Everyday Mathematics®

The University of Chicago School Mathematics Project

Teacher's Lesson Guide
Volume 1

Chicago, IL • Columbus, OH • New York, NY

The University of Chicago School Mathematics Project (UCSMP)

Max Bell, Director, UCSMP Elementary Materials Component; Director, *Everyday Mathematics* First Edition; James McBride, Director, *Everyday Mathematics* Second Edition; Andy Isaacs, Director, *Everyday Mathematics* Third Edition; Amy Dillard, Associate Director, *Everyday Mathematics* Third Edition; Rachel Malpass McCall, Associate Director, *Everyday Mathematics* Common Core State Standards Edition

Authors

Max Bell, John Bretzlauf, Amy Dillard, Robert Hartfield, Andy Isaacs, James McBride, Kathleen Pitvorec, Denise Porter‡, Peter Saecker, Noreen Winningham*, Robert Balfanz†, William Carroll†

*Third Edition only †First Edition only ‡Common Core State Standards Edition only

Technical Art

Diana Barrie

Third Edition Teachers in Residence

Fran Goldenberg, Sandra Vitantonio

Mathematics and Technology Advisor

James Flanders

UCSMP Editorial

Rosina Busse, Laurie K. Thrasher, David B. Spangler

ELL Consultant

Kathryn B. Chval

Contributors

Regina Littleton (Office Manager), Kriszta Miner (Project Manager), Sandra R. Overcash, Serena Hohmann, Sally S. Johnson, Colleen M. Kelly, Kimberley Dawn Sowa, Tracy Lynn Selock, Tammy Belgrade, Diana Carry, Debra Dawson, Kevin Dorken, Laurel Hallman, Ann Hemwall, Elizabeth Homewood, Linda Klaric, Lee Kornhauser, Judy Korshak-Samuels, Deborah Arron Leslie, Joseph C. Liptak, Sharon McHugh, Janet M. Meyers, Susan Mieli, Donna Nowatzki, Sheila Sconiers, Kevin J. Smith, Theresa Sparlin, Laura Sunseri, Kim Van Haitsma, John Wilson, Mary Wilson, Carl Zmola, Theresa Zmola

Photo Credits

Cover (l)Steven Hunt/Stone/Getty Images, (c)Martin Mistretta/Stone/Getty Images, (r)Digital Stock/CORBIS, (bkgd)Pier/Stone/Getty Images; **Back Cover** Martin Mistretta/Stone/Getty Images; **ii xx** The McGraw-Hill Companies; **xxv** (tr)The McGraw-Hill Companies (b)Jasper James/The Image Bank/Getty Images; **xxvi** (t)The McGraw-Hill Companies, (b)Siede Preis/Photodisc/Getty Images; **xxvii** (t)Pete Saloutos/Flirt/CORBIS, (b)Michael Nelson/Taxi/Getty Images; **xxviii** (t)Rosemary Calvert/Getty Images, (b)Stockbyte/Getty Images; **xxix** (t)TATSUHIKO SAWADA/amana images/Getty Images, (b)Lew Robertson/Flirt/CORBIS; **xxx** C Squared Studios/Getty Images; **xxxi** Gazimal/Iconica/Getty Images; **xxxii** The McGraw-Hill Companies; **xxxiv** Emma Lee/Life File/Photodisc/Getty Images; **xxxv** Brand X Pictures/Getty Images; **xxxvi** The McGraw-Hill Companies; **xxxvii** (t)George Doyle/Stockbyte/Getty Images, (b)The McGraw-Hill Companies; **xxxviii** Nicholas Eveleigh/Iconica/Getty Images; **xxxix** C Squared Studios/Getty Images; **2** (tr)John E. Kelly/foodPix/Getty Images, (b)Brand X/Getty Images; **3** Steve Wisbauer/Photodisc/Getty Images; **14 15** The McGraw-Hill Companies; **66** Steve Wisbauer/Photodisc/Getty Images; **67** Chris Walsh/IFA-Bilderteam/Stock Image/Getty Images; **77** Tom Schierlitz/Stone/Getty Images; **79** Stockbyte/Getty Images; **142** (l)The McGraw-Hill Companies, (r) Travel Ink/Photodisc/Getty Images; **143** Kuttig-Travel/Alamy; **153 172** The McGraw-Hill Companies; **216** Jed Share/Riser/Getty Images; **217** Maps.com/CORBIS; **229** C Squared Studios/Photodisc/Getty Images; **276** The McGraw-Hill Companies; **287** David Lees/CORBIS; **288** Jack Hollingsworth/Spirit/CORBIS; **289** (t)Visions of America/Joe Sohm/Getty Images, (b)Tom Merton/Photodisc/Getty Images; **364** (l)Barry Gregg/CORBIS, (r)Joe Raedle/Getty Images News/Getty Images; **375** Southern Stock/Photonica/Getty Images; **376** Ann Monn/Brand X Pictures/Getty Images; **377 490** The McGraw-Hill Companies; **Icons** (NCTM l-r)Sharon Hoogstraten/Courtesy of Dave Wyman, Jules Frazier/Photodisc/Getty Images, Comstock/PunchStock, Sundell Larsen/Getty Images, PhotoAlto/PunchStock, Four Elements/V262/CORBIS, Juan Silva/Stockbyte/Getty Images, Digital Vision/Getty Images; (iTLG)C Squared Studios/Getty Images; (Online Content Support)Image Source; (Objective)Brand X Pictures/PunchStock/Getty Images.

This material is based upon work supported by the National Science Foundation under Grant No. ESI-9252984. Any opinions, findings, conclusions, or recommendations expressed in this material are those of the authors and do not necessarily reflect the views of the National Science Foundation.

everydaymath.com

Education

Send all inquiries to:
McGraw-Hill Education
STEM Learning Solutions Center
P.O. Box 812960
Chicago, IL 60681

ISBN: 978-0-07-657682-1
MHID: 0-07-657682-5

Printed in the United States of America.

1 2 3 4 5 6 7 8 9 RMN 17 16 15 14 13 12 11

McGraw-Hill is committed to providing instructional materials in Science, Technology, Engineering, and Mathematics (STEM) that give all students a solid foundation, one that prepares them for college and careers in the 21st century.

The University of Chicago School Mathematics Project (UCSMP)

Acknowledgements

The first edition of *Everyday Mathematics* was made possible by sustained support over several years from the GTE Corporation and the National Science Foundation; additional help came from the Amoco Foundation through its support of the University of Chicago School Mathematics Project (UCSMP). Earlier projects supported by the National Science Foundation, the National Institute of Education, and the Benton Foundation provided us with insights into the surprising capabilities of young children.

Development of the second edition of *Everyday Mathematics* was funded by the Everyday Learning Corporation and the authors; development of the third edition was supported by McGraw-Hill, the University of Chicago, and the authors. For all of these editions, many University of Chicago and UCSMP colleagues have been helpful. For this Common Core State Standards edition, Deborah Arron Leslie, Rachel Malpass McCall, Cheryl G. Moran, Mary Ellen Dairyko, Rebecca W. Maxcy, Denise Porter, and Sarah R. Burns formed a committee that provided invaluable guidance on many key issues. Rachel Malpass McCall's work as Associate Director of the Common Core State Standards Edition was especially important to the success of the project. We also acknowledge dedicated and resourceful assistance on production and technical tasks by many people at the University of Chicago and at the McGraw-Hill School Education Group.

Over the years that UCSMP has been working in schools, feedback and advice from teachers willing to take risks in trying development versions of our materials have been essential and enormously helpful. There are too many such teachers to list, but their contributions are gratefully acknowledged.

Andy Isaacs
Director, Third Edition and Common Core State Standards Edition

James McBride
Director, Second Edition

Max Bell
Director, First Edition

Contents

Everyday Mathematics

A Mission to Improve Mathematics

The University of Chicago School Mathematics Project

Everyday Mathematics was developed by the University of Chicago School Mathematics Project (UCSMP) in order to enable students in elementary grades to learn more mathematical content and become life-long mathematical thinkers.

- The National Science Foundation and Amoco, GTE, and other leading corporations supported the project through substantial, long-term funding.
- A strong partnership among researchers, mathematics educators, classroom teachers, students, and administrators was developed.
- A consistent, core author team at the University of Chicago School Mathematics Project collaborated on all grade levels to provide a cohesive and well-articulated Pre-K through Grade 6 curriculum.
- The *Everyday Mathematics* curriculum is completely aligned to the NCTM Curriculum Focal Points and the Connections to the Curriculum Focal Points for Grades Pre-K through 6.

"We, our funders, and our users believe strongly that even the best curricula of decades ago are not adequate for today's youth."

University of Chicago School Mathematics Project

Research Foundation

Everyday Mathematics began with the premise that students can, and must, learn more mathematics than has been expected from them in the past. This premise is based on research the UCSMP author team and others undertook prior to writing the curriculum. Following are some major findings of this research:

- The typical U.S. mathematics curriculum is arithmetic-driven, slow-paced, isolated in its instruction, and broad—rather than deep—in its content.
- International studies show that U.S. students learn much less mathematics than students in other countries.
- Children are capable of learning more mathematics in a richer curriculum.
- All children can be successful mathematical thinkers.
- Mathematics is meaningful to children when it is varied, rich, and rooted in real-world problems and applications.

Instructional Design

The *Everyday Mathematics* instructional design was carefully crafted to capitalize on student interest and maximize student learning. Among its features are the following:

- High expectations for all students
- Concepts and skills developed over time and in a wide variety of contexts
- Balance among mathematical strands
- Dynamic applications
- Multiple methods and strategies for problem solving
- Concrete modeling as a pathway to abstract understanding
- Collaborative learning in partner and small-group activities
- Cross-curricular applications and connections
- Built-in professional development for teachers

"Our teachers in Grades 6–8 tell me that students using the *Everyday Mathematics* program in earlier grades are arriving in their classrooms with a deeper understanding of mathematical concepts and are ready to start the year at a much higher level."

Principal Kenneth Tucker, Pre-K to 8

Meeting Standards, Achieving Results

The *Everyday Mathematics* program is celebrating more than 25 years of research and development. The program offers schools results unmatched by any other elementary mathematics program.

Research, Validation, Results

As part of the research for *Everyday Mathematics,* the authors at the University of Chicago School Mathematics Project examined successful curricula from around the world, researched how children learn mathematics, and studied the actual use of mathematics by people in their everyday lives. The results of this research were used to establish the scope and sequence for the mathematical content of the *Everyday Mathematics* program.

Field Testing

The program was written and field tested one grade-level at a time, beginning with Kindergarten. Field tests gathered information from classroom teachers and students in three main areas: teacher preparation of materials, student response to materials, and student achievement. Based on teacher and student feedback, the authors revised the curriculum before *Everyday Mathematics* was published.

Learner Verification

The best way to show the effectiveness of a program is to study it over time. Several independent research studies have been conducted which provide evidence for the effectiveness of *Everyday Mathematics*. For example, *Everyday Mathematics* was the focus of a five-year longitudinal study conducted by researchers at Northwestern University. Reports from this study and others are available through the University of Chicago School Mathematics Project or McGraw-Hill.

Everyday Mathematics **Timeline of Research and Development**

	Pre-1989	1989	1990	1991	1992	1993	1994	1995	1996	1997
Pre-K										
Kindergarten	PUBLISH								FEEDBACK • WRITE • FIELD-TEST	
Grade 1	WRITE • FIELD-TEST REWRITE • PUBLISH									◆
Grade 2		WRITE • FIELD-TEST • REWRITE • PUBLISH								◆
Grade 3			WRITE • FIELD-TEST • REWRITE • PUBLISH							◆
Grade 4					WRITE • FIELD-TEST • REWRITE • PUBLISH					
Grade 5						WRITE • FIELD-TEST • REWRITE • PUBLISH				
Grade 6							WRITE • FIELD-TEST • REWRITE • PUBLISH			

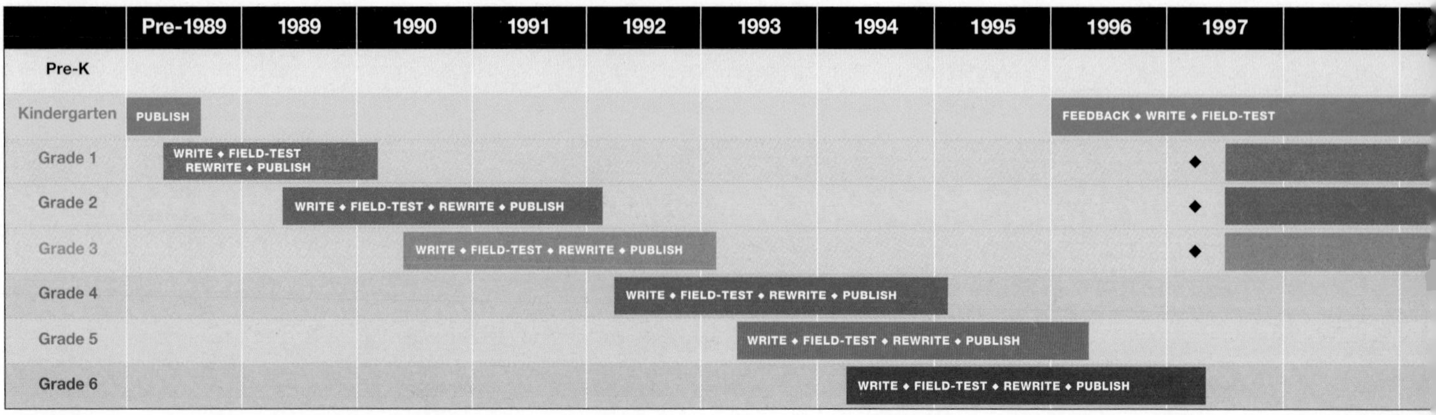

Tri-State Student Achievement Study

The ARC Center, a National Science Foundation (NSF) funded project, located at the Consortium for Mathematics and its Applications (COMAP), has carried out a study of the effects of standards-based mathematics programs on student performance on state-mandated standardized tests in Massachusetts, Illinois, and Washington.

The findings of the study are based on the records of over 78,000 students: 39,701 who had used the *Everyday Mathematics* curriculum for at least two years, and 38,481 students from comparison schools. The students were carefully matched by reading level, socioeconomic status, and other variables.

Results showed that the average scores of students in the *Everyday Mathematics* schools were consistently higher than the average scores of students in the comparison schools. (A complete report is available from COMAP or McGraw-Hill.)

A report based on 78,000 students showed that average standardized test scores were significantly higher for students in *Everyday Mathematics* schools than for students in comparison schools.

What Works Clearinghouse

Everyday Mathematics is the only elementary math program found by the What Works Clearinghouse to have potentially positive effects on students' math achievement, among those with a medium to large extent of evidence. The studies of *Everyday Mathematics* cited in the What Works Clearinghouse findings included a total of approximately 12,600 students in Grades 3–5. The students were from a range of socioeconomic backgrounds and attended schools in urban, suburban, and rural communities in multiple states.

Closing the Gap

Many districts, by using the *Everyday Mathematics* program, have helped minority students increase achievement, reducing the minority/majority achievement gap while maintaining growth for all students. This helps schools and districts meet adequate yearly progress requirements set forth by No Child Left Behind legislation. District information is available by contacting McGraw-Hill.

	1998	1999	2000	2001	2002	2003	2004	2005	2006	2007	2008	2009	2010
				FEEDBACK ◆ WRITE ◆ FIELD-TEST ◆ PUBLISH				FEEDBACK ◆ WRITE FIELD-TEST ◆ PUBLISH					
	PUBLISH – 2ND EDITION					▲	FEEDBACK ◆ WRITE ◆ FIELD-TEST ◆ PUBLISH – 3RD EDITION						●
	FEEDBACK ◆ WRITE ◆ FIELD-TEST ◆ PUBLISH – 2ND EDITION					▲	FEEDBACK ◆ WRITE ◆ FIELD-TEST ◆ PUBLISH – 3RD EDITION						●
	FEEDBACK ◆ WRITE ◆ FIELD-TEST ◆ PUBLISH – 2ND EDITION					▲	FEEDBACK ◆ WRITE ◆ FIELD-TEST ◆ PUBLISH – 3RD EDITION						●
	FEEDBACK ◆ WRITE ◆ FIELD-TEST ◆ PUBLISH – 2ND EDITION					▲	FEEDBACK ◆ WRITE ◆ FIELD-TEST ◆ PUBLISH – 3RD EDITION						●
	◆	FEEDBACK ◆ WRITE ◆ FIELD-TEST ◆ PUBLISH – 2ND EDITION				▲	FEEDBACK ◆ WRITE ◆ FIELD-TEST ◆ PUBLISH – 3RD EDITION						●
	◆	FEEDBACK ◆ WRITE ◆ FIELD-TEST ◆ PUBLISH – 2ND EDITION				▲	FEEDBACK ◆ WRITE ◆ FIELD-TEST ◆ PUBLISH – 3RD EDITION						●
	◆	FEEDBACK ◆ WRITE ◆ FIELD-TEST ◆ PUBLISH – 2ND EDITION				▲	FEEDBACK ◆ WRITE ◆ FIELD-TEST ◆ PUBLISH – 3RD EDITION						●

◆ = 1st edition update ▲ = 2nd edition update ● = 3rd edition update

Everyday Mathematics

Everyday Mathematics Grade-Level Goals for Grade 5

The Program Goals and Grade-Level Goals for Grade 5 are listed in the chart below.

Number and Numeration

Program Goal: Understand the meanings, uses, and representations of numbers.	
Place value and notation	**Goal 1** Read and write whole numbers and decimals; identify places in such numbers and the values of the digits in those places; use expanded notation to represent whole numbers and decimals.
Meanings and uses of fractions	**Goal 2** Solve problems involving percents and discounts; describe and explain strategies used; identify the unit whole in situations involving fractions.
Number theory	**Goal 3** Identify prime and composite numbers; factor numbers; find prime factorizations.
Program Goal: Understand equivalent names for numbers.	
Equivalent names for whole numbers	**Goal 4** Use numerical expressions involving one or more of the basic four arithmetic operations, grouping symbols, and exponents to give equivalent names for whole numbers; convert between base-10, exponential, and repeated-factor notations.
Equivalent names for fractions, decimals, and percents	**Goal 5** Use numerical expressions to find and represent equivalent names for fractions, decimals, and percents; use and explain multiplication and division rules to find equivalent fractions and fractions in simplest form; convert between fractions and mixed numbers; convert between fractions, decimals, and percents.
Program Goal: Understand common numerical relations.	
Comparing and ordering numbers	**Goal 6** Compare and order rational numbers; use area models, benchmark fractions, and analyses of numerators and denominators to compare and order fractions and mixed numbers; describe strategies used to compare fractions and mixed numbers.

Operations and Computation

Program Goal: Compute accurately.	
Addition and subtraction procedures	**Goal 1** Use manipulatives, mental arithmetic, paper-and-pencil algorithms and models, and calculators to solve problems involving the addition and subtraction of whole numbers, decimals, and signed numbers; describe the strategies used and explain how they work.
Multiplication and division facts	**Goal 2** Demonstrate automaticity with multiplication and division fact extensions.
Multiplication and division procedures	**Goal 3** Use manipulatives, mental arithmetic, paper-and-pencil algorithms and models, and calculators to solve problems involving the multiplication of whole numbers and decimals and the division of multidigit whole numbers and decimals by whole numbers; express remainders as whole numbers or fractions as appropriate; describe the strategies used and explain how they work.

Operations and Computation (cont.)

Program Goal: Compute accurately. (cont.)	
Procedures for addition and subtraction of fractions	**Goal 4** Use mental arithmetic, paper-and-pencil algorithms and models, and calculators to solve problems involving the addition and subtraction of fractions and mixed numbers; describe the strategies used and explain how they work.
Procedures for multiplication and division of fractions	**Goal 5** Use area models, mental arithmetic, paper-and pencil algorithms and models, and calculators to solve problems involving the multiplication of fractions and mixed numbers; use visual models, paper-and-pencil methods, and calculators to solve problems involving the division of fractions; describe the strategies used.
Program Goal: Make reasonable estimates.	
Computational estimation	**Goal 6** Make reasonable estimates for whole number and decimal addition, subtraction, multiplication, and division problems and fraction and mixed number addition and subtraction problems; explain how the estimates were obtained.
Program Goal: Understand meanings of operations.	
Models for the operations	**Goal 7** Use repeated addition, arrays, area, and scaling to model multiplication and division; use ratios expressed as words, fractions, percents, and with colons; solve problems involving ratios of parts of a set to the whole set.

Data and Chance

Program Goal: Select and create appropriate graphical representations of collected or given data.	
Data collection and representation	**Goal 1** Collect and organize data or use given data to create graphic displays with reasonable titles, labels, keys, and intervals.
Program Goal: Analyze and interpret data.	
Data analysis	**Goal 2** Use the maximum, minimum, range, median, mode, and mean and graphs to ask and answer questions, draw conclusions, and make predictions.
Program Goal: Understand and apply basic concepts of probability.	
Qualitative probability	**Goal 3** Describe events using *certain, very likely, likely, unlikely, very unlikely, impossible,* and other basic probability terms; use *more likely, equally likely, same chance, 50–50, less likely,* and other basic probability terms to compare events; explain the choice of language.
Quantitative probability	**Goal 4** Predict the outcomes of experiments, test the predictions using manipulatives, and summarize the results; compare predictions based on theoretical probability with experimental results; use summaries and comparisons to predict future events; express the probability of an event as a fraction, decimal, or percent.

Measurement and Reference Frames

Program Goal: Understand the systems and processes of measurement; use appropriate techniques, tools, units, and formulas in making measurements.	
Length, weight, and angles	**Goal 1** Estimate length with and without tools; measure length with tools to the nearest $\frac{1}{8}$ inch and millimeter; estimate the measure of angles with and without tools; use tools to draw angles with given measures.
Area, perimeter, volume, and capacity	**Goal 2** Describe and use strategies to find the perimeter of polygons and the area of circles; choose and use appropriate methods, including formulas, to find the areas of rectangles, parallelograms, and triangles, and the volume of a prism; define *pi* as the ratio of a circle's circumference to its diameter.

Measurement and Reference Frames (cont.)

Program Goal: Understand the systems and processes of measurement; use appropriate techniques, tools, units, and formulas in making measurements. (cont.)	
Units and systems of measurement	**Goal 3** Describe relationships among U.S. customary units of measure and among metric units of measure.
Program Goal: Use and understand reference frames.	
Coordinate systems	**Goal 4** Use ordered pairs of numbers to name, locate, and plot points in all four quadrants of a coordinate grid.

Geometry

Program Goal: Investigate characteristics and properties of two- and three-dimensional geometric shapes.	
Lines and angles	**Goal 1** Identify, describe, compare, name, and draw right, acute, obtuse, straight, and reflex angles; determine angle measures in vertical and supplementary angles and by applying properties of sums of angle measures in triangles and quadrangles.
Plane and solid figures	**Goal 2** Describe, compare, and classify plane and solid figures using appropriate geometric terms; identify congruent figures and describe their properties.
Program Goal: Apply transformations and symmetry in geometric situations.	
Transformations and symmetry	**Goal 3** Identify, describe, and sketch examples of reflections, translations, and rotations.

Patterns, Functions, and Algebra

Program Goal: Understand patterns and functions.	
Patterns and functions	**Goal 1** Extend, describe, and create numeric patterns; describe rules for patterns and use them to solve problems; write rules for functions involving the four basic arithmetic operations; represent functions using words, symbols, tables, and graphs and use those representations to solve problems.
Program Goal: Use algebraic notation to represent and analyze situations and structures.	
Algebraic notation and solving number sentences	**Goal 2** Determine whether number sentences are true or false; solve open number sentences and explain the solutions; use a letter variable to write an open sentence to model a number story; use a pan-balance model to solve linear equations in one unknown.
Order of operations	**Goal 3** Evaluate numeric expressions containing grouping symbols and nested grouping symbols; insert grouping symbols and nested grouping symbols to make number sentences true; describe and use the precedence of multiplication and division over addition and subtraction.
Properties of the arithmetic operations	**Goal 4** Describe and apply properties of arithmetic.

Common Core State Standards

Everyday Mathematics fully aligns with the national Common Core State Standards for Mathematics. Both are founded on cross-disciplinary skills such as critical thinking and problem solving. The Standards for Mathematical Practice, described in the Common Core State Standards, form a cohesive match with the already-proven instructional design of *Everyday Mathematics*. Both require students to:

- Make sense of problems and persevere in solving them.
- Reason abstractly and quantitatively.
- Construct viable arguments and critique the reasoning of others.
- Model with mathematics.
- Use appropriate tools strategically.
- Attend to precision.
- Look for and make use of structure.
- Look for and express regularity in repeated reasoning.

Everyday Mathematics fully meets all of the Common Core State Standards for Mathematics, Grades K–6.

In *Everyday Mathematics*, the Grade-Level Goals, which state the core content that is assessed at each grade level, align with the Standards for Mathematical Content. *Everyday Mathematics* has a long track record of success resulting from constant revision based on evidence of what works. *Everyday Mathematics* is a world-class mathematics curriculum that fully meets the Common Core State Standards for Grades K–6.

Instruction and Planning

The *Teacher's Lesson Guide* includes a comprehensive grade-level correlation that shows the *Everyday Mathematics* lessons that cover each of the Standards for Mathematical Content. Correlation documents for the complete *Everyday Mathematics* program are available at everydaymathonline.com.

Everyday Mathematics offers a variety of print and technology materials to meet instructional needs and to help incorporate these standards in the classroom curriculum.

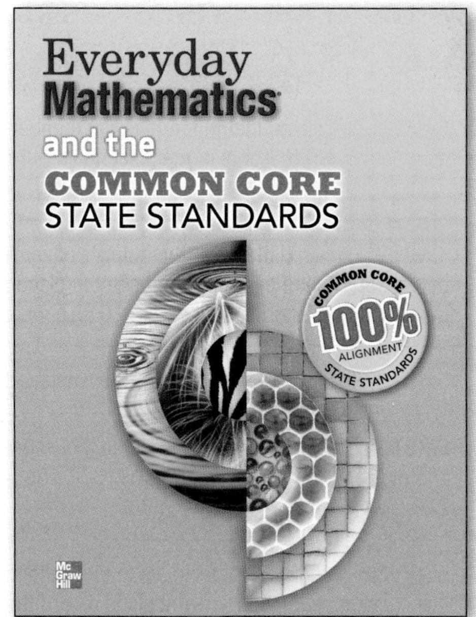

Assessment

Everyday Mathematics provides many opportunities and tools for assessment. Assessment results show students' progress toward the *Everyday Mathematics* Grade-Level Goals and the Common Core State Standards.

Professional Development

Professional Development is offered at implementation, for continued support, and is built into the program materials to help teachers successfully implement the Common Core State Standards with the *Everyday Mathematics* program.

Common Core State Standards and *Everyday Mathematics*

The *Everyday Mathematics* curriculum is completely aligned to the *K-12 Common Core State Standards* for Kindergarten through Grade 6.

Common Core State Standards for Grade 5	*Everyday Mathematics* Grade 5 Lessons*
OPERATIONS AND ALGEBRAIC THINKING 5.OA	
Write and interpret numerical expressions.	
5.OA.1. Use parentheses, brackets, or braces in numerical expressions, and evaluate expressions with these symbols.	**1•9,** 2•4, 4•1, 4•3, 5•12, **7•4, 7•5,** 7•7, 8•7, 10•3, 11•6 Project 2
5.OA.2. Write simple expressions that record calculations with numbers, and interpret numerical expressions without evaluating them. *For example, express the calculation "add 8 and 7, then multiply by 2" as $2 \times (8 + 7)$. Recognize that $3 \times (18932 + 921)$ is three times as large as $18932 + 921$ without having to calculate the indicated sum or product.*	**1•1, 1•3, 1•4, 1•7, 1•8, 2•4, 3•2, 4•1, 4•6,** 4•7, **7•4, 7•5, 10•3**
Analyze patterns and relationships.	
5.OA.3. Generate two numerical patterns using two given rules. Identify apparent relationships between corresponding terms. Form ordered pairs consisting of corresponding terms from the two patterns, and graph the ordered pairs on a coordinate plane. *For example, given the rule "Add 3" and the starting number 0, and given the rule "Add 6" and the starting number 0, generate terms in the resulting sequences, and observe that the terms in one sequence are twice the corresponding terms in the other sequence. Explain informally why this is so.*	**10•3, 10•4, 10•6**
NUMBER AND OPERATIONS IN BASE TEN 5.NBT	
Understand the place value system.	
5.NBT.1. Recognize that in a multi-digit number, a digit in the ones place represents 10 times as much as it represents in the place to its right and $\frac{1}{10}$ of what it represents in the place to its left.	**2•2, 2•3, 2•10, 7•2**
5.NBT.2. Explain patterns in the number of zeros of the product when multiplying a number by powers of 10, and explain patterns in the placement of the decimal point when a decimal is multiplied or divided by a power of 10. Use whole-number exponents to denote powers of 10.	**1•1, 1•2, 1•5, 1•6,** 1•8, **1•9, 2•1,** 2•7, 2•8, **2•9,** 3•2, **3•5, 3•8,** 3•9, **4•1,** 4•7, 4•8, **7•1, 7•2,** 7•3, 7•4, **7•7, 9•1, 9•5, 10•1,** 10•3, **11•6**
5.NBT.3. Read, write, and compare decimals to thousandths.	
5.NBT.3a. Read and write decimals to thousandths using base-ten numerals, number names, and expanded form, e.g., $347.392 = 3 \times 100 + 4 \times 10 + 7 \times 1 + 3 \times (\frac{1}{10}) + 9 \times (\frac{1}{100}) + 2 \times (\frac{1}{1000})$.	**2•2, 2•3, 2•4,** 2•5, **2•8, 3•9, 5•5, 5•6, 5•7, 5•8, 5•9,** 6•2, 6•3
5.NBT.3b. Compare two decimals to thousandths based on meanings of the digits in each place, using $>$, $=$, and $<$ symbols to record the results of comparisons.	**2•2, 2•5, 3•1,** 3•5, **7•9**
5.NBT.4. Use place value understanding to round decimals to any place.	**2•3, 2•5, 2•7, 2•8, 3•6, 5•5, 5•6,** 5•8, 6•1, 6•4, 9•8, 10•7, **10•8, 11•3,** 12•7

***Bold lesson numbers indicate that content from the standard is being taught. Lesson numbers not in bold indicate that content from the standard is being reviewed or practiced.**

Common Core State Standards for Grade 5	***Everyday Mathematics* Grade 5 Lessons**
Perform operations with multi-digit whole numbers and with decimals to hundredths.	
5.NBT.5. Fluently multiply multi-digit whole numbers using the standard algorithm.	7•10, 9•2, 10•1, 10•3, **Algorithm Projects 5 and 6**
5.NBT.6. Find whole-number quotients of whole numbers with up to four-digit dividends and two-digit divisors, using strategies based on place value, the properties of operations, and/or the relationship between multiplication and division. Illustrate and explain the calculation by using equations, rectangular arrays, and/or area models.	**4•1, 4•2, 4•4, 4•6,** 7•10, **Algorithm Project 7**
5.NBT.7. Add, subtract, multiply, and divide decimals to hundredths, using concrete models or drawings and strategies based on place value, properties or operations, and/or the relationship between addition and subtraction; relate the strategy to a written method and explain the reasoning used.	**2•2, 2•3, 2•4,** 2•5, **2•7, 2•8, 2•9, 4•5, 4•6,** 5•11, 6•5, 6•7, 7•10, 9•8, 9•10, 10•6, 12•2, **Algorithm Projects 2, 4, 6, 8, and 9**
NUMBERS AND OPERATIONS—FRACTIONS 5.NF	
Use equivalent fractions as a strategy to add and subtract fractions.	
5 NF.1. Add and subtract fractions with unlike denominators (including mixed numbers) by replacing given fractions with equivalent fractions in such a way as to produce an equivalent sum or difference of fractions with like denominators. *For example,* $\frac{2}{3} + \frac{5}{4} = \frac{8}{12} + \frac{15}{12} = \frac{23}{12}$. *(In general,* $\frac{a}{b} + \frac{c}{d} = \frac{(ad + bc)}{bd}$*.)*	**5•3, 6•8, 6•9, 6•10, 7•6, 7•10, 8•1, 8•2, 8•3, 8•4, 11•7**
5.NF.2. Solve word problems involving addition and subtraction of fractions referring to the same whole, including cases of unlike denominators, e.g., by using visual fraction models or equations to represent the problem. Use benchmark fractions and number sense of fractions to estimate mentally and assess the reasonableness of answers. *For example, recognize an incorrect result* $\frac{2}{5} + \frac{1}{2} = \frac{3}{7}$*, by observing that* $\frac{3}{7} < \frac{1}{2}$.	**5•3, 6•8, 6•9, 6•10, 7•10, 8•1, 8•2, 8•3, 8•4,** 8•11, **9•6,** 10•6, 11•7
Apply and extend previous understandings of multiplication and division to multiply and divide fractions.	
5.NF.3. Interpret a fraction as division of the numerator by the denominator ($\frac{a}{b} = a \div b$). Solve word problems involving division of whole numbers leading to answers in the form of fractions or mixed numbers, e.g., by using visual fraction models or equations to represent the problem. *For example, interpret* $\frac{3}{4}$ *as the result of dividing 3 by 4, noting that* $\frac{3}{4}$ *multiplied by 4 equals 3, and that when 3 wholes are shared equally among 4 people each person has a share of size* $\frac{3}{4}$*. If 9 people want to share a 50-pound sack of rice equally by weight, how many pounds of rice should each person get? Between what two whole numbers does your answer lie?*	**5•1, 5•6, 6•8,** 7•11
5.NF.4. Apply and extend previous understandings of multiplication to multiply a fraction or whole number by a fraction.	
5.NF.4a. Interpret the product $(\frac{a}{b}) \times q$ as *a* parts of a partition of *q* into *b* equal parts; equivalently, as the result of a sequence of operations $a \times q \div b$. *For example, use a visual fraction model to show* $(\frac{2}{3}) \times 4 = \frac{8}{3}$*, and create a story context for this equation. Do the same with* $(\frac{2}{3}) \times (\frac{4}{5}) = \frac{8}{15}$*. (In general,* $(\frac{a}{b}) \times (\frac{c}{d}) = \frac{ac}{bd}$*.)*	**8•5, 8•6, 8•7, 8•8,** 9•1
5.NF.4b. Find the area of a rectangle with fractional side lengths by tiling it with unit squares of appropriate unit fraction side lengths, and show that the area is the same as would be found by multiplying the side lengths. Multiply fractional side lengths to find areas of rectangles, and represent fraction products as rectangular areas.	**8•8, 9•4,** 9•10, **11•7**

Common Core State Standards for Grade 5	*Everyday Mathematics* Grade 5 Lessons
5.NF.5. Interpret multiplication as scaling (resizing), by:	
5.NF.5a. Comparing the size of a product to the size of one factor on the basis of the size of the other factor, without performing the indicated multiplication.	**1•4,** 3•8, **4•1, 8•5, 8•6, 8•8,** 10•2
5.NF.5b. Explaining why multiplying a given number by a fraction greater than 1 results in a product greater than the given number (recognizing multiplication by whole numbers greater than 1 as a familiar case); explaining why multiplying a given number by a fraction less than 1 results in a product smaller than the given number; and relating the principle of fraction equivalence $\frac{a}{b} = \frac{(n \times a)}{(n \times b)}$ to the effect of multiplying $\frac{a}{b}$ by 1.	**6•9, 8•1, 8•6, 8•7, 8•8**
5.NF.6. Solve real world problems involving multiplication of fractions and mixed numbers, e.g., by using visual fraction models or equations to represent the problem.	**8•5, 8•6, 8•7, 8•8,** 9•7
5.NF.7. Apply and extend previous understandings of division to divide unit fractions by whole numbers and whole numbers by unit fractions.	
5.NF.7a. Interpret division of a unit fraction by a non-zero whole number, and compute such quotients. *For example, create a story context for* $(\frac{1}{3}) \div 4$, *and use a visual fraction model to show the quotient. Use the relationship between multiplication and division to explain that* $(\frac{1}{3}) \div 4 = \frac{1}{12}$ *because* $(\frac{1}{12}) \times 4 = \frac{1}{3}$.	**8•12, 9•4,** 11•4, 12•1, **12•3, 12•5**
5.NF.7b. Interpret division of a whole number by a unit fraction, and compute such quotients. *For example, create a story context for* $4 \div (\frac{1}{5})$, *and use a visual fraction model to show the quotient. Use the relationship between multiplication and division to explain that* $4 \div (\frac{1}{5}) = 20$ *because* $20 \times (\frac{1}{5}) = 4$.	**8•12, 9•4, 11•4,** 12•1, **12•3, 12•5**
5.NF.7c. Solve real world problems involving the division of unit fractions by non-zero whole numbers and division of whole numbers by unit fractions, e.g., by using visual fraction models and equations to represent the problem. *For example, how much chocolate will each person get if 3 people share* $\frac{1}{2}$ *lb. of chocolate equally? How many* $\frac{1}{3}$*-cup servings are in 2 cups of raisins?*	**8•12, 9•4,** 11•7, 12•1, 12•3, **12•5**
MEASUREMENT AND DATA 5.MD	
Convert like measurement units within a given measurement system.	
5.MD.1. Convert among different-sized standard measurement units within a given measurement system (e.g., convert 5 cm to 0.05 m), and use these conversions in solving multi-step, real world problems.	**2•1, 2•10,** 6•2, **9•10, 10•5,** 10•9, **11•3, 11•5,** 11•6, **Project 6**
Represent and interpret data.	
5.MD.2. Make a line plot to display a data set of measurements in fractions of a unit $(\frac{1}{2}, \frac{1}{4}, \frac{1}{8})$. Use operations of fractions for this grade to solve problems involving information presented in line plots. *For example, given different measurements of liquid in identical beakers, find the amount of liquid each beaker would contain if the total amount in all the beakers were distributed equally.*	**2•5, 6•1, 7•10, 10•2, 11•7**

Common Core State Standards for Grade 5	*Everyday Mathematics* Grade 5 Lessons
Geometric measurement: understand concepts of volume and relate volume to multiplication and to addition.	
5.MD.3. Recognize volume as an attribute of solid figures and understand concepts of volume measurement.	
5.MD.3a. A cube with side length 1 unit, called a "unit cube" is said to have "one cubic unit" of volume, and can be used to measure volume.	9•3, 9•4, **9•8, 9•9, 9•10,** 10•1, **11•1,** 11•3, **Project 9**
5.MD.3b. A solid figure which can be packed without gaps and overlaps using *n* unit cubes is said to have a volume of *n* cubic units.	**9•8, 9•10,** 10•1, **11•1,** 11•3, **Project 9**
5.MD.4. Measure volumes by counting unit cubes, using cubic cm, cubic in, cubic ft, and improvised units.	9•3, 9•4, **9•8, 9•10,** 10•1, **11•1,** 11•3, **Project 9**
5.MD.5. Relate volume to the operations of multiplication and addition and solve real world and mathematical problems involving volume.	
5.MD.5a. Find the volume of a right rectangular prism with whole-number side lengths by packing it with unit cubes, and show that the volume is the same as would be found by multiplying the edge of lengths, equivalently by multiplying the height by the area of the base. Represent three-fold whole-number products as volumes, e.g., to represent the associative property of multiplication.	**9•8, 9•10,** 10•3, **11•1, 11•3,** 11•7, Project 9
5.MD.5b. Apply the formulas $V = l \times w \times h$ and $V = b \times h$ for rectangular prisms to find volumes of right rectangular prisms with whole-number edge lengths in the context of solving real world and mathematical problems.	9•3, **9•4, 9•8, 9•9, 9•10,** 10•1, 10•3, **11•1, 11•3,** 11•7, **Project 9**
5.MD.5c. Recognize volume as additive. Find volumes of solid figures composed of two non-overlapping right rectangular prisms by adding the volumes of the non-overlapping parts, applying this technique to solve real world problems.	**9•9, 11•5, Project 9**
GEOMETRY 5.G	
Graph points on the coordinate plane to solve real-world and mathematical problems.	
5.G.1. Use a pair of perpendicular number lines, called axes, to define a coordinate system, with the intersection of the lines (the origin) arranged to coincide with the 0 on each line and a given point in the plane located by using an ordered pair of numbers, called its coordinates. Understand that the first number indicates how far to travel from the origin in the direction of one axis, and the second number indicates how far to travel in the direction of the second axis, with the convention that the names of the two axes and the coordinates correspond (e.g., *x*-axis and *x*-coordinate, *y*-axis and *y*-coordinate).	**9•1, 9•2, 9•3, 10•4, 10•6, 10•7, 12•8**
5.G.2. Represent real world and mathematical problems by graphing points in the first quadrant of the coordinate plane, and interpret coordinate values of points in the context of the situation.	**9•1, 9•2, 9•3, 10•4, 10•6**
Classify two-dimensional figures into categories based on their properties.	
5.G.3. Understand that attributes belonging to a category of two-dimensional figures also belong to all subcategories of that category. *For example, all rectangles have four right angles and squares are rectangles, so all squares have four right angles.*	**3•4, 3•7, 3•8, 4•1,** 8•3
5.G.4. Classify two-dimensional figures in a hierarchy based on properties.	**3•7, 3•8, 4•1,** 8•3

Components at a Glance

Student Materials

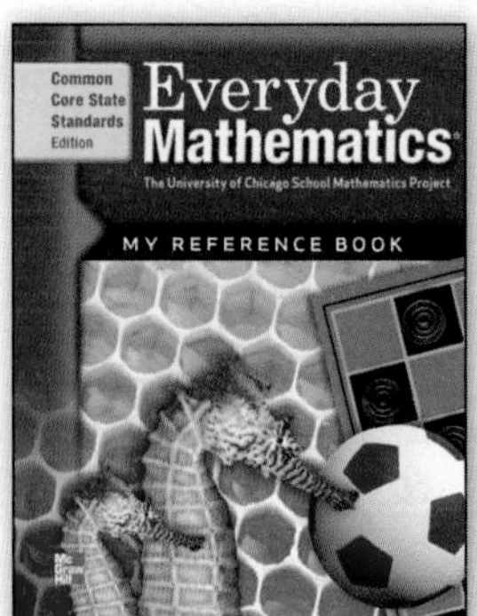

My Reference Book (Grades 1 and 2)
This hardcover book is a child's first mathematical reference book. *My Reference Book* contains explanations of key concepts as well as directions for games.

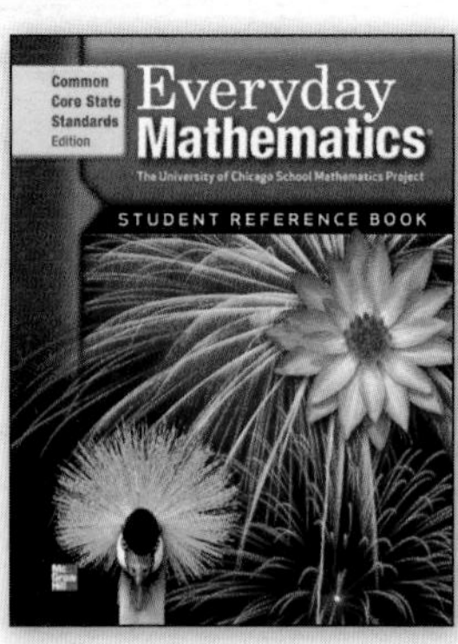

Student Reference Book (Grades 3–6)
Contains explanations of key mathematical content, along with directions for the *Everyday Mathematics* games. This hardbound book supports student learning in the classroom and at home.

Student Math Journal, Volumes 1 & 2 (Grades 1–6)
These consumable books provide daily support for classroom instruction. They provide a long-term record of each student's mathematical development.

Teacher Materials

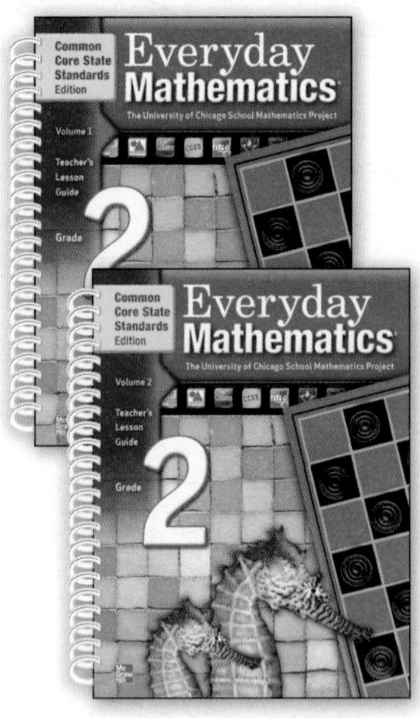

Teacher's Lesson Guide, Volumes 1 & 2 (Grades 1–6)
The core of the *Everyday Mathematics* program, the *Teacher's Lesson Guide* provides teachers with easy-to-follow lessons organized by instructional unit, as well as built-in mathematical content support. Lessons include planning and assessment tips and multilevel differentiation strategies to support all learners.

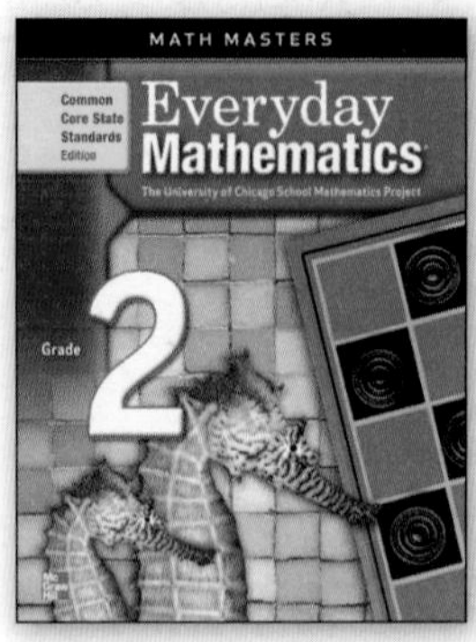

Math Masters (Grades 1–6)
Blackline masters that support daily lesson activities. Includes Home/Study Links, lesson-specific masters, game masters, and project masters.

Minute Math®+ (Grades 1–3)
5-Minute Math (Grades 4–6)
Brief activities for transition time and for spare moments throughout the day.

▶ Teacher Resources

Teacher's Reference Manual Contains comprehensive background information about mathematical content and program management for grades Early Childhood, 1–3, and 4–6.

Home Connection Handbook Enhances home-school communication for teachers and administrators. Includes masters for easy planning for grades Early Childhood, 1–3, and 4–6.

Differentiation Handbook (Grades 1–6)
Grade-specific handbooks that help teachers plan strategically in order to reach the needs of diverse learners.

Assessment Handbook (Grades 1–6)
Grade-specific handbooks provide explanations of key features of assessment in the *Everyday Mathematics* program. Includes all assessment masters.

Multilingual Handbook (Grades 1–6) Grade-specific component provides lesson-specific support to help meet the needs of a multilingual classroom. Includes a brief summary and an example for each lesson. Content provided in English, Spanish, traditional Chinese, Vietnamese, Arabic, and Hmong.

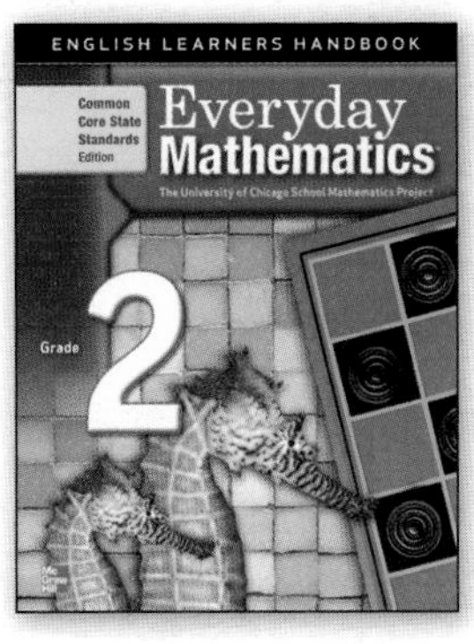

English Learners Handbook (Grades 1–6)
Grade-specific component provides lesson-specific comprehension strategies to aid in meeting the needs of a multilingual classroom. Also included are language development notes.

Content by Strand Poster
To help with pacing, the Key Concepts and Skills for each content strand are presented by month. Provides overview of program content for each grade level. Reverse side is a poster of the Grade-Level Goals.

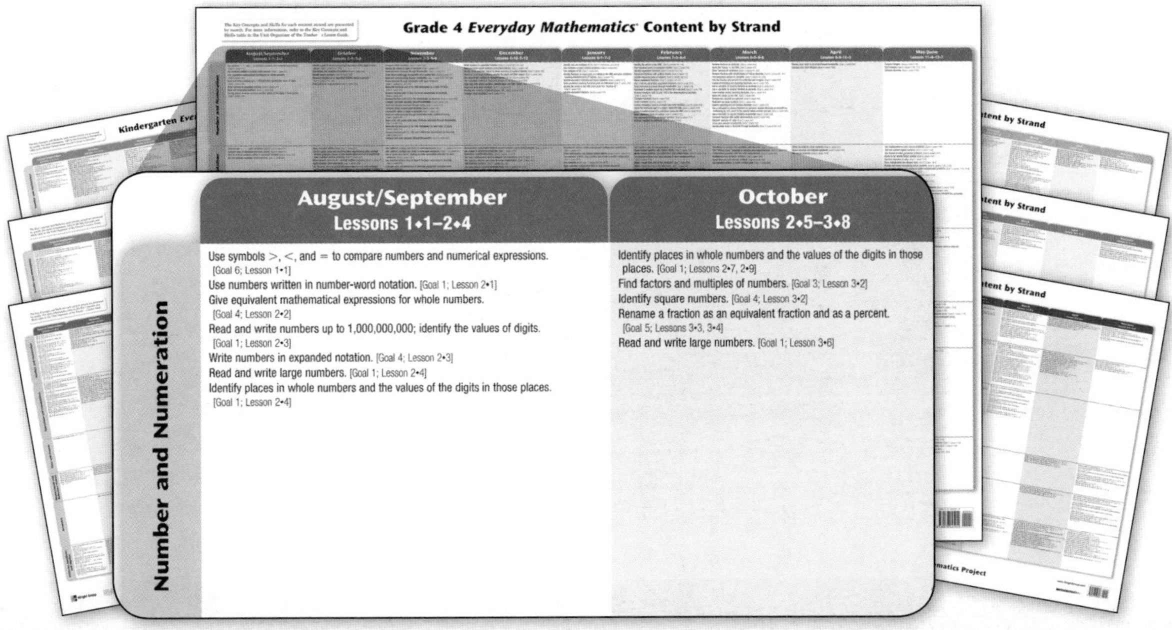

Everyday Mathematics

Technology at a Glance

Integrated technology enhances instruction and engages learners. *Everyday Mathematics* offers integrated technology for planning and teaching, practice, assessment, and home connections. Learn more and access all technology resources online at **www.everydaymathonline.com**.

Planning and Teaching

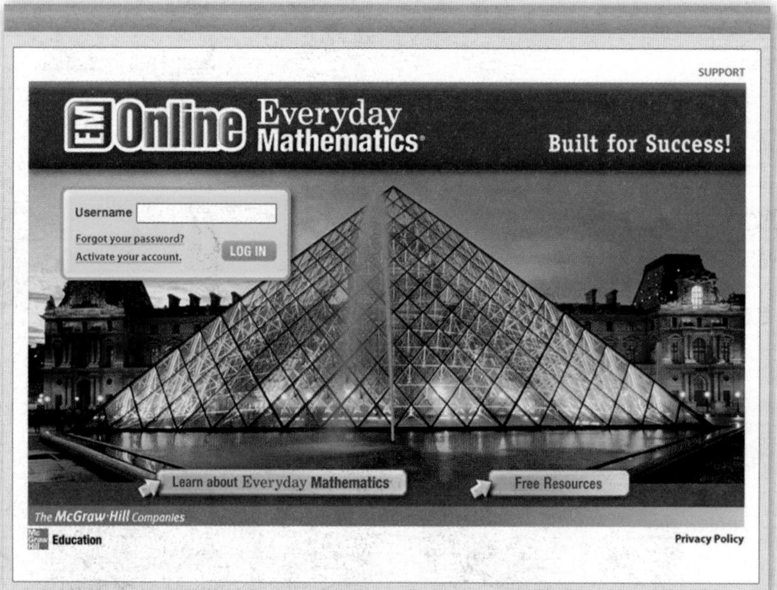

everydaymathonline.com

Offers an eSuite of fully integrated online tools that provide rich, interactive classroom experiences and solutions for students and teachers.

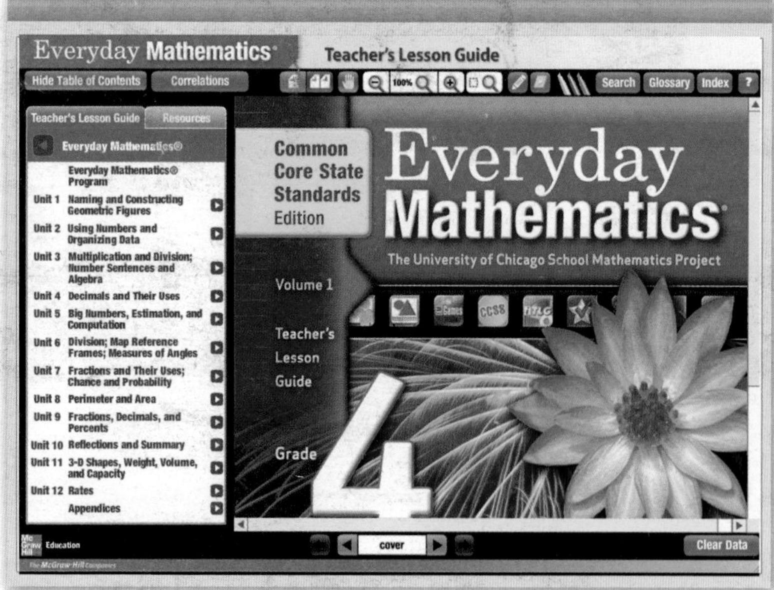

Interactive Teacher's Lesson Guide (iTLG)*

Enables digital access to the entire *Everyday Mathematics* program. Includes access to all components found in the Classroom Resource Package. Content is searchable by word or phase so all pages related to a specific topic can be found quickly and easily. Available online or on CD-ROM.

*Available as separate purchase

Planning and Teaching continued

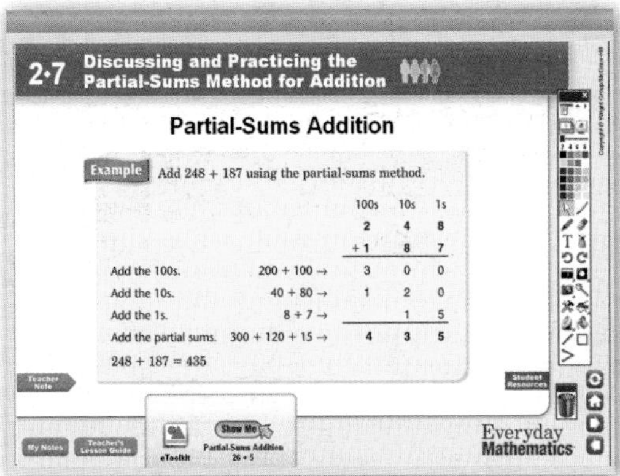

ePresentations*
Provide engaging lessons on your favorite interactive whiteboard for every lesson, except for the Progress Checks. Available online through the ePlanner Deluxe.

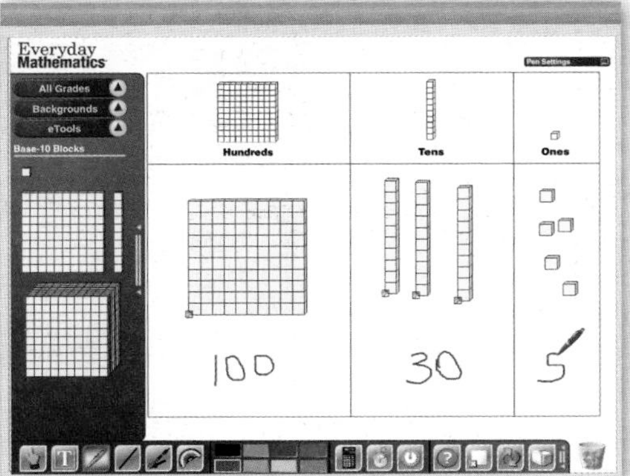

eToolkit*
Includes all the online tools and virtual manipulatives necessary to teach an *Everyday Mathematics* lesson. Available online through the ePlanner Deluxe.

Home Connections

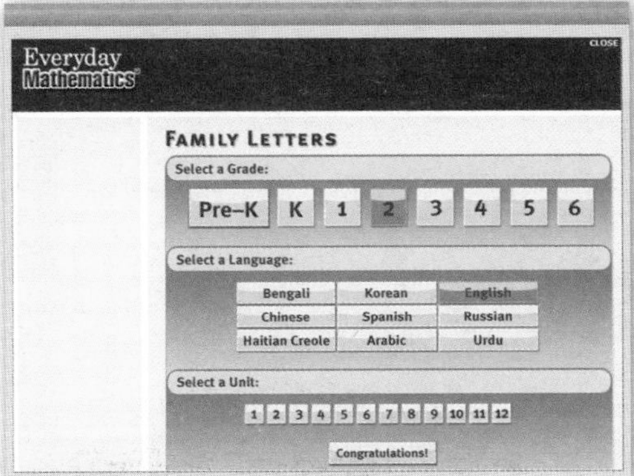

Family Letters** Support students at home by sharing each unit's key content and vocabulary, directions to games, Do-Anytime Activities, and answers to most Home Links/Study Links. Available online in nine different languages.

Practice

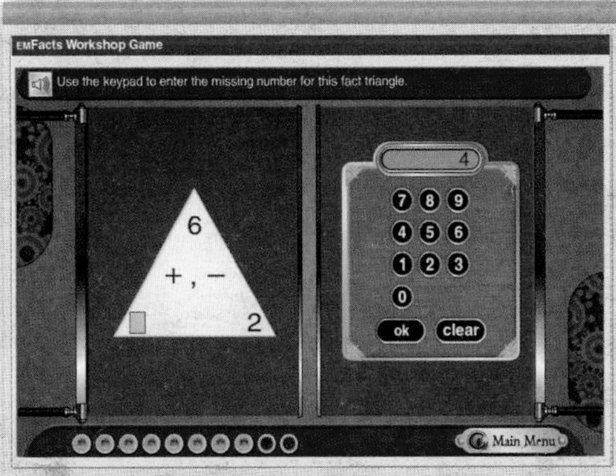

EM Facts Workshop Game
Provides interactive practice for students on basic facts and computation. Available online only.

Assessment

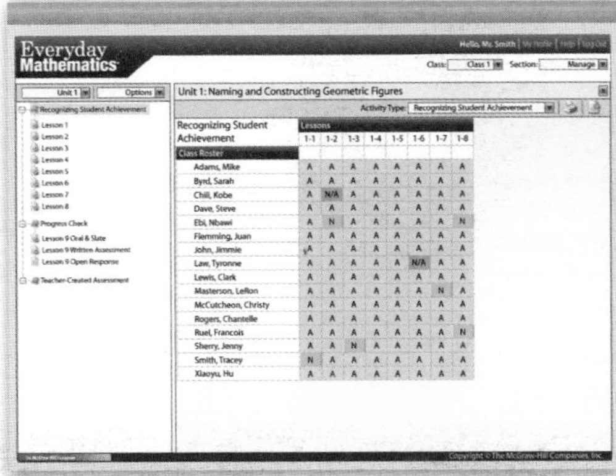

Assessment Management Spreadsheets
This electronic tool can be used to monitor and record students' progress.

After information on student performance is entered, the Assessment Management Spreadsheets provide reports showing students' progress toward Grade-Level Goals. Available online only.

*Available as separate purchase
**Languages other than English and Spanish available as separate purchase

Everyday Mathematics

Planning and Instructional Support

Each unit organizer provides an overview of the content for the unit. Also included is support for ongoing learning and practice, problem solving, and differentiated instruction. Detailed content support relating to the unit instruction is provided in Mathematical Background.

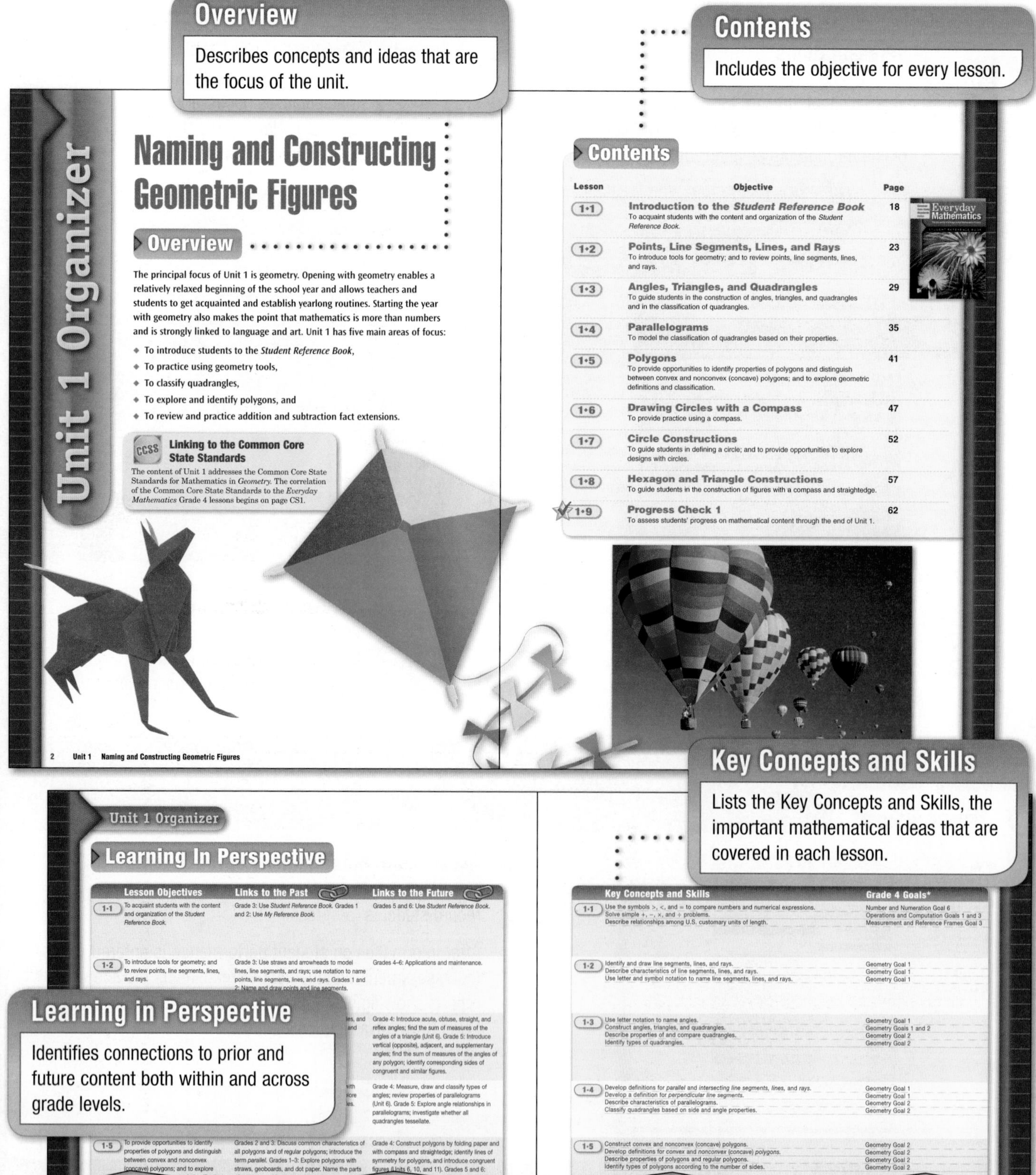

Overview
Describes concepts and ideas that are the focus of the unit.
Contents
Includes the objective for every lesson.
Key Concepts and Skills
Lists the Key Concepts and Skills, the important mathematical ideas that are covered in each lesson.
Learning in Perspective
Identifies connections to prior and future content both within and across grade levels.

Unit 1 Organizer

Naming and Constructing Geometric Figures

Overview

The principal focus of Unit 1 is geometry. Opening with geometry enables a relatively relaxed beginning of the school year and allows teachers and students to get acquainted and establish yearlong routines. Starting the year with geometry also makes the point that mathematics is more than numbers and is strongly linked to language and art. Unit 1 has five main areas of focus:

- To introduce students to the *Student Reference Book*,
- To practice using geometry tools,
- To classify quadrangles,
- To explore and identify polygons, and
- To review and practice addition and subtraction fact extensions.

Linking to the Common Core State Standards

The content of Unit 1 addresses the Common Core State Standards for Mathematics in *Geometry*. The correlation of the Common Core State Standards to the *Everyday Mathematics* Grade 4 lessons begins on page CS1.

2 Unit 1 Naming and Constructing Geometric Figures

Contents

Unit 1 Organizer

Learning In Perspective

	Lesson Objectives	Links to the Past	Links to the Future
1-1	To acquaint students with the content and organization of the *Student Reference Book*.	Grade 3: Use *Student Reference Book*. Grades 1 and 2: Use *My Reference Book*.	Grades 5 and 6: Use *Student Reference Book*.
1-2	To introduce tools for geometry; and to review points, line segments, lines, and rays.	Grade 3: Use straws and arrowheads to model lines, line segments, and rays; use notation to name points, line segments, lines, and rays. Grades 1 and 2: Name and draw points and line segments.	Grades 4–6: Applications and maintenance.
1-5	To provide opportunities to identify properties of polygons and distinguish between convex and nonconvex (concave) polygons; and to explore ... classification.	Grades 2 and 3: Discuss common characteristics of all polygons and of regular polygons; introduce the term *parallel*. Grades 1–3: Explore polygons with straws, geoboards, and dot paper. Name the parts of a polygon: side, vertex, and angle.	Grade 4: Construct polygons by folding paper and with compass and straightedge; identify lines of symmetry for polygons, and introduce congruent figures (Units 6, 10, and 11). Grades 5 and 6: ...

	Key Concepts and Skills	Grade 4 Goals*
1-1	Use the symbols >, <, and = to compare numbers and numerical expressions. Solve simple +, −, ×, and ÷ problems. Describe relationships among U.S. customary units of length.	Number and Numeration Goal 6 Operations and Computation Goals 1 and 3 Measurement and Reference Frames Goal 3
1-2	Identify and draw line segments, lines, and rays. Describe characteristics of line segments, lines, and rays. Use letter and symbol notation to name line segments, lines, and rays.	Geometry Goal 1 Geometry Goal 1 Geometry Goal 1
1-3	Use letter notation to name angles. Construct angles, triangles, and quadrangles. Describe properties of and compare quadrangles. Identify types of quadrangles.	Geometry Goal 1 Geometry Goals 1 and 2 Geometry Goal 2 Geometry Goal 2
1-4	Develop definitions for *parallel* and *intersecting line segments, lines,* and *rays*. Develop a definition for *perpendicular line segments*. Describe characteristics of parallelograms. Classify quadrangles based on side and angle properties.	Geometry Goal 1 Geometry Goal 1 Geometry Goal 2 Geometry Goal 2
1-5	Construct convex and nonconvex (concave) polygons. Develop definitions for *convex* and *nonconvex (concave) polygons*. Describe properties of polygons and regular polygons. Identify types of polygons according to the number of sides.	Geometry Goal 2 Geometry Goal 2 Geometry Goal 2 Geometry Goal 2

Ongoing Practice

Highlights essential activities that provide review and practice for maintaining skills. These activities include Math Boxes, Home/Study Links, games, and Extra Practice.

Unit 1 Organizer

A Balanced Curriculum

Ongoing Practice

Everyday Mathematics provides numerous opportunities for ongoing practice. These activities are embedded throughout the lessons:

Mental Math and Reflexes activities promote speed and accuracy in mental computation.

Math Boxes offer mixed practice and are paired across lessons as shown in the brackets below. This makes them useful as assessment tools. The last one or two boxes on each page preview the next unit's content.

Mixed practice	[1•1, 1•3], [1•2, 1•4], [1•5, 1•7], [1•6, 1•8]
Mixed practice with multiple choice	1•1, 1•4, 1•5, 1•8
Mixed practice with writing/reasoning opportunity	1•3, 1•4, 1•6, 1•7

Study Links are daily homework assignments that review the content of the lesson and often contain ongoing facts practice or computation practice.

5-Minute Math problems are offered for additional practice in Lesson 1•3.

EM Facts Workshop Game provides online practice of basic facts and computation.

EXTRA PRACTICE **Extra Practice** activities are included in Lessons 1•3, 1•6, and 1•8.

Daily Assessments

Includes the assessment opportunities in each lesson to assess progress toward Grade-Level Goals.

Assessment Support

Identifies useful pages in the *Assessment Handbook* for each unit.

Unit 1 Organizer

Balanced Assessment

Daily Assessments

- **Recognizing Student Achievement** – A daily assessment that is included in every lesson to evaluate students' progress toward the Grade 4 Grade-Level Goals.
- **Informing Instruction** – Notes that appear throughout the unit to help anticipate students' common errors and suggest appropriate problem-solving strategies.

Lesson	Recognizing Student Achievement	Informing Instruction
1•1	Demonstrate automaticity with addition fact extensions. [OC Goal 1]	
1•2	Describe a line segment and a line. [GEO Goal 1]	Connect points to other points.
1•3	Compare and contrast plane figures. [GEO Goal 2]	Consider the measures of angles rather than the lengths of rays.
1•4	Understand parallel line segments. [GEO Goal 1]	
1•5	Explain the properties of polygons. [GEO Goal 2]	Distinguish regular polygons from other polygons.
1•6	Understand right angles. [GEO Goal 1]	
1•7	Construct circles with a compass. [GEO Goal 2]	
1•8	Demonstrate automaticity with subtraction fact extensions. [OC Goal 1]	Connect consecutive marks to form a regular hexagon.

[NN] Number and Numeration [OC] Operations and Computation [DC] Data and Chance
[MRF] Measurement and Reference Frames [GEO] Geometry [PFA] Patterns, Functions, and Algebra

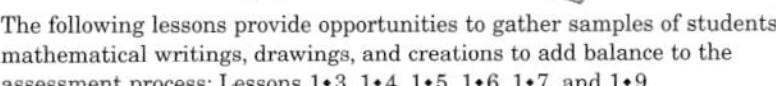

Portfolio Opportunities

The following lessons provide opportunities to gather samples of students' mathematical writings, drawings, and creations to add balance to the assessment process: Lessons 1•3, 1•4, 1•5, 1•6, 1•7, and 1•9.

See pages 16 and 17 in the *Assessment Handbook* for more information about portfolios and how to use them.

Unit Assessment

Progress Check 1 – A cumulative assessment of concepts and skills taught in Unit 1, providing information for evaluating students' progress and planning for future instruction. These assessments include oral/slate, written, and open-response activities, as shown below in the sample Progress Check lesson opener.

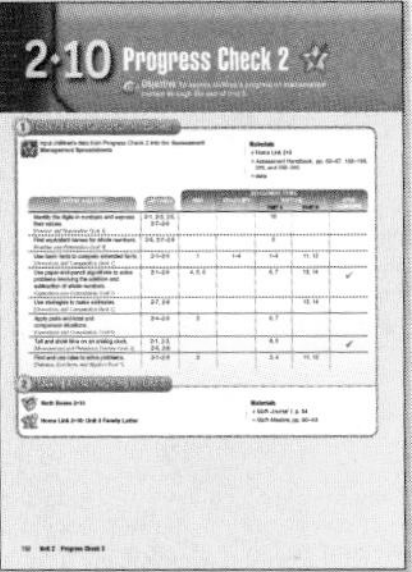

Core Assessment Resources

Assessment Handbook

- **Unit 1 Assessment Overview,** pages 52–59
- **Unit 1 Assessment Masters,** pages 154–158
- **Unit 1 Individual Profiles of Progress,** pages 246, 247, and 302
- **Unit 1 Class Checklists,** pages 248, 249, and 303
- **Beginning-of-Year Assessment,*** pages 227A–227D
- **Math Logs,** pages 306–308
- **Exit Slip,** page 311
- **Other Student Assessment Forms,** pages 304, 305, 309, and 310

*The Beginning-of-Year Assessment is one of the screening tools that can be used to help identify which concepts and skills students have learned and to help plan instruction for the upcoming year.

Assessment Management Spreadsheets

The Assessment Management Spreadsheets consist of the Digital Class Checklists and Individual Profile of Progress Checklists. Use them to monitor, record, and report student progress.

Unit 1 Organizer

Addressing All Needs

Differentiated Instruction

Adjusting the Activity – suggests adaptations that target advanced learners, English language learners, or learners who need additional instructional support.

ELL SUPPORT / ELL – provides lesson-specific suggestions to help English language learners understand and process the mathematical content.

READINESS – accesses students' prior knowledge or previews content that prepares students to engage in the lesson's Part 1 activities.

EXTRA PRACTICE – provides additional opportunities to apply the mathematical content of the lesson.

ENRICHMENT – enables students to apply or further explore the mathematical content of the lesson.

Lesson	Adjusting the Activity	ELL Support/ ELL	Readiness	Extra Practice	Enrichment
1•1	•	•	•		•
1•2	•	•	•		•
1•3	•	•	•	•	•
1•4	•	•	•		•
1•5	•	•	•		•
1•6	•			•	•
1•7	•	•			•
1•8	•		•	•	•

Differentiated Instruction

Highlights the many facets of differentiated instruction in each unit. Includes English language learner support, as well as Enrichment, Readiness, and Extra Practice activities.

3-Part Lesson Plan

3-Part Lesson

1. **Teaching the Lesson** Provides main instructional activities for the lesson.
2. **Ongoing Learning and Practice** Supports previously introduced concepts and skills; essential for maintaining skills.
1. **Differentiation Options** Includes options for supporting the needs of all students; usually an extension of Part 1, Teaching the Lesson.

Technology Resources

Suggests appropriate digital resources that support instruction of the lesson.

Lesson Opener

At-a-glance view of the 3-part lesson, highlighting materials, vocabulary, assessment, and more!

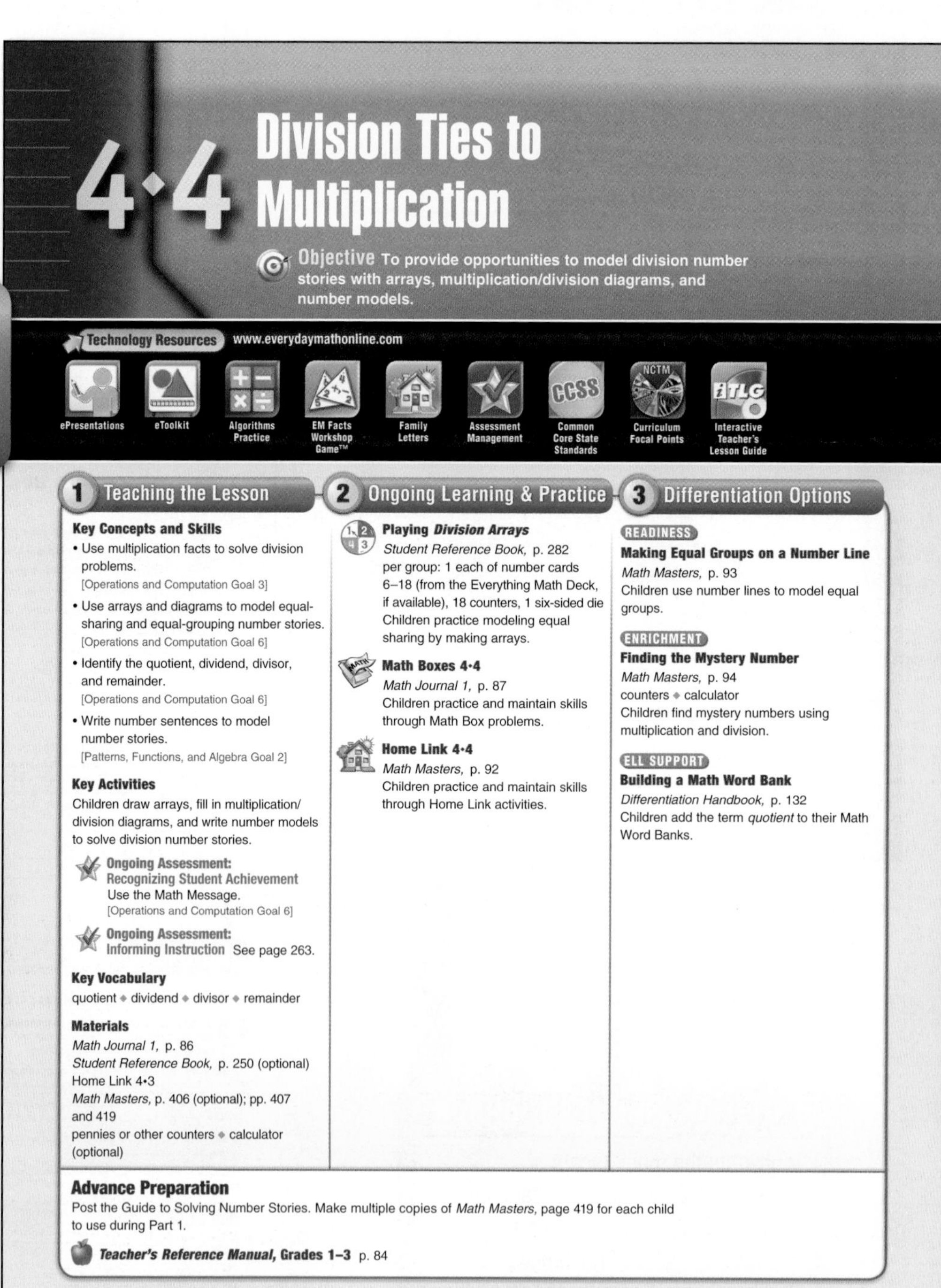

4•4 **Division Ties to Multiplication**

Objective To provide opportunities to model division number stories with arrays, multiplication/division diagrams, and number models.

Technology Resources www.everydaymathonline.com

ePresentations · eToolkit · Algorithms Practice · EM Facts Workshop Game™ · Family Letters · Assessment Management · Common Core State Standards · Curriculum Focal Points · Interactive Teacher's Lesson Guide

1 Teaching the Lesson

Key Concepts and Skills
- Use multiplication facts to solve division problems. [Operations and Computation Goal 3]
- Use arrays and diagrams to model equal-sharing and equal-grouping number stories. [Operations and Computation Goal 6]
- Identify the quotient, dividend, divisor, and remainder. [Operations and Computation Goal 6]
- Write number sentences to model number stories. [Patterns, Functions, and Algebra Goal 2]

Key Activities
Children draw arrays, fill in multiplication/division diagrams, and write number models to solve division number stories.

Ongoing Assessment: Recognizing Student Achievement Use the Math Message. [Operations and Computation Goal 6]

Ongoing Assessment: Informing Instruction See page 263.

Key Vocabulary
quotient • dividend • divisor • remainder

Materials
Math Journal 1, p. 86
Student Reference Book, p. 250 (optional)
Home Link 4•3
Math Masters, p. 406 (optional); pp. 407 and 419
pennies or other counters • calculator (optional)

2 Ongoing Learning & Practice

Playing *Division Arrays*
Student Reference Book, p. 282
per group: 1 each of number cards 6–18 (from the Everything Math Deck, if available), 18 counters, 1 six-sided die
Children practice modeling equal sharing by making arrays.

Math Boxes 4•4
Math Journal 1, p. 87
Children practice and maintain skills through Math Box problems.

Home Link 4•4
Math Masters, p. 92
Children practice and maintain skills through Home Link activities.

3 Differentiation Options

READINESS
Making Equal Groups on a Number Line
Math Masters, p. 93
Children use number lines to model equal groups.

ENRICHMENT
Finding the Mystery Number
Math Masters, p. 94
counters • calculator
Children find mystery numbers using multiplication and division.

ELL SUPPORT
Building a Math Word Bank
Differentiation Handbook, p. 132
Children add the term *quotient* to their Math Word Banks.

Advance Preparation
Post the Guide to Solving Number Stories. Make multiple copies of *Math Masters,* page 419 for each child to use during Part 1.

***Teacher's Reference Manual,* Grades 1–3** p. 84

260 Unit 4 Multiplication and Division

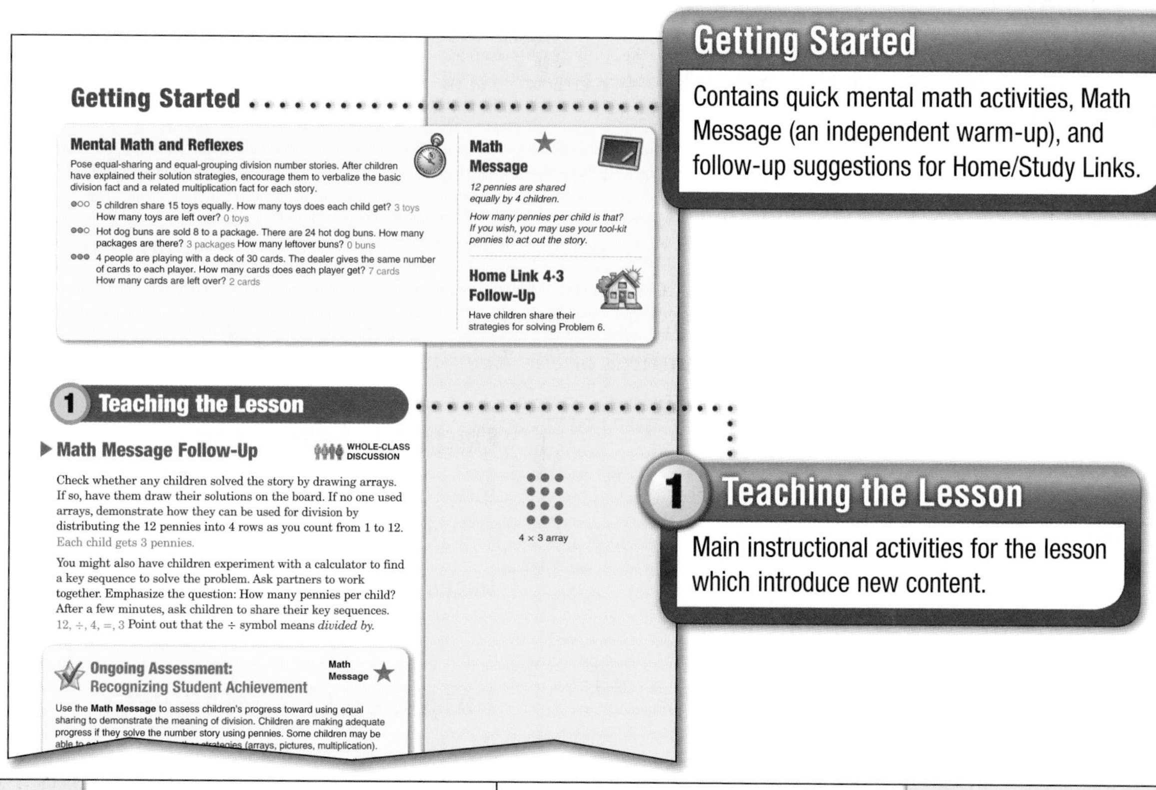

Getting Started

Contains quick mental math activities, Math Message (an independent warm-up), and follow-up suggestions for Home/Study Links.

1 Teaching the Lesson

Main instructional activities for the lesson which introduce new content.

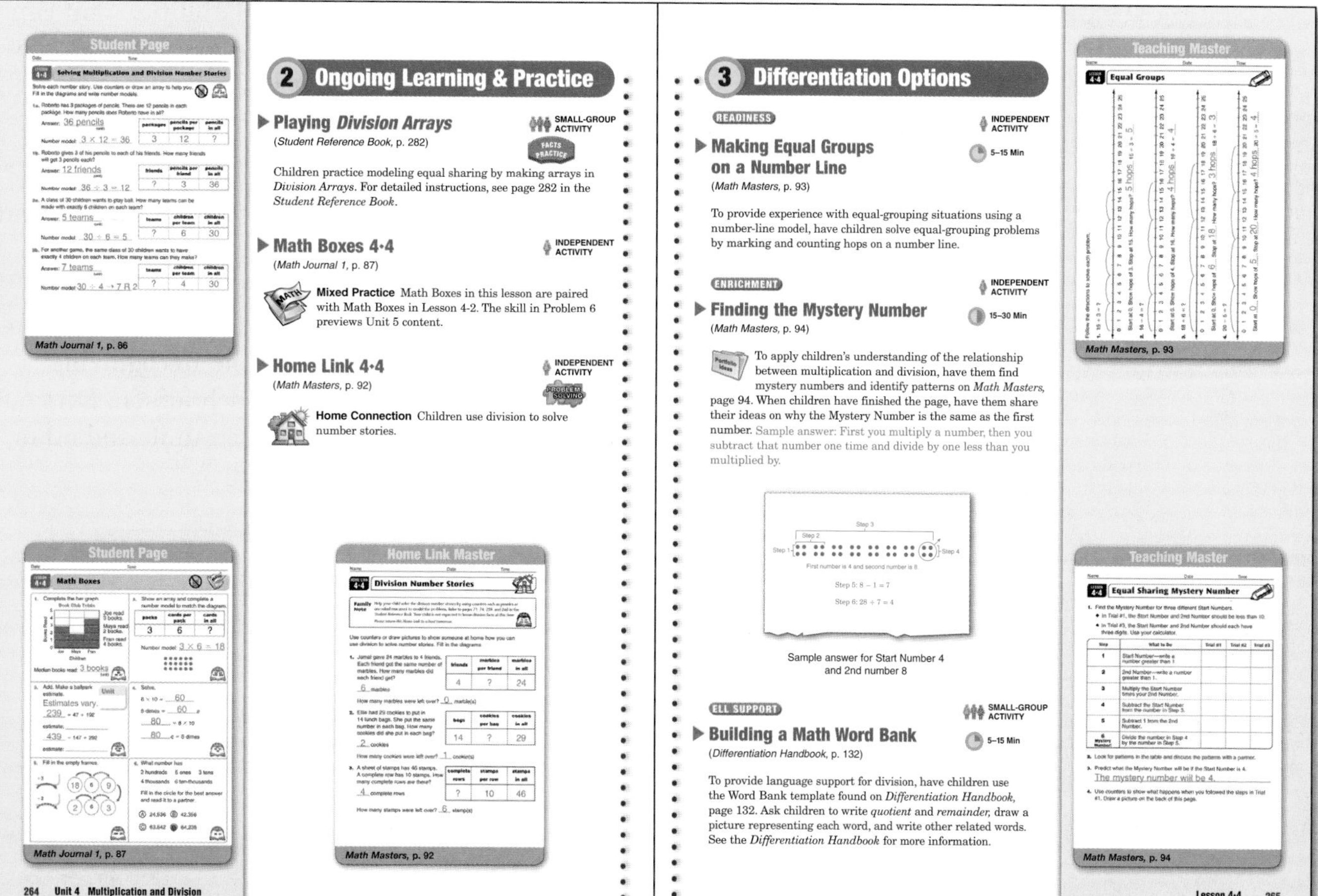

2 Ongoing Learning & Practice

Activities provide essential review and practice for maintaining skills. Includes *Everyday Mathematics* games appropriate for revisiting mathematics skills, as well as Math Boxes and Home/Study Links.

3 Differentiation Options

Includes Readiness activities which cover mathematical content necessary for student success in the lesson. English Language Learner Support, Enrichment, and Extra Practice are also key features of the Differentiation Options.

Everyday Mathematics

Assessment

In *Everyday Mathematics,* assessment is like a motion picture revealing the development of each student's mathematical understanding over time, while giving the teacher useful feedback about the instructional needs of both individual students and the class as a whole. The *Assessment Handbook* contains a complete explanation of the philosophy of assessment and assessment features of the *Everyday Mathematics* program.

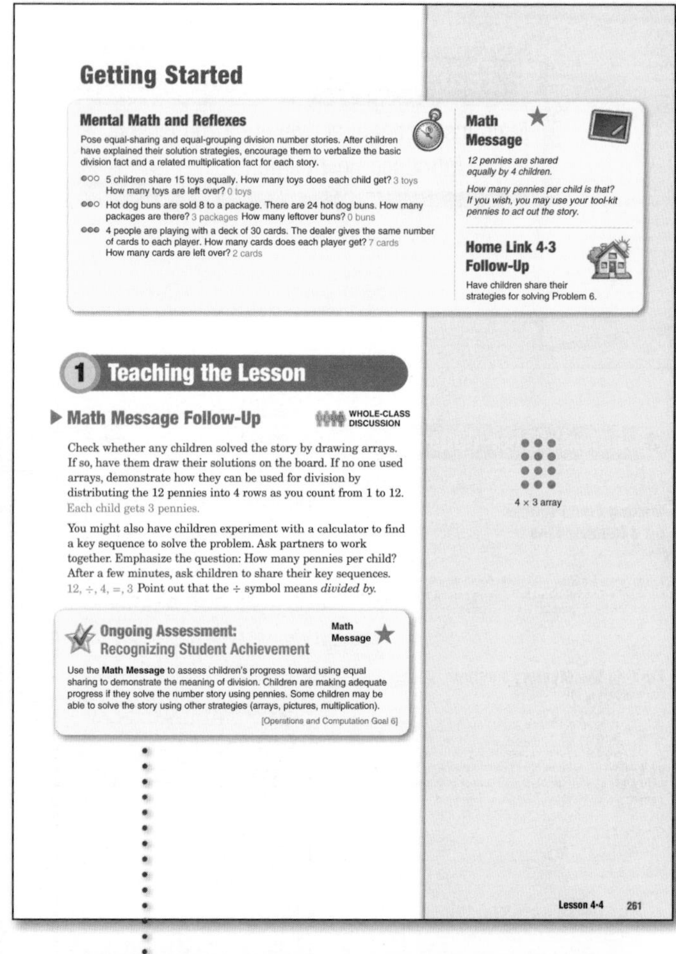

Getting Started

Mental Math and Reflexes

Pose equal-sharing and equal-grouping division number stories. After children have explained their solution strategies, encourage them to verbalize the basic division fact and a related multiplication fact for each story.

●○○ 5 children share 15 toys equally. How many toys does each child get? 3 toys How many toys are left over? 0 toys

●●○ Hot dog buns are sold 8 to a package. There are 24 hot dog buns. How many packages are there? 3 packages How many leftover buns? 0 buns

●●● 4 people are playing with a deck of 30 cards. The dealer gives the same number of cards to each player. How many cards does each player get? 7 cards How many cards are left over? 2 cards

Math Message

12 pennies are shared equally by 4 children.

How many pennies per child is that? If you wish, you may use your tool-kit pennies to act out the story.

Home Link 4·3 Follow-Up

Have children share their strategies for solving Problem 6.

1 Teaching the Lesson

▶ Math Message Follow-Up

WHOLE-CLASS DISCUSSION

Check whether any children solved the story by drawing arrays. If so, have them draw their solutions on the board. If no one used arrays, demonstrate how they can be used for division by distributing the 12 pennies into 4 rows as you count from 1 to 12. Each child gets 3 pennies.

You might also have children experiment with a calculator to find a key sequence to solve the problem. Ask partners to work together. Emphasize the question: How many pennies per child? After a few minutes, ask children to share their key sequences. 12, ÷, 4, =, 3 Point out that the ÷ symbol means *divided by.*

4 × 3 array

Ongoing Assessment: Recognizing Student Achievement

Math Message

Use the **Math Message** to assess children's progress toward using equal sharing to demonstrate the meaning of division. Children are making adequate progress if they solve the number story using pennies. Some children may be able to solve the story using other strategies (arrays, pictures, multiplication).

[Operations and Computation Goal 6]

Lesson 4·4 261

Recognizing Student Achievment

Each lesson contains a Recognizing Student Achievement note. The notes highlight tasks that can be used to monitor student progress.

Ongoing Assessment

Ongoing Assessment: Recognizing Student Achievement is included in every lesson.

Ongoing Assessment: Informing Instruction is included in many lessons to help you guide instruction.

Purposes of Assessment

Formative Assessments provide information about students' current knowledge and abilities that can be used to plan or inform instruction. Information from almost any assessment task in *Everyday Mathematics* might be useful for planning future instruction.

Summative Assessments measure student growth and achievement and provide information that may be used to assign grades or otherwise evaluate students' performance. Summative assessments in *Everyday Mathematics* include the Recognizing Student Achievement tasks in each lesson, Part A of the written assessments in each unit, and other assessments labeled "fair to grade."

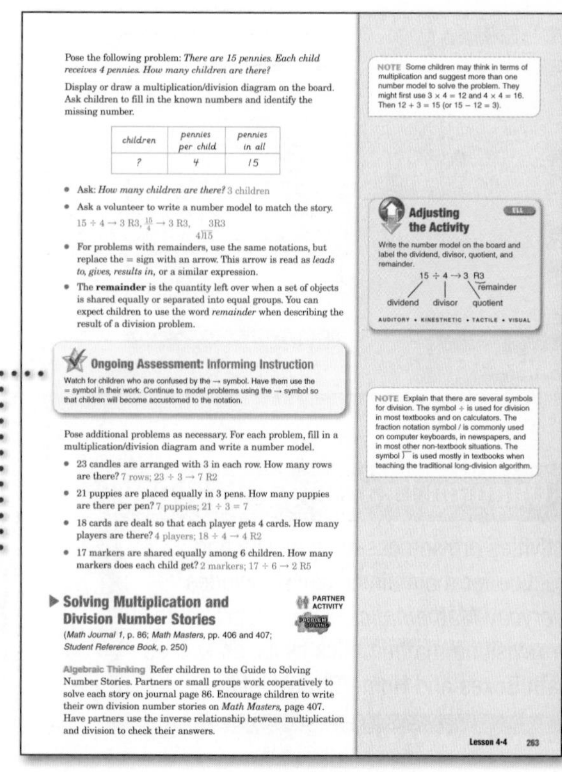

Pose the following problem: *There are 15 pennies. Each child receives 4 pennies. How many children are there?*

Display or draw a multiplication/division diagram on the board. Ask children to fill in the known numbers and identify the missing number.

children	pennies per child	pennies in all
?	4	15

- Ask: *How many children are there?* 3 children
- Ask a volunteer to write a number model to match the story. 15 ÷ 4 → 3 R3, $\frac{15}{4}$ → 3 R3, $4\overline{)15}$ 3R3
- For problems with remainders, use the same notations, but replace the = sign with an arrow. This arrow is read as *leads to, gives, results in,* or a similar expression.
- The **remainder** is the quantity left over when a set of objects is shared equally or separated into equal groups. You can expect children to use the word *remainder* when describing the result of a division problem.

NOTE Some children may think in terms of multiplication and suggest more than one number model to solve the problem. They might first use 3 × 4 = 12 and 4 × 4 = 16. Then 12 + 3 = 15 (or 15 − 12 = 3).

Adjusting the Activity

ELL

Write the number model on the board and label the dividend, divisor, quotient, and remainder.

15 ÷ 4 → 3 R3 (dividend, divisor, quotient, remainder)

AUDITORY • KINESTHETIC • TACTILE • VISUAL

Ongoing Assessment: Informing Instruction

Watch for children who are confused by the → symbol. Have them use the = symbol in their work. Continue to model problems using the → symbol so that children will become accustomed to the notation.

NOTE Explain that there are several symbols for division. The symbol ÷ is used for division in most textbooks and on calculators. The fraction notation symbol / is commonly used on computer keyboards, in newspapers, and in most other non-textbook situations. The symbol $\overline{)\ }$ is used mostly in textbooks when teaching the traditional long-division algorithm.

Pose additional problems as necessary. For each problem, fill in a multiplication/division diagram and write a number model.

- 23 candles are arranged with 3 in each row. How many rows are there? 7 rows; 23 ÷ 3 → 7 R2
- 21 puppies are placed equally in 3 pens. How many puppies are there per pen? 7 puppies; 21 ÷ 3 = 7
- 18 cards are dealt so that each player gets 4 cards. How many players are there? 4 players; 18 ÷ 4 → 4 R2
- 17 markers are shared equally among 6 children. How many markers does each child get? 2 markers; 17 ÷ 6 → 2 R5

▶ Solving Multiplication and Division Number Stories

PARTNER ACTIVITY

PROBLEM SOLVING

(*Math Journal 1*, p. 86; *Math Masters*, pp. 406 and 407; *Student Reference Book*, p. 250)

Algebraic Thinking Refer children to the Guide to Solving Number Stories. Partners or small groups work cooperatively to solve each story on journal page 86. Encourage children to write their own division number stories on *Math Masters*, page 407. Have partners use the inverse relationship between multiplication and division to check their answers.

Lesson 4·4 263

Informing Instruction

Suggests how to use observation of students' work to effectively adapt instruction.

Periodic Assessment

The Progress Check lessons, included for each unit, provide several types of periodic assessment.

Online Assessment Tools

The Assessment Management Spreadsheets provide additional opportunities to monitor student progress and inform instruction.

Written Assessment

Each Written Assessment has two parts: Part A Recognizing Student Achievement (summative assessment), and Part B Informing Instruction (formative assessment).

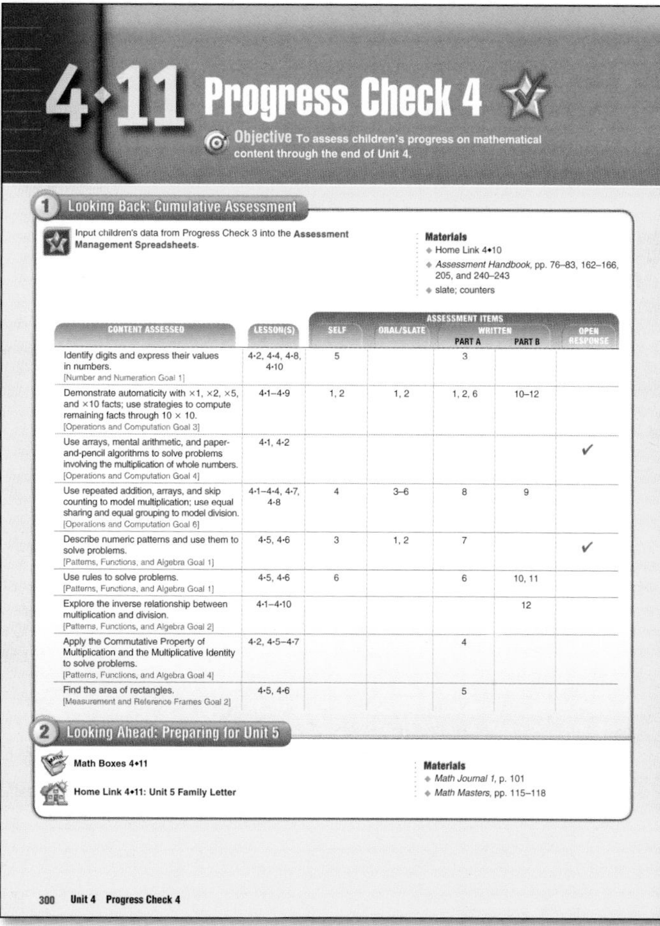

4•11 Progress Check 4

Objective To assess children's progress on mathematical content through the end of Unit 4.

1 Looking Back: Cumulative Assessment

Input children's data from Progress Check 3 into the **Assessment Management Spreadsheets**.

Materials
- Home Link 4•10
- *Assessment Handbook*, pp. 76–83, 162–166, 205, and 240–243
- slate; counters

CONTENT ASSESSED	LESSON(S)	ASSESSMENT ITEMS				
		SELF	ORAL/SLATE	WRITTEN PART A	WRITTEN PART B	OPEN RESPONSE
Identify digits and express their values in numbers. [Number and Numeration Goal 1]	4•2, 4•4, 4•8, 4•10	5		3		
Demonstrate automaticity with ×1, ×2, ×5, and ×10 facts; use strategies to compute remaining facts through 10 × 10. [Operations and Computation Goal 3]	4•1–4•9	1, 2	1, 2	1, 2, 6	10–12	
Use arrays, mental arithmetic, and paper-and-pencil algorithms to solve problems involving the multiplication of whole numbers. [Operations and Computation Goal 4]	4•1, 4•2					✓
Use repeated addition, arrays, and skip counting to model multiplication; use equal sharing and equal grouping to model division. [Operations and Computation Goal 6]	4•1–4•4, 4•7, 4•8	4	3–6	8	9	
Describe numeric patterns and use them to solve problems. [Patterns, Functions, and Algebra Goal 1]	4•5, 4•6	3	1, 2	7		✓
Use rules to solve problems. [Patterns, Functions, and Algebra Goal 1]	4•5, 4•6	6		6	10, 11	
Explore the inverse relationship between multiplication and division. [Patterns, Functions, and Algebra Goal 2]	4•1–4•10				12	
Apply the Commutative Property of Multiplication and the Multiplicative Identity to solve problems. [Patterns, Functions, and Algebra Goal 4]	4•2, 4•5–4•7			4		
Find the area of rectangles. [Measurement and Reference Frames Goal 2]	4•5, 4•6			5		

2 Looking Ahead: Preparing for Unit 5

Math Boxes 4•11

Home Link 4•11: Unit 5 Family Letter

Materials
- *Math Journal 1*, p. 101
- *Math Masters*, pp. 115–118

300 Unit 4 Progress Check 4

Progress Check

Provides multiple assessment options. Includes Oral and Slate Assessments, Written Assessment, Open Response, and Self Assessment.

Open Response

Each unit provides an Open Response question. Sample student responses as well as rubrics for every Open Response question are found in the *Assessment Handbook.*

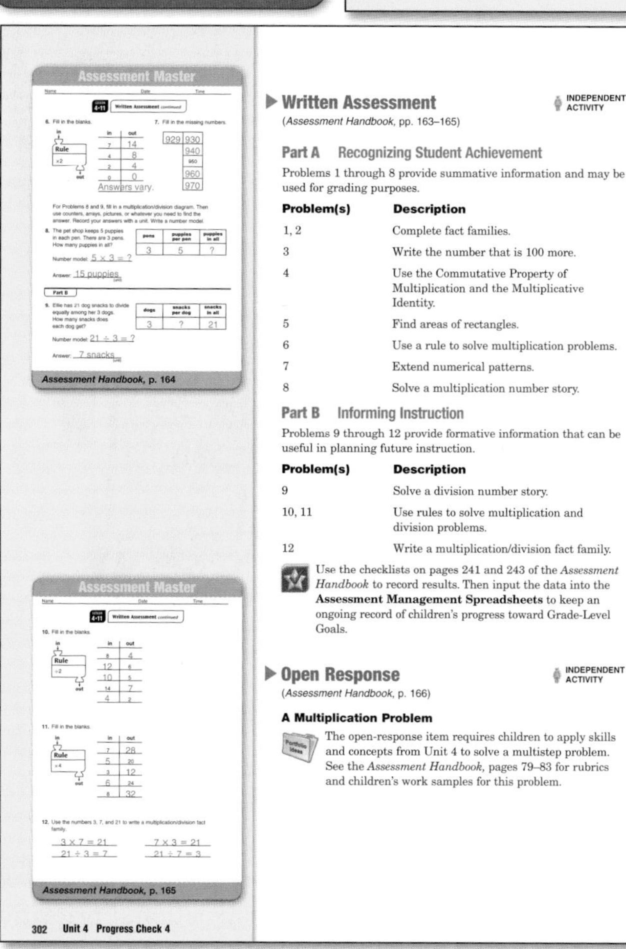

Assessment Master

Assessment Handbook, p. 164

Assessment Master

Assessment Handbook, p. 165

Written Assessment INDEPENDENT ACTIVITY
(*Assessment Handbook*, pp. 163–165)

Part A Recognizing Student Achievement

Problems 1 through 8 provide summative information and may be used for grading purposes.

Problem(s)	Description
1, 2	Complete fact families.
3	Write the number that is 100 more.
4	Use the Commutative Property of Multiplication and the Multiplicative Identity.
5	Find areas of rectangles.
6	Use a rule to solve multiplication problems.
7	Extend numerical patterns.
8	Solve a multiplication number story.

Part B Informing Instruction

Problems 9 through 12 provide formative information that can be useful in planning future instruction.

Problem(s)	Description
9	Solve a division number story.
10, 11	Use rules to solve multiplication and division problems.
12	Write a multiplication/division fact family.

Use the checklists on pages 241 and 243 of the *Assessment Handbook* to record results. Then input the data into the **Assessment Management Spreadsheets** to keep an ongoing record of children's progress toward Grade-Level Goals.

Open Response INDEPENDENT ACTIVITY
(*Assessment Handbook*, p. 166)

A Multiplication Problem

The open-response item requires children to apply skills and concepts from Unit 4 to solve a multistep problem. See the *Assessment Handbook*, pages 79–83 for rubrics and children's work samples for this problem.

302 Unit 4 Progress Check 4

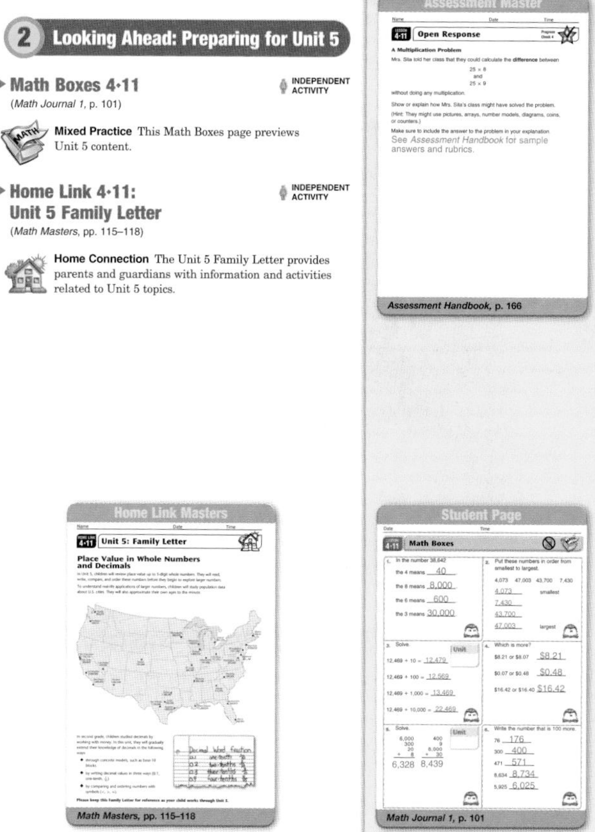

2 Looking Ahead: Preparing for Unit 5

Math Boxes 4•11 INDEPENDENT ACTIVITY
(*Math Journal 1*, p. 101)

Mixed Practice This Math Boxes page previews Unit 5 content.

Home Link 4•11: Unit 5 Family Letter INDEPENDENT ACTIVITY
(*Math Masters*, pp. 115–118)

Home Connection The Unit 5 Family Letter provides parents and guardians with information and activities related to Unit 5 topics.

Assessment Master

Assessment Handbook, p. 166

Home Link Masters

Math Masters, pp. 115–118

Student Page

Math Journal 1, p. 101

Lesson 4•11 303

Professional Development

Everyday Mathematics believes it is critical to support teachers with the materials necessary to enable students to meet higher expectations of mathematical achievement. In addition to district-specific training offered at implementation and for continued support, numerous professional development opportunities are built into the *Everyday Mathematics* program.

Teacher's Reference Manual

An invaluable resource that contains comprehensive background information about mathematical content as well as a guide to help organize the curriculum, the students, and the program materials.

Teacher's Lesson Guide

Professional development is embedded throughout, including Mathematical Background in each unit organizer to highlight the major content ideas presented and to help establish instructional priorities.

Supporting Students and Home

Family Involvement

Within *Everyday Mathematics* there are several opportunities for supporting the home–school connection.

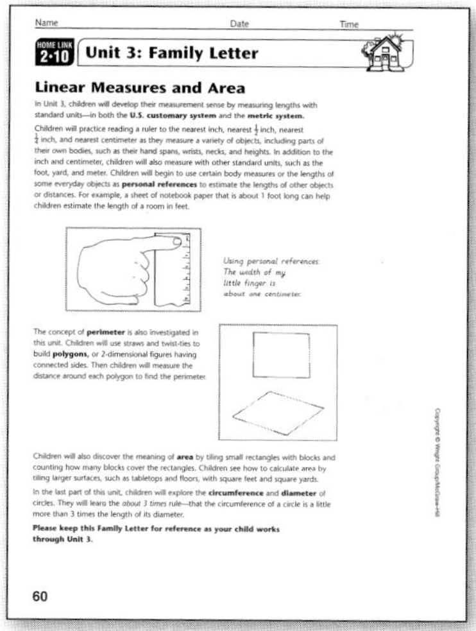

Name Date Time

HOME LINK 2·10 **Unit 3: Family Letter**

Linear Measures and Area

In Unit 3, children will develop their measurement sense by measuring lengths with standard units—in both the **U.S. customary system** and the **metric system.**

Children will practice reading a ruler to the nearest inch, nearest $\frac{1}{2}$ inch, nearest $\frac{1}{4}$ inch, and nearest centimeter as they measure a variety of objects, including parts of their own bodies, such as their hand spans, wrists, necks, and heights. In addition to the inch and centimeter, children will also measure with other standard units, such as the foot, yard, and meter. Children will begin to use certain body measures or the lengths of some everyday objects as **personal references** to estimate the lengths of other objects or distances. For example, a sheet of notebook paper that is about 1 foot long can help children estimate the length of a room in feet.

Using personal references: The width of my little finger is about one centimeter.

The concept of **perimeter** is also investigated in this unit. Children will use straws and twist-ties to build **polygons,** or 2-dimensional figures having connected sides. Then children will measure the distance around each polygon to find the perimeter.

Children will also discover the meaning of **area** by tiling small rectangles with blocks and counting how many blocks cover the rectangles. Children see how to calculate area by tiling larger surfaces, such as tabletops and floors, with square feet and square yards.

In the last part of this unit, children will explore the **circumference** and **diameter** of circles. They will learn the *about 3 times* rule—that the circumference of a circle is a little more than 3 times the length of its diameter.

Please keep this Family Letter for reference as your child works through Unit 3.

Copyright © Wright Group/McGraw-Hill

60

Family Letters

Each unit's Family Letter explains the unit's key content and vocabulary and provides directions for appropriate games, Do-Anytime Activities, and answers to most Home/Study Links for the unit.

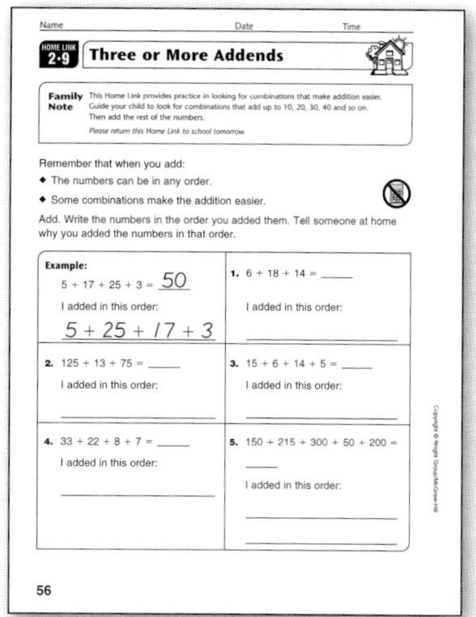

Name Date Time

HOME LINK 2·9 **Three or More Addends**

Family Note This Home Link provides practice in looking for combinations that make addition easier. Guide your child to look for combinations that add up to 10, 20, 30, 40 and so on. Then add the rest of the numbers.

Please return this Home Link to school tomorrow.

Remember that when you add:

- The numbers can be in any order.
- Some combinations make the addition easier.

Add. Write the numbers in the order you added them. Tell someone at home why you added the numbers in that order.

Example: 5 + 17 + 25 + 3 = 50 I added in this order: 5 + 25 + 17 + 3	**1.** 6 + 18 + 14 = ____ I added in this order: ________
2. 125 + 13 + 75 = ____ I added in this order: ________	**3.** 15 + 6 + 14 + 5 = ____ I added in this order: ________
4. 33 + 22 + 8 + 7 = ____ I added in this order: ________	**5.** 150 + 215 + 300 + 50 + 200 = ____ I added in this order: ________

Copyright © Wright Group/McGraw-Hill

56

Home Links/Study Links

Each lesson has a Home/Study Link. They show families what students are doing in mathematics.

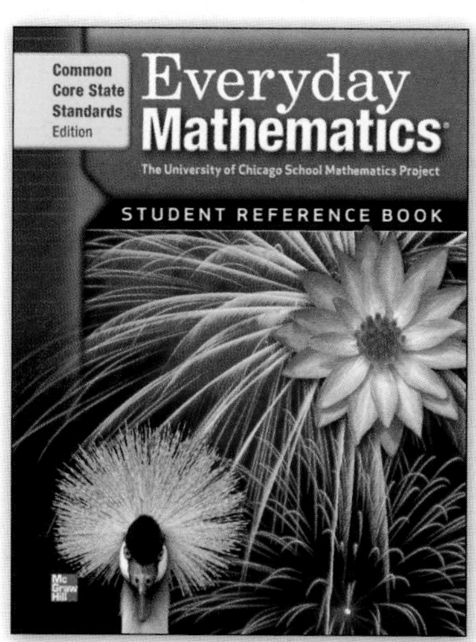

Student Reference Book and My Reference Book

These books are resources that can be sent home to provide parents with support on lesson content. The reference books include explanations and examples of mathematical topics, as well as directions for *Everyday Mathematics* games.

Home Connection Handbook

This teacher- and administrator-focused handbook provides support for communicating with families. Includes blackline masters for easier communication.

EM Online Access all technology resources online at everydaymathonline.com

NCTM Curriculum Focal Points and *Everyday Mathematics*

The *Everyday Mathematics* curriculum is completely aligned to the NCTM Curriculum Focal Points and the Connections to the Curriculum Focal Points for Pre-Kindergarten through Grade 6.

NCTM Curriculum Focal Points for Grade 5	*Everyday Mathematics* Grade 5 Lessons
Number and Operations and Algebra: Developing an understanding of and fluency with division of whole numbers.	
Students apply their understanding of models for division, place value, properties, and the relationship of division to multiplication as they develop, discuss, and use efficient, accurate, and generalizable procedures to find quotients involving multidigit dividends.	1•4, 4•1, 4•2, 4•4
Students select appropriate methods and apply them accurately to estimate quotients or calculate them mentally, depending on the context and numbers involved.	2•1, 4•4, 4•6, 4•7
Students develop fluency with efficient procedures, including the standard algorithm, for dividing whole numbers, understand why the procedures work (on the basis of place value and properties of operations), and use them to solve problems.	1•5, 1•8, 4•1, 4•2, 4•4, 4•6 Algorithm Project 7
Students consider the context in which a problem is situated to select the most useful form of the quotient for the solution, and they interpret it appropriately.	4•2, 4•5, 4•6
Number and Operations: Developing an understanding of and fluency with addition and subtraction of fractions and decimals.	
Students apply their understandings of fractions and fraction models to represent the addition and subtraction of fractions with unlike denominators as equivalent calculations with like denominators.	5•1, 5•2, 5•3, 5•6, 6•8, 6•9, 8•1, 8•2, 8•3
Students apply their understandings of decimal models, place value, and properties to add and subtract decimals.	2•2, 2•3, 2•4
Students develop fluency with standard procedures for adding and subtracting fractions and decimals.	2•2, 2•3, 5•7, 6•9, 6•10, 8•1, 8•2, 8•3, 8•4, Algorithm Projects 2, 4
Students make reasonable estimates of fraction and decimal sums and differences.	2•2, 2•3, 5•5
Students add and subtract fractions and decimals to solve problems, including problems involving measurement.	2•2, 2•3, 2•4, 2•5, 5•1, 5•3, 6•10, 8•2, 8•3, 8•4
Geometry and Measurement and Algebra: Describing three-dimensional shapes and analyzing their properties, including volume and surface area.	
Students relate two-dimensional shapes to three-dimensional shapes and analyze properties of polyhedral solids, describing them by the number of edges, faces, or vertices as well as the types of faces.	3•7, 3•9, 3•10, 9•8, 9•9, 11•1, 11•2, 11•4
Students recognize volume as an attribute of three-dimensional space.	9•8, 11•3, 11•4
Students understand that they can quantify volume by finding the total number of same-sized units of volume that they need to fill the space without gaps or overlaps.	9•8, 11•3, 11•4

NCTM Curriculum Focal Points for Grade 5	*Everyday Mathematics* Grade 5 Lessons
Geometry and Measurement and Algebra: Describing three-dimensional shapes and analyzing their properties, including volume and surface area. (cont.)	
Students understand that a cube that is 1 unit on an edge is the standard unit for measuring volume. They select appropriate units, strategies, and tools for solving problems that involve estimating or measuring volume.	9•8, 9•9, 11•3, 11•4, 11•5
Students decompose three-dimensional shapes and find surface areas and volumes of prisms.	9•8, 9•9, 11•1, 11•5, 11•7
As students work with surface area, they find and justify relationships among the formulas for the areas of different polygons. They measure necessary attributes of shapes to use area formulas to solve problems.	9•4, 9•5, 9•6, 10•9, 11•3, 11•7 Projects 6, 7

NCTM Connections to the Curriculum Focal Points	*Everyday Mathematics* Grade 5 Lessons
Algebra	
Students use patterns, models, and relationships as contexts for writing and solving simple equations and inequalities.	4•6, 4•7, 9•4, 9•5, 9•6, 9•8, 10•1, 10•2, 10•3, 10•9, 11•3, 11•7
Students create graphs of simple equations.	10•4, 10•5, 10•6
Students explore prime and composite numbers and discover concepts related to the addition and subtraction of fractions as they use factors and multiples, including applications of common factors and common multiples. They develop an understanding of the order of operations and use it for all operations.	1•6, 1•9, 6•10, 7•4, 7•5, 12•1 Projects 1, 2
Measurement	
Students' experiences connect their work with solids and volume to their earlier work with capacity and weight or mass.	9•10, 11•3, 11•4, 11•5, 11•6
Students solve problems that require attention to both approximation and precision of measurement.	2•1, 2•5, 3•3, 3•4, 3•5, 3•6, 3•9, 3•10, 4•3, 6•2
Data Analysis	
Students apply their understanding of whole numbers, fractions, and decimals as they construct and analyze double-bar and line graphs and use ordered pairs on coordinate grids.	5•9, 6•6, 7•6, 9•1, 9•2, 9•3, 10•4, 10•5, 10•6, 10•7, 12•7
Number and Operations	
Building on their work in grade 4, students extend their understanding of place value to numbers through millions and millionths in various contexts.	2•1, 3•2, 7•2, 7•3 Project 5
They apply what they know about multiplication of whole numbers to larger numbers. Students also explore contexts that they can describe with negative numbers (e.g., situations of owing money or measuring elevations above and below sea level).	2•1, 2•7, 2•8, 2•9, 7•1, 7•2, 7•3, 7•7

The Curriculum Focal Points identify key mathematical ideas for these grades. They are not discrete topics or a checklist to be mastered; rather, they provide a framework for the majority of instruction at a particular grade level and the foundation for future mathematics study.

Contents

Volume 1

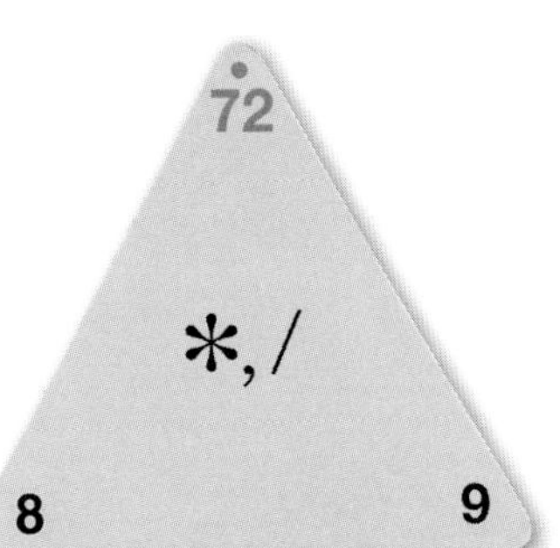

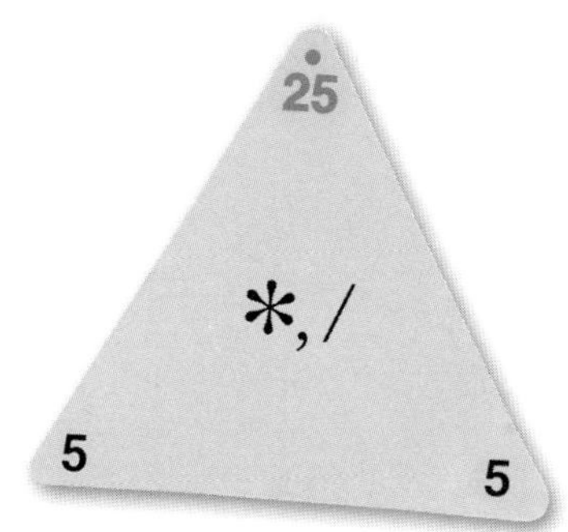

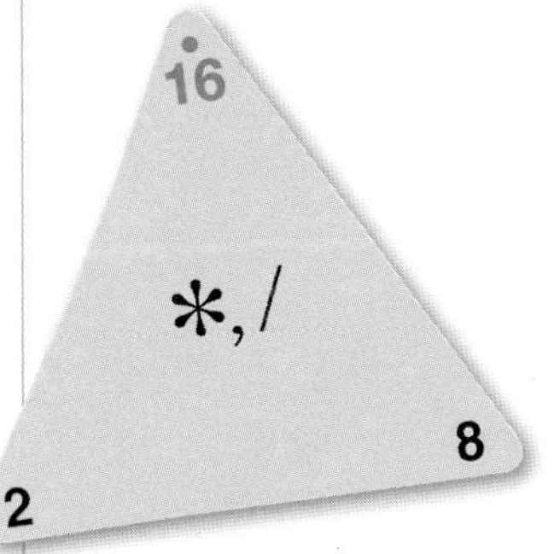

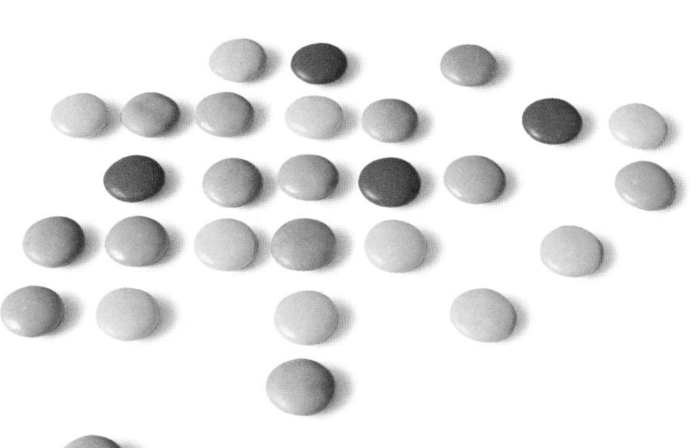

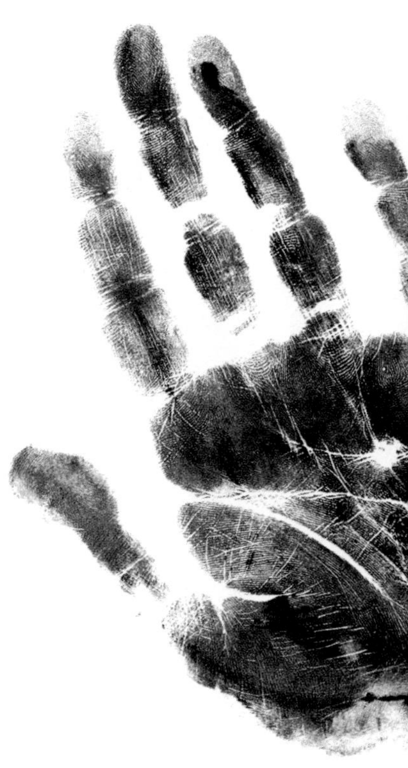

Volume 2

4
1
6
7
8

Welcome to *Everyday Mathematics,* the elementary school mathematics curriculum developed by the University of Chicago School Mathematics Project (UCSMP). *Everyday Mathematics* offers you and your students a broad, rich, and balanced experience in mathematics. *Fifth Grade Everyday Mathematics* emphasizes the following content strands, skills, and concepts:

- **Number and Numeration** Reading, writing, and comparing negative numbers, fractions, whole numbers through billions, and decimals through thousandths; reading, writing, and interpreting whole-number powers of 10; translating between exponential and standard notation; understanding and identifying prime, composite, and square numbers.
- **Operations and Computation** Using paper-and-pencil algorithms to add, subtract, multiply, and divide multidigit whole numbers and decimals; using mental arithmetic to compute and to estimate; translating among fractions, decimals, and percents; prime factoring; converting between fractions and mixed numbers; adding and subtracting fractions and mixed numbers with unlike denominators; finding least common multiples and greatest common factors; multiplying and dividing fractions.
- **Data and Chance** Comparing probabilities for different outcomes; comparing theoretical and experimental probabilities; expressing probabilities as fractions, decimals, and percents; drawing justifiable conclusions from data; displaying data in more than one way; formulating a question, carrying out a survey or experiment, recording data, and communicating results; drawing and interpreting stem-and-leaf plots and bar, line, and circle graphs; understanding mean, median, and mode.
- **Measurement and Reference Frames** Measuring and estimating length, area, volume, weight, and capacity; converting and computing with common units of measure.
- **Geometry** Constructing a circle with a given radius or diameter; defining and creating tessellations; measuring and drawing angles; identifying and defining triangles; plotting points in four quadrants; using translations, reflections, and rotations; solving perimeter, area, and volume problems; understanding the relationship between the volumes of cones/pyramids and cylinders/prisms; finding the surface areas of prisms and cylinders and the areas of circles; identifying angle relationships in triangles and in quadrilaterals.
- **Patterns, Functions, and Algebra** Evaluating simple algebraic expressions; finding rules for patterns; finding the nth term in a sequence; solving simple open number sentences and simple rate problems; working with equations by doing the same thing on both sides; understanding simple direct proportion; using variables and equations to represent situations; graphing ordered pairs.

Everyday Mathematics is a comprehensive program that will help you and your students experience mathematical processes as a part of everyday work and play. These processes will gradually shape your students' ways of thinking about mathematics and will foster the development of their mathematical intuition and understanding. By the end of the year, we think you will agree that the rewards are worth the effort.

Everyday Mathematics emphasizes the following:

- A realistic approach to problem solving in everyday situations, other applications, and purely mathematical contexts.
- Frequent and distributed practice of basic skills through ongoing program routines and mathematical games.
- An instructional approach that revisits topics regularly to ensure full concept development and long-term retention of learning.
- Activities that explore a wide variety of mathematical content and offer opportunities for students to apply their skills and understandings to geometry, measurement, and algebra.

Professional Preparation

Components for *Fifth Grade Everyday Mathematics*

Go to...	When you need...	
Teacher's Lesson Guide	• daily lessons • daily assessment suggestions • readiness, enrichment, and extra practice suggestions	• unit support information • key vocabulary • scope and sequence • Grade-Level Goals • English language learners support
Teacher's Reference Manual	• background on mathematical content	• ideas for curriculum and classroom management
Assessment Handbook	• suggestions for ongoing and periodic assessment • Grade-Level Goals across all grades	• assessment masters • sample rubrics for open-response items
Differentiation Handbook	• suggestions for meeting diverse needs	• unit-specific ideas
5-Minute Math	• brief activities for transition time and extra practice	
Content by Strand Poster	• Key Concepts and Skills organized by content strand and paced by month	• Program Goals and Grade-Level Goals
Home Connection Handbook	• suggestions for home-school communication	• masters for easy planning
Student Reference Book	• concise explanations of fundamental mathematics • worked examples	• game directions • a reference for students, parents, and others
Student Math Journal	• a yearlong record of each student's mathematical development	• paired Math Boxes for mixed practice • activity sheets
Math Masters	• blackline masters for lessons, Study Links, projects, teaching aids, and games	
English Learners Handbook	• comprehensive instructional strategies that maximize understanding	• methods that accelerate the acquisition of academic language and improve students' comprehension
Multilingual Handbook	• brief lesson summaries with examples in 6 languages	• lesson vocabulary in 11 languages

Suggested Reading & Lesson Preparation

In order to prepare for effective classroom and curriculum management, we suggest the following before you teach *Everyday Mathematics* for the first time:

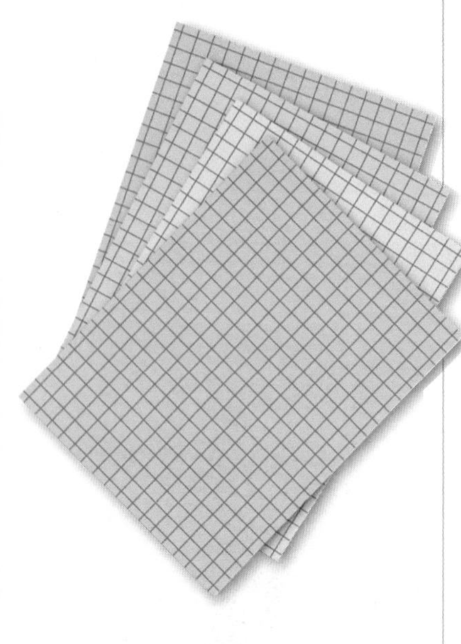

Reading and Planning

- ☐ Review each component in your Classroom Resource Package (CRP). Locate information and materials so that you can find them as needed throughout the school year.
- ☐ Browse through the *Teacher's Reference Manual,* the *Assessment Handbook,* the *Differentiation Handbook,* the *Home Connection Handbook,* and the *Student Reference Book.*
- ☐ Read the Management Guide in the *Teacher's Reference Manual,* which has many useful tips and explanations.
- ☐ Before you teach each unit, including Unit 1, read the Unit Organizer in the *Teacher's Lesson Guide* and refer to the Advance Preparation section in each lesson. Also, read the relevant sections of the *Teacher's Reference Manual,* the *Assessment Handbook,* and the *Differentiation Handbook.*
- ☐ Prepare a daily math schedule. *Everyday Mathematics* lessons have several parts that can be done at different times throughout the day. Your schedule should include time for Getting Started activities (Math Message, Mental Math and Reflexes, and Study Link Follow-Up); Teaching the Lesson discussions and activities; Ongoing Learning & Practice activities, including Math Boxes and games; and possibly Differentiation Options.
- ☐ Prepare materials that will be used throughout the year. Special items for consideration include:
    - For the Mental Math and Reflexes routine, gather slates and chalk (or dry-erase boards and markers) and old socks for erasers.
    - Prepare a lost-and-found box for misplaced items.
    - Assign an ID number to each student to simplify matching students and manipulatives.
- ☐ Prepare a supply of paper:
    - Blank $8\frac{1}{2}$" by 11" (full-, half-, and quarter-size sheets)
    - Grid paper (1 cm; see *Math Masters,* page 436)
- ☐ Obtain the optional books listed in the literature links section of the Unit Organizer for upcoming units.
- ☐ Review the following games. Try the games with a colleague or small group of students. Consider any adaptations you may need to make for various abilities:
    - *Name That Number* (*Student Reference Book,* page 325)
    - *Multiplication Top-It* (*Student Reference Book,* page 334)
    - *Factor Captor* (*Student Reference Book,* page 306)
    - *Polygon Capture* (*Student Reference Book,* page 328)
- ☐ Create an Arrays Museum. See *Teacher's Lesson Guide,* Lesson 1-2, page 21.

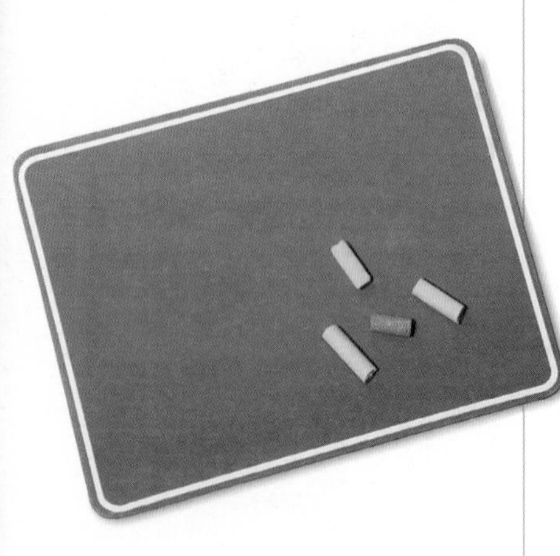

- ☐ Gather Everything Math Decks or decks of playing cards. See *Teacher's Lesson Guide,* Lesson 1-3, page 30.
- ☐ Create Tool Kits. See *Teacher's Reference Manual.*
- ☐ Gather dice, centimeter cubes, counters, calculators, an overhead calculator (optional), pennies, Fact Triangles, and dictionaries. See *Teacher's Reference Manual* and *Teacher's Lesson Guide* Unit 1 Organizer, page 12.

Organizing Your Classroom

Items for Display

Before the school year begins, we suggest that you gather the following items for classroom display. When using the posters with English language learners, display either the English version only or both the English and Spanish versions simultaneously; do not display the Spanish version only. By taking time to prepare these items your first year, and laminating them if possible, you will be able to reuse them year after year. See the Management Guide of your *Teacher's Reference Manual* for more information and suggestions.

- ☐ Poster 1: Probability Meter (English/Spanish)
- ☐ Poster 2: *, / Facts Table (English/Spanish)
- ☐ Poster 3: Class Number Grid (English/Spanish)

Classroom Setup

The following items should be considered as you set up your classroom for *Everyday Mathematics.* Try several arrangements until you find one that is comfortable and effective for you and your students. Visit other classrooms in your building to observe and discuss what works for your colleagues.

- ☐ Prepare and label a location in the classroom where students can deposit their written work such as Math Messages, Study Links, Exit Slips, and so on.
- ☐ Arrange the classroom to allow for easy access to manipulatives and to facilitate efficient transitions for individual, partner, and small-group activities.
- ☐ Organize class and individual manipulatives for easy access and efficient use of storage space.
- ☐ Allow space for math center(s). Selected games and activities can then be left in this space for ongoing practice or free exploration.
- ☐ Identify a place where the daily Math Message will be posted. See the *Teacher's Reference Manual* for information about the Math Message.
- ☐ One or more computers with Internet access can let students use software and Web sites that are recommended in *Fifth Grade Everyday Mathematics.*

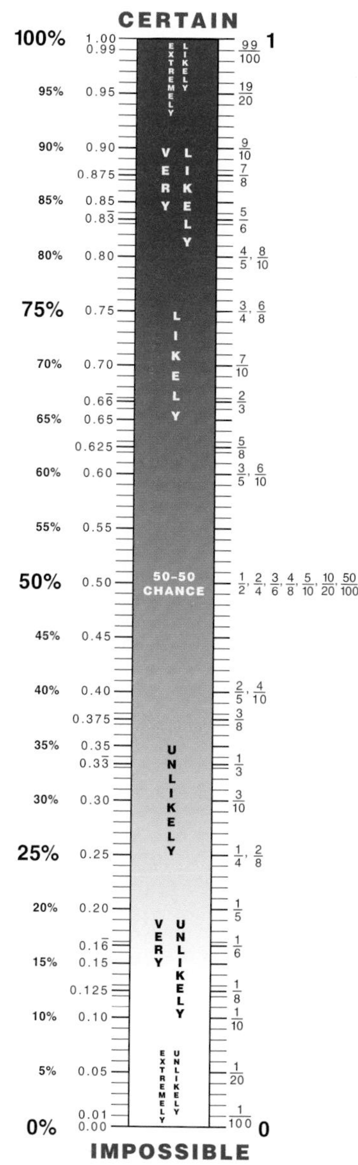

Probability Meter

Manipulatives

The table below lists the materials that are used throughout *Fifth Grade Everyday Mathematics.* Some lessons call for a few additional materials, which you or your students can bring in at the appropriate time.

Additional Valuable Classroom Resources

- Overhead Projector Materials
- Class Data Pad
- World and U.S. Maps

Quantity	Item
1 set	Base-10 Blocks
1 per student	Calculators (Texas Instruments TI-15 or Casio *fx*-55 recommended)*
1 per student	Compass, Helix
1 pkg (2,000)	Connectors (twist ties)
1 set	Cup Set, Standard Measuring
1 per student	Dice, Dot
3 pkgs (18 total)	Dice, Polyhedral
15 decks	Everything Math Decks
1 per student	Geometry Templates (in Student Materials Set)
1	Liter Pitcher
1	Liter Volume Cube
1 per student	Slates (marker boards)
10	Meter Sticks, Dual Scale
1	Number Line, –35 to 180
1 set	Pattern Blocks
1	Rocker Balance
1 pkg (500)	Straws
15	Tape Measures, Retractable
1	Tape Measure, 30m/100'
1 per student	Tool-Kit Bags*
15	Transparent Mirrors

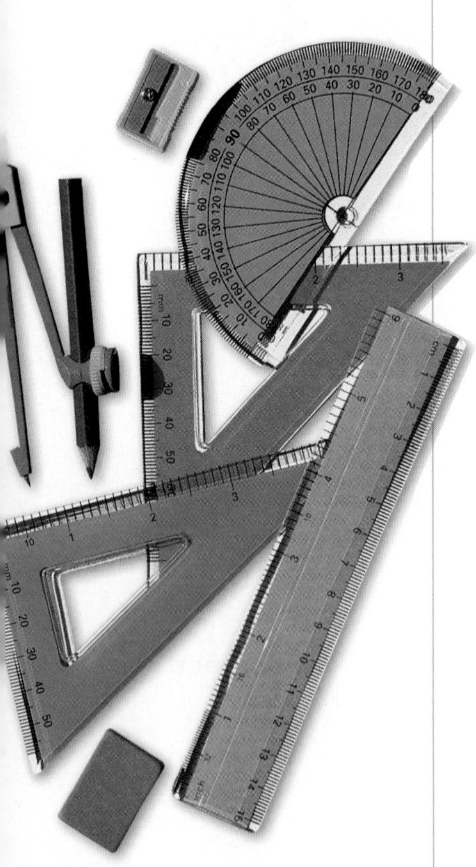

All of the items above are available from Wright Group/McGraw-Hill. They may be purchased either as a comprehensive classroom manipulative kit or as individual components. The manipulative kit provides multiple classroom quantities and comes packaged in durable plastic tubs with labels.

**Calculators and tool-kit bags are available from Wright Group/McGraw-Hill for individual purchase only.*

Instruction

The following sections introduce instructional procedures and suggestions for implementing *Everyday Mathematics.* Teachers are encouraged to read these pages and refer to them as needed throughout the school year.

Program Routines

Everyday Mathematics uses a number of program routines that are incorporated throughout all grade levels. These routines provide a consistent and familiar format for ongoing practice and applications.

Below is a list of the program routines you will encounter in *Fifth Grade Everyday Mathematics*. The lesson in which each routine is first used has been noted. Refer to the Management Guide in the *Teacher's Reference Manual* for more information.

Mental Math and Reflexes (Lesson 1-1)
Math Message (Lesson 1-1)
Math Boxes (Lesson 1-1)
Study Links (Lesson 1-1)
Fact Triangles (Lesson 1-2)
Games (Lesson 1-3)
Name-Collection Boxes (Lesson 1-9)
"What's My Rule?"/Function Machines (Lesson 7-8)

Students who have used *Fourth Grade Everyday Mathematics* will be familiar with the above routines, so most can be reintroduced with a minimum of explanation.

Games

A significant amount of practice in *Everyday Mathematics* is formatted as games, which are accordingly integral to the program and must not be omitted. Establish a games routine during the first unit and maintain it throughout the year. Once established, the routine will become self-sustaining, as much by the students' enthusiasm as by your effort. Make sure that all students are afforded time to play the games, especially those students who require the most practice.

Suggestions for building games into your instructional program:

- Include games as part of your daily morning routine.
- Devote the first or last 10 minutes of each math class to playing games from the current unit.
- Designate one math class per week as Games Day. Set up stations that feature the unit games. Ask parent volunteers to assist in the rotation of students through these stations.
- Set up a Games Corner that features some of the students' favorite games. Encourage students to visit this corner during free time. Change the games frequently to maintain student interest.

The American Tour

In *Fifth Grade Everyday Mathematics,* students go on a yearlong American Tour, collecting, analyzing, and representing information about our nation. The tour is easily linked to American history and other social studies and language arts topics. The *Student Reference Book* has a special American Tour section, which is a source of information for the yearlong project. This section contains maps, data about the states, and essays of interest. The American Tour is introduced in Lesson 3-1.

Museums

Everyday Mathematics encourages the development of classroom museums, using a bulletin board or table where related items can be collected, categorized, and labeled. *Fifth Grade Everyday Mathematics* includes the following museums:

- Array Museum (Lesson 1-2)
- Tessellation Museum (Lesson 3-8)
- Fraction, Decimals, and Percents Museum (Lesson 5-1)
- Rates and Ratios Museum (Lesson 10-4)

Projects

Fifth Grade Everyday Mathematics provides nine optional projects, each of which includes an array of mathematics activities focusing on a theme that interests students. The Unit Organizers in the *Teacher's Lesson Guide* include reminders about these projects at appropriate times throughout the year. With the exception of the yearlong American Tour, projects typically take one to two days to complete, depending upon how many of the suggested activities are used.

Projects involve a range of concepts and skills; integrate mathematics with science, social studies, art, and language arts; and allow the teacher to assess students' abilities to apply the mathematics they have learned in cross-curricular contexts. Projects are also often memorable for students.

Refer to the Management Guide in the *Teacher's Reference Manual* and the Unit Organizers in the *Teacher's Lesson Guide* for more information. Detailed explanations for the projects are found at the back of the *Teacher's Lesson Guide.*

Assessment

Everyday Mathematics supports a balanced approach to assessment that provides information for guiding instruction and for evaluating student performance. Assessment takes place on an ongoing basis as students complete their everyday work and in special periodic assessments, such as the Progress Check lesson at the end of each unit. Information for assessment is gathered through teacher observations while students are working, and through students' written products.

Refer to the *Assessment Handbook* and the Unit Organizers in the *Teacher's Lesson Guide* for detailed information regarding student assessment.

Differentiation

Everyday Mathematics has been designed to accommodate a wide range of student backgrounds and abilities, including English language learners. The program also includes many tools and suggestions to help teachers differentiate instruction to meet students' diverse needs, including Readiness, Enrichment, Extra Practice, and ELL activities in Part 3 of the lessons, and Adjusting the Activity suggestions in Parts 1 and 2. Differentiated instruction gives students multiple options for taking in information, making sense of ideas, building skills, and communicating what they have learned.

Refer to the *Differentiation Handbook* and the Unit Organizers in the *Teacher's Lesson Guide* for detailed information about differentiation in *Everyday Mathematics.*

Providing for Home–School Connections

Comprehensive and consistent home–school communication is essential for successful implementation of *Everyday Mathematics. Everyday Mathematics* provides a number of support materials to facilitate this communication. The *Home Connection Handbook* has many suggestions and tools that can help you introduce parents and primary caregivers to the *Everyday Mathematics* curriculum. Grade-specific Family Letters and Study Links in the *Math Masters* facilitate ongoing communication and engage parents as partners in the learning process. Individual assessment checklists in the *Assessment Handbook* enable teachers to document in detail the progress of each student, and they are a valuable communication tool during parent conferences.

Refer to the *Home Connection Handbook* for more information.

4–6 Games Correlation Chart

Games	Grade 4 Lesson	Grade 5 Lesson	Grade 6 Lesson	Basic Facts	Operations	Calculator	Numeration	Geometry	Data	Algebra	Measurement/ Ref. Frames	Mental Math	Strategy
				Skill and Concept Areas									
Addition Top-It (Extended-Facts Version)	1•2			●	●		●					●	
Addition Top-It (Decimal Version)		2•2			●		●					●	
Algebra Election		4•7	6•11		●	●			●	●	●		●
Angle Add-Up	6•6				●			●			●		
Angle Tangle	6•6	3•6	5•1		●			●			●		
Base-10 Exchange	4•2						●						
Baseball Multiplication	3•3	*		●	●							●	
Beat the Calculator	3•5	*		●	●	●						●	
Beat the Calculator (Extended-Facts Version)		1•3		●	●	●						●	
Build-It		8•1	4•2				●						●
Buzz and *Bizz Buzz*	3•2				●		●						
Calculator 10,000	*				●	●							
Chances Are	7•11								●				
Coin Top-It	4•3				●		●					●	
Coordinate Search		12•8									●		●
Credits/Debits Game	10•6		3•7		●							●	
Credits/Debits Game (Advanced Version)	11•6	7•8	6•3		●							●	
Divisibility Dash		4•4	2•6	●	●		●					●	●
Division Arrays	3•5			●	●							●	
Division Dash	6•3	4•2			●							●	
Division Top-It	*	4•5	2•7		●		●					●	
Doggone Decimal			2•4		●	●	●					●	●
Estimation Squeeze		5•5				●	●					●	
Exponent Ball		7•1	2•10		●	●	●					●	
Factor Bingo		1•7		●	●		●					●	
Factor Captor		1•4	3•2	●	●		●					●	●
Factor Top-It		*		●	●		●					●	
Finish First		6•2		●	●							●	
First to 100		4•7	8•12	●	●					●		●	
Fishing for Digits	2•4				●	●	●						●
500		7•8			●								
Frac-Tac-Toe		5•7	4•8		●		●					●	●
Fraction Action, Fraction Friction		8•4	4•4		●		●					●	
Fraction Capture		6•9	4•1		●							●	●
Fraction Match	7•6						●					●	●
Fraction Of	7•2	5•11			●		●					●	●
Fraction/Percent Concentration	9•3	5•8				●	●					●	
Fraction Spin		8•5			●		●						●
Fraction Top-It	7•9	5•1					●					●	
Fraction Top-It (Advanced Version)		6•8			●		●					●	
Fraction/Whole Number Top-It		*	6•1		●		●					●	

Number indicates first exposure at grade level. *Available in the Games section of the *Student Reference Book.*

Games Correlation Chart *continued*

Games	Grade 4 Lesson	Grade 5 Lesson	Grade 6 Lesson	Skill and Concept Areas									
				Basic Facts	Operations	Calculator	Numeration	Geometry	Data	Algebra	Measurement/ Ref. Frames	Mental Math	Strategy
Getting to One	7•10	*	3•10			●	●						●
Grab Bag	7•3		7•1		●				●	●		●	●
Greedy			7•7						●			●	●
Grid Search	6•8										●		●
Hidden Treasure		9•1									●		●
High-Number Toss	2•7	2•10	1•2				●						●
High-Number Toss (Decimal Version)		2•5	1•11		●		●						●
Landmark Shark			1•5						●			●	●
Mixed-Number Spin		8•3	4•7		●		●			●		●	●
Multiplication Bull's-Eye		2•7	2•5		●	●	●					●	
Multiplication Top-It	3•3	3•3	2•5	●	●		●					●	
Multiplication Top-It (Extended-Facts Version)		1•8		●	●		●					●	
Multiplication Wrestling	5•2	*	9•1		●		●			●		●	●
Name That Number	2•2	1•9	1•8		●		●			●		●	●
Number Top-It (7-Digit Numbers)	5•11	2•10	2•1				●						●
Number Top-It (Decimals)	4•4	5•6					●						●
Over and Up Squares	6•9		1•6								●		●
Percent/Sector Match-Up			1•9				●						●
Polygon Capture		3•7	5•8					●					
Polygon Pair-Up	1•6							●					
Product Pile-Up	4•3			●			●					●	●
Rugs and Fences	8•7	11•4								●	●	●	●
Scientific Notation Toss		7•3	2•9				●						●
Seega	3•6												●
Sides and Angles: Triangles		3•6						●			●		
Solution Search			6•12		●					●			●
Spoon Scramble		12•6	5•4				●					●	
Spreadsheet Scramble			3•7		●							●	●
Sprouts	1•2							●					●
Subtraction Target Practice	2•9	*			●	●							●
Subtraction Target Practice (Decimal Version)		2•3			●	●							●
Subtraction Top-It (Extended-Facts Version)	1•4			●	●		●					●	
Sz'kwa	1•4							●					●
3-D Shape Sort		11•2	5•10					●					
Top-It with Positive and Negative Numbers		7•11	6•4		●		●					●	
Triangle Sort		3•6						●					
Venn Diagram Challenge			7•6					●	●				●
What's My Attribute Rule?		3•7						●					●
Where Do I Fit In?		3•6						●					
X and O—Tic-Tac-Toe			5•4								●		●

Number indicates first exposure at grade level. *Available in the Games section of the *Student Reference Book*.

Unit 1 Organizer

Number Theory

Overview

Unit 1 builds on students' understanding of factors and products to explore topics from the branch of mathematics called *number theory.* The new material in this unit builds on students' prior informal work with multiplication and division of whole numbers. Number theory makes the point that mathematics is more than computation. Since number theory features a technical vocabulary where precise meanings of words really matter, it is strongly linked to language arts. Unit 1 has five main areas of focus:

- To introduce students to the *Student Reference Book,*
- To review rectangular arrays and multiplication number models,
- To review and practice factoring,
- To introduce prime, composite, and square numbers, and
- To develop exponents and square roots concepts.

CCSS Linking to the Common Core State Standards

The content of Unit 1 addresses the Common Core State Standards for Mathematics in *Number and Operations in Base Ten.* The correlation of the Common Core State Standards to the *Everyday Mathematics* Grade 5 lessons begins on page CS1.

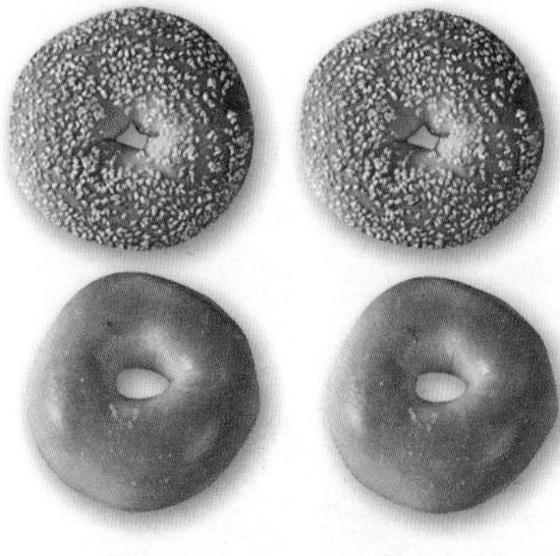

Contents

Learning In Perspective

	Lesson Objectives	Links to the Past	Links to the Future
1•1	To acquaint students with the content and organization of the *Math Journal* and *Student Reference Book.*	Starting in third grade, students use the *Student Reference Book* to find information and solve problems.	In sixth grade, students use the *Student Reference Book* to find information and solve problems.
1•2	To review rectangular arrays and the use of multiplication number models to represent such arrays.	In fourth grade, students use arrays to find factors of numbers.	In sixth grade, students apply rectangular arrays to multiplicative situations.
1•3	To provide a review of the meanings of *factor* and *product;* and to provide opportunities to factor numbers and apply multiplication facts.	In fourth grade, students define *factor* and *product,* and practice multiplication facts with Fact Triangles and games.	In sixth grade, students develop and apply rules for multiplying and dividing positive and negative numbers.
1•4	To review divisibility concepts.	In fourth grade, students use Fact Triangles to reinforce the relationship between division and multiplication.	In Unit 1, students represent a number as a product of factors and a product of prime factors.
1•5	To introduce divisibility rules for division by 2, 3, 5, 6, 9, and 10; and how to use a calculator to test for divisibility by a whole number.	In fourth grade, students define *dividend, divisor, quotient,* and *remainder.*	In Units 2 and 5, students solve division problems by partitioning dividends into "friendly" numbers.
1•6	To introduce the classification of whole numbers as either prime or composite.	In fourth grade, students use arrays to find factors of numbers and classify the numbers as prime or composite.	In sixth grade, students apply knowledge of number properties to solve problems.
1•7	To introduce square numbers and the exponent key on a calculator.	In fourth grade, students find the square of a number and write it in exponential notation.	In sixth grade, students use squares and square roots of numbers in applications of the Pythagorean Theorem.
1•8	To introduce the concept of square roots and the use of the square-root key on a calculator.	In fourth grade, students model square numbers with arrays and find the square of a number.	In sixth grade, students use squares and square roots of numbers in applications of the Pythagorean Theorem.
1•9	To review equivalency concepts for whole numbers; and to introduce factor strings and prime factorization.	In first through fourth grade, students use a Name-Collection Box routine to express numbers in many ways.	In sixth grade, students use greatest common factors and least common multiples to solve problems.

	Key Concepts and Skills	Grade 5 Goals*
1•1	Identify places in whole numbers and express the values of digits in those places.	Number and Numeration Goal 1
	Identify places in decimals and express the values of digits in those places.	Number and Numeration Goal 1
1•2	Find factors of a number.	Number and Numeration Goal 3
	Write number sentences for rectangular arrays.	Operations and Computation Goal 7
	Use the turn-around rule for multiplication.	Patterns, Functions, and Algebra Goal 4
1•3	Write number models for rectangular arrays.	Operations and Computation Goal 7
	Find all factors of a number.	Number and Numeration Goal 3
	Solve and apply multiplication facts.	Operations and Computation Goal 2
1•4	Describe numbers as odd or even using rectangular arrays.	Number and Numeration Goal 3
	Find factors using divisibility.	Number and Numeration Goal 3
	Apply multiplication/division facts by using rules of divisibility and finding factors.	Operations and Computation Goal 2
1•5	Use divisibility rules to solve problems.	Number and Numeration Goal 3
	Explore the relationship between the operations of multiplication and division.	Operations and Computation Goal 2
1•6	Define and classify prime and composite numbers.	Number and Numeration Goal 3
	Find factors of a number.	Number and Numeration Goal 3
1•7	Rename square number factor pairs in exponential and standard notation.	Number and Numeration Goal 4
	Investigate the properties of square numbers.	Operations and Computation Goal 7
	Use array patterns to define square numbers.	Patterns, Functions, and Algebra Goal 1
1•8	Use exponential notation to name square numbers, and explore the relationship between square numbers and square roots.	Number and Numeration Goal 4
1•9	Find factor strings for numbers.	Number and Numeration Goal 3
	Write the prime factorization for numbers.	Number and Numeration Goal 3
	Rename numbers as factor strings or products of exponents.	Number and Numeration Goal 4
	Use exponents to rename numbers.	Number and Numeration Goal 4

*See the Appendix for a complete list of Grade 5 Goals.

A Balanced Curriculum

Ongoing Practice

Everyday Mathematics provides numerous opportunities for ongoing practice. These activities are embedded throughout the lessons:

Mental Math and Reflexes activities promote speed and accuracy in mental computation.

Math Boxes offer mixed practice and are paired across lessons as shown in the brackets below. This makes them useful as assessment tools. The last one or two boxes on each page preview the next unit's content.

Mixed practice	[1•1, 1•3], [1•2, 1•4], [1•5, 1•7, 1•9], [1•6, 1•8]
Mixed practice with multiple choice	1•3
Mixed practice with writing/reasoning opportunity	1•1, 1•3, 1•5, 1•6, 1•8

Study Links are daily homework assignments that review the content of the lesson and often contain ongoing facts practice or computation practice.

5-Minute Math problems are offered for additional practice in Lessons 1•1, 1•3, 1•6, and 1•8.

EM Facts Workshop Game provides online practice of basic facts and computation.

EXTRA PRACTICE **Extra Practice** activities are included in Lessons 1•1, 1•3, 1•5, 1•6, 1•8, and 1•9.

Practice through Games

Games are an essential component of practice in the *Everyday Mathematics* program. Games offer skills practice and promote strategic thinking. See the *Differentiation Handbook* for ways to adapt games to meet students' needs.

Lesson	Game	Skill Practiced
1•3	*Beat the Calculator* (Extended-Facts Version)	Practice multiplication fact extensions [OC Goal 2]
1•8	*Multiplication Top-It* (Extended-Facts Version)	Practice multiplication fact extensions [OC Goal 2]
1•4, 1•5, 1•6	*Factor Captor*	Apply multiplication facts and finding factors [NN Goal 3 and OC Goal 2]
1•7	*Factor Bingo*	Identify factors and multiples [NN Goal 3]
1•9	*Name That Number*	Use number properties, arithmetic operations, and basic facts to find equivalent names for numbers [NN Goal 4]

[NN] Number and Numeration
[MRF] Measurement and Reference Frames
[OC] Operations and Computation
[GEO] Geometry
[DC] Data and Chance
[PFA] Patterns, Functions, and Algebra

Problem Solving 

Experts at problem solving and mathematical modeling generally do these things:

- Identify the problem.
- Decide what information is needed to solve the problem.
- Play with and study the data to find patterns and meaning.
- Identify and use mathematical procedures to solve the problem.
- Decide whether the solution makes sense and whether it can be applied to other problems.

The table below lists some of the opportunities in this unit for students to practice these strategies.

Lessons that teach *through* problem solving, not just *about* problem solving

Lesson	Activity
1•2, 1•7	Find all possible rectangular arrays that represent a number; identify the square numbers.
1•3	Find factor pairs.
1•4, 1•6, 1•9	Find as many factors as possible for given whole numbers.
1•5	Use divisibility tests to check whether given numbers are divisible by 2, 3, 5, 6, 9, or 10.
1•6	Develop a winning strategy for the game *Factor Captor.*
1•8	Unsquare numbers.
1•9	Play *Name That Number.*

See Chapter 18: Problem Solving in the *Teacher's Reference Manual* for more information.

The Language of Mathematics

Everyday Mathematics provides lesson-specific suggestions to help all students acquire, process, and express mathematical ideas. Throughout Unit 1, there are lesson-specific language development notes that address the needs of English language learners, indicated by ELL.

ELL SUPPORT Activities to support English language learners are in Part 3 of Lessons 1•2, 1•3, and 1•5.

The *English Learners Handbook* and the *Differentiation Handbook* have suggestions for promoting language development and acquisition of mathematics vocabulary. See Unit 1 in each handbook.

Literacy Connection

Lesson 1•1 *Math Talk: Mathematical Ideas in Poems for Two Voices,* by Theoni Pappas, Wide World Publishing, 1993

Lesson 1•9 *12 Ways to Get to 11,* by Eve Merriam, Aladdin, 1996

For more literacy connections, see the *Home Connection Handbook,* Grades 4–6.

Unit 1 Vocabulary

Commutative Property of Multiplication
composite number
divisibility rule
divisible by
even number
exponent
exponent key
exponential notation
factor
factor pair
factor rainbow
factor string
length of factor string
name-collection box
number model
odd number
prime factorization
prime number
product
quotient
rectangular array
remainder
square array
square number
square root
square-root key
turn-around rule (for multiplication)
unsquaring a number

Cross-Curricular Links 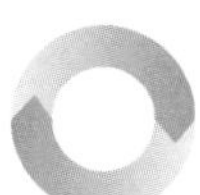

Language Arts – Lesson 1•1

Social Studies – Lessons 1•6, 1•9

Balanced Assessment

Daily Assessments

- **Recognizing Student Achievement** – A daily assessment that is included in every lesson to evaluate students' progress toward the Grade 5 Grade-Level Goals.
- **Informing Instruction** – Notes that appear throughout the unit to help anticipate students' common errors and suggest appropriate problem-solving strategies.

Lesson	Recognizing Student Achievement	Informing Instruction
1•1	Understand place value. [NN Goal 1]	
1•2	Build arrays and identify factors to describe them. [OC Goal 7]	
1•3	Identify factor pairs. [NN Goal 3]	
1•4	Describe strategies that maximize scoring in *Factor Captor.* [NN Goal 3]	
1•5	Understand place value. [NN Goal 1]	
1•6	Factor numbers in the form of arrays. [NN Goal 3]	Find the rule for number line problems.
1•7	Understand square numbers and exponential notation for square numbers. [NN Goal 4]	Graphically highlight the structure of square arrays.
1•8	Solve and compare multiplication fact extensions. [OC Goal 2]	
1•9	Correctly identify factors of a number. [NN Goal 3]	Use varied numbers and expressions in name-collection boxes.

[NN] Number and Numeration
[MRF] Measurement and Reference Frames
[OC] Operations and Computation
[GEO] Geometry
[DC] Data and Chance
[PFA] Patterns, Functions, and Algebra

Portfolio Opportunities

The following lessons provide opportunities to gather samples of students' mathematical writings, drawings, and creations to add balance to the assessment process: Lessons 1•1, 1•2, 1•3, 1•5, 1•6, 1•8, and 1•10.

See pages 16 and 17 in the *Assessment Handbook* for more information about portfolios and how to use them.

Unit Assessment

Progress Check 1 – A cumulative assessment of concepts and skills taught in Unit 1, providing information for evaluating students' progress and planning for future instruction. These assessments include oral/slate, written, and open-response activities, as shown below in the sample Progress Check lesson opener.

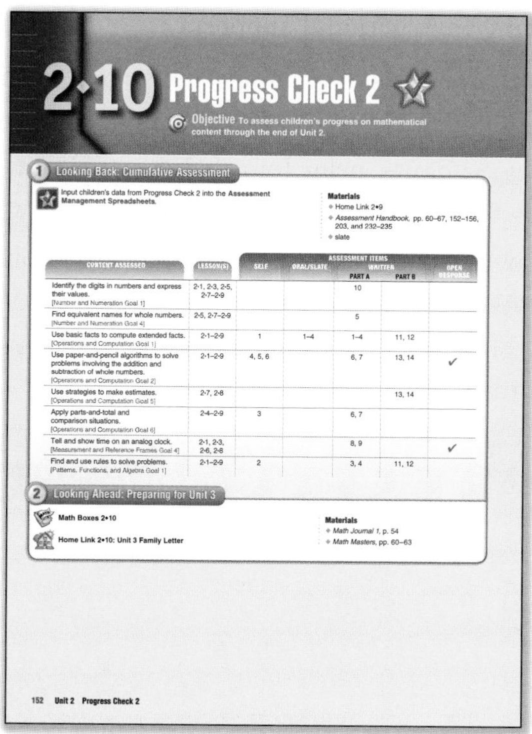

2•10 Progress Check 2

Objective To assess children's progress on mathematical content through the end of Unit 2.

1 Looking Back: Cumulative Assessment

Input children's data from Progress Check 2 into the **Assessment Management Spreadsheets.**

Materials
- Home Link 2•9
- *Assessment Handbook,* pp. 60–67, 152–156, 203, and 232–235
- slate

CONTENT ASSESSED	LESSON(S)	ASSESSMENT ITEMS				
		SELF	ORAL/SLATE	WRITTEN		OPEN RESPONSE
				PART A	PART B	
Identify the digits in numbers and express their values. [Number and Numeration Goal 1]	2·1, 2·3, 2·5, 2·7–2·9			10		
Find equivalent names for whole numbers. [Number and Numeration Goal 4]	2·5, 2·7–2·9			5		
Use basic facts to compute extended facts. [Operations and Computation Goal 1]	2·1–2·9	1	1–4	1–4	11, 12	
Use paper-and-pencil algorithms to solve problems involving the addition and subtraction of whole numbers. [Operations and Computation Goal 2]	2·1–2·9	4, 5, 6		6, 7	13, 14	✓
Use strategies to make estimates. [Operations and Computation Goal 5]	2·7, 2·8				13, 14	
Apply parts-and-total and comparison situations. [Operations and Computation Goal 6]	2·4–2·9	3		6, 7		
Tell and show time on an analog clock. [Measurement and Reference Frames Goal 4]	2·1, 2·3, 2·6, 2·8			8, 9		✓
Find and use rules to solve problems. [Patterns, Functions, and Algebra Goal 1]	2·1–2·9	2		3, 4	11, 12	

2 Looking Ahead: Preparing for Unit 3

Math Boxes 2•10

Home Link 2•10: Unit 3 Family Letter

Materials
- *Math Journal 1,* p. 54
- *Math Masters,* pp. 60–63

152 Unit 2 Progress Check 2

Core Assessment Resources

Assessment Handbook

- **Unit 1 Assessment Overview,** pages 52–59
- **Unit 1 Assessment Masters,** pages 154–157
- **Unit 1 Individual Profiles of Progress,** pages 246, 247, and 302
- **Unit 1 Class Checklists,** pages 248, 249, and 303
- **Beginning-of-Year Assessment,*** pages 51A, 51B, 222A, and 222B
- **Quarterly Checklist: Quarter 1,** pages 294 and 295
- **Math Logs,** pages 306–308
- **Exit Slip,** page 311
- **Other Student Assessment Forms,** pages 304, 305, 309, and 310

*The Beginning-of-Year Assessment is one of the screening tools that can be used to help identify which concepts and skills students have learned and to help plan instruction for the upcoming year.

Assessment Management Spreadsheets

The Assessment Management Spreadsheets consist of the Digital Class Checklists and Individual Profile of Progress Checklists. Use them to monitor, record, and report student progress.

Addressing All Needs

Differentiated Instruction

Adjusting the Activity – suggests adaptations that target advanced learners, English language learners, or learners who need additional instructional support.

ELL SUPPORT / **ELL** – provides lesson-specific suggestions to help English language learners understand and process the mathematical content.

READINESS – accesses students' prior knowledge or previews content that prepares students to engage in the lesson's Part 1 activities.

EXTRA PRACTICE – provides additional opportunities to apply the mathematical content of the lesson.

ENRICHMENT – enables students to apply or further explore the mathematical content of the lesson.

Lesson	Adjusting the Activity	ELL Support/ ELL	Readiness	Extra Practice	Enrichment
1•1			•	•	
1•2	•	•	•		•
1•3	•	•	•	•	
1•4	•		•		•
1•5	•	•	•	•	•
1•6	•	•		•	•
1•7		•	•		•
1•8	•	•		•	•
1•9	•	•	•	•	•

Additional Resources

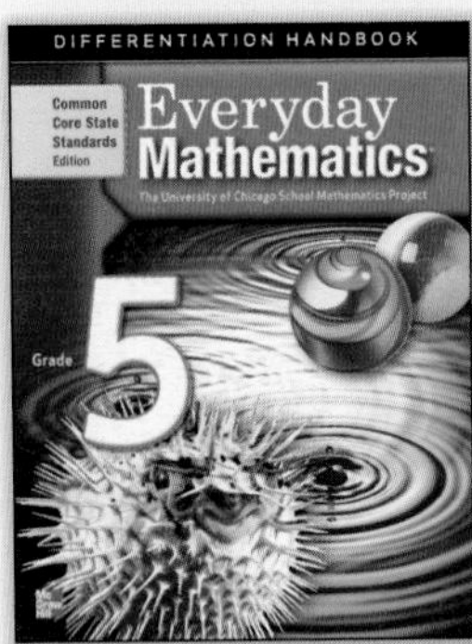

Differentiation Handbook
Provides ideas and strategies for differentiating instruction.
Pages 50–56

English Learners Handbook
Contains lesson-specific comprehension strategies.
Pages 1–9

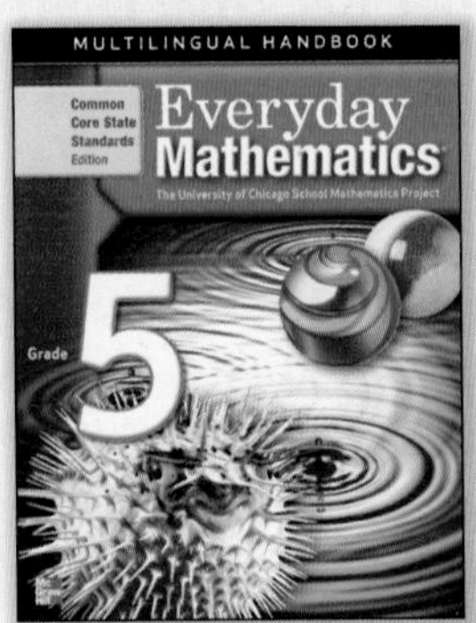

Multilingual Handbook
Previews concepts and vocabulary. It is written in six languages.
Pages 1–18

Planning Tips

Multiage Classroom

Companion Lessons from Grades 4 and 6 can help you meet instructional needs of a multiage classroom. The full Scope and Sequence can be found in the Appendix.

Grade 4	1•1		3•2–3•4	3•2–3•4			5•9		
Grade 5	**1•1**	**1•2**	**1•3**	**1•4**	**1•5**	**1•6**	**1•7**	**1•8**	**1•9**
Grade 6					6•4	6•5	2•9, 2•11, 6•5	6•5	

Pacing for Success

Pacing depends on a number of factors, such as students' individual needs and how long your school has been using *Everyday Mathematics.* At the beginning of Unit 1, you may want to use tools available at www.everydaymathonline.com to help you set your pace.

Home Support

Unit 1 Family Letter (English/Spanish) provides families with an overview, Do-Anytime Activities, Building Skills through Games, a list of vocabulary, and answers to the daily homework (Study Links). Family Letters in English, Spanish, and seven other languages are also available online.

Study Links are the daily homework assignments. They consist of active projects and ongoing review problems.

Home Support Resources

Home Connection Handbook
Offers ideas and reproducible masters for communicating with families. See Table of Contents for unit information.

Student Reference Book
Provides a resource for students and parents.
Pages 10, 306, 325, 333, 334

Technology Resources

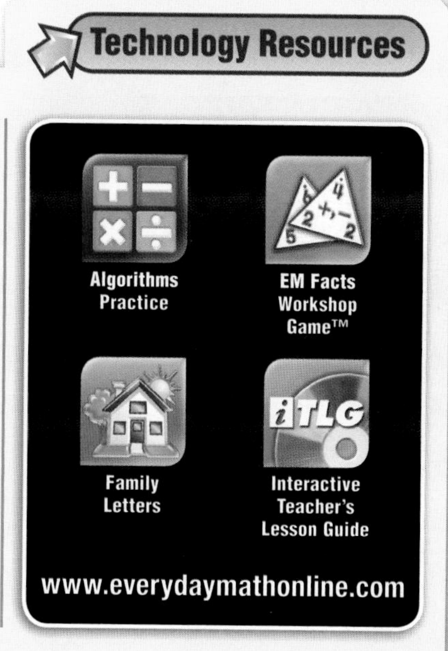

Materials

Technology Resources www.everydaymathonline.com

ePresentations

eToolkit

Algorithms Practice

EM Facts Workshop Game™

Family Letters

Assessment Management

Common Core State Standards

Curriculum Focal Points

Interactive Teacher's Lesson Guide

Lesson	Masters	Manipulative Kit	Other Items
1•1	Teaching Aid Master, p. 412 *Math Masters,* p. 7	slate or marker boards	chalk or dry-erase markers
1•2	Teaching Aid Master, p. 413* Study Link Master, p. 8 Teaching Masters, pp. 9 and 10	per group: 40 centimeter cubes, 2 dice; slate	18 counters; Class Data Pad
1•3	Teaching Masters, pp. 11 and 13 Study Link Master, p. 12 *Differentiation Handbook,* p. 143	per group: 4 each of number cards 1–10; centimeter cubes	18 counters; Class Data Pad; calculator
1•4	Teaching Aid Master, p. 414 Game Masters, pp. 453–455 Transparency of *Math Masters,* p. 453* Study Link Master, p. 14		per group: 50 counters; scissors; calculator; half-sheet of paper
1•5	Study Link Master, p. 15 Game Masters, pp. 453–454 Teaching Masters, pp. 11 and 16 *Differentiation Handbook,* p. 142	per group: 3 dice	overhead calculator*; per group: 66 counters or centimeter cubes; calculator
1•6	Study Link Master, p. 17 Teaching Masters, pp. 18 and 19		blank paper or colored construction paper; markers; Class Data Pad*
1•7	Teaching Aid Masters, pp. 413 and 414* Study Link Master, p. 20 Game Master, p. 452 Teaching Master, p. 21 *Math Journal 1,* inside front cover	per group: 4 each of number cards 2–9; centimeter cubes	25 counters; calculator
1•8	Study Link Master, p. 22 Game Master, p. 493 Teaching Master, p. 23	per group: 4 each of number cards 1–10; slate or paper	overhead calculator*; calculator
1•9	Teaching Masters, pp. 11, 25–28 Study Link Master, p. 24	per group: 4 each of number cards 0–9	quarter sheet of paper; Class Data Pad; calculator
1•10	Assessment Masters, pp. 154–157 Study Link Masters, pp. 29–32	slate	

*Denotes optional materials

Mathematical Background

The discussion below highlights the major content ideas presented in Unit 1 and helps to establish instructional priorities.

Number Theory (Lessons 1◆1–1◆10)

Number theory is the branch of theoretical mathematics that focuses on whole numbers and their properties. Because number theory methods and results often can be stated simply, this area of mathematics attracts nonprofessionals interested in mathematics, including elementary students. Number theory is one of a number of topics studied in *Everyday Mathematics* that reinforce the idea that there is more to mathematics than computation.

For additional information about number theory, see Section 9.8 of the *Teacher's Reference Manual.*

Note

The *Everyday Mathematics* authors believe that people should learn and practice the special skills involved in obtaining information from mathematics books, almanacs, encyclopedias, and other resources. Regular use of the *Student Reference Book* can be an important aspect of your language arts program.

The *Student Reference Book* (Lesson 1◆1)

The *Student Reference Book* is a resource book containing summaries of the principle mathematics concepts and skills students encounter in their study. It provides reinforcement of critical mathematics topics and calculator usage, as well as rules of mathematical games, reference tables, a glossary of mathematical terms, and information for American Tour activities. Presented in a concise, reference-oriented format, these materials invite students to look up needed information on their own. An icon appears in the journal to indicate pages in the *Student Reference Book* where there is information on the topic at hand.

To learn more about the *Student Reference Book,* see Section 1.2.9 of the *Teacher's Reference Manual.*

Arrays as Representations of Products and Quotients (Lesson 1•2)

2 × 6 array
2 × 6 = 12
12 ÷ 6 = 2
12 ÷ 2 = 6

34 ÷ 5 → 6 R4
34 ÷ 6 → 5 R4

Arrays have been featured as "pictures" of products and quotients since *First Grade Everyday Mathematics.* Students of *Everyday Mathematics* know that, since multiplication and division are inextricably linked, arrays represent division as well as multiplication. For multiplication, the number of rows and the number of columns in an array are factors, and the total number of objects in the array is the product. For division, the total number of objects in the array is the dividend; the number of rows (or the number of columns) is the divisor; and the number of columns (or the number of rows) is the quotient. If a given dividend (total) cannot be displayed as a rectangular array in which the number of rows or columns is equal to the divisor (because there are too few leftover objects to make another row or column), the array corresponds to a division problem with a remainder.

What may be new to students is the linking of arrays to various subsets of whole numbers: to even numbers, whose arrays have two rows or columns; to prime numbers, whose arrays have only a single row or column; and to square numbers, whose arrays have the same number of rows as columns.

See Section 10.3.2 of the *Teacher's Reference Manual* for more information about arrays.

Automatic "Reflexes" for Multiplication and Division

(Lessons 1•2–1•8)

Unit 1 sets up a screening procedure to determine which students have automaticity with the basic multiplication facts. Most fifth-grade students have already achieved mastery of these facts. However, there may be a few students who are unlikely to ever achieve quick, automatic recall. These students should be encouraged to compensate in various ways. Games provide additional practice to help build automaticity. The Multiplication/ Division Facts Table and calculator are possible tools for students to utilize until automaticity is reached.

In *Everyday Mathematics,* students apply their knowledge of basic facts to solve extended facts for both multiplication and division. Students have learned that both basic and extended division facts are linked to multiplication facts—once you know a multiplication fact, you know at least one, and usually two, division facts. In Unit 1, many of the Mental Math and Reflexes problems focus on building automatic recall of extended multiplication and division facts. The Mental Math and Reflexes extend the basic multiplication facts (7 * 8) to products of ones and tens (7 * 80 or 70 * 8) and products of tens and tens (70 * 80). Facility with extended facts is important because it provides powerful mental arithmetic strategies that can be used when working with large numbers. Students should also begin to see the patterns associated with the number of zeros that are attached (or removed) when multiplying or dividing by powers of 10.

For more information about automatic basic fact "reflexes," see Sections 16.3.2 and 16.3.3 of the *Teacher's Reference Manual.*

Factors and Factorization

(Lessons 1•3–1•6 and 1•9)

Factors are numbers that are multiplied together. Usually they are whole numbers, positive or negative integers, fractions, or decimals; in number theory, however, *factor* always means a whole number. Factors have many applications, and the terms *prime number, composite number, prime factorization, square number,* and *square root of a number* are all defined in terms of factors.

To learn more about factors and factorization, see Section 9.8.1 of the *Teacher's Reference Manual.*

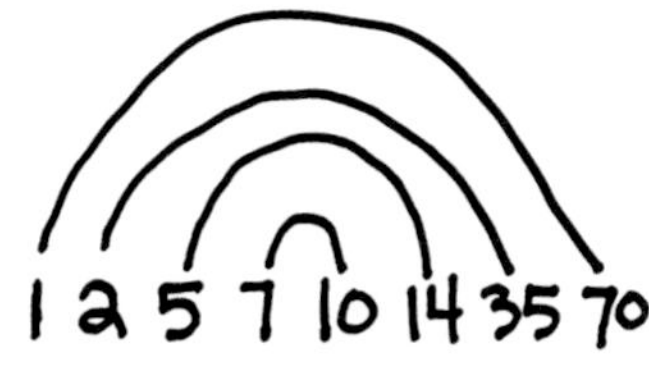

My factor rainbow for the number 70

Project Note

Use Project 1, The Sieve of Eratosthenes, to identify and look for patterns in prime numbers from 1 to 100.

Use Project 2, Deficient, Abundant, and Perfect Numbers, to classify the whole numbers through 50 according to the sums of their proper factors.

Tests for Divisibility (Lesson 1•5)

Students of *Everyday Mathematics* learned to recognize even numbers as early as first grade. They found that an even number must end in 0, 2, 4, 6, or 8. This means that an even number must have 2 as a factor, or stated another way, an even number must be divisible by 2. Similarly, from many counting-on exercises, most students know that numbers that end in 0 have 10 as a factor (are divisible by 10), and numbers that end in either 0 or 5 have 5 as a factor (are divisible by 5). The new divisibility tests of this lesson involve surprising facts: Numbers, however large, whose digits add up to a multiple of 9 must have 9 as a factor and, hence, are divisible by 9. A similar rule applies to divisibility by 3. By combining rules for divisibility by 2, 3, 5, 9, and 10, other rules can be formulated. For example, if a number is divisible by both 2 and 3, it is divisible by 6; even numbers divisible by 9 are divisible by 18; and so on.

See Section 9.8.1 of the *Teacher's Reference Manual* to learn more about divisibility tests.

Squaring and Unsquaring, or Square Numbers and Square Roots

(Lessons 1•7 and 1•8)

Except for informal exposures in Grades K–4, these lessons are the first time *Everyday Mathematics* focuses on square numbers and square roots.

NOTE: Starting in *Fourth Grade Everyday Mathematics,* the asterisk (∗) is used in place of the traditional "×" symbol and the slash (/) in place of the traditional "÷" symbol. Both the asterisk and the slash are used in computer applications, such as spreadsheets. Use both the traditional operation symbols and the asterisk and slash when writing them in number sentences.

See Section 10.1.2 of the *Teacher's Reference Manual* for more information about squaring and "unsquaring" numbers.

1•1 Introduction to the *Student Reference Book*

Objective To acquaint students with the content and organization of the *Math Journal* and *Student Reference Book.*

Technology Resources www.everydaymathonline.com

ePresentations

eToolkit

Algorithms Practice

EM Facts Workshop Game™

Family Letters

Assessment Management

Common Core State Standards

Curriculum Focal Points

Interactive Teacher's Lesson Guide

1 Teaching the Lesson

Key Concepts and Skills

- Identify places in whole numbers and express the values of digits in those places. [Number and Numeration Goal 1]
- Identify places in decimals and express the values of digits in those places. [Number and Numeration Goal 1]

Key Activities

Students examine their journals and discuss the introduction and overview. They become familiar with the *Student Reference Book* by using it to solve problems and to find information.

Materials

Math Journal 1, pp. 1–3
Student Reference Book
slate or marker board ◆ chalk or dry-erase marker

2 Ongoing Learning & Practice

Math Boxes 1•1

Math Journal 1, p. 4
Math Masters, p. 412
Students practice and maintain skills through Math Box problems.

Ongoing Assessment: Recognizing Student Achievement
Use Math Boxes, Problems 2 and 5.
[Number and Numeration Goal 1]

Study Link 1•1: Unit 1 Family Letter

Math Masters, pp. 2–6
Students take home the Study Link Family Letter introducing *Everyday Mathematics* and Unit 1.

3 Differentiation Options

READINESS

Following Written Directions

Math Masters, p. 7
Students practice following written directions.

EXTRA PRACTICE

5-Minute Math

5-Minute Math™, pp. 4–6, 82–84, and 168–170
Students write numbers using Roman numerals and standard notation.

Advance Preparation

Refer to Suggested Reading & Lesson Preparation, Organizing Your Classroom, Manipulatives, and Instruction in the *Teacher's Lesson Guide,* pages xxxii–xxxvii.

For the optional Readiness activity in Part 3, duplicate and cut *Math Masters,* page 7 into half-sheets. For a mathematics and literacy connection, obtain a copy of ***Math Talk*** by Theoni Pappas (Wide World Publishing, 1993).

For Lesson 1•2, begin to collect examples of arrays for the Array Museum display. Starting with Lesson 1•2, students will use counters in many of the activities. See the materials list in each lesson for the approximate number needed per student. Keep extras readily available.

***Teacher's Reference Manual,* Grades 4–6** pp. 8–15, 79–83

Getting Started

Mental Math and Reflexes

Establish and use your slate procedure for the following problems. Pose basic multiplication facts and extended facts. Have students write the products for each set of problems. At the end of each set, ask students to describe the pattern they see in the products. *Suggestions:*

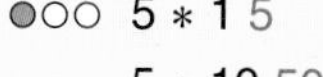

●○○	●●○	●●●
5 ∗ 1 5	7 ∗ 3 21	8 ∗ 5 40
5 ∗ 10 50	7 ∗ 30 210	8 ∗ 50 400
5 ∗ 100 500	7 ∗ 300 2,100	8 ∗ 500 4,000
5 ∗ 1,000 5,000	7 ∗ 3,000 21,000	8 ∗ 5,000 40,000

Math Message

Look through your journal for things that may be different from your fourth grade journal. Read "Welcome to Fifth Grade Everyday Mathematics" on page 1. Underline any words or terms that you do not know or that you think are interesting.

1 Teaching the Lesson

▶ Math Message Follow-Up

WHOLE-CLASS ACTIVITY

(*Math Journal 1,* p.1)

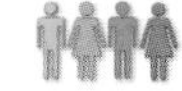

Ask students to share features of the journal that they found while browsing. The following journal features should be included in the discussion:

▷ The last pages in the journal are perforated Activity Sheets that will be torn out at appropriate times.

▷ The inside front cover and the reference pages before the Activity Sheets in the journal contain quick resources for students to use in their work.

Discuss journal page 1 with the class. Ask students to share the terms that they have questions about or that they found interesting. Follow-up questions might involve asking students whether they agree on specific shared items and why or why not.

▶ Examining the *Student Reference Book*

WHOLE-CLASS DISCUSSION

Ask students to browse through the *Student Reference Book.* After a few minutes, bring the class together to discuss the organization and use of the book. Point out the Index and how the Glossary and the color coding for topic selections might inform its use. As a class, read page xi, "How to Use the *Student Reference Book.*"

Choose a page in the *Student Reference Book,* such as "Place Value for Whole Numbers" on page 4. Work through the page to model how a student would use it. Have students try the Check Your Understanding problems and check their answers. Encourage them to analyze any mistakes by finding what they did incorrectly.

Interactive whiteboard-ready **ePresentations** are available at www.everydaymathonline.com to help you teach the lesson.

NOTE The Mental Math and Reflexes activities in Unit 1 are designed to increase students' automatic recall of extended multiplication facts. Refer students to *Student Reference Book,* pages 18 and 21 as needed.

NOTE Some students may benefit from doing the **Readiness** activity before you begin Part 1 of each lesson. See the Readiness activity in Part 3 for details.

Student Page

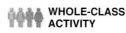

Date Time

LESSON 1·1 Welcome to *Fifth Grade Everyday Mathematics*

Much of what you have learned up to now in *Everyday Mathematics* has been basic training in mathematics and its uses. This year, you will extend the skills and ideas you have learned, and you will also study other ideas in mathematics—many of which your older brothers and sisters, or even your parents, may not have learned until high school. The authors of *Everyday Mathematics* believe that today's fifth graders can learn more and do more than fifth graders in the past.

Here are some of the things you will be asked to do in *Fifth Grade Everyday Mathematics:*

- Practice and extend your knowledge of numbers and their properties, as well as your ability to use measurements and estimation.
- Review and extend your skills in doing arithmetic, using a calculator, and thinking about problems and their solutions. You will work with and learn the notations for fractions, decimals, percents, large whole numbers, exponents, and negative numbers.
- Continue your work with algebra, using variables in place of numbers to represent and analyze situations.
- Refine your understanding of geometry. You will define and classify geometric figures more completely than before. You will construct figures and transformations. You will find the perimeter and area of 2-dimensional shapes, and the volume and surface area of 3-dimensional figures.
- You will study the history, people, and environment of the United States through numerical data. You will learn to interpret many kinds of maps, graphs, and tables and use them to solve problems. Look at journal page 2. Without telling anyone, write a secret number in the margin at the top of the page in the right hand corner.
- You will use data that comes from questionnaires and experiments to explore probability and statistics.

We want you to become better at using mathematics so you may better understand your world. We hope that you enjoy the activities in *Fifth Grade Everyday Mathematics* and that they will help you appreciate the beauty and usefulness of mathematics in your daily activities.

Math Journal 1, p. 1

Student Page

Date ______ Time ______

LESSON 1·1 ***Student Reference Book* Scavenger Hunt**

Solve the problems on this page and page 3. Use your *Student Reference Book* to find information about each problem, and then record the page numbers.

	Problem Points	Page Points
1. Circle the prime numbers in the following list: ① 2 6 9 ⑬ 20 ㉛ 63 72 — SRB page 12		
2. 5 meters = 500 centimeters — SRB page 184		
3. 300 mm = 30 cm — SRB page 184		
4. What is the perimeter of this figure? 22 ft (4 ft by 7 ft rectangle) — SRB page 186		
5. Name two fractions equivalent to $\frac{4}{6}$. Sample answers: $\frac{2}{3}$ and $\frac{8}{12}$ — SRB page 56 59 65		
6. Is angle *RST* acute or obtuse? acute — SRB page 139		

Math Journal 1, p. 2

Student Page

Date ______ Time ______

LESSON 1·1 ***Student Reference Book* Scavenger Hunt** *continued*

	Problem Points	Page Points
7. a. What is the definition of a scalene triangle? A triangle whose sides all have different lengths b. Draw and label a scalene triangle. — SRB page 144		
8. What materials do you need to play *Top-It* games? Number cards 1–10, 4 of each; calculator (optional)		

Choose one of the versions of *Top-It*, and play it with a partner.

SRB page 333–336

Record your scavenger hunt scores in the table below. Then calculate the totals.

Problem Number	Problem Points	Page Points	Total Points = Problem Points + Page Points
1			
2			
3			
4			
5			
6			
7			
8			
	Total Points		

Math Journal 1, p. 3

Occasionally, an icon appears on student pages to indicate where information on the current topic can be found in the *Student Reference Book*. In the Math Boxes for this lesson, students will find and write the *Student Reference Book* page numbers related to the problems.

▶ Solving Problems Using the *Student Reference Book*

(*Math Journal 1*, pp. 2 and 3; *Student Reference Book*)

Language Arts Link As students solve these problems on topics covered in previous grades of *Everyday Mathematics*, many will need to refer to the *Student Reference Book* for help. Using the Table of Contents, Glossary, and Index in the book will help students gain and practice reference skills.

Ask students to score their answers as follows:

▷ 3 points for each correctly answered problem

▷ 5 points for each correct page number from the *Student Reference Book* (There may be more than one correct page number.)

The focus of this activity should be on locating pages in the *Student Reference Book* that provide assistance with difficult problems, rather than obtaining correct answers. Scoring 3 points for a correct answer, but 5 points for citing a page, emphasizes this goal.

Have students complete journal pages 2 and 3. Circulate and assist. When most students have completed the assignment, review the answers and the page references. Emphasize that students should work through and be expected to understand the examples in the *Student Reference Book.* As the subheading at the bottom of many pages indicates, they can check their understanding by working the problems.

Helpful information for problems is often found in several places in the *Student Reference Book.* Encourage students to find multiple sources.

Have students calculate two separate scores—one for total correct answers (problem points), and one for total correct pages (page points)—and find the sum of the two scores. Lastly, direct students to turn to page 2 of their journals, and ask who wrote the secret number in the top right-hand corner. Those students who read and followed the instructions embedded in the student letter on journal page 1 should add 10 extra points to their total points.

2 Ongoing Learning & Practice

Math Boxes 1•1

INDEPENDENT ACTIVITY

(*Math Journal 1,* p. 4; *Math Masters,* p. 412)

Mixed Practice Math Boxes are an important routine for reviewing and maintaining skills. Students can complete them either independently or with partners. Circulate and assist. This is an opportunity to observe students' progress. Use the Math Boxes grid (*Math Masters,* page 412) to create problems for individualized extra practice.

Call attention to the no-calculator icon. When students see this icon next to a problem or a set of problems, it means that they are not to use a calculator to solve the problem(s). For example, see Math Boxes on journal page 4.

The Math Boxes problems in Unit 1 address skills that students practiced in *Fourth Grade Everyday Mathematics.*

Math Boxes in this lesson are paired with Math Boxes in Lesson 1-3. The skill in Problem 6 previews Unit 2 content.

Remind students to find and write the *Student Reference Book* page number(s) related to each problem on *Math Journal 1,* page 4.

Writing/Reasoning Have students write a response to the following: *Look at the fact family you wrote for Problem 4. You can say that 14 is 7 times as great as 2. You can also say that 14 is 2 times as great as 7. Write similar statements for* $8 * 6 = 48$*.* Sample answers: 48 is 6 times as great as 8; 48 is 8 times as great as 6. The number that is 6 times as great as 8 is 48.

Ongoing Assessment: Recognizing Student Achievement

Math Boxes Problems 2 and 5

Use **Math Boxes, Problems 2 and 5** to assess students' understanding of place value. Students are making adequate progress if they are able to correctly position and identify digits and their values in whole numbers through the hundred thousands and decimals through the hundredths.

[Number and Numeration Goal 1]

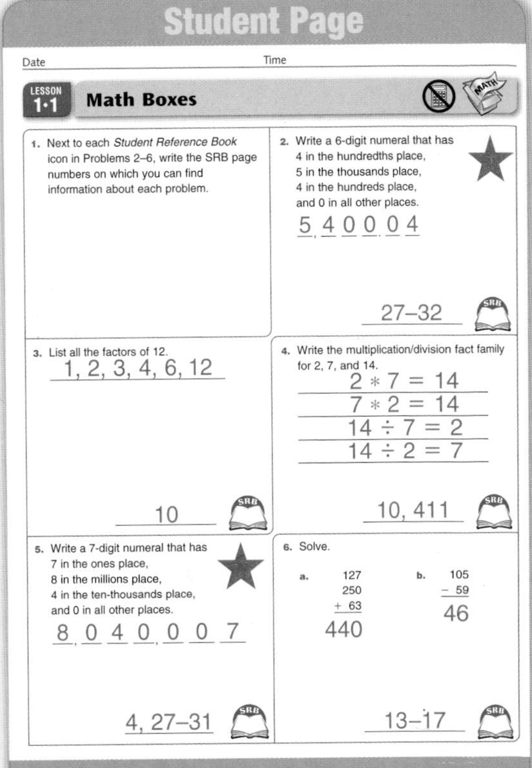

Student Page

Date Time

LESSON 1•1 **Math Boxes**

1. Next to each *Student Reference Book* icon in Problems 2–6, write the SRB page numbers on which you can find information about each problem.

2. Write a 6-digit numeral that has 4 in the hundredths place, 5 in the thousands place, 4 in the hundreds place, and 0 in all other places.
5 4 0 0. 0 4
27–32

3. List all the factors of 12.
1, 2, 3, 4, 6, 12
10

4. Write the multiplication/division fact family for 2, 7, and 14.
$2 * 7 = 14$
$7 * 2 = 14$
$14 \div 7 = 2$
$14 \div 2 = 7$
10, 411

5. Write a 7-digit numeral that has 7 in the ones place, 8 in the millions place, 4 in the ten-thousands place, and 0 in all other places.
8 0 4 0 0 0 7
4, 27–31

6. Solve.
a. 127 + 250 + 63 = 440
b. 105 − 59 = 46
13–17

Math Journal 1, p. 4

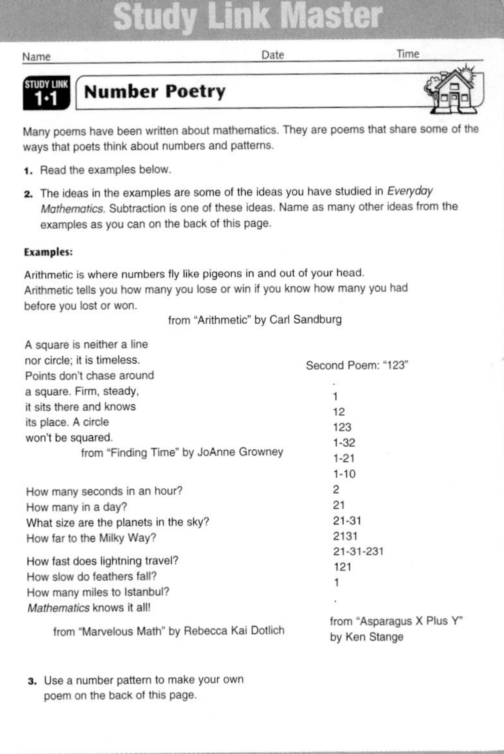

Study Link Master

Name Date Time

STUDY LINK 1•1 **Number Poetry**

Many poems have been written about mathematics. They are poems that share some of the ways that poets think about numbers and patterns.

1. Read the examples below.
2. The ideas in the examples are some of the ideas you have studied in *Everyday Mathematics.* Subtraction is one of these ideas. Name as many other ideas from the examples as you can on the back of this page.

Examples:

Arithmetic is where numbers fly like pigeons in and out of your head.
Arithmetic tells you how many you lose or win if you know how many you had before you lost or won.
from "Arithmetic" by Carl Sandburg

A square is neither a line
nor circle; it is timeless.
Points don't chase around
a square. Firm, steady,
it sits there and knows
its place. A circle
won't be squared.
from "Finding Time" by JoAnne Growney

How many seconds in an hour?
How many in a day?
What size are the planets in the sky?
How far to the Milky Way?
How fast does lightning travel?
How slow do feathers fall?
How many miles to Istanbul?
Mathematics knows it all!
from "Marvelous Math" by Rebecca Kai Dotlich

Second Poem: "123"
.
1
12
123
1-32
1-21
1-10
2
21
21-31
2131
21-31-231
121
1
.
from "Asparagus X Plus Y" by Ken Stange

3. Use a number pattern to make your own poem on the back of this page.

Math Masters, p. 2

Study Link Master

Name Date Time

STUDY LINK 1•1 **Unit 1: Family Letter**

Introduction to *Fifth Grade Everyday Mathematics*

Welcome to *Fifth Grade Everyday Mathematics.* This curriculum was developed by the University of Chicago School Mathematics Project to offer students a broad background in mathematics.

The features of the program described below are to help familiarize you with the structure and expectations of *Everyday Mathematics.*

A problem-solving approach based on everyday situations Students learn basic math skills in a context that is meaningful by making connections between their own knowledge and experience and mathematics concepts.

Frequent practice of basic skills Students practice basic skills in a variety of engaging ways. In addition to completing daily review exercises covering a variety of topics and working with multiplication and division fact families in different formats, students play games that are specifically designed to develop basic skills.

An instructional approach that revisits concepts regularly Lessons are designed to take advantage of previously learned concepts and skills and to build on them throughout the year.

A curriculum that explores mathematical content beyond basic arithmetic Mathematics standards around the world indicate that basic arithmetic skills are only the beginning of the mathematical knowledge students will need as they develop critical-thinking skills. In addition to basic arithmetic, *Everyday Mathematics* develops concepts and skills in the following topics—number and numeration; operations and computation; data and chance; geometry; measurement and reference frames; and patterns, functions, and algebra.

Everyday Mathematics provides you with ample opportunities to monitor your child's progress and to participate in your child's mathematical experiences. Throughout the year, you will receive Family Letters to keep you informed of the mathematical content your child is studying in each unit. Each letter includes a vocabulary list, suggested Do-Anytime Activities for you and your child, and an answer guide to selected Study Link (homework) activities.

Please keep this Family Letter for reference as your child works through Unit 1.

Math Masters, p. 3

▶ Study Link 1•1: Unit 1 Family Letter

INDEPENDENT ACTIVITY

(*Math Masters,* pp. 2–6)

Home Connection It is intended that the activities in *Fifth Grade Everyday Mathematics* will help students appreciate the beauty and widespread usefulness of mathematics, as well as improve their mathematical skills so that they may better understand their world.

Students read the poetry examples on Study Link 1-1 and identify the mathematical ideas in the examples and/or other ideas the poems stimulated. They write a number pattern poem.

The Family Letter provides an introduction to the content of *Fifth Grade Everyday Mathematics* and to the topics covered in Unit 1. Consider distributing this letter to parents during your introductory meeting or curriculum night.

NOTE Consider obtaining a copy of *Math Talk* by Theoni Pappas for additional examples of math poetry.

3 Differentiation Options

READINESS

INDEPENDENT ACTIVITY

▶ Following Written Directions

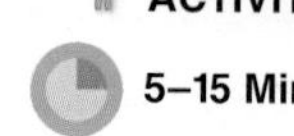

5–15 Min

(*Math Masters,* p. 7)

To explore a variety of problem-solving situations, have students follow the directions on *Math Masters,* page 7. This lesson requires that students are able to translate the ideas and instructions they read in the *Math Journal* and the *Student Reference Book* into their individual classroom behaviors and performance. It is suggested that students complete the Readiness activity before beginning the lesson. The activity is designed as a playful reminder for students to take the time to read all directions carefully before they begin their work.

Teaching Master

Name Date Time

LESSON 1•1 **Following Written Directions**

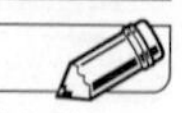

Read the directions *carefully.* Do *not* do anything until you have read all ten instructions.

1. Draw a square inside of a rectangle on this page.
2. Find the sum of the student fingers and toes in your class.
3. Stand up. Cover your eyes with your hands, and turn 90 degrees to the right.
4. Pat the top of your head with your right hand and, at the same time, rub your stomach in a clockwise direction with your left hand. Sit down.
5. As loudly as you can, count backwards from 10.
6. Find the sum of the digits for today's date.
7. Estimate how many miles you walked in the last 2 months.
8. Try to touch the tip of your nose with your tongue.
9. If you reach into a bag where there is a \$1 bill, a \$5 bill, and a \$10 bill, what is the chance that, without looking, you will pull a \$10 bill? Whisper your answer to a neighbor.
10. Do not do any of the first 9 activities. Instead, turn over your paper and wait for your teacher's instructions.

Name Date Time

LESSON 1•1 **Following Written Directions**

Read the directions *carefully.* Do *not* do anything until you have read all ten instructions.

1. Draw a square inside of a rectangle on this page.
2. Find the sum of the student fingers and toes in your class.
3. Stand up. Cover your eyes with your hands, and turn 90 degrees to the right.
4. Pat the top of your head with your right hand and, at the same time, rub your stomach in a clockwise direction with your left hand. Sit down.
5. As loudly as you can, count backwards from 10.
6. Find the sum of the digits for today's date.
7. Estimate how many miles you walked in the last 2 months.
8. Try to touch the tip of your nose with your tongue.
9. If you reach into a bag where there is a \$1 bill, a \$5 bill, and a \$10 bill, what is the chance that, without looking, you will pull a \$10 bill? Whisper your answer to a neighbor.
10. Do not do any of the first 9 activities. Instead, turn over your paper and wait for your teacher's instructions.

Math Masters, p. 7

EXTRA PRACTICE

SMALL-GROUP ACTIVITY

▶ 5-Minute Math

5–15 Min

To offer students more experience with number representation, see *5-Minute Math,* pages 4–6, 82–84, and 168–170.

1•2 Rectangular Arrays

Objectives To review rectangular arrays and the use of multiplication number models to represent such arrays.

Technology Resources www.everydaymathonline.com

ePresentations

eToolkit

Algorithms Practice

EM Facts Workshop Game™

Family Letters

Assessment Management

Common Core State Standards

Curriculum Focal Points

Interactive Teacher's Lesson Guide

1 Teaching the Lesson

Key Concepts and Skills

- Find factors of a number. [Number and Numeration Goal 3]
- Write number sentences for rectangular arrays. [Operations and Computation Goal 7]
- Use the turn-around rule for multiplication. [Patterns, Functions, and Algebra Goal 4]

Key Activities

Students discuss rectangular arrays using examples in the Arrays Museum and ones they draw or make with counters. They write multiplication number models to represent rectangular arrays.

Ongoing Assessment: Recognizing Student Achievement
Use journal page 5.
[Operations and Computation Goal 7]

Key Vocabulary

rectangular array ◆ number model ◆ Commutative Property of Multiplication ◆ turn-around rule (for multiplication)

Materials

Math Journal 1, p. 5
Student Reference Book, p. 10
Study Link 1•1
Math Masters, p. 413 (optional)
18 counters ◆ Class Data Pad ◆ slate

2 Ongoing Learning & Practice

Recognizing Patterns in Extended Facts
Math Journal 1, pp. 6 and 7
Students practice solving extended multiplication and division fact problems using Fact Triangles.

Math Boxes 1•2
Math Journal 1, p. 8
Students practice and maintain skills through Math Box problems.

Study Link 1•2
Math Masters, p. 8
Students practice and maintain skills through Study Link activities.

3 Differentiation Options

READINESS

Defining Rows and Columns
Math Masters, p. 9
per partnership: 40 centimeter cubes ◆ 2 dice
Students practice building arrays.

ENRICHMENT

Exploring Magic Square and Heterosquare Arrays
Math Masters, p. 10
Students explore rectangular arrays by solving magic square and heterosquare array problems.

ELL SUPPORT

Describing Exhibits in the Arrays Museum
Students practice new vocabulary by describing items in the Arrays Museum.

Advance Preparation

Post the "Working with a Partner" principles. See *Teacher's Reference Manual,* pages 46–48. Prepare a display area for the Class Data Pad and Arrays Museum. Collect several arrays as examples. Refer to *Teacher's Reference Manual,* page 13.

***Teacher's Reference Manual,* Grades 4–6** pp. 16, 79–83, 107–111, 267–271

Getting Started

Mental Math and Reflexes

FACTS PRACTICE

Pose basic and extended division facts.
Have students write the answers for each set of problems. At the end of each set, ask students to describe the patterns they see among the dividends, divisors, and quotients. *Suggestions:*

●○○	●●○	●●●
7 ÷ 1 7	28 ÷ 4 7	56 ÷ 7 = 8
70 ÷ 10 7	280 ÷ 40 7	560 ÷ 70 = 8
700 ÷ 100 7	2,800 ÷ 400 7	560,000 ÷ 70,000 = 8
7,000 ÷ 1,000 7	28,000 ÷ 4,000 7	

Math Message

Arrange 12 counters into as many different rectangular arrays as you can. Then choose and draw one of the arrays.

Study Link 1·1 Follow-Up

Discuss student's responses and their number pattern poems. Ask: *If you were writing a poem about arithmetic, how would you finish this sentence:* Arithmetic is…? List the mathematics vocabulary that students use on the Class Data Pad. Emphasize how using mathematics vocabulary makes communicating their ideas to others easier and more efficient.

NOTE Some students may benefit from doing the **Readiness** activity before you begin Part 1 of each lesson. See the Readiness activity in Part 3 for details.

Interactive whiteboard-ready **ePresentations** are available at www.everydaymathonline.com to help you teach the lesson.

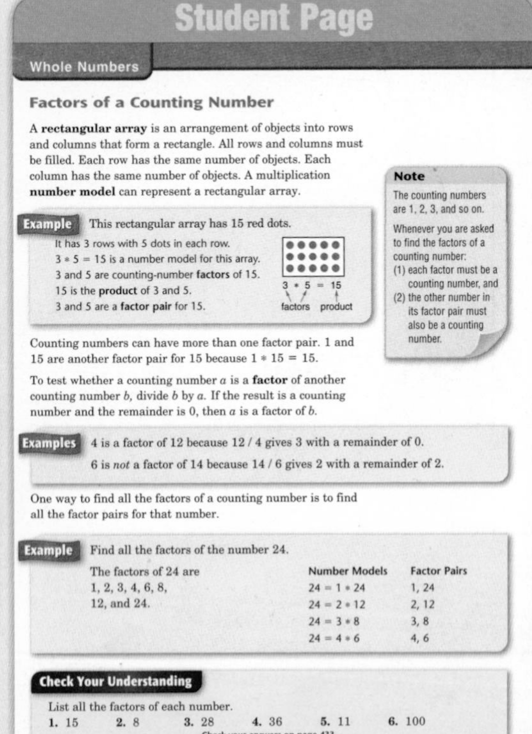

Student Page

Whole Numbers

Factors of a Counting Number

A **rectangular array** is an arrangement of objects into rows and columns that form a rectangle. All rows and columns must be filled. Each row has the same number of objects. Each column has the same number of objects. A multiplication **number model** can represent a rectangular array.

Example This rectangular array has 15 red dots.

It has 3 rows with 5 dots in each row.
3 ∗ 5 = 15 is a number model for this array.
3 and 5 are counting-number **factors** of 15.
15 is the **product** of 3 and 5.
3 and 5 are a **factor pair** for 15.

3 ∗ 5 = 15
factors product

Note
The counting numbers are 1, 2, 3, and so on.
Whenever you are asked to find the factors of a counting number:
(1) each factor must be a counting number, and
(2) the other number in its factor pair must also be a counting number.

Counting numbers can have more than one factor pair. 1 and 15 are another factor pair for 15 because 1 ∗ 15 = 15.

To test whether a counting number *a* is a **factor** of another counting number *b*, divide *b* by *a*. If the result is a counting number and the remainder is 0, then *a* is a factor of *b*.

Examples 4 is a factor of 12 because 12 / 4 gives 3 with a remainder of 0.
6 is *not* a factor of 14 because 14 / 6 gives 2 with a remainder of 2.

One way to find all the factors of a counting number is to find all the factor pairs for that number.

Example Find all the factors of the number 24.

The factors of 24 are 1, 2, 3, 4, 6, 8, 12, and 24.

Number Models	Factor Pairs
24 = 1 ∗ 24	1, 24
24 = 2 ∗ 12	2, 12
24 = 3 ∗ 8	3, 8
24 = 4 ∗ 6	4, 6

Check Your Understanding

List all the factors of each number.
1. 15 **2.** 8 **3.** 28 **4.** 36 **5.** 11 **6.** 100

Check your answers on page 433.

Student Reference Book, p. 10

1 Teaching the Lesson

▶ Math Message Follow-Up

WHOLE-CLASS DISCUSSION

ELL

Ask students to share the **rectangular arrays** they drew. Have one student describe the array and another draw the array from the description. To support English language learners, clarify the noun/adjective relationship between *rectangle* and *rectangular*. Mentally note students' use and understanding of appropriate vocabulary (rows, columns, in each row, in each column).

Array possibilities for 12: 1-by-12, 12-by-1, 2-by-6, 6-by-2, 3-by-4, and 4-by-3.

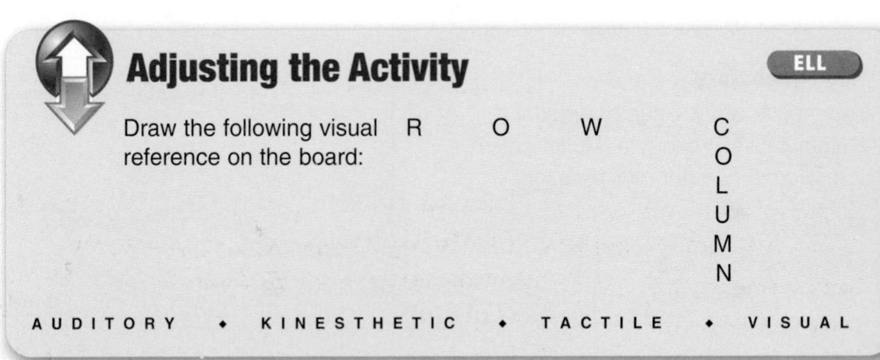

Adjusting the Activity

ELL

Draw the following visual reference on the board:

R O W

C
O
L
U
M
N

AUDITORY • KINESTHETIC • TACTILE • VISUAL

▶ Reviewing Arrays

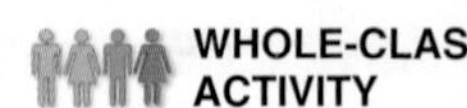

WHOLE-CLASS ACTIVITY

(*Student Reference Book*, p. 10; *Math Masters*, p. 413)

Algebraic Thinking Display examples of rectangular arrays from the Arrays Museum. Stress these key elements:

▷ Each row has the same number of objects.

▷ Each column also has the same number of objects.

▷ Each array has a rectangular shape.

Ask students to name the number of rows and columns in each example.

During this unit, students should collect other examples of arrays to add to the Arrays Museum.

Adjusting the Activity

Consider reserving a section of the Arrays Museum for arrangements that are "almost arrays" but do not satisfy all the conditions for rectangular arrays. Examples include some calculator keypads; certain playing cards, such as the nine of diamonds; a double-3 domino; and a calendar month, such as the month of August.

August						
S	M	T	W	T	F	S
1	2	3	4	5	6	7
8	9	10	11	12	13	14
15	16	17	18	19	20	21
22	23	24	25	26	27	28
29	30	31				

This is not an array:
The fifth row has only 3 days.

AUDITORY ◆ KINESTHETIC ◆ TACTILE ◆ VISUAL

Arrays were first introduced in *Second Grade Everyday Mathematics.* Have students focus on labeling arrays in terms of rows and columns and representing arrays with **number models.** Assign student groups to:

1. Read page 10 in the *Student Reference Book.*
2. Complete one of the Check Your Understanding problems.
3. Draw a rectangular array from one of their factor pairs and write the number model that represents the array.

Circulate and assist.

Review multiplication number models as a way of representing rectangular arrays. Have groups present their arrays and number models.

Rectangular arrays can help students visualize factors and the **Commutative Property of Multiplication.** Ask students to take out and arrange 6 counters into an array. Show students' responses on the board or transparency of *Math Masters,* page 413 until all four possibilities have been displayed and discussed. (*See margin.*)

To avoid confusion when naming an r-by-c array, let r represent the number of rows and c the number of objects in each row (the number of columns).

Point out that both the 3-row-by-2-column and the 2-row-by-3-column arrays have the same number of dots, but not the same number of rows and columns. Tell students that this models a property of multiplication. The order in which two numbers are multiplied makes no difference in their product: $2 * 3 = 6$ and $3 * 2 = 6$.

3-row-by-2-column array
Number model: $3 * 2 = 6$

2-row-by-3-column array
Number model: $2 * 3 = 6$

1-row-by-6-column array
Number model: $1 * 6 = 6$

6-row-by-1-column array
Number model: $6 * 1 = 6$

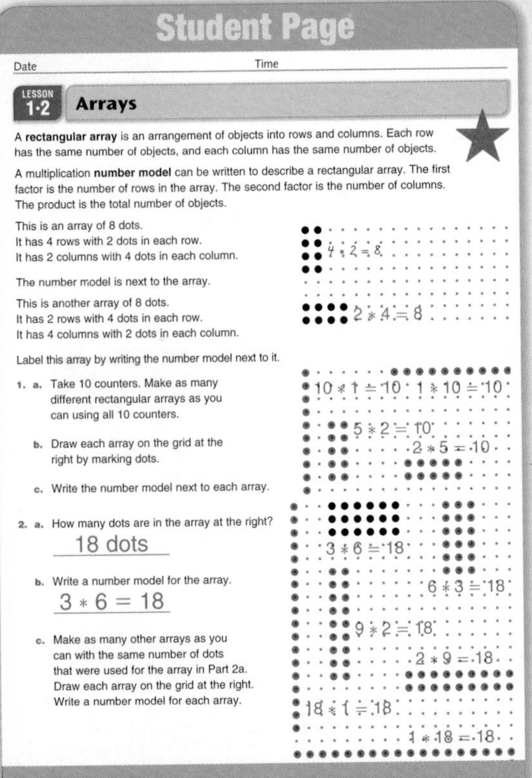
Student Page

Date Time

LESSON 1·2 **Arrays**

A **rectangular array** is an arrangement of objects into rows and columns. Each row has the same number of objects, and each column has the same number of objects.

A multiplication **number model** can be written to describe a rectangular array. The first factor is the number of rows in the array. The second factor is the number of columns. The product is the total number of objects.

This is an array of 8 dots.
It has 4 rows with 2 dots in each row.
It has 2 columns with 4 dots in each column.

4 * 2 = 8

The number model is next to the array.

This is another array of 8 dots.
It has 2 rows with 4 dots in each row.
It has 4 columns with 2 dots in each column.

2 * 4 = 8

Label this array by writing the number model next to it.

1. a. Take 10 counters. Make as many different rectangular arrays as you can using all 10 counters.
   b. Draw each array on the grid at the right by marking dots.
   c. Write the number model next to each array.

10 * 1 = 10   1 * 10 = 10   5 * 2 = 10   2 * 5 = 10

2. a. How many dots are in the array at the right? 18 dots
   b. Write a number model for the array. 3 * 6 = 18
   c. Make as many other arrays as you can with the same number of dots that were used for the array in Part 2a. Draw each array on the grid at the right. Write a number model for each array.

3 * 6 = 18   6 * 3 = 18   9 * 2 = 18   2 * 9 = 18   18 * 1 = 18   1 * 18 = 18

Math Journal, p. 5

Student Page

Date Time

LESSON 1·2 **Multiplication and Division Extended Facts**

Read the information about extended multiplication and division facts on *Student Reference Book,* pages 18 and 21. If you know the basic multiplication and division facts, then you can solve extended fact problems such as 30 * 20 and 1,800 / 30 mentally. Just as there are four related facts for each basic fact, there are also four related facts in an extended fact family.

2 * 3 = 6
3 * 2 = 6
6 / 2 = 3
6 / 3 = 2

(Fact Triangle: 6; *, /; 2, 3)

20 * 30 = 600
30 * 20 = 600
600 / 20 = 30
600 / 30 = 20

(Fact Triangle: 600; *, /; 20, 30)

20 * 30 = ? *Think:* 2[3s] = 6. Then 20[30s] is 100 times as much. 20 * 30 = 600

1. Write the extended fact family represented by each of these Fact Triangles.

a. 30 * 70 = 2,100
70 * 30 = 2,100
2,100 / 70 = 30
2,100 / 30 = 70

(Fact Triangle: 2,100; *, /; 30, 70)

b. 60 * 20 = 1,200
20 * 60 = 1,200
1,200 / 20 = 60
1,200 / 60 = 20

(Fact Triangle: 1,200; *, /; 60, 20)

Math Journal 1, p. 6

Students have used this property of multiplication in turn-around facts as shortcuts to learning new facts. Ask if students know what this property is called. Some students will respond that the property is the **turn-around rule** for multiplication. Some students might know to use the term *Commutative Property of Multiplication,* but do not insist that students use this term.

Adjusting the Activity

ELL

Teach students a physical representation of the Commutative Property of Multiplication to indicate "turn-around" facts. This gesture demonstrates the idea of switching the numbers and can be used to remind students when the turn-around rule is being applied.

AUDITORY ◆ KINESTHETIC ◆ TACTILE ◆ VISUAL

▶ Finding All Possible Rectangular Arrays for a Number

(*Math Journal 1,* p. 5)

Review the "Working with a Partner" principles. Ask students for additional suggestions to help make the classroom more pleasant when students are working with partners or in small groups.

Ask partners to make all possible rectangular arrays using 8 counters. 1-by-8, 8-by-1, 2-by-4, 4-by-2 Partners then work on journal page 5. Circulate and assist.

NOTE Some students might find it easier to work on a full sheet of dot paper for Problem 2. (*Math Masters,* p. 413)

Ongoing Assessment: Recognizing Student Achievement

Journal Page 5

Use **journal page 5** to assess students' ability to build arrays and identify factors that describe arrays. Students are making adequate progress if they correctly arrange and label the arrays for both 10 and 18 by using counters and/or drawing on the journal page.

[Operations and Computation Goal 7]

2 Ongoing Learning & Practice

Recognizing Patterns in Extended Facts

PARTNER ACTIVITY

(*Math Journal 1,* pp. 6 and 7)

Students write the extended fact families represented by the numbers on multiplication and division Fact Triangles. They describe patterns in the number of zeros in the factors and products.

Math Boxes 1•2

INDEPENDENT ACTIVITY

(*Math Journal 1,* p. 8)

Mixed Practice Math Boxes in this lesson are paired with Math Boxes in Lesson 1-4. The skill in Problem 5 previews Unit 2 content.

Study Link 1•2

INDEPENDENT ACTIVITY

(*Math Masters,* p. 8)

Home Connection Students build and draw rectangular arrays to represent numbers and write the associated number models.

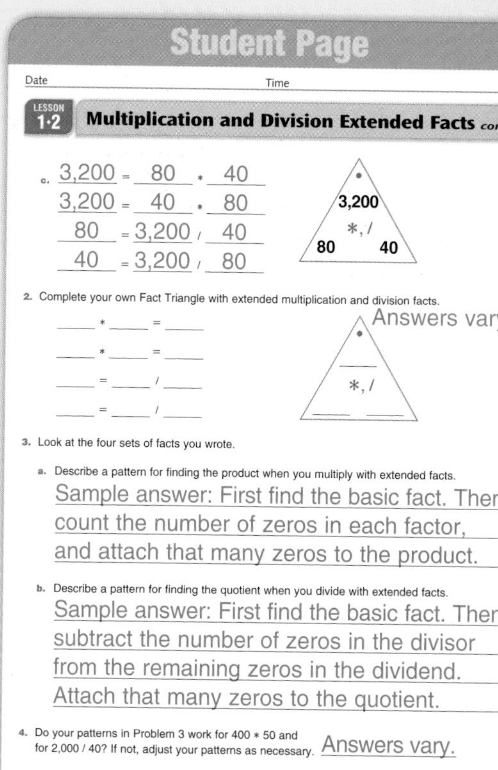

Student Page

Date Time

LESSON 1•2 **Multiplication and Division Extended Facts** *cont.*

c. 3,200 = 80 * 40
3,200 = 40 * 80
80 = 3,200 / 40
40 = 3,200 / 80

2. Complete your own Fact Triangle with extended multiplication and division facts.

Answers vary.

____ * ____ = ____
____ * ____ = ____
____ = ____ / ____
____ = ____ / ____

3. Look at the four sets of facts you wrote.

a. Describe a pattern for finding the product when you multiply with extended facts.
Sample answer: First find the basic fact. Then count the number of zeros in each factor, and attach that many zeros to the product.

b. Describe a pattern for finding the quotient when you divide with extended facts.
Sample answer: First find the basic fact. Then subtract the number of zeros in the divisor from the remaining zeros in the dividend. Attach that many zeros to the quotient.

4. Do your patterns in Problem 3 work for 400 * 50 and for 2,000 / 40? If not, adjust your patterns as necessary. Answers vary.

Math Journal 1, p. 7

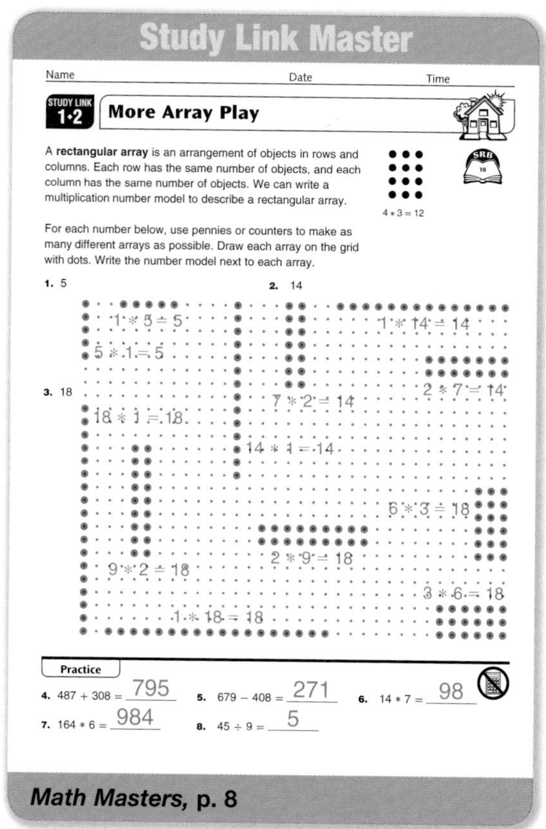

Study Link Master

Name Date Time

STUDY LINK 1•2 **More Array Play**

A **rectangular array** is an arrangement of objects in rows and columns. Each row has the same number of objects, and each column has the same number of objects. We can write a multiplication number model to describe a rectangular array.

4 * 3 = 12

For each number below, use pennies or counters to make as many different arrays as possible. Draw each array on the grid with dots. Write the number model next to each array.

1. 5
1 * 5 = 5
5 * 1 = 5

2. 14
1 * 14 = 14
7 * 2 = 14
2 * 7 = 14
14 * 1 = 14

3. 18
18 * 1 = 18
6 * 3 = 18
2 * 9 = 18
9 * 2 = 18
3 * 6 = 18
1 * 18 = 18

Practice

4. 487 + 308 = 795
5. 679 − 408 = 271
6. 14 * 7 = 98
7. 164 * 6 = 984
8. 45 ÷ 9 = 5

Math Masters, p. 8

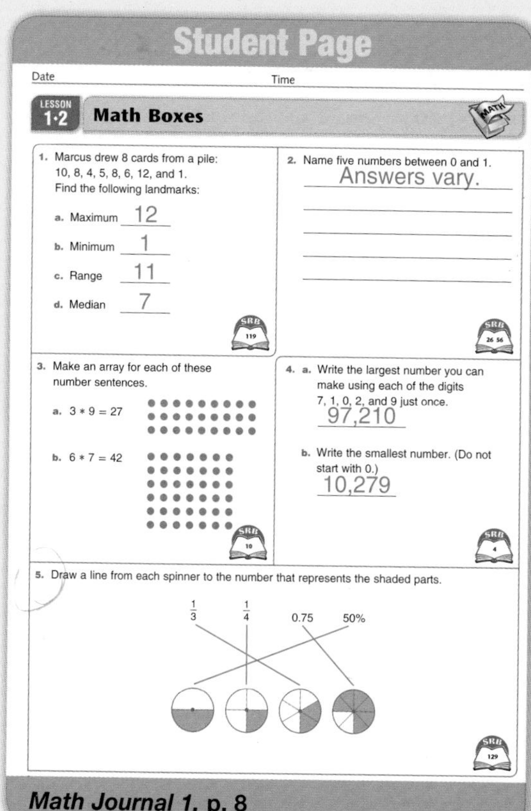

Student Page

Date Time

LESSON 1•2 **Math Boxes**

1. Marcus drew 8 cards from a pile: 10, 8, 4, 5, 8, 6, 12, and 1. Find the following landmarks:
a. Maximum 12
b. Minimum 1
c. Range 11
d. Median 7

2. Name five numbers between 0 and 1.
Answers vary.

3. Make an array for each of these number sentences.
a. 3 * 9 = 27
b. 6 * 7 = 42

4. a. Write the largest number you can make using each of the digits 7, 1, 0, 2, and 9 just once. 97,210
b. Write the smallest number. (Do not start with 0.) 10,279

5. Draw a line from each spinner to the number that represents the shaded parts.

$\frac{1}{3}$ $\frac{1}{4}$ 0.75 50%

Math Journal 1, p. 8

Name _______________ Date _______ Time _______

LESSON 1·2 **Rows and Columns**

A rectangular array is an arrangement of objects in rows and columns. Each row has the same number of objects, and each column has the same number of objects.

Work with a partner to build arrays. For each array, take turns rolling dice. The first die is the number of rows. Write this number in the table under Rows. The second die is the number of cubes in each row. Write this number under Columns. Then use centimeter cubes to build the array on the dot grid. How many cubes are in the array? Write this number under Array Total on the dot grid table.

Rows	Columns	Array Total

Rows	Columns	Array Total

Math Masters, p. 9

Name _______________ Date _______ Time _______

LESSON 1·2 **Magic Square and Heterosquare Arrays**

A rectangular array is an arrangement of objects in rows and columns. The objects in an array can be numbers or numerical expressions. The Multiplication/Division Facts Table on the inside front cover of your journal is an example of numbers arranged in an array. The objects can also be words or symbols that represent elements of a given situation. For example, a plan for after-school snacks could be arranged in a 1-by-5 array, using *A* for apple, *B* for banana, and so on.

A magic square is an array of positive whole numbers. The sum of the numbers in each row, column, and diagonal will be the same.

1. Complete this magic square.

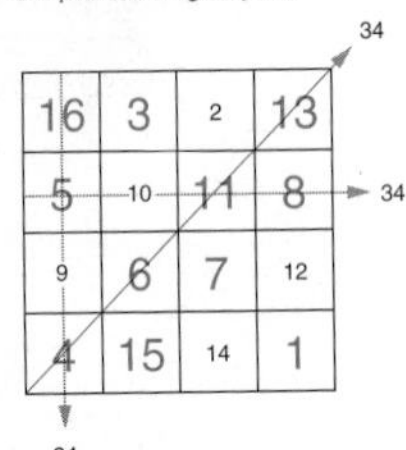

16	3	2	13
5	10	11	8
9	6	7	12
4	15	14	1

34, 34, 34

A heterosquare is like a magic square, except that the sum of the numbers in each row, column, and diagonal are different. A 3-by-3 array for a heterosquare will have an arrangement of the numbers 1–9.

2. Complete this heterosquare, and write the sum for each row, column, and the two diagonals.

7	6	5	18
8	1	4	13
9	2	3	14
24	9	12	

Diagonals: 15, 11

3. Create a magic square or heterosquare for your partner to solve.
Answers vary.

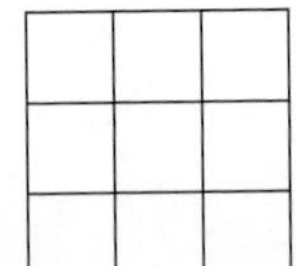

Math Masters, p. 10

3 Differentiation Options

READINESS

PARTNER ACTIVITY

15–30 Min

▶ Defining Rows and Columns

(*Math Masters,* p. 9)

To explore factoring numbers using a concrete model, have students build arrays and find the total number of counters for each array. Have students describe their arrays using the words *row* and *column.*

ENRICHMENT

PARTNER ACTIVITY

15–30 Min

▶ Exploring Magic Square and Heterosquare Arrays

(*Math Masters,* p. 10)

To further explore rectangular arrays, have students solve magic square and heterosquare array problems. Arrays are also used to organize numbers, numerical expressions, and symbols to represent rules. In a magic square, the rule is that the sum of each row, column, and diagonal is the same. In a heterosquare, these sums will be different. Partners complete these two types of arrays and make an array of either type using their own numbers. Have students display their arrays in the Arrays Museum.

This activity also provides practice with adding, subtracting, and comparing whole numbers.

ELL SUPPORT

SMALL-GROUP ACTIVITY

5–15 Min

▶ Describing Exhibits in the Arrays Museum

To provide language support for multiplication, have students look at the Arrays Museum. Ask them to describe the arrays in the museum using language from the lesson. They might describe the rows, columns, shape, and the contents of the arrays.

Planning Ahead

Remind students to collect examples of arrays for the Arrays Museum. The Arrays Museum will be used again in Lesson 1-3 and in subsequent lessons.

1•3 Factors

Objectives To provide a review of the meanings of *factor* and *product;* and to provide opportunities to factor numbers and apply multiplication facts.

Technology Resources www.everydaymathonline.com

ePresentations

eToolkit

Algorithms Practice

EM Facts Workshop Game™

Family Letters

Assessment Management

Common Core State Standards

Curriculum Focal Points

Interactive Teacher's Lesson Guide

1 Teaching the Lesson

Key Concepts and Skills

- Find all factors of a number. [Number and Numeration Goal 3]
- Solve and apply multiplication facts. [Operations and Computation Goal 2]
- Write number models for rectangular arrays. [Operations and Computation Goal 7]

Key Activities

Students are introduced to a multiplication facts routine. Students form rectangular arrays, write number models for the arrays, and list factor pairs for whole numbers.

Ongoing Assessment: Recognizing Student Achievement
Use journal page 10.
[Number and Numeration Goal 3]

Key Vocabulary

factor ◆ product ◆ factor pair

Materials

Math Journal 1, pp. 9 and 10
Study Link 1•2
Math Masters, p. 11
Class Data Pad ◆ 18 counters

2 Ongoing Learning & Practice

Playing *Beat the Calculator* (Extended-Facts Version)
Student Reference Book, p. 299
per partnership: 4 each of number cards 1–10 (from the Everything Math Deck, if available), calculator
Students practice and apply extended multiplication facts.

Math Boxes 1•3
Math Journal 1, p. 11
Students practice and maintain skills through Math Box problems.

Study Link 1•3
Math Masters, p. 12
Students practice and maintain skills through Study Link activities.

3 Differentiation Options

READINESS

Factoring Numbers with Cube Arrays
Student Reference Book, p. 10
Math Masters, p. 13
centimeter cubes
Students build arrays for numbers with centimeter cubes and record the factor pairs.

EXTRA PRACTICE

5-Minute Math
5-Minute Math™, pp. 13 and 90
Students factor whole numbers.

EXTRA PRACTICE

Practicing Multiplication Facts
Math Journal 1, p. 9
Math Masters, p. 11
Students use a multiplication facts routine.

ELL SUPPORT

Building a Math Word Bank
Differentiation Handbook, p. 143
Students add the terms *factor, product,* and *multiplication* to their Math Word Banks.

Advance Preparation

***Teacher's Reference Manual,* Grades 4–6** pp. 79–83, 107–111, 267–271

Getting Started

Mental Math and Reflexes

Pose the following problems, and have students write an expression for each. Students are not expected to calculate the answers. Answers may vary.

●○○ The sum of 5 and 4 $5 + 4$

The product of 5 and 6 $5 * 6$

Double 4 $2 * 4$

●●○ Five times the sum of 2 and 3 $5 * (2 + 3)$

Six times the sum of 5 and 2 $6 * (5 + 2)$

Eight times the product of 3 and 2 $8 * (3 * 2)$

●●● Double the sum of 5 and 4 $2(5 + 4)$

Triple the sum of 6 and 2 $3 * (6 + 2)$

Add 4 and 3, and multiply the sum by 9 $9(4 + 3)$

Math Message

Solve Problem 1 at the top of journal page 10.

Study Link 1·2 Follow-Up

Ask a volunteer to explain his or her solution to Problem 2. Emphasize the use of appropriate vocabulary.

Discuss the sample arrays and solicit possible grouping categories for the Arrays Museum. Encourage students to provide more examples.

NOTE Some students may benefit from doing the **Readiness** activity before you begin Part 1 of each lesson. See the Readiness activity in Part 3 for details.

Interactive whiteboard-ready ePresentations are available at www.everydaymathonline.com to help you teach the lesson.

Student Page

Date Time

LESSON 1·3 **Multiplication Facts Master Lists**

Make a check mark next to each fact you missed and need to study. When you have learned a fact, write "OK" next to the check mark.

Multiplication Facts

3s	5s	7s	9s
3 * 3	5 * 3	7 * 3	9 * 3
3 * 4	5 * 4	7 * 4	9 * 4
3 * 5	5 * 5	7 * 5	9 * 5
3 * 6	5 * 6	7 * 6	9 * 6
3 * 7	5 * 7	7 * 7	9 * 7
3 * 8	5 * 8	7 * 8	9 * 8
3 * 9	5 * 9	7 * 9	9 * 9
		7 * 10	9 * 10

Multiplication Facts

4s	6s	8s	10s
4 * 3	6 * 3	8 * 3	10 * 3
4 * 4	6 * 4	8 * 4	10 * 4
4 * 5	6 * 5	8 * 5	10 * 5
4 * 6	6 * 6	8 * 6	10 * 6
4 * 7	6 * 7	8 * 7	10 * 7
4 * 8	6 * 8	8 * 8	10 * 8
4 * 9	6 * 9	8 * 9	10 * 9
	6 * 10	8 * 10	10 * 10

Math Journal 1, p. 9

1 Teaching the Lesson

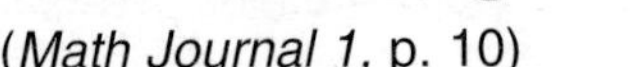

▶ Math Message Follow-Up

WHOLE-CLASS DISCUSSION

ELL

(*Math Journal 1*, p. 10)

Have volunteers write their number models for 14 on the board.

Remind students that in a number model such as $3 * 5 = 15$ or $5 * 3 = 15$, the 3 and the 5 are called **factors**; and 15, the result of multiplying, is called the **product** of 3 and 5. The factors 3 and 5 are a **factor pair** for the number 15. To support English language learners, write a number model labeled with the terms *factor* and *product* on the Class Data Pad. Also, discuss the everyday and mathematical meanings of the words *factor* and *product*.

Ask: *What is another factor pair for 15?* 1 and 15 The factors 1 and 15 are another factor pair for 15. For all numbers, 1 and n are always factors of n. *Are there other whole-number factor pairs for 15?* no

▶ Introducing the Multiplication Facts Routine

WHOLE-CLASS ACTIVITY

FACTS PRACTICE

(*Math Journal 1*, p. 9; *Math Masters*, p. 11)

The authors of *Everyday Mathematics* expect that most fifth-grade students will have automaticity of the multiplication facts and are building toward automatic recall of the extended facts. Facility with extended facts is important because it provides powerful mental arithmetic strategies that can be used when working with large numbers. Mastery of the basic facts helps students make quick estimates and compute with larger numbers. Use the following facts routine to screen the class to determine which students have automaticity with the basic multiplication facts. Although multiplication facts will not be addressed in Part 1 of the

remaining lessons, this routine may be used in Part 3 to continue practice with multiplication facts. Achieving automatic recall of the basic facts helps students to develop automaticity of the extended multiplication facts. Use the following steps:

1. Have each student number a sheet of paper from 1 to 16.
2. Dictate 10 problems from list A on *Math Masters,* page 11; five problems from list B; and one problem from the bonus problems. Repeat each problem only once. Proceed fairly rapidly.
3. Students write their answers on their papers.
4. Go over the problems, reading the answers. Students correct any mistakes and record them by making check marks next to the problems on the Master List on journal page 9. These are the problems they will target to study in order to reach automaticity. As students improve, they write "OK" next to their check marks on journal page 9. Students who have not reached automaticity for all of the facts should be encouraged to use this list as a guide for continued study.

As students work with their facts, emphasize the turn-around rule for multiplication to help them recognize the facts they already know. Circle the problems on *Math Masters,* page 11 that are missed most frequently so that you use them again for continued practice.

NOTE This facts routine will appear in Part 3 of Lessons 1-3, 1-5, and 1-9.

Adjusting the Activity

Prepare a written quiz or a transparency of the problems as an alternative. With the transparency, you can use a sheet of paper to cover the problems, uncovering them one at a time as you read.

AUDITORY • KINESTHETIC • TACTILE • VISUAL

Finding Factor Pairs

(*Math Journal 1,* p. 10)

With the class, list all the whole-number factor pairs for the number 18. Record the list on the board or on a transparency. 1 and 18, 2 and 9, 3 and 6 Remind students that each of the turn-around facts uses only 2 factors. 1 * 18 and 18 * 1 use the factors 1 and 18. If students have trouble finding factor pairs, ask them to use counters to make all possible arrays for 18. Then write a number model for each array. 1 * 18 = 18, 18 * 1 = 18, 2 * 9 = 18, 9 * 2 = 18, 3 * 6 = 18, 6 * 3 = 18

Teaching Master

Name Date Time

LESSON 1·3 **Multiplication Facts**

A List					
3 * 6 = 18					
6 * 3 = 18					
3 * 7 = 21					
7 * 3 = 21					
3 * 8 = 24					
8 * 3 = 24					
3 * 9 = 27					
9 * 3 = 27					
4 * 6 = 24					
6 * 4 = 24					
4 * 7 = 28					
7 * 4 = 28					
4 * 8 = 32					
8 * 4 = 32					
4 * 9 = 36					
9 * 4 = 36					
5 * 7 = 35					
7 * 5 = 35					
5 * 9 = 45					
9 * 5 = 45					
6 * 6 = 36					
6 * 7 = 42					
7 * 6 = 42					
6 * 8 = 48					
8 * 6 = 48					
6 * 9 = 54					
9 * 6 = 54					
7 * 7 = 49					
7 * 8 = 56					
8 * 7 = 56					
7 * 9 = 63					
9 * 7 = 63					
8 * 8 = 64					
8 * 9 = 72					
9 * 8 = 72					
9 * 9 = 81					

B List					
3 * 3 = 9					
3 * 4 = 12					
4 * 3 = 12					
3 * 5 = 15					
5 * 3 = 15					
4 * 4 = 16					
4 * 5 = 20					
5 * 4 = 20					
5 * 5 = 25					
5 * 6 = 30					
6 * 5 = 30					
5 * 8 = 40					
8 * 5 = 40					
6 * 10 = 60					
10 * 6 = 60					
7 * 10 = 70					
10 * 7 = 70					
8 * 10 = 80					
10 * 8 = 80					
9 * 10 = 90					
10 * 9 = 90					
10 * 10 = 100					

Bonus Problems					
11 * 11 = 121					
11 * 12 = 132					
5 * 12 = 60					
12 * 6 = 72					
7 * 12 = 84					
12 * 8 = 80					
9 * 12 = 108					
10 * 12 = 120					
5 * 13 = 65					
15 * 7 = 105					
12 * 12 = 144					
6 * 14 = 84					

Math Masters, p. 11

NOTE Although a factor may be a whole number, decimal, or fraction, Unit 1 deals with whole-number factors only. The work with factors in this unit involves basic multiplication and division facts.

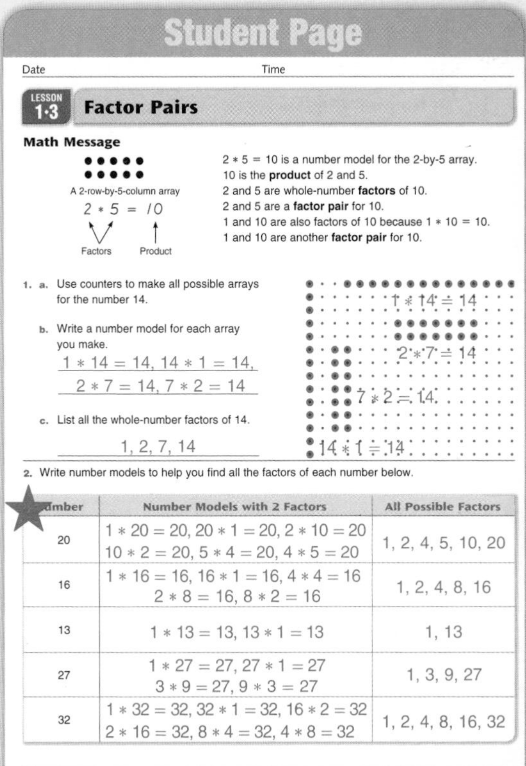
Student Page

Date Time

LESSON 1·3 **Factor Pairs**

Math Message

A 2-row-by-5-column array

2 * 5 = 10

Factors Product

2 * 5 = 10 is a number model for the 2-by-5 array.
10 is the **product** of 2 and 5.
2 and 5 are whole-number **factors** of 10.
2 and 5 are a **factor pair** for 10.
1 and 10 are also factors of 10 because 1 * 10 = 10.
1 and 10 are another **factor pair** for 10.

1. a. Use counters to make all possible arrays for the number 14.

b. Write a number model for each array you make.
1 * 14 = 14, 14 * 1 = 14,
2 * 7 = 14, 7 * 2 = 14

c. List all the whole-number factors of 14.
1, 2, 7, 14

1 * 14 = 14
2 * 7 = 14
7 * 2 = 14
14 * 1 = 14

2. Write number models to help you find all the factors of each number below.

Number	Number Models with 2 Factors	All Possible Factors
20	1 * 20 = 20, 20 * 1 = 20, 2 * 10 = 20 10 * 2 = 20, 5 * 4 = 20, 4 * 5 = 20	1, 2, 4, 5, 10, 20
16	1 * 16 = 16, 16 * 1 = 16, 4 * 4 = 16 2 * 8 = 16, 8 * 2 = 16	1, 2, 4, 8, 16
13	1 * 13 = 13, 13 * 1 = 13	1, 13
27	1 * 27 = 27, 27 * 1 = 27 3 * 9 = 27, 9 * 3 = 27	1, 3, 9, 27
32	1 * 32 = 32, 32 * 1 = 32, 16 * 2 = 32 2 * 16 = 32, 8 * 4 = 32, 4 * 8 = 32	1, 2, 4, 8, 16, 32

Math Journal 1, p. 10

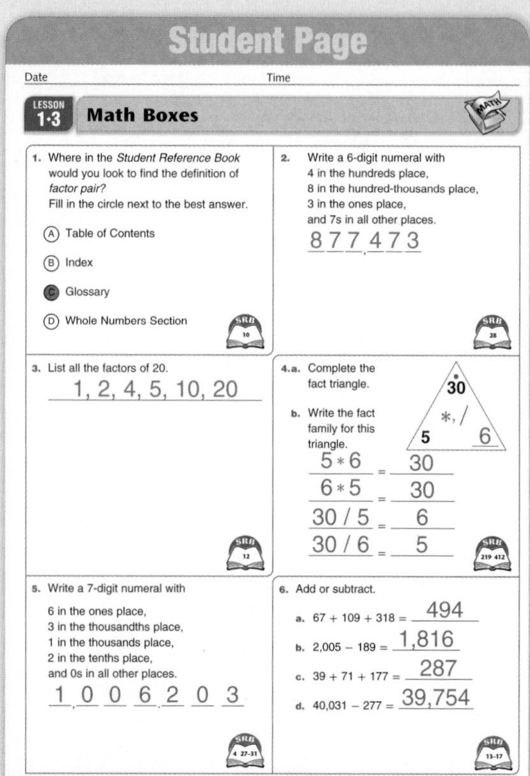

Student Page

Date Time

LESSON 1·3 **Math Boxes**

1. Where in the *Student Reference Book* would you look to find the definition of *factor pair?*
Fill in the circle next to the best answer.
Ⓐ Table of Contents
Ⓑ Index
● Glossary
Ⓓ Whole Numbers Section

2. Write a 6-digit numeral with 4 in the hundreds place, 8 in the hundred-thousands place, 3 in the ones place, and 7s in all other places.
877,473

3. List all the factors of 20.
1, 2, 4, 5, 10, 20

4. a. Complete the fact triangle.
b. Write the fact family for this triangle.
5 ∗ 6 = 30
6 ∗ 5 = 30
30 / 5 = 6
30 / 6 = 5

5. Write a 7-digit numeral with 6 in the ones place, 3 in the thousandths place, 1 in the thousands place, 2 in the tenths place, and 0s in all other places.
1,006.203

6. Add or subtract.
a. 67 + 109 + 318 = 494
b. 2,005 − 189 = 1,816
c. 39 + 71 + 177 = 287
d. 40,031 − 277 = 39,754

Math Journal 1, p. 11

Have students work independently to complete Problem 2 on journal page 10. Encourage students to use their knowledge of the multiplication facts to solve the problem.

Ongoing Assessment Recognizing Student Achievement

Journal Page 10 Problem 2 ★

Use **journal page 10, Problem 2** to assess students' ability to identify factor pairs. Students are making adequate progress if they have used factor pairs to write correct multiplication number models for the numbers in this problem.

[Number and Numeration Goal 3]

2 Ongoing Learning & Practice

▶ Playing *Beat the Calculator* (Extended-Facts Version)

(*Student Reference Book*, p. 299)

PARTNER ACTIVITY

Students practice multiplication of extended facts by playing *Beat the Calculator* (Extended-Facts Version).

NOTE Use a permanent marker to change ordinary decks of playing cards so they will have the same frequency of each number card as an Everything Math Deck.

- Mark each of the 4 aces with the number 1.
- Mark each of the 4 queens with the number 0.
- Mark the 4 jacks and the 4 kings with the numbers 11–18.
- Mark the 2 jokers with the numbers 19 and 20.

▶ Math Boxes 1·3

INDEPENDENT ACTIVITY

(*Math Journal 1*, p. 11)

Mixed Practice Math Boxes in this lesson are paired with Math Boxes in Lesson 1-1. The skill in Problem 6 previews Unit 2 content.

Writing/Reasoning Have students write a response to the following: *Willa wrote the following true statements based on the fact family she wrote for Problem 4: 30 is 5 times as great as 6, and 30 is 6 times as great as 5. Write similar statements for 7 ∗ 6 = 42.* Sample answers: 42 is 7 times as great as 6; 42 is 6 times as great as 7. The number that is 6 times as great as 7 is 42.

▶ Study Link 1·3

INDEPENDENT ACTIVITY

(*Math Masters*, p. 12)

Home Connection Students match arrays, factor pairs, and products. Encourage students to bring examples of arrays to school.

Study Link Master

Name Date Time

STUDY LINK 1·3 **Number Models for Arrays**

Complete the chart. You will need to find each missing part and write it in the correct space.

	Array	Number Model	Factors	Product
1		6 ∗ 4 = 24	6, 4	24
2		2 ∗ 12 = 24; 12 ∗ 2 = 24	2, 12	24
3		3 ∗ 8 = 24	3, 8	24
4		1 ∗ 15 = 15; 15 = 1 ∗ 15	1, 15	15
5		3 ∗ 5 = 15; 5 ∗ 3 = 15	3, 5	15
6		1 ∗ 5 = 5	1, 5	5

Reminder: Look for examples of arrays and bring them to school.

Practice

7. 12 / 3 = 4
8. 1,288 + 2,631 = 3,919
9. 307 ∗ 9 = 2,763
10. 306 − 147 = 159

Math Masters, p. 12

3 Differentiation Options

READINESS

PARTNER ACTIVITY

5–15 Min

Factoring Numbers with Cube Arrays

(*Student Reference Book*, p. 10; *Math Masters*, p. 13)

To provide experience finding factor pairs using concrete models, have students build arrays with centimeter cubes. This activity highlights the relationships between arrays, factor pairs, and all possible factor pairs of a number.

EXTRA PRACTICE

SMALL-GROUP ACTIVITY

5–15 Min

5-Minute Math

To offer students more experience factoring whole numbers, see *5-Minute Math*, pages 13 and 90.

EXTRA PRACTICE

SMALL-GROUP ACTIVITY

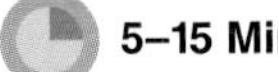

5–15 Min

Practicing Multiplication Facts

(*Math Journal 1*, p. 9; *Math Masters*, p. 11)

To provide additional practice with basic multiplication facts, have students use the facts routine introduced in Lesson 1-3. See *Teacher's Lesson Guide,* pages 28 and 29 to review the procedure.

ELL SUPPORT

SMALL-GROUP ACTIVITY

5–15 Min

Building a Math Word Bank

(*Differentiation Handbook*, p. 143)

To provide language support for multiplication, have students use the Word Bank Template found on *Differentiation Handbook*, page 143. Ask students to write the terms *factor, product,* and *multiplication,* draw pictures relating to each term, and write other related words. See the *Differentiation Handbook* for more information.

Teaching Master

Name Date Time

LESSON 1·3 **Factoring Numbers with Cube Arrays**

Use centimeter cubes to build arrays for the following numbers. With each array write the **factor pair.** Remember that the number of rows in the array is one **factor** and that the number of columns in the array is the other **factor.**

SRB 10

Continue to build every possible array until you have all of the factors for the number.

1. 14 Factors: 1, 14, 2, 7
2. 8 Factors: 1, 8, 2, 4
3. 10 Factors: 1, 10, 2, 5
4. 20 Factors: 1, 20, 2, 10, 4, 5
5. 33 Factors: 1, 33, 3, 11
6. Can you tell when you have all of the factors for a number before you have built every possible array? Yes Explain. Answers vary.

Try This

7. Write three true statements about factors. Answers vary.

Math Masters, p. 13

1•4 The *Factor Captor* Game

Objective To review divisibility concepts.

www.everydaymathonline.com

ePresentations

eToolkit

Algorithms Practice

EM Facts Workshop Game™

Family Letters

Assessment Management

Common Core State Standards

Curriculum Focal Points

Interactive Teacher's Lesson Guide

1 Teaching the Lesson

Key Concepts and Skills

- Describe numbers as odd or even using rectangular arrays. [Number and Numeration Goal 3]
- Find factors using divisibility. [Number and Numeration Goal 3]
- Apply multiplication/division facts by using rules of divisibility and finding factors. [Operations and Computation Goal 2]

Key Activities

Students review what it means for a number to be divisible by another number. They practice finding factors by playing *Factor Captor.*

Ongoing Assessment: Recognizing Student Achievement
Use *Math Masters,* page 453.
[Number and Numeration Goal 3]

Key Vocabulary

remainder ◆ even number ◆ odd number ◆ divisible by

Materials

Student Reference Book, p. 306
Study Link 1•3
Math Masters, pp. 414, 453, and 454
transparency of *Math Masters,* p. 453 (optional) ◆ half-sheet of paper ◆ calculator ◆ per partnership: 50 counters

2 Ongoing Learning & Practice

Using Fact Triangles to Practice Extended Multiplication Facts

Math Journal 1, Activity Sheet 1
scissors
Students use ∗, / Fact Triangles to increase accuracy with extended multiplication facts.

Math Boxes 1•4

Math Journal 1, p. 12
Students practice and maintain skills through Math Box problems.

Study Link 1•4

Math Masters, pp. 14, 453, and 454
Students practice and maintain skills through Study Link activities.

3 Differentiation Options

READINESS

Exploring Multiplication and Division Relationships

Student Reference Book
Students explore number and operations relationships in multiplication/division fact families.

ENRICHMENT

Playing *Factor Captor* with the 1–110 Grid

Math Masters, p. 455
Students apply strategies for finding factors of larger numbers.

Advance Preparation

For Part 1, each partnership will need 1 copy of *Factor Captor* Grid 1 (*Math Masters,* page 453). Each student will need 1 additional copy of *Factor Captor* Grid 1 to take home with Study Link 1•4. Consider copying *Factor Captor* Grid 2 (*Math Masters,* page 454) for students' use during the lesson. For Part 2, students will need to cut out the Fact Triangles from Activity Sheet 1.

***Teacher's Reference Manual,* Grades 4–6** pp. 79–83, 267–271

Getting Started

Mental Math and Reflexes

Pose the following problems, and have students write an expression for each. Students are not expected to calculate the answers. Answers may vary.

●○○ 9 less than 18 $18 - 9$
The product of 8 and 2 $8 * 2$
Double 8 $2 * 8$

●●○ 3 times the product of 2 and 4 $3 * (2 * 4)$
Double the sum of 5 and 3 $2 * (5 + 3)$
7 times the sum of 3 and 2 $7 * (3 + 2)$

●●● Multiply 4 and 2, and then triple the product $3(4 * 2)$
5 less than the product of $7 * 6$ $7 * 6 - 5$
Double the sum of 9 and 1 $2(9 + 1)$

Math Message

Which of the following numbers are factors of 36? 1, 2, 3, 4, 5, 6, 7, 8, 9, and 10? Record your answers on a half-sheet of paper. 1, 2, 3, 4, 6, 9

Write the multiplication facts you know for 36. Sample answers: $1 * 36$, $2 * 18$, $3 * 12$

Study Link 1·3 Follow-Up

Have partners compare answers and resolve differences.

Then have students share and display their examples of arrays.

1 Teaching the Lesson

▶ Math Message Follow-Up

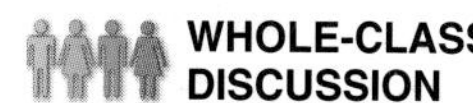

WHOLE-CLASS DISCUSSION

Give students an opportunity to compare answers with a partner. List their **factors** on the board or a transparency. Prompt students to support their answers. *For example:*

- How do we know 4 is a factor of 36? Because $4 * 9 = 36$; therefore, 4 and 9 are factors of 36.
- How do we know 5 is not a factor of 36? There is no whole number that can be multiplied by 5 to get an answer of 36.

Students might mention that 4 is a factor of 36 because 36 divided by 4 "comes out even," or that 5 is not a factor of 36 because 36 divided by 5 "doesn't come out even." Clarify that when it is said that division comes out even, it means there is a **remainder** of zero. If the numbers do not divide evenly, then the remainder is greater than zero.

Extend students' knowledge of factors by asking them to think about factors in relationship to each other. Ask: *What number is 4 times as great as 9?* 36 *What number is 9 times as great as 4?* 36 Explain that you may also compare the size of the product of two factors with the size of either factor. Write the following example on the board: 36 is 4 times as great as 9, and 36 is 9 times as great as 4. Ask partners to think about other pairs of factors that they could use in a similar statement using 36 as the product. Sample answers: 36 is 6 times as great as 6; 36 is 18 times as great as 2; 36 is 3 times as great as 12.

NOTE Some students may benefit from doing the **Readiness** activity before you begin Part 1 of each lesson. See the Readiness activity in Part 3 for details.

Interactive whiteboard-ready ePresentations are available at www.everydaymathonline.com to help you teach the lesson.

Adjusting the Activity

The list of factors for 36 is incomplete. Ask students to name the other factors of 36 greater than 10. 12, 18, and 36 Encourage them to support their answers. Sample answers: Because $1 * 36 = 36$; $2 * 18 = 36$; $3 * 12 = 36$; the list contains single members of a factor pair; 1, 2, and 3 are missing the other factor in their pair.

AUDITORY ◆ KINESTHETIC ◆ TACTILE ◆ VISUAL

Reviewing the Meaning of Divisibility

Begin this review with discussion starters like these:

- We know a great deal about rectangular arrays. What connections can we make?
- If a number can be represented by a rectangular array with 2 rows, what true statements can we make about the number? 2 is a factor; the number is an **even number;** the number is divisible by 2.
- If a number can be represented by a rectangular array with 2 columns, what true statements can we make about the number? 2 is a factor; the number is even; the number is divisible by 2.
- Suppose a number cannot be represented by an array with 2 rows or 2 columns? For instance, why can't 3 be represented by an array with 2 rows? 3 is an **odd number;** 3 is not divisible by 2; 2 is not a factor of 3.

Follow up on students' use of division vocabulary:

- Arrays model multiplication. Does multiplication have a relationship to division?

Ask students to share what they know about division. Illustrate the relationship between factors and divisibility with problems such as the following:

- Is 54 divisible by 9? Yes. 54 divided by 9 is 6 with remainder 0; $9 * 6 = 54$.
- Is 25 divisible by 6? No. 25 divided by 6 is 4 with remainder 1; 6 is not a factor of 25.
- Is 8 a factor of 48? Yes. 48 is divisible by 8, $8 * 6$ is 48.
- Is 4 a factor of 30? No. 30 is not divisible by 4.

Remind the class that a number is **divisible by** another number if the result of the division is a whole number, with a remainder of zero. For example, 28 is divisible by 7 because 28 divided by 7 is 4 with a remainder of zero. Since 28 is divisible by 7, 7 is a factor of 28.

NOTE *Everyday Mathematics* emphasizes the relationship between multiplication and division. For example, to find the quotient of 42 divided by 7, students are encouraged to think: *7 times what number is 42?* The concepts of factors and divisibility are just another way of expressing the relationship between the operations. For example, you can say that 7 is a factor of 42, because 42 is divisible by 7.

Playing *Factor Captor*

(*Student Reference Book,* p. 306; *Math Masters,* pp. 453 and 454)

Factor Captor is an effective way for students to practice finding factors and to improve their fluency with multiplication facts.

Student Page

Games

Factor Captor

Materials
- 1 calculator for each player
- paper and pencil for each player
- 1 *Factor Captor* Grid—either Grid 1 or Grid 2 (*Math Masters,* pp. 453 and 454)
- coin-size counters (48 for Grid 1; 70 for Grid 2)

Players 2

Skill Finding factors of a number

Object of the game To have the higher total score.

Directions

1. To start the first round, Player 1 chooses a 2-digit number on the number grid, covers it with a counter, and records the number on scratch paper. This is Player 1's score for the round.
2. Player 2 covers all of the factors of Player 1's number. Player 2 finds the sum of the factors and records it on scratch paper. This is Player 2's score for the round.

A factor may only be covered once during a round.

3. If Player 2 missed any factors, Player 1 can cover them with counters and add them to his or her score.
4. In the next round, players switch roles. Player 2 chooses a number that is not covered by a counter. Player 1 covers all factors of that number.
5. Any number that is covered by a counter is no longer available and may not be used again.
6. The first player in a round may not cover a number that is less than 10, unless no other numbers are available.
7. Play continues with players trading roles after each round, until all numbers on the grid have been covered. Players then use their calculators to find their total scores. The player with the higher score wins the game.

Grid 1 (Beginning Level)

1	2	2	2	2	2
2	3	3	3	3	3
3	4	4	4	4	5
5	5	5	6	6	7
7	8	8	9	9	10
10	11	12	13	14	15
16	18	20	21	22	24
25	26	27	28	30	32

Grid 2 (Advanced Level)

1	2	2	2	2	2	3
3	3	3	3	4	4	4
4	5	5	5	5	6	6
6	7	7	8	8	9	9
10	10	11	12	13	14	15
16	17	18	19	20	21	22
23	24	25	26	27	28	30
32	33	34	35	36	38	39
40	42	44	45	46	48	49
50	51	52	54	55	56	60

Example

Round 1: James covers 27 and scores 27 points. Emma covers 1, 3, and 9, and scores $1 + 3 + 9 = 13$ points.

Round 2: Emma covers 18 and scores 18 points. James covers 2, 3, and 6, and scores $2 + 3 + 6 = 11$ points. Emma covers 9 with a counter, because 9 is also a factor of 18. Emma adds 9 points to her score.

Student Reference Book, p. 306

Game Master

Name Date Time

Factor Captor Grid 1

1	2	2	2	2	2
2	3	3	3	3	3
3	4	4	4	4	5
5	5	5	6	6	7
7	8	8	9	9	10
10	11	12	13	14	15
16	18	20	21	22	24
25	26	27	28	30	32

453

Math Masters, p. 453

Go over the rules on page 306 of the *Student Reference Book* with the class, and play a few practice rounds using a transparency of *Factor Captor* Grid 1 (*Math Masters*, p. 453). Partners then play the game on their own. Consider allowing students to repeat the game a second time using Grid 2 (*Math Masters,* p. 454), or to take both grids home with Study Link 1-4.

Ongoing Assessment: Recognizing Student Achievement

Math Masters Page 453

Use ***Factor Captor*** **Grid 1** (*Math Masters,* page 453) to assess students' ability to identify factors. Have them complete an Exit Slip (*Math Masters,* page 414) by writing a response to the following: *Describe a strategy for getting the highest score when playing* Factor Captor. Students are making adequate progress if their description refers to numbers with the fewest factors as being the better choice.

[Number and Numeration Goal 3]

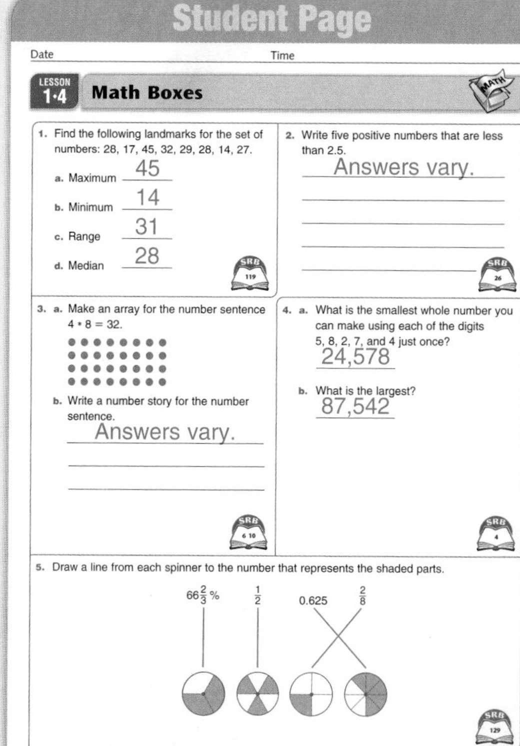

Student Page

Date Time

LESSON 1•4 **Math Boxes**

1. Find the following landmarks for the set of numbers: 28, 17, 45, 32, 29, 28, 14, 27.
   a. Maximum 45
   b. Minimum 14
   c. Range 31
   d. Median 28

2. Write five positive numbers that are less than 2.5.
   Answers vary.

3. a. Make an array for the number sentence 4 * 8 = 32.
   b. Write a number story for the number sentence.
   Answers vary.

4. a. What is the smallest whole number you can make using each of the digits 5, 8, 2, 7, and 4 just once? 24,578
   b. What is the largest? 87,542

5. Draw a line from each spinner to the number that represents the shaded parts.
   $66\frac{2}{3}\%$ $\frac{1}{2}$ 0.625 $\frac{2}{8}$

Math Journal 1, **p. 12**

2 Ongoing Learning & Practice

Using Fact Triangles to Practice Extended Multiplication Facts

PARTNER ACTIVITY

(*Math Journal 1,* Activity Sheet 1)

Partners cut out the Fact Triangles from Activity Sheet 1 and write the extended facts they want to practice on the triangles. (Ask students to use pencil so that the triangles can be reused.) Partners take turns drawing the top triangle and reading the number at the ● or at either bottom corner. The other partner responds with the missing number. (*See margin.*) The missing number will be either the product (420) or one of the two factors (60 or 7).

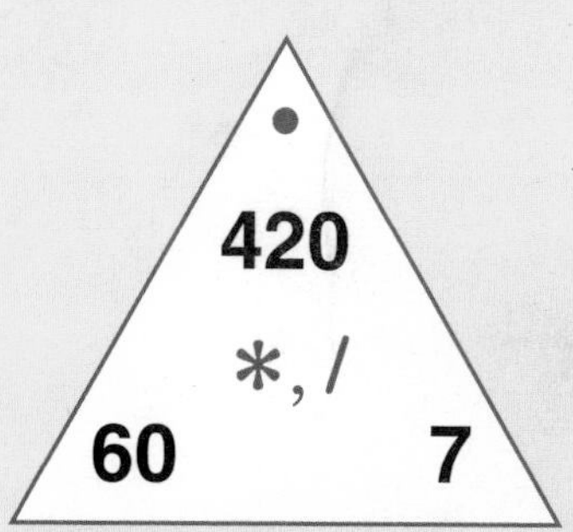

Example: 420, 60, and 7; 60 * 7 = 420

Math Boxes 1•4

INDEPENDENT ACTIVITY

(*Math Journal 1,* p. 12)

Mixed Practice Math Boxes in this lesson are paired with Math Boxes in Lesson 1-2. The skill in Problem 5 previews Unit 2 content.

Study Link 1•4

INDEPENDENT ACTIVITY

(*Math Masters*, pp. 14, 453, and 454)

Home Connection Students find as many factors as they can for whole numbers. Give each student a copy of one or both Factor Captor grids (*Math Masters*, pages 453 and 454), so they can play *Factor Captor* with someone at home.

Study Link Master

Name Date Time

STUDY LINK 1•4 **Factors**

To find the factors of a number, ask yourself: *Is 1 a factor of the number? Is 2 a factor? Is 3 a factor?* Continue with larger numbers. For example, to find all the factors of 15, ask yourself these questions.

	Yes/No	Number Sentence	Factor Pair
Is 1 a factor of 15?	Yes	1 * 15 = 15	1, 15
Is 2 a factor of 15?	No		
Is 3 a factor of 15?	Yes	3 * 5 = 15	3, 5
Is 4 a factor of 15?	No		

1. You don't need to go any further. Can you tell why?
   The next number to try is 5, but 5 is already listed as a factor. Also, any factor greater than 5 would already be named because it would be paired with a factor less than 5.

So the factors of 15 are 1, 3, 5, and 15.

List as many factors as you can for each of the numbers below.

2. 25 1, 5, 25
3. 28 1, 2, 4, 7, 14, 28
4. 42 1, 2, 3, 6, 7, 14, 21, 42
5. 100 1, 2, 4, 5, 10, 20, 25, 50, 100

Practice

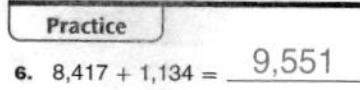

6. 8,417 + 1,134 = 9,551
7. 73 − 25 = 48
8. 6,924 * 6 = 41,544
9. 634 − 193 = 441
10. 56 / 8 = 7

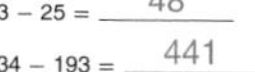

Math Masters, **p. 14**

3 Differentiation Options

READINESS

PARTNER ACTIVITY

5–15 Min

▶ Exploring Multiplication and Division Relationships

(*Student Reference Book*)

To explore the inverse relationship between multiplication and division, have students do the following fact-family activity. Introduce the activity: *A fact family begins with 3 numbers. In a multiplication/division fact family, these numbers are used to name 2 multiplication facts and 2 division facts.*

▷ Write $8 * 7 = 56$ on a transparency or the board. Ask students to name the parts of this number sentence. 8 and 7 are factors, and 56 is the product.

▷ Write $56 \div 8 = 7$ on a transparency or the board. Ask students to name the parts of this number sentence. 56 is the dividend; 8 is the divisor; and 7 is the quotient.

▷ Ask students to compare the size of the product (56) to the size of one of its factors based on the size of the other factor. Sample answers: 56 is 8 times as many as 7, or 56 is 7 times as many as 8.

In a fact family, each number can be thought of in different ways. In the fact family for 8, 7, and 56, 8 and 7 can be factors in multiplication, and divisors or quotients in division; 56 can be the product in multiplication, and the dividend in division.

Ask several students to write multiplication facts on the board. Use these facts for questions like the following:

- What numbers are in this fact family?
- If I now write a division number sentence for this fact family, what number will be the dividend?
- What number will be the divisor?

NOTE If students are not familiar with the names of the parts of division number sentences, read the definitions for *dividend, divisor,* and *quotient* in the *Student Reference Book* glossary as a class.

ENRICHMENT

SMALL-GROUP ACTIVITY

15–30 Min

COMPUTATION PRACTICE

▶ Playing *Factor Captor* with the 1–110 Grid

(*Math Masters*, p. 455)

To apply strategies for finding factors of larger numbers, including the use of prime factors, use the 1–110 Grid (*Math Masters,* page 455) to play *Factor Captor*. The activity is suggested for groups of 3 or 4 students who are fluent with finding factors. Have students note differences between Grid 1 and the 1–110 Grid. Encourage students to use language such as, "There are more prime numbers," or "There are not as many factors available because no numbers repeat."

Game Master

Name Date Time

***Factor Captor* 1–110 Grid**

1	2	3	4	5	6	7	8	9	10
11	12	13	14	15	16	17	18	19	20
21	22	23	24	25	26	27	28	29	30
31	32	33	34	35	36	37	38	39	40
41	42	43	44	45	46	47	48	49	50
51	52	53	54	55	56	57	58	59	60
61	62	63	64	65	66	67	68	69	70
71	72	73	74	75	76	77	78	79	80
81	82	83	84	85	86	87	88	89	90
91	92	93	94	95	96	97	98	99	100
101	102	103	104	105	106	107	108	109	110

Math Masters, p. 455

1•5 Divisibility

Objectives To introduce divisibility rules for division by 2, 3, 5, 6, 9, and 10; and how to use a calculator to test for divisibility by a whole number.

www.everydaymathonline.com

ePresentations

eToolkit

Algorithms Practice

EM Facts Workshop Game™

Family Letters

Assessment Management

Common Core State Standards

Curriculum Focal Points

Interactive Teacher's Lesson Guide

1 Teaching the Lesson

Key Concepts and Skills

- Use divisibility rules to solve problems. [Number and Numeration Goal 3]
- Explore the relationship between the operations of multiplication and division. [Operations and Computation Goal 2]

Key Activities

Students use a calculator to test for divisibility by a whole number. They learn and practice divisibility rules.

Key Vocabulary

factor rainbow ◆ divisible by ◆ quotient ◆ divisibility rule

Materials

Math Journal 1, pp. 13 and 14
Study Link 1•4
calculator ◆ overhead calculator (optional)

2 Ongoing Learning & Practice

Playing *Factor Captor*

Student Reference Book, p. 306
Math Masters, pp. 453 and 454
counters or centimeter cubes ◆ calculator
Students practice finding factors of a number.

Math Boxes 1•5

Math Journal 1, p. 15
Students practice and maintain skills through Math Box problems.

Ongoing Assessment: Recognizing Student Achievement
Use Math Boxes, Problem 4.
[Number and Numeration Goal 1]

Study Link 1•5

Math Masters, p. 15
Students practice and maintain skills through Study Link activities.

3 Differentiation Options

READINESS

Practicing Divisibility with Counters

per partnership: 66 counters, 3 dice
Students use dice and counters to predict divisibility relationships between 2 numbers.

EXTRA PRACTICE

Practicing Multiplication Facts

Math Journal 1, p. 9
Math Masters, p. 11
Students use a multiplication facts routine.

ENRICHMENT

Exploring a Test for Divisibility by 4

Math Masters, p. 16
Students use place-value concepts to investigate a test for divisibility by 4.

ELL SUPPORT

Building a Math Word Bank

Differentiation Handbook, p. 142
Students add the terms *divisor, dividend, quotient,* and *remainder* to their Math Word Banks.

Advance Preparation

***Teacher's Reference Manual,* Grades 4–6** pp. 79–83, 267–269

Getting Started

Mental Math and Reflexes

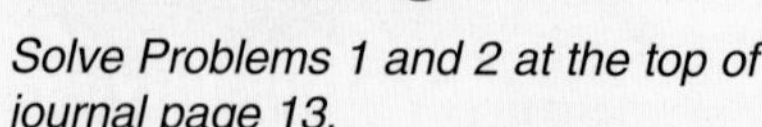

Pose basic and extended multiplication/division facts. Have students write the answers for each set of problems. At the end of each set, ask students to describe the patterns. *Suggestions:*

●○○	●●○	●●●
5 * 5 25	6 * 3 18	8 * 4 32
5 * 50 250	60 * 3 180	80 * 40 3,200
5 * 500 2,500	600 * 3 1,800	800 * 400 320,000
5 * 5,000 25,000	6,000 * 3 18,000	8,000 * 4,000 32,000,000

Math Message

Solve Problems 1 and 2 at the top of journal page 13.

Study Link 1·4 Follow-Up

Have partners compare answers. Ask the class how they know that all possible factors have been listed. Have volunteers model using a **factor rainbow** to pair factors for 25, 28, 42, and 100. If there is an odd number of factors, the middle factor is paired with itself. Explain that this only happens with square numbers.

NOTE Some students may benefit from doing the **Readiness** activity before you begin Part 1 of each lesson. See the Readiness activity in Part 3 for details.

NOTE If possible, use an overhead calculator to model the keystrokes and calculator displays for lesson examples.

Interactive whiteboard-ready ePresentations are available at www.everydaymathonline.com to help you teach the lesson.

NOTE Factor rainbows are introduced in the Study Link Follow-Up. This tool helps students identify all of the factors for a given number. The rainbow is a visual representation of the factor pairs and provides a way to check if the factor list is complete. Share the factor rainbow in the Study Link Follow-Up with the class. Factor rainbows will be used again in Lesson 1-6.

1 Teaching the Lesson

▶ Math Message Follow-Up

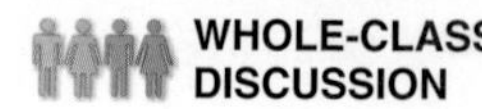

WHOLE-CLASS DISCUSSION

(*Math Journal 1,* p. 13)

Students share solution strategies. Use students' responses to emphasize to the class that even numbers are numbers that are **divisible by** 2.

▶ Using a Calculator to Test for Divisibility by a Whole Number

INDEPENDENT ACTIVITY

(*Math Journal 1,* p. 13)

Recall for students the class discussion on the review of divisibility in Lesson 1-4. Remind students that a whole number (the dividend) is divisible by a whole number (the divisor) if the remainder in the division is zero. The result or **quotient,** must be a whole number. If the remainder is not zero, then the number being divided is not divisible by the second number.

If your students use calculators that display answers to division problems as a quotient and a whole number remainder, you might want to demonstrate the procedure. With the TI-15 calculator, this is done by pressing the (Int÷) key instead of the (÷) key. With the Casio *fx*-55, use the (÷R) key. For example, If you press 27 (Int÷) 5 (Enter), or 27 (÷R) 5 (Enter), the display will show a quotient of 5 with a remainder of 2.

Adjusting the Activity

Write the number model from the first example on journal page 13 on the board with each number appropriately labeled, including a remainder of zero.

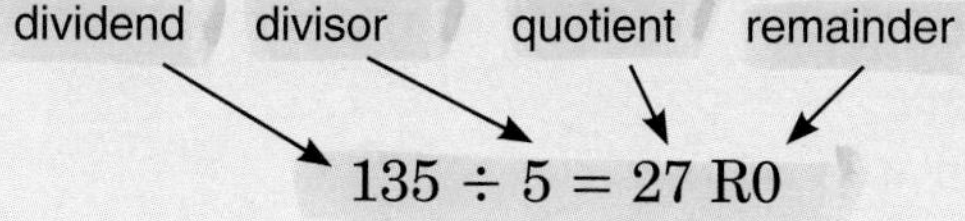

AUDITORY ◆ KINESTHETIC ◆ TACTILE ◆ VISUAL

When testing for divisibility with a calculator that does not display remainders, the first number is not divisible by the second number if the quotient has a decimal part. Ask students to use their calculators to test whether 27 is divisible by 9. 27 is divisible by 9 because the result is 3—a whole number. Test whether 27 is divisible by 5. 27 is not divisible by 5 because the result is 5.4—not a whole number.

Allow 5 to 10 minutes for students to complete Problems 3–10 on the journal page 13.

▶ Introducing Divisibility Rules

(*Math Journal 1,* p. 14)

Ask: *How can you know that a number is divisible by 2 without actually doing the division?* Numbers that end in 0, 2, 4, 6, or 8 are divisible by 2. *Can you tell whether a number is divisible by 10 without dividing?* Yes; numbers that end in 0 are divisible by 10. *Can you tell whether a number is divisible by 3 without dividing?* Allow students to explore this question before continuing. There are rules that let us test for divisibility without dividing or using a calculator.

1. Go over the divisibility-by-3 rule on journal page 14: *A number is divisible by 3 if the sum of its digits is divisible by 3.*
2. Illustrate by using the rule to test several examples.
   - Is 237 divisible by 3? Yes. 2 + 3 + 7 = 12, and 12 is divisible by 3.
   - Is 415 divisible by 3? No. 4 + 1 + 5 = 10, and 10 is not divisible by 3.
3. Ask students to provide examples of a number that is divisible by 3 and a number that is not. Encourage them to apply the divisibility-by-3 test first. Then have them check that it works by carrying out the division on their calculators.

Assign small groups to present examples for the remaining **divisibility rules** (5, 6, or 9).

Students complete Problems 1–3 independently. Have them check each other's work.

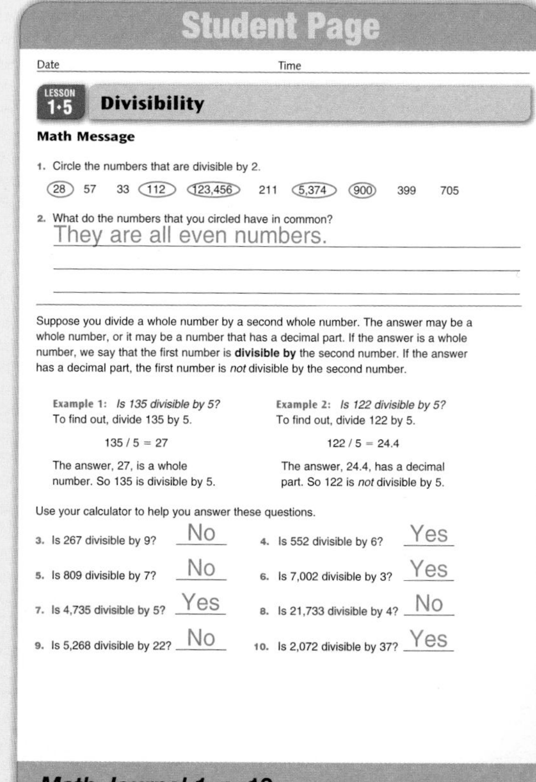

Student Page

Date Time

LESSON 1·5 **Divisibility**

Math Message

1. Circle the numbers that are divisible by 2.

(28) 57 33 (112) (123,456) 211 (5,374) (900) 399 705

2. What do the numbers that you circled have in common?
They are all even numbers.

Suppose you divide a whole number by a second whole number. The answer may be a whole number, or it may be a number that has a decimal part. If the answer is a whole number, we say that the first number is **divisible by** the second number. If the answer has a decimal part, the first number is *not* divisible by the second number.

Example 1: *Is 135 divisible by 5?*
To find out, divide 135 by 5.
135 / 5 = 27
The answer, 27, is a whole number. So 135 is divisible by 5.

Example 2: *Is 122 divisible by 5?*
To find out, divide 122 by 5.
122 / 5 = 24.4
The answer, 24.4, has a decimal part. So 122 is *not* divisible by 5.

Use your calculator to help you answer these questions.

3. Is 267 divisible by 9? No
4. Is 552 divisible by 6? Yes
5. Is 809 divisible by 7? No
6. Is 7,002 divisible by 3? Yes
7. Is 4,735 divisible by 5? Yes
8. Is 21,733 divisible by 4? No
9. Is 5,268 divisible by 22? No
10. Is 2,072 divisible by 37? Yes

Math Journal 1, p. 13

Student Page

Date Time

LESSON 1·5 **Divisibility Rules**

For many numbers, even large ones, it is possible to test for divisibility without actually dividing.

Here are the most useful divisibility rules:

- All numbers are **divisible by 1.**
- All even numbers (ending in 0, 2, 4, 6, or 8) are **divisible by 2.**
- A number is **divisible by 3** if the sum of its digits is divisible by 3.
  Example: 246 is divisible by 3 because 2 + 4 + 6 = 12, and 12 is divisible by 3.
- A number is **divisible by 6** if it is divisible by both 2 and 3.
  Example: 246 is divisible by 6 because it is divisible by 2 and by 3.
- A number is **divisible by 9** if the sum of its digits is divisible by 9.
  Example: 51,372 is divisible by 9 because 5 + 1 + 3 + 7 + 2 = 18, and 18 is divisible by 9.
- A number is **divisible by 5** if it ends in 0 or 5.
- A number is **divisible by 10** if it ends in 0.

1. Test each number below for divisibility. Then check on your calculator.

	Divisible...					
Number	by 2?	by 3?	by 6?	by 9?	by 5?	by 10?
75		✓			✓	
7,960	✓				✓	✓
384	✓	✓	✓			
3,725					✓	
90	✓	✓	✓	✓	✓	✓
36,297		✓		✓		

2. Find a 3-digit number that is divisible by both 3 and 5.
Sample answers: 735; 540

3. Find a 4-digit number that is divisible by both 6 and 9.
Sample answers: 1,800; 5,454

Math Journal 1, p. 14

Student Page

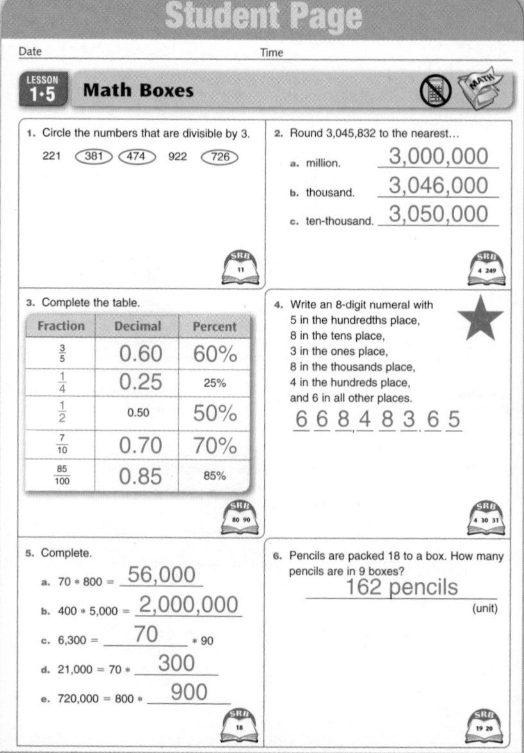

Date Time

LESSON 1·5 **Math Boxes**

1. Circle the numbers that are divisible by 3.

221 (381) (474) 922 (726)

2. Round 3,045,832 to the nearest...

a. million. 3,000,000

b. thousand. 3,046,000

c. ten-thousand. 3,050,000

3. Complete the table.

Fraction	Decimal	Percent
$\frac{3}{5}$	0.60	60%
$\frac{1}{4}$	0.25	25%
$\frac{1}{2}$	0.50	50%
$\frac{7}{10}$	0.70	70%
$\frac{85}{100}$	0.85	85%

4. Write an 8-digit numeral with 5 in the hundredths place, 8 in the tens place, 3 in the ones place, 8 in the thousands place, 4 in the hundreds place, and 6 in all other places.

6 6 8 4 8 3 . 6 5

5. Complete.

a. 70 ∗ 800 = 56,000

b. 400 ∗ 5,000 = 2,000,000

c. 6,300 = 70 ∗ 90

d. 21,000 = 70 ∗ 300

e. 720,000 = 800 ∗ 900

6. Pencils are packed 18 to a box. How many pencils are in 9 boxes?

162 pencils (unit)

Math Journal 1, p. 15

NOTE As students continue to develop their strategies for *Factor Captor,* they will find that as more numbers are used, the scoring rules increasingly reward a player for planning ahead and anticipating an opponent's moves.

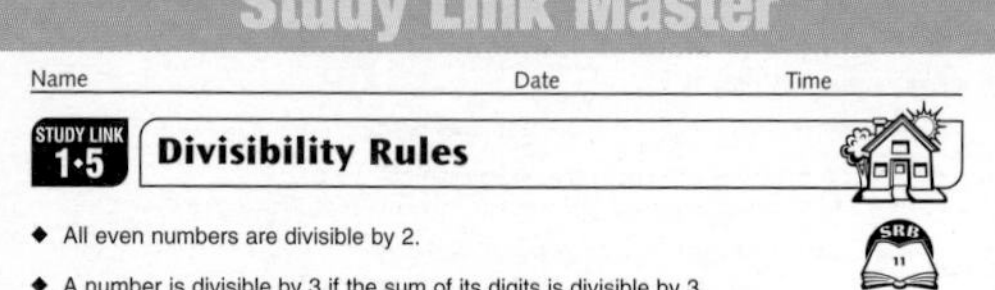

Study Link Master

Name Date Time

STUDY LINK 1·5 **Divisibility Rules**

- All even numbers are divisible by 2.
- A number is divisible by 3 if the sum of its digits is divisible by 3.
- A number is divisible by 6 if it is divisible by both 2 and 3.
- A number is divisible by 9 if the sum of its digits is divisible by 9.
- A number is divisible by 5 if it ends in 0 or 5.
- A number is divisible by 10 if it ends in 0.

1. Use divisibility rules to test whether each number is divisible by 2, 3, 5, 6, 9, or 10.

	Number	Divisible... by 2?	by 3?	by 6?	by 9?	by 5?	by 10?
★	998,876	✓					
	5,890	✓				✓	✓
★	36,540	✓	✓	✓	✓	✓	✓
	33,015		✓			✓	
	1,098	✓	✓	✓	✓		

A number is divisible by 4 if the tens and ones digits form a number that is divisible by 4.

Example: 47,836 is divisible by 4 because 36 is divisible by 4.

It isn't always easy to tell whether the last two digits form a number that is divisible by 4. A quick way to check is to divide the number by 2 and then divide the result by 2. It's the same as dividing by 4, but is easier to do mentally.

Example: 5,384 is divisible by 4 because 84 / 2 = 42 and 42 / 2 = 21.

2. Place a star next to any number in the table that is divisible by 4.

Practice

3. 250 ∗ 7 = 1,750

4. 1,931 + 4,763 + 2,059 = 8,753

5. (20 + 30) ∗ 5 = 250

6. 78 ÷ 6 = 13

Math Masters, p. 15

2 Ongoing Learning & Practice

▶ Playing *Factor Captor*

PARTNER ACTIVITY

FACTS PRACTICE

(*Student Reference Book*, p. 306; *Math Masters*, pp. 453–454)

Students practice finding factors of a number by playing *Factor Captor.* Students have the option of playing any of the two *Factor Captor* grids. If students are using Grid 2 for the first time, suggest that they omit the last two rows of the gameboard.

▶ Math Boxes 1·5

INDEPENDENT ACTIVITY

(*Math Journal 1*, p. 15)

Mixed Practice Math Boxes in this lesson are paired with Math Boxes in Lessons 1-7 and 1-9. The skills in Problems 5 and 6 preview Unit 2 content.

Writing/Reasoning Have students write a response to the following: *Explain how you solved Problem 6.* Sample answer: Because there are 18 pencils per box and 9 boxes total, I multiplied 18 ∗ 9: 10 ∗ 9 is 90 and 8 ∗ 9 is 72; 90 + 72 = 162. There are 162 pencils in all.

Ongoing Assessment: Recognizing Student Achievement

Math Boxes Problem 4

Use **Math Boxes, Problem 4** to assess students' understanding of place value. Students are making adequate progress if they are able to correctly position and identify digits and their values in whole numbers through the hundred-thousands and decimals through the hundredths.

[Number and Numeration Goal 1]

▶ Study Link 1·5

INDEPENDENT ACTIVITY

(*Math Masters*, p. 15)

Home Connection Students use divisibility rules to test whether numbers are divisible by 2, 3, 5, 6, 9, or 10. They learn the divisibility rule for 4 and recheck the numbers for those that are also divisible by 4.

3 Differentiation Options

READINESS

PARTNER ACTIVITY

15–30 Min

▶ Practicing Divisibility with Counters

To explore the concept of divisibility using a concrete model, have students use counters to determine whether a number is divisible by the numbers 1–6.

Partners take turns rolling three dice. Make a two-digit number with two of the dice, and count out that number of counters. They predict whether the number of counters is divisible by the number on the third die. Then partners check the prediction by dividing the counters into the number of groups indicated on the third die.

EXTRA PRACTICE

SMALL-GROUP ACTIVITY

5–15 Min

▶ Practicing Multiplication Facts

(*Math Journal 1,* p. 9; *Math Masters,* p. 11)

To provide additional practice with basic multiplication facts, have students use the facts routine introduced in Lesson 1-3. See *Teacher's Lesson Guide,* pages 28 and 29 to review the procedure.

ENRICHMENT

PARTNER ACTIVITY

5–15 Min

▶ Exploring a Test for Divisibility by 4

(*Math Masters,* p. 16)

To further explore divisibility, have students use place-value concepts to investigate why only the last 2 digits in a number determine whether the number is divisible by 4.

ELL SUPPORT

SMALL-GROUP ACTIVITY

5–15 Min

▶ Building a Math Word Bank

(*Differentiation Handbook,* p. 142)

To provide language support for division, have students use the Word Bank Template found on *Differentiation Handbook,* page 142. Ask students to write the terms *divisor, dividend, quotient,* and *remainder;* draw a picture representing each term; and write other related words. See the *Differentiation Handbook* for more information.

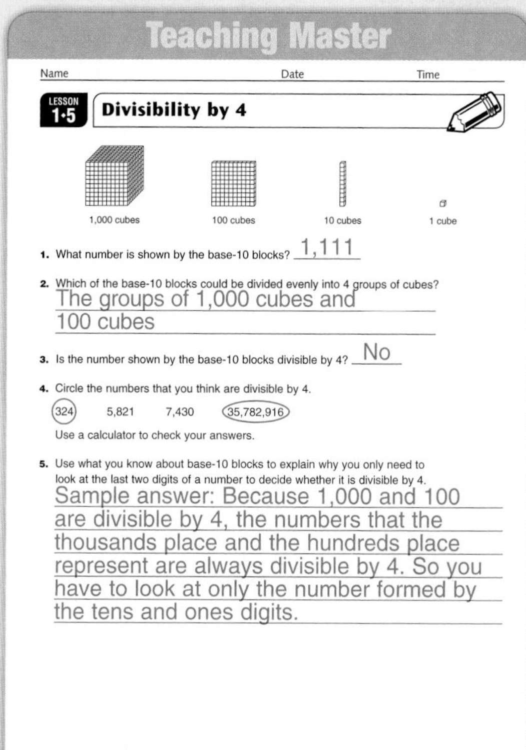

Teaching Master

Name Date Time

LESSON 1·5 **Divisibility by 4**

1,000 cubes 100 cubes 10 cubes 1 cube

1. What number is shown by the base-10 blocks? 1,111
2. Which of the base-10 blocks could be divided evenly into 4 groups of cubes? The groups of 1,000 cubes and 100 cubes
3. Is the number shown by the base-10 blocks divisible by 4? No
4. Circle the numbers that you think are divisible by 4.
   (324) 5,821 7,430 (35,782,916)
   Use a calculator to check your answers.
5. Use what you know about base-10 blocks to explain why you only need to look at the last two digits of a number to decide whether it is divisible by 4.
   Sample answer: Because 1,000 and 100 are divisible by 4, the numbers that the thousands place and the hundreds place represent are always divisible by 4. So you have to look at only the number formed by the tens and ones digits.

Math Masters, p. 16

1•6 Prime and Composite Numbers

Objective To introduce the classification of whole numbers greater than 1 as either prime or composite.

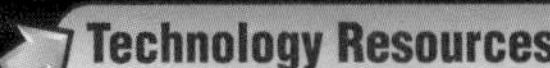

Technology Resources www.everydaymathonline.com

ePresentations

eToolkit

Algorithms Practice

EM Facts Workshop Game™

Family Letters

Assessment Management

Common Core State Standards

Curriculum Focal Points

Interactive Teacher's Lesson Guide

1 Teaching the Lesson

Key Concepts and Skills

- Define and classify prime and composite numbers. [Number and Numeration Goal 3]
- Find factors of a number. [Number and Numeration Goal 3]

Key Activities

Students use arrays and factor rainbows to develop definitions for prime and composite numbers; classify the numbers 2–39 as prime or composite; and use their understanding of prime numbers to develop strategies for playing *Factor Captor.*

Ongoing Assessment: Recognizing Student Achievement Use the Math Message. [Number and Numeration Goal 3]

Key Vocabulary

composite number ◆ prime number

Materials

Math Journal 1, pp. 16 and 17
Student Reference Book, p. 306
Study Link 1•5
blank paper or colored construction paper ◆ markers ◆ Class Data Pad (optional)

2 Ongoing Learning & Practice

Completing Number-Line Patterns

Math Journal 1, p. 18
Students use their knowledge of number relationships to complete patterns by filling in missing values on number lines.

Ongoing Assessment: Informing Instruction See page 45.

Math Boxes 1•6

Math Journal 1, p. 19
Students practice and maintain skills through Math Box problems.

Study Link 1•6

Math Masters, p. 17
Students practice and maintain skills through Study Link activities.

3 Differentiation Options

ENRICHMENT

Exploring Goldbach's Conjecture

Math Masters, pp. 18 and 19
Students investigate Goldbach's conjecture by expressing whole numbers as the sum of two prime numbers.

EXTRA PRACTICE

5-Minute Math

5-Minute Math™, p. 177
Students differentiate between prime and composite numbers.

Advance Preparation

Make the following display labels for the Arrays Museum: Prime Numbers and Composite Numbers.

***Teacher's Reference Manual,* Grades 4–6** pp. 79–82, 267–269, 275–277

Getting Started

Mental Math and Reflexes

Write problems on the board or the Class Data Pad. Students answer each problem and then explain the patterns they see in the number of zeros.

●○○	●●○	●●●
18 ÷ 9 2	5 * 7 35	72 ÷ 9 = 8
180 ÷ 90 2	5 * 70 350	720 ÷ 90 = 8
1,800 ÷ 900 2	3,500 ÷ 700 5	7,200 ÷ 900 = 8
18,000 ÷ 9,000 2	35,000 ÷ 7,000 5	72,000 ÷ 9,000 = 8

Math Message

Draw all possible rectangular arrays for these numbers: 2, 4, 5, 10, 11, and 16.

Study Link 1·5 Follow-Up

Have partners compare answers and resolve differences.

1 Teaching the Lesson

▶ Math Message Follow-Up

WHOLE-CLASS DISCUSSION

Draw a vertical line on the board or a transparency. Have volunteers record all possible arrays and the factor rainbow for each number. Use the left side of the line to record arrays for 4, 10, and 16 and the right side to record the arrays for 2, 5, and 11. (*See margin.*)

4-dot arrays
1 by 4
2 by 2
4 by 1

1 2 4

10-dot arrays
1 by 10
2 by 5
5 by 2
10 by 1

1 2 5 10

16-dot arrays
1 by 16
2 by 8
4 by 4
8 by 2
16 by 1

1 2 4 8 16

2-dot arrays
1 by 2
2 by 1

1 2

5-dot arrays
1 by 5
5 by 1

1 5

11-dot arrays
1 by 11
11 by 1

1 11

Ongoing Assessment: Recognizing Student Achievement

Math Message 

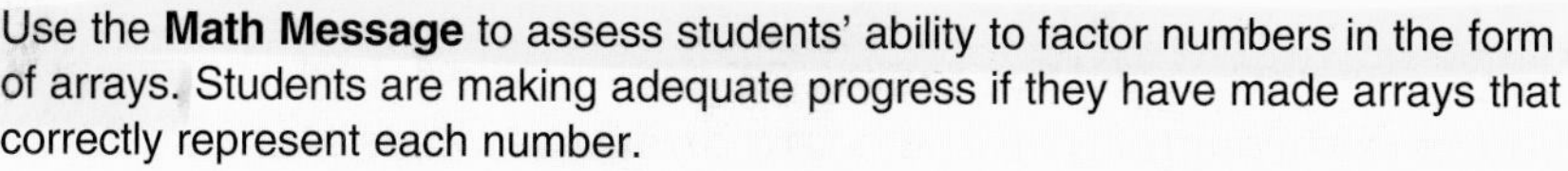

Use the **Math Message** to assess students' ability to factor numbers in the form of arrays. Students are making adequate progress if they have made arrays that correctly represent each number.

[Number and Numeration Goal 3]

▶ Defining Prime and Composite Numbers

WHOLE-CLASS ACTIVITY

ELL

Ask students to compare the information they collected on the left side of the Math Message Follow-Up display with the information collected on the right side. Be sure that the following observations are included in the discussion:

▷ Each number on the right side is represented by exactly two arrays. Each array has either one row or one column. Each number on the left side is represented by more than two arrays. At least one array has more than one row and more than one column.

Student Page

Date Time

LESSON 1·6 **Prime and Composite Numbers**

A **prime number** has exactly two factors—1 and the number itself.
A **composite number** has more than two factors.

1. List all the factors of each number in the table. Write *P* if it is a prime number or *C* if it is a composite number.

Number	Factors	P or C	Number	Factors	P or C
2	1, 2	P	21	1, 3, 7, 21	C
3	1, 3	P	22	1, 2, 11, 22	C
4	1, 2, 4	C	23	1, 23	P
5	1, 5	P	24	1, 2, 3, 4, 6, 8, 12, 24	C
6	1, 2, 3, 6	C	25	1, 5, 25	C
7	1, 7	P	26	1, 2, 13, 26	C
8	1, 2, 4, 8	C	27	1, 3, 9, 27	C
9	1, 3, 9	C	28	1, 2, 4, 7, 14, 28	C
10	1, 2, 5, 10	C	29	1, 29	P
11	1, 11	P	30	1, 2, 3, 5, 6, 10, 15, 30	C
12	1, 2, 3, 4, 6, 12	C	31	1, 31	P
13	1, 13	P	32	1, 2, 4, 8, 16, 32	C
14	1, 2, 7, 14	C	33	1, 3, 11, 33	C
15	1, 3, 5, 15	C	34	1, 2, 17, 34	C
16	1, 2, 4, 8, 16	C	35	1, 5, 7, 35	C
17	1, 17	P	36	1, 2, 3, 4, 6, 9, 12, 18, 36	C
18	1, 2, 3, 6, 9, 18	C	37	1, 37	P
19	1, 19	P	38	1, 2, 19, 38	C
20	1, 2, 4, 5, 10, 20	C	39	1, 3, 13, 39	C

2. How many factors does each prime number have? two
3. Can a composite number have exactly 2 factors? No
   If yes, give an example of such a composite number. Answers vary.

Math Journal 1, p. 16

Student Page

Date Time

LESSON 1·6 ***Factor Captor* Strategies**

Work alone to answer the questions below. Then compare your answers to your partner's. If your answers don't agree with your partner's answers, try to convince your partner that your answers are correct.

1	2	3	4	5	6	7	8	9	10
11	12	13	14	15	16	17	18	19	20
21	22	23	24	25	26	27	28	29	30

1. Suppose you played *Factor Captor* using the above number grid. No numbers have been covered yet. Which is the best number choice you could make? Why?
Sample answer: I could cover 29 and score 29 points. My opponent could then cover only 1 and would score 1 point.

2. Suppose the 29 and 1 squares have already been covered. Which is the best number choice you could make? Why?
Sample answer: I could cover 23 and score 23 points. My opponent could not cover any number and would score 0 points.

3. Suppose that the 29, 23, and 1 squares have already been covered. Which is the best number choice you could make? Why?
Sample answer: I could cover 25 and score 25 points. My opponent could then cover only 5 and would score 5 points.

***Math Journal 1*, p. 17**

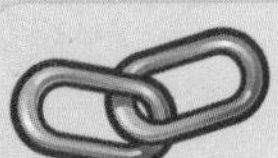

Links to the Past

Students are first introduced to prime and composite numbers in Grade 4.

Student Page

Date Time

LESSON 1·6 **Number-Line Patterns**

Find the patterns and fill in the missing values on the number lines.

1. 0, 8, 16, 24, 32, 40, 48, 56, 64
2. 0, $\frac{1}{2}$, 1, $1\frac{1}{2}$, 2, $2\frac{1}{2}$, 3, $3\frac{1}{2}$, 4, $4\frac{1}{2}$
3. 12, 32, 52, 72, 92, 112, 132, 152, 172
4. −15, −12, −9, −6, −3, 0, 3, 6, 9
5. Create your own number-line pattern for a partner to solve. Answers vary.
6. Explain your solution strategy for your partner's number-line pattern.
Answers vary.

***Math Journal 1*, p. 18**

▷ Each number on the right side has exactly two factors. Each number on the left side has more than two factors.

Tell students that the numbers on the left side are called **composite numbers** and that the numbers on the right side are called **prime numbers.** To support English language learners, write *prime numbers* and *composite numbers* along with the definitions to label the right and left sides of the Math Message Follow-Up display. Summarize as follows:

▷ A prime number is a counting number greater than 1 that has exactly two factors—1 and the number itself.

▷ A composite number is a counting number greater than 1 that has more than two factors.

The number 1 is considered neither prime nor composite. This is a mathematical convention—something that has been agreed on by mathematicians.

Assign or allow students to select one number from the Math Message Follow-Up display for their small group to make a dot array/factor rainbow poster. The groups place their posters for display in the Arrays Museum. Position the *Prime Number* and *Composite Number* display labels to guide students in arranging their posters.

▶ Classifying Prime and Composite Numbers

PARTNER ACTIVITY

(*Math Journal 1,* p. 16)

Assign journal page 16. Students first find all factors for each number and then classify them as prime or composite. Circulate and assist.

Bring the class together to go over the answers. List the prime numbers through 39 on the board or on the Class Data Pad.
2, 3, 5, 7, 11, 13, 17, 19, 23, 29, 31, 37

Adjusting the Activity

As an ongoing project for the rest of the unit, ask students to add other prime numbers to the list. Keep this class list of prime numbers on display. Whenever a prime number is proposed, the class should check that it is a prime number. The next five prime numbers to add to the list are 41, 43, 47, 53, and 59.

AUDITORY ◆ KINESTHETIC ◆ TACTILE ◆ VISUAL

▶ Developing a Strategy for *Factor Captor*

(*Math Journal 1,* p. 17; *Student Reference Book,* p. 306)

Students determine the best first three moves for a game of *Factor Captor,* played on a number grid consisting of the whole numbers up to 30. Encourage students first to work independently to find these moves on their own, and then to discuss their solutions with their partners. Students should conclude that it is usually (though not always) to their advantage to cover the highest available prime number.

Example: The best choice for a first move is 29, since it results in a score of 29 against a score of 1 for the other player, for a net score of 28. Some students may have chosen 30, but this would result in a score of 42 for the other player since the available factors of 30 are 1, 2, 3, 5, 6, 10, and 15.

The best choice for a second move is 23, which results in a net score of 23 because the number 1 has already been covered.

The best choice for a third move is 25, resulting in a net score of 20. Some students may have chosen 19 with a net score of 19, having concluded that the best move is to choose the highest available prime number, but not in this case.

Adjusting the Activity

Discuss situations that result in negative net scores.
Example: If player 1 scores 30 and player 2 scores 42, then player 1's net score is −12.

AUDITORY ◆ KINESTHETIC ◆ TACTILE ◆ VISUAL

2 Ongoing Learning & Practice

▶ Completing Number-Line Patterns

PARTNER ACTIVITY

(*Math Journal 1,* p. 18)

Algebraic Thinking Students use their knowledge of number relationships to analyze and complete patterns by filling in the missing values on number lines.

Ongoing Assessment: Informing Instruction

Watch for students who have difficulty finding the rule for the pattern in Problem 3. One strategy is to take the difference between two given values and divide by the number of "hops" between them.

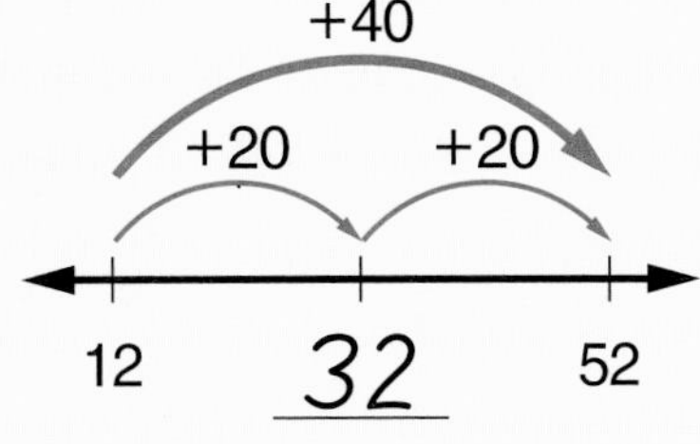

Student Page

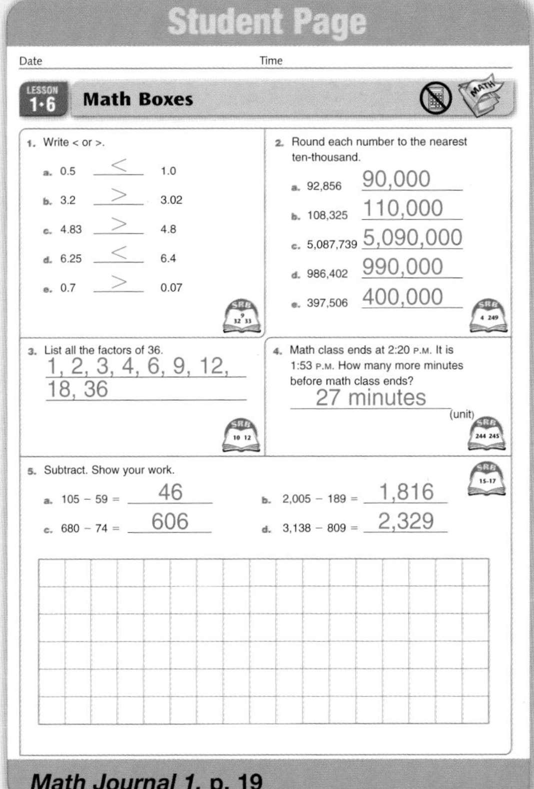

Date Time

LESSON 1·6 **Math Boxes**

1. Write < or >.
   a. 0.5 < 1.0
   b. 3.2 > 3.02
   c. 4.83 > 4.8
   d. 6.25 < 6.4
   e. 0.7 > 0.07

2. Round each number to the nearest ten-thousand.
   a. 92,856 90,000
   b. 108,325 110,000
   c. 5,087,739 5,090,000
   d. 986,402 990,000
   e. 397,506 400,000

3. List all the factors of 36.
   1, 2, 3, 4, 6, 9, 12, 18, 36

4. Math class ends at 2:20 P.M. It is 1:53 P.M. How many more minutes before math class ends?
   27 minutes (unit)

5. Subtract. Show your work.
   a. 105 − 59 = 46
   b. 2,005 − 189 = 1,816
   c. 680 − 74 = 606
   d. 3,138 − 809 = 2,329

Math Journal 1, p. 19

Study Link Master

Name Date Time

STUDY LINK 1·6 **Prime and Composite Numbers**

A **prime number** is a whole number that has exactly two factors—1 and the number itself. A **composite number** is a whole number that has more than two factors.

For each number:

- List all of its factors.
- Write whether the number is prime or composite.
- Circle all of the factors that are prime numbers.

	Number	Factors	Prime or Composite?
1	11	1, (11)	prime
2	18	1, (2), (3), 6, 9, 18	composite
3	24	1, (2), (3), 4, 6, 8, 12, 24	composite
4	28	1, (2), 4, (7), 14, 28	composite
5	36	1, (2), (3), 4, 6, 9, 12, 18, 36	composite
6	49	1, (7), 49	composite
7	50	1, (2), (5), 10, 25, 50	composite
8	70	1, (2), (5), (7), 10, 14, 35, 70	composite
9	100	1, (2), 4, (5), 10, 20, 25, 50, 100	composite

Practice

10. 4,065 + 2,803 + 2,954 = 9,822
11. 392 − 158 = 234
12. 1,532 ∗ 14 = 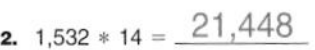 21,448
13. 39 / 4 → 9 R3
14. 48 ∗ 15 =  720

Math Masters, p. 17

Teaching Master

Name ______ Date ______ Time ______

LESSON 1•6 **Goldbach's Conjecture**

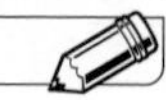

1. Write each of the following numbers as the sum of two prime numbers. Sample answers:

Examples: 56 = 43 + 13   26 = 13 + 13

a. 6 = 3 + 3   b. 12 = 7 + 5

c. 18 = 13 + 5   d. 22 = 11 + 11

e. 24 = 17 + 7   f. 34 = 31 + 3

The answers to these problems are examples of **Goldbach's Conjecture.** A **conjecture** is something you believe is true even though you can't be certain that it is true. Goldbach's Conjecture might be true, but no one has ever proven it. Anyone who can either prove or disprove Goldbach's Conjecture will become famous.

2. Work with a partner. Find and write as many of the addition expressions as you can for the numbers in the grid on page 19.

3. Can any of the numbers in the grid be written as the sum of two prime numbers in more than one way? If so, give an example. Show all possible ways.
Yes. 18: 7 + 11, 13 + 5; 24: 19 + 5, 11 + 13; 22: 19 + 3, 5 + 17; 34: 29 + 5, 11 + 23, 3 + 31

Try This

4. Write 70 as the sum of two primes in as many ways as you can.
3 + 67, 11 + 59, 17 + 53, 23 + 47, 29 + 41

Math Masters, p. 18

NOTE Provide ongoing facts practice to help students maintain skills. Students who are not yet proficient to the level of automatic recall should not be penalized. Rather, use individualized support to help them achieve effective study approaches.

Teaching Master

Name ______ Date ______ Time ______

LESSON 1•6 **Goldbach's Conjecture** *continued*

Write each number below as the sum of two prime numbers.
Answers vary.

4: 2 + 2	6: 3 + 3	8: 5 + 3	10: 5 + 5	12: 7 + 5
14: 7 + 7	16: 11 + 5	18: 11 + 7	20: 13 + 7	22: 11 + 11
24: 13 + 11	26: 23 + 3	28: 23 + 5	30: 23 + 7	32: 29 + 3
34: 31 + 3	36: 31 + 5	38: 31 + 7	40: 37 + 3	42: 5 + 37
44: 41 + 3	46: 41 + 5	48: 41 + 7	50: 47 + 3	52: 23 + 29
54: 47 + 7	56: 53 + 3	58: 41 + 17	60: 23 + 37	62: 59 + 3
64: 61 + 3	66: 43 + 23	68: 31 + 37	70: 59 + 11	72: 31 + 41
74: 31 + 43	76: 73 + 3	78: 31 + 47	80: 37 + 43	82: 79 + 3
84: 41 + 43	86: 83 + 3	88: 41 + 47	90: 43 + 47	92: 89 + 3
94: 41 + 53	96: 43 + 53	98: 31 + 67	100: 41 + 59	102: 41 + 61

Math Masters, p. 19

▶ Math Boxes 1•6

INDEPENDENT ACTIVITY

(*Math Journal 1,* p. 19)

Mixed Practice Math Boxes in this lesson are paired with Math Boxes in Lesson 1-8. The skill in Problem 5 previews Unit 2 content.

Writing/Reasoning Have students write a response to the following: *Explain how you know your answer is correct for Problem 4.* Sample answer: I know that 1:53 P.M. is 7 minutes less than 2:00 P.M. because there are 60 minutes in an hour and 60 − 53 = 7. 2:20 P.M. is 20 minutes past the hour. So there are 27 minutes before the math class ends because 20 + 7 = 27.

▶ Study Link 1•6

INDEPENDENT ACTIVITY

(*Math Masters,* p. 17)

Home Connection Students find the factors of whole numbers and identify numbers as prime or composite.

3 Differentiation Options

ENRICHMENT

PARTNER ACTIVITY

▶ Exploring Goldbach's Conjecture

15–30 Min

(*Math Masters,* pp. 18 and 19)

Social Studies Link To further investigate prime numbers, have students explore Goldbach's conjecture. Christian Goldbach (1690–1764) had a theory—every even number greater than 2 can be written as the sum of two prime numbers. Students rename whole numbers as the sum of two prime numbers. In this activity students apply their knowledge of number properties and addition facts.

Have students complete Problem 1 on *Math Masters,* page 18. When most students have finished, read and discuss the introduction to Problem 2. Then have students complete pages 18 and 19. Also, *Math Masters,* page 19 can be used to organize the collection of students' addition expressions for the even numbers 1–102. Enlarge and post the page where students can add the solutions from their individual pages as they are found.

EXTRA PRACTICE

SMALL-GROUP ACTIVITY

▶ 5-Minute Math

5–15 Min

To offer students more experience with prime and composite numbers see *5-Minute Math,* page 177.

1•7 Square Numbers

Objectives To introduce square numbers and the exponent key on a calculator.

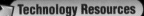

www.everydaymathonline.com

ePresentations

eToolkit

Algorithms Practice

EM Facts Workshop Game™

Family Letters

Assessment Management

Common Core State Standards

Curriculum Focal Points

Interactive Teacher's Lesson Guide

1 Teaching the Lesson

Key Concepts and Skills

- Rename square number factor pairs in exponential and standard notation.
  [Number and Numeration Goal 4]
- Investigate the properties of square numbers.
  [Operations and Computation Goal 7]
- Use array patterns to define square numbers.
  [Patterns, Functions, and Algebra Goal 1]

Key Activities

Students form arrays to identify square numbers and investigate their properties. They use exponential notation to represent square numbers and use the exponent key on a calculator.

Ongoing Assessment: Informing Instruction See page 48.

Ongoing Assessment: Recognizing Student Achievement Use an Exit Slip (*Math Masters,* page 414).
[Number and Numeration Goal 4]

Key Vocabulary

square array ◆ square number ◆ exponential notation ◆ exponent key ◆ exponent

Materials

Math Journal 1, pp. 20 and 21
Study Link 1•6
Math Masters, pp. 413 and 414
25 counters ◆ calculator

2 Ongoing Learning & Practice

Playing *Factor Bingo*
Math Masters, p. 452
per partnership: 4 each of number cards 2–9 (from the Everything Math Deck, if available) ◆ 12 counters
Students practice applying multiplication facts and number properties, recognizing factors, and factoring numbers.

Math Boxes 1•7
Math Journal 1, p. 22
Students practice and maintain skills through Math Box problems.

Study Link 1•7
Math Masters, p. 20
Students practice and maintain skills through Study Link activities.

3 Differentiation Options

READINESS

Investigating Square Number Facts
Math Journal 1, inside front cover
centimeter cubes
Students relate doubles facts and square arrays.

ENRICHMENT

Completing Patterns
Math Masters, p. 21
counters
Students investigate dot patterns in rectangular and nonrectangular arrays.

Advance Preparation

For Part 1, check that the calculators your students are using have an exponent key of some kind.

***Teacher's Reference Manual,* Grades 4–6** pp. 79–83, 94–98, 267–269

Getting Started

Mental Math and Reflexes

Pose the following problems, and have students write an expression for each. Students are not expected to calculate the answers. Answers may vary.

●○○ The sum of 8 and 6 $8 + 6$
The product of 7 and 5 $7 * 5$
The product of 4 and 3 $4 * 3$

●●○ 7 more than the product of 2 and 5 $7 + (2 * 5)$
2 more than double 8 $2 + (2 * 8)$
Double 5 and then add 4 more $(5 + 5) + 4$

●●● 6 less than the product of 10 and 6 $(10 * 6) - 6$
8 less than the sum of 10 and 5 $(10 + 5) - 8$
7 less than the product of 8 and 7 $(8 * 7) - 7$

Math Message

Use counters to try and make a rectangular array with an equal number of rows and columns for each number: 14, 16, and 18.

Which numbers make this kind of array?

Study Link 1·6 Follow-Up

Have partners compare answers and resolve differences.

NOTE Some students may benefit from doing the **Readiness** activity before you begin Part 1 of each lesson. See the Readiness activity in Part 3 for details.

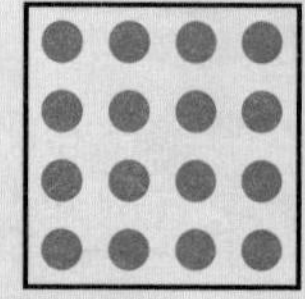

Square array for the square number 16.

1 Teaching the Lesson

▶ Math Message Follow-Up

Survey the class to determine which numbers could be represented by an array with the same number of rows and columns. Of the three numbers, 16 is the only one that can be represented in this way (4-by-4 array). Ask a volunteer to draw this array on the board. Ask another student to draw a square next to the array. Ask: *How is a 4-by-4 array similar to a square?* Sample answers: The shapes are alike; the sides of a square are equal; the rows and columns in the array are equal. Explain that when an array has the same number of rows and columns, it is shaped like a square and is called a **square array.** The number it represents is called a **square number.** Draw a square around the array on the board before continuing. Since 16 can be represented by a square array, the number 16 is a square number. (*See margin.*)

After students complete the Math Message Follow-Up, ask them to look at and describe the pattern in the arrays at the top of *Math Journal 1,* page 20. Sample answers: It is a pattern of squares. Each square is bigger than the one before it with one more row and column. For each array, the rows and columns have the same number of dots. Starting at 1, the number of dots added to each array is always odd. For example, $1 + 3 = 4, 4 + 5 = 9, 9 + 7 = 16$, and so on. Ask: *How many dots would need to be added for the next square number?* 9

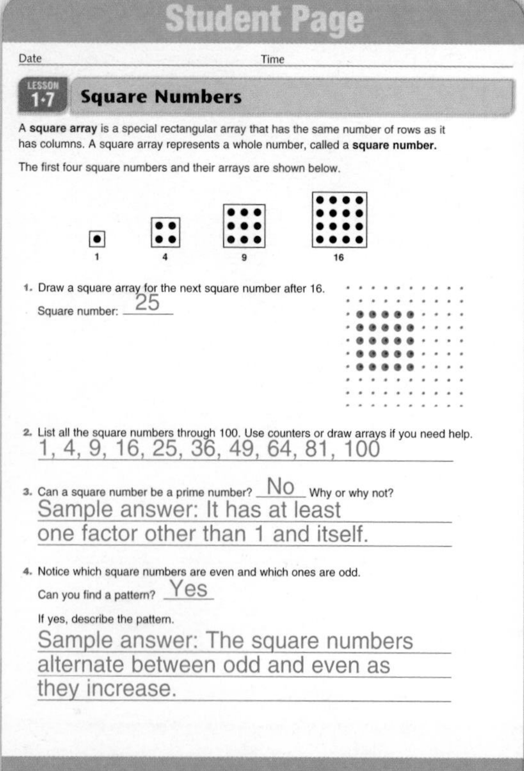

Student Page

Date Time

LESSON 1·7 **Square Numbers**

A **square array** is a special rectangular array that has the same number of rows as it has columns. A square array represents a whole number, called a **square number.**

The first four square numbers and their arrays are shown below.

1 4 9 16

1. Draw a square array for the next square number after 16.
Square number: 25

2. List all the square numbers through 100. Use counters or draw arrays if you need help.
1, 4, 9, 16, 25, 36, 49, 64, 81, 100

3. Can a square number be a prime number? No Why or why not?
Sample answer: It has at least one factor other than 1 and itself.

4. Notice which square numbers are even and which ones are odd.
Can you find a pattern? Yes
If yes, describe the pattern.
Sample answer: The square numbers alternate between odd and even as they increase.

Math Journal 1, p. 20

Ongoing Assessment: Informing Instruction

Watch for students who have trouble seeing the structure of square arrays. Ask them to draw a 4-by-4 array and instead of drawing a square around the array, draw lines connecting the outside dots. Do the same with an 8-by-2 array. Ask students to describe the shape formed by the lines on the two arrays. One array has a square shape, and the other array is shaped like a rectangle.

Finding Other Square Numbers

Write the numbers 1, 2, 3, and 4 on the board. Ask: *Can square arrays be drawn for these numbers?* Students should respond that the numbers 2 and 3 cannot be represented by square arrays, but the number 4 can be. They may or may not include the number 1 as well. Erase the numbers 2 and 3, and ask a volunteer to draw the square array for the number 4 underneath the number on the board. Draw a square around the array. Ask another volunteer to draw the square array for the number 1.

Students might argue that the single dot for 1 is not an array. Guide them to see that the array for the number 1 should be thought of as a square array. Ask: *How many objects are in the array?* 1 *How many rows are in the array set?* 1 *How many columns are in the array set?* 1 Then ask them to write the multiplication number model that represents this array. $1 * 1 = 1$ Because we can answer these questions in the same manner for any square array, we consider the single dot for 1 to be a square array.

Explain that a complete listing of square arrays starts with an array that has one row and one column, each containing one dot. The second square array has two rows and two columns, each containing two dots. Ask: *How many rows and how many columns does the third square array have?* 3 Ask a volunteer to draw this square array.

Numbers that can be represented by square arrays are called square numbers. The first square number is 1. The second square number is 4. *What is the third square number?* 9 Write the number 9 on the board above the 3-by-3 array. *What is the fourth square number?* 16 Write *square numbers* above the display of numbers and arrays on the board.

Investigating the Properties of Square Numbers

(*Math Journal 1,* pp. 20 and 21; *Math Masters,* p. 413)

On journal page 20, students list all the square numbers through 100. Students should complete this page independently and then compare answers with a partner. Encourage students to use counters or to draw arrays on dot paper (*Math Masters,* page 413) as they look for square numbers. Circulate and assist.

The first part of journal page 21 introduces **exponential notation** for square numbers. The second part introduces the calculator keys used to square a number. On the TI-15 an **exponent key** [^] is used. On the Casio *fx*-55, the [x^2] key is used. If students' calculators have a key for squaring numbers, they should use it to solve Problems 6–12. If their calculators do not have this key, they can find the answers by multiplying. To support English language learners, discuss the common meaning of *key* as well as its meaning in this context.

Student Page

Date ______ Time ______

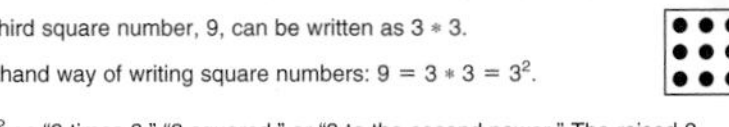

LESSON 1·7 Square Numbers *continued*

Any square number can be written as the product of a number multiplied by itself.

Example: The third square number, 9, can be written as $3 * 3$.

There is a shorthand way of writing square numbers: $9 = 3 * 3 = 3^2$.

You can read 3^2 as "3 times 3," "3 squared," or "3 to the second power." The raised 2 is called an **exponent.** It tells that 3 is used as a factor 2 times. Numbers written with an exponent are said to be in **exponential notation.**

Be careful! The number 3^2 is not the same as the product of $3 * 2$.
$3 * 2 = 6$, but 3^2 equals $3 * 3$, which is 9.

5. Fill in the blanks.

Product	Exponential Notation	Square Number
$4 * 4$	4^2	16
$7 * 7$	7^2	49
$10 * 10$	10^2	100
$11 * 11$	11^2	121

Some calculators have a key that can be used to find the square of a number. Depending on the calculator, this key might be marked with the symbol [^] or the symbol [x^2].

6. Use your calculator to find 3 squared.
   Write the key sequence that you used. Answers vary.
   What does the display show? 9

If your calculator has an exponent key, use it to solve the following problems. If not, you can use the multiplication key.

7. $8^2 =$ 64
8. $12^2 =$ 144
9. $14^2 =$ 196
10. $20^2 =$ 400
11. $43^2 =$ 1,849
12. $67^2 =$ 4,489
13. Start with 4. Square it. Now square the result. What do you get? 256

Math Journal 1, p. 21

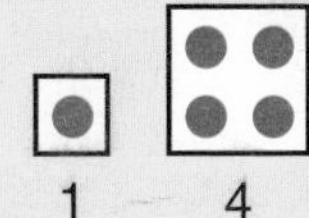

Square arrays for the square numbers 1 and 4

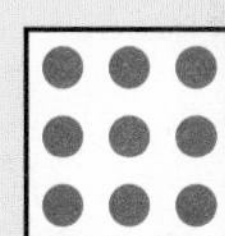

Square array for the square number 9

Links to the Future

Calculator use in *Everyday Mathematics* is designed to provide students with practice in knowing when and how to use this mathematical tool. Throughout fifth grade, calculator practice is included within lessons, and beginning in Unit 3 as a part of the Mental Math and Reflexes activities. Provide students with ready access to calculators in the same way that they have access to the Geometry Template and other tools.

Game Master

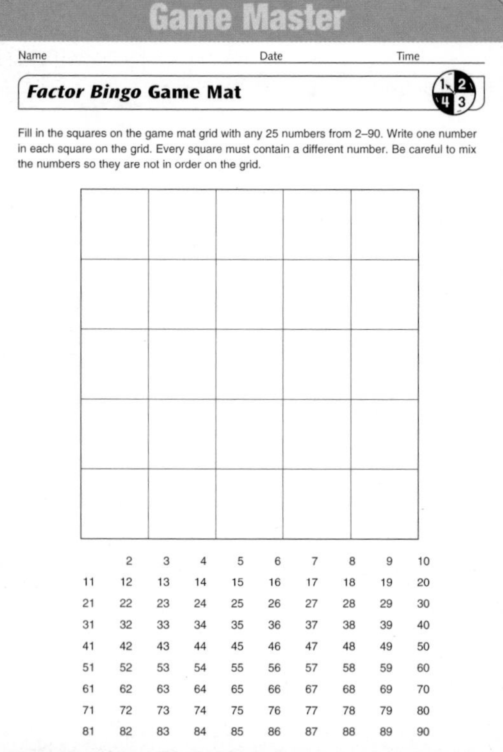

Name Date Time

Factor Bingo Game Mat

Fill in the squares on the game mat grid with any 25 numbers from 2–90. Write one number in each square on the grid. Every square must contain a different number. Be careful to mix the numbers so they are not in order on the grid.

	2	3	4	5	6	7	8	9	10
11	12	13	14	15	16	17	18	19	20
21	22	23	24	25	26	27	28	29	30
31	32	33	34	35	36	37	38	39	40
41	42	43	44	45	46	47	48	49	50
51	52	53	54	55	56	57	58	59	60
61	62	63	64	65	66	67	68	69	70
71	72	73	74	75	76	77	78	79	80
81	82	83	84	85	86	87	88	89	90

Math Masters, p. 452

Student Page

Date Time

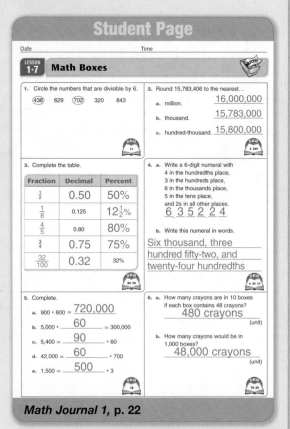

LESSON 1·7 **Math Boxes**

1. Circle the numbers that are divisible by 6.
(438) 629 (702) 320 843

2. Round 15,783,406 to the nearest…
a. million. 16,000,000
b. thousand. 15,783,000
c. hundred-thousand. 15,800,000

3. Complete the table.

Fraction	Decimal	Percent
$\frac{1}{2}$	0.50	50%
$\frac{1}{8}$	0.125	$12\frac{1}{2}$%
$\frac{4}{5}$	0.80	80%
$\frac{3}{4}$	0.75	75%
$\frac{32}{100}$	0.32	32%

4. a. Write a 6-digit numeral with 4 in the hundredths place, 3 in the hundreds place, 6 in the thousands place, 5 in the tens place, and 2s in all other places.
6 3 5 2 . 2 4
b. Write this numeral in words.
Six thousand, three hundred fifty-two, and twenty-four hundredths

5. Complete.
a. 900 ∗ 800 = 720,000
b. 5,000 ∗ 60 = 300,000
c. 5,400 = 90 ∗ 60
d. 42,000 = 60 ∗ 700
e. 1,500 = 500 ∗ 3

6. a. How many crayons are in 10 boxes if each box contains 48 crayons?
480 crayons (unit)
b. How many crayons would be in 1,000 boxes?
48,000 crayons (unit)

Math Journal 1, p. 22

After students have completed both pages, discuss the answers. Focus your questioning to make sure students understand the answers to Problems 3 and 4. Students could draw arrays on the board to explain their answers in addition to their written explanations on the journal page. Ask students to tell a partner the definition for **exponent.** Tell a different partner the definition for *exponential notation*. Partners are responsible for understanding each other's definitions.

Discuss the difference between doubling a number and squaring a number. Illustrate this difference by asking students to first double a number and then to square the same number. Ask: *What do you get when you double 10?* 20 *When you square 10?* 100 *What is the number model for doubling 10?* 10 + 10; 10 ∗ 2 *What is the number model for squaring 10?* 10 ∗ 10; 10^2

Ongoing Assessment: Recognizing Student Achievement

Exit Slip 

Use an Exit Slip (*Math Masters,* page 414) to assess students' understanding of square numbers and exponential notation for square numbers. Have students write a response to the following: *Describe a square number and why it is possible to write a square number using an exponent.* Students are making adequate progress if their explanation refers to repeated factors in number models and/or if there are the same number of rows and columns in an array that represents a square number.

[Number and Numeration Goal 4]

2 Ongoing Learning & Practice

▶ Playing *Factor Bingo*

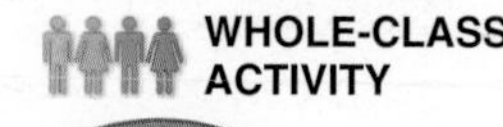

WHOLE-CLASS ACTIVITY

(*Math Masters,* p. 452)

Students relate multiplication facts to a common factor by playing *Factor Bingo.*

Directions

1. Shuffle the deck of number cards. Turn over and announce the top card. This is the target factor.
2. Each player places a counter on one square containing a number that is a multiple of the target factor.
3. Turn over the next card and continue in the same way.
4. The first player to get five counters in a row, column, or diagonal calls out, "Bingo!" and wins the game. A player who places 12 counters anywhere on the game mat may also call out "Bingo!" and win the game.
5. Play should continue until there is a winner. Reshuffle the deck as needed.

Math Boxes 1•7

INDEPENDENT ACTIVITY

(*Math Journal 1*, p. 22)

Mixed Practice Math Boxes in this lesson are paired with Math Boxes in Lessons 1-5 and 1-9. The skills in Problems 5 and 6 preview Unit 2 content.

Study Link 1•7

INDEPENDENT ACTIVITY

(*Math Masters*, p. 20)

Home Connection Students solve problems involving square numbers, identify a square array, and explain why the array represents a square number.

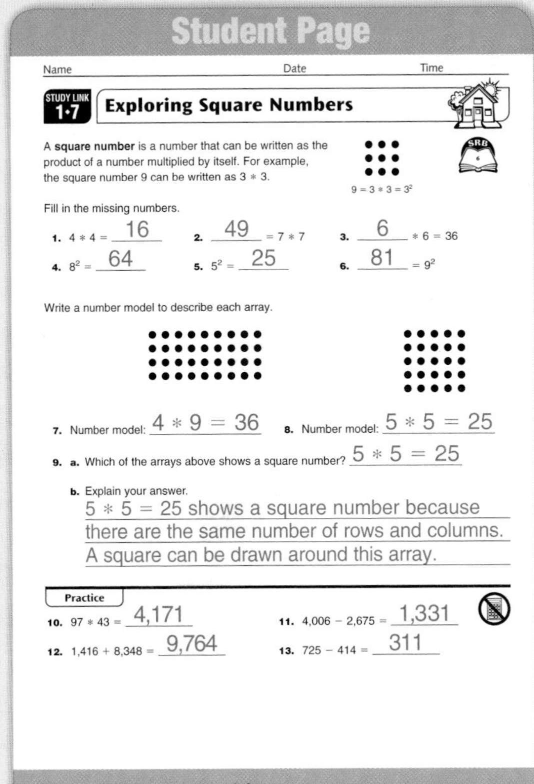

Student Page

Name ____ Date ____ Time ____

STUDY LINK 1•7 **Exploring Square Numbers**

A **square number** is a number that can be written as the product of a number multiplied by itself. For example, the square number 9 can be written as 3 ∗ 3.

9 = 3 ∗ 3 = 3^2

Fill in the missing numbers.

1. 4 ∗ 4 = 16
2. 49 = 7 ∗ 7
3. 6 ∗ 6 = 36
4. 8^2 = 64
5. 5^2 = 25
6. 81 = 9^2

Write a number model to describe each array.

7. Number model: 4 ∗ 9 = 36
8. Number model: 5 ∗ 5 = 25
9. a. Which of the arrays above shows a square number? 5 ∗ 5 = 25

   b. Explain your answer.
   5 ∗ 5 = 25 shows a square number because there are the same number of rows and columns. A square can be drawn around this array.

Practice

10. 97 ∗ 43 = 4,171
11. 4,006 − 2,675 = 1,331
12. 1,416 + 8,348 = 9,764
13. 725 − 414 = 311

Math Masters, p. 20

3 Differentiation Options

READINESS

Investigating Square Number Facts

SMALL-GROUP ACTIVITY

15–30 Min

(*Math Journal 1*, inside front cover)

To explore the relationship between the doubles multiplication facts and square numbers, have students build arrays for the square numbers. Students use the Multiplication/Division Facts Table on the inside front cover of their journals to write the facts from the diagonal running from the upper left-hand corner to the lower right-hand corner of the table. Then they use centimeter cubes to make arrays for each of these facts.

Ask students which arrays are similar. They should notice that all of these numbers are doubles facts and can be represented by arrays with the same number of rows as columns.

ENRICHMENT

Completing Patterns

INDEPENDENT ACTIVITY

5–15 Min

(*Math Masters*, p. 21)

To further investigate dot patterns in rectangular and non-rectangular arrays, have students draw, label, and describe dot patterns. Encourage students to think about and discuss how the dot patterns and the corresponding number patterns are related.

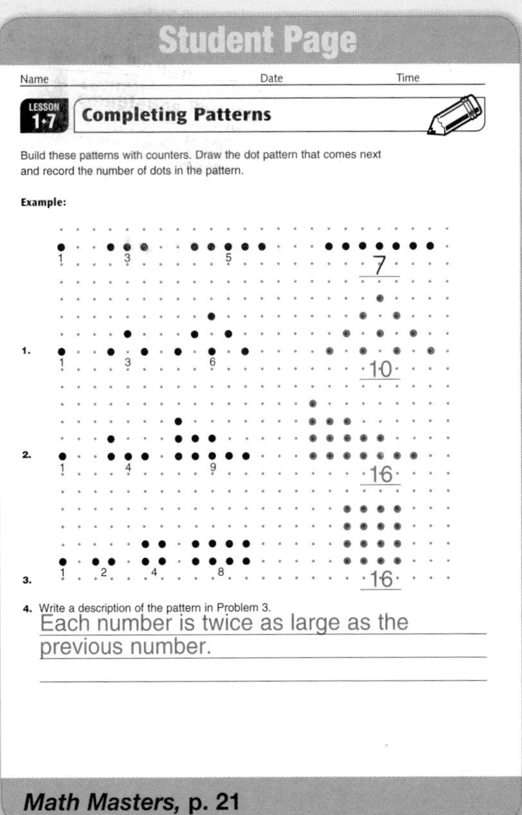

Student Page

Name ____ Date ____ Time ____

LESSON 1•7 **Completing Patterns**

Build these patterns with counters. Draw the dot pattern that comes next and record the number of dots in the pattern.

Example: 1, 3, 5, 7

1. 1, 3, 6, 10
2. 1, 4, 9, 16
3. 1, 2, 4, 8, 16
4. Write a description of the pattern in Problem 3.
   Each number is twice as large as the previous number.

Math Masters, p. 21

1•8 Unsquaring Numbers

Objective To introduce the concept of square roots and the use of the square-root key on a calculator.

www.everydaymathonline.com

ePresentations

eToolkit

Algorithms Practice

EM Facts Workshop Game™

Family Letters

Assessment Management

Common Core State Standards

Curriculum Focal Points

Interactive Teacher's Lesson Guide

1 Teaching the Lesson

Key Concepts and Skills

- Use exponential notation to name square numbers, and explore the relationship between square numbers and square roots. [Number and Numeration Goal 4]

Key Activities

Students investigate "unsquaring" numbers without using the square-root key on a calculator and use the square-root key to test their answers. They explore properties of square numbers and their square roots.

Key Vocabulary

unsquaring a number ◆ square root ◆ square-root key

Materials

Math Journal 1, p. 23
Study Link 1•7
calculator ◆ overhead calculator (optional) ◆ 16 counters (optional)

2 Ongoing Learning & Practice

Playing *Multiplication Top-It* (Extended-Facts Version)
Student Reference Book, p. 334
Math Masters, p. 493
per partnership: 4 each of number cards 1–10 (from the Everything Math Deck, if available), calculator
Students use their knowledge of extended facts to form and compare numbers.

Ongoing Assessment: Recognizing Student Achievement
Use *Math Masters,* page 493.
[Operations and Computation Goal 2]

Math Boxes 1•8
Math Journal 1, p. 24
Students practice and maintain skills through Math Box problems.

Study Link 1•8
Math Masters, p. 22
Students practice and maintain skills through Study Link activities.

3 Differentiation Options

ENRICHMENT

Comparing Numbers with Their Squares
Math Masters, p. 23
calculator
Students investigate the relationship between numbers and their squares.

EXTRA PRACTICE

5-Minute Math
5-Minute Math™, p. 108
slate or paper
Students practice using the square root sign.

Advance Preparation

Familiarize yourself with the use of the square root key on your students' calculators.

***Teacher's Reference Manual,* Grades 4–6** pp. 74, 75, 79–83, 94–98, 267–269

Getting Started

Mental Math and Reflexes

Pose the following problems. Have students write an expression as you describe the calculation. Students are not expected to calculate the solution. Answers may vary.

●○○ The sum of 9 and 8 $9 + 8$

7 less than 7 $7 - 7$

The quotient of 24 divided by 6 $24 / 6$

●●○ 7 less than the product of 2 and 9 $(2 * 9) - 7$

Double 8 and then add 0 more $(2 * 8) + 0$

0 times the sum of 8 and 2 $0 * (8 + 2)$

●●● 8 less than the sum of 10 and 5 $(10 + 5) - 8$

3 more than triple 3 $3 + (3 * 3)$

10 less than triple 10 $(3 * 10) - 10$

Math Message

Find the numbers that make these statements true.

$\square * \square = 4$

$\square^2 = 81$

Study Link 1·7 Follow-Up

Have partners compare answers and resolve differences.

1 Teaching the Lesson

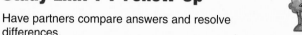

Interactive whiteboard-ready ePresentations are available at www.everydaymathonline.com to help you teach the lesson.

Math Message Follow-Up

WHOLE-CLASS DISCUSSION

Algebraic Thinking Ask a volunteer to read the first problem. Some number times some number equals 4. *What numbers could the placeholders in this problem represent?* The factors of 4; 1 and 4; 2 Write the first problem on the board or a transparency, replacing both placeholders with the letter n. Ask students what number the letter n (the variable) represents. 2 Explain that the variable can only represent one number if the number sentence is true. Tell students that unknown numbers will be represented using variables as the placeholders. Rewrite the second problem using the variable m. $m^2 = 81$ Ask a volunteer to read the problem. m squared equals 81; $m * m$ equals 81 *What is the number* m *that makes this number sentence true?* 9

"Unsquaring" Numbers

Begin this activity by explaining that solving problems like the Math Message problems requires **unsquaring a number.** We needed to undo the operation that squared the number. If students square a number, they multiply it by itself to get the product. Given the product of a squared number, they have to undo the multiplication in order to identify the number that was squared.

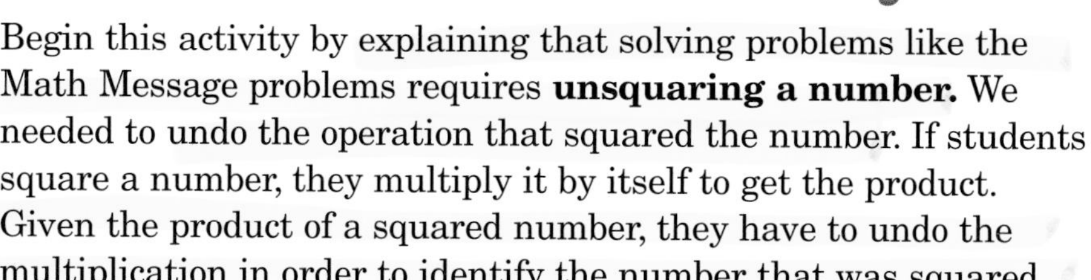

$4 * 4 = p$	Square the number 4 to find p.
$n * n = 16$	Unsquare the number 16 to find n.

The difference between squaring and unsquaring a number

Adjusting the Activity

Have students use counters to build the square array for 16. Note that when 16 is unsquared, the result is the same as the number of rows, or the number of columns, of the original square.

AUDITORY ◆ KINESTHETIC ◆ TACTILE ◆ VISUAL

Ask: *What number, multiplied by itself, is equal to 289?* Give students a few minutes to find the number. They may use their calculators if they wish.

After a few minutes, survey the class for their solution strategies. Most students will have used one of the following approaches:

▷ The random method: Some students might have tried various numbers without using a system to guide their choices.

▷ The "squeeze" method: Some students might have tried various numbers, each time using the result to help select their next choice. To unsquare 289, you might:

- Try 10: $10^2 = 100$; much less than 289
- Try 20: $20^2 = 400$; more than 289

Then try numbers between 10 and 20, probably closer to 20 than to 10.

- Try 18: $18^2 = 324$; still too large, but closer.
- Try 17: $17^2 = 289$; the answer is 17.

▷ Endings and products: When students established an interval, such as the interval from 10 to 20, some might have reasoned that since 17 ends in 7, and $7 * 7 = 49$; then 17 should be the next choice because 289 also ends in 9.

If students mention using the square-root key on their calculator, acknowledge that this is an efficient way of unsquaring a number, but the focus on this portion of the lesson is to help them understand the process of squaring and unsquaring numbers before they use the calculator function.

Give students a few more square numbers to unsquare. (*See margin.*) Challenge them to use as few guesses as possible.

Suggested square numbers for students to "unsquare"

196 14	10,000 100
1,024 32	676 26
7,225 85	3,136 56
441 21	900 30
1,849 43	5,041 71

Tell students that when they unsquare a number, they have found the **square root** of the number. *What number squared is 64?* 8 *So what is 64 unsquared?* 8, because $8 * 8 = 64$ *What is the square root of 64?* 8

▶ Finding the Square Root of Numbers

(*Math Journal 1*, p. 23)

Allow partners a few minutes to complete Problems 1 and 2. Survey the class for suggestions for checking the answers in Problem 1. Most students will respond with the following possibilities:

▷ Multiply the square root of a number by itself.

▷ Use the **square-root key**, for example [√], on the calculator to find the square root of a number.

To support English language learners, write the following on the board: $8^2 = 8 * 8 = 64$. *The square of 8 is 64. The square root of 64 is 8.*

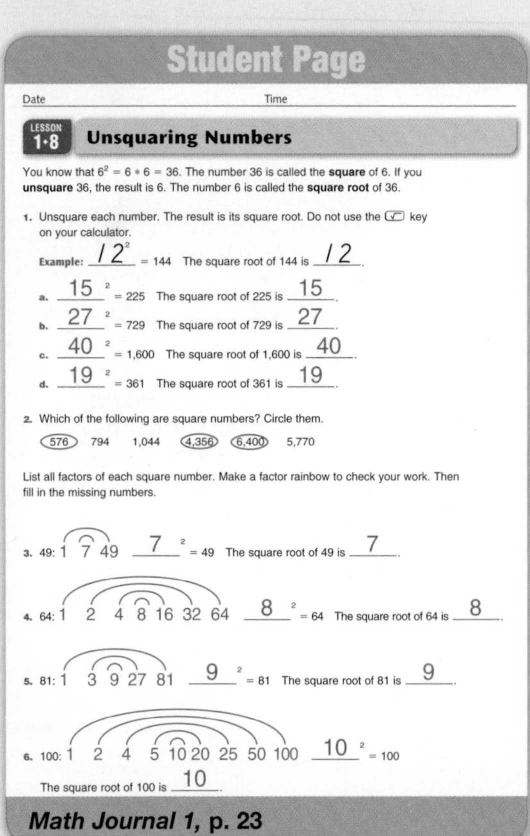

Student Page

Date Time

LESSON 1·8 **Unsquaring Numbers**

You know that $6^2 = 6 * 6 = 36$. The number 36 is called the **square** of 6. If you **unsquare** 36, the result is 6. The number 6 is called the **square root** of 36.

1. Unsquare each number. The result is its square root. Do not use the [√] key on your calculator.

Example: $12^2 = 144$ The square root of 144 is 12.

a. $15^2 = 225$ The square root of 225 is 15.

b. $27^2 = 729$ The square root of 729 is 27.

c. $40^2 = 1{,}600$ The square root of 1,600 is 40.

d. $19^2 = 361$ The square root of 361 is 19.

2. Which of the following are square numbers? Circle them.

(576) 794 1,044 (4,356) (6,400) 5,770

List all factors of each square number. Make a factor rainbow to check your work. Then fill in the missing numbers.

3. 49: 1 7 49 $7^2 = 49$ The square root of 49 is 7.

4. 64: 1 2 4 8 16 32 64 $8^2 = 64$ The square root of 64 is 8.

5. 81: 1 3 9 27 81 $9^2 = 81$ The square root of 81 is 9.

6. 100: 1 2 4 5 10 20 25 50 100 $10^2 = 100$

The square root of 100 is 10.

Math Journal 1, p. 23

Explain that in the same way that the class has used a calculator to test the result of other computations, they will use a calculator to test that they have accurately found the square-root of a number. If available, use an overhead calculator to demonstrate how to use the square-root function key. Model for students how to test the answers in Problem 2. Emphasize the following points:

- If the display shows a whole number, then the original number is a square number. For example, 576 is a square number because using the square-root key displays a whole number—24.
- If the display shows a decimal, then the original number is not a square number. For example, 794 is not a square number because using the square-root key displays a decimal—28.178006 (rounded to 6 decimal places).

Ask students to check the remaining numbers in Problem 2. Partners complete the remaining problems on journal page 23.

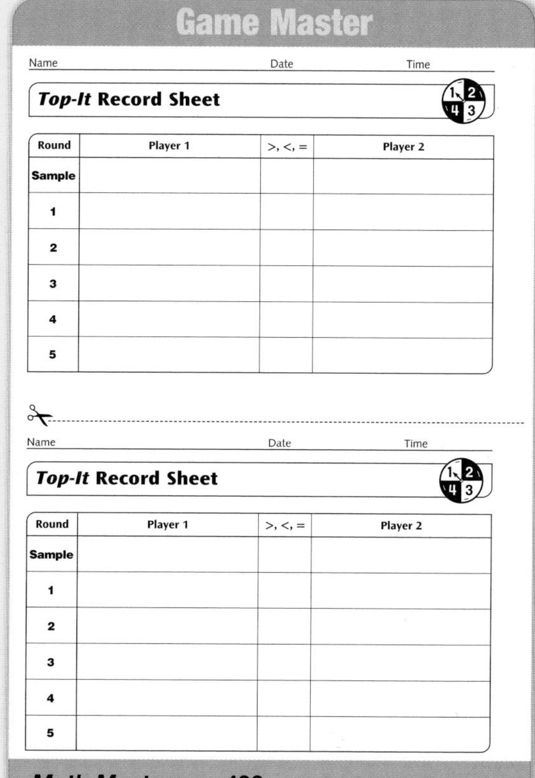

Game Master

Name Date Time

***Top-It* Record Sheet**

Round	Player 1	>, <, =	Player 2
Sample			
1			
2			
3			
4			
5			

Name Date Time

***Top-It* Record Sheet**

Round	Player 1	>, <, =	Player 2
Sample			
1			
2			
3			
4			
5			

***Math Masters,* p. 493**

2 Ongoing Learning & Practice

Playing *Multiplication Top-It* (Extended-Facts Version)

PARTNER ACTIVITY

(*Student Reference Book*, p. 334; *Math Masters*, p. 493)

Students apply their knowledge of basic multiplication facts to extended facts by playing *Multiplication Top-It* (Extended-Facts Version). Students use the same rules as described on *Student Reference Book,* page 334; however, they attach a zero to the first card drawn and multiply by the second card drawn. For example, suppose 5 is the first number drawn; 7 is the second number drawn. The student would compute: $5 * 10 = 50; 50 * 7 = 350$.

Ongoing Assessment: Recognizing Student Achievement

***Math Masters* Page 493**

Use the ***Top-It* Record Sheet** (*Math Masters,* page 493) to assess students' ability to solve and compare multiplication extended fact problems. Have the class record and compare 70 ∗ 8 and 50 ∗ 9 for the sample record. Partners record their first five rounds. Students are making adequate progress if they correctly solve and compare all five extended facts. Some students may be able to solve and compare problems with both factors multiplied by 10: 70 ∗ 80.

[Operations and Computation Goal 2]

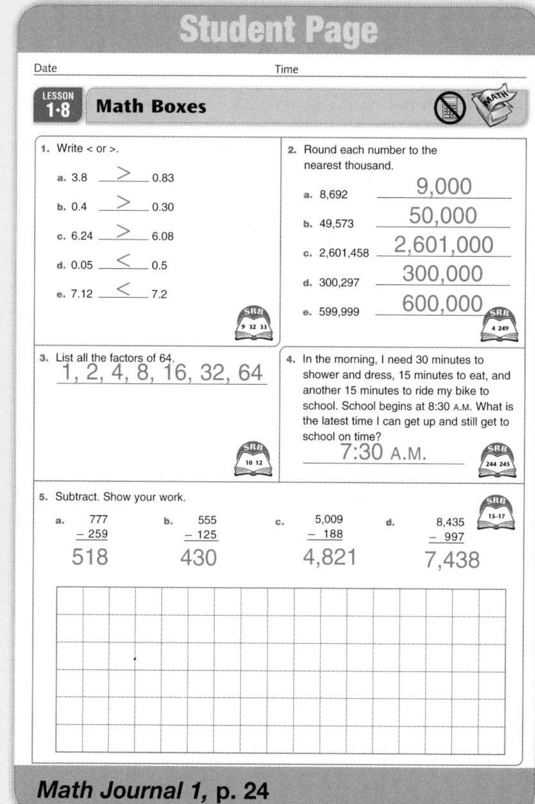

Student Page

Date Time

LESSON 1•8 **Math Boxes**

1. Write < or >.
   a. 3.8 __>__ 0.83
   b. 0.4 __>__ 0.30
   c. 6.24 __>__ 6.08
   d. 0.05 __<__ 0.5
   e. 7.12 __<__ 7.2

SRB 9 32 33

2. Round each number to the nearest thousand.
   a. 8,692 __9,000__
   b. 49,573 __50,000__
   c. 2,601,458 __2,601,000__
   d. 300,297 __300,000__
   e. 599,999 __600,000__

SRB 4 249

3. List all the factors of 64.
   1, 2, 4, 8, 16, 32, 64

SRB 10 12

4. In the morning, I need 30 minutes to shower and dress, 15 minutes to eat, and another 15 minutes to ride my bike to school. School begins at 8:30 A.M. What is the latest time I can get up and still get to school on time?
   7:30 A.M.

SRB 244 245

5. Subtract. Show your work.
   a. 777 − 259 = 518
   b. 555 − 125 = 430
   c. 5,009 − 188 = 4,821
   d. 8,435 − 997 = 7,438

SRB 15-17

***Math Journal 1,* p. 24**

Math Boxes 1•8

INDEPENDENT ACTIVITY

(*Math Journal 1,* p. 24)

Mixed Practice Math Boxes in this lesson are paired with Math Boxes in Lesson 1-6. The skill in Problem 5 previews Unit 2 content.

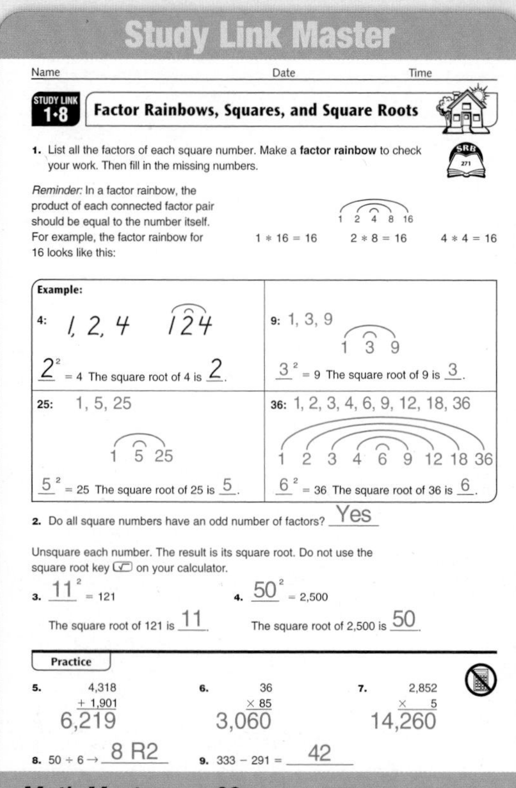

Study Link Master

Name Date Time

STUDY LINK 1·8 **Factor Rainbows, Squares, and Square Roots**

1. List all the factors of each square number. Make a **factor rainbow** to check your work. Then fill in the missing numbers.

Reminder: In a factor rainbow, the product of each connected factor pair should be equal to the number itself. For example, the factor rainbow for 16 looks like this:

1 2 4 8 16

1 ∗ 16 = 16   2 ∗ 8 = 16   4 ∗ 4 = 16

Example: 4: 1, 2, 4 (rainbow 1 2 4) 2^2 = 4 The square root of 4 is 2.	9: 1, 3, 9 (rainbow 1 3 9) 3^2 = 9 The square root of 9 is 3.
25: 1, 5, 25 (rainbow 1 5 25) 5^2 = 25 The square root of 25 is 5.	36: 1, 2, 3, 4, 6, 9, 12, 18, 36 (rainbow 1 2 3 4 6 9 12 18 36) 6^2 = 36 The square root of 36 is 6.

2. Do all square numbers have an odd number of factors? Yes

Unsquare each number. The result is its square root. Do not use the square root key on your calculator.

3. 11^2 = 121 The square root of 121 is 11

4. 50^2 = 2,500 The square root of 2,500 is 50

Practice

5. 4,318 + 1,901 = 6,219

6. 36 × 85 = 3,060

7. 2,852 × 5 = 14,260

8. 50 ÷ 6 → 8 R2

9. 333 − 291 = 42

Math Masters, p. 22

Writing/Reasoning Have students write a response to the following: *Was Jason correct when he said that 64 is a prime number in Problem 3? Explain your answer.* Sample answer: Jason was not correct. The factors of 64 are 1, 2, 4, 8, 16, 32, and 64. Because it has more than two factors, it is a composite number. A prime number has only two factors.

▶ Study Link 1·8

INDEPENDENT ACTIVITY

(*Math Masters*, p. 22)

Home Connection Students list all the factors of the first 4 square numbers, write numbers in exponential notation, and identify square roots.

3 Differentiation Options

ENRICHMENT

PARTNER ACTIVITY

15–30 Min

▶ Comparing Numbers with Their Squares

(*Math Masters*, p. 23)

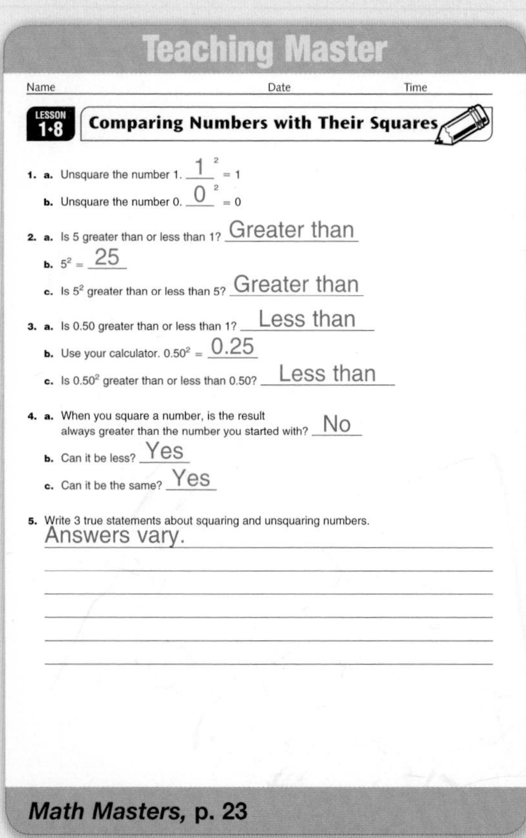

Teaching Master

Name Date Time

LESSON 1·8 **Comparing Numbers with Their Squares**

1. a. Unsquare the number 1. 1^2 = 1
   b. Unsquare the number 0. 0^2 = 0
2. a. Is 5 greater than or less than 1? Greater than
   b. 5^2 = 25
   c. Is 5^2 greater than or less than 5? Greater than
3. a. Is 0.50 greater than or less than 1? Less than
   b. Use your calculator. 0.50^2 = 0.25
   c. Is 0.50^2 greater than or less than 0.50? Less than
4. a. When you square a number, is the result always greater than the number you started with? No
   b. Can it be less? Yes
   c. Can it be the same? Yes
5. Write 3 true statements about squaring and unsquaring numbers. Answers vary.

Math Masters, p. 23

To further explore factoring numbers, have students investigate the relationship between numbers and their squares. Ask students to think about the following question as they work the problems for this activity: *When you square a number, will the result be greater than, less than, or equal to the number?*

Guide students to recognize that squaring a number does not necessarily result in a number that is greater than the original number. For example, both 0 and 1 are equal to their squares. (*See Problem 1.*) Ask students what they noticed about the numbers and relationships they found in Problem 3. The number 0.50 is a decimal; the square was smaller. Explain that the square of a number that is greater than 0, but less than 1, is always less than the original number. Ask volunteers to suggest other numbers between 0 and 1 for partners to square.

EXTRA PRACTICE

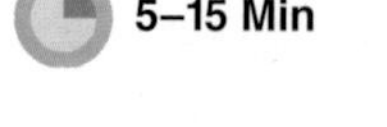

SMALL-GROUP ACTIVITY

5–15 Min

▶ *5-Minute Math*

To offer students more experience with using the square root sign, see *5-Minute Math,* page 108.

1•9 Factor Strings and Prime Factorizations

 **Objectives** To review equivalency concepts for whole numbers; and to introduce factor strings and prime factorization.

Technology Resources www.everydaymathonline.com

ePresentations

eToolkit

Algorithms Practice

EM Facts Workshop Game™

Family Letters

Assessment Management

Common Core State Standards

Curriculum Focal Points

Interactive Teacher's Lesson Guide

1 Teaching the Lesson

Key Concepts and Skills

- Find factor strings for numbers. [Number and Numeration Goal 3]
- Write the prime factorization for numbers. [Number and Numeration Goal 3]
- Rename numbers as factor strings or products of exponents. [Number and Numeration Goal 4]
- Use exponents to rename numbers. [Number and Numeration Goal 4]

Key Activities

Students use name-collection boxes to review the idea that numbers can be represented in many different ways. They represent composite numbers as factor strings, identify the prime factorization of a number, and use factor trees to find the prime factorization of numbers.

 **Ongoing Assessment: Informing Instruction** See page 58.

 **Ongoing Assessment: Recognizing Student Achievement** Use journal page 25. [Number and Numeration Goal 3]

Key Vocabulary

name-collection box ◆ factor string ◆ length of factor string ◆ prime factorization

Materials

Math Journal 1, pp. 25 and 26
Study Link 1•8
Math Masters, p. 25
quarter sheet of paper ◆ Class Data Pad

2 Ongoing Learning & Practice

Playing *Name That Number*
Student Reference Book, p. 325
per partnership: 4 each of number cards 0–9 (from the Everything Math Deck, if available), calculator
Students practice arithmetic operations to find equivalent names for numbers.

Math Boxes 1•9
Math Journal 1, p. 27
Students practice and maintain skills through Math Box problems.

Study Link 1•9
Math Masters, p. 24
Students practice and maintain skills through Study Link activities.

3 Differentiation Options

READINESS
Using the Sieve of Eratosthenes
Math Masters, pp. 26 and 27
Students identify the prime numbers between 1 and 30.

EXTRA PRACTICE
Practicing Multiplication Facts
Math Journal 1, p. 9
Math Masters, p. 11
Students use a multiplication facts routine.

ENRICHMENT
Exploring Palindromic Squares
Math Masters, p. 28
Students explore square numbers that are also palindromes.

Advance Preparation

Prepare a name-collection box for 16 on the Class Data Pad to use in the Math Message Follow-up.

For a mathematics and literacy connection, obtain a copy of ***12 Ways to Get to 11*** by Eve Merriam (Aladdin, 1996).

 ***Teacher's Reference Manual,* Grades 4–6** pp. 79–83

Getting Started

Mental Math and Reflexes

Write problems on the board or the Class Data Pad. Have students record their answers for each set of problems. At the end of each set, ask students to describe the pattern they see.

●○○ 5 ∗ 3 15
5 ∗ 30 150
5 ∗ 300 1,500
5 ∗ 3,000 15,000

●●○ 8 ∗ 7 56
8 ∗ __70__ = 560
8 ∗ __700__ = 5,600
8 ∗ __7,000__ = 56,000

●●● 60 ∗ __90__ = 5,400
60 ∗ __900__ = 54,000
600 ∗ __900__ = 540,000

Math Message

8 + 8 and 4 ∗ 4 are two names for the number 16. On a quarter-sheet of paper, write at least five other names for 16.

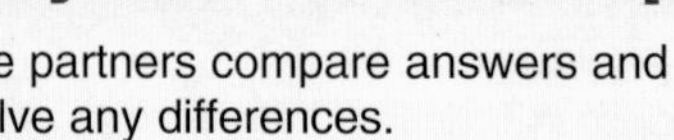

Study Link 1·8 Follow-Up

Have partners compare answers and resolve any differences.

NOTE Some students may benefit from doing the **Readiness** activity before you begin Part 1 of each lesson. See the Readiness activity in Part 3 for details.

Interactive whiteboard-ready ePresentations are available at www.everydaymathonline.com to help you teach the lesson.

16
4^2
$\sqrt{256}$
(4 + 6) ∗ 6 − 4 ∗ 11
XVI

A typical name-collection box for 16. There are infinite possibilities.

1 Teaching the Lesson

▶ Math Message Follow-Up

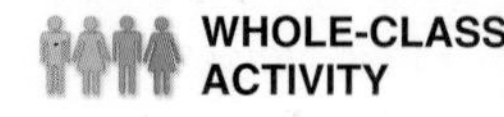

Representing a number in many equivalent ways is an important concept in *Everyday Mathematics*. Display a **name-collection box** for 16 on the Class Data Pad. (*See margin.*) Ask students to share equivalent names for 16, comparing each other's choices (and possibly thinking of new ones). Record equivalent names in the name-collection box.

Ongoing Assessment: Informing Instruction

Watch for students who write only addition or subtraction expressions in name-collection boxes. Encourage them to use more than one operation in their expressions and to use other types of numbers, such as square roots and exponents.

▶ Introducing Factor Strings

Explain that another form of an equivalent name for a number is called a **factor string.** A factor string is a multiplication expression that has at least two factors that are greater than 1. In a factor string, the number 1 may not be used as a factor. For example, a factor string for the number 24 is 2 ∗ 3 ∗ 4. To support English language learners, write *factor string* and its definition on the Class Data Pad. Include the example.

We compare factor strings by comparing their lengths. In the example, the factor string has three factors, so the **length of the factor string** is 3. Note that the turn-around rule for multiplication applies to factor strings: 2 ∗ 3 ∗ 4 and 3 ∗ 4 ∗ 2 are considered to be the same factor string.

▷ Ask students to find other factor strings for 24. Remind students to exclude 1 as a factor. Record all possible factor strings on the board. (*See margin.*)

Ask students to find the factor string for 7. Most students will automatically answer 1 ∗ 7. Ask: *What type of number is 7?* Prime number The number 1 may not be used in a factor string, so there are no factor strings for prime numbers.

▷ Have students find all possible factor strings for other numbers, such as 30, 50, 54, and 72. Record them in tables on the board.

▷ Share students' strategies for finding the longest factor strings. For example, for the number 36, you might start with 4 ∗ 9 and then rename 4 as 2 ∗ 2 and 9 as 3 ∗ 3. Another strategy is to try the prime numbers in order:

- Is 2 a factor of 36? Yes; so 36 = 2 ∗ 18
- Is 2 a factor of 18? Yes; so 36 = 2 ∗ 2 ∗ 9
- Is 2 a factor of 9? No
- Is 3 a factor of 9? Yes; so 36 = 2 ∗ 2 ∗ 3 ∗ 3

Adjusting the Activity

Remind students that divisibility rules can be used to find the prime factorization of a number. Model using the divisibility rules to find the prime factorization of 126. 2 ∗ 3 ∗ 3 ∗ 7

AUDITORY ◆ KINESTHETIC ◆ TACTILE ◆ VISUAL

Ask: *What kind of numbers are the factors in the longest possible factor string for any number?* Prime numbers The longest factor string for a number is called the **prime factorization** of the number. For example, the prime factorization of 24 is 2 ∗ 2 ∗ 2 ∗ 3. To support English language learners, write *prime factorization* and its definition the Class Data Pad. Include the example.

▶ Finding Factor Strings and Prime Factorization

PARTNER ACTIVITY
ELL

(*Math Journal 1,* pp. 25 and 26)

Have partners complete both journal pages. Circulate and assist. Problems 3 and 4 offer additional practice writing and decoding exponential notation. To support English language learners, clarify the meaning of *exponent* before students complete the journal page.

Student Page

Date Time

LESSON 1·9 **Factor Strings**

A **factor string** is a name for a number written as a product of two or more factors. In a factor string, 1 may not be used as a factor.

The **length of a factor string** is equal to the number of factors in the string. The longest factor string for a number is made up of prime numbers. The longest factor string for a number is called the **prime factorization** of that number.

Example:

Number	Factor Strings	Length
20	2 ∗ 10	2
	4 ∗ 5	2
	2 ∗ 2 ∗ 5	3

The order of the factors is not important. For example, 2 ∗ 10 and 10 ∗ 2 are the same factor string.

The longest factor string for 20 is 2 ∗ 2 ∗ 5. So the prime factorization of 20 is 2 ∗ 2 ∗ 5.

1. Find all the factor strings for each number below.

a.

Number	Factor Strings	Length
12	3 ∗ 4	2
	2 ∗ 6	2
	3 ∗ 2 ∗ 2	3

b.

Number	Factor Strings	Length
16	4 ∗ 4	2
	4 ∗ 2 ∗ 2	3
	8 ∗ 2	2
	2 ∗ 2 ∗ 2 ∗ 2	4

c.

Number	Factor Strings	Length
18	9 ∗ 2	2
	6 ∗ 3	2
	3 ∗ 3 ∗ 2	3

d.

Number	Factor Strings	Length
28	7 ∗ 4	2
	14 ∗ 2	2
	7 ∗ 2 ∗ 2	3

Math Journal 1, p. 25

Number	Factor String	Length
24	2 ∗ 3 ∗ 4	3
	4 ∗ 6	2
	2 ∗ 12	2
	3 ∗ 8	2
	2 ∗ 2 ∗ 6	3
	2 ∗ 2 ∗ 2 ∗ 3	4

Student Page

Date Time

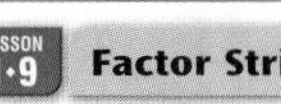

LESSON 1·9 **Factor Strings** *continued*

2. Write the prime factorization (the longest factor string) for each number.

a. 27 = 3 ∗ 3 ∗ 3
b. 40 = 2 ∗ 2 ∗ 2 ∗ 5
c. 36 = 2 ∗ 2 ∗ 3 ∗ 3
d. 42 = 2 ∗ 3 ∗ 7
e. 48 = 2 ∗ 2 ∗ 2 ∗ 2 ∗ 3
f. 60 = 2 ∗ 2 ∗ 3 ∗ 5
g. 100 = 2 ∗ 2 ∗ 5 ∗ 5

An **exponent** is a raised number that shows how many times the number to its left is used as a factor.

Examples: 5^2 ← exponent — 5^2 means 5 ∗ 5, which is 25. 5^2 is read as "5 squared" or as "5 to the second power."

10^3 ← exponent — 10^3 means 10 ∗ 10 ∗ 10, which is 1,000. 10^3 is read as "10 cubed" or as "10 to the third power."

2^4 ← exponent — 2^4 means 2 ∗ 2 ∗ 2 ∗ 2, which is 16. 2^4 is read as "2 to the fourth power."

3. Rewrite each number written in exponential notation as a product of factors. Then find the answer.

Examples: 2^3 = 2 ∗ 2 ∗ 2 = 8

2^2 ∗ 9 = 2 ∗ 2 ∗ 9 = 36

a. 10^4 = 10 ∗ 10 ∗ 10 ∗ 10 = 10,000

b. 3^2 ∗ 5 = 3 ∗ 3 ∗ 5 = 45

c. 2^4 ∗ 10^2 = 2 ∗ 2 ∗ 2 ∗ 2 ∗ 10 ∗ 10 = 1,600

4. Rewrite each product using exponents.

Examples: 5 ∗ 5 ∗ 5 = 5^3 5 ∗ 5 ∗ 3 ∗ 3 = 5^2 ∗ 3^2

a. 3 ∗ 3 ∗ 3 ∗ 3 = 3^4
b. 4 ∗ 7 ∗ 7 = 4 ∗ 7^2
c. 2 ∗ 5 ∗ 5 ∗ 7 = 2 ∗ 5^2 ∗ 7
d. 2 ∗ 2 ∗ 2 ∗ 5 ∗ 5 = 2^3 ∗ 5^2

Math Journal 1, p. 26

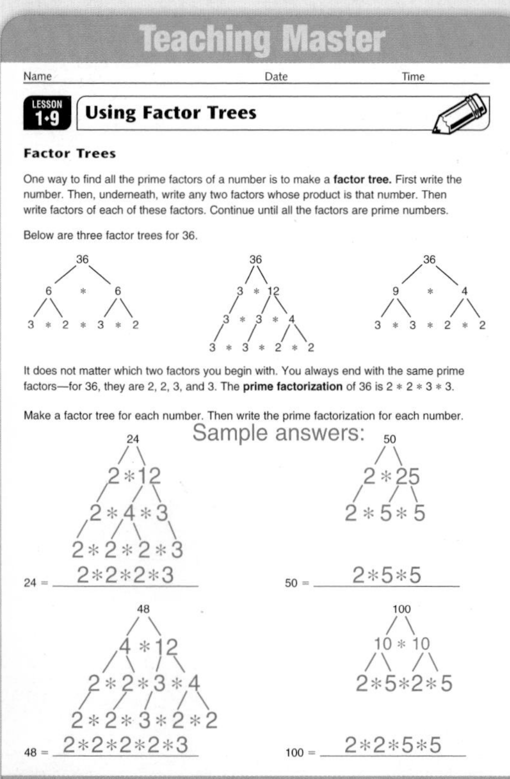

Teaching Master

Name Date Time

LESSON 1·9 **Using Factor Trees**

Factor Trees

One way to find all the prime factors of a number is to make a **factor tree.** First write the number. Then, underneath, write any two factors whose product is that number. Then write factors of each of these factors. Continue until all the factors are prime numbers.

Below are three factor trees for 36.

36 → 6 * 6 → 3 * 2 * 3 * 2

36 → 3 * 12 → 3 * 3 * 4 → 3 * 3 * 2 * 2

36 → 9 * 4 → 3 * 3 * 2 * 2

It does not matter which two factors you begin with. You always end with the same prime factors—for 36, they are 2, 2, 3, and 3. The **prime factorization** of 36 is 2 * 2 * 3 * 3.

Make a factor tree for each number. Then write the prime factorization for each number.

Sample answers:

24 → 2∗12 → 2∗4∗3 → 2∗2∗2∗3
24 = 2∗2∗2∗3

50 → 2∗25 → 2∗5∗5
50 = 2∗5∗5

48 → 4∗12 → 2∗2∗3∗4 → 2∗2∗3∗2∗2
48 = 2∗2∗2∗2∗3

100 → 10∗10 → 2∗5∗2∗5
100 = 2∗2∗5∗5

Math Masters, **p. 25**

Ongoing Assessment: Recognizing Student Achievement

Journal Page 25

Use **journal page 25** to assess students' facility with finding factors of a number. Students are making adequate progress if they have correctly written more than one factor string for each number.

[Number and Numeration Goal 3]

▶ Finding the Prime Factorization Using Factor Trees

WHOLE-CLASS ACTIVITY

PROBLEM SOLVING

(*Math Masters,* p. 25)

Explain that sometimes it is helpful to organize factors when we are looking for the longest factor string (the prime factorization). One way to do this is to make a factor tree. As a class, read the directions on the teaching master. Students then work together to find the prime factorization for the numbers 24 and 50. Circulate and assist.

2 Ongoing Learning & Practice

▶ Playing *Name That Number*

PARTNER ACTIVITY

PROBLEM SOLVING

(*Student Reference Book,* p. 325)

Students practice applying number properties, equivalent names, arithmetic operations, and basic facts by playing *Name That Number*.

▶ Math Boxes 1·9

INDEPENDENT ACTIVITY

(*Math Journal 1,* p. 27)

Mixed Practice Math Boxes in this lesson are paired with Math Boxes in Lessons 1-5 and 1-7. The skills in Problems 5 and 6 preview Unit 2 content.

▶ Study Link 1·9

INDEPENDENT ACTIVITY

(*Math Masters*, p. 24)

Home Connection Students write numbers with exponents as factor strings and vice versa. Then they find the prime factorization numbers and express the prime factorization using exponents.

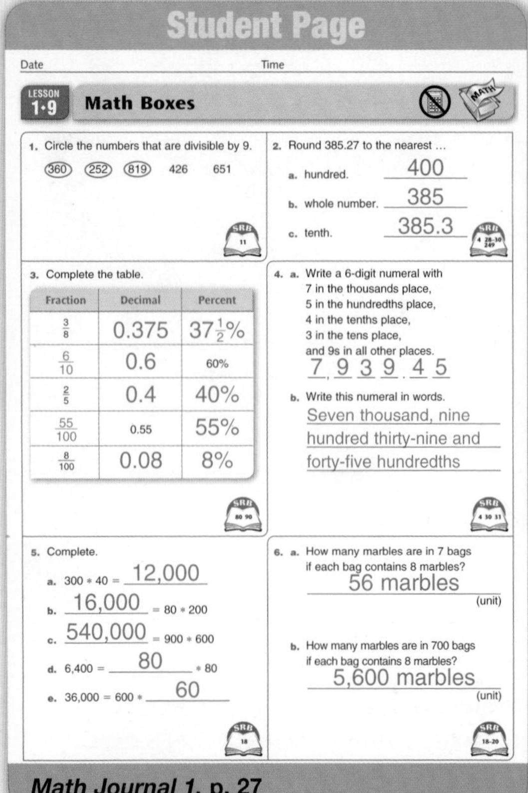

Student Page

Date Time

LESSON 1·9 **Math Boxes**

1. Circle the numbers that are divisible by 9.
(360) (252) (819) 426 651

2. Round 385.27 to the nearest ...
a. hundred. 400
b. whole number. 385
c. tenth. 385.3

3. Complete the table.

Fraction	Decimal	Percent
$\frac{3}{8}$	0.375	$37\frac{1}{2}\%$
$\frac{6}{10}$	0.6	60%
$\frac{2}{5}$	0.4	40%
$\frac{55}{100}$	0.55	55%
$\frac{8}{100}$	0.08	8%

4. a. Write a 6-digit numeral with 7 in the thousands place, 5 in the hundredths place, 4 in the tenths place, 3 in the tens place, and 9s in all other places.
7 9 3 9 . 4 5
b. Write this numeral in words.
Seven thousand, nine hundred thirty-nine and forty-five hundredths

5. Complete.
a. 300 ∗ 40 = 12,000
b. 16,000 = 80 ∗ 200
c. 540,000 = 900 ∗ 600
d. 6,400 = 80 ∗ 80
e. 36,000 = 600 ∗ 60

6. a. How many marbles are in 7 bags if each bag contains 8 marbles?
56 marbles (unit)
b. How many marbles are in 700 bags if each bag contains 8 marbles?
5,600 marbles (unit)

Math Journal 1, **p. 27**

3 Differentiation Options

READINESS

INDEPENDENT ACTIVITY

Using the Sieve of Eratosthenes

15–30 Min

(*Math Masters,* pp. 26 and 27)

Social Studies Link To explore the concept of prime numbers, have students use the Sieve of Eratosthenes to find the prime numbers. *Math Masters,* page 27 provides a grid that will allow students to identify all of the prime numbers from 1 to 30. Have students describe patterns they see in the marked-up grid. Encourage them to use vocabulary words such as *row, column,* and *diagonal.*

Math Masters, page 26
Problem 7 Answers 2, 3, 5, 7, 11, 13, 17, 19, 23, 29

EXTRA PRACTICE

SMALL-GROUP ACTIVITY

Practicing Multiplication Facts

5–15 Min

(*Math Journal 1,* p. 9; *Math Masters,* p. 11)

To provide additional practice of basic multiplication facts, have students use the facts routine introduced in Lesson 1-3. See *Teacher's Lesson Guide,* pages 28 and 29 to review the procedure.

ENRICHMENT

INDEPENDENT ACTIVITY

Exploring Palindromic Squares

15–30 Min

(*Math Masters,* p. 28)

To explore the relationship between numbers and their squares, have students find palindrome numbers by looking at the arrangement of their digits. Students list 3- and 4-digit palindrome numbers. Then they square these to find palindromic squares—the square of a palindrome number that is also a palindrome number.

Study Link Master

Name Date Time

STUDY LINK 1•9 **Exponents**

An **exponent** is a raised number that shows how many times the number to its left is used as a factor.

Examples: 5^2 ← exponent; 10^3 ← exponent; 2^4 ← exponent
5^2 means 5 ∗ 5, which is 25.
10^3 means 10 ∗ 10 ∗ 10, which is 1,000.
2^4 means 2 ∗ 2 ∗ 2 ∗ 2, which is 16.

1. Write each of the following as a factor string. Then find the product.
Example: 2^3 = 2∗2∗2 = 8
a. 10^4 = 10∗10∗10∗10 = 10,000
b. 7^2 = 7∗7 = 49
c. 20^3 = 20∗20∗20 = 8,000

2. Write each factor string using an exponent.
Example: 6 ∗ 6 ∗ 6 ∗ 6 = 6^4
a. 11 ∗ 11 = 11^2
b. 9 ∗ 9 ∗ 9 = 9^3
c. 50 ∗ 50 ∗ 50 ∗ 50 = 50^4

3. Write each of the following as a factor string that does *not* have any exponents. Then use your calculator to find the product.
Example: $2^3 * 3$ = 2 ∗ 2 ∗ 2 ∗ 3 = 24
a. $2 * 3^3 * 5^2$ = 2 ∗ 3 ∗ 3 ∗ 3 ∗ 5 ∗ 5 = 1,350
b. $2^4 * 4^2$ = 2 ∗ 2 ∗ 2 ∗ 2 ∗ 4 ∗ 4 = 256

4. Write the prime factorization of each number. Then write it using exponents.
Example: 18 = 2 ∗ 3 ∗ 3 = $2 * 3^2$
a. 40 = 2 ∗ 2 ∗ 2 ∗ 5 = $2^3 * 5$
b. 90 = 2 ∗ 3 ∗ 3 ∗ 5 = $2 * 3^2 * 5$

Practice

5. 6,383 − 1,342 = 5,041
6. 48 ∗ 15 = 720
7. 7)354 → 50 R4
8. 50,314 + 48,826 = 99,140
9. 84 ÷ 7 = 12
10. 701 ∗ 68 = 47,668

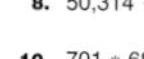

Math Masters, p. 24

Teaching Master

Name Date Time

LESSON 1•9 **Palindromic Squares**

Palindrome numbers are numbers that read the same forward or backward. A single-digit number is also a palindrome. The two-digit palindrome numbers are 11, 22, 33, 44, 55, 66, 77, 88, and 99. The table below lists samples of 3-digit and 4-digit palindromes.

1. Find 3-digit and 4-digit numbers to add to the table.
Sample answers:

Palindrome Numbers	
3-digit	4-digit
101, 111	1,001; 1,111
202, 222	2,002; 2,222
303, 333	3,003; 3,333
404, 414, 424, 434, 444	4,004; 4,114; 4,224; 4,334;
454, 464, 474, 484, 494	4,444; 4,554; 4,664; 4,774;
	4,884; 4,994

Sometimes finding the square of a palindrome number results in a square number that is also a palindrome number—a palindromic square. For example, 111^2 = 12,321.

2. Which 3 single-digit numbers have palindromic squares? 1, 2, and 3
3. Which 2-digit numbers have palindromic squares? 11 and 22
4. Find the numbers from the table that have a palindromic square and write the number model.
Example: 101^2 = 10,201
Sample answers: 111^2 = 12,321; 202^2 = 40,804; $1{,}001^2$ = 1,002,001; $1{,}111^2$ = 1,234,321

Math Masters, p. 28

1•10 Progress Check 1 

Objective To assess students' progress on mathematical content through the end of Unit 1.

1 Looking Back: Cumulative Assessment

The **Beginning-of-Year Assessment** in the *Assessment Handbook* is a written assessment that you may use to gauge students' readiness for the content they will encounter early in fifth grade.

 Input student data from Progress Check 1 and the Beginning-of-Year Assessment into the **Assessment Management Spreadsheets**.

Materials
- Study Link 1•9
- *Assessment Handbook,* pp. 52–59, 154–157, 216, and 246–249
- Beginning-of-Year Assessment (*Assessment Handbook,* pp. 51A, 51B, 227A–227D, and 242)
- slate

CONTENT ASSESSED	LESSON(S)	ASSESSMENT ITEMS				
		SELF	ORAL/SLATE	WRITTEN PART A	WRITTEN PART B	OPEN RESPONSE
Write whole numbers and decimals; identify the value of digits. [Number and Numeration Goal 1]	1•1, 1•5	6		7		
Factor numbers. [Number and Numeration Goal 3]	1•2–1•4, 1•6, 1•9	7		2, 5		✓
Identify numbers as prime and composite. [Number and Numeration Goal 3]	1•4, 1•6, 1•9	3	1	3, 4, 6		
Use prime factorization. [Number and Numeration Goal 3]	1•9	1			8	
Use rules of divisibility. [Number and Numeration Goal 3]	1•4, 1•5	5	2		11, 12	✓
Convert between exponential notation, repeated factor, and standard notation. [Number and Numeration Goal 4]	1•7–1•9	2	3, 4		8, 9, 10	
Demonstrate automaticity with multiplication fact extensions. [Operations and Computation Goal 2]	1•3–1•9	4	5			
Use arrays to model multiplication and division. [Operations and Computation Goal 7]	1•2, 1•3, 1•7			1		✓

2 Looking Ahead: Preparing for Unit 2

 **Math Boxes 1•10**

 **Home Link 1•10: Unit 2 Family Letter**

Materials
- *Math Journal 1,* p. 28
- *Math Masters,* pp. 29–32

Getting Started

Math Message • Self Assessment

Complete the Self Assessment. (Assessment Handbook, p. 154)

Study Link 1·9 Follow-Up

Have students compare answers and correct errors.

1 Looking Back: Cumulative Assessment

Math Message Follow-Up

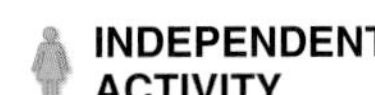

INDEPENDENT ACTIVITY

(Self Assessment, *Assessment Handbook*, p. 154)

The Self Assessment offers students the opportunity to reflect upon their progress.

Oral and Slate Assessments

WHOLE-CLASS ACTIVITY

Problems 1 and 5 provide summative information and can be used for grading purposes. Problems 2, 3, and 4 provide formative information that can be useful in planning future instruction.

Oral Assessment

1. Write the following:
   - an even number between 100 and 120 102, 104, 106, 108, 110, 112, 114, 116, 118
   - a prime number between 20 and 25 23
   - a composite number that is less than 100 Answers vary.
   - an odd number between 40 and 50; 41, 43, 45, 47, 49 *Keep your slate up if it is a prime number.* 41, 43, 47
2. Write 345 and 282 on the board or a transparency.
   - Is 345 divisible by 2? No By 3? Yes By 5? Yes By 6? No By 9? No By 10? No
   - Is 282 divisible by 2? Yes By 3? Yes By 4? No By 5? No By 6? Yes By 9? No By 10? No

Slate Assessment

3. What is 7 squared? 49 5 squared? 25 8 squared? 64 What number squared equals 16? 4
4. What is the square root of 36? 6 81? 9 100? 10 144? 12
5. Solve.
   - 8 ∗ 4 32 8 ∗ 40 320 80 ∗ 40 3,200
   - 90 ∗ 7 630 90 ∗ 70 6,300 900 ∗ 700 630,000

Assessment Master

Name ________ Date ________ Time ________

LESSON 1·10 **Self Assessment** Progress Check 1

Think about each skill listed below. Assess your progress by checking the most appropriate box.

Skills	I can do this on my own and explain how to do it.	I can do this on my own.	I can do this if I get help or look at an example.
1. Use prime factorization.			
2. Convert between exponential, repeated factor, and standard notation.			
3. Find and identify prime and composite numbers.			
4. Solve extended multiplication facts.			
5. Use divisibility tests to find factors and divisors.			
6. Read and write whole numbers through billions and decimals through thousandths.			
7. Factor numbers.			

Assessment Handbook, p. 154

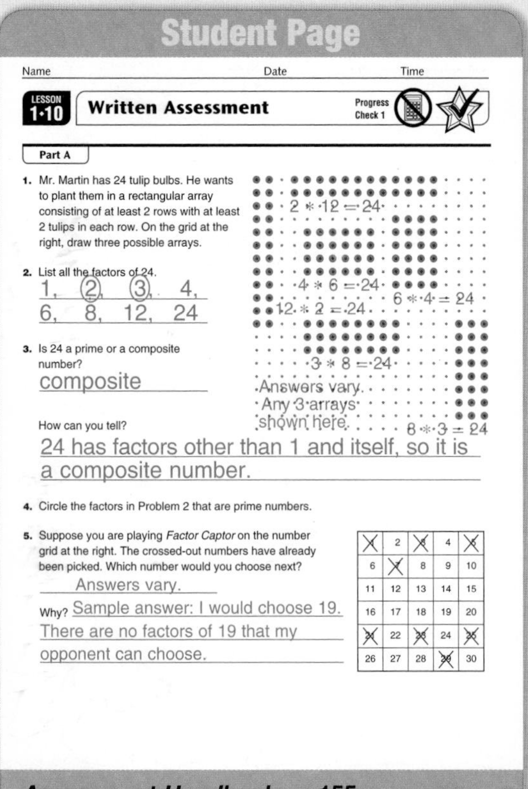
Student Page

Name ______ Date ______ Time ______

LESSON 1·10 **Written Assessment** Progress Check 1

Part A

1. Mr. Martin has 24 tulip bulbs. He wants to plant them in a rectangular array consisting of at least 2 rows with at least 2 tulips in each row. On the grid at the right, draw three possible arrays.
   2 * 12 = 24; 4 * 6 = 24; 6 * 4 = 24; 12 * 2 = 24; 3 * 8 = 24; 8 * 3 = 24
   Answers vary. Any 3 arrays shown here.
2. List all the factors of 24.
   1, (2), (3), 4, 6, 8, 12, 24
3. Is 24 a prime or a composite number?
   composite
   How can you tell?
   24 has factors other than 1 and itself, so it is a composite number.
4. Circle the factors in Problem 2 that are prime numbers.
5. Suppose you are playing *Factor Captor* on the number grid at the right. The crossed-out numbers have already been picked. Which number would you choose next?
   Answers vary.
   Why? Sample answer: I would choose 19. There are no factors of 19 that my opponent can choose.

X	2	X	4	X
6	X	8	9	10
11	12	13	14	15
16	17	18	19	20
X	22	X	24	X
26	27	28	X	30

Assessment Handbook, p. 155

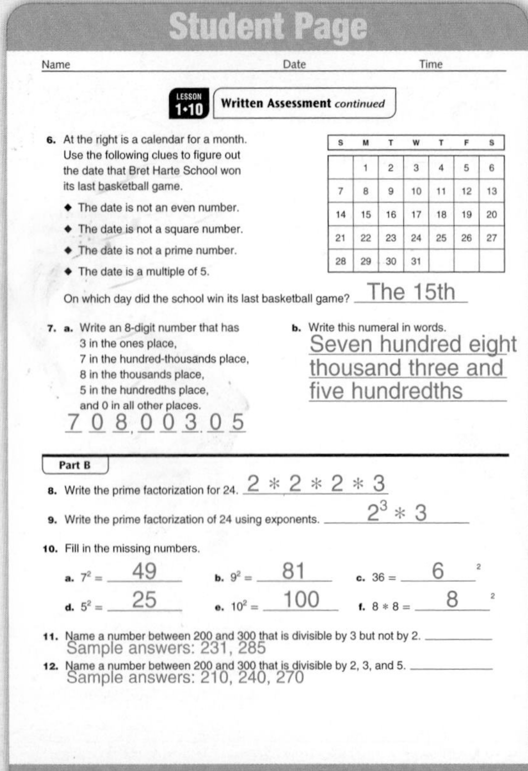
Student Page

Name ______ Date ______ Time ______

LESSON 1·10 **Written Assessment** *continued*

6. At the right is a calendar for a month. Use the following clues to figure out the date that Bret Harte School won its last basketball game.
   - The date is not an even number.
   - The date is not a square number.
   - The date is not a prime number.
   - The date is a multiple of 5.

S	M	T	W	T	F	S
	1	2	3	4	5	6
7	8	9	10	11	12	13
14	15	16	17	18	19	20
21	22	23	24	25	26	27
28	29	30	31			

   On which day did the school win its last basketball game? The 15th
7. a. Write an 8-digit number that has 3 in the ones place, 7 in the hundred-thousands place, 8 in the thousands place, 5 in the hundredths place, and 0 in all other places.
   7 0 8, 0 0 3. 0 5
   b. Write this numeral in words.
   Seven hundred eight thousand three and five hundredths

Part B

8. Write the prime factorization for 24. 2 * 2 * 2 * 3
9. Write the prime factorization of 24 using exponents. $2^3 * 3$
10. Fill in the missing numbers.
    a. 7^2 = 49 b. 9^2 = 81 c. 36 = 6^2
    d. 5^2 = 25 e. 10^2 = 100 f. 8 * 8 = 8^2
11. Name a number between 200 and 300 that is divisible by 3 but not by 2. Sample answers: 231, 285
12. Name a number between 200 and 300 that is divisible by 2, 3, and 5. Sample answers: 210, 240, 270

Assessment Handbook, p. 156

▶ Written Assessment

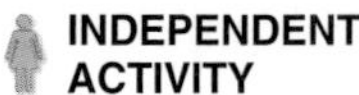

(*Assessment Handbook,* p. 155 and 156)

Everyday Mathematics students are expected to master a variety of mathematical concepts and skills over time. The curriculum frequently revisits topics, concepts, and skills. For this reason, the written assessment includes items recently introduced as well as items that assess long-term retention and mastery.

The written assessment is only one part of a balanced assessment plan. Use it along with other assessment tools in the program. See the *Assessment Handbook* for additional information.

Part A Recognizing Student Achievement

The Recognizing Student Achievement, or *summative,* part of the written assessment is designed to help teachers assess students' progress toward Grade 5 Goals. The items in this section can be used for grading purposes since the curriculum to this point has provided multiple exposures to the content of the problems that appear in this part.

Problem(s)	Description
1	Use arrays to model multiplication.
2, 5	Factor numbers.
3, 4, 6	Identify numbers as prime or composite.
7	Write whole numbers and decimals and identify the value of digits.

Part B Informing Instruction

The Informing Instruction, or *formative,* part of the written assessment can help teachers make decisions about how best to approach concepts and skills the next time they appear. The items in this part of the written assessment are intended to inform future instruction.

Problem(s)	Description
8	Write the prime factorization of a number.
9	Use exponents to write prime factorization.
10	Rename numbers in exponential and standard notations.
11, 12	Identify divisibility.

Use the checklists on pages 247 and 249 of the *Assessment Handbook* to record results. Then input the data into the **Assessment Management Spreadsheets** to keep an ongoing record of students' progress toward Grade-Level Goals.

Open Response

INDEPENDENT ACTIVITY

(*Assessment Handbook,* p. 157)

Divisibility

The open-response item requires students to apply skills and concepts from Unit 1 to solve a multistep problem. See *Assessment Handbook,* pages 55–59, for rubrics and students' work samples for this problem.

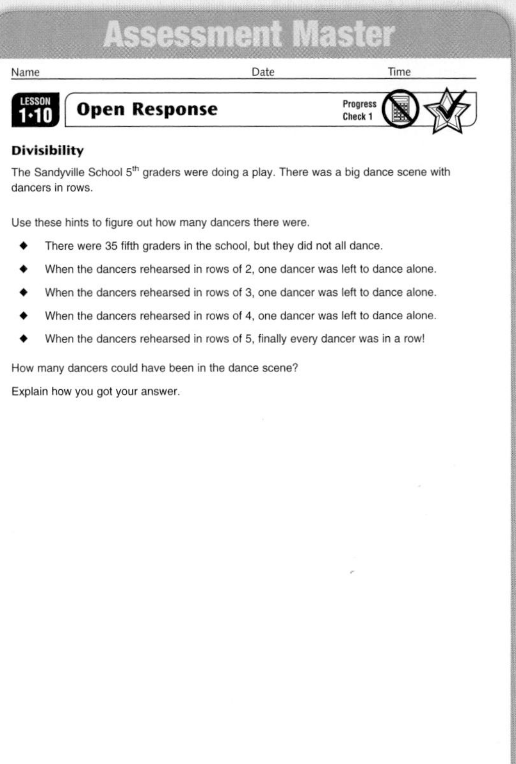
Assessment Master

Name Date Time

LESSON 1•10 **Open Response** Progress Check 1

Divisibility

The Sandyville School 5th graders were doing a play. There was a big dance scene with dancers in rows.

Use these hints to figure out how many dancers there were.

- There were 35 fifth graders in the school, but they did not all dance.
- When the dancers rehearsed in rows of 2, one dancer was left to dance alone.
- When the dancers rehearsed in rows of 3, one dancer was left to dance alone.
- When the dancers rehearsed in rows of 4, one dancer was left to dance alone.
- When the dancers rehearsed in rows of 5, finally every dancer was in a row!

How many dancers could have been in the dance scene?

Explain how you got your answer.

Assessment Handbook, **p. 157**

2 Looking Ahead: Preparing for Unit 2

Math Boxes 1•10

INDEPENDENT ACTIVITY

(*Math Journal 1,* p. 28)

Mixed Practice This Math Boxes page previews Unit 2 content.

Study Link 1•10: Unit 2 Family Letter

(*Math Masters,* pp. 29–32)

Home Connection The Unit 2 Family Letter provides parents and guardians with information and activities related to Unit 2 topics.

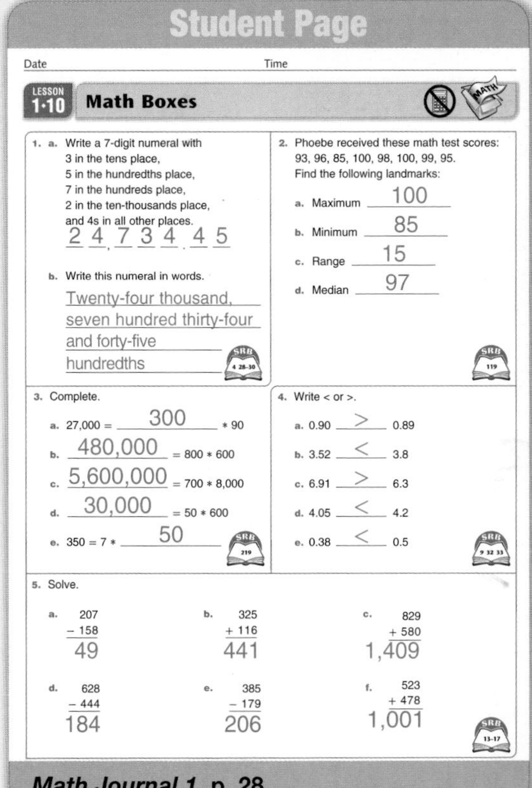
Student Page

Date Time

LESSON 1•10 **Math Boxes**

1. a. Write a 7-digit numeral with 3 in the tens place, 5 in the hundredths place, 7 in the hundreds place, 2 in the ten-thousands place, and 4s in all other places.
   2 4 , 7 3 4 . 4 5
   b. Write this numeral in words.
   Twenty-four thousand, seven hundred thirty-four and forty-five hundredths

2. Phoebe received these math test scores: 93, 96, 85, 100, 98, 100, 99, 95. Find the following landmarks:
   a. Maximum 100
   b. Minimum 85
   c. Range 15
   d. Median 97

3. Complete.
   a. 27,000 = 300 * 90
   b. 480,000 = 800 * 600
   c. 5,600,000 = 700 * 8,000
   d. 30,000 = 50 * 600
   e. 350 = 7 * 50

4. Write < or >.
   a. 0.90 > 0.89
   b. 3.52 < 3.8
   c. 6.91 > 6.3
   d. 4.05 < 4.2
   e. 0.38 < 0.5

5. Solve.
   a. 207 − 158 = 49
   b. 325 + 116 = 441
   c. 829 + 580 = 1,409
   d. 628 − 444 = 184
   e. 385 − 179 = 206
   f. 523 + 478 = 1,001

Math Journal 1, **p. 28**

Unit 2 Organizer

Estimation and Computation

Overview

Unit 2 addresses three topics: estimation, computational procedures, and data analyses. Algorithms for addition, subtraction, and multiplication are reviewed and extended to decimals. *Everyday Mathematics* continues to emphasize data analysis and probabilities linked to data gathering. Students also extend their understanding of numbers through an exploration that addresses the differences between millions, billions, and trillions. Unit 2 has six main areas of focus:

- To devise an estimation strategy to solve a problem,
- To subtract multidigit numbers using the trade-first and partial-differences methods,
- To review and apply vocabulary associated with chance events,
- To make magnitude estimates for products of multidigit numbers,
- To review and practice the partial-products and lattice methods for multiplication of numbers, and
- To understand the relative sizes of 1 million, 1 billion, and 1 trillion.

CCSS Linking to the Common Core State Standards

The content of Unit 2 addresses the Common Core State Standards for Mathematics in *Number and Operations in Base Ten*. The correlation of the Common Core State Standards to the *Everyday Mathematics* Grade 5 lessons begins on page CS1.

Contents

Learning In Perspective

	Lesson Objectives	Links to the Past	Links to the Future
2·1	To develop estimation strategies when finding an exact answer is impractical.	In Grade 4, students examine situations in which making an estimate is appropriate, and they practice estimating solutions.	In Grade 6, students develop estimation strategies for decimal operations.
2·2	To review place-value concepts and the use of the partial-sums and column-addition methods.	In Grade 4, students read and write numbers up to hundred-millions and extend basic concepts and notation for decimals to thousandths.	In Grade 6, students develop proficiency with the partial-sums algorithm for decimal addition.
2·3	To review the trade-first and partial-differences methods for subtraction.	In Grade 4, students review the trade-first and counting-up methods and are introduced to the partial-differences method of solving multidigit subtraction problems.	In Grade 6, students develop proficiency with the trade-first algorithm for decimal subtraction.
2·4	To review the use of mathematical models to solve number stories.	In Grade 4, students follow problem-solving steps and write open sentences for number stories.	In Grade 6, students solve inequalities; define equivalent equations; and use a systematic method to simplify and solve equations.
2·5	To provide experiences with estimating reaction times and with using statistical landmarks to describe experimental data.	In Grade 4, students organize and display data with a tally chart and determine the maximum, minimum, range, and mode of a set of data.	In Grade 6, students use larger data sets and more complicated contexts for data organization and analysis.
2·6	To review vocabulary associated with chance events and to introduce the Probability Meter.	In Grade 4, students review basic ideas of probability, including fairness and expected results. They compare predicted and actual results from an experiment with equally likely outcomes.	In Grade 6, students find probabilities for events when all of the outcomes are equally likely.
2·7	To provide experiences with making and using magnitude estimates for products of multidigit numbers, including decimals.	In Grade 4, students estimate whether a product is in the tens, hundreds, thousands, or greater.	In Grade 6, students estimate and calculate quotients of whole-number and decimal dividends.
2·8	To review the partial-products method for whole numbers and decimals.	In Grade 4, students extend the partial-products method of multiplication of whole numbers and decimals.	In Grade 6, students develop proficiency with the partial-products and lattice algorithms for decimal multiplication.
2·9	To review and provide practice with the lattice method for multiplication of whole numbers and decimals.	In Grade 4, students extend the lattice method of multiplication of whole numbers and decimals.	In Grade 6, students discuss the traditional shortcut for placing the decimal point correctly in decimal products.
2·10	To provide experience with comparing the relative sizes of 1 million, 1 billion, and 1 trillion and using a sample to make an estimate.	In Grade 4, students extend place value concepts to hundred-millions and place value as powers of 10.	In Grade 6, students read and write both large and small numbers in scientific notation.

	Key Concepts and Skills	Grade 5 Goals*
2•1	Find the median for a data set.	Data and Chance Goal 2
	Estimate linear distance using a map scale.	Measurement and Reference Frames Goal 1
	Convert between inches, feet, and miles.	Measurement and Reference Frames Goal 3
	Calculate travel times for a given distance at a given rate of speed.	Patterns, Functions, and Algebra Goal 1
2•2	Write numbers in expanded notation.	Number and Numeration Goal 1
	Use paper-and-pencil algorithms for multidigit addition problems.	Operations and Computation Goal 1
	Make magnitude estimates for addition.	Operations and Computation Goal 6
2•3	Explore algorithms for multidigit subtraction problems.	Operations and Computation Goal 1
	Make magnitude estimates for subtraction.	Operations and Computation Goal 6
2•4	Solve addition and subtraction problems for whole numbers and decimals.	Operations and Computation Goal 1
	Make magnitude estimates for addition and subtraction number stories.	Operations and Computation Goal 6
	Use open number sentences to solve number stories.	Patterns, Functions, and Algebra Goal 2
2•5	Read and write decimals to the hundredths place.	Number and Numeration Goal 1
	Order decimals to the hundredths place.	Number and Numeration Goal 6
	Use line plots to organize reaction-time data.	Data and Chance Goal 1
	Find statistical landmarks.	Data and Chance Goal 2
	Compare and draw conclusions about collected data.	Data and Chance Goal 2
2•6	Record data in a table.	Data and Chance Goal 1
	Find landmarks for a data set.	Data and Chance Goal 2
	Describe events using basic probability terms.	Data and Chance Goal 3
	Predict the outcome and respond to the results of a thumbtack experiment.	Data and Chance Goal 4
	Express the probability of an event as a fraction, decimal, or percent.	Data and Chance Goal 4
2•7	Use place value to make magnitude estimates for products.	Number and Numeration Goal 1
	Make magnitude estimates for problems.	Operations and Computation Goal 6
	Round numbers to make magnitude estimates for multiplication problems.	Operations and Computation Goal 6
2•8	Solve whole-number and decimal problems using the partial-products algorithm.	Operations and Computation Goal 3
	Make magnitude estimates.	Operations and Computation Goal 6
	Use magnitude estimates to place the decimal point in products.	Operations and Computation Goal 6
2•9	Apply multiplication facts.	Operations and Computation Goal 2
	Use the lattice method for multiplying whole numbers and decimals.	Operations and Computation Goal 3
	Use magnitude estimates to verify lattice method solutions.	Operations and Computation Goal 6
2•10	Read and write large numbers.	Number and Numeration Goal 1
	Compare order of magnitude for large numbers.	Number and Numeration Goal 6
	Make reasonable estimates for whole number multiplication problems.	Operations and Computation Goal 6

*See the Appendix for a complete list of Grade 5 Goals.

A Balanced Curriculum

Ongoing Practice

Everyday Mathematics provides numerous opportunities for ongoing practice. These activities are embedded throughout the lessons:

Mental Math and Reflexes activities promote speed and accuracy in mental computation.

Math Boxes offer mixed practice and are paired across lessons as shown in the brackets below. This makes them useful as assessment tools. The last one or two boxes on each page preview the next unit's content.

Mixed practice	[2•1, 2•3], [2•2, 2•4], [2•5, 2•7], [2•6, 2•9], [2•8, 2•10]
Mixed practice with multiple choice	2•1, 2•8, 2•10
Mixed practice with writing/reasoning opportunity	2•2, 2•3, 2•4, 2•5, 2•6, 2•7

Study Links are daily homework assignments that review the content of the lesson and often contain ongoing facts practice or computation practice.

5-Minute Math problems are offered for additional practice in Lessons 2•7 and 2•9.

EM Facts Workshop Game provides online practice of basic facts and computation.

EXTRA PRACTICE **Extra Practice** activities are included in Lessons 2•7, 2•9, and 2•10.

Practice through Games

Games are an essential component of practice in the *Everyday Mathematics* program. Games offer skills practice and promote strategic thinking. See the *Differentiation Handbook* for ways to adapt games to meet students' needs.

Lesson	Game	Skill Practiced
2•2	*Addition Top-It* (Decimal Version)	Using addition methods with decimals [OC Goal 1]
2•3	*Subtraction Target Practice* (Decimal Version)	Practicing subtraction with decimals [OC Goal 1]
2•4	*Name That Number*	Practicing arithmetic operations [NN Goal 4]
2•5	*High-Number Toss: Decimal Version*	Writing and comparing decimals [NN Goals 1 and 6]
2•7	*Multiplication Bull's-Eye*	Practicing estimating products [OC Goal 6]
2•9	*Factor Bingo*	Practicing skills relating to factoring [NN Goal 3]
2•10	*High-Number Toss*	Reading, writing, and comparing large numbers [NN Goals 1 and 6]
2•10	*Number Top-It*	Reading and comparing large numbers [NN Goals 1 and 6]

[NN] Number and Numeration
[MRF] Measurement and Reference Frames
[OC] Operations and Computation
[GEO] Geometry
[DC] Data and Chance
[PFA] Patterns, Functions, and Algebra

Problem Solving 

Experts at problem solving and mathematical modeling generally do these things:

- Identify the problem.
- Decide what information is needed to solve the problem.
- Play with and study the data to find patterns and meaning.
- Identify and use mathematical procedures to solve the problem.
- Decide whether the solution makes sense and whether it can be applied to other problems.

The table below lists some of the opportunities in this unit for students to practice these strategies.

Lessons that teach *through* problem solving, not just *about* problem solving

Lesson	Activity
2•1	Find how many footsteps you will have to take to get to a destination.
2•4, 2•8	Solve number stories involving addition and subtraction.
2•5	Find which of your hands has a quicker reaction time.
2•6	Find what the chance is that a thumbtack will land point down.
2•10	Find how long it would take you to tap your desk 1 million times, without any interruptions.

See Chapter 18: Problem Solving in the *Teacher's Reference Manual* for more information.

The Language of Mathematics

Everyday Mathematics provides lesson-specific suggestions to help all students acquire, process, and express mathematical ideas. Throughout Unit 2, there are lesson-specific language development notes that address the needs of English language learners, indicated by ELL.

ELL SUPPORT Activities to support English language learners are in Part 3 of Lesson 2•2.

The *English Learners Handbook* and the *Differentiation Handbook* have suggestions for promoting language development and acquisition of mathematics vocabulary. See Unit 2 in each handbook.

Unit 2 Vocabulary

algorithm
ballpark estimate
certain
column-addition method
difference
digit
elapsed time
estimate
expanded notation
false number sentence
impossible
lattice
lattice method
magnitude estimate
maximum
mean (average)
median
minimum
minuend
mode
number sentence
open number sentence
operation symbol
partial-differences method
partial-products method
partial-sums method
place
place value
Probability Meter Poster
range
reaction time
relation symbol
sample
solution
stimulus
subtrahend
trade-first method
true number sentence
value
variable

Literacy Connection

Counting on Frank, by Rod Clement, Houghton Mifflin, 2006

How Much Is a Million? by David M. Schwartz, HarperCollins Publishers, 1985

For more literacy connections, see the *Home Connection Handbook,* Grades 4–6.

Cross-Curricular Links 

Social Studies – Lesson 2•1

Science – Lesson 2•5

Language Arts – Lesson 2•2

Balanced Assessment

Daily Assessments

- **Recognizing Student Achievement** – A daily assessment that is included in every lesson to evaluate students' progress toward the Grade 5 Grade-Level Goals.
- **Informing Instruction** – Notes that appear throughout the unit to help anticipate students' common errors and suggest appropriate problem-solving strategies.

Lesson	Recognizing Student Achievement	Informing Instruction
2•1	Solve extended facts problems mentally. [OC Goal 2]	
2•2	Solve multidigit addition problems. [OC Goal 1]	
2•3	Use the trade-first method with subtraction problems. [OC Goal 1]	
2•4	Write open number sentences to model given situations. [PFA Goal 2]	
2•5	Compare decimals. [NN Goal 6]	
2•6	Explain the structure of the Probability Meter. [NN Goal 5]	Identify denominators.
2•7	Add and subtract whole numbers. [OC Goal 1]	Recognize place-value columns as multiples of powers of 10.
2•8	Make reasonable magnitude estimates based on number sentences. [OC Goal 6]	Use expanded notation to identify the value of digits in numbers.
2•9	Use a multiplication method. [OC Goal 3]	Use the lattice multiplication facts table.
2•10	Know place value and compare numbers. [NN Goals 1 and 6]	Develop a strategy and make an estimate.

[NN] Number and Numeration
[MRF] Measurement and Reference Frames
[OC] Operations and Computation
[GEO] Geometry
[DC] Data and Chance
[PFA] Patterns, Functions, and Algebra

Portfolio Opportunities

The following lessons provide opportunities to gather samples of students' mathematical writings, drawings, and creations to add balance to the assessment process: Lessons 2•2, 2•3, 2•4, 2•5, 2•6, 2•7, 2•9, and 2•11.

See pages 16 and 17 in the *Assessment Handbook* for more information about portfolios and how to use them.

Unit Assessment

Progress Check 2 – A cumulative assessment of concepts and skills taught in Unit 2 and in the previous unit, providing information for evaluating students' progress and planning for future instruction. These assessments include oral/slate, written, and open-response activities, as shown below in the sample Progress Check lesson opener.

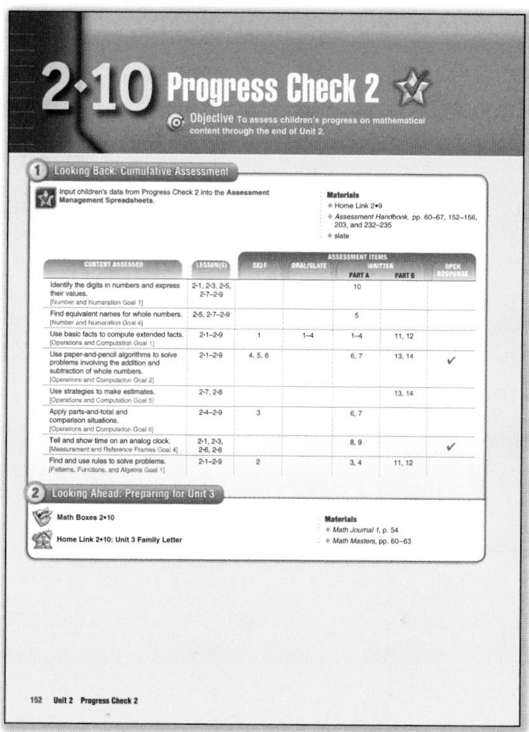

2•10 Progress Check 2

Objective To assess children's progress on mathematical content through the end of Unit 2.

1 Looking Back: Cumulative Assessment

Input children's data from Progress Check 2 into the **Assessment Management Spreadsheets.**

Materials
- Home Link 2•9
- *Assessment Handbook,* pp. 60–67, 152–156, 203, and 232–235
- slate

Content Assessed	Lesson(s)	Assessment Items: Self	Oral/Slate	Written: Part A	Written: Part B	Open Response
Identify the digits in numbers and express their values. [Number and Numeration Goal 1]	2•1, 2•3, 2•5, 2•7–2•9			10		
Find equivalent names for whole numbers. [Number and Numeration Goal 4]	2•5, 2•7–2•9			5		
Use basic facts to compute extended facts. [Operations and Computation Goal 1]	2•1–2•9	1	1–4	1–4	11, 12	
Use paper-and-pencil algorithms to solve problems involving the addition and subtraction of whole numbers. [Operations and Computation Goal 2]	2•1–2•9	4, 5, 6		6, 7	13, 14	✓
Use strategies to make estimates. [Operations and Computation Goal 5]	2•7, 2•8				13, 14	
Apply parts-and-total and comparison situations. [Operations and Computation Goal 6]	2•4–2•9	3		6, 7		
Tell and show time on an analog clock. [Measurement and Reference Frames Goal 4]	2•1, 2•3, 2•6, 2•8			8, 9		✓
Find and use rules to solve problems. [Patterns, Functions, and Algebra Goal 1]	2•1–2•9	2		3, 4	11, 12	

2 Looking Ahead: Preparing for Unit 3

Math Boxes 2•10

Home Link 2•10: Unit 3 Family Letter

Materials
- *Math Journal 1,* p. 54
- *Math Masters,* pp. 60–63

152 **Unit 2 Progress Check 2**

Core Assessment Resources

Assessment Handbook

- **Unit 2 Assessment Overview,** pages 60–67
- **Unit 2 Assessment Masters,** pages 158–163
- **Unit 2 Individual Profiles of Progress,** pages 250, 251, and 302
- **Unit 2 Class Checklists,** pages 252, 253, and 303
- **Math Logs,** pages 306–308
- **Exit Slip,** page 311
- **Other Student Assessment Forms,** pages 304, 305, 309, and 310

Assessment Management Spreadsheets

The Assessment Management Spreadsheets consist of the Digital Class Checklists and Individual Profile of Progress Checklists. Use them to monitor, record, and report student progress.

Addressing All Needs

Differentiated Instruction

Adjusting the Activity – suggests adaptations that target advanced learners, English language learners, or learners who need additional instructional support.

ELL SUPPORT / ELL – provides lesson-specific suggestions to help English language learners understand and process the mathematical content.

READINESS – accesses students' prior knowledge or previews content that prepares students to engage in the lesson's Part 1 activities.

EXTRA PRACTICE – provides additional opportunities to apply the mathematical content of the lesson.

ENRICHMENT – enables students to apply or further explore the mathematical content of the lesson.

Lesson	Adjusting the Activity	ELL Support/ ELL	Readiness	Extra Practice	Enrichment
2•1	•		•		•
2•2	•	•	•		•
2•3		•	•		•
2•4		•	•		•
2•5	•	•	•		•
2•6	•		•		•
2•7		•	•	•	•
2•8		•	•		•
2•9				•	•
2•10			•	•	•

Additional Resources

Differentiation Handbook
Provides ideas and strategies for differentiating instruction.
Pages 57–63

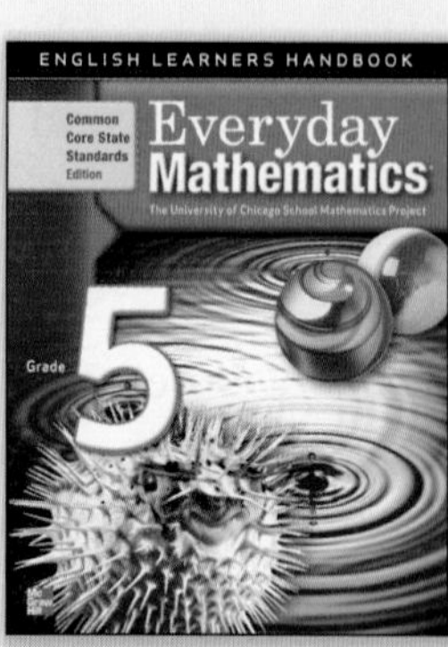

English Learners Handbook
Contains lesson-specific comprehension strategies.
Pages 10–19

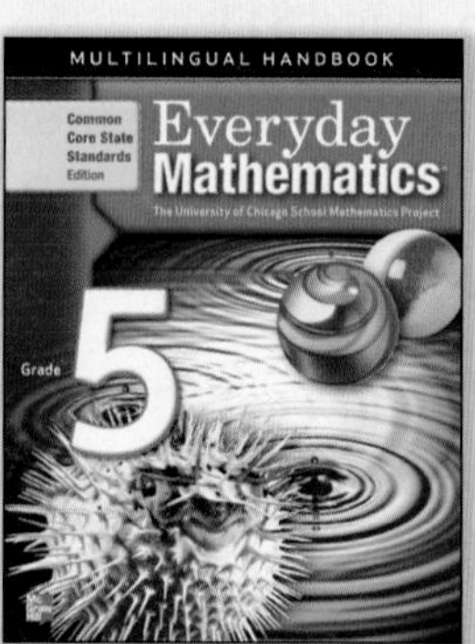

Multilingual Handbook
Previews concepts and vocabulary. It is written in six languages.
Pages 19–38

Planning Tips

Multiage Classroom

Companion Lessons from Grades 4 and 6 can help you meet instructional needs of a multiage classroom. The full Scope and Sequence can be found in the Appendix.

Grade 4		2•3, 2•4, 2•7, 4•5	2•3, 2•4, 4•5	3•6, 3•9, 6•1			5•4	3•2–3•4, 5•1	3•2–3•4, 5•7	5•8	
Grade 5	**2•1**	**2•2**	**2•3**	**2•4**	**2•5**	**2•6**	**2•7**	**2•8**	**2•9**	**2•10**	**2•11**
Grade 6		2•3	2•3	6•3		7•1–7•3		2•5, 2•6		2•1	

Pacing for Success

Pacing depends on a number of factors, such as students' individual needs and how long your school has been using *Everyday Mathematics*. At the beginning of Unit 2, you may want to use tools available at www.everydaymathonline.com to help you set your pace.

Home Support

Unit 2 Family Letter (English/Spanish) provides families with an overview, Do-Anytime Activities, Building Skills through Games, a list of vocabulary, and answers to the daily homework (Study Links). Family Letters in English, Spanish, and seven other languages are also available online.

Study Links are the daily homework assignments. They consist of active projects and ongoing review problems.

Home Support Resources

Home Connection Handbook
Offers ideas and reproducible masters for communicating with families. See Table of Contents for unit information.

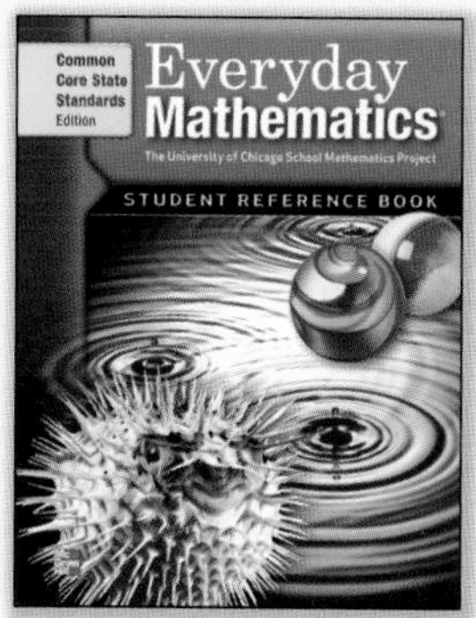

Student Reference Book
Provides a resource for students and parents.

Pages 5, 13–21, 28–30, 35, 36, 38–40, 119–121, 226, 227, 242, 243, 249, 321, 323, 325, 326, 331, 333, 339, 398, 402

Technology Resources

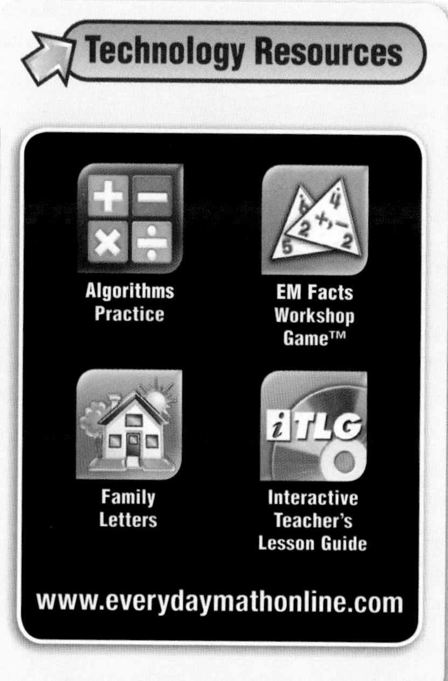

Materials

Technology Resources www.everydaymathonline.com

ePresentations

eToolkit

Algorithms Practice

EM Facts Workshop Game™

Family Letters

Assessment Management

Common Core State Standards

Curriculum Focal Points

Interactive Teacher's Lesson Guide

Lesson	Masters	Manipulative Kit	Other Items
2•1	Study Link Master, p. 33 Teaching Masters, pp. 34 and 35	per group: yardstick, meterstick, or tape measure	per group: road map, 1 page from a residential telephone directory; clock or watch; calculator
2•2	Teaching Aid Master, p. 415 Study Link Master, p. 36 Teaching Masters, pp. 37 and 38 *Differentiation Handbook,* p. 142	per group: 4 each of number cards 1–10; base-10 blocks; slate	2 counters
2•3	Teaching Masters, pp. 40 and 415 Study Link Master, p. 39	per group: 4 each of number cards 1–10; slate; per group: 120 wooden craft sticks or straws, rubber bands or twist-ties	counters
2•4	Teaching Masters, pp. 41, 42, 44, and 45 Teaching Aid Master, p. 415 Study Link Master, p. 43	per partnership: 1 complete deck of number cards	
2•5	Study Link Master, p. 46 Teaching Masters, pp. 47 and 48	per partnership: 4 each of number cards 0–9	timer such as a stopwatch, a digital watch, or a clock; stick-on notes; scissors; calculator
2•6	Teaching Aid Master, p. 414* Study Link Master, p. 49 Teaching Masters, pp. 50–52 Game Master, p. 511		*Probability Meter* Poster; per group: stick-on note; 10 thumbtacks, two-color counters, or pennies; small cup; scissors; calculator
2•7	Study Link Master, p. 53 Teaching Masters, pp. 54 and 66A	per partnership: 4 each of number cards 0–9; 1 six-sided die	
2•8	Teaching Aid Master, p. 415* Study Link Master, p. 55 Teaching Masters, pp. 56 and 57 Transparencies of *Math Masters,* pp. 416 and 417	per partnership: base-10 blocks	per group: dry-erase marker and eraser
2•9	Teaching Masters, pp. 58 and 60 Teaching Aid Masters, pp. 414 and 418 Study Link Master, p. 59 Game Master, p. 452	4 each of number cards 2–9	Geometry Template; 12 pennies or counters
2•10	Study Link Master, p. 61 Teaching Masters, pp. 62 and 66B Game Masters, pp. 487, 491, and 492	per group: 4 each of number cards 0–9	Class Data Pad; blank paper or construction paper; markers or crayons; watch or timer with second hand; calculator
2•11	Assessment Masters, pp. 158–163 Study Link Masters, pp. 63–66	slate	

*Denotes optional materials

Mathematical Background

The discussion below highlights the major content ideas presented in Unit 2 and helps establish instructional priorities.

Estimation Challenge (Lesson 2◆1)

The Estimation Challenge is an *Everyday Mathematics* routine presented several times during the year. Students will develop effective estimation strategies to solve problems where finding an exact answer is difficult, time consuming, or even impossible. Typically, the problem will be introduced in class and discussed briefly. Then students will be given one or more days to think about the problem and prepare their estimates. The spirit of the challenge is one of open inquiry to promote both estimation skills and problem formulation.

Refer to the *Teacher's Reference Manual,* Section 16.1, for more information about estimation.

Addition and Subtraction Algorithms (Lessons 2◆2 and 2◆3)

Lessons 2-2 and 2-3 focus on algorithms for addition and subtraction. Students first review methods for adding and subtracting multidigit whole numbers. These methods are then extended to decimals.

Computational algorithms are systematic procedures, and they are important in mathematics. In this calculator and computer age, however, the plain truth is that if a person has many calculations to do, the sensible choice is to reach for a calculator, to program the calculations into a computer, or to use a computer spreadsheet or other software to make the calculations. This is not to say that students should not learn to perform paper-and-pencil calculations, but students must also develop the number sense to understand calculations, their relationships, and applications.

Read more about addition and subtraction algorithms in Sections 11.2.1 and 11.2.2 of the *Teacher's Reference Manual.*

Magnitude Estimates (Lesson 2◆7)

It is often useful to know a rough answer to a problem: Is the number less than 1? Is it in the hundreds? In the thousands? In the millions? In the billions? In science and in other applications, "orders of magnitude" are powers of 10, and magnitude estimates are powers-of-10 estimates.

The magnitude-estimate routine invites students to estimate the magnitude of answers to problems in advance. Eventually this routine will become intuitive when students are solving problems: "Is the answer I'm looking for in the tens? Hundreds? Thousands?" With well-developed intuition, students know when they have gotten an inaccurate result on a calculator or when information doesn't make sense.

For more information about magnitude estimates, refer to Sections 16.1 and 16.2 in the *Teacher's Reference Manual.*

Note

Students should not use their calculators while exploring and practicing the algorithms for adding and subtracting multidigit numbers. The journal pages, Study Links, and Assessment Masters with these lessons are marked with the "no-calculator" icon to remind students of this. However, calculator usage is encouraged in other parts of the program. For example, students might use a calculator in solving an Estimation Challenge or the problems in Lesson 2-10.

Project Note

To teach U.S. traditional addition and subtraction, see Algorithm Projects 1, 2, 3, and 4.

About how many blueberries do you think are in this bowl?

Project Notes

To teach U.S. traditional multiplication, see Algorithm Projects 5 and 6.

Use Project 3, An Ancient Multiplication Algorithm, to examine a multiplication algorithm that was invented in Egypt more than 4,000 years ago.

Use Project 4, "Magic" Computation Tricks, to figure out, perform, and explain computation tricks.

Multiplication Algorithms

(Lessons 2•8 and 2•9)

In *Third* and *Fourth Grade Everyday Mathematics,* students were introduced to two multiplication algorithms: the partial-products algorithm and the lattice algorithm.

The partial-products algorithm reinforces place-value skills, supports mental arithmetic, and provides practice with column addition. It encourages students to say to themselves which numbers, rather than which digits, are being multiplied. For example, in the problem below, the first partial product is not 3 times 7, but 30 seventies, or 30 * 70.

The lattice algorithm, an ancient method invented in India, is popular with students because it requires only simple computations and makes it fairly easy to get a correct answer.

Both multiplication algorithms easily extend to decimals.

See Section 11.2.3 in the *Teacher's Reference Manual* for more information on multiplication algorithms.

The Partial Products Algorithm

75	
* 32	
2100	(30 * 70)
150	(30 * 5)
140	(2 * 70)
10	(2 * 5)
2400	

Lattice algorithm

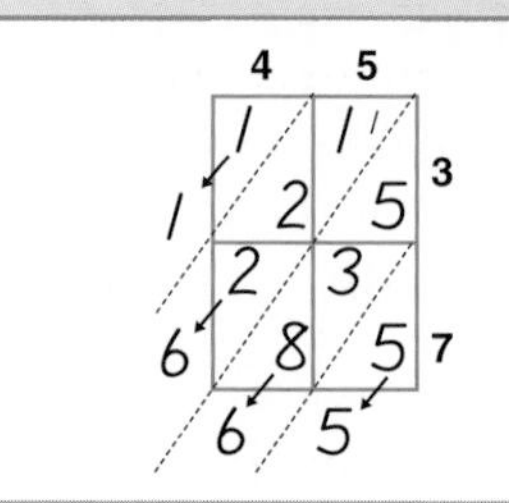

Note

For students who have already learned reliable addition and subtraction algorithms, these lessons remind them that there is more than one way to solve a problem. Students who are still struggling have another opportunity to learn reliable methods that will work for them.

Everyday Mathematics exposes students to several methods for operations with whole numbers and decimals. For each operation, all students are expected to know a particular algorithm. But they are encouraged to use whatever algorithm they like to solve problems.

Using Open Sentences in Problem Solving (Lesson 2•4)

Beginning in Grade 1, students have used situation diagrams to help them solve number stories and to summarize their solutions with number sentences. In Grade 4, students used diagrams to help them write and solve open sentences (sentences containing a variable) for number stories. In Lesson 2-4, situation diagrams are used to help students transition to fifth grade number stories and the writing of open sentences for number stories without first using a situation diagram. (See the *Teacher's Reference Manual* for a discussion of situation diagrams.) Work with number sentences will be extended throughout fifth and sixth grades in *Everyday Mathematics,* thus providing a solid foundation for the content of future middle- and high-school mathematics courses.

Learn more about using open sentences in problem solving in Sections 1.3.5 and 17.2.4 of the *Teacher's Reference Manual.*

Collecting, Organizing, and Describing Data (Lessons 2•5 and 2•6)

Working with data provides both context and motivation for developing number skills and for practicing computation strategies. Many sources of data will be used during the school year. Students will gather their data in various ways. The lessons in this unit rely on counting and measuring in the classroom. In future lessons, students will collect data by observing and measuring at home, by taking surveys, and by recording information from reference books.

In Lesson 2-5 students use data landmarks maximum, minimum, median, mean, and mode as reference points when they discuss features of the data. This is similar to cartographers' use of landmarks when they discuss maps.

The Probability Meter Poster is introduced in Lesson 2-6. It is used to record the data results that describe the chances or probabilities of events, and is big enough to accommodate large displays of collected chance results—for a single day, or for much longer. The meter is a number line from 0 to 1 that is marked to show fraction, decimal, and percent divisions. It can be used to find equivalent fractions, to convert fractions to decimals or to percents, to compare fractions or decimals, and so on.

Note

The Grab-it Gauge used in Lesson 2-5 to measure reaction time has been calibrated to show the distance that an object will drop during the first $\frac{1}{4}$ second of free fall. (Because a falling object accelerates and will drop 4 feet during the first $\frac{1}{2}$ second, the gauge would have to be 4 feet long to measure reaction times up to $\frac{1}{2}$ second.)

Consult Sections 12.1 and 12.2 in the *Teacher's Reference Manual* to learn more about collecting, organizing, and describing data.

Comparing Millions, Billions, and Trillions (Lesson 2•10)

Lesson 2-10 is designed to provide exposure to the magnitude of large numbers. Few people comprehend what "1,000 times as much" really means. To help students grasp the concept of 1,000 times, you might provide examples like the following:

- What can you buy with $2 versus $2,000? $20 versus $20,000?
- What type of transportation might you use to travel 24 miles? 24,000 miles?
- How long might it take you to read 2 pages of a book? 2,000 pages?

For more information about estimating and comparing between millions, billions, and trillions, refer to Sections 16.1 and 16.2 in the *Teacher's Reference Manual.*

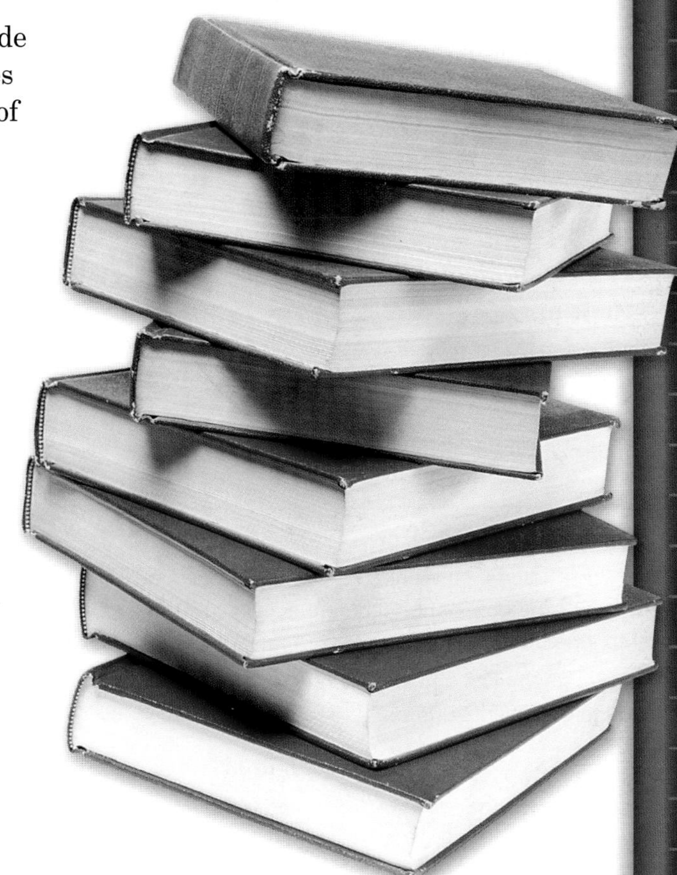

2•1 Estimation Challenge

Objective To develop estimation strategies when finding an exact answer is impractical.

Technology Resources www.everydaymathonline.com

EMePresentations Intervention System

eToolkit

Algorithms Practice

EM Facts Workshop Game™

Family Letters

Assessment Management

Common Core State Standards

Curriculum Focal Points

Interactive Teacher's Lesson Guide

1 Teaching the Lesson

Key Concepts and Skills

- Find the median for a data set. [Data and Chance Goal 2]
- Estimate linear distance using a map scale. [Measurement and Reference Frames Goal 1]
- Convert between inches, feet, and miles. [Measurement and Reference Frames Goal 3]
- Calculate travel times for a given distance at a given rate of speed. [Patterns, Functions, and Algebra Goal 1]

Key Activities

Students develop strategies to estimate the time it would take to walk from school to a designated location.

Ongoing Assessment: Recognizing Student Achievement
Use Mental Math and Reflexes.
[Operations and Computation Goal 2]

Key Vocabulary

estimate ◆ median

Materials

Math Journal 1, pp. 29 and 30
Student Reference Book, pp. 18 and 21
Class Data Pad ◆ per group: 1 copy of a road map; 1 yardstick, meterstick, or tape measure ◆ clock or watch ◆ calculator

2 Ongoing Learning & Practice

Math Boxes 2•1
Math Journal 1, p. 31
Students practice and maintain skills through Math Box problems.

Study Link 2•1
Math Masters, p. 33
Students practice and maintain skills through Study Link activities.

3 Differentiation Options

READINESS

Identifying Estimation Strategies
Math Masters, p. 34
Students develop a strategy for estimating the total number of objects in a visual field.

ENRICHMENT

Estimating Totals
Math Masters, p. 35
per group: 1 page from a residential telephone directory
Students devise a strategy for estimating the number of names on a phone book page.

Advance Preparation

For Part 1, students will need a map that shows both the school and a chosen location that is 40 to 200 miles away. For the optional Enrichment activity in Part 3, students need an original page—not a copy—from a telephone book.

For a mathematics and literacy connection, obtain a copy of ***Counting On Frank*** by Rod Clement (Houghton Mifflin, 2006).

***Teacher's Reference Manual,* Grades 4–6** pp. 256–261

Getting Started

Mental Math and Reflexes  

Write problems on the board or the Class Data Pad. Students answer and then explain the patterns they see in the number of zeros in the products.

●○○	●●○	●●●
7 * 3 21	4 * 6 24	9 [8s] 72
7 * 30 210	4 * 60 240	90 [8s] 720
70 * 30 2,100	40 * 60 2,400	900 [80s] 72,000

Math Message

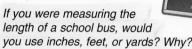

If you were measuring the length of a school bus, would you use inches, feet, or yards? Why?

Use the unit of measure you chose. Estimate the length of a school bus.

Ongoing Assessment: Recognizing Student Achievement

Mental Math and Reflexes 

Use the **Mental Math and Reflexes** to assess students' ability to solve extended facts problems mentally. Students are making adequate progress if they are able to correctly solve the ●○○ and ●●○ problems. Some students might be able to solve the ●●● problems.

[Operations and Computation Goal 2]

1 Teaching the Lesson

▶ Mental Math and Reflexes Follow-Up

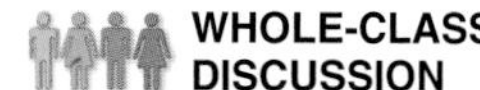

WHOLE-CLASS DISCUSSION

(*Student Reference Book,* pp. 18 and 21)

The Mental Math and Reflexes problems in Unit 2 continue to focus on extended multiplication and division facts with emphasis on the patterns formed by zeros in the product or quotient. The patterns in these problems are used in the multiplication algorithms in Lesson 2-7. Refer students to pages 18 and 21 of the *Student Reference Book* to review using these patterns when solving multiplication and division problems involving powers of 10. Students also use their knowledge of place value to write numbers in expanded notation.

▶ Math Message Follow-Up

WHOLE-CLASS DISCUSSION

Ask students to share reasons for choosing a particular unit of measure over the other units. Most students will not have chosen inches. The discussion could include the reasons why the Math Message did not ask students to measure a school bus. Ask: *Is an actual measure of a school bus more useful than an* ***estimate?*** Sample answer: No. It depends on the situation. An estimate is adequate in many everyday situations. *Which is easier to obtain: the actual measurement or an estimate?* An estimate

Interactive whiteboard-ready ePresentations are available at www.everydaymathonline.com to help you teach the lesson.

NOTE In *Everyday Mathematics,* brackets are used in phrases that name multiples. For example, 900 [80s] is read as 900 eighties.

Student Page

Date ______ Time ______

LESSON 2·1 **Estimation Challenge**

Sometimes you will be asked to solve a problem for which it is difficult or even impossible to find an exact answer. Your job will be to make your best estimate and then defend it. We call this kind of problem an Estimation Challenge.

Estimation challenges can be difficult, and they take time to solve. Usually, you will work with a partner or as part of a small group.

Estimation Challenge Problem

Imagine that you are living in a time when there are no cars, trains, or planes. You do not own a horse, a boat, or any other means of transportation.

You plan to travel to ______ (location given by your teacher). You will have to walk there.

Answers vary.

Information needed to solve the problem.

Definition of a *step.* 1 mile = 5,280 feet

Length of a step

1. About how many miles is it from your school to your destination?

   About ______ miles

2. a. About how many footsteps will you have to take to get from your school to your destination?

   About ______ footsteps

   b. What did you do to estimate the number of footsteps you would take?

   ______

Math Journal 1, p. 29

Student Page

Date ______ Time ______

LESSON 2·1 **Estimation Challenge** *continued*

3. a. Suppose that you did not stop to rest, eat, sleep, or for any other reason. About how long would it take you to get from school to your destination? Answers vary.

About ______ hours

b. What did you do to estimate how long it would take you?

______

4. Suppose you start from school at 7:00 A.M. on Monday. You take time out to rest, eat, sleep, and for other reasons.

a. List reasons that you might stop along the way. For each reason, write about how long you would stop.

Reason for Stopping	Length of Stop

b. At about what time, and on what day of the week, would you expect to reach your destination?

Time: About ______ Day: ______

5. Who did you work with on this Estimation Challenge? ______

Math Journal 1, **p. 30**

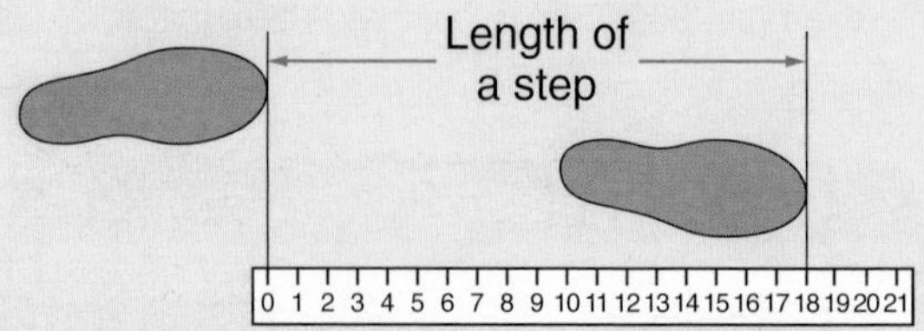

Measure of a step from toe to toe

Adjusting the Activity

A strategy for finding the median is to write the individual step lengths on separate pieces of paper, sort them so the numbers are in ascending order, and then identify the median—the middle number, or the mean of the two middle numbers.

AUDITORY ♦ KINESTHETIC ♦ TACTILE ♦ VISUAL

▶ Introducing the Estimation Challenge Problem

SMALL-GROUP ACTIVITY

PROBLEM SOLVING

(*Math Journal 1*, pp. 29 and 30)

Social Studies Link Introduce the Estimation Challenge Problem presented in the journal. This activity presents an opportunity for students to use estimation as a practical strategy for solving a problem where obtaining the exact answer is impractical. Divide the class into partnerships or small groups of 3 to 5 students. The Estimation Challenge Problem asks students to estimate how many footsteps and the amount of time it would take to travel from school to a chosen destination.

Distribute a yardstick, meterstick, or tape measure, and one copy of the road map to each group. If maps are not available, give students the approximate distance to the location, and have them record this information in Problem 1 on journal page 29.

Ask students to look over Problems 2–4. Survey the class for questions, and discuss why it is not possible to find exact answers. Sample answers: Step length will vary. Walking speed will vary. Number of stops along the way and the lengths of these stops cannot be predicted exactly.

Encourage students to devise their own solution strategies. Direct them to record the length of a step for each member of their group. Circulate and assist.

For students who need help planning how to proceed, suggest the following:

1. Use the scale of miles on the road map to find the distance between school and the destination.
2. Measure the length of a typical step. Use this information to calculate the approximate number of steps in 1 mile. (1 mile = 5,280 feet)
3. Estimate the number of steps for the distance between the two locations.
4. Estimate an average distance a student might walk in 1 minute. Use this information to estimate the amount of time it would take to walk the given distance.

For a group measure, students might find the **median** step length for their group and use this length as their typical step. Then they must determine whether to calculate the number of steps in a mile, using inches or feet. A median step length of 18 inches will take about 3,520 steps to walk a mile. (5,280 feet per mile ∗ 12 inches per foot ÷ 18 inches per step = 3,520 steps per mile, or 5,280 ÷ 1.5 feet per step = 3,520)

Having found the number of steps in a mile, for a distance of 200 miles, it would take about 704,000 steps to walk 200 miles: 200 miles ∗ 3,520 steps per mile = 704,000 steps.

Next students estimate the time it would take to walk this number of steps. Have students walk for 1 minute and count their steps. Students then find the median number of steps for their group. If the median number of steps for 1 minute is 120 steps and each step is about $1\frac{1}{2}$ feet, a student will walk about 180 feet in 1 minute (120 steps per min $*$ 1.5 ft per step = 180 ft per min). It would take about 30 minutes to walk 1 mile (5,280 ft per mile ÷ 180 ft per min = 29.33 min per mile; but it is easier to work with half-hour increments rather than minute increments). Having found the time it takes to walk 1 mile, students then multiply the number of miles by this time. It would take about 100 hours to walk 200 miles without stops (200 miles $*$ 0.5 hours per mile = 100 hours).

Students estimate the time needed for stops along the way and add this time to 100 hours. Finally, they calculate their arrival time and day.

Adjusting the Activity

In the interest of time, you might have students find and use the class median for the length of 1 step and the number of steps walked in 1 minute.

AUDITORY ◆ KINESTHETIC ◆ TACTILE ◆ VISUAL

Sharing Results

(*Math Journal 1,* pp. 29 and 30)

When students have completed Problems 2–4 of the Estimation Challenge Problem, invite the class to share their estimates and strategies.

Suggestions:

- What information that was needed to solve the problems was not given to you?
- Did your group encounter any especially interesting or troublesome calculations? How were these resolved?
- How did you determine how long it would take to walk the distance and when you would reach your destination?

To follow-up, you might ask students to support the reasonableness of their calculations and estimates.

To conclude Part 1 of this lesson, use students' individual measures for the length of a step to find the median length for the class and then the number of steps in a mile for this length.

If students used the median to solve the estimation challenge, recall the earlier discussion and clarify how the use of the median contributed to the reasonableness of their estimates. Ask: *Why might using the median be a better choice than using the minimum or maximum?* During the discussion, review the definition of median and its use in estimation.

Student Page

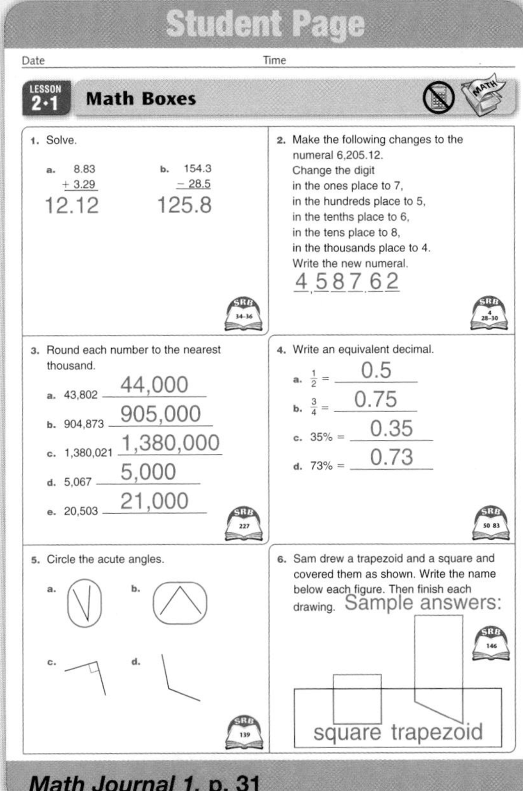
Date Time

LESSON 2·1 **Math Boxes**

1. Solve.
a. 8.83 + 3.29 = 12.12
b. 154.3 − 28.5 = 125.8

2. Make the following changes to the numeral 6,205.12. Change the digit in the ones place to 7, in the hundreds place to 5, in the tenths place to 6, in the tens place to 8, in the thousands place to 4. Write the new numeral. 4 5 8 7 6 2

3. Round each number to the nearest thousand.
a. 43,802 44,000
b. 904,873 905,000
c. 1,380,021 1,380,000
d. 5,067 5,000
e. 20,503 21,000

4. Write an equivalent decimal.
a. $\frac{1}{2}$ = 0.5
b. $\frac{3}{4}$ = 0.75
c. 35% = 0.35
d. 73% = 0.73

5. Circle the acute angles.
a. b. c. d.

6. Sam drew a trapezoid and a square and covered them as shown. Write the name below each figure. Then finish each drawing. Sample answers:
square trapezoid

Math Journal 1, p. 31

NOTE Students will need to record the class median step length and number of steps in a mile for use with the Study Link assignment.

Study Link Master

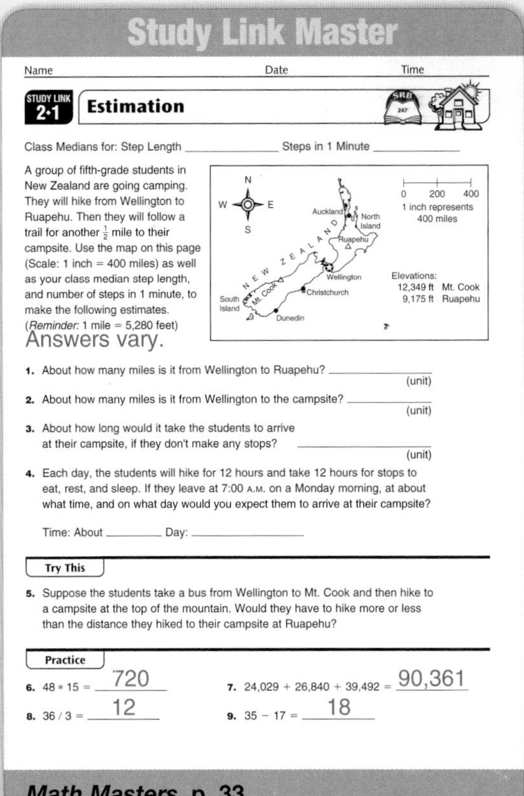
Name Date Time

STUDY LINK 2·1 **Estimation**

Class Medians for: Step Length ______ Steps in 1 Minute ______

A group of fifth-grade students in New Zealand are going camping. They will hike from Wellington to Ruapehu. Then they will follow a trail for another $\frac{1}{2}$ mile to their campsite. Use the map on this page (Scale: 1 inch = 400 miles) as well as your class median step length, and number of steps in 1 minute, to make the following estimates. (*Reminder:* 1 mile = 5,280 feet)

Answers vary.

1. About how many miles is it from Wellington to Ruapehu? ______ (unit)
2. About how many miles is it from Wellington to the campsite? ______ (unit)
3. About how long would it take the students to arrive at their campsite, if they don't make any stops? ______ (unit)
4. Each day, the students will hike for 12 hours and take 12 hours for stops to eat, rest, and sleep. If they leave at 7:00 A.M. on a Monday morning, at about what time, and on what day would you expect them to arrive at their campsite?

Time: About ______ Day: ______

Try This

5. Suppose the students take a bus from Wellington to Mt. Cook and then hike to a campsite at the top of the mountain. Would they have to hike more or less than the distance they hiked to their campsite at Ruapehu?

Practice

6. 48 ∗ 15 = 720
7. 24,029 + 26,840 + 39,492 = 90,361
8. 36 / 3 = 12
9. 35 − 17 = 18

Math Masters, p. 33

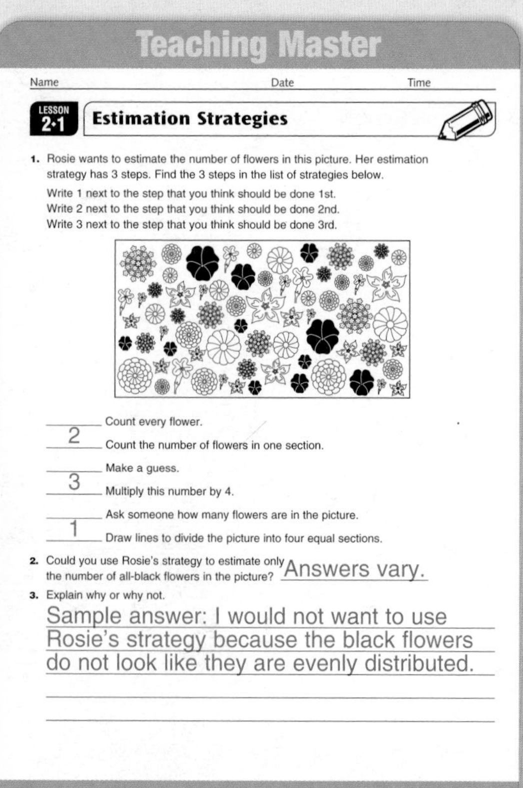
Teaching Master

Name Date Time

LESSON 2·1 **Estimation Strategies**

1. Rosie wants to estimate the number of flowers in this picture. Her estimation strategy has 3 steps. Find the 3 steps in the list of strategies below.
Write 1 next to the step that you think should be done 1st.
Write 2 next to the step that you think should be done 2nd.
Write 3 next to the step that you think should be done 3rd.

____ Count every flower.
__2__ Count the number of flowers in one section.
____ Make a guess.
__3__ Multiply this number by 4.
____ Ask someone how many flowers are in the picture.
__1__ Draw lines to divide the picture into four equal sections.

2. Could you use Rosie's strategy to estimate only the number of all-black flowers in the picture? Answers vary.
3. Explain why or why not.
Sample answer: I would not want to use Rosie's strategy because the black flowers do not look like they are evenly distributed.

Math Masters, p. 34

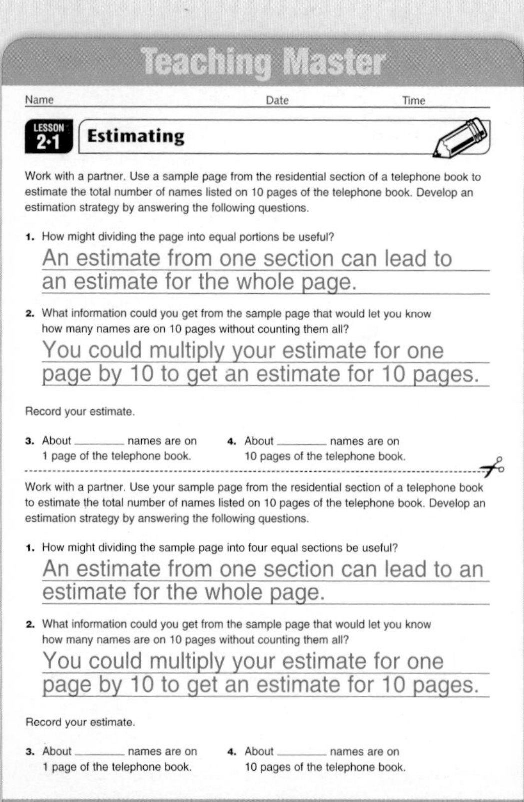
Teaching Master

Name Date Time

LESSON 2·1 **Estimating**

Work with a partner. Use a sample page from the residential section of a telephone book to estimate the total number of names listed on 10 pages of the telephone book. Develop an estimation strategy by answering the following questions.

1. How might dividing the page into equal portions be useful?
An estimate from one section can lead to an estimate for the whole page.
2. What information could you get from the sample page that would let you know how many names are on 10 pages without counting them all?
You could multiply your estimate for one page by 10 to get an estimate for 10 pages.

Record your estimate.

3. About ______ names are on 1 page of the telephone book.
4. About ______ names are on 10 pages of the telephone book.

Work with a partner. Use your sample page from the residential section of a telephone book to estimate the total number of names listed on 10 pages of the telephone book. Develop an estimation strategy by answering the following questions.

1. How might dividing the sample page into four equal sections be useful?
An estimate from one section can lead to an estimate for the whole page.
2. What information could you get from the sample page that would let you know how many names are on 10 pages without counting them all?
You could multiply your estimate for one page by 10 to get an estimate for 10 pages.

Record your estimate.

3. About ______ names are on 1 page of the telephone book.
4. About ______ names are on 10 pages of the telephone book.

Math Masters, p. 35

2 Ongoing Learning & Practice

▶ Math Boxes 2·1

INDEPENDENT ACTIVITY

(*Math Journal* 1, p. 31)

Mixed Practice Math Boxes in this lesson are paired with Math Boxes in Lesson 2-3. The skills in Problems 5 and 6 preview Unit 3 content.

▶ Study Link 2·1

INDEPENDENT ACTIVITY

(*Math Masters,* p. 33)

Home Connection Students use the class median for the step length and the number of steps in a minute to estimate the time needed to walk between two points shown on a map.

3 Differentiation Options

READINESS

SMALL-GROUP ACTIVITY

5–15 Min

▶ Identifying Estimation Strategies

(*Math Masters,* p. 34)

To provide experience in developing estimation strategies, have students identify a strategy to estimate the total number of objects in a visual field. Discuss the difference between making an estimate and making a guess. Estimates use a strategy and pertinent information. When students finish, have them share their strategies and explain how they know that their estimates are reasonable. The goal is not for students to make the estimate, but rather to develop an estimation strategy.

ENRICHMENT

SMALL-GROUP ACTIVITY

5–15 Min

▶ Estimating Totals

(*Math Masters,* p. 35)

To apply students' understanding of estimation skills, have students develop a strategy for estimating the number of names on a phone book page. Direct students to complete *Math Masters,* page 35 as a guide to making their estimates. When students finish, have them share their strategies and explain how they know that their estimates are reasonable. Ask students to generalize their strategies to other types of telephone book pages.

2·2 Addition of Whole Numbers and Decimals

 **Objectives** To review place-value concepts and the use of the partial-sums and column-addition methods.

Technology Resources www.everydaymathonline.com

ePresentations

eToolkit

Algorithms Practice

EM Facts Workshop Game™

Family Letters

Assessment Management

Common Core State Standards

Curriculum Focal Points

Interactive Teacher's Lesson Guide

1 Teaching the Lesson

Key Concepts and Skills

- Write numbers in expanded notation. [Number and Numeration Goal 1]
- Use paper-and-pencil algorithms for multidigit addition problems. [Operations and Computation Goal 1]
- Make magnitude estimates for addition. [Operations and Computation Goal 6]

Key Activities

Students review place-value concepts and write numbers in expanded notation. They review addition of whole numbers and decimals with the partial-sums and column-addition methods.

Ongoing Assessment: Recognizing Student Achievement Use journal page 33. [Operations and Computation Goal 1]

Key Vocabulary

place ◆ value ◆ digit ◆ algorithm ◆ partial-sums method ◆ place value ◆ expanded notation ◆ column-addition method

Materials

Math Journal 1, pp. 32 and 33
Student Reference Book, pp. 13, 14, 28–30, and 35
Study Link 2•1
Math Masters, p. 415
slate

2 Ongoing Learning & Practice

Playing *Addition Top-It* (Decimal Version)
Student Reference Book, p. 333
per partnership: 4 each of the number cards 1–10 (from the Everything Math Deck, if available); 2 counters
Students practice place-value concepts, use addition methods, and compare numbers.

Math Boxes 2•2
Math Journal 1, p. 34
Students practice and maintain skills through Math Box problems.

Study Link 2•2
Math Masters, p. 36
Students practice and maintain skills through Study Link activities.

3 Differentiation Options

READINESS
Building Numbers with Base-10 Blocks
Math Masters, p. 37
base-10 blocks
Students use base-10 blocks to explore the partial-sums method of addition.

ENRICHMENT
Using Place Value to Solve Addition Problems
Math Masters, p. 38
Students apply place-value and addition concepts to solve problems.

ELL SUPPORT
Building a Math Word Bank
Differentiation Handbook, p. 142
Students define and illustrate the term *expanded notation.*

Advance Preparation

Plan to spend two days on this lesson. Distribute copies of the computation grid on *Math Masters,* page 415 for students to use as they do addition problems. Make and display a poster showing expanded notation for a whole number and a decimal.

 ***Teacher's Reference Manual,* Grades 4–6** pp. 119–122

Getting Started

Mental Math and Reflexes

Read the numbers orally and have students write them in expanded notation on their slates. Remind students that expanded notation expresses a number as the sum of the values of each digit. For example, 906 is equivalent to 9 hundreds + 0 tens + 6 ones, and 0.796 is equivalent to 7 tenths + 9 hundredths + 6 thousandths. In expanded notation, 906 is written as 900 + 6, and 0.796 may be written as 0.7 + 0.09 + 0.006 or as $7 * (\frac{1}{10}) + 9 * (\frac{1}{100}) + 6 * (\frac{1}{1,000})$. Encourage students to write the decimal numbers in fraction notation. Sample answers are given.

●○○ 35 30 + 5
0.35 $3 * (\frac{1}{10}) + 5 * (\frac{1}{100})$
52 50 + 2
0.52 $5 * (\frac{1}{10}) + 2 * (\frac{1}{100})$

●●○ 241 200 + 40 + 1
0.241 $2 * (\frac{1}{10}) + 4 * (\frac{1}{100}) + 1 * (\frac{1}{1,000})$
162 100 + 60 + 2
0.467 $4 * (\frac{1}{10}) + 6 * (\frac{1}{100}) + 7 * (\frac{1}{1,000})$

●●● 0.109 $1 * (\frac{1}{10}) + 9 * (\frac{1}{1,000})$
0.708 $7 * (\frac{1}{10}) + 8 * (\frac{1}{1,000})$
0.084 $8 * (\frac{1}{100}) + 4 * (\frac{1}{1,000})$
7,904 7,000 + 900 + 4

Math Message

Use the information on Student Reference Book, *pages 28–30 to solve the Check Your Understanding Problems on the bottom of page 30.*

Study Link 2·1 Follow-Up

Have partners discuss their strategies and identify one thing that they did the same and one thing that they did differently. Have volunteers share their findings.

- On **Day 1** of this lesson, students should complete the Mental Math and Reflexes and the Math Message. They should review and discuss the partial-sums addition method.
- On **Day 2** of this lesson, do the Study Link Follow-Up. Then review and discuss the column-addition method. Finally, have students complete the Part 2 activities.

Student Page

Decimals and Percents

You use facts about the place-value chart each time you make trades using base-10 blocks.

Example Suppose that a flat is worth 1. Then a long is worth $\frac{1}{10}$, or 0.1; and a cube is worth $\frac{1}{100}$, or 0.01.

You can trade one long for ten cubes because one $\frac{1}{10}$ equals ten $\frac{1}{100}$s.

You can trade ten longs for one flat because ten $\frac{1}{10}$s equals one 1.

You can trade ten cubes for one long because ten $\frac{1}{100}$s equals one $\frac{1}{10}$.

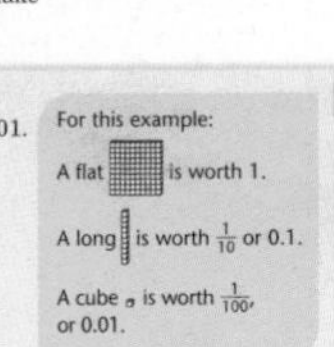

For this example:
A flat is worth 1.
A long is worth $\frac{1}{10}$ or 0.1.
A cube is worth $\frac{1}{100}$, or 0.01.

Left to Right in the Place-Value Chart

Study the place-value chart below. Look at the numbers that name the places. As you move from *left to right* along the chart, each number is $\frac{1}{10}$ **as large as the number to its left.**

Example

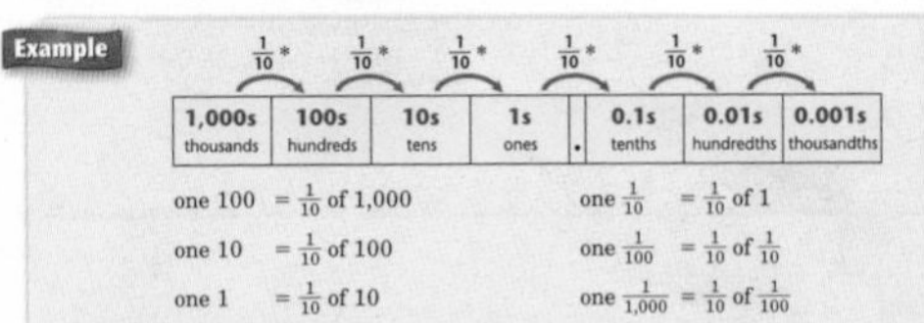

1,000s thousands	100s hundreds	10s tens	1s ones	.	0.1s tenths	0.01s hundredths	0.001s thousandths

one 100 $= \frac{1}{10}$ of 1,000   one $\frac{1}{10} = \frac{1}{10}$ of 1
one 10 $= \frac{1}{10}$ of 100   one $\frac{1}{100} = \frac{1}{10}$ of $\frac{1}{10}$
one 1 $= \frac{1}{10}$ of 10   one $\frac{1}{1,000} = \frac{1}{10}$ of $\frac{1}{100}$

Check Your Understanding

1. What is the value of the digit 2 in each of these numbers?
   a. 20,006.8
   b. 0.02
   c. 34.502
2. Using the digits 9, 3, and 5, what is
   a. the smallest decimal that you can write?
   b. the largest decimal less than 1 that you can write?
   c. the decimal closest to 0.5 that you can write?

Check your answers on page 434.

***Student Reference Book*, p. 30**

1 Teaching the Lesson

▶ Math Message Follow-Up

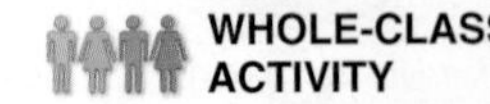

WHOLE-CLASS ACTIVITY

(*Student Reference Book*, pp. 28–30)

Ask students to use the information they read in the *Student Reference Book* to think of one true statement they could make about the base-ten number system.

Adjusting the Activity

Refer students to the place-value chart on page 30 of the *Student Reference Book.* Ask them to look over the headings on the chart and describe any patterns they see. The numbers decrease in size from left to right; the columns on the right side of the chart have a decimal point and the left side does not; the 0s increase by one for each column as you move outward from the center in either direction.

AUDITORY ◆ KINESTHETIC ◆ TACTILE ◆ VISUAL

Survey the class and use their responses to discuss the following:

▷ Each **place** has a **value** that is 10 times the value of the place to its right. For example, 1,000 is 10 times as much as 100; 100 is 10 times as much as 10; 10 is 10 times as much as 1; 1 is 10 times as much as 0.1; and 0.1 is 10 times as much as 0.01.

▷ Each place has a value that is one-tenth the value of the place to its left. For example, 100 is $\frac{1}{10}$ of 1,000; 10 is $\frac{1}{10}$ of 100; 1 is $\frac{1}{10}$ of 10; 0.1 is $\frac{1}{10}$ of 1; and 0.01 is $\frac{1}{10}$ of 0.1.

Ask students how these relationships guide them in writing the decimals in Problem 2 on *Student Reference Book*, page 30. Sample answers: Place the largest **digits** rightmost when forming the smallest decimal; place the largest digits leftmost when forming the largest decimal; place the 5 in the tenths place and the other two digits so the larger is to the right to form the decimal that is closest to 0.5. Explain that knowing these relationships also helps with comparing and ordering numbers by their relative sizes.

Ask students to listen closely as you read the numbers from Problem 1 on *Student Reference Book*, page 30. Tell them that you will include some mistakes. Read the numbers as 200,068; 0.2; and, 34.052. For each number, ask students to tell a partner what mistake was made. Then ask volunteers to describe the mistake and to read the number correctly. 200,068—no decimal point; 0.2—decimal point in the wrong position; 34.052 reverses the tenths and hundredths.

Tell students that clocks operate on a base-60 number system for minutes, and base-12 or base-24 (with military clocks) for hours. Have volunteers compare these systems and the base-10 systems.

▶ Reviewing Algorithms: Partial-Sums Method

WHOLE-CLASS DISCUSSION

(*Math Journal 1,* p. 32; *Student Reference Book,* pp. 13, 29, and 35; *Math Masters,* p. 415)

Most fifth-grade students have mastered an **algorithm** of their choice for addition. If they are comfortable with that algorithm, there is no reason for them to change it. However, all students are expected to know the **partial-sums method** for addition. This method helps students develop their understanding of **place value** and addition. In the partial-sums method, addition is performed from left to right, column by column. The sum for each column is recorded on a separate line. The partial sums are added either at each step or at the end.

Ask students to read *Student Reference Book,* page 29 and then write the numbers 348 and 177 in **expanded notation.** 300 + 40 + 8 = 348 and 100 + 70 + 7 = 177 Provide additional examples for students to write in expanded notation if needed. Then refer to page 13 in the *Student Reference Book* and demonstrate adding 348 + 177 using the partial-sums method. Ask students to describe any relationships they see between the expanded notation and the partial-sums method. Sample answer: Both methods use the value of the digits.

Ask students to write the numbers 4.56 and 7.9 in expanded notation. $4 + 5 * 0.1 + 6 * 0.01 = 4.56$ and $7 + 9 * 0.1 = 7.9$ Provide additional decimal examples for students to write in expanded notation if needed. Then refer to page 35 in the *Student Reference Book* and demonstrate adding 4.56 + 7.9 using the partial-sums method. Ask: *What are the similarities and differences between expanded notation and the partial-sums method with whole numbers and with decimals?* Sample answers: Both methods for whole numbers and decimals use the value of the digits. With decimals, you have to line up the places correctly, either by affixing 0s to the end of the numbers, or by aligning the digits in the ones place.

Have students independently solve the problems on journal page 32 and then check each other's answers.

Algorithm Project The focus of this lesson is the partial-sums and column-addition methods for adding whole numbers and decimals. To teach U.S. traditional addition with whole numbers and with decimals, see Algorithm Project 1 on page A1 and Algorithm Project 2 on page A6.

Expanded Notation

Number	Expanded Form
34.15	$3 * 10 + 4 * 1 + 1 * 0.1 + 5 * 0.01$
27.94	$2 * 10 + 7 * 1 + 9 * 0.1 + 4 * 0.01$
18.795	$1 * 10 + 8 * 1 + 7 * 0.1 + 9 * 0.01 + 5 * 0.001$
72.089	$7 * 10 + 2 * 1 + 0 * 0.1 + 8 * 0.01 + 9 * 0.001$

Expanded form may also be written with fractions instead of decimals. For example: $34.15 = 3 * 10 + 4 * 1 + 1 * (\frac{1}{10}) + 5 * (\frac{1}{100})$.

NOTE Display a poster showing the expanded notation of a whole number and of a decimal to provide students with a readily accessible example.

Language Arts Link The word *algorithm* is used to name a step-by-step procedure for solving a mathematical problem. The word is derived from the name of a ninth-century Muslim mathematician, Al-Khowarizimi. Encourage students to research the etymology of other mathematical terms.

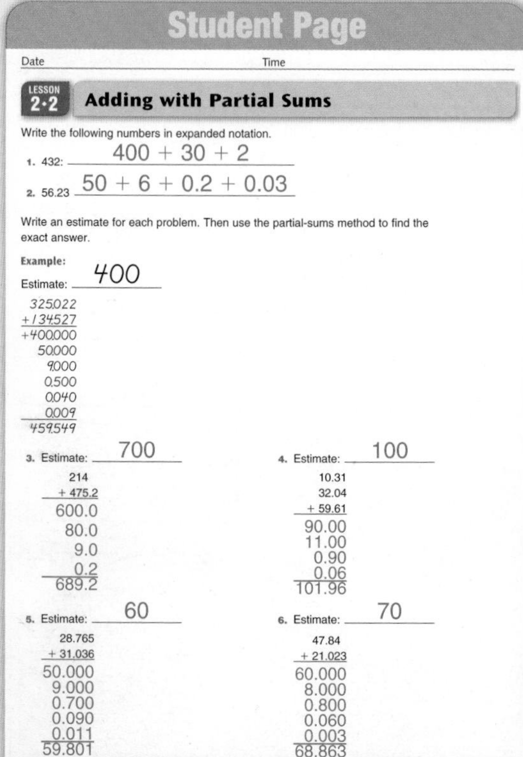

Student Page

Date Time

LESSON 2·2 **Adding with Partial Sums**

Write the following numbers in expanded notation.

1. 432: 400 + 30 + 2
2. 56.23 50 + 6 + 0.2 + 0.03

Write an estimate for each problem. Then use the partial-sums method to find the exact answer.

Example:

Estimate: 400

```
 325.022
+134.527
+400.000
  50.000
   9.000
   0.500
   0.040
   0.009
 459.549
```

3. Estimate: 700

```
  214
+ 475.2
  600.0
   80.0
    9.0
    0.2
  689.2
```

4. Estimate: 100

```
  10.31
  32.04
+ 59.61
  90.00
  11.00
   0.90
   0.06
 101.96
```

5. Estimate: 60

```
  28.765
+ 31.036
  50.000
   9.000
   0.700
   0.090
   0.011
  59.801
```

6. Estimate: 70

```
  47.84
+ 21.023
  60.000
   8.000
   0.800
   0.060
   0.003
  68.863
```

Math Journal 1, p. 32

NOTE Remind students always to say aloud, or to themselves, the numbers that they are adding when they use the partial-sums method. *For example:* 500 + 200, not 5 + 2; 70 + 60, not 7 + 6.

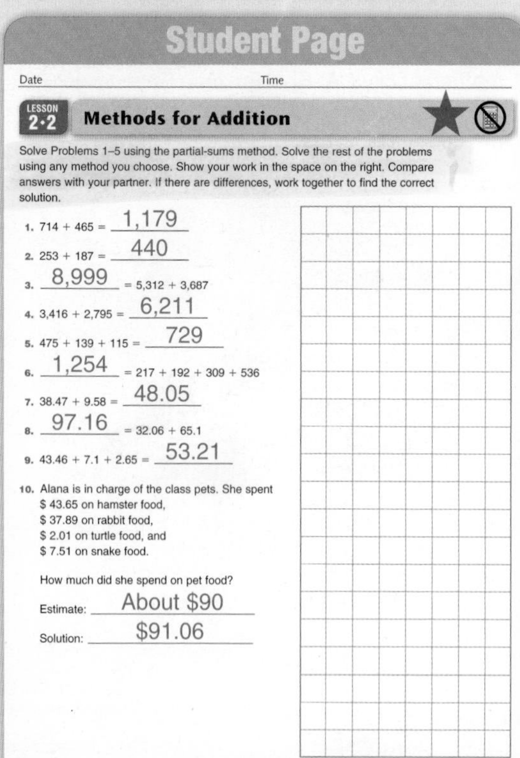

Student Page

Date Time

LESSON 2·2 **Methods for Addition**

Solve Problems 1–5 using the partial-sums method. Solve the rest of the problems using any method you choose. Show your work in the space on the right. Compare answers with your partner. If there are differences, work together to find the correct solution.

1. 714 + 465 = 1,179
2. 253 + 187 = 440
3. 8,999 = 5,312 + 3,687
4. 3,416 + 2,795 = 6,211
5. 475 + 139 + 115 = 729
6. 1,254 = 217 + 192 + 309 + 536
7. 38.47 + 9.58 = 48.05
8. 97.16 = 32.06 + 65.1
9. 43.46 + 7.1 + 2.65 = 53.21
10. Alana is in charge of the class pets. She spent
    $ 43.65 on hamster food,
    $ 37.89 on rabbit food,
    $ 2.01 on turtle food, and
    $ 7.51 on snake food.

    How much did she spend on pet food?

    Estimate: About $90

    Solution: $91.06

Math Journal 1, p. 33

▶ Reviewing Algorithms: Column-Addition Method

(*Student Reference Book*, pp. 13 and 35; *Math Masters*, p. 415)

The **column-addition method** is similar to the traditional algorithm most adults know. It can become an alternate method for students who are still struggling with addition.

Demonstrate the method using examples like those on pages 13 and 35 of the *Student Reference Book*. In this method, each column of numbers is added separately, and in any order.

- ▷ If adding results in a single digit in each column, the sum has been found.
- ▷ If the sum in any column is a 2-digit number, it is renamed and part of it is added to the sum in the column on its left.

This adjustment serves the same purpose as "carrying" in the traditional algorithm.

Ask students to compare the examples of column addition on pages 13 and 35 of the *Student Reference Book*. Assign each small group one of the following problems to solve using the column addition method. Encourage students to use concrete models or drawings and strategies based on place value, properties of operations, and/or the relationship between addition and subtraction. Have students write about their method and explain the reasoning they used to solve the assigned problem. Volunteers share the group's solution using the board or a transparency.

39 + 23 62	607 + 46 + 239 892	7,069 + 3,481 10,550
0.7 + 0.29 0.99	1.56 + 8.72 10.28	48.26 + 7.94 56.2

▶ Adding Whole Numbers and Decimals

PARTNER ACTIVITY

(*Math Journal 1*, p. 33; *Student Reference Book*, pp. 13, 14, and 35; *Math Masters*, p. 415)

Encourage students to estimate and solve the problems independently and then check each other's work. Using the computation grid helps students line up digits and/or decimal points. Encourage students to try the methods described on pages 13, 14, and 35 of the *Student Reference Book*.

Journal Page 33 Problems 1 and 2 ★

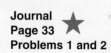

Use **journal page 33** to assess students' ability to solve multidigit addition problems. Students are making adequate progress if they correctly use the partial-sums method to solve Problems 1 and 2.

[Operations and Computation Goal 1]

Sharing Results

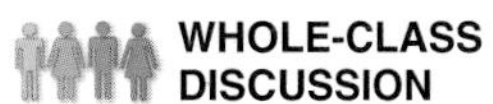

(*Math Journal 1*, pp. 32 and 33)

Bring the class together to share solutions. Some possible discussion questions include the following:

- What are some of the advantages or disadvantages of different methods for addition?
- When might a particular method be useful? When might it not be useful?
- How did students use their estimates on journal page 32? Did they make estimates for any subsequent problems?

Ask students to explain the reasoning they used to solve some of the problems on *Math Journal 1,* page 33.

2 Ongoing Learning & Practice

Playing *Addition Top-It* (Decimal Version)

(*Student Reference Book*, p. 333; *Math Masters,* p. 493)

Addition Top-It (Decimal Version) provides practice adding decimals, comparing numbers, and understanding place-value concepts. Direct students to play a decimal version of *Addition Top-It, Student Reference Book,* page 333. Use this variation:

- ▷ Each player draws 4 cards and forms 2 numbers that each has a whole-number portion and a decimal portion. Players should consider how to form their numbers to make the largest sum possible. Use counters or pennies to represent the decimal point.
- ▷ Each player finds the sum of the 2 numbers and then writes the sum in expanded form.
- ▷ Each player records his or her sum on *Math Masters,* page 493 to form a number sentence using >, <, or =.
- ▷ The player with the largest sum takes all of the cards.

Math Boxes 2•2

INDEPENDENT ACTIVITY

(*Math Journal 1,* p. 34)

Mixed Practice Math Boxes in this lesson are paired with Math Boxes in Lesson 2-4. The skill in Problem 6 previews Unit 3 content.

Writing/Reasoning Have students write a response for the following: *Leroy rounded 56.199 to 60. Rosina said that he was incorrect. Do you agree or disagree with Rosina?* Sample answer: It depends on whether Leroy intended to round to the nearest 10 or the nearest whole number; 56.199 rounded to the nearest 10 is 60; 56.199 rounded to the nearest whole number is 56.

Student Page

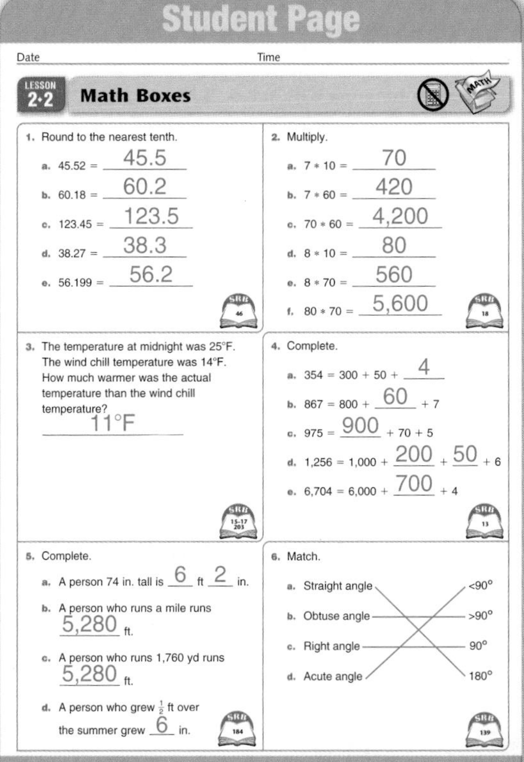

Date Time

LESSON 2•2 **Math Boxes**

1. Round to the nearest tenth.
   a. 45.52 = 45.5
   b. 60.18 = 60.2
   c. 123.45 = 123.5
   d. 38.27 = 38.3
   e. 56.199 = 56.2

2. Multiply.
   a. 7 ∗ 10 = 70
   b. 7 ∗ 60 = 420
   c. 70 ∗ 60 = 4,200
   d. 8 ∗ 10 = 80
   e. 8 ∗ 70 = 560
   f. 80 ∗ 70 = 5,600

3. The temperature at midnight was 25°F. The wind chill temperature was 14°F. How much warmer was the actual temperature than the wind chill temperature? 11°F

4. Complete.
   a. 354 = 300 + 50 + 4
   b. 867 = 800 + 60 + 7
   c. 975 = 900 + 70 + 5
   d. 1,256 = 1,000 + 200 + 50 + 6
   e. 6,704 = 6,000 + 700 + 4

5. Complete.
   a. A person 74 in. tall is 6 ft 2 in.
   b. A person who runs a mile runs 5,280 ft.
   c. A person who runs 1,760 yd runs 5,280 ft.
   d. A person who grew $\frac{1}{2}$ ft over the summer grew 6 in.

6. Match.
   a. Straight angle — 180°
   b. Obtuse angle — >90°
   c. Right angle — 90°
   d. Acute angle — <90°

Math Journal 1, p. 34

NOTE Remind students of the benefits of making estimates prior to solving problems. Estimation as an ongoing practice helps students to become flexible with mental computation and to check their answers for reasonableness.

Study Link Master

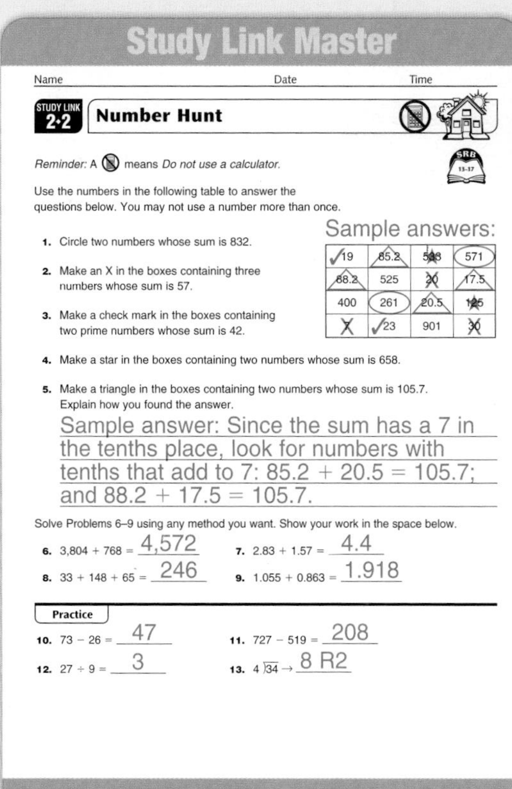

Name Date Time

STUDY LINK 2•2 **Number Hunt**

Reminder: A (no calculator symbol) means *Do not use a calculator.*

Use the numbers in the following table to answer the questions below. You may not use a number more than once.

1. Circle two numbers whose sum is 832.
2. Make an X in the boxes containing three numbers whose sum is 57.
3. Make a check mark in the boxes containing two prime numbers whose sum is 42.
4. Make a star in the boxes containing two numbers whose sum is 658.
5. Make a triangle in the boxes containing two numbers whose sum is 105.7. Explain how you found the answer.

Sample answers:

19	85.2	583	571
88.2	525	8	17.5
400	261	20.5	135
14	23	901	35

Sample answer: Since the sum has a 7 in the tenths place, look for numbers with tenths that add to 7: 85.2 + 20.5 = 105.7; and 88.2 + 17.5 = 105.7.

Solve Problems 6–9 using any method you want. Show your work in the space below.

6. 3,804 + 768 = 4,572
7. 2.83 + 1.57 = 4.4
8. 33 + 148 + 65 = 246
9. 1.055 + 0.863 = 1.918

Practice

10. 73 − 26 = 47
11. 727 − 519 = 208
12. 27 ÷ 9 = 3
13. 4)34 → 8 R2

Math Masters, p. 36

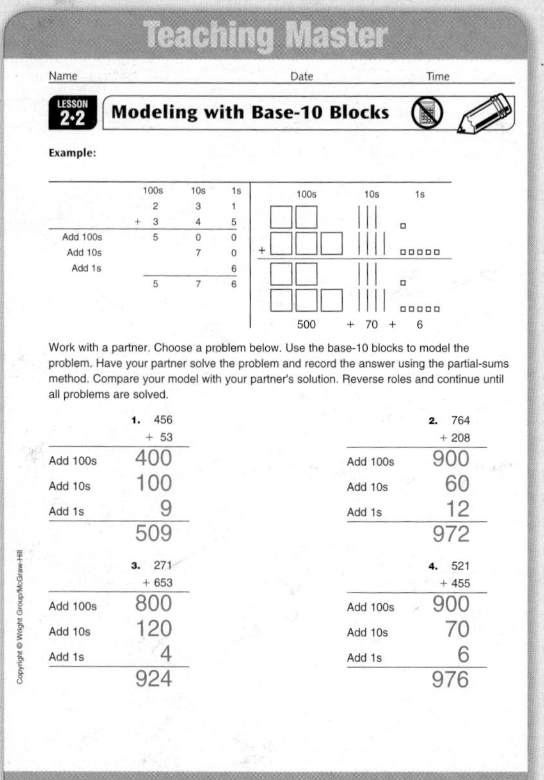

Teaching Master

Name Date Time

LESSON 2·2 **Modeling with Base-10 Blocks**

Example:

	100s	10s	1s
	2	3	1
	+ 3	4	5
Add 100s	5	0	0
Add 10s		7	0
Add 1s			6
	5	7	6

500 + 70 + 6

Work with a partner. Choose a problem below. Use the base-10 blocks to model the problem. Have your partner solve the problem and record the answer using the partial-sums method. Compare your model with your partner's solution. Reverse roles and continue until all problems are solved.

1. 456 + 53
Add 100s 400
Add 10s 100
Add 1s 9
509

2. 764 + 208
Add 100s 900
Add 10s 60
Add 1s 12
972

3. 271 + 653
Add 100s 800
Add 10s 120
Add 1s 4
924

4. 521 + 455
Add 100s 900
Add 10s 70
Add 1s 6
976

Math Masters, p. 37

▶ Study Link 2·2

INDEPENDENT ACTIVITY

(*Math Masters*, p. 36)

Home Connection Students practice finding sums. Students can solve problems using any method they choose.

3 Differentiation Options

READINESS

PARTNER ACTIVITY

15–30 Min

COMPUTATION PRACTICE

▶ Building Numbers with Base-10 Blocks

(*Math Masters*, p. 37)

To explore place value and expanded notation using concrete models, have students use base-10 blocks to model numbers. After students complete *Math Masters*, page 37, discuss the relationship between expanded notation and base-10 block representations. Have students also share how they used the blocks to add the numbers.

ENRICHMENT

PARTNER ACTIVITY

15–30 Min

▶ Using Place Value to Solve Addition Problems

(*Math Masters*, p. 38)

To apply students' understanding of place value and addition algorithms, have them use the sum of one problem to help them find the solution of other problems. After students complete Problems 1 and 2 on *Math Masters,* page 38, discuss their strategies. Ask students to explain how these strategies might be useful when solving addition problems. Sample answer: I could find related addends that are easier to work with than those in the original problem and use what I know about place value to help me solve the problem.

Teaching Master

Name Date Time

LESSON 2·2 **Place-Value Strategies**

Use your favorite addition algorithm to solve the first problem in each column. Then use the answer to the first problem in each column to help you solve the remaining problems.

1. 3,058 + 2,182 = 5,240
a. 3,058 + 2,282 = 5,340
b. 3,058 + 2,082 = 5,140
c. 3,058 + 2,582 = 5,640
d. 3,058 + 2,181 = 5,239

2. 7,401 + 2,659 = 10,060
a. 7,401 + 2,679 = 10,080
b. 7,401 + 2,669 = 10,070
c. 7,401 + 2,689 = 10,090
d. 7,401 + 2,699 = 10,100

3. Explain the strategy you used to solve the problem sets above.
I identified which digit in the second number changed. Then I adjusted the sum of the original problem by that amount.

Math Masters, p. 38

ELL SUPPORT

SMALL-GROUP ACTIVITY

5–15 Min

▶ Building a Math Word Bank

(*Differentiation Handbook,* p. 142)

To provide language support for number notation, have students use the Word Bank Template found on *Differentiation Handbook,* page 142. Ask students to write the term *expanded notation,* draw pictures relating to the term, and write other related words. See the *Differentiation Handbook* for more information.

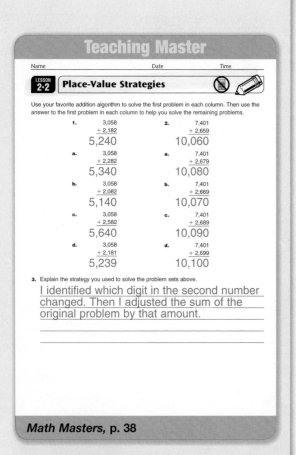

2•3 Subtraction of Whole Numbers and Decimals

Objective To review the trade-first and partial-differences methods for subtraction.

Technology Resources www.everydaymathonline.com

ePresentations

eToolkit

Algorithms Practice

EM Facts Workshop Game™

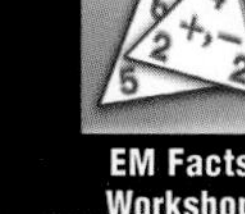
Family Letters

Assessment Management

Common Core State Standards

Curriculum Focal Points

Interactive Teacher's Lesson Guide

1 Teaching the Lesson

Key Concepts and Skills

- Explore algorithms for multidigit subtraction problems.
  [Operations and Computation Goal 1]
- Make magnitude estimates for subtraction.
  [Operations and Computation Goal 6]

Key Activities

Students discuss the trade-first and partial-differences methods; they use these and other methods to solve problems.

Ongoing Assessment: Recognizing Student Achievement
Use journal page 35.
[Operations and Computation Goal 1]

Key Vocabulary

trade-first method ◆ minuend ◆ subtrahend ◆ difference ◆ partial-differences method

Materials

Math Journal 1, p. 35
Student Reference Book, pp. 15–17, 35, and 36
Study Link 2•2
Math Masters, p. 415
slate

2 Ongoing Learning & Practice

Playing *Subtraction Target Practice* (Decimal Version)
Student Reference Book, p. 331
per partnership: 4 each of number cards 1–10 (from the Everything Math Deck, if available), counters
Students practice place-value concepts, subtraction methods, and comparing numbers.

Math Boxes 2•3
Math Journal 1, p. 36
Students practice and maintain skills through Math Box problems.

Study Link 2•3
Math Masters, p. 39
Students practice and maintain skills through Study Link activities.

3 Differentiation Options

READINESS

Making and Breaking Apart Numbers
Math Masters, p. 40
per partnership: 120 wooden craft sticks or straws; rubber bands or twist ties
Students explore subtraction concepts by making and breaking apart multiples of 10.

ENRICHMENT

Comparing Methods of Subtraction
Student Reference Book, pp. 15–17
Students compare different subtraction methods.

Advance Preparation

For Part 1, distribute copies of the computation grid on *Math Masters,* page 415 to encourage students to align digits when they write problems.

***Teacher's Reference Manual,* Grades 4–6** pp. 122–126

Getting Started

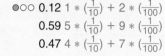

Mental Math and Reflexes

Dictate the numbers and have students write the numbers in expanded notation on their slates using fractions to record the decimal portion. For example, $0.392 = 3 * (\frac{1}{10}) + 9 * (\frac{1}{100}) + 2 * (\frac{1}{1,000})$.

●○○ 0.12 $1 * (\frac{1}{10}) + 2 * (\frac{1}{100})$
0.59 $5 * (\frac{1}{10}) + 9 * (\frac{1}{100})$
0.47 $4 * (\frac{1}{10}) + 7 * (\frac{1}{100})$

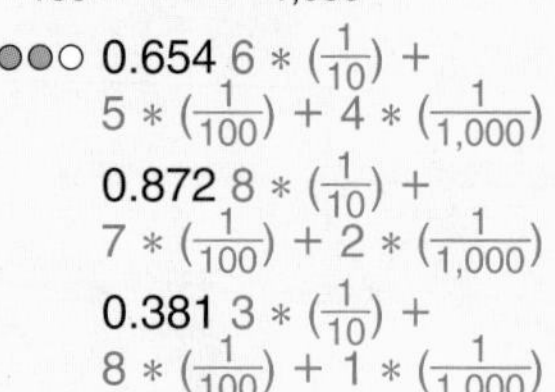
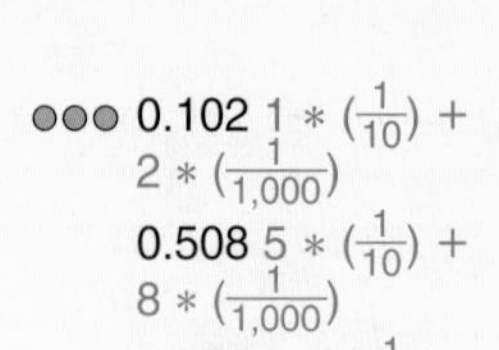

●●○ 0.654 $6 * (\frac{1}{10}) + 5 * (\frac{1}{100}) + 4 * (\frac{1}{1,000})$
0.872 $8 * (\frac{1}{10}) + 7 * (\frac{1}{100}) + 2 * (\frac{1}{1,000})$
0.381 $3 * (\frac{1}{10}) + 8 * (\frac{1}{100}) + 1 * (\frac{1}{1,000})$

●●● 0.102 $1 * (\frac{1}{10}) + 2 * (\frac{1}{1,000})$
0.508 $5 * (\frac{1}{10}) + 8 * (\frac{1}{1,000})$
0.093 $9 * (\frac{1}{100}) + 3 * (\frac{1}{1,000})$

Math Message

Estimate and solve each problem. Be prepared to discuss how you used place value and rounding in your estimate.

81 − 47 = ? 34 *8.1 − 4.7 = ?* 3.4

Study Link 2·2 Follow-Up

Partners compare answers and resolve differences. Ask volunteers to share their strategies for Problems 1–5.

NOTE As you go over the Study Link answers, discuss how to use the process of elimination as an estimation strategy. For example, to find two numbers with a sum of 832:

- ▷ Eliminate 901 because it is greater than 832.
- ▷ Eliminate all combinations of pairs of numbers in the 500s because each of their sums is greater than 1,000.
- ▷ Eliminate any combination of two 2-digit numbers because these sums are less than 800.

1 Teaching the Lesson

▶ Math Message Follow-Up

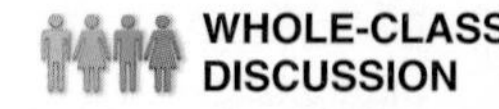

WHOLE-CLASS DISCUSSION

Briefly discuss the solutions for the two problems and the estimation strategies used. Follow up with questions regarding magnitude differences of the two solutions and related place-value concepts. Ask: *The value of 3 in 34 is how many times as great as the value of 3 in 3.4?* Sample answer: The 3 in 34 is ten times as great as the 3 in 3.4. *How does the value of the 4 in 3.4 compare to the value of the 4 in 34?* Sample answer: The 4 in 3.4 is $\frac{1}{10}$ the value of the 4 in 34.

▶ Reviewing Subtraction Algorithms

WHOLE-CLASS ACTIVITY

ELL

(*Student Reference Book*, pp. 15–17, 35, and 36; *Math Masters*, p. 415)

Using the Trade-First Method

Students in previous grades of *Everyday Mathematics* used the **trade-first method** to find differences. It is an algorithm all students are expected to know even if they favor other subtraction methods. To support English language learners, discuss the different meanings of the word *trade.* Use examples like those on *Student Reference Book,* pages 15 and 35 to demonstrate this method. Problems are written vertically. Subtraction is performed separately in each column. Briefly introduce the terms **minuend, subtrahend** and **difference.** Students are not expected to know these terms.

19	minuend
− 5	subtrahend
4	difference

Reinforce the use of estimation by asking volunteers to make an estimate prior to solving each problem.

Student Page

Whole Numbers

Subtraction Algorithms

Trade-First Subtraction Method

The **trade-first method** is similar to the method for subtracting that most adults in the United States were taught.

- ♦ If each digit in the top number is greater than or equal to the digit below it, subtract separately in each column.
- ♦ If any digit in the top number is less than the digit below it, adjust the top number before doing any subtracting. Adjust the top number by "trading."

Example Subtract 275 from 463 using the trade-first method.

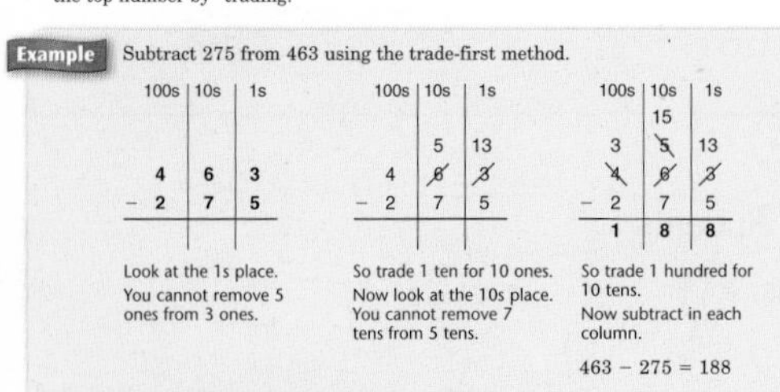

100s	10s	1s
4	6	3
− 2	7	5

Look at the 1s place. You cannot remove 5 ones from 3 ones.

100s	10s	1s
	5	13
4	~~6~~	~~3~~
− 2	7	5

So trade 1 ten for 10 ones. Now look at the 10s place. You cannot remove 7 tens from 5 tens.

100s	10s	1s
	15	
3	~~5~~	13
~~4~~	~~6~~	~~3~~
− 2	7	5
1	8	8

So trade 1 hundred for 10 tens. Now subtract in each column.

463 − 275 = 188

Larger numbers with 4 or more digits are subtracted in the same way.

Check Your Understanding

Subtract.

1. 75 − 37 2. 853 − 471 3. 651 − 285 4. 704 − 442 5. 7,345 − 3,066

Check your answers on page 433.

Student Reference Book, p. 15

Example: If each digit of the minuend is greater than or equal to the digit directly below it, subtract separately in each column.

$$\begin{array}{r} 93 \\ -\,21 \\ \hline 72 \end{array} \qquad \begin{array}{r} 6.48 \\ -\,3.45 \\ \hline 3.03 \end{array} \qquad \begin{array}{r} 54{,}729 \\ -\,34{,}026 \\ \hline 20{,}703 \end{array}$$

If any digit of the minuend is less than the digit directly below it, then the minuend is adjusted *before* subtracting. The minuend is adjusted by "trading." For example, we might need to trade 1 of the tens for 10 ones and 1 of the hundreds for 10 tens.

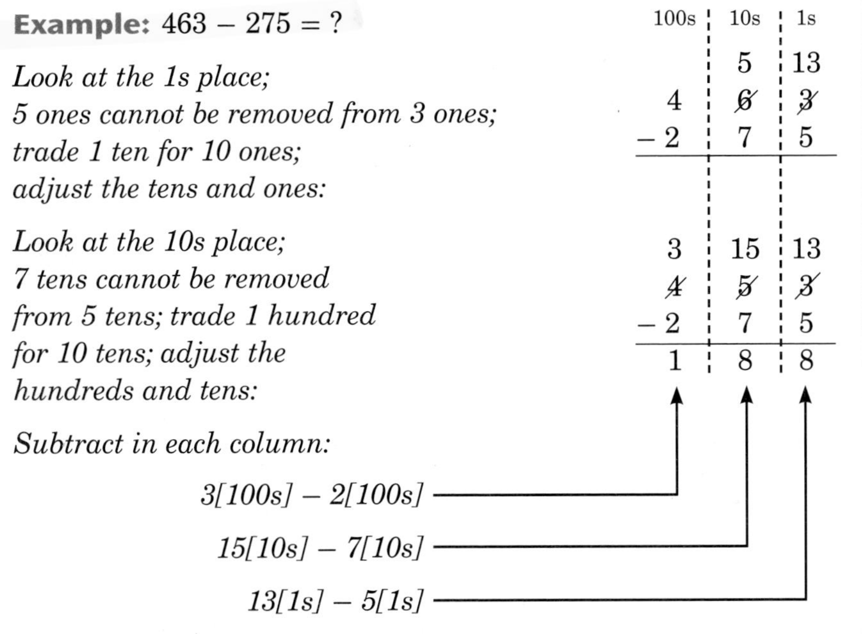

Example: 463 – 275 = ?

Look at the 1s place; 5 ones cannot be removed from 3 ones; trade 1 ten for 10 ones; adjust the tens and ones:

100s	10s	1s
	5	13
4	~~6~~	~~3~~
– 2	7	5

Look at the 10s place; 7 tens cannot be removed from 5 tens; trade 1 hundred for 10 tens; adjust the hundreds and tens:

100s	10s	1s
3	15	13
~~4~~	~~5~~	~~3~~
– 2	7	5
1	8	8

Subtract in each column:

3[100s] – 2[100s]

15[10s] – 7[10s]

13[1s] – 5[1s]

The authors of *Everyday Mathematics* recommend that trading be done from right to left. But it can also be done from left to right. What's important is that the student makes trades correctly and that the final adjusted minuend has each digit greater than or equal to the digit directly below it. Point out that decimal subtraction is done in the same way as whole-number subtraction.

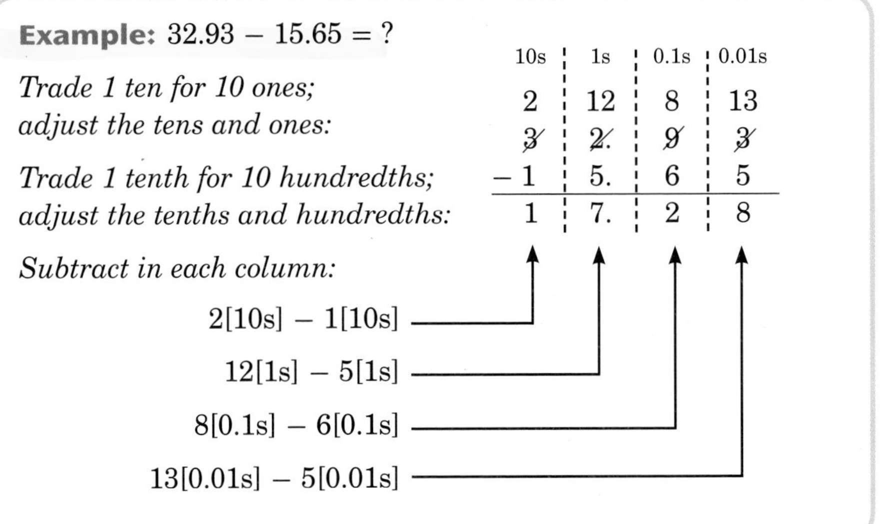

Example: 32.93 – 15.65 = ?

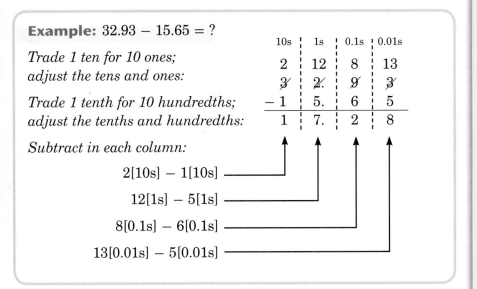

Trade 1 ten for 10 ones; adjust the tens and ones:

Trade 1 tenth for 10 hundredths; adjust the tenths and hundredths:

10s	1s	0.1s	0.01s
2	12	8	13
~~3~~	~~2~~.	~~9~~	~~3~~
– 1	5.	6	5
1	7.	2	8

Subtract in each column:

2[10s] – 1[10s]

12[1s] – 5[1s]

8[0.1s] – 6[0.1s]

13[0.01s] – 5[0.01s]

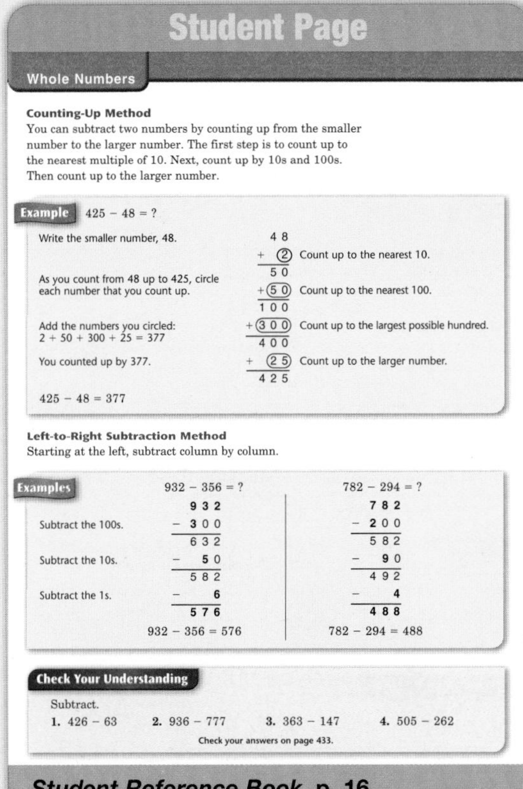

Student Page

Whole Numbers

Counting-Up Method

You can subtract two numbers by counting up from the smaller number to the larger number. The first step is to count up to the nearest multiple of 10. Next, count up by 10s and 100s. Then count up to the larger number.

Example 425 – 48 = ?

Write the smaller number, 48. — 48

As you count from 48 up to 425, circle each number that you count up. — + ② Count up to the nearest 10. — 50 — + ⑤⓪ Count up to the nearest 100. — 100

Add the numbers you circled: 2 + 50 + 300 + 25 = 377 — + ③⓪⓪ Count up to the largest possible hundred. — 400

You counted up by 377. — + ②⑤ Count up to the larger number. — 425

425 – 48 = 377

Left-to-Right Subtraction Method

Starting at the left, subtract column by column.

Examples

	932 – 356 = ?	782 – 294 = ?
	932	782
Subtract the 100s.	– 300	– 200
	632	582
Subtract the 10s.	– 50	– 90
	582	492
Subtract the 1s.	– 6	– 4
	576	488
	932 – 356 = 576	782 – 294 = 488

Check Your Understanding

Subtract.

1. 426 – 63 2. 936 – 777 3. 363 – 147 4. 505 – 262

Check your answers on page 433.

***Student Reference Book*, p. 16**

NOTE Adjusting by trading serves the same purpose as "borrowing and renaming" does in the traditional subtraction algorithm. Because all trades are done first—*before* any subtractions—there is much less chance of computational error than with the traditional subtraction algorithm.

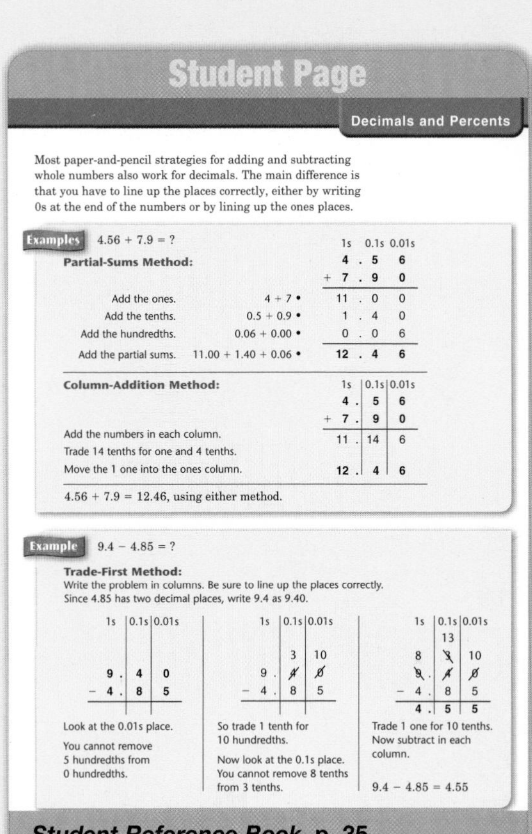

Student Page

Decimals and Percents

Most paper-and-pencil strategies for adding and subtracting whole numbers also work for decimals. The main difference is that you have to line up the places correctly, either by writing 0s at the end of the numbers or by lining up the ones places.

Examples 4.56 + 7.9 = ?

Partial-Sums Method:

		1s	0.1s	0.01s
		4 .	5	6
		+ 7 .	9	0
Add the ones.	4 + 7 →	11 .	0	0
Add the tenths.	0.5 + 0.9 →	1 .	4	0
Add the hundredths.	0.06 + 0.00 →	0 .	0	6
Add the partial sums.	11.00 + 1.40 + 0.06 →	12 .	4	6

Column-Addition Method:

	1s	0.1s	0.01s
	4 .	5	6
	+ 7 .	9	0
Add the numbers in each column.	11 .	14	6
Trade 14 tenths for one and 4 tenths. Move the 1 one into the ones column.	12 .	4	6

4.56 + 7.9 = 12.46, using either method.

Example 9.4 – 4.85 = ?

Trade-First Method:

Write the problem in columns. Be sure to line up the places correctly. Since 4.85 has two decimal places, write 9.4 as 9.40.

1s	0.1s	0.01s
9 .	4	0
– 4 .	8	5

Look at the 0.01s place. You cannot remove 5 hundredths from 0 hundredths.

1s	0.1s	0.01s
	3	10
9 .	~~4~~	~~0~~
– 4 .	8	5

So trade 1 tenth for 10 hundredths. Now look at the 0.1s place. You cannot remove 8 tenths from 3 tenths.

1s	0.1s	0.01s
	13	
8	~~3~~	10
~~9~~ .	~~4~~	~~0~~
– 4 .	8	5
4 .	5	5

Trade 1 one for 10 tenths. Now subtract in each column.

9.4 – 4.85 = 4.55

***Student Reference Book*, p. 35**

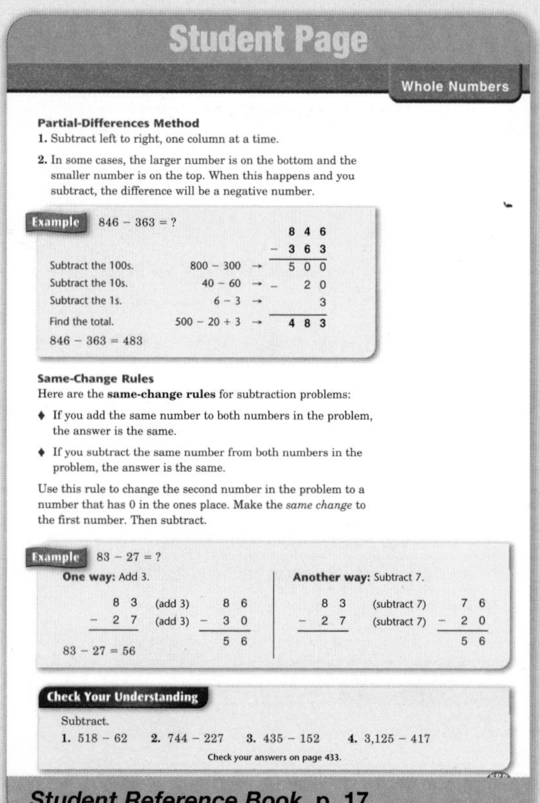

Student Page

Whole Numbers

Partial-Differences Method

1. Subtract left to right, one column at a time.
2. In some cases, the larger number is on the bottom and the smaller number is on the top. When this happens and you subtract, the difference will be a negative number.

Example 846 − 363 = ?

			8 4 6
			− 3 6 3
Subtract the 100s.	800 − 300	→	5 0 0
Subtract the 10s.	40 − 60	→	− 2 0
Subtract the 1s.	6 − 3	→	3
Find the total.	500 − 20 + 3	→	4 8 3

846 − 363 = 483

Same-Change Rules

Here are the **same-change rules** for subtraction problems:

- If you add the same number to both numbers in the problem, the answer is the same.
- If you subtract the same number from both numbers in the problem, the answer is the same.

Use this rule to change the second number in the problem to a number that has 0 in the ones place. Make the *same change* to the first number. Then subtract.

Example 83 − 27 = ?

One way: Add 3.

83	(add 3)	86
− 27	(add 3)	− 30
		56

83 − 27 = 56

Another way: Subtract 7.

83	(subtract 7)	76
− 27	(subtract 7)	− 20
		56

Check Your Understanding

Subtract.

1. 518 − 62 **2.** 744 − 227 **3.** 435 − 152 **4.** 3,125 − 417

Check your answers on page 433.

Student Reference Book, p. 17

Algorithm Project The focus of this lesson is the trade-first and partial-differences methods for subtracting whole numbers and decimals. To teach U.S. traditional subtraction with whole numbers and with decimals, see Algorithm Project 3 on page A11 and Algorithm Project 4 on page A16.

Remind students to make sure they align the numbers properly in columns. Students may find it helpful to separate these columns with vertical lines and to write place-value reminders such as 100s, 10s, and 1s above the columns. Continue to reinforce the use of estimation by asking volunteers to make an estimate prior to solving each problem.

Using the Partial-Differences Method

Use an example similar to the one on *Student Reference Book* page 17 to demonstrate the **partial-differences method.**

Example: 4,261 − 2,637 = ?

			4,261
			− 2,637
Subtract the thousands:	4,000 − 2,000	→	+ 2,000
Subtract the hundreds:	200 − 600	→	− 400
Subtract the tens:	60 − 30	→	+ 30
Subtract the ones:	1 − 7	→	− 6
Find the total:	2,000 − 400 + 30 − 6	→	1,624

Summarize:

- ▷ The subtraction is performed from left to right, column by column.
- ▷ In some columns, the larger number (or digit) is on the bottom and the smaller number (or digit) is on the top. When this happens, the result of the subtraction is a negative number.
- ▷ To find the final answer, the partial differences are added or subtracted.

Point out that decimal subtraction is done in the same way as whole-number subtraction. Encourage students to use concrete models or drawings and strategies based on place value, properties of operations, and/or the relationship between addition and subtraction.

Example: 76.38 − 39.81 = ?

			76.38
			− 39.81
Subtract the tens:	70 − 30	→	+ 40.00
Subtract the ones:	6 − 9	→	− 3.00
Subtract the tenths:	0.3 − 0.8	→	− 0.50
Subtract the hundredths:	0.08 − 0.01	→	+ 0.07
Find the total:	40.00 − 3.00 − 0.50 + 0.07	=	36.57

Ask: *How would you write the solution, 36.57, in expanded notation?* Sample answer: 3 * 10 + 6 * 1 + 5 * 0.1 + 7 * 0.01

Remind students to think about the values they are subtracting, not just the method. Subtracting 36.570 − 0.005 is easier if they think 0.070 − 0.005, or 0.010 − 0.005.

▶ Subtracting Whole Numbers and Decimals

PARTNER ACTIVITY

COMPUTATION PRACTICE

(*Math Journal 1,* p. 35)

Students solve subtraction problems independently and then check each other's work. Circulate and assist. Remind students to estimate prior to solving each problem. Encourage students to use concrete models or drawings and strategies based on place value, properties of operations, and/or the relationship between addition and subtraction. Ask students to write about their method and explain the reasoning they used to solve one of the problems.

Ongoing Assessment: Recognizing Student Achievement

Journal page 35 Problems 1 and 2 ★

Use **journal page 35, Problems 1 and 2** to assess students' ability to use the trade-first method. Students are making adequate progress if they correctly solve both problems.

[Operations and Computation Goal 1]

Bring the class together to share solutions. Some possible discussion questions include the following:

- How did you use your estimates?
- What are some of the advantages or disadvantages of different methods for subtraction?
- When might a particular method be useful? When might it not be useful?

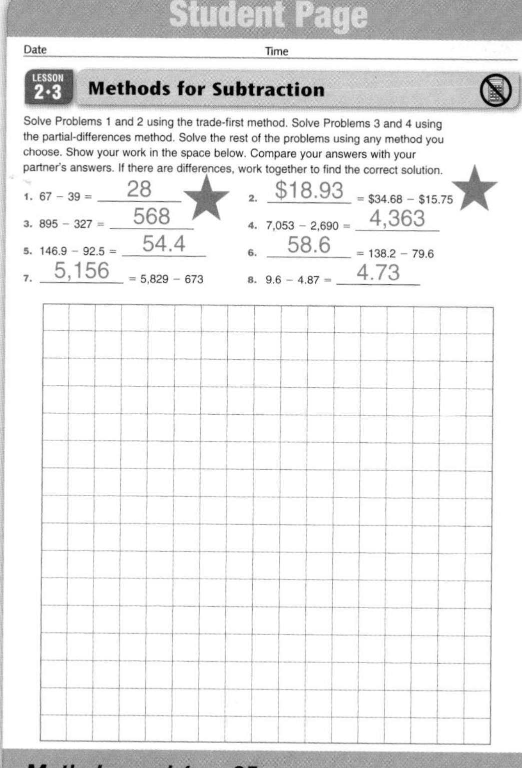

Student Page

Date Time

LESSON 2·3 **Methods for Subtraction**

Solve Problems 1 and 2 using the trade-first method. Solve Problems 3 and 4 using the partial-differences method. Solve the rest of the problems using any method you choose. Show your work in the space below. Compare your answers with your partner's answers. If there are differences, work together to find the correct solution.

1. 67 − 39 = 28 ★
2. $18.93 = $34.68 − $15.75 ★
3. 895 − 327 = 568
4. 7,053 − 2,690 = 4,363
5. 146.9 − 92.5 = 54.4
6. 58.6 = 138.2 − 79.6
7. 5,156 = 5,829 − 673
8. 9.6 − 4.87 = 4.73

Math Journal 1, p. 35

2 Ongoing Learning & Practice

▶ Playing *Subtraction Target Practice* (Decimal Version)

PARTNER ACTIVITY

COMPUTATION PRACTICE

(*Student Reference Book,* p. 331)

Students practice subtracting, applying place-value concepts, and comparing numbers by playing *Subtraction Target Practice* (Decimal Version). Direct students to play a decimal version of the game found on page 331 of the *Student Reference Book.* Use this variation:

▷ Start at 20.

▷ When 2 cards are turned over, use them to form a decimal number that has one digit in the ones place and one digit in the tenths place. (Use a penny or counter for the decimal point.)

▷ These numbers become the minuends. The game continues until one player reaches 0 without going below 0.

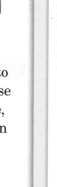

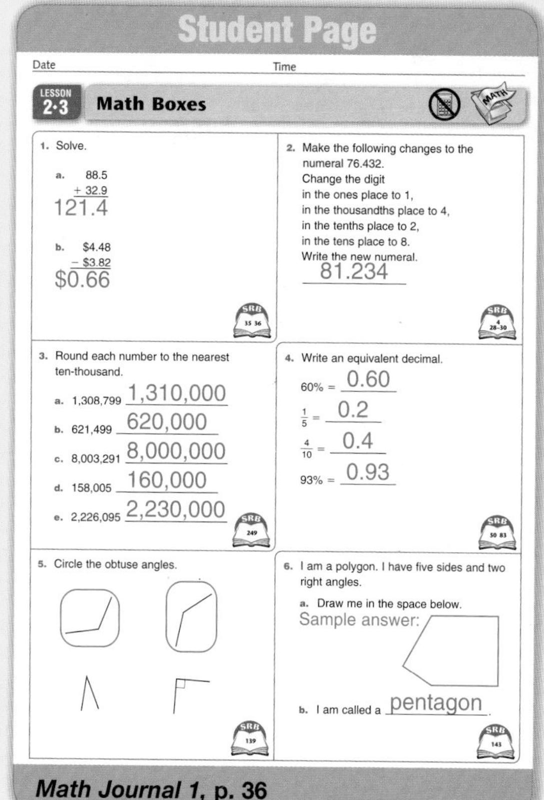

Student Page

Date Time

LESSON 2·3 **Math Boxes**

1. Solve.
   a. 88.5 + 32.9 = 121.4
   b. $4.48 − $3.82 = $0.66
2. Make the following changes to the numeral 76.432. Change the digit in the ones place to 1, in the thousandths place to 4, in the tenths place to 2, in the tens place to 8. Write the new numeral. 81.234
3. Round each number to the nearest ten-thousand.
   a. 1,308,799 1,310,000
   b. 621,499 620,000
   c. 8,003,291 8,000,000
   d. 158,005 160,000
   e. 2,226,095 2,230,000
4. Write an equivalent decimal.
   60% = 0.60
   $\frac{1}{5}$ = 0.2
   $\frac{4}{10}$ = 0.4
   93% = 0.93
5. Circle the obtuse angles.
6. I am a polygon. I have five sides and two right angles.
   a. Draw me in the space below. Sample answer:
   b. I am called a pentagon.

Math Journal 1, p. 36

Study Link Master

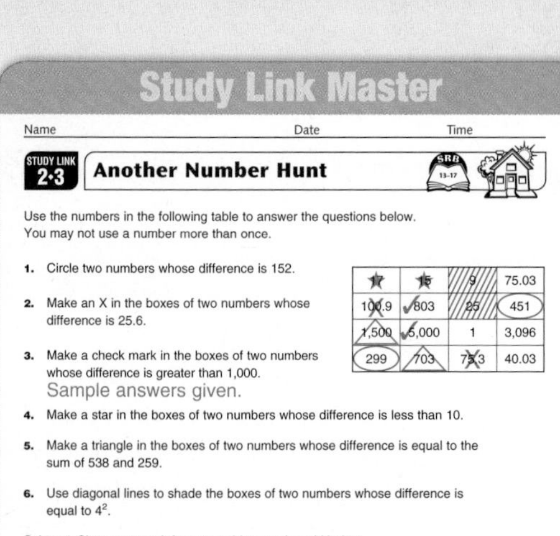

Name Date Time

STUDY LINK 2·3 **Another Number Hunt**

Use the numbers in the following table to answer the questions below. You may not use a number more than once.

1. Circle two numbers whose difference is 152.
2. Make an X in the boxes of two numbers whose difference is 25.6.
3. Make a check mark in the boxes of two numbers whose difference is greater than 1,000.
Sample answers given.

17	15	9	75.03
100.9	803	25	451
1,500	5,000	1	3,096
299	703	75.3	40.03

4. Make a star in the boxes of two numbers whose difference is less than 10.
5. Make a triangle in the boxes of two numbers whose difference is equal to the sum of 538 and 259.
6. Use diagonal lines to shade the boxes of two numbers whose difference is equal to 4^2.

Subtract. Show your work for one problem on the grid below.

7. 247 − 186 = 61
8. 137 = 405 − 268
9. 24.5 − 18.7 = 5.8
10. 18.85 = 62.7 − 43.85

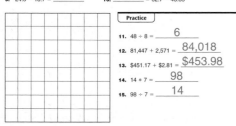

Practice

11. 48 ÷ 8 = 6
12. 81,447 + 2,571 = 84,018
13. $451.17 + $2.81 = $453.98
14. 14 ∗ 7 = 98
15. 98 ÷ 7 = 14

Math Masters, p. 39

Teaching Master

Name Date Time

LESSON 2·3 **Make and Break Apart**

Directions

- Make 10s by putting your wooden craft sticks or straws into bundles of 10.
- Use these bundles to model the subtraction problems.
- Then use your models to solve the problems.

Example: 22 − 7

To begin, you need 2 bundles of 10 and 2 ones.

10 + 10 + 2 = 22

To subtract 7, you need to break apart one bundle. Now you have 12 ones. Remove 7 ones.

10 + 5 = 15 7

Solution: 15

1. 10 − 4 = 6
2. 32 − 6 = 26
3. 71 − 23 = 48
4. 22 − 9 = 13
5. 56 − 38 = 18
6. 110 − 62 = 48

Math Masters, p. 40

▶ Math Boxes 2·3

INDEPENDENT ACTIVITY

(*Math Journal 1,* p. 36)

Mixed Practice Math Boxes in this lesson are paired with Math Boxes in Lesson 2-1. The skills in Problems 5 and 6 preview Unit 3 content.

Writing/Reasoning Have students write a response to the following: *Explain how you know which angles in Problem 5 are obtuse without measuring them?* If the angle looks greater than a right angle, the angle is probably obtuse.

▶ Study Link 2·3

INDEPENDENT ACTIVITY

(*Math Masters,* p. 39)

Home Connection Students practice estimating and finding differences. Students can solve problems using any method they choose.

3 Differentiation Options

READINESS

PARTNER ACTIVITY

15–30 Min

▶ Making and Breaking Apart Numbers

(*Math Masters,* p. 40)

To provide experience trading between place-value columns, have students make tens by bundling wooden craft sticks or straws with rubber bands or twist ties. They break apart these bundles to model subtraction.

ENRICHMENT

PARTNER ACTIVITY

15–30 Min

▶ Comparing Methods of Subtraction

(*Student Reference Book,* pp. 15–17)

To further explore subtraction algorithms, have students compare the subtraction methods in the *Student Reference Book.* Their comparisons should focus on which methods make it easy to do mental arithmetic and which methods make it easy to do pencil-and-paper computations. Have students make posters illustrating in which steps they recommend using mental arithmetic.

2•4 Addition and Subtraction Number Stories

 **Objective** To review the use of mathematical models to solve number stories.

Technology Resources www.everydaymathonline.com

 ePresentations
 eToolkit
 Algorithms Practice
 EM Facts Workshop Game™
 Family Letters
 Assessment Management
 Common Core State Standards
 Curriculum Focal Points
 Interactive Teacher's Lesson Guide

1 Teaching the Lesson

Key Concepts and Skills

- Solve addition and subtraction problems for whole numbers and decimals. [Operations and Computation Goal 1]
- Make magnitude estimates for addition and subtraction number stories. [Operations and Computation Goal 6]
- Use open number sentences to solve number stories. [Patterns, Functions, and Algebra Goal 2]

Key Activities

Students review the use of situation diagrams; they write and solve open number sentences that model addition and subtraction number stories.

 **Ongoing Assessment: Recognizing Student Achievement** Use journal pages 37 and 38. [Patterns, Functions, and Algebra Goal 2]

Key Vocabulary

number sentence ♦ true number sentence ♦ false number sentence ♦ variable ♦ open number sentence ♦ relation symbol ♦ operation symbol ♦ solution

Materials

Math Journal 1, pp. 37 and 38
Student Reference Book, pp. 226, 227, 242, and 243
Study Link 2•3
Math Masters, pp. 41, 42, and 415

2 Ongoing Learning & Practice

Playing *Name That Number*
Student Reference Book, p. 325
per partnership: 1 complete deck of number cards (the Everything Math Deck, if available) ♦ calculator
Students apply their knowledge of number properties and equivalent names, and practice arithmetic operations and basic facts.

 **Math Boxes 2•4**
Math Journal 1, p. 39
Students practice and maintain skills through Math Box problems.

 **Study Link 2•4**
Math Masters, p. 43
Students practice and maintain skills through Study Link activities.

3 Differentiation Options

READINESS

Using Situation Diagrams
Math Masters, p. 44
Students use situation diagrams to write open number sentences.

ENRICHMENT

Solving Number Stories and Open Number Sentences
Math Masters, p. 45
Students write and solve number sentences for complicated number stories.

Advance Preparation

For Part 1, prepare a classroom chart showing the four steps on A Guide for Number Stories in the *Student Reference Book* on page 243. Consider making this a permanent part of your classroom displays. Copy and cut *Math Masters,* page 42 so that each small group has one problem to solve.

 ***Teacher's Reference Manual,* Grades 4–6** pp. 19, 291, 292

Getting Started

Mental Math and Reflexes

Dictate the numbers and have students write the numbers in expanded notation on their slates using fractions to record the decimal portion. For example, 8.392 $= 8 * 1 + 3 * (\frac{1}{10}) + 9 * (\frac{1}{100}) + 2 * (\frac{1}{1{,}000})$.

●○○ 1.6 $1 * 1 + 6 * (\frac{1}{10})$

5.4 $5 * 1 + 4 * (\frac{1}{10})$

16.3 $1 * 10 + 6 * 1 + 3 * (\frac{1}{10})$

●●○ 7.12 $7 * 1 + 1 * (\frac{1}{10}) + 2 * (\frac{1}{100})$

42.01 $4 * 10 + 2 * 1 + 1 * (\frac{1}{100})$

28.69 $2 * 10 + 8 * 1 + 6 * (\frac{1}{10}) + 9 * (\frac{1}{100})$

●●● 243.05 $2 * 100 + 4 * 10 + 3 * 1 + 5 * (\frac{1}{100})$

102.36 $1 * 100 + 2 * 1 + 3 * (\frac{1}{10}) + 6 * (\frac{1}{100})$

401.309 $4 * 100 + 1 * 1 + 3 * (\frac{1}{10}) + 9 * (\frac{1}{1{,}000})$

Math Message

Niko has $8.00. Does he have enough money to buy 3 fancy pencils for $1.98 each and an eraser for $1.73? Yes *What is the total cost of 3 pencils and 1 eraser?* $7.67

Study Link 2·3 Follow-Up

Have partners compare answers and resolve differences.

1 Teaching the Lesson

▶ Math Message Follow-Up

(*Student Reference Book,* pp. 226 and 227)

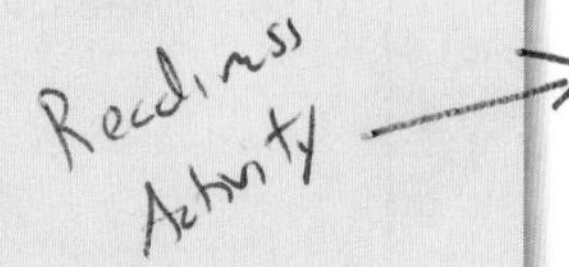

Algebraic Thinking Ask a volunteer to read the Math Message problem, stopping after the first question. Survey the class for their responses, and ask how they estimated their answers. Ask another volunteer to read the second question. Before students share their answers, refer to page 226 of the *Student Reference Book.* Ask students to discuss with a partner which diagram they would use to model the situation in the Math Message problem. Ask volunteers to explain their choices. Ask: *After thinking about using situation diagrams, would you change your original plan for solving the problem?*

Use this discussion to emphasize that mathematical models help organize the given and the unknown information in a problem, making the problem easier to understand.

Another way to model situations is to use number models to organize the information. Ask partners to refer to page 227 of the *Student Reference Book* and then write a **number sentence** to model the Math Message problem. As partners finish, have them write their number sentences on the board. Sample answers: $3 * 1.98 + 1.73 = 7.67$, and $7.67 < 8.00$; $(3 * p) + e =$ total cost, $(3 * 1.98) + 1.73 = 5.94 + 1.73 = 7.67$. Survey the class for true statements about number sentences. Use student responses and examples to discuss the following points. To support English language learners, write the key ideas on the board during the discussion.

▷ Number sentences are similar to language sentences except that they use math symbols instead of words.

▷ Some number sentences are true and some are false. For example, $10 - 2 = 8$ is a **true number sentence.** The number sentence $8 / 2 > 4 * 100$ is a **false number sentence.**

NOTE Relation Symbols
< means *is less than*
> means *is greater than*
= means *is equal to*

Operation Symbols
+ means *plus*
− means *minus*
× or * means *times*
÷ or / means *divided by*

- ▷ Number sentences that contain a **variable** are called open number sentences. **Open number sentences** are neither true nor false. Only when we replace the variable with a number do we get a number sentence that is either true or false.
- ▷ A number sentence must have a **relation symbol.** (*See margin, page 98.*) Students should be familiar with the relation symbols shown in the margin. For example, the number sentence $10 - 2 = 8$ contains the $=$ relation symbol. The number sentence $8 / 2 < 4 * 100$ contains the $<$ relation symbol.
- ▷ Number sentences also contain numbers and **operation symbols.** (*See margin, page 98.*) For example, the number sentence $10 - 2 = 8$ contains three numbers (10, 2, and 8) and the operation symbol, $-$. The number sentence $8 / 2 < 4 * 100$ contains four numbers (8, 2, 4, and 100) and the operation symbols, / and $*$.

▶ Using Open Number Sentences

WHOLE-CLASS ACTIVITY

(*Student Reference Book,* pp. 242 and 243; *Math Masters,* p. 41 and 42)

Algebraic Thinking Ask: *What does it mean to be a good problem solver?* Many fifth-grade students mistakenly view the good problem solver as someone who knows right away what to do to get the correct answer. Use follow-up questions to help students recognize that problem solving is a creative activity. Emphasize that there is more than one way to do most things. People think differently, and what seems easy for some may be difficult for others.

The good problem solver is someone who has learned ways to organize information to find a solution when he or she is not sure how to get the correct answer. One way to become a good problem solver is to solve many different kinds of problems.

Refer students to pages 242 and 243 in the *Student Reference Book.* Read the four steps of the guide, and then read one of the Check Your Understanding problems. Ask students the questions under Step 1. Have volunteers respond and check the class for consensus on the responses. Ask students to identify the type of situation in the problem: parts-and-total, change-to-more, change-to-less, or comparison. Remind students that recognizing the type of situation helps them understand the problem and plan what to do. Allow partners a few minutes to complete Steps 2 and 3 independently.

Bring the class together to discuss Step 4. Explain that writing a number model for the problem in Step 2 means writing an open number sentence that will help solve the problem. Writing a number model in Step 4 means writing a number sentence, using the appropriate numbers from the problem, and showing the **solution.** If the number sentence is true, the solution is correct.

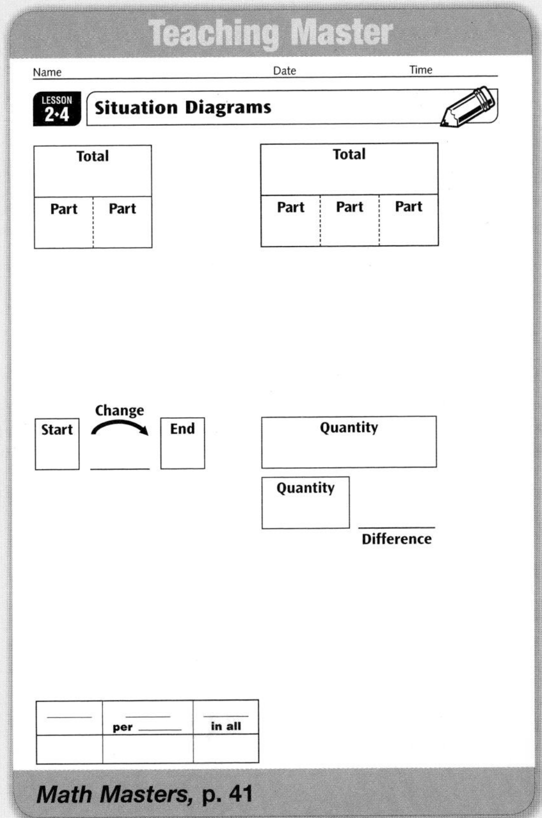
Teaching Master

Name Date Time

LESSON 2·4 **Situation Diagrams**

Math Masters, p. 41

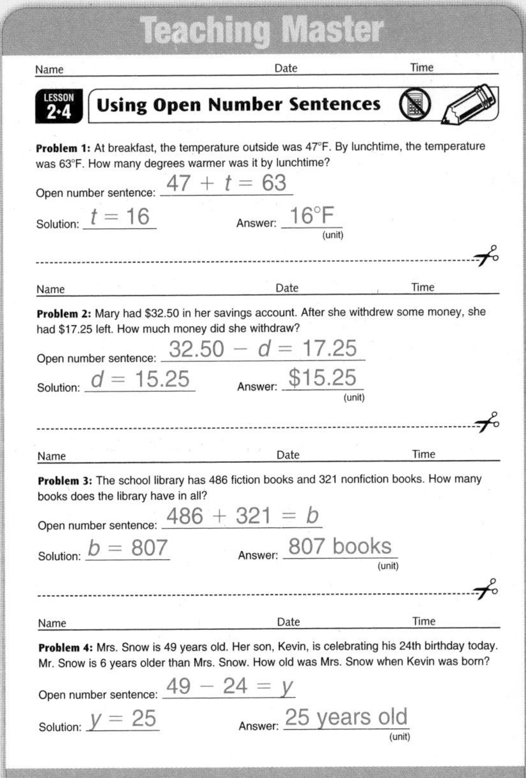
Teaching Master

Name Date Time

LESSON 2·4 **Using Open Number Sentences**

Problem 1: At breakfast, the temperature outside was 47°F. By lunchtime, the temperature was 63°F. How many degrees warmer was it by lunchtime?

Open number sentence: $47 + t = 63$

Solution: $t = 16$ Answer: 16°F (unit)

Name Date Time

Problem 2: Mary had \$32.50 in her savings account. After she withdrew some money, she had \$17.25 left. How much money did she withdraw?

Open number sentence: $32.50 - d = 17.25$

Solution: $d = 15.25$ Answer: \$15.25 (unit)

Name Date Time

Problem 3: The school library has 486 fiction books and 321 nonfiction books. How many books does the library have in all?

Open number sentence: $486 + 321 = b$

Solution: $b = 807$ Answer: 807 books (unit)

Name Date Time

Problem 4: Mrs. Snow is 49 years old. Her son, Kevin, is celebrating his 24th birthday today. Mr. Snow is 6 years older than Mrs. Snow. How old was Mrs. Snow when Kevin was born?

Open number sentence: $49 - 24 = y$

Solution: $y = 25$ Answer: 25 years old (unit)

Math Masters, p. 42

Have students work in small groups. Give each small group one copy of *Math Masters,* page 41, and a copy of one of the problems from *Math Masters,* page 42. Have students share their processes and solutions. Prompt students to include the following points:

▷ The type of situation that the number story represents. There may be more than one appropriate situation diagram for each number story.

▷ How the group decided on a letter variable to use for the missing number in their open number sentence. Remind students that the variable can be any letter, but it often helps if the letter serves as a reminder of what is to be found.

▷ How the variable and the other numbers in the story are related in their open number sentence.

Problem 1: At breakfast, the temperature outside was 47°F. By lunchtime, the temperature had gone up to 63°F. How many degrees warmer was it by lunchtime? 16 degrees

This is a change-to-more story, in which we want to find how much the starting number increased. The missing number is the number of degrees the temperature increased. The variable could be t (for temperature) or d (for degrees), for example.

Problem 2: Mary had $32.50 in her savings account. After she withdrew some money, she had $17.25 left in her account. How much money did she withdraw from her account? Mary withdrew $15.25.

This is a change-to-less story. We want to find how much the starting number decreased. The missing number is the amount of money she withdrew. The variable could be any letter agreed on by the group.

Problem 3: The school library has 486 fiction books and 321 nonfiction books. How many books does the library have in all? 807 books

This is a parts-and-total story where two or more separate parts are known, and we want to find the total. The missing number is the total number of books in the library. The variable could be t (for total) or any letter agreed upon by the group.

Problem 4: Mrs. Snow is 49 years old. Her son, Kevin, is celebrating his 24th birthday today. Mr. Snow is 6 years older than Mrs. Snow. How old was Mrs. Snow when Kevin was born? Mrs. Snow was 25 years old when Kevin was born.

This is a **comparison story** involving the difference between two quantities. The missing number is the difference between the two ages. The variable could be d (for difference) or any letter agreed upon by the group.

NOTE Mr. Snow's age is not relevant to the solution of the problem. Remind students that understanding the problem helps them recognize when they have all the information needed to answer the question. Then they can avoid being distracted by other information in the problem.

Student Page

Date ______ Time ______

LESSON 2·4 Addition and Subtraction Stories

For each problem on pages 37 and 38, fill in the blanks and solve the problem.

Example: Maria had 2 decks of cards. One of the decks had only 36 cards instead of 52. The rest were missing from the deck. How many cards were missing?

- List the numbers needed to solve the problem. 36 and 52
- Describe what you want to find. The number of missing cards
- Write an open sentence: $36 + c = 52$
- Find the missing number in the open sentence. Solution: $c = 16$
- Write the answer to the number story. Answer: 16 cards (unit)

1. Anthony got a new bike. He rode 18 miles the first week, 27 miles the second week, and 34 miles the third week. How many miles did he ride altogether?
   a. List the numbers needed to solve the problem. 18, 27, and 34
   b. Describe what you want to find. The total number of miles
   c. Open sentence: $18 + 27 + 34 = m$
   d. Solution: $m = 79$ e. Answer: 79 miles (unit)

2. Regina has $23.08. Her sister has $16.47. Her brother has only $5.00. How much more money does Regina have than her sister?
   a. List the numbers needed to solve the problem. 23.08 and 16.47
   b. Describe what you want to find. How much more money Regina has than her sister
   c. Open sentence: $23.08 - 16.47 = r$
   d. Solution: $r = 6.61$ e. Answer: $6.61

3. Lucas was making breakfast for 12 friends. He started with 19 eggs. He bought 1 dozen more eggs. How many eggs did he have to cook for breakfast?
   a. List the numbers needed to solve the problem. 19 and 12
   b. Describe what you want to find. The total number of eggs
   c. Open sentence: $19 + 12 = e$
   d. Solution: $e = 31$ e. Answer: 31 eggs

Math Journal 1, p. 37

NOTE You can expect that many students will be able to solve simple addition and subtraction number stories without first having to write an open number sentence. The main purpose of this lesson is to introduce the use of open number sentences so students can use them to solve more complex problems.

Student Page

Date ______ Time ______

LESSON 2·4 Addition and Subtraction Stories *continued*

4. Nicholas earned $48 mowing lawns one weekend. With the money he earned, he bought 2 CDs that cost a total of $23. How much money did he have left?
   a. List the numbers needed to solve the problem. 48 and 23
   b. Describe what you want to find. The amount of money left
   c. Open sentence: $48 - 23 = d$
   d. Solution: $d = 25$ e. Answer: $25 (unit)

Circle the open sentence that best matches each story and then solve the problem.

5. Patrick paints color-by-number pictures. He spent 24 hours painting in June and 37 hours painting in July. One picture had 18 different colors. How many hours did he paint in the two months?

   $18 + h = 37$ $24 + h = 37$ ($37 + 24 = h$) $37 - h = 18$

   Answer: 61 hours (unit)

6. Sue walked 2 miles to Jan's house. Then both girls walked 2 miles to Tad's house. Sue took 28 minutes to get to Jan's house. The girls took 45 minutes to get to Tad's house. How much longer did it take to get to Tad's than to Jan's?

   $2 * 28 = m$ $2 + 28 + m = 45$ $m - 28 = 45$ ($45 - 28 = m$)

   Answer: 17 minutes (unit)

Circle the number sentence that matches the problem.

7. Ralph and Adeline saved their money for 6 weeks. Ralph saved $27.23. Adeline saved $34.98. How much more did Adeline save than Ralph?
   a. $\$27.23 + \$34.98 = s$
   b. $6 * s = \$34.98$
   (c.) $\$27.23 + s = \$34.98$
   d. $6 + s = \$34.98 - \$27.23$

   Answer: $7.75 (unit)

8. Tanya's guinea pig is 5 years old and 10.25 inches long. Monique's guinea pig is 2 years old and 11.5 inches. Jamal's guinea pig is 4 years old and 9.3 inches. What is the difference in length between the shortest and the longest guinea pig?
   (a.) $11.5 - 9.3 = d$ b. $11.5 - 10.25 = d$
   c. $d = 2 + 5 + 9.3$ d. $d = 11.5 + 9.3$

   Answer: 2.2 inches (unit)

Math Journal 1, p. 38

Solving Addition and Subtraction Number Stories

PARTNER ACTIVITY

(*Math Journal 1,* pp. 37 and 38; *Math Masters,* p. 415)

Algebraic Thinking Distribute a computation grid to each student. Go over the example on journal page 37 with the class. Then have partners complete the pages.

Ongoing Assessment: Recognizing Student Achievement

Journal pages 37 and 38 Problems 1, 3, and 4

Use **journal pages 37 and 38, Problems 1, 3, and 4** to assess students' ability to write open number sentences to model given situations. Students are making adequate progress if they have written the correct open number sentence for Problems 1, 3, and 4.

[Patterns, Functions, and Algebra Goal 2]

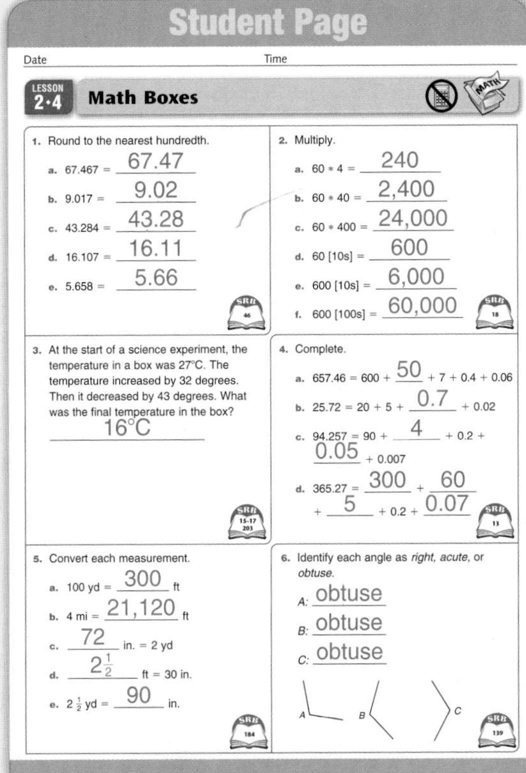

Student Page

Date Time

LESSON 2·4 **Math Boxes**

1. Round to the nearest hundredth.
   a. 67.467 = 67.47
   b. 9.017 = 9.02
   c. 43.284 = 43.28
   d. 16.107 = 16.11
   e. 5.658 = 5.66

2. Multiply.
   a. 60 ∗ 4 = 240
   b. 60 ∗ 40 = 2,400
   c. 60 ∗ 400 = 24,000
   d. 60 [10s] = 600
   e. 600 [10s] = 6,000
   f. 600 [100s] = 60,000

3. At the start of a science experiment, the temperature in a box was 27°C. The temperature increased by 32 degrees. Then it decreased by 43 degrees. What was the final temperature in the box?
   16°C

4. Complete.
   a. 657.46 = 600 + 50 + 7 + 0.4 + 0.06
   b. 25.72 = 20 + 5 + 0.7 + 0.02
   c. 94.257 = 90 + 4 + 0.2 + 0.05 + 0.007
   d. 365.27 = 300 + 60 + 5 + 0.2 + 0.07

5. Convert each measurement.
   a. 100 yd = 300 ft
   b. 4 mi = 21,120 ft
   c. 72 in. = 2 yd
   d. $2\frac{1}{2}$ ft = 30 in.
   e. $2\frac{1}{2}$ yd = 90 in.

6. Identify each angle as *right, acute,* or *obtuse.*
   A: obtuse
   B: obtuse
   C: obtuse

Math Journal 1, p. 39

2 Ongoing Learning & Practice

Playing *Name That Number*

PARTNER ACTIVITY

(*Student Reference Book,* p. 325)

Students play *Name That Number* to practice applying their knowledge of number properties, equivalent names, arithmetic operations, and basic facts. This game supports the development of flexibility with mental and paper-and-pencil computation.

For an added challenge, players can turn over two cards and place them next to each other. The numbers on the cards become the digits of the target number. The target number may be a 2-, 3-, or 4-digit number.

Math Boxes 2·4

INDEPENDENT ACTIVITY

(*Math Journal 1,* p. 39)

Mixed Review Math Boxes in this lesson are paired with Math Boxes in Lesson 2-2. The skill in Problem 6 previews Unit 3 content.

Writing/Reasoning Have students write a response to the following: *Explain how 60 ∗ 4 from Problem 2 can help you solve 240 ÷ 60.* Both problems are part of the same multiplication/division fact family. Knowing that 60 ∗ 4 = 240 lets you know right away that 240 ÷ 60 = 4.

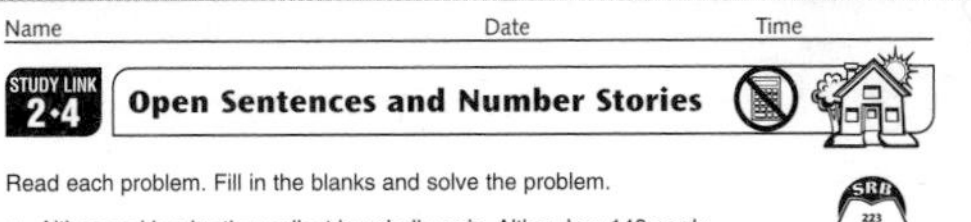

Study Link Master

Name Date Time

STUDY LINK 2·4 **Open Sentences and Number Stories**

Read each problem. Fill in the blanks and solve the problem.

1. Althea and her brother collect baseball cards. Althea has 148 cards. Her brother has 127 cards. How many cards do they have altogether?
   a. List the numbers needed to solve the problem. 148 and 127
   b. Describe what you want to find. Total number of cards
   c. Open number sentence: 148 + 127 = *b*
   d. Solution: *b* = 275 e. Answer: 275 baseball cards (unit)

2. Mark bought a hamburger for $3.89 and a drink for $1.49. If he paid with a $20 bill, how much change did he receive?
   a. List the numbers needed to solve the problem. 20.00; 3.89; 1.49
   b. Describe what you want to find. The amount of change
   c. Open number sentence: 20.00 − 3.89 − 1.49 = *c*, or 20 − (3.89 + 1.49) = *c*
   d. Solution: *c* = 14.62 e. Answer: $14.62 (unit)

3. Fran has four pieces of ribbon. Each piece of ribbon is a different length: 0.6 meters long, 1.15 meters long, 1.35 meters long, and 0.925 meters long. How many meters of ribbon does Fran have in all?
   a. List the numbers needed to solve the problem. 0.6, 1.15, 1.35, 0.925
   b. Describe what you want to find. The length of the ribbons
   c. Open number sentence: *b* = 0.6 + 1.15 + 1.35 + 0.925
   d. Solution: *b* = 4.025
   e. Answer: 4.025 meters (unit)

Math Masters, p. 43

Teaching Master

Name Date Time

LESSON 2•4 **Using Situation Diagrams**

- Use the information in each problem to fill in the diagram.
- Use a ? to show the missing number.
- Write an open number sentence with the information from the diagram.

1. Two angles of a triangle measure 45° and 55°. What is the sum of the measures of the two angles?

   Open number sentence: $s = 45 + 55$

Total	
?	
Part	Part
45	55

2. There are 64 tennis balls in a basket. If 35 of them are orange and the rest are green, how many tennis balls are green?

   Open number sentence: $35 + g = 64$

Total	
64	
Part	Part
35	?

3. Elvin had \$15.00 to spend at the school bazaar. He spent \$12.75. How much money did he have left?

   Open number sentence: $15.00 - 12.75 = d$

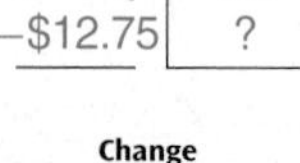

Start	Change	End
\$15.00	−\$12.75	?

4. a. At 7 A.M., the temperature is 76°F. The temperature is expected to drop by 17° by 4 P.M. What will the temperature be at 4 P.M.?

   Open number sentence: $76 - 17 = t$

Start	Change	End
76	−17	?

   b. What would the temperature be at 4 P.M. if the temperature increased by 17°?

   Open number sentence: $76 + 17 = t$

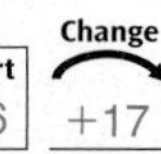

Start	Change	End
76	+17	?

Math Masters, **p. 44**

Teaching Master

Name Date Time

LESSON 2•4 **Writing Open Number Sentences**

Write an open number sentence and solve the problem.

1. Chan brought his collection of 1,500 sports cards to school. He has 156 basketball cards and 625 football cards. The rest were baseball cards. How many baseball cards did Chan bring?

   a. Open number sentence: $b = 1{,}500 - (156 + 625)$; $156 + 625 = c$; $1{,}500 - c = b$

   b. Solution: $b = 719$ c. Answer: 719 baseball cards (unit)

2. Abdul took a bus downtown to see a movie. The bus ride to the theater took 15 minutes. If the movie was $2\frac{1}{4}$ hours long, how many hours and minutes was Abdul away from home?

   a. Open number sentence: $m = 2.25 * 60 + (2 * 15)$ or, $h = 2.25 + (2 * 0.25)$

   b. Solution: $m = 165$, or $h = 2.75$

   c. Answer: 2 hours, 45 minutes (unit)

3. Julie paid \$14.08 to fill her gas tank with 10 gallons of gas before starting a trip from Chicago to Topeka, Kansas. After driving about 305 miles, she bought 10 more gallons of gas in Iowa and paid \$11.85. How much more did she pay for a gallon of gas in Chicago than in Iowa?

   a. Open number sentence: $(14.08 / 10) - (11.85 / 10) = g$, or $(14.08 - 11.85) / 10 = g$

   b. Solution: $g = 0.223$ c. Answer: About \$0.22 per gallon (unit)

Math Masters, **p. 45**

▶ Study Link 2•4

INDEPENDENT ACTIVITY

(*Math Masters,* p. 43)

Home Connection Students solve addition and subtraction number stories. Remind students to use the steps in A Guide to Solving Number Stories on *Student Reference Book,* page 243 to help them solve the problems.

3 Differentiation Options

READINESS

INDEPENDENT ACTIVITY

▶ Using Situation Diagrams

5–15 Min

(*Math Masters,* p. 44)

Algebraic Thinking To provide experience using situation diagrams to write open-number sentences, have students solve the problems on *Math Masters,* page 44. When students have finished, have them explain how the diagram helps them determine where the placeholder goes in the number sentence.

ENRICHMENT

PARTNER ACTIVITY

▶ Solving Number Stories and Open Number Sentences

15–30 Min

(*Math Masters,* p. 45)

Algebraic Thinking To apply students' understanding of open-number sentences, have them solve multistep number stories on *Math Masters,* page 45.

NOTE Students may use parentheses to model a problem with a single open number sentence. Others will use several separate number sentences for a problem. Parentheses will be formally reviewed in Unit 7.

2•5 Estimate Your Reaction Time

Objective To provide experiences with estimating reaction times and with using statistical landmarks to describe experimental data.

Technology Resources www.everydaymathonline.com

ePresentations

eToolkit

Algorithms Practice

EM Facts Workshop Game™

Family Letters

Assessment Management

Common Core State Standards

Curriculum Focal Points

Interactive Teacher's Lesson Guide

1 Teaching the Lesson

Key Concepts and Skills

- Read and write decimals to the hundredths place. [Number and Numeration Goal 1]
- Order decimals to the hundredths place. [Number and Numeration Goal 6]
- Use line plots to organize reaction-time data. [Data and Chance Goal 1]
- Find statistical landmarks. [Data and Chance Goal 2]
- Compare and draw conclusions about collected data. [Data and Chance Goal 2]

Key Activities

Students review how to find the mean of a set of data. They experiment to collect reaction time data. They find statistical landmarks and estimate individual reaction times.

Ongoing Assessment: Recognizing Student Achievement
Use Mental Math and Reflexes.
[Number and Numeration Goal 6]

Key Vocabulary

stimulus ◆ reaction time ◆ elapsed time ◆ mean (average) ◆ mode ◆ range ◆ minimum ◆ maximum

Materials

Math Journal 1, pp. 40, 41, and Activity Sheet 2
Student Reference Book, pp. 119–121, 249
Study Link 2•4
calculator ◆ timer such as a stopwatch, a digital watch, or a clock ◆ Class Data Pad ◆ stick-on notes ◆ scissors

2 Ongoing Learning & Practice

Playing *High Number Toss: Decimal Version*
Student Reference Book, p. 321
Math Masters, p. 511
per partnership: 4 each of number cards 0–9 (from the Everything Math Deck, if available)
Students practice concepts of place value and standard notation by writing and comparing decimals.

Math Boxes 2•5
Math Journal 1, p. 42
Students practice and maintain skills through Math Box problems.

Study Link 2•5
Math Masters, p. 46
Students practice and maintain skills through Study Link activities.

3 Differentiation Options

READINESS

Missing Decimals on the Number Line
Math Masters, p. 47
calculator
Students use a calculator to find the pattern on a decimal number line and use the pattern to fill in the missing numbers.

ENRICHMENT

Interpreting Data
Math Masters, p. 48
Students explore the relationship between data organization and its interpretation.

Advance Preparation

For Part 1, you will need a timing device that measures to the nearest second. Prepare two line plot scales on chart paper or the board for students to plot their individual data with stick-on notes. (*See page 106.*)

***Teacher's Reference Manual,* Grades 4–6** pp. 158–169

Getting Started

Mental Math and Reflexes

Remind students of the relation symbols for *is greater than* (>), *is less than* (<), and *is equal to* (=). Orally give students decimal pairs and have them write a number sentence showing the relationship. *Suggestions:*

●○○	●●○	●●●
8.0 _>_ 0.08	0.04 _>_ 0.004	0.015 _<_ 0.02
0.6 _>_ 0.006	0.809 _<_ 0.899	0.011 _<_ 0.110
0.55 _=_ 0.550	0.20 _>_ 0.045	0.080 _=_ 0.0800

Math Message

Cut out the Grab-It Gauge on Activity Sheet 2.

Study Link 2·4 Follow-Up

Have partners compare answers and resolve differences. Ask volunteers to share how they decided which numbers were needed to solve the problems.

Ongoing Assessment: Recognizing Student Achievement

Mental Math and Reflexes ★

Use the **Mental Math and Reflexes** problem to assess students' ability to compare decimals. Students are making adequate progress if they are able to correctly solve ●○○ and ●●○ problems. Some students might be able to solve the ●●● problems.

[Number and Numeration Goal 6]

NOTE Remind students that the time that passes between a given starting and ending time is *elapsed time.* For practice with *elapsed time,* see www.everydaymathonline.com.

1 Teaching the Lesson

▶ Math Message Follow-Up

WHOLE-CLASS DISCUSSION

(*Math Journal 1,* Activity Sheet 2)

Science Link Explain that the class will use the Grab-It Gauge to measure the time it takes each of them to react to a **stimulus.** Ask students to give an example of a stimulus. Summarize the discussion by defining a stimulus as something that causes a response. For example, your eyes may tear when you chop onions because the onion's gases are a stimulus.

▶ Estimating a Mean Reaction Time for the Class

WHOLE-CLASS ACTIVITY

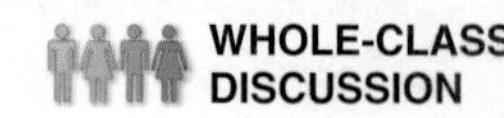

(*Student Reference Book,* pp. 121 and 249)

In this lesson, students will conduct an experiment to estimate how fast they react to stimuli. Explain that by doing this experiment, they will be able to estimate the average time it takes a student to react to having his or her right hand squeezed. This is called the **reaction time.**

Assign two students to be Timers; one is the "Start Timer" and the other is the "Stop Timer." Before you begin, explain the experiment. Practice once or twice, and then perform the experiment.

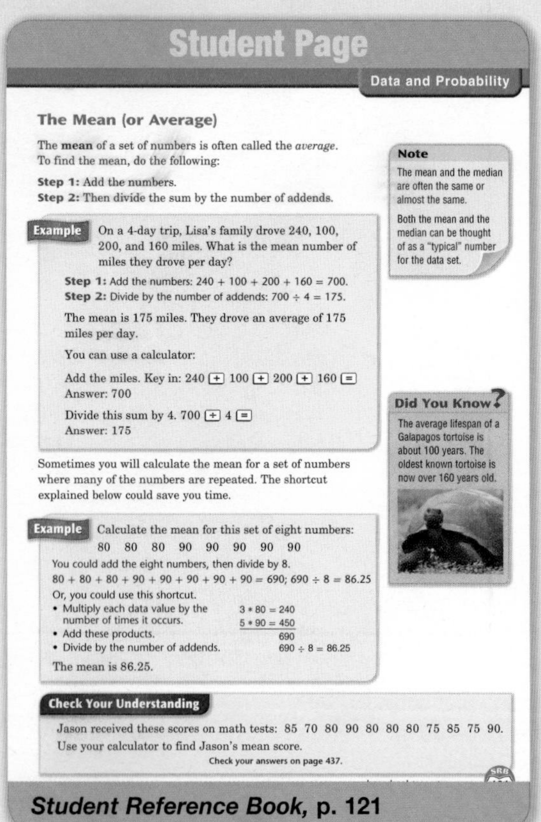

Student Page

Data and Probability

The Mean (or Average)

The **mean** of a set of numbers is often called the *average.* To find the mean, do the following:

Step 1: Add the numbers.
Step 2: Then divide the sum by the number of addends.

Example On a 4-day trip, Lisa's family drove 240, 100, 200, and 160 miles. What is the mean number of miles they drove per day?

Step 1: Add the numbers: 240 + 100 + 200 + 160 = 700.
Step 2: Divide by the number of addends: 700 ÷ 4 = 175.

The mean is 175 miles. They drove an average of 175 miles per day.

You can use a calculator:

Add the miles. Key in: 240 [+] 100 [+] 200 [+] 160 [=]
Answer: 700

Divide this sum by 4. 700 [÷] 4 [=]
Answer: 175

Note The mean and the median are often the same or almost the same.

Both the mean and the median can be thought of as a "typical" number for the data set.

Sometimes you will calculate the mean for a set of numbers where many of the numbers are repeated. The shortcut explained below could save you time.

Example Calculate the mean for this set of eight numbers:
80 80 80 90 90 90 90 90

You could add the eight numbers, then divide by 8.
80 + 80 + 80 + 90 + 90 + 90 + 90 + 90 = 690; 690 ÷ 8 = 86.25

Or, you could use this shortcut.
- Multiply each data value by the number of times it occurs. 3 ∗ 80 = 240; 5 ∗ 90 = 450
- Add these products. 690
- Divide by the number of addends. 690 ÷ 8 = 86.25

The mean is 86.25.

Did You Know? The average lifespan of a Galapagos tortoise is about 100 years. The oldest known tortoise is now over 160 years old.

Check Your Understanding

Jason received these scores on math tests: 85 70 80 90 80 80 80 75 85 75 90.
Use your calculator to find Jason's mean score.

Check your answers on page 437.

Student Reference Book, p. 121

Procedure

1. The Leader and all the students, except the Timers, hold hands and form a large circle around the room.
2. As the Leader, give the Start Timer the signal to start timing as you gently squeeze the hand of the person on your left. The Start Timer records the time on the board.
3. The person on your left squeezes the hand of the person on his or her left.
4. The squeeze continues around the circle until it reaches the Leader, who calls out "Stop!"
5. The Stop Timer records the stop time. Both Timers then calculate the **elapsed time** in seconds and record it on the board. This is the total reaction time.

Have students close their eyes during the experiment so they can't anticipate the squeeze by watching it travel from person to person.

To support English language learners, write *elapsed time* and *total reaction time* on the board and discuss their meanings. Ask students to use their calculators to find the **mean** reaction time per student. (Divide the total reaction time by the total number of people in the circle.) Explain that both *mean* and *average* describe the same data landmark. Refer students to *Student Reference Book,* page 121, if needed.

Ask students to read the result in their calculator display to a partner. Read the result for the class and record it on the Class Data Pad. Ask whether it would be practical to use the entire decimal for further experiments. Use their responses to clarify the use of the nearest tenth of a second for the mean reaction time.

Ask volunteers to explain how they would use the calculator display after dividing to find the nearest tenth of a second. Review rounding to the nearest tenth. Refer students to page 249 of the *Student Reference Book,* if necessary. Discuss when it might be better to round to the nearest hundredth. Review that procedure.

Rounding to the Nearest Tenth

Use the hundredths digit to round to the nearest tenth:

If the hundredths digit is 4 or less, round down.

$0.5\underline{4}2 \rightarrow 0.5$ $\quad 0.4\underline{3}1538 \rightarrow 0.4$ $\quad 0.4\underline{1}94949 \rightarrow 0.4$

If the hundredths digit is 5 or more, round up.

$0.4\underline{5} \rightarrow 0.5$ $\quad 0.5\underline{5}1674 \rightarrow 0.6$ $\quad 0.4\underline{9}1 \rightarrow 0.5$

Rounding to the Nearest Hundredth

Use the thousandths digit to round to the nearest hundredth:

If the thousandths digit is 4 or less, round down.

$0.54\underline{2} \rightarrow 0.54$ $\quad 0.43\underline{1}538 \rightarrow 0.43$

If the thousandths digit is 5 or more, round up.

$0.55\underline{6}74 \rightarrow 0.56$ $\quad 0.41\underline{9}4949 \rightarrow 0.42$

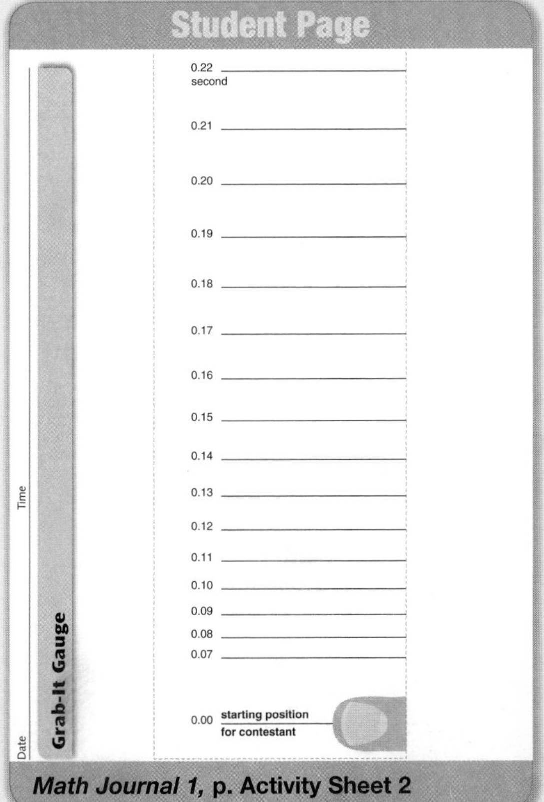

Math Journal 1, p. Activity Sheet 2

Student Page

Date Time

LESSON 2·5 Estimating Your Reaction Time

Tear out Activity Sheet 2 from the back of your journal. Cut out the Grab-It Gauge.

It takes two people to perform this experiment. The "Tester" holds the Grab-It Gauge at the top. The "Contestant" gets ready to catch the gauge by placing his or her thumb and index finger at the bottom of the gauge, *without quite touching it.* (*See diagram.*)

When the Contestant is ready, the Tester lets go of the gauge. The Contestant tries to grab it with his or her thumb and index finger as quickly as possible.

The number grasped by the Contestant shows that person's reaction time, to the nearest hundredth of a second. The Contestant then records that reaction time in the data table shown below.

Partners take turns being Tester and Contestant. Each person should perform the experiment 10 times with each hand.

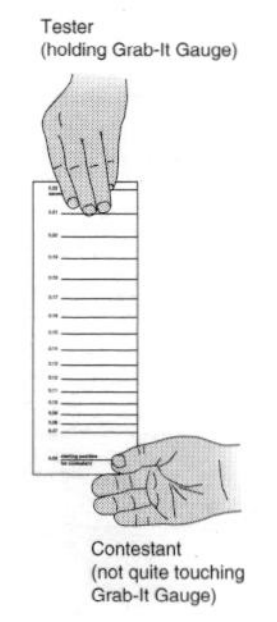

Reaction Time (in seconds)			
Left Hand		Right Hand	
1.	6.	1.	6.
2.	7.	2.	7.
3.	8.	3.	8.
4.	9.	4.	9.
5.	10.	5.	10.

Math Journal 1, p. 40

Student Page

Date Time

LESSON 2·5 Estimating Your Reaction Time *continued*

Use the results of your Grab-It experiment to answer the following questions.

Answers vary.

1. What was the **maximum** reaction time for your left hand? ______ right hand? ______
2. What was the **minimum** reaction time for your left hand? ______ right hand? ______
3. What was the **range** of reaction times for your left hand? ______ right hand? ______
4. What reaction time was the **mode** for your left hand? ______ right hand? ______
5. What was the **median** reaction time for your left hand? ______ right hand? ______
6. What was the **mean** reaction time for your left hand? ______ right hand? ______
7. If you could use just one number to estimate your reaction time, which number would you choose as the best estimate? Circle one.

   minimum maximum mode median mean

   Explain. ______

8. Which of your hands reacted more quickly in the Grab-It experiment? ______

Math Journal 1, p. 41

▶ Estimating Individual Reaction Times

PARTNER ACTIVITY

PROBLEM SOLVING

(*Math Journal 1,* pp. 40, 41, and Activity Sheet 2)

Ask students whether they think their left or right hand is quicker. Some students might reason that if they are right-handed, their right hand would react more quickly than their left hand; and conversely if they are left-handed. Tell them that they will perform an experiment to check which hand reacts more quickly.

Go over the directions for the experiment on journal page 40. Discuss the markings on the Grab-It Gauge. The times increase by 0.01 second as you go from the bottom of the gauge to the top.

Have two students demonstrate how to use the Grab-It Gauge. Partners then proceed with the experiment. Independently, they record the results of the experiment, find the statistical landmarks for the data, and record their conclusions.

Adjusting the Activity

Refer students to the *Student Reference Book,* pages 119–121, for the definitions and directions for finding statistical landmarks.

AUDITORY ◆ KINESTHETIC ◆ TACTILE ◆ VISUAL

▶ Displaying Reaction Time in Line Plots

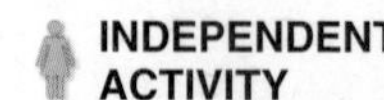

As students finish recording data and conclusions on their journal pages, direct the girls to write *girl* and the boys to write *boy* on each of two stick-on notes. Then each student writes the median time for the right hand on one stick-on note and the median time for the left hand on the other stick-on note. Students then use the lines you have prepared to make two line plots, one for each hand, by putting their stick-on notes in the appropriate places. Display one line plot over the other for ease of comparison.

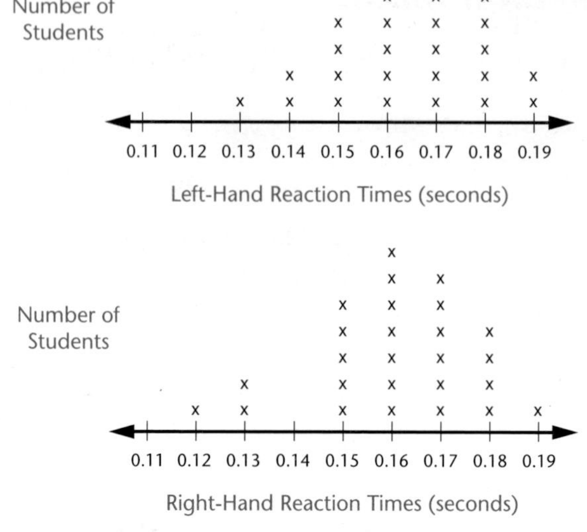

▶ Sharing Results

(*Math Journal 1,* pp. 40 and 41)

Bring the class together to discuss the results of the experiment. Ask students which landmarks they chose as the best estimates of their reaction times and why. The **mode,** median, and mean can be justified as reasonable estimates of their typical reaction time. The **range** cannot. The **minimum** is an estimate of their fastest reaction time but is not a good estimate of their typical reaction time. The **maximum** is an estimate of their slowest reaction time but is not a good estimate of their typical reaction time.

Refer to the line plots, and ask students to compare the shapes of these two line plots.

- Are the stick-on notes evenly spread? Do some occur in clusters? Are there gaps? What meaning do these shapes have?
- From your results, as well as the results of your classmates, are you able to state a rule about reaction times and left-handed or right-handed people? Do you have enough data?

NOTE Studies have shown that a right-handed person can react with the right hand about 3% faster than with the left hand and conversely for a left-handed person. Students would probably need to collect much more data to detect such slight differences.

- Would a difference of one or two hundredths in the medians make a meaningful difference? Not necessarily, considering that the tool and the method of measuring are not precise.
- Why might it be important to know a reaction time? In what sports or professions would this information be useful? Sample answer: It might be important for professional athletes in sports such as baseball or hockey, or in other professions such as pilots or astronauts.

2 Ongoing Learning & Practice

▶ Playing *High Number Toss: Decimal Version*

- When Finished w/ Math boxes

(*Student Reference Book,* p. 321; *Math Masters,* p. 511)

Students play *High Number Toss: Decimal Version* to practice writing and comparing decimals. They form, write, read, and compare decimal numbers. Provide students with a reminder box on the board noting that < means *is less than* and > means *is greater than.* After each round, ask students to record the decimals they formed on *Math Masters,* page 511, and use <, >, and = to compare them. If necessary, refer students to *Student Reference Book,* pages 32 and 33 to review comparing of decimals.

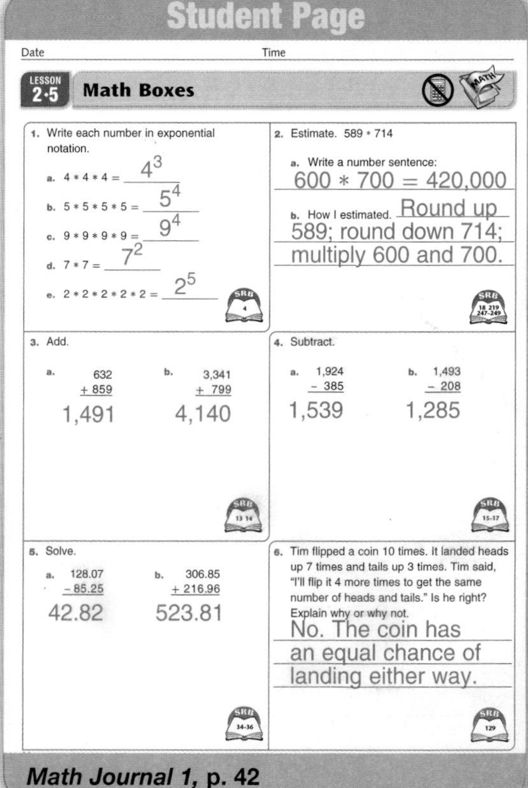

Student Page

Date Time

LESSON 2·5 **Math Boxes**

1. Write each number in exponential notation.
   a. 4 * 4 * 4 = 4^3
   b. 5 * 5 * 5 * 5 = 5^4
   c. 9 * 9 * 9 * 9 = 9^4
   d. 7 * 7 = 7^2
   e. 2 * 2 * 2 * 2 * 2 = 2^5

2. Estimate. 589 * 714
   a. Write a number sentence: 600 * 700 = 420,000
   b. How I estimated. Round up 589; round down 714; multiply 600 and 700.

3. Add.
   a. 632 + 859 = 1,491
   b. 3,341 + 799 = 4,140

4. Subtract.
   a. 1,924 − 385 = 1,539
   b. 1,493 − 208 = 1,285

5. Solve.
   a. 128.07 − 85.25 = 42.82
   b. 306.85 + 216.96 = 523.81

6. Tim flipped a coin 10 times. It landed heads up 7 times and tails up 3 times. Tim said, "I'll flip it 4 more times to get the same number of heads and tails." Is he right? Explain why or why not.
   No. The coin has an equal chance of landing either way.

Math Journal 1, p. 42

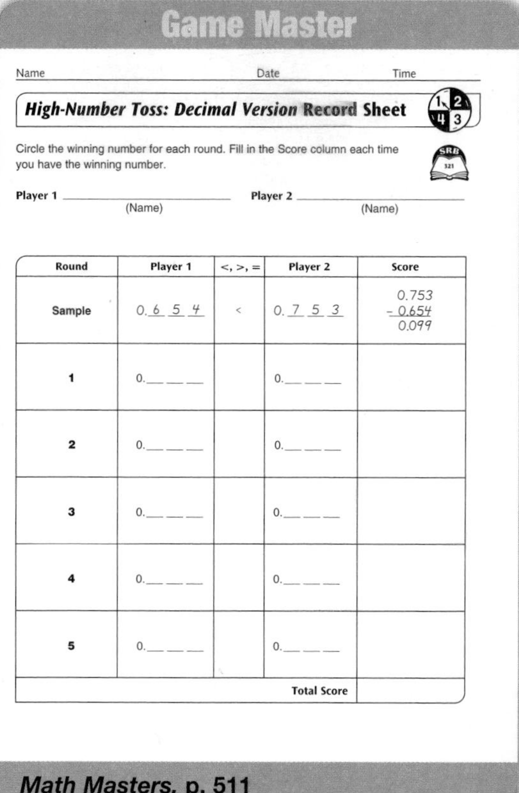

Game Master

Name Date Time

High-Number Toss: Decimal Version Record Sheet

Circle the winning number for each round. Fill in the Score column each time you have the winning number.

Player 1 ________ (Name) Player 2 ________ (Name)

Round	Player 1	<, >, =	Player 2	Score
Sample	0. 6 5 4	<	0. 7 5 3	0.753 − 0.654 = 0.099
1	0.___		0.___	
2	0.___		0.___	
3	0.___		0.___	
4	0.___		0.___	
5	0.___		0.___	
			Total Score	

Math Masters, p. 511

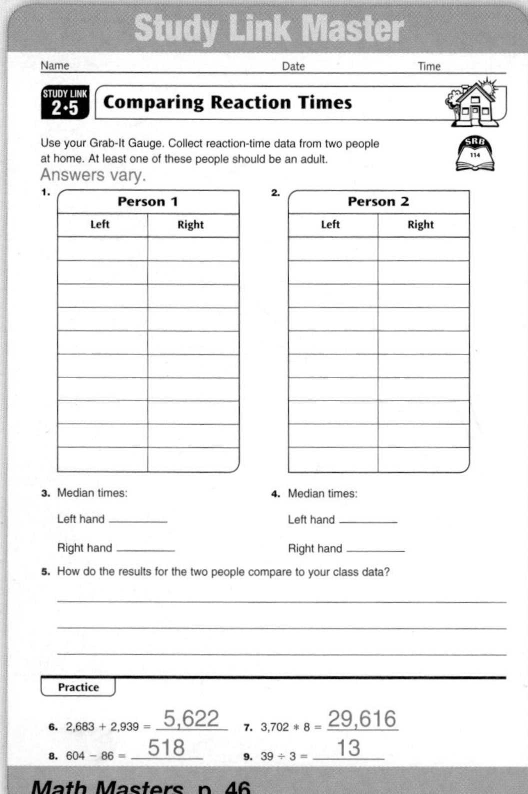
Study Link Master

Name Date Time

STUDY LINK 2·5 **Comparing Reaction Times**

Use your Grab-It Gauge. Collect reaction-time data from two people at home. At least one of these people should be an adult.

Answers vary.

1.

Person 1	
Left	Right

2.

Person 2	
Left	Right

3. Median times:
Left hand ______
Right hand ______

4. Median times:
Left hand ______
Right hand ______

5. How do the results for the two people compare to your class data?

Practice

6. 2,683 + 2,939 = 5,622
7. 3,702 ∗ 8 = 29,616
8. 604 − 86 = 518
9. 39 ÷ 3 = 13

Math Masters, p. 46

Math Boxes 2·5

INDEPENDENT ACTIVITY

(*Math Journal 1,* p. 42)

Mixed Practice Math Boxes in this lesson are paired with Math Boxes in Lesson 2-7. The skill in Problem 6 previews Unit 3 content.

Writing/Reasoning Have students write a response to the following: *Explain how you solved Problem 5a. Include in your explanation the strategies and reasoning used.* Answers vary.

Study Link 2·5

INDEPENDENT ACTIVITY

(*Math Masters,* p. 46)

Home Connection Students use the Grab-It Gauge to collect data from two people at home. They compare the results with the class data for the experiment. Remind students that they will need to take their Grab-It Gauges home.

3 Differentiation Options

READINESS

SMALL-GROUP ACTIVITY

5–15 Min

Missing Decimals on the Number Line

(*Math Masters,* p. 47)

To explore ordering decimals, have students skip-count on a calculator to find missing numbers on a number line. Students use a calculator to find patterns and calculate missing numbers on number lines. Then they fill in the missing numbers. Remind students to read the numbers quietly to themselves as they work.

ENRICHMENT

SMALL-GROUP ACTIVITY

5–15 Min

Interpreting Data

(*Math Masters,* p. 48)

To further explore organizing and analyzing data, have students use the data collected on the line plots from Part 1 to reorganize the reaction times by gender and then interpret the meaning of the data. From this new vantage point, have students prepare a presentation to explain the data. Encourage them to include pictures or graphs of their findings.

Teaching Master

Name Date Time

LESSON 2·5 **Decimal Number-Line Puzzles**

Step 1: Clear your calculator. Look at the number line.

Step 2: Enter the end number, subtract the start number, and divide by the number of jumps between. The result is the interval number.

Step 3: Enter the start number and add the interval number. This is the first missing number. Add the interval again to get the next missing number, and so on.

Example:

End number − start number = difference 6 − 4 = 2

Difference ÷ hops = interval 2 ÷ 5 = 0.4

4 + 0.4 = 4.4; 4.4 + 0.4 = 4.8; 4.8 + 0.4 = 5.2; 5.2 + 0.4 = 5.6; 5.6 + 0.4 = 6.0

4.0 4.4 4.8 5.2 5.6 6.0

1. Jumps: 8
6 6.1 6.2 6.3 6.4 6.5 6.6 6.7 6.8

2. Jumps: 5
1.4 1.96 2.52 3.08 3.64 4.2

3. Jumps: 6
1.34 2.68 4.02 5.36 6.7 8.04 9.38

Try This

4. Jumps: 6
4.568 9.136 13.704 18.272 22.84 27.408 31.976 36.544 41.112

Math Masters, p. 47

2•6 Chance Events

Objectives To review vocabulary associated with chance events and to introduce the Probability Meter.

www.everydaymathonline.com

ePresentations

eToolkit

Algorithms Practice

EM Facts Workshop Game™

Family Letters

Assessment Management

Common Core State Standards

Curriculum Focal Points

Interactive Teacher's Lesson Guide

1 Teaching the Lesson

Key Concepts and Skills

- Record data in a table. [Data and Chance Goal 1]
- Find landmarks for a data set. [Data and Chance Goal 2]
- Describe events using basic probability terms. [Data and Chance Goal 3]
- Predict the outcome and respond to the results of a thumbtack experiment. Express the probability of an event as a fraction, decimal, or percent. [Data and Chance Goal 4]

Key Activities

Students describe the probability of various chance events and record these probabilities on the Probability Meter Poster.

Ongoing Assessment: Recognizing Student Achievement Use an Exit Slip (*Math Masters,* page 414). [Numbers and Numeration Goal 5]

Ongoing Assessment: Informing Instruction See page 112.

Key Vocabulary

impossible ◆ certain ◆ Probability Meter Poster

Materials

Math Journal 1, pp. 43 and 44
Student Reference Book, p. 402
Study Link 2•5 ◆ *Math Masters,* p. 414
Probability Meter ◆ calculator ◆ per partnership: stick-on note, 10 thumbtacks (or two-color counters or pennies), small cup

2 Ongoing Learning & Practice

Estimating Magnitude for Addition and Subtraction

Math Journal 1, p. 45
Students practice making magnitude estimates and number models for addition and subtraction problems.

Math Boxes 2•6

Math Journal 1, p. 46
Students practice and maintain skills through Math Box problems.

Study Link 2•6

Math Masters, p. 49
Students practice and maintain skills through Study Link activities.

3 Differentiation Options

READINESS

Comparing Fractions, Decimals, and Percents

Student Reference Book, p. 398
Math Masters, p. 50
scissors ◆ glue or paste (optional)
Students order fractions, decimals, and percents.

ENRICHMENT

Making Spinners

Math Masters, pp. 51 and 52
scissors
Students design spinners based on fraction, decimal, and percent relationships, as well as probability concepts.

Advance Preparation

Cut out the Probability Meter Poster. Tape the pieces together at the 50% mark, and post it. For Part 1, pennies or counters may be substituted for thumbtacks. Change the journal page directions accordingly. Do not use pushpins.

***Teacher's Reference Manual,* Grades 4–6** pp. 155–158

Getting Started

Mental Math and Reflexes

Dictate the fractions, repeating each problem once. Maintain a brisk pace. Have students write the decimal and percent equivalents on their slates.

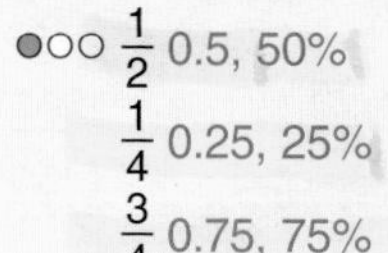

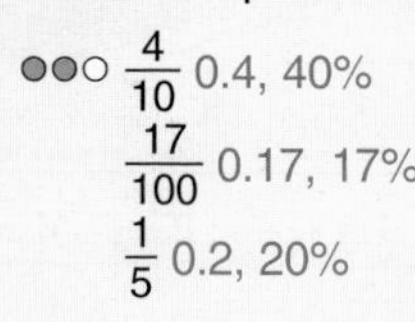

●○○ $\frac{1}{2}$ 0.5, 50%
$\frac{1}{4}$ 0.25, 25%
$\frac{3}{4}$ 0.75, 75%

●●○ $\frac{4}{10}$ 0.4, 40%
$\frac{17}{100}$ 0.17, 17%
$\frac{1}{5}$ 0.2, 20%

●●● $\frac{1}{3}$ $0.\overline{3}$, $33\frac{1}{3}$%
$\frac{2}{3}$ $0.\overline{6}$, $66\frac{2}{3}$%
$\frac{2}{5}$ 0.4, 40%

Math Message

Complete journal page 43.

Study Link 2·5 Follow-Up

Survey the class for the results of the home experiments. Ask: What true statements can you make to compare the results of your home experiment with the class experiments?

1 Teaching the Lesson

▶ Math Message Follow-Up

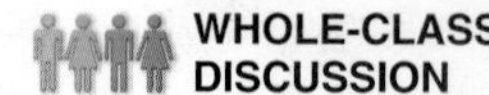

WHOLE-CLASS DISCUSSION

(*Math Journal 1,* p. 43)

Students of *Everyday Mathematics* have conducted spinner experiments since third grade. Use the spinners on *Math Journal 1,* page 43 to encourage students to describe probability concepts using decimal and percent names, as well as fractions. *For example:*

- If you spin many times, you should land on black half the time. That's a 50% chance that black will come up. There are only two conditions. It is **impossible** to land on neither black nor white; and it is **certain** that you will land on either black or white. The sum of the probabilities of the two conditions is 100%.
- It's hard to predict, but if you spin numerous times, black will come up about 1 out of 4 spins. This can be described as $\frac{1}{4}$ of the time, about 25% of the time, or 0.25 ($\frac{25}{100}$) of the time. Conversely $\frac{3}{4}$ of the time, or 0.75 ($\frac{75}{100}$) of the time, something other than black will come up. The sum of the probabilities of the outcomes of an experiment expressed as fractions or decimals will always equal 1.

For some events students must make educated guesses; therefore, their answers will vary. Structure questions so disagreements among students provide opportunities for them to explain and support their thinking.

Student Page

LESSON 2·6 **Describing Chances**

1. Circle the number that best describes the chance of landing in the blue area.

	Spinner	Chance of Landing on Blue
a.		0.25 (50%) $\frac{2}{3}$ 0.75 90%
b.		0.25 50% ($\frac{2}{3}$) 0.75 90%
c.		(0.25) 50% $\frac{2}{3}$ 0.75 90%
d.		0.25 50% $\frac{2}{3}$ 0.75 (90%)

2. Use the words and phrases from the Word Bank. Write how you would describe the chance of the event happening or not happening.

Word Bank				
certain	extremely likely	very likely	50–50 chance	
impossible	extremely unlikely	very unlikely	unlikely	likely

Example: Most people will fly in an airplane at least once during their lifetime. *extremely likely*

Sample answers:

Event	Chance
a. The sun will rise tomorrow.	certain
b. An adult is able to swim.	very likely
c. A newborn baby will be a girl.	50–50 chance
d. A long-distance call will result in a busy signal.	unlikely
e. There will be an earthquake in California during the next year.	likely
f. A house in the United States will catch on fire during the next year.	extremely unlikely

***Math Journal 1,* p. 43**

Introducing the Probability Meter Poster

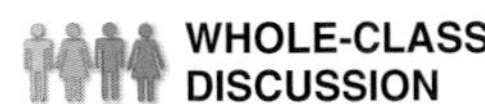

WHOLE-CLASS DISCUSSION

(*Student Reference Book*, p. 402)

Spinners are one graphic model for chance situations. The **Probability Meter Poster** is a model for displaying chance situations. Probability can be described using fractions, decimals, and percents, and also using a variety of words and phrases. Survey the class for words and phrases they would use to describe the chance of an event happening or not happening. Sample answers: 1 out of 4, one-fourth of the time, 25% of the time, the chances are, one may expect Model using students' responses in sentences: an event is likely or unlikely; there is a 1 out of 4 chance that the event will or will not happen, and so on.

Refer students to the class Probability Meter Poster on *Student Reference Book,* page 402. Survey the class for true statements about the Probability Meter. Guide the discussion to include and clarify the following points:

- ▷ The Probability Meter Poster is part of a vertical number line from 0 to 1 that is divided into 100 equal parts by thin black lines, showing on both sides, like a thermometer.
- ▷ Each thin line sections off $\frac{1}{100}$, or 0.01, or 1% of the Probability Meter Poster. (There are also some thicker lines that show simple fractions between sections.)
- ▷ Fractions, decimals, and percents appear on the meter. For some numbers, such as $\frac{3}{4}$ and $\frac{1}{10}$, all three names for the number appear. Fractions appear on the right.
- ▷ The meter is shaded to indicate the level of probability from impossible (0, 0.00, 0%) to certain (1, 1.00, 100%).

Demonstrate how to display probabilities on the meter. For example, a large sample of birth records shows that 51% are boys and 49% are girls. Assign volunteers to place stick-on notes in the correct locations on the meter to show these probabilities. (*See margin.*) Ask students to use the information on the meter to interpret this data. The chance is that more boys than girls will be born; the chance of a baby boy is 2% more than for a girl.

Repeat this process using the following statements:

- ▷ There is about a 1% chance of a person's house catching on fire during the next year.
- ▷ There is about a $\frac{2}{3}$ chance that an adult knows how to swim.

Ask how the probabilities of these events might have been obtained. *For example:*

- How do we know that about 2 out of 3 adults can swim? By asking a large number of adults whether they can swim
- How do we know that there is 1 chance in 100 that a house will catch on fire during the next year? By using fire reports to estimate the number of house fires per year

Explain that statisticians estimate probability using surveys (of many people), telephone records, fire reports, and so on. Ask

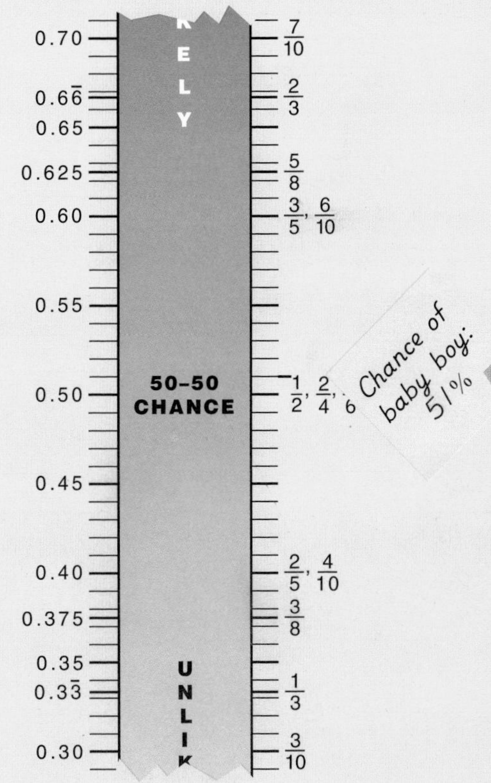

Student Page

Date Time

LESSON 2·6 **A Thumbtack Experiment**

Make a guess: If you drop a thumbtack, is it more likely to land with the point up or with the point down? Answers vary.

The experiment described below will enable you to make an estimate of the chance that a thumbtack will land point down.

1. Work with a partner. You should have 10 thumbtacks and 1 small cup. Do the experiment at your desk or a table so you are working over a smooth, hard surface.

   Place the 10 thumbtacks inside the cup. Shake the cup a few times, and then carefully drop the tacks onto the desk surface. Record the number of thumbtacks that land point up and the number that land point down.

   Toss the 10 thumbtacks 9 more times and record the results each time.

Toss	Number Landing Point Up	Number Landing Point Down
1		
2		
3		
4		
5		
6		
7		
8		
9		
10		
	Total Up =	Total Down =

2. In making your 10 tosses, you dropped a total of 100 thumbtacks.

   What fraction of the thumbtacks landed point down? ______

3. Write this fraction on a small stick-on note. Also write it as a decimal and as a percent.

4. For the whole class, the chance that a tack will land point down is ______.

Math Journal 1, p. 44

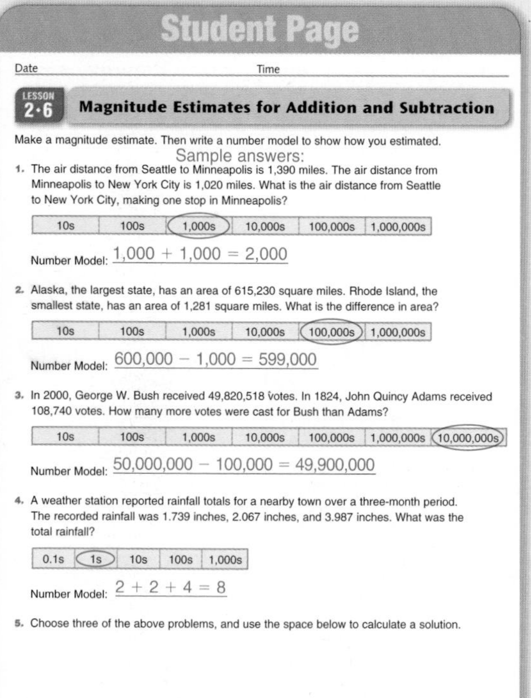

Student Page

Date Time

LESSON 2·6 **Magnitude Estimates for Addition and Subtraction**

Make a magnitude estimate. Then write a number model to show how you estimated.
Sample answers:

1. The air distance from Seattle to Minneapolis is 1,390 miles. The air distance from Minneapolis to New York City is 1,020 miles. What is the air distance from Seattle to New York City, making one stop in Minneapolis?

10s	100s	(1,000s)	10,000s	100,000s	1,000,000s

Number Model: 1,000 + 1,000 = 2,000

2. Alaska, the largest state, has an area of 615,230 square miles. Rhode Island, the smallest state, has an area of 1,281 square miles. What is the difference in area?

10s	100s	1,000s	10,000s	(100,000s)	1,000,000s

Number Model: 600,000 − 1,000 = 599,000

3. In 2000, George W. Bush received 49,820,518 votes. In 1824, John Quincy Adams received 108,740 votes. How many more votes were cast for Bush than Adams?

10s	100s	1,000s	10,000s	100,000s	1,000,000s	(10,000,000s)

Number Model: 50,000,000 − 100,000 = 49,900,000

4. A weather station reported rainfall totals for a nearby town over a three-month period. The recorded rainfall was 1.739 inches, 2.067 inches, and 3.987 inches. What was the total rainfall?

0.1s	(1s)	10s	100s	1,000s

Number Model: 2 + 2 + 4 = 8

5. Choose three of the above problems, and use the space below to calculate a solution.

Math Journal 1, p. 45

Student Page

Date Time

LESSON 2·6 **Math Boxes**

1. Give the value of the **boldface** digit in each numeral.
   a. 287,051 80 thousand
   b. 7,042,690 2 thousand
   c. 28,609,381 8 million
   d. 506,344,526 5 hundred
   e. 47,381,296 40 million

2. Solve.
   a. 3 + n = 17 n = 14
   b. 35 − r = 10 r = 25
   c. 67 + t = 113 t = 46
   d. 5.9 − b = 2 b = 3.9
   e. 3.25 + n = 12.75 n = 9.50

3. Write the prime factorization of 32.
   $2 * 2 * 2 * 2 * 2 = 2^5$

4. Multiply.
   30 ∗ 900 = 27,000
   400 ∗ 100 = 40,000
   800 ∗ 6,000 = 4,800,000
   2,000 ∗ 500 = 100,000
   420,000 = 600 ∗ 700

5. Measure angle *TAG* to the nearest degree.
   Angle *TAG*: 78°

6. Cross out the shapes below that are *not* polygons.

Math Journal 1, p. 46

students to use the meter labels to express the probabilities of their postings. It is extremely unlikely that a house will catch on fire during the next year; it is likely that adults know how to swim.

Conclude this discussion by summarizing the phrases shown on the Probability Meter Poster. Emphasize that each phrase identifies an approximate location on the meter. Explain that the class will use the Probability Meter poster throughout the year to display the chances of various events happening.

Adjusting the Activity

Point out the color intensity inside the meter and its relationship to the labels along the side.

AUDITORY ◆ KINESTHETIC ◆ TACTILE ◆ VISUAL

▶ Estimating the Chance That a Thumbtack Will Land Point Down

(*Math Journal 1*, p. 44; *Math Masters*, p. 414)

1. Introduce the problem.

Tell the class that if you drop a thumbtack, it will land with the point up or with the point down. Demonstrate these two positions with thumbtacks. (Do *not* toss the thumbtacks.)

Ask students to guess whether a thumbtack is more likely to land with the point up or with the point down and to record their guesses at the top of journal page 44. Take a vote and record the class results on the board.

2. Perform an experiment to check students' guesses.

Have students read the instructions in Problem 1 on the journal page. Demonstrate how you want students to shake and toss a set of 10 thumbtacks. Then distribute 1 cup, 10 tacks, and a stick-on note to each partnership.

Each partnership then makes a total of 10 tosses of 10 thumbtacks and records the results of each toss in their journals. Partners record the fraction of the thumbtacks that landed point down in their journals and on a stick-on note. This should be a fraction with a denominator of 100. Partners also write the equivalent decimal and percent names. For example, if students observed 35 point-down outcomes out of 100, they would write $\frac{35}{100}$, 0.35, and 35%.

Ongoing Assessment: Informing Instruction

Watch for students who are having trouble assigning a denominator to the fraction representing their findings. Remind them that the denominator represents the total. Ask them to suppose they tossed 100 thumbtacks once and identify the denominator. Explain that each toss is like having a new set of thumbtacks. So 10 tosses of 10 thumbtacks is 10 ∗ 10, or 100 thumbtacks.

Next, they post their stick-on notes on the Probability Meter Poster with a corner of the note pointing to the appropriate line on the meter.

3. Interpret the results of the experiment.

Bring the class together to interpret the results. Student results will likely vary. Explain that by combining results from all partnerships, students can make a reasonable estimate of the chance that a thumbtack will land point down.

a. First make a rough estimate. Students use the distribution of stick-on notes to estimate the fraction of thumbtacks landing point down for the whole class.

b. Next find the fraction of thumbtacks landing point down for the whole class by adding the results shown on all the stick-on notes.

Students use calculators to divide this total by the total number of throws, which is 100 times the number of partnerships represented by the stick-on notes. For example, if 12 partnerships tossed 1,200 thumbtacks and 491 of these landed point down, students would divide 491 by 1,200, rounding the result to the nearest hundredth. 0.41; which can also be written as $\frac{41}{100}$, or 41%.

Students record this class estimate in Problem 4. Post it on the Probability Meter Poster with a corner of the stick-on note pointing to the correct line on the meter. (See margin.) Remove the partnership stick-on notes from the meter.

Study Link Master

Name Date Time

STUDY LINK 2·6 **How Likely Is Rain?**

Many years ago, weather reports described the chances of rain with phrases such as *very likely, unlikely,* and *extremely unlikely.* Today, the chances of rain are almost always reported as percents. For example, "There is a 50% chance of rain tonight."

1. Use the Probability Meter Poster to translate phrases into percents.

Sample answers:

Phrase	Percent
Unlikely	30%
Very likely	80%
Very unlikely	15%
Likely	70%
Extremely unlikely	5%

2. Use the Probability Meter Poster to translate percents into phrases.

Percent	Phrase
30%	Unlikely
5%	Extremely unlikely
99%	Extremely likely
20%	Very unlikely
80%	Very likely
35%	Unlikely
65%	Likely
45%	50–50 chance

CERTAIN

IMPOSSIBLE

Math Masters, p. 49

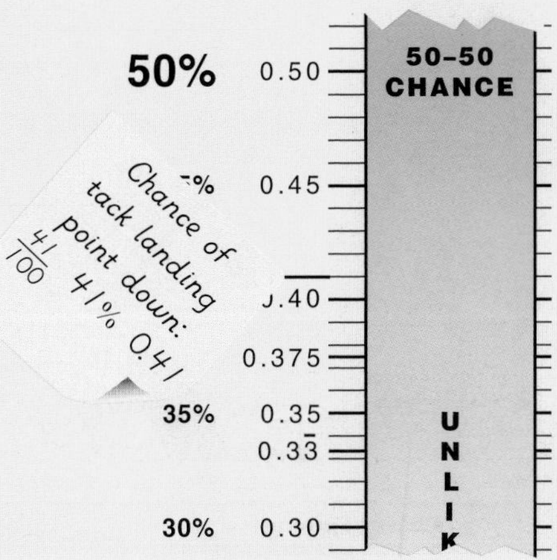

Ongoing Assessment: Recognizing Student Achievement

Exit Slip

Use an **Exit Slip** (*Math Masters,* page 414) to assess students' ability to explain the structure of the Probability Meter. Have students write a response to the following: *Why is the Probability Meter labeled with fractions, decimals, and percents?* Students are making adequate progress if they demonstrate an understanding that these notations are ways to express probability.

[Numbers and Numeration Goal 5]

2 Ongoing Learning & Practice

▶ Estimating Magnitude for Addition and Subtraction

INDEPENDENT ACTIVITY

(*Math Journal 1,* p. 45)

Students practice making magnitude estimates for addition and subtraction.

▶ Math Boxes 2·6

INDEPENDENT ACTIVITY

(*Math Journal 1,* p. 46)

Mixed Practice Math Boxes in this lesson are paired with Math Boxes in Lesson 2-9. The skills in Problems 5 and 6 preview Unit 3 content.

Portfolio Ideas

Writing/Reasoning Have students write a response to the following: *Write a number story for Problem 2a.* Sample answer: Rachel had 3 shells in her collection before she went to the beach. She has 17 shells in her collection now. How many shells did she find at the beach?

▶ Study Link 2·6

INDEPENDENT ACTIVITY

(*Math Masters,* p. 49)

Home Connection Students use the Probability Meter Poster to translate between probabilities expressed in words and probabilities expressed with percents.

3 Differentiation Options

READINESS

INDEPENDENT ACTIVITY

▶ Comparing Fractions, Decimals, and Percents

5–15 Min

(*Student Reference Book,* p. 398; *Math Masters,* p. 50)

Portfolio Ideas

To explore ordering fractions, decimals, and percents, have students order the cards from *Math Masters,* page 50. Students cut out the cards and order them from smallest to largest. They can use the table in the front of their journals and the Fraction-Decimal Number Line on page 398 of the *Student Reference Book* to help them.

Students can glue or tape the cards to make a permanent record of the activity.

ENRICHMENT

SMALL-GROUP ACTIVITY

▶ Making Spinners

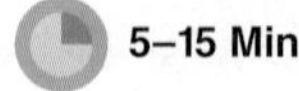
5–15 Min

(*Math Masters,* pp. 51 and 52)

To apply students' understanding of probability concepts and further explore the language of probability, have students draw spinners to match given situations. Each group of six students cuts apart the six clues and the six spinners. Each student gets one clue and one spinner. Students design a spinner that matches their set of clues, and then mix the clues and the spinners. The group tries to find the appropriate matches.

Teaching Master

Name Date Time

LESSON 2·6 **Order Fractions, Decimals, Percents**

Cut out the cards and order them from smallest to largest.
Use the table in the front of the journal to help you.

$\frac{1}{2}$	$33\frac{1}{3}\%$	0.25	$\frac{3}{4}$
20%	0.60	$\frac{4}{5}$	0.10
30%	0.70	$\frac{9}{10}$	$12\frac{1}{2}\%$
0.625	$87\frac{1}{2}\%$	$\frac{2}{3}$	$16\frac{2}{3}\%$

Math Masters, p. 50

Teaching Master

Name Date Time

LESSON 2·6 **Making Spinners**

Choosing a Pants Color There is a 30% chance of choosing blue pants. There is a $\frac{1}{4}$ chance of choosing black pants. There is a 0.1 chance of choosing white pants. There is twice the probability of choosing red pants as there is of choosing white pants. There is a 15 out of 100 chance of choosing brown pants.	**Choosing a Favorite Color** 28% of the people said red was their favorite color. $\frac{1}{3}$ of the people reported that blue was their favorite color. One-half as many people favored white as favored blue. 0.1 of the people chose brown as their favorite color. 3 out of 25 people named black as their favorite color.
Drawing Colored Chips from a Bag There is a 1 out of 5 chance of drawing a white chip. There is a 20% chance of drawing a blue chip. The probability of drawing black is 0.3. The chance of drawing a red chip is 15%. A brown chip is as likely to be drawn as a red chip.	**Choosing a Car Color** 7 out of 70 people chose white. 25% of the people chose black. 0.15 of the people chose red. $\frac{4}{12}$ of the people chose blue. $\frac{1}{6}$ of the people chose brown.
Choosing a Notebook Color 3 out of 20 people favored brown. 20% of the people favored blue. $\frac{1}{4}$ of the people favored black. 0.3 of the people favored red. Half as many people favored white as favored blue.	**Choosing a Sock Color** 1 out of 8 socks sold are red. $\frac{5}{25}$ of the socks sold are blue. $37\frac{1}{2}\%$ of the socks sold are black. 0.2 of the socks sold are white. Half as many brown socks are sold as white socks.

Math Masters, p. 51

2•7 Estimating Products

Objective To provide experiences with making and using magnitude estimates for products of multidigit numbers, including decimals.

www.everydaymathonline.com

ePresentations

eToolkit

Algorithms Practice

EM Facts Workshop Game™

Family Letters

Assessment Management

Common Core State Standards

Curriculum Focal Points

Interactive Teacher's Lesson Guide

1 Teaching the Lesson

Key Concepts and Skills

- Use place value to make magnitude estimates for products. [Number and Numeration Goal 1]
- Make magnitude estimates for problems. [Operations and Computation Goal 6]
- Round numbers to make magnitude estimates for multiplication problems. [Operations and Computation Goal 6]

Key Activities

Students use rounding to estimate the place value of products and mark their estimates on a magnitude bar. Students practice estimating products by playing *Multiplication Bull's-Eye.*

Ongoing Assessment: Informing Instruction See page 117.

Key Vocabulary

magnitude estimate

Materials

Math Journal 1, p. 47
Student Reference Book, pp. 5 and 323
Study Link 2•6
Class Data Pad ◆ per partnership: 4 each of number cards 0–9 (from the Everything Math Deck, if available), 1 six-sided die, calculator

2 Ongoing Learning & Practice

Experimenting with Spinners
Math Journal 1, p. 48
Students apply probability concepts by designing spinners.

Math Boxes 2•7
Math Journal 1, p. 49
Students practice and maintain skills through Math Box problems.

Ongoing Assessment: Recognizing Student Achievement
Use Math Boxes, Problems 3 and 4.
[Operations and Computation Goal 1]

Study Link 2•7
Math Masters, p. 53
Students practice and maintain skills through Study Link activities.

3 Differentiation Options

READINESS

Practicing Extended Facts
Student Reference Book, p. 18
Math Masters, p. 54
4 each of number cards 0–9 (from the Everything Math Deck, if available)
Students investigate a shortcut for solving extended multiplication facts.

EXTRA PRACTICE

5-Minute Math
5-Minute Math™, pp. 19, 95, and 182
Students practice estimation.

ENRICHMENT

Using Multiplication Patterns
Student Reference Book, p. 5
Math Masters, p. 66A
Students analyze why there are patterns in the number of zeros in the factors and products.

Advance Preparation

For the Math Message, prepare 3 chart-paper-size name-collection boxes. Label the name-collection boxes 1, 10, and 100, respectively. Position these in separate locations around the classroom, or post them together on the board.

***Teacher's Reference Manual,* Grades 4–6** pp. 256–264

Getting Started

Mental Math and Reflexes

FACTS PRACTICE

Write the problems on the board or the Class Data Pad so students can visually recognize the patterns.

●○○	●●○	●●●
8 * 4 32	60 * 2 120	30 [10s] 300
8 * 40 320	60 * 20 1,200	300 [10s] 3,000
80 * 400 32,000	60 * 200 12,000	300 [100s] 30,000

Math Message

Use the numbers 10, 6, 9, 8, and 5 to make expressions that are equivalent names for 1, 10, and 100. Use addition, subtraction, multiplication, division, or exponents, and try to use all 5 numbers.

Record your expressions on the class name-collection box for that number.

Study Link 2·6 Follow-Up

Briefly review the answers.

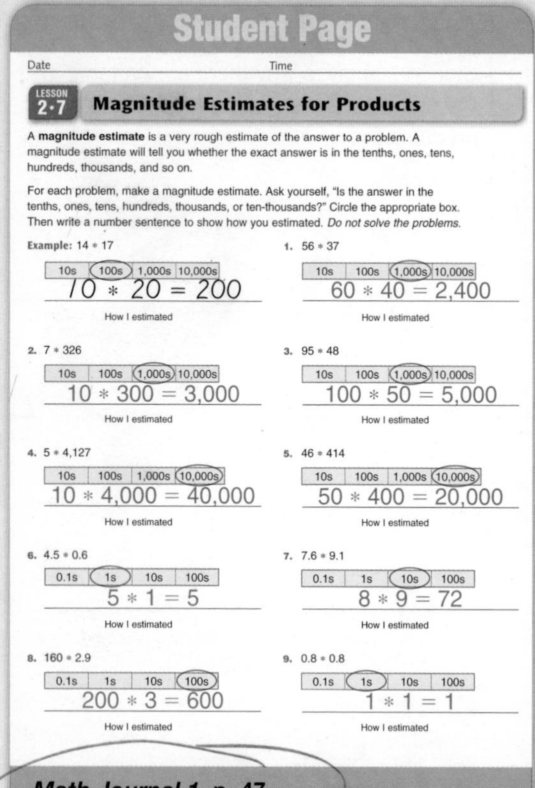

Student Page

Date Time

LESSON 2·7 **Magnitude Estimates for Products**

A **magnitude estimate** is a very rough estimate of the answer to a problem. A magnitude estimate will tell you whether the exact answer is in the tenths, ones, tens, hundreds, thousands, and so on.

For each problem, make a magnitude estimate. Ask yourself, "Is the answer in the tenths, ones, tens, hundreds, thousands, or ten-thousands?" Circle the appropriate box. Then write a number sentence to show how you estimated. *Do not solve the problems.*

Example: 14 * 17
10s | (100s) | 1,000s | 10,000s
10 * 20 = 200
How I estimated

1. 56 * 37
10s | 100s | (1,000s) | 10,000s
60 * 40 = 2,400
How I estimated

2. 7 * 326
10s | 100s | (1,000s) | 10,000s
10 * 300 = 3,000
How I estimated

3. 95 * 48
10s | 100s | (1,000s) | 10,000s
100 * 50 = 5,000
How I estimated

4. 5 * 4,127
10s | 100s | 1,000s | (10,000s)
10 * 4,000 = 40,000
How I estimated

5. 46 * 414
10s | 100s | 1,000s | (10,000s)
50 * 400 = 20,000
How I estimated

6. 4.5 * 0.6
0.1s | (1s) | 10s | 100s
5 * 1 = 5
How I estimated

7. 7.6 * 9.1
0.1s | 1s | (10s) | 100s
8 * 9 = 72
How I estimated

8. 160 * 2.9
0.1s | 1s | 10s | (100s)
200 * 3 = 600
How I estimated

9. 0.8 * 0.8
0.1s | (1s) | 10s | 100s
1 * 1 = 1
How I estimated

Math Journal 1, p. 47

1 Teaching the Lesson

▶ Math Message Follow-Up

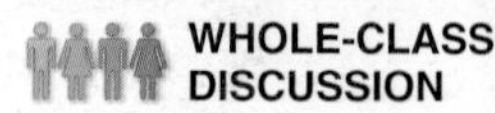

WHOLE-CLASS DISCUSSION

Allow students time to discuss and compare the expressions in the three name-collection boxes. Survey the class for expressions that individual students had not considered. Ask students to compare the differences between strategies they used to rename 1 and strategies they used to rename 10. Have students compare strategies they used to rename 10 to strategies they used to rename 100. One approach is to look for ways to make multiples. For example, any expression that names 10 can be squared to name 100.

▶ Estimating Products

WHOLE-CLASS DISCUSSION

ELL

(*Math Journal 1*, p. 47)

Through much of their work with arithmetic, students are encouraged to make an estimate prior to solving a problem. As students work with larger numbers, particularly using multiplication or division, making **magnitude estimates** allows them to know whether the solution to a problem is reasonable. This is true whether they are working with a calculator, or using paper and a pencil.

Remind students that a magnitude estimate is a very rough estimate that answers questions such as: *Is the solution in the tens? Hundreds? Thousands?*

Pose the following problem: *Is the result of 14 * 17 in the tens? Hundreds? Thousands?* Ask students to justify their answers. The product of 14 * 17 must be greater than 10 * 10 = 100; it must be less than 20 * 20 = 400. So the product is in the hundreds.

Explain that because magnitude estimates predict answers in terms of multiples of 10, one approach is to round the factors first.

To support English language learners, discuss the common meaning of *round* and its meaning in this context. Discuss the rounding approach to estimate a product of two numbers:

1. Round both factors to the nearest multiple of a power of 10.

Ask a volunteer to count by a multiple of a power of 10. Repeat until students have counted by 10, 100, and 1,000. Encourage students to count by larger multiples as well. Ask: *What is the nearest multiple of a power of 10 for* x*?* Ask questions using several sample numbers. Suggestions: 76; 220; 4,892. Restate student responses. For example, *The nearest multiple of a power of 10 for 76 is 80 because 76 rounded to the nearest 10 is 80.* Similarly, 220 rounded to the nearest 100 is 200; 4,892 rounded to the nearest 1,000 is 5,000.

2. Then find the product of the rounded numbers.

For example, to estimate 14 ∗ 17, round 14 to 10 and 17 to 20. Since 10 ∗ 20 = 200, 14 ∗ 17 is in the hundreds.

Emphasize the use of "friendly numbers," that is, numbers that are close to the numbers being multiplied and easy to work with. A friendly number is a number that students can use in their heads for mental arithmetic. Write these problems on a transparency or the board: 420 ∗ 43,892; 6,748 ∗ 3,480; and 88,889 ∗ 4,965. Ask a volunteer to round both factors to the nearest multiple of a power of 10. 400 ∗ 40,000; 7,000 ∗ 3,000; and 90,000 ∗ 5,000 Ask: *Which friendly numbers would you multiply mentally to find the product of the rounded numbers?* Sample answers: 4 ∗ 4; 7 ∗ 3; 9 ∗ 5 Point out that because the goal is to make use of mental arithmetic when making magnitude estimates, one student's friendly numbers might be different from another's.

Ongoing Assessment: Informing Instruction

Watch for students who do not recognize place-value columns as multiples of powers of 10. Refer them to the Place-Value Chart on page 205 in the journal.

Remind students that when they make estimates, they are not attempting to find the exact answers to the problems.

Ask students to use rounding to make a magnitude estimate of the product in Problem 1 (56 ∗ 37) on journal page 47. They should write the number sentence they used for their estimate, showing the rounded factors and solution, and then use their solution to circle the magnitude of the answer. Ask volunteers to explain what they did. (*See estimate diagram below.*) Sample answers: Round 56 to 60. Round 37 to 40. Then multiply 60 ∗ 40 and write 60 ∗ 40 = 2,400 on the line. Finally, circle thousands because the magnitude estimate indicates that 56 ∗ 37 is in the thousands.

10s	100s	(1,000s)	10,000s

60 ∗ 40 = 2,400

How I estimated

NOTE Magnitude estimates for products and quotients are made in the same way. Students will practice making magnitude estimates for quotients in Unit 3.

NOTE Make a classroom display of the steps for this rounding approach to making magnitude estimates to serve as a quick, available reference for students.

Games

Multiplication Bull's-Eye

Materials ☐ number cards 0–9 (4 of each)
☐ 1 six-sided die
☐ 1 calculator

Players 2

Skill Estimating products of 2- and 3-digit numbers

Object of the game To score more points.

Directions

1. Shuffle the deck and place it number-side down on the table.
2. Players take turns. When it is your turn:
   - Roll the die. Look up the target range of the product in the table at the right.
   - Take 4 cards from the top of the deck.
   - Use the cards to try to form 2 numbers whose product falls within the target range. **Do not use a calculator.**
   - Multiply the 2 numbers on your calculator to determine whether the product falls within the target range. If it does, you have hit the bull's-eye and score 1 point. If it doesn't, you score 0 points.
   - Sometimes it is impossible to form 2 numbers whose product falls within the target range. If this happens, you score 0 points for that turn.
3. The game ends when each player has had 5 turns.
4. The player scoring more points wins the game.

Number on Die	Target Range of Product
1	500 or less
2	501 – 1,000
3	1,001 – 3,000
4	3,001 – 5,000
5	5,001 – 7,000
6	more than 7,000

Example Tom rolls a 3, so the target range of the product is from 1,001 to 3,000. He turns over a 5, a 7, a 9, and a 2.

Tom uses estimation to try to form 2 numbers whose product falls within the target range—for example, 97 and 25.

He then finds the product on the calculator: 97 ∗ 25 = 2,425.

Since the product is between 1,001 and 3,000, Tom has hit the bull's-eye and scores 1 point.

Some other possible winning products from the 5, 7, 2, and 9 cards are: 25 ∗ 79, 27 ∗ 59, 9 ∗ 257, and 2 ∗ 579.

Student Reference Book, p. 323

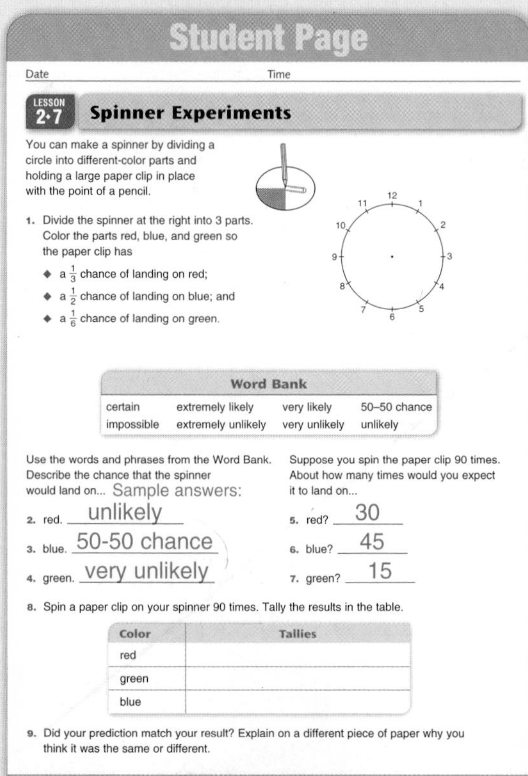

Student Page

Date Time

LESSON 2·7 **Spinner Experiments**

You can make a spinner by dividing a circle into different-color parts and holding a large paper clip in place with the point of a pencil.

1. Divide the spinner at the right into 3 parts. Color the parts red, blue, and green so the paper clip has
   - a $\frac{1}{3}$ chance of landing on red;
   - a $\frac{1}{2}$ chance of landing on blue; and
   - a $\frac{1}{6}$ chance of landing on green.

Word Bank			
certain	extremely likely	very likely	50–50 chance
impossible	extremely unlikely	very unlikely	unlikely

Use the words and phrases from the Word Bank. Describe the chance that the spinner would land on... Sample answers:

2. red. unlikely
3. blue. 50-50 chance
4. green. very unlikely

Suppose you spin the paper clip 90 times. About how many times would you expect it to land on...

5. red? 30
6. blue? 45
7. green? 15

8. Spin a paper clip on your spinner 90 times. Tally the results in the table.

Color	Tallies
red	
green	
blue	

9. Did your prediction match your result? Explain on a different piece of paper why you think it was the same or different.

Math Journal 1, p. 48

Direct students to Problem 6, and explain that the same strategy can be used to make magnitude estimates for products of decimals. Ask volunteers to tell how they would estimate, and record their responses on the board or a transparency. Sample answer: Round 4.5 to 5; round 0.6 to 1; multiply $5 * 1 = 5$; circle ones because the magnitude estimate indicates that $4.5 * 0.6$ is in the ones.

Students finish the problems on their own. When most students have finished, write some of the problems on the board and have students describe how they estimated. Allow them to present any different strategies. Conclude by emphasizing that magnitude estimates are usually reserved for work with very large or very small numbers, but that the process of rounding to make an estimate can be used in a variety of situations.

▶ Playing *Multiplication Bull's-Eye*

PARTNER ACTIVITY

(*Student Reference Book,* p. 323)

The purpose of this game is to provide practice in estimating products. While the rules of the game call for two players, the game can also be played by one player. If a student plays alone, the game ends after 10 turns, and the goal of the game becomes to top previous scores. Go over the rules of the game on page 323 in the *Student Reference Book.* Play a few rounds with the class.

2 Ongoing Learning & Practice

▶ Experimenting with Spinners

PARTNER ACTIVITY

(*Math Journal 1,* p. 48) work w/ partner

Students make a spinner to match given criteria. Then they use the language of probability to describe events. When most students have finished, ask: *Suppose you spin the paper clip 36 times. About how many times might it land on a color other than blue?* 18 times *About how many times might it land on red or blue?* 30 times

▶ Math Boxes 2·7

INDEPENDENT ACTIVITY

(*Math Journal 1,* p. 49)

When finished w/ p.48 work on these independently

Mixed Practice Math Boxes in this lesson are paired with Math Boxes in Lesson 2-5. The skill in Problem 6 previews Unit 3 content.

Writing/Reasoning Have students write a response to the following: *Explain how you solved Problem 5b. Include in your explanation the strategies and reasoning used.* Answers vary.

Student Page

Date Time

LESSON 2·7 **Math Boxes**

1. Write the repeated-factor notations.
   a. $3^4 = 3 * 3 * 3 * 3$
   b. $5^3 =$ $5 * 5 * 5$
   c. $7^4 =$ $7 * 7 * 7 * 7$
   d. $2^5 =$ $2 * 2 * 2 * 2 * 2$
   e. $10^3 =$ $10 * 10 * 10$

2. Estimate. 247 ∗ 974
   a. Write your estimate as a number sentence: $200 * 1{,}000 = 200{,}000$
   b. How I estimated. Round down 247 and round up 974; then multiply 200 and 1,000.

3. Add.
   a. 3,672 + 1,319 = 4,991
   b. 1,654 + 2,020 = 3,674

4. Subtract.
   a. 322 − 199 = 123
   b. 602 − 483 = 119

5. Solve.
   a. 18.95 − 6.07 = 12.88
   b. 215.29 + 38.75 = 254.04

6. When rolling a pair of dice, is there a better chance of rolling a 7 or a 9? Explain. Sample answer: There is a better chance of rolling a 7 because you can roll 7 three different ways but you can roll a 9 only two different ways.

Math Journal 1, p. 49

Ongoing Assessment: Recognizing Student Achievement

Math Boxes Problems 3 and 4 ★

Use **Math Boxes, Problems 3 and 4** to assess students' ability to add and subtract whole numbers. Students are making adequate progress if they demonstrate successful strategies for solving these problems.

[Operations and Computation Goal 1]

▶ Study Link 2·7

INDEPENDENT ACTIVITY

(*Math Masters,* p. 53)

Home Connection Students practice making magnitude estimates. Remind them to round each number and then multiply the products. Stress that students should not find exact answers.

3 Differentiation Options

READINESS

INDEPENDENT ACTIVITY

▶ Practicing Extended Facts

5–15 Min

(*Student Reference Book,* p. 18; *Math Masters,* p. 54)

To explore multiplication patterns, have students use their knowledge of basic facts and multiplication patterns to help them solve extended fact problems. Have students describe or write about patterns they see in their problems. Ask students to refer to *Student Reference Book,* page 18, if necessary.

EXTRA PRACTICE

SMALL-GROUP ACTIVITY

▶ *5-Minute Math*

5–15 Min

To offer students more experience with estimation, see *5-Minute Math* pages 19, 95, and 182.

ENRICHMENT

INDEPENDENT ACTIVITY

▶ Using Multiplication Patterns

5–15 Min

(*Student Reference Book,* p. 5; *Math Masters,* p. 66A)

To apply their understanding of patterns in the number of zeros in the product when multiplying by powers of 10, students analyze the connections between the patterns and rewrite factors as numbers in expanded form.

Study Link Master

Name Date Time

STUDY LINK 2·7 Magnitude Estimates

A **magnitude estimate** is a very rough estimate. It tells whether the exact answer falls in the tenths, ones, tens, hundreds, thousands, and so on. For each problem, make a magnitude estimate. Ask yourself: *Is the answer in the tenths, ones, tens, hundreds, thousands, or ten-thousands?* Circle the appropriate box. Do not solve the problems.

Example: 18 ∗ 21 — 10s | (100s) | 1,000s | 10,000s — 20 ∗ 20 = 400 (How I estimated)

1. 73 ∗ 28 — 10s | 100s | (1,000s) | 10,000s — 70 ∗ 30 = 2,100 (How I estimated)

2. 12 ∗ 708 — 10s | 100s | (1,000s) | 10,000s — 10 ∗ 700 = 7,000 (How I estimated)

3. 98 ∗ 105 — 10s | 100s | 1,000s | (10,000s) — 100 ∗ 100 = 10,000 (How I estimated)

4. 17 ∗ 2.2 — (10s) | 100s | 1,000s | 10,000s — 20 ∗ 2 = 40 (How I estimated)

5. 2.6 ∗ 3.9 — 0.1s | 1s | (10s) | 100s — 3 ∗ 4 = 12 (How I estimated)

Try This

6. Use the digits 4, 5, 6, and 8. Make as many factor pairs as you can that have a product between 3,000 and 5,000. Use a calculator to solve the problems.
Sample answers: 45 ∗ 68 = 3,060; 684 ∗ 5 = 3,420; and 864 ∗ 5 = 4,320

Math Masters, p. 53

Teaching Master

Name Date Time

LESSON 2·7 Using Multiplication Patterns

Find information about **Powers of 10** on page 5 of your *Student Reference Book.* Study the example below. Then try to use the same strategy to solve Problems 1 and 2.

20 ∗ 300 = (2 ∗ 10) ∗ (3 ∗ 100)	Write each factor in expanded form.
= 2 ∗ 10 ∗ 3 ∗ 100	Remove the parentheses.
= 2 ∗ 3 ∗ 10 ∗ 100	Use the Commutative Property so that the powers of 10 are together.
= (2 ∗ 3) ∗ (10 ∗ 100)	Multiply the basic fact, and multiply the powers of 10.
= 6 ∗ 1,000	Multiply the partial products.
= 6,000	

Solve the problems. Show your work.

1. 900 ∗ 70 = 63,000
2. 500 ∗ 6,000 = 3,000,000
3. Explain why you think counting zeros works in solving multiplication problems involving powers of 10.
Sample answer: Each time you multiply by 10, you are attaching another 0. When you rewrite the numbers in expanded form, you can see that the zeros you attach come from the powers of 10.
4. Use what you know about counting zeros in multiplication to help you figure out the missing numbers below.
4,200 ∗ 200 = 840,000
50,000 ∗ 40 = 2,000,000
250 ∗ 200,000 = 50,000,000
5. On the back of this page, write two problems of your own that can be solved by counting zeros.

Math Masters, p. 66A

2•8 Multiplication of Whole Numbers and Decimals

Objectives To review the partial-products method for whole numbers and decimals.

Technology Resources www.everydaymathonline.com

ePresentations

eToolkit

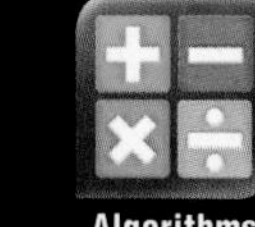
Algorithms Practice

EM Facts Workshop Game™

Family Letters

Assessment Management

Common Core State Standards

Curriculum Focal Points

Interactive Teacher's Lesson Guide

1 Teaching the Lesson

Key Concepts and Skills

- Solve whole-number and decimal problems using the partial-products algorithm.
  [Operations and Computation Goal 3]
- Make magnitude estimates.
  [Operations and Computation Goal 6]
- Use magnitude estimates to place the decimal point in products.
  [Operations and Computation Goal 6]

Key Activities

Students review the partial-products method for whole numbers. They use magnitude estimates to solve multiplication problems involving whole numbers and decimals.

Ongoing Assessment: Informing Instruction See page 122.

Ongoing Assessment: Recognizing Student Achievement Use journal page 50.
[Operations and Computation Goal 6]

Key Vocabulary

partial-products method ◆ magnitude estimate ◆ ballpark estimate

Materials

Math Journal 1, pp. 50 and 51
Student Reference Book, pp. 19, 38, and 39
Study Link 2•7
Math Masters, p. 415 (optional)
Class Data Pad

2 Ongoing Learning & Practice

Solving Number Stories

Math Journal 1, p. 52
Students solve addition and subtraction number stories by writing and solving open number sentences.

Math Boxes 2•8

Math Journal 1, p. 53
Students practice and maintain skills through Math Box problems.

Study Link 2•8

Math Masters, p. 55
Students practice and maintain skills through Study Link activities.

3 Differentiation Options

READINESS

Modeling the Partial-Products Method

Math Masters, pp. 56, 416, and 417
per group: transparencies of *Math Masters,* pp. 416 and 417; base-10 blocks; dry erase marker; eraser
Students use base-10 blocks to practice multiplication using a concrete model.

ENRICHMENT

Multiplying Numbers That End in 9

Math Masters, p. 57
Students explore a calculation strategy for multiplying by 9.

Advance Preparation

Make copies of the computation grid (*Math Masters,* page 415) available for students' use throughout Part 1. For the optional Readiness activity in Part 3, make transparencies of *Math Masters,* pages 416 and 417, cut them out, and tape them together with clear tape.

***Teacher's Reference Manual,* Grades 4–6** pp. 126–132

Getting Started

Mental Math and Reflexes

Write problems on the board or the Class Data Pad, so students can visually recognize the patterns. Ask students to share the patterns of decimal point placement and the value of the digits in the products of each set. Sample answer: In the first set of problems, the decimal point moves to the left and the value of each digit is $\frac{1}{10}$ the value it was in the previous problem.

●○○	●●○	●●●
3 * 8 24	6 * 8 48	7 * 9 63
3 * 0.8 2.4	6 * 0.8 4.8	0.7 * 0.9 0.63
3 * 0.08 0.24	0.6 * 0.8 0.48	0.7 * 0.09 0.063

Math Message

Estimate the solution to this problem. Write a number sentence showing how you found your estimate. Be prepared to discuss how you used rounding in your estimate.

*3.7 * 6.2* 4 * 6 = 24

Study Link 2·7 Follow-Up

Have partners compare answers and correct any errors. Ask students to share solutions to Problem 6.

1 Teaching the Lesson

▶ Math Message Follow-Up

WHOLE-CLASS DISCUSSION

Ask volunteers to share their estimates and number models. Ask: *How does estimating products of decimals differ from estimating products of whole numbers?* Emphasize that when the decimal is less than 1, comparisons to other decimals can help students make an appropriate estimate. For example, they can compare the decimal to 0.5 or 0.33 or compare it to 1.

Emphasize that when estimating with decimals, rounding can also help make an appropriate estimate. For example, in this problem, rounding each number to the nearest whole number is helpful; 3.7 is rounded to 4, and 6.2 is rounded to 6.

▶ Reviewing the Partial-Products Method with Whole Numbers

WHOLE-CLASS DISCUSSION

(*Student Reference Book,* p. 19)

The **partial-products method** for multiplication has been stressed since *Third Grade Everyday Mathematics*. It is an algorithm that all students are expected to know because it helps students develop a good understanding of place-value and multiplication concepts. It has the added benefit of facilitating student use of mental arithmetic as they solve problems.

Refer students to page 19 of the *Student Reference Book*. With the partial-products method, each part of one factor is multiplied by each part of the other factor. Each partial product is written on a separate line. These partial products are then added. This process is usually fairly simple and has the additional benefit of providing practice with column addition.

Algorithm Project The focus of this lesson is the partial-products method for multiplying whole numbers and decimals. To teach U.S. traditional multiplication with whole numbers and with decimals, see Algorithm Project 5 on page A22 and Algorithm Project 6 on page A27.

NOTE The partial-products method is a direct application of the *Distributive Property of Multiplication over Addition.* For more practice with the Distributive Property, see www.everydaymathonline.com.

NOTE Working from left to right is consistent with the process of estimating products. Point out for students that when they have found the partial product for the leftmost digits, they have a *ballpark estimate* for the product. To support English language learners, discuss the meaning of *ballpark estimate.*

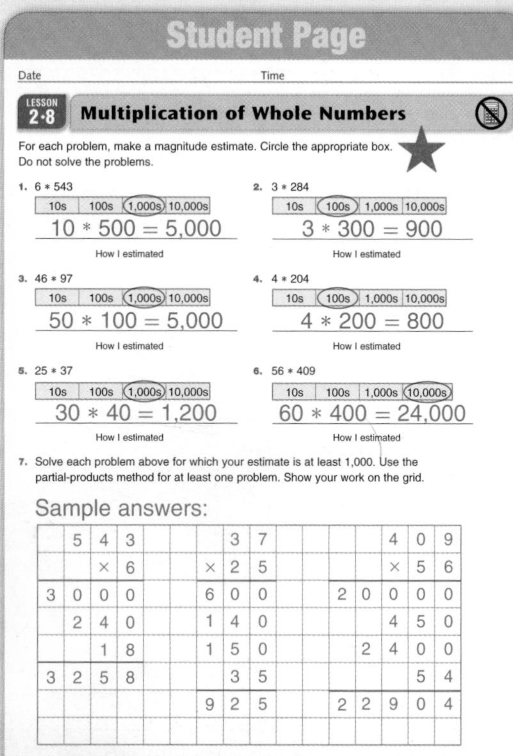
Student Page

Date Time

LESSON 2·8 **Multiplication of Whole Numbers**

For each problem, make a magnitude estimate. Circle the appropriate box. Do not solve the problems.

1. 6 * 543 — 10s | 100s | (1,000s) | 10,000s — 10 * 500 = 5,000 — How I estimated
2. 3 * 284 — 10s | (100s) | 1,000s | 10,000s — 3 * 300 = 900 — How I estimated
3. 46 * 97 — 10s | 100s | (1,000s) | 10,000s — 50 * 100 = 5,000 — How I estimated
4. 4 * 204 — 10s | (100s) | 1,000s | 10,000s — 4 * 200 = 800 — How I estimated
5. 25 * 37 — 10s | 100s | (1,000s) | 10,000s — 30 * 40 = 1,200 — How I estimated
6. 56 * 409 — 10s | 100s | 1,000s | (10,000s) — 60 * 400 = 24,000 — How I estimated
7. Solve each problem above for which your estimate is at least 1,000. Use the partial-products method for at least one problem. Show your work on the grid.

Sample answers:

543	37	409
× 6	× 25	× 56
3000	600	20000
240	140	450
18	150	2400
3258	35	54
	925	22904

Math Journal 1, p. 50

Go through the following example with the class. Then distribute computation grids (*Math Masters*, page 415) and have students solve the Check Your Understanding problems using this method.

Example: 43 * 26 = ?		100s	10s	1s
Think of 26 as 20 + 6:			2	6
Think of 43 as 40 + 3:		*	4	3
Multiply each part of 26	40 * 20 →	8	0	0
by each part of 43:	40 * 6 →	2	4	0
	3 * 20 →		6	0
	3 * 6 →		1	8
Add four partial products:		11	1	8

NOTE Make sure the digits students write are properly aligned in columns. It will also help if they write place-value reminders (such as 100s, 10s, and 1s) above the columns.

Ongoing Assessment: Informing Instruction

Watch for students who do not recognize the value of the digits in a number. Have them write the factors in expanded notation.

NOTE To provide additional practice using the Distributive Property, have students play the game *Multiplication Wrestling.* See *Student Reference Book,* page 324 for directions.

▶ Reviewing Multiplication of Decimals

COMPUTATION PRACTICE

(*Student Reference Book,* pp. 38 and 39)

Ask students to solve the following problem: 1.3 * 5. After a couple of minutes, have them share their solution strategies and explain their reasoning. Encourage students to use drawings or strategies based on their place-value knowledge. Expect that they may have difficulty because one of the factors is a decimal.

Explain that one way to solve multiplication problems containing decimal factors is to multiply as though both factors were whole numbers and then adjust the product. Specifically:

1. First make a **magnitude estimate** of the product.
2. Multiply the numbers as though they were whole numbers.
3. Then use the magnitude estimate as a guide to inserting the decimal point at the correct location in the answer.

Example: 1.3 * 5 = ?

1. Make a magnitude estimate: 1.3 rounds to 1; because 1 * 5 = 5, the product will be in the ones. Ask students to justify how they would round 1.3. Answers vary.
2. Ignore the decimal point and multiply 13 * 5 as though both factors were whole numbers: 13 * 5 = 65.

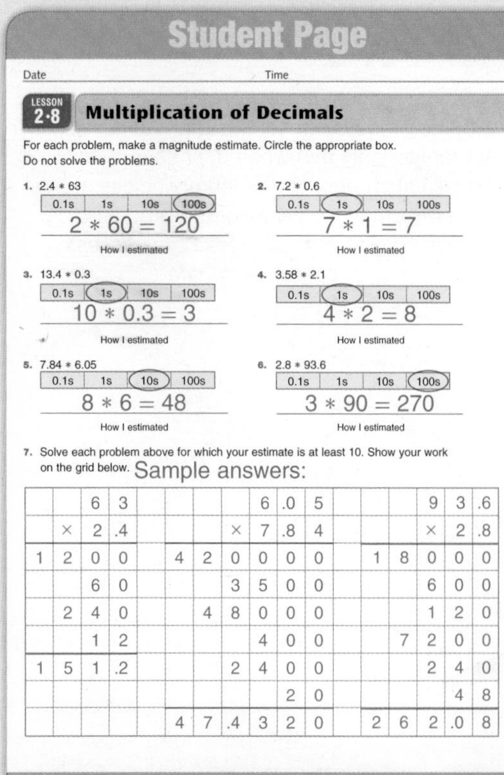
Student Page

Date Time

LESSON 2·8 **Multiplication of Decimals**

For each problem, make a magnitude estimate. Circle the appropriate box. Do not solve the problems.

1. 2.4 * 63 — 0.1s | 1s | 10s | (100s) — 2 * 60 = 120 — How I estimated
2. 7.2 * 0.6 — 0.1s | (1s) | 10s | 100s — 7 * 1 = 7 — How I estimated
3. 13.4 * 0.3 — 0.1s | (1s) | 10s | 100s — 10 * 0.3 = 3 — How I estimated
4. 3.58 * 2.1 — 0.1s | (1s) | 10s | 100s — 4 * 2 = 8 — How I estimated
5. 7.84 * 6.05 — 0.1s | 1s | (10s) | 100s — 8 * 6 = 48 — How I estimated
6. 2.8 * 93.6 — 0.1s | 1s | 10s | (100s) — 3 * 90 = 270 — How I estimated
7. Solve each problem above for which your estimate is at least 10. Show your work on the grid below.

Sample answers:

63	6.05	9.36
× 2.4	× 7.84	× 2.8
1200	420000	18000
60	3500	600
240	48000	120
12	400	7200
151.2	2400	240
	20	48
	47.4320	262.08

Math Journal 1, p. 51

3. Since the magnitude estimate is in the ones, the product must be in the ones. The answer must be 6.5. So, 1.3 * 5 = 6.5.

Ask partners to solve several multiplication problems in which one of the factors is a decimal. *Suggestions:* 25 * 0.6 15; 400 * 1.7 680.

Next use examples like those on pages 38 and 39 of the *Student Reference Book* to demonstrate how to find the product of two decimals.

Example: 3.4 * 4.6 = ?

1. Round 3.4 to 3 and 4.6 to 5. Since 3 * 5 = 15, the product will be in the tens.
2. Ignore the decimal points and multiply 34 * 46 as though both factors were whole numbers: 34 * 46 = 1,564.
3. Since the magnitude estimate is in the tens, the product must be in the tens. The answer must be 15.64. Thus, 3.4 * 4.6 = 15.64.

Refer students to *Student Reference Book,* page 39. Introduce the strategy of placing the decimal point in a product by counting the number of decimal places to the right of the decimal point in each factor. Have students try this strategy to solve the Check Your Understanding problems on page 39 of the *Student Reference Book.* This strategy is especially useful with numbers that have many decimal places.

Ask partners to solve several multiplication problems in which both factors are decimals. *Suggestions:* 6.3 * 1.8 11.34; 0.71 * 3.2 2.272.

NOTE There are borderline cases where a magnitude estimate is not accurate enough to guide the correct placement of the decimal point in a product. For example, 3.4 * 3.4 → 3 * 3 = 9. Place the decimal point to make the product as close to 9 as possible: 34 * 34 = 1,156; 3.4 * 3.4 = 11.56. Remind students that the placement of the decimal point should result in a product that is reasonable.

▶ Practicing Multiplication of Whole Numbers and Decimals

PARTNER ACTIVITY

(*Math Journal 1,* pp. 50 and 51)

Students estimate the answers to Problems 1–6 on journal page 50 and Problems 1–6 on journal page 51. They will find the exact answer only for some, not all, of these problems. Students may use whatever method they prefer to make a **ballpark estimate.** They should write the number sentence they used to make their estimate on the line and then circle the magnitude of their estimate.

Have students complete both pages. Then have partners check each other's solutions. When they have finished, write Problem 6 from *Math Journal 1,* page 51 on the board. Ask students to explain the strategies and reasoning they used to estimate and solve the problem. Explanations should include how they placed the decimal point and should reflect their understanding of decimal place values.

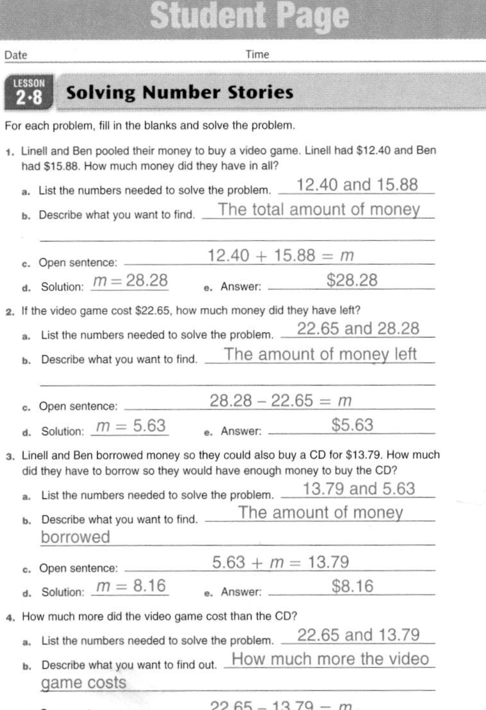
Student Page

Date Time

LESSON 2·8 **Solving Number Stories**

For each problem, fill in the blanks and solve the problem.

1. Linell and Ben pooled their money to buy a video game. Linell had $12.40 and Ben had $15.88. How much money did they have in all?
   a. List the numbers needed to solve the problem. 12.40 and 15.88
   b. Describe what you want to find. The total amount of money
   c. Open sentence: 12.40 + 15.88 = m
   d. Solution: m = 28.28 e. Answer: $28.28
2. If the video game cost $22.65, how much money did they have left?
   a. List the numbers needed to solve the problem. 22.65 and 28.28
   b. Describe what you want to find. The amount of money left
   c. Open sentence: 28.28 – 22.65 = m
   d. Solution: m = 5.63 e. Answer: $5.63
3. Linell and Ben borrowed money so they could also buy a CD for $13.79. How much did they have to borrow so they would have enough money to buy the CD?
   a. List the numbers needed to solve the problem. 13.79 and 5.63
   b. Describe what you want to find. The amount of money borrowed
   c. Open sentence: 5.63 + m = 13.79
   d. Solution: m = 8.16 e. Answer: $8.16
4. How much more did the video game cost than the CD?
   a. List the numbers needed to solve the problem. 22.65 and 13.79
   b. Describe what you want to find out. How much more the video game costs
   c. Open sentence: 22.65 – 13.79 = m
   d. Solution: m = 8.86 e. Answer: $8.86

Math Journal 1, p. 52

NOTE Some students will use friendly numbers to make an estimate rather than rounding. Making the appropriate magnitude estimate is the important concept, not whether the student uses rounding to make an estimate.

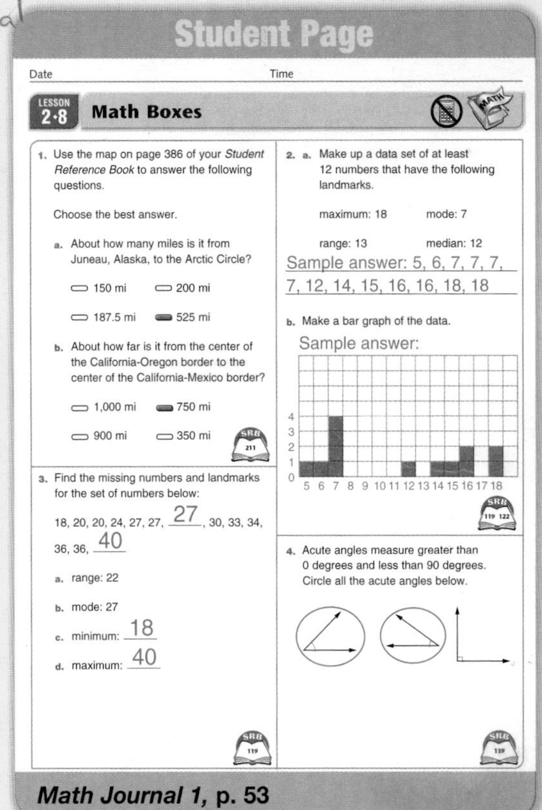
Student Page

Date Time

LESSON 2·8 **Math Boxes**

1. Use the map on page 386 of your *Student Reference Book* to answer the following questions.
   Choose the best answer.
   a. About how many miles is it from Juneau, Alaska, to the Arctic Circle?
      ○ 150 mi ○ 200 mi ○ 187.5 mi ● 525 mi
   b. About how far is it from the center of the California-Oregon border to the center of the California-Mexico border?
      ○ 1,000 mi ● 750 mi ○ 900 mi ○ 350 mi
2. a. Make up a data set of at least 12 numbers that have the following landmarks.
   maximum: 18 mode: 7
   range: 13 median: 12
   Sample answer: 5, 6, 7, 7, 7, 7, 12, 14, 15, 16, 16, 18, 18
   b. Make a bar graph of the data.
   Sample answer:
3. Find the missing numbers and landmarks for the set of numbers below:
   18, 20, 20, 24, 27, 27, 27, 30, 33, 34, 36, 36, 40
   a. range: 22
   b. mode: 27
   c. minimum: 18
   d. maximum: 40
4. Acute angles measure greater than 0 degrees and less than 90 degrees. Circle all the acute angles below.

Math Journal 1, p. 53

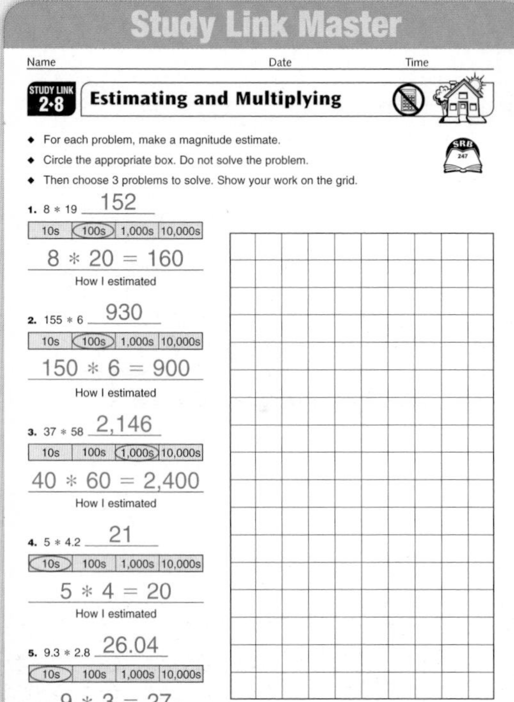

Study Link Master

Name Date Time

STUDY LINK 2•8 **Estimating and Multiplying**

SRB 247

- For each problem, make a magnitude estimate.
- Circle the appropriate box. Do not solve the problem.
- Then choose 3 problems to solve. Show your work on the grid.

1. 8 * 19 152
   10s (100s) 1,000s 10,000s
   8 * 20 = 160
   How I estimated

2. 155 * 6 930
   10s (100s) 1,000s 10,000s
   150 * 6 = 900
   How I estimated

3. 37 * 58 2,146
   10s 100s (1,000s) 10,000s
   40 * 60 = 2,400
   How I estimated

4. 5 * 4.2 21
   (10s) 100s 1,000s 10,000s
   5 * 4 = 20
   How I estimated

5. 9.3 * 2.8 26.04
   (10s) 100s 1,000s 10,000s
   9 * 3 = 27
   How I estimated

***Math Masters,* p. 55**

Teaching Master

Name Date Time

LESSON 2•8 **Model the Partial-Products Method**

Materials ☐ array grid (*Math Masters,* pp. 416 and 417)
☐ base-10 blocks

Directions
- Draw a line around rows and columns on the grid to model each problem.
- Cover the array you made using as few base-10 blocks as possible.
- Solve using the partial-products method.
- Then match each part of the array with a partial product.
- Record the solution, filling in the sentences to match the blocks you used.

1. 6 * 23 = 138

In each of 6 rows there are...	2 longs, so there are 120 cubes. 3 cubes, so there are 18 cubes. There are 138 cubes in all.	Write the problem showing the partial products. 120 + 18 = 138

2. 26 * 18 = 468

In each of 20 rows there are...	1 longs, so there are 200 cubes. 8 cubes, so there are 160 cubes.	Write the problem showing the partial products. 200 + 160 + 60 + 48 = 468
In each of 6 rows there are...	1 longs, so there are 60 cubes. 8 cubes, so there are 48 cubes. There are 468 cubes in all.	

***Math Masters,* p. 56**

Ongoing Assessment: Recognizing Student Achievement

Journal Page 50 Problems 1–6 ★

Use **journal page 50, Problems 1–6** to assess students' understanding of how to make magnitude estimates. Students are making adequate progress if they make reasonable magnitude estimates based on their number sentences.

[Operations and Computation Goal 6]

2 Ongoing Learning & Practice

▶ Solving Number Stories

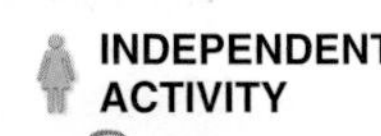
INDEPENDENT ACTIVITY

(*Math Journal 1,* p. 52)

Algebraic Thinking Students solve addition and subtraction number stories. They write an open number sentence for each problem and solve the open sentence to find the answer to the problem.

▶ Math Boxes 2•8

INDEPENDENT ACTIVITY

(*Math Journal 1,* p. 53)

Mixed Practice Math Boxes in this lesson are paired with Math Boxes in Lesson 2-10. The skill in Problem 4 previews Unit 3 content.

▶ Study Link 2•8

INDEPENDENT ACTIVITY

(*Math Masters,* p. 55) Homework

Home Connection Students make magnitude estimates for multiplication problems in which the factors are whole numbers and/or decimals. They then select 3 problems to solve for exact answers.

3 Differentiation Options

READINESS

SMALL-GROUP ACTIVITY

5–15 Min

▶ Modeling the Partial-Products Method

(*Math Masters,* pp. 56, 416, and 417)

To provide experience with multiplication using a concrete model, have students solve multidigit multiplication problems with base-10 blocks. Use transparencies of *Math Masters,* pages 416 and 417. (*See Advance Preparation.*) Place the assembled grids on a table. Do not use an overhead projector. Gather a small group of students around the table. Use an overhead marker to show a 4-by-28 array. (*See Figure 1.*)

Have students cover the array using as few base-10 blocks as possible.

Guide students' use of the partial-products method to solve 4 * 28. Match each part of the 4-by-28 array with a partial product. (*See Figure 2.*)

1. There are 2 longs in each of 4 rows, so there are 80 cubes.
2. There are 8 cubes in each of 4 rows, so there are 32 cubes.
3. There are 80 + 32, or 112 cubes in all.

Clear the masters. Now use an overhead marker to mark off a 17-by-32 array.

Ask students to cover the array using as few base-10 blocks (flats, rods, and cubes) as possible.

Guide students' use of the partial-products method to solve 17 * 32. Now match each part of the 17-by-32 array with a partial product.

1. There are 10 rows with 30 cubes in each row (3 flats).
2. There are 7 rows with 30 cubes in each row (21 longs).
3. There are 10 rows with 2 cubes in each row (2 longs).
4. There are 7 rows with 2 cubes in each row (14 cubes).
5. There are 300 + 210 + 20 + 14, or 544 cubes in all.

Ask students to work with partners using base-10 blocks to solve the multiplication problems on *Math Masters*, p. 56.

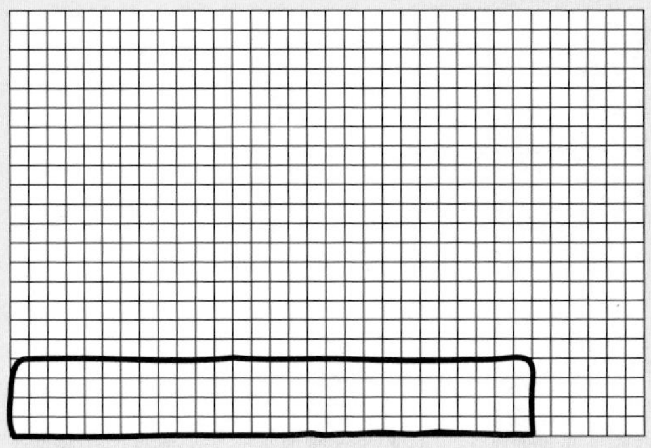

Figure 1: Array model of 4 * 28

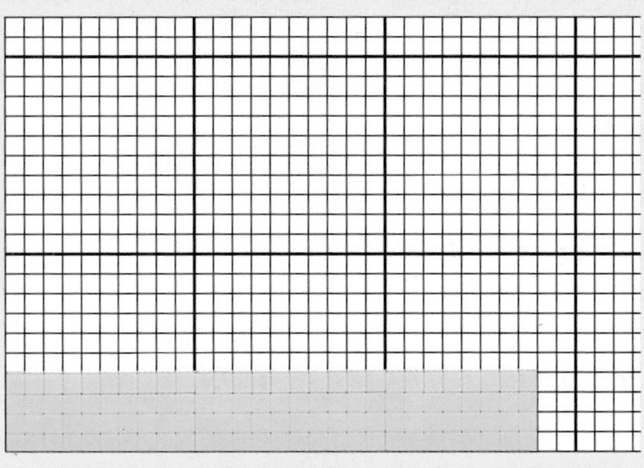

Figure 2: Base-10 block model of 4 * 28

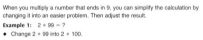

ENRICHMENT

INDEPENDENT ACTIVITY

Multiplying Numbers That End in 9

(*Math Masters,* p. 57)

To further explore multiplication strategies, have students solve problems using a mental multiplication strategy. Students read *Math Masters,* page 57 and use the mental math strategy given to answer the questions on the page. If necessary, read and discuss Example 1 as a class.

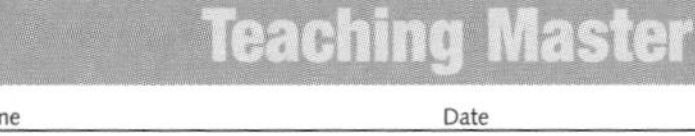

Teaching Master

Name Date Time

LESSON 2·8 **A Mental Calculation Strategy**

When you multiply a number that ends in 9, you can simplify the calculation by changing it into an easier problem. Then adjust the result.

Example 1: 2 * 99 = ?

- Change 2 * 99 into 2 * 100.
- Find the answer: 2 * 100 = 200
- Ask: *How is the answer to 2 * 100 different from the answer to 2 * 99?* 100 is 1 more than 99, and you multiplied by 2. So 200 is 2 more than the answer to 2 * 99.
- Adjust the answer to 2 * 100 to find the answer to 2 * 99: 200 − 2 = 198. So 2 * 99 = 198.

Example 2: 3 * 149 = ?

- Change 3 * 149 into 3 * 150.
- Find the answer: 3 * 150 = (3 * 100) + (3 * 50) = 450.
- Ask: *How is the answer to 3 * 150 different from the answer to 3 * 149?* 150 is 1 more than 149, and you multiplied by 3. So 450 is 3 more than the answer to 3 * 149.
- Adjust: 450 − 3 = 447. So 3 * 149 = 447.

Use this strategy to calculate these products mentally.

1. 5 * 49 245
2. 5 * 99 495
3. 8 * 99 792
4. 4 * 199 796
5. 2 * 119 238
6. 3 * 98 294

Math Masters, p. 57

2·9 The Lattice Method of Multiplication

Objective To review and practice the lattice method for multiplication of whole numbers and decimals.

Technology Resources www.everydaymathonline.com

ePresentations

eToolkit

Algorithms Practice

EM Facts Workshop Game™

Family Letters

Assessment Management

Common Core State Standards

Curriculum Focal Points

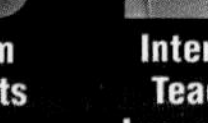
Interactive Teacher's Lesson Guide

1 Teaching the Lesson

Key Concepts and Skills

- Apply multiplication facts.
  [Operations and Computation Goal 2]
- Use the lattice method for multiplying whole numbers and decimals.
  [Operations and Computation Goal 3]
- Use magnitude estimates to verify lattice method solutions.
  [Operations and Computation Goal 6]

Key Activities

Students review and practice the lattice method for multiplying multidigit whole numbers. They practice the lattice method for multiplying decimals.

Ongoing Assessment: Informing Instruction See page 129.

Ongoing Assessment: Recognizing Student Achievement Use an Exit Slip (*Math Masters,* page 414).
[Operations and Computation Goal 3]

Key Vocabulary

lattice method ◆ lattice

Materials

Math Journal 1, pp. 54 and 55
Student Reference Book, pp. 20 and 40
Study Link 2•8
Math Masters, pp. 58, 414, and 418
Class Data Pad

2 Ongoing Learning & Practice

Playing *Factor Bingo*
Math Masters, p. 452
per group: 4 each of number cards 2–9 (from the Everything Math Deck, if available) ◆ 12 counters
Students practice applying multiplication facts and number properties, recognizing factors, and factoring numbers.

Multiplying and Dividing by Powers of 10
Math Journal 1, pp. 56A and 56B
Students practice multiplying and dividing by powers of 10.

Math Boxes 2•9
Math Journal 1, p. 56
Students practice and maintain skills through Math Box problems.

Study Link 2•9
Math Masters, p. 59
Students practice and maintain skills through Study Link activities.

3 Differentiation Options

ENRICHMENT

Exploring an Ancient Multiplication Method
Math Masters,p. 60
Students analyze an ancient multiplication method and use that method to solve a multiplication problem.

EXTRA PRACTICE

5-Minute Math
5-Minute Math™, p. 186
Students practice multiplying decimals.

EXTRA PRACTICE

Multiplying Decimals
Math Masters, p. 414
Students practice multiplying decimals and writing about their strategies.

Advance Preparation

For Part 1, draw a 1-by-3 and a 2-by-2 lattice on the board. You might find it helpful to copy the lattice computation grids on *Math Masters,* page 57 on a transparency. Each student will need 2 copies of *Math Masters,* page 418.

***Teacher's Reference Manual,* Grades 4–6** pp. 126–132

Getting Started

Mental Math and Reflexes

Write problems on the board or the Class Data Pad so students can visually recognize the patterns of decimal point placement in the products. Ask students to describe the patterns they notice in each set.

●○○	●●○	●●●
6 * 3 18	8 * 7 56	8 * 5 40
6 * 0.3 1.8	8 * 0.7 5.6	8 * 0.5 4
6 * 0.03 0.18	0.8 * 0.7 0.56	0.8 * 0.5 0.4

Math Message

Study the problems in Column A on journal page 54. Then use lattice multiplication to solve the problems in Column B.

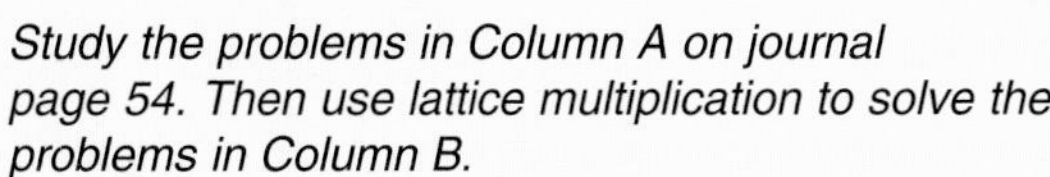

Study Link 2·8 Follow-Up

Allow students five minutes to work together to compare their answers and correct any errors.

1 Teaching the Lesson

> **Algorithm Project** The focus of this lesson is the lattice method for multiplying whole numbers and decimals. To teach U.S. traditional multiplication with whole numbers and with decimals, see Algorithm Project 5 on page A22 and Algorithm Project 6 on page A27.

▶ Math Message Follow-Up

(*Math Journal 1,* p. 54)

Ask volunteers to demonstrate on the board how they solved the problems. Note students' explanations of their processes, including their vocabulary, for use in the following review.

▶ Reviewing the Lattice Method of Multiplication

(*Student Reference Book,* pp. 20 and 40; *Math Journal 1,* p. 54; *Math Masters,* p. 418)

The **lattice method** for multiplying has been used since *Third Grade Everyday Mathematics*. This method is very easy to use because it relies almost entirely on the recall of the basic multiplication facts.

Use the student examples on the board from the Math Message Follow-Up to emphasize the vocabulary of the lattice method.

- ▷ The box with squares and diagonals is called a **lattice.** Ask students how they know what size lattice to use and where to write the factors. The factors tell which size lattice to use. Write the second factor above the lattice and the first factor on the right side. Some students might think of the rectangular array model for multiplication: The number of digits in the first factor is the number of rows, and the number of digits in the second factor is the number of columns.
- ▷ Multiply the digits. Write the answers. Ask students how they know where to write these partial products. Write the answers in the square where the multiplied digits intersect on the lattice, 1 digit per diagonal. Some students may note that each partial product is never more than 2 digits: Tens go in the left diagonal and ones go in the right diagonal.

Student Page

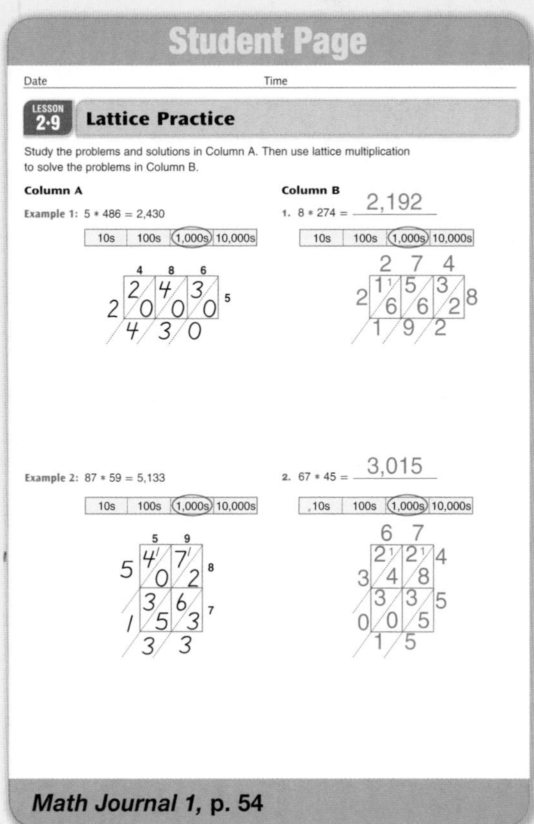

Math Journal 1, p. 54

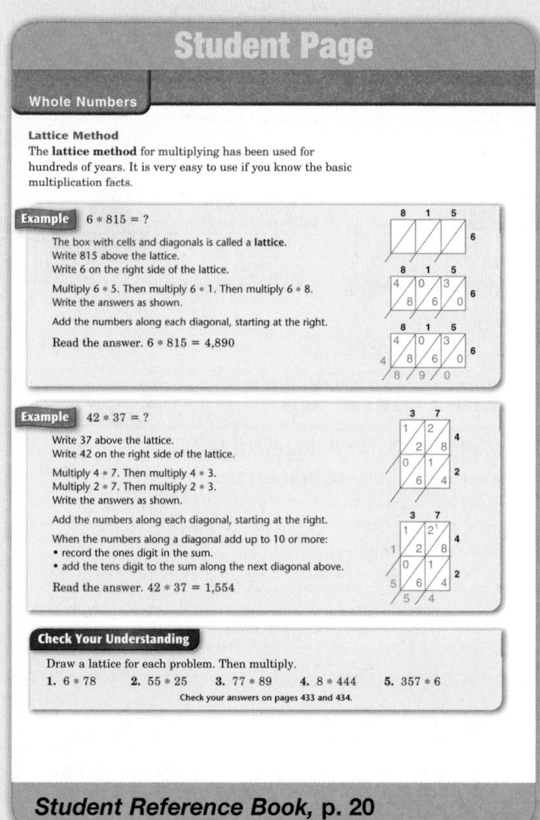

Student Page

Whole Numbers

Lattice Method

The **lattice method** for multiplying has been used for hundreds of years. It is very easy to use if you know the basic multiplication facts.

Example 6 * 815 = ?

The box with cells and diagonals is called a **lattice**.
Write 815 above the lattice.
Write 6 on the right side of the lattice.

Multiply 6 * 5. Then multiply 6 * 1. Then multiply 6 * 8.
Write the answers as shown.

Add the numbers along each diagonal, starting at the right.

Read the answer. 6 * 815 = 4,890

Example 42 * 37 = ?

Write 37 above the lattice.
Write 42 on the right side of the lattice.

Multiply 4 * 7. Then multiply 4 * 3.
Multiply 2 * 7. Then multiply 2 * 3.
Write the answers as shown.

Add the numbers along each diagonal, starting at the right.

When the numbers along a diagonal add up to 10 or more:
- record the ones digit in the sum.
- add the tens digit to the sum along the next diagonal above.

Read the answer. 42 * 37 = 1,554

Check Your Understanding

Draw a lattice for each problem. Then multiply.

1. 6 * 78 **2.** 55 * 25 **3.** 77 * 89 **4.** 8 * 444 **5.** 357 * 6

Check your answers on pages 433 and 434.

Student Reference Book, p. 20

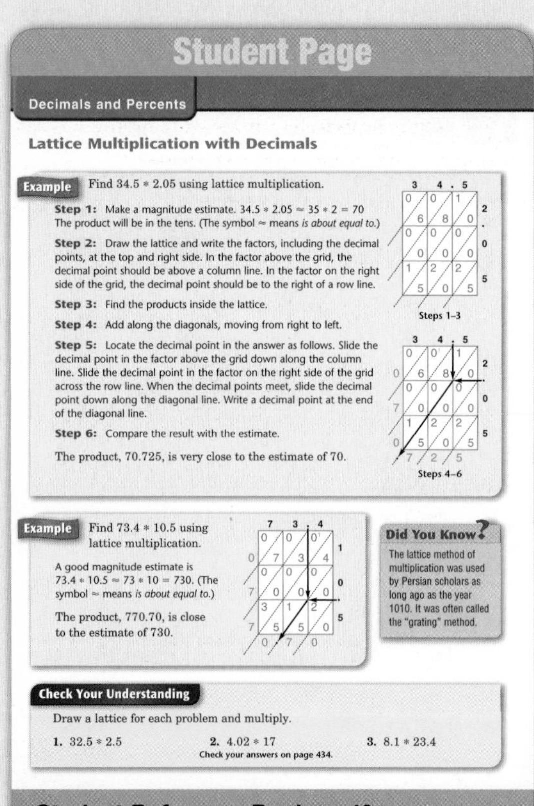

Student Page

Decimals and Percents

Lattice Multiplication with Decimals

Example Find 34.5 * 2.05 using lattice multiplication.

Step 1: Make a magnitude estimate. 34.5 * 2.05 ≈ 35 * 2 = 70
The product will be in the tens. (The symbol ≈ means *is about equal to.*)

Step 2: Draw the lattice and write the factors, including the decimal points, at the top and right side. In the factor above the grid, the decimal point should be above a column line. In the factor on the right side of the grid, the decimal point should be to the right of a row line.

Step 3: Find the products inside the lattice.

Step 4: Add along the diagonals, moving from right to left.

Step 5: Locate the decimal point in the answer as follows. Slide the decimal point in the factor above the grid down along the column line. Slide the decimal point in the factor on the right side of the grid across the row line. When the decimal points meet, slide the decimal point down along the diagonal line. Write a decimal point at the end of the diagonal line.

Step 6: Compare the result with the estimate.

The product, 70.725, is very close to the estimate of 70.

Steps 1–3

Steps 4–6

Example Find 73.4 * 10.5 using lattice multiplication.

A good magnitude estimate is 73.4 * 10.5 ≈ 73 * 10 = 730. (The symbol ≈ means *is about equal to.*)

The product, 770.70, is close to the estimate of 730.

Did You Know?

The lattice method of multiplication was used by Persian scholars as long ago as the year 1010. It was often called the "grating" method.

Check Your Understanding

Draw a lattice for each problem and multiply.

1. 32.5 * 2.5 **2.** 4.02 * 17 **3.** 8.1 * 23.4

Check your answers on page 434.

Student Reference Book, p. 40

▷ Add the numbers along each diagonal. Ask students how they know where to begin the addition. Begin with the diagonal in the bottom right-hand corner. Explain that the extended diagonal lines outside of the lattice squares are the answer spaces. Ask students how the sum is written when the sum on a diagonal is 10 or more. Write the ones digit in the answer space and the tens digit at the top of the next diagonal.

Review these steps by demonstrating with the following problem.

The Lattice Method for Multiplying Whole Numbers

Example: $42 * 37 = ?$

1. Write 37 above the lattice.
Write 42 on the right side.

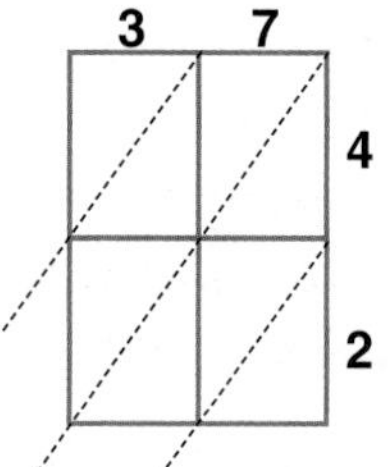

2. Multiply $4 * 7$.
Then multiply $4 * 3$.
Multiply $2 * 7$.
Then multiply $2 * 3$.
Write the answers as shown.

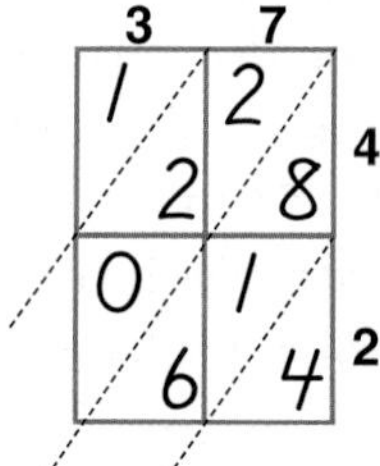

3. Add the numbers along each diagonal. Begin with the diagonal in the bottom right-hand corner. The sum of the numbers in the second diagonal is 15, so write 1 above the 2 in the third diagonal. The sum of the numbers in that diagonal is $1 + 2 + 2 = 5$.

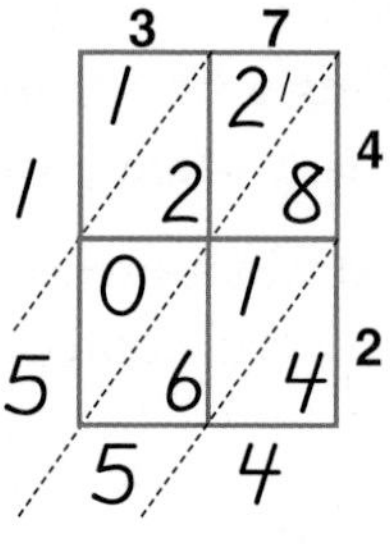

4. Stress that the answer is shown, starting on the upper left side of the lattice and continuing below the lattice.
$42 * 37 = 1{,}554$

Pass out two lattice-computation grids (*Math Masters*, page 418) to each student. Students work with partners to use the lattice method to solve several multiplication problems in which both factors are whole numbers. Remind students to make a magnitude estimate for the problem before beginning the lattice. *Suggestions:* $7 * 37$; $43 * 96$; $32 * 146$; $513 * 658$.

Ongoing Assessment: Informing Instruction

Watch for students who are still having difficulty with the automatic recall of multiplication facts. Provide them with copies of the lattice multiplication facts table (*Math Masters,* page 58).

The Lattice Method for Multiplying Decimals

An advantage of the lattice method is that products of decimals are as easy to calculate as products of whole numbers, and the grid automatically locates the placement of the decimal point in the answer.

▷ When writing the factors above and on the right side of the lattice, include the decimal points. In the factor above the grid, the decimal point should be above a column line. In the factor on the right side of the grid, the decimal point should be to the right of a row line.

▷ Locate the decimal point in the answer as follows: Slide the decimal point in the factor above the grid down. Slide the decimal point in the factor on the right side of the grid across. The decimal points will intersect on a diagonal line. Slide that decimal point down along the diagonal line. Place a decimal point at the end of the diagonal line.

4.2 * 3.7 = 15.54

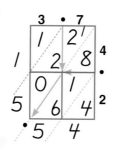

Model how to use the lattice to locate the decimal point in problems with factors such as 0.5 and in problems where one factor is a whole number such as 3.7 * 42.

Have students work with partners to use the lattice method to solve several multiplication problems in which at least one factor is a decimal. Remind students to make a magnitude estimate for the problem before beginning the lattice. *Suggestions:* 7 * 3.7 25.9; 4.3 * 9.6 41.28; 32 * 14.6 467.2; 5.13 * 6.58 33.7554.

Multiplying Whole Numbers and Decimals by the Lattice Method

INDEPENDENT ACTIVITY

(*Math Journal 1,* p. 55)

Students solve the problems independently and then check each other's work. Circulate and assist. Bring the class together to share magnitude estimates and solutions and to explain strategies and the reasoning used.

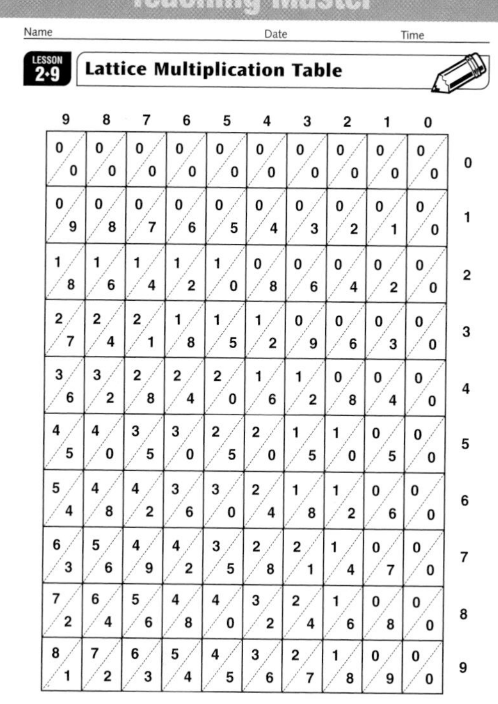

Teaching Master

Name Date Time

LESSON 2·9 **Lattice Multiplication Table**

	9	8	7	6	5	4	3	2	1	0
0	0/0	0/0	0/0	0/0	0/0	0/0	0/0	0/0	0/0	0/0
1	0/9	0/8	0/7	0/6	0/5	0/4	0/3	0/2	0/1	0/0
2	1/8	1/6	1/4	1/2	1/0	0/8	0/6	0/4	0/2	0/0
3	2/7	2/4	2/1	1/8	1/5	1/2	0/9	0/6	0/3	0/0
4	3/6	3/2	2/8	2/4	2/0	1/6	1/2	0/8	0/4	0/0
5	4/5	4/0	3/5	3/0	2/5	2/0	1/5	1/0	0/5	0/0
6	5/4	4/8	4/2	3/6	3/0	2/4	1/8	1/2	0/6	0/0
7	6/3	5/6	4/9	4/2	3/5	2/8	2/1	1/4	0/7	0/0
8	7/2	6/4	5/6	4/8	4/0	3/2	2/4	1/6	0/8	0/0
9	8/1	7/2	6/3	5/4	4/5	3/6	2/7	1/8	0/9	0/0

Math Masters, p. 58

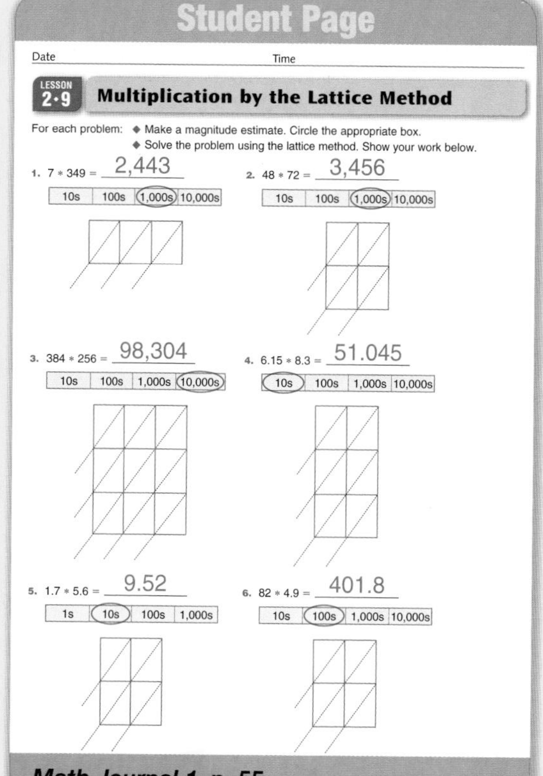

Student Page

Date Time

LESSON 2·9 **Multiplication by the Lattice Method**

For each problem: ◆ Make a magnitude estimate. Circle the appropriate box.
◆ Solve the problem using the lattice method. Show your work below.

1. 7 * 349 = 2,443 — 10s | 100s | (1,000s) | 10,000s
2. 48 * 72 = 3,456 — 10s | 100s | (1,000s) | 10,000s
3. 384 * 256 = 98,304 — 10s | 100s | 1,000s | (10,000s)
4. 6.15 * 8.3 = 51.045 — (10s) | 100s | 1,000s | 10,000s
5. 1.7 * 5.6 = 9.52 — 1s | (10s) | 100s | 1,000s
6. 82 * 4.9 = 401.8 — 10s | (100s) | 1,000s | 10,000s

Math Journal 1, p. 55

Student Page

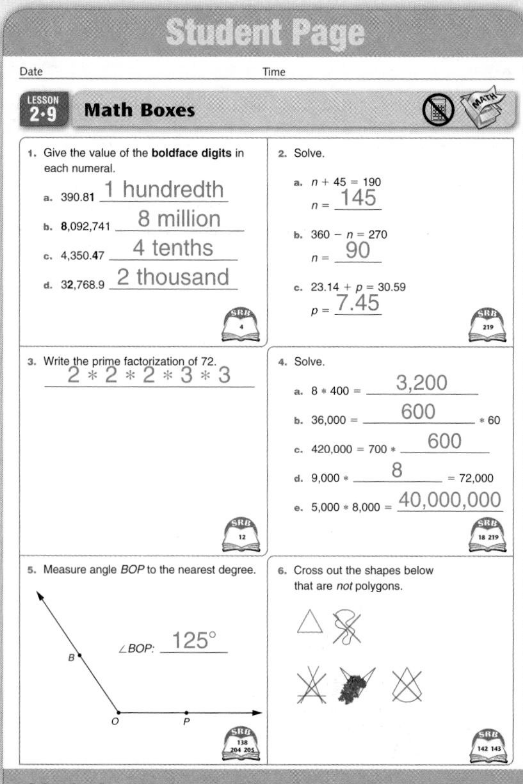
Date Time

LESSON 2·9 **Math Boxes**

1. Give the value of the **boldface digits** in each numeral.
   a. 390.81 1 hundredth
   b. 8,092,741 8 million
   c. 4,350.47 4 tenths
   d. 32,768.9 2 thousand

2. Solve.
   a. n + 45 = 190
      n = 145
   b. 360 − n = 270
      n = 90
   c. 23.14 + p = 30.59
      p = 7.45

3. Write the prime factorization of 72.
   2 ∗ 2 ∗ 2 ∗ 3 ∗ 3

4. Solve.
   a. 8 ∗ 400 = 3,200
   b. 36,000 = 600 ∗ 60
   c. 420,000 = 700 ∗ 600
   d. 9,000 ∗ 8 = 72,000
   e. 5,000 ∗ 8,000 = 40,000,000

5. Measure angle BOP to the nearest degree.
   ∠BOP: 125°

6. Cross out the shapes below that are *not* polygons.

Math Journal 1, p. 56

Study Link Master

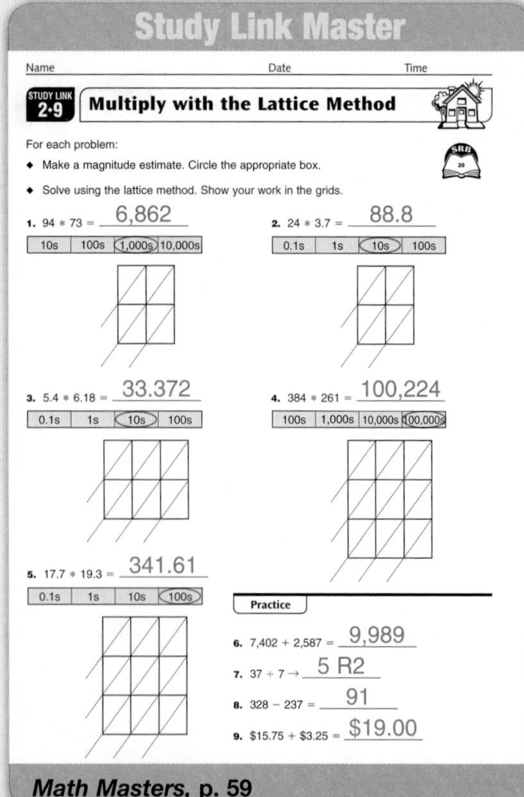
Name Date Time

STUDY LINK 2·9 **Multiply with the Lattice Method**

For each problem:
- Make a magnitude estimate. Circle the appropriate box.
- Solve using the lattice method. Show your work in the grids.

1. 94 ∗ 73 = 6,862
   10s | 100s | 1,000s | 10,000s
2. 24 ∗ 3.7 = 88.8
   0.1s | 1s | 10s | 100s
3. 5.4 ∗ 6.18 = 33.372
   0.1s | 1s | 10s | 100s
4. 384 ∗ 261 = 100,224
   100s | 1,000s | 10,000s | 100,000s
5. 17.7 ∗ 19.3 = 341.61
   0.1s | 1s | 10s | 100s

Practice

6. 7,402 + 2,587 = 9,989
7. 37 ÷ 7 → 5 R2
8. 328 − 237 = 91
9. $15.75 + $3.25 = $19.00

Math Masters, p. 59

Ongoing Assessment: Recognizing Student Achievement

Exit Slip

Use an **Exit Slip** (*Math Masters,* page 414) to assess students' ability to use a multiplication method of their choice. Have students write a response to the following: *Explain how to use the multiplication method of your choice to solve 82 ∗ 75 = ? and 8.2 ∗ 7.5 = ?* Students are making adequate progress if their explanations support their multiplication strategy and appropriate placement of the decimal.

[Operations and Computation Goal 3]

2 Ongoing Learning & Practice

▶ Playing *Factor Bingo*

(*Math Masters,* p. 452)

Students practice applying multiplication facts and number properties, recognizing factors, and factoring numbers by playing *Factor Bingo.* See this lesson guide, page 50, for game directions. It can also be played as a whole-class activity.

▶ Multiplying and Dividing by Powers of 10

(*Math Journal 1,* pp. 56A and 56B)

Students practice multiplying and dividing by powers of 10.

▶ Math Boxes 2·9

INDEPENDENT ACTIVITY

(*Math Journal 1,* p. 56)

Mixed Practice Math Boxes in this lesson are paired with Math Boxes in Lesson 2-6. The skills in Problems 4 and 5 preview Unit 3 content.

▶ Study Link 2·9

Homework

INDEPENDENT ACTIVITY

(*Math Masters,* p. 59)

Home Connection Students make estimates and then solve multiplication problems by the lattice method.

3 Differentiation Options

ENRICHMENT

PARTNER ACTIVITY

15–30 Min

Exploring an Ancient Multiplication Method

(*Math Masters,* p. 60)

To apply students' understanding of multiplication, have them explore and analyze how to use an ancient Egyptian method of multiplying. When students have finished, have them describe the pattern that is used in the Egyptian method.

NOTE This method is also used in Project 3: An Ancient Multiplication Algorithm. See page 446 in this lesson guide.

EXTRA PRACTICE

SMALL-GROUP ACTIVITY

5–10 Min

5-Minute Math

To offer students more experience with multiplying decimals, see *5-Minute Math*, page 186.

EXTRA PRACTICE

INDEPENDENT ACTIVITY

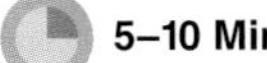

5–10 Min

Decimal Computation

(*Math Masters,* p. 414)

To offer students more experience with decimal multiplication, have them record the following problems onto an Exit Slip, *Math Masters,* page 414. Ask students to make magnitude estimates for each product and then solve the problems. Students should use their estimates to ensure that their answers are reasonable. Have them write an explanation of their reasoning in solving Problem a.

a. 3.35 * 8.4 = 28.14

b. 16.05 * 400 = 6,420

c. 82.6 * 6.5 = 536.9

d. 61.04 * 3.9 = 238.056

Student Page

Date ______ Time ______

LESSON 2·9 Dividing by Powers of 10

Use the strategy described in Extended Division Facts on page 21 of the *Student Reference Book* to solve Problems 1–6.

Example: 45,000 / 100 = ?	Divide a whole number that ends in zero by a power of 10.
45,000 / 100 = 45,000	Count the number of zeros in the divisor (power of 10).
45,000 / 100 = 45,0~~00~~	Cross out the same number of zeros in the answer (quotient) as there are zeros in the divisor (power of 10), starting in the ones place.
45,000 / 100 = 450	The numbers not crossed out give the answer.

1. 3,200 / 10 = 320
2. 78,000 / 10 = 7,800
3. 902,000 / 100 = 9,020
4. 35,000 / 1,000 = 35
5. 450,000 / 5,000 = 90
6. 28,000 / 40 = 700

Solve the following problems. Show your work.

7. Every year, Mrs. Connick asked her students to bring in bottle caps for charity. It took Mrs. Connick 10 years to collect one million bottle caps. About how many bottle caps did each class collect every year?
   100,000 bottle caps

8. The entire fifth grade collected about 8,000 buttons for their Math Fun Fair estimation jar. There are 200 fifth-grade students. If each student collected the same number of buttons, about how many buttons did each student bring in?
   40 buttons

9. Elves love to bake cookies. Last year, they had a contest to see who could bake the most cookies in a week. Effie, the fastest elf, baked 70 cookies an hour. She baked for 10 hours per day. About how many cookies did she bake in a week?
   4,900 cookies

Math Journal 1, p. 56A

Student Page

Date ______ Time ______

LESSON 2·9 Multiplying and Dividing Decimals by Powers of 10

Study the problems below.

3.27 * 10 = 32.7 0.438 * 100 = 43.8

7694 * $\frac{1}{10}$ = 7.694 2462 * $\frac{1}{100}$ = 2.462

1. Explain a strategy for finding a product when you multiply a number by a power of 10 greater than 1. Do the same for a power of 10 less than 1.
   Sample answer: When multiplying by 10, 100, or 1,000, you move the decimal point to the right; when multiplying by 0.1, 0.01, or 0.001, you move the decimal point to the left.

Study the problems below.

3.27 ÷ 10 = 0.327 43.8 ÷ 100 = 0.438

769.4 ÷ 1,000 = 0.7694 2462 ÷ 10,000 = 0.2462

2. Explain a strategy for finding the quotient when you divide a number by a power of 10 greater than 1.
   Sample answer: When dividing by 10, 100, or 1,000, you move the decimal point one place to the left for each 0 in the power of 10.

3. Use your strategies to solve the problems below.
   a. 59.87 * 10 = 598.7
   b. 20.477 * 1,000 = 20,477
   c. 6.32 * $\frac{1}{10}$ = 0.632
   d. 959.8 * $\frac{1}{100}$ = 9.598
   e. 56.02 ÷ 100 = 0.5602
   f. 49,034 ÷ 1,000 = 49.034

Math Journal 1, p. 56B

2•10 Comparing Millions, Billions, and Trillions

Objectives To provide experience with comparing the relative sizes of 1 million, 1 billion, and 1 trillion and using a sample to make an estimate.

Technology Resources www.everydaymathonline.com

ePresentations

eToolkit

Algorithms Practice

EM Facts Workshop Game™

Family Letters

Assessment Management

Common Core State Standards

Curriculum Focal Points

Interactive Teacher's Lesson Guide

1 Teaching the Lesson

Key Concepts and Skills

- Read and write large numbers. [Number and Numeration Goal 1]
- Compare order of magnitude for large numbers. [Number and Numeration Goal 6]
- Make reasonable estimates for whole number multiplication problems. [Operations and Computation Goal 6]

Key Activities

Students review time conversion factors. They count the number of times they can tap their desks in 10 seconds and estimate how long it would take to tap 1 million times. Students then estimate how long it would take to tap 1 billion and 1 trillion times.

Ongoing Assessment: Informing Instruction See page 134.

Key Vocabulary

sample

Materials

Math Journal 1, p. 57
Study Link 2•9
Class Data Pad ◆ blank paper or construction paper ◆ markers or crayons ◆ watch or timer with second hand ◆ calculator

2 Ongoing Learning & Practice

Playing *High-Number Toss*
Student Reference Book, p. 320
Math Masters, p. 487
per partnership: 1 die ◆ 1 sheet of paper
Students practice concepts of place value and standard notation by writing and comparing large numbers.

Ongoing Assessment: Recognizing Student Achievement
Use *Math Masters,* page 487.
[Numbers and Numeration Goals 1 and 6]

Math Boxes 2•10
Math Journal 1, p. 58
Students practice and maintain skills through Math Box problems.

Study Link 2•10
Math Masters, p. 61
Students practice and maintain skills through Study Link activities.

3 Differentiation Options

READINESS

Playing *Number Top-It* (7-Digit Numbers)
Student Reference Book, p. 326
Math Masters, pp. 491 and 492
per partnership: 4 each of number cards 0–9 (from the Everything Math Deck, if available)
Students apply place-value concepts to form, read, and compare large numbers.

EXTRA PRACTICE

Comparing Powers of 10 Using Place Value
Math Masters, p. 66B
Students apply place value for powers of 10.

ENRICHMENT

Applying Estimation Strategies
Math Masters, p. 62
Students make time estimates and identify the number models used for their estimation strategies.

Advance Preparation

For Part 1, use the Class Data Pad to record and display the Mental Math and Reflexes problems and responses.
For the optional Readiness activity in Part 3, make one game mat for each partnership by copying, cutting, and taping together *Math Masters,* pages 491 and 492.

For a mathematics and literary connection, obtain a copy of ***How Much Is a Million?*** by David M. Schwartz (HarperCollins Publishers, 1985).

***Teacher's Reference Manual,* Grades 4–6** pp. 256–264

Getting Started

Mental Math and Reflexes

Have students practice conversions between units of time. Use the Class Data Pad to record the correct responses. Keep this display up for students to refer to during the lesson.

How many seconds are in...

●○○ 1 minute? 60
●○○ 3 minutes? 180
●●○ 100 minutes? 6,000

How many minutes are in...

●○○ 1 hour? 60
●○○ 5 hours? 300
●●○ 50 hours? 3,000

How many hours are in...

●○○ 1 day? 24
●○○ 2 days? 48
●●● 200 days? 4,800

How many days are in...

●○○ 1 year? 365, except 366 in leap years
●●○ 10 years? about 3,650
●●● 100 years? about 36,500

Math Message

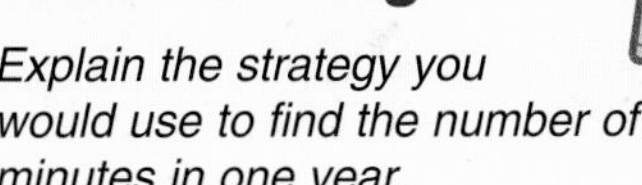

Explain the strategy you would use to find the number of minutes in one year.

Study Link 2·9 Follow-Up

Have partners share answers and resolve any differences.

1 Teaching the Lesson

▶ Math Message Follow-Up

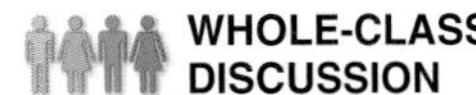

WHOLE-CLASS DISCUSSION

Have students in small groups discuss their individual strategies. The group then decides which steps they would use to find the number of minutes in a year. Each group should make a poster, using construction paper and markers or crayons, to list their steps and place the poster on display. Allow time for students to read the displayed group posters. Ask volunteers to identify the similarities and differences in the strategies. Guide the class discussion to focus on summarizing the strategies. Sample answers: Convert a year into a unit of time that can be converted to minutes; convert a year into days; convert these days into hours and the hours into minutes.

NOTE Include a walkabout in the follow-up to this Math Message: Display the group posters in separate areas of your classroom, and allow students time to browse until they have read all the posters.

▶ Solving a Tapping Problem with Sampling Strategies

WHOLE-CLASS DISCUSSION

PROBLEM SOLVING

(*Math Journal 1,* p. 57)

Ask students to refer to the Useful Information chart on journal page 57. Pose several questions from the first row of information to highlight these large number relationships for students. *What is 1,000 times 1 million?* 1 billion *One billion has what relationship to 1 trillion?* One trillion is 1,000 times 1 billion. Ask a volunteer to read the question labeled Make a guess. Ask students to guess how long it would take them to tap their desks 1 million times without any interruptions. Have students

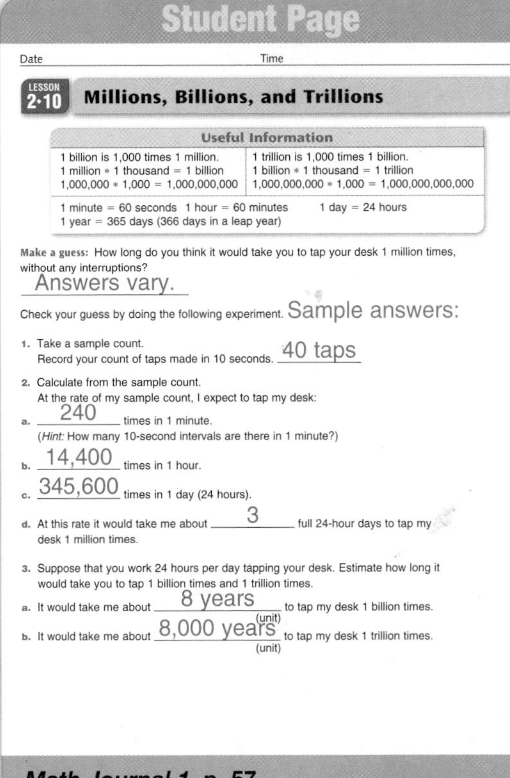

Student Page

Date ______ Time ______

LESSON 2·10 **Millions, Billions, and Trillions**

Useful Information	
1 billion is 1,000 times 1 million. 1 million * 1 thousand = 1 billion 1,000,000 * 1,000 = 1,000,000,000	1 trillion is 1,000 times 1 billion. 1 billion * 1 thousand = 1 trillion 1,000,000,000 * 1,000 = 1,000,000,000,000
1 minute = 60 seconds 1 hour = 60 minutes 1 day = 24 hours 1 year = 365 days (366 days in a leap year)	

Make a guess: How long do you think it would take you to tap your desk 1 million times, without any interruptions?

Answers vary.

Check your guess by doing the following experiment. Sample answers:

1. Take a sample count.
   Record your count of taps made in 10 seconds. 40 taps

2. Calculate from the sample count.
   At the rate of my sample count, I expect to tap my desk:
   a. 240 times in 1 minute.
   (*Hint:* How many 10-second intervals are there in 1 minute?)
   b. 14,400 times in 1 hour.
   c. 345,600 times in 1 day (24 hours).
   d. At this rate it would take me about 3 full 24-hour days to tap my desk 1 million times.

3. Suppose that you work 24 hours per day tapping your desk. Estimate how long it would take you to tap 1 billion times and 1 trillion times.
   a. It would take me about 8 years (unit) to tap my desk 1 billion times.
   b. It would take me about 8,000 years (unit) to tap my desk 1 trillion times.

Math Journal 1, p. 57

Student Page

Games

High-Number Toss

Materials □ 1 six-sided die
□ 1 sheet of paper for each player

Players 2

Skill Place value, exponential notation

Object of the game To make the largest numbers possible.

Directions

1. Each player draws 4 blank lines on a sheet of paper to record the numbers that come up on the rolls of the die.
   Player 1: ___ ___ ___ | ___
   Player 2: ___ ___ ___ | ___
2. Player 1 rolls the die and writes the number on any of his or her 4 blank lines. It does not have to be the first blank—it can be any of them. *Keep in mind that the larger number wins!*
3. Player 2 rolls the die and writes the number on one of his or her blank lines.
4. Players take turns rolling the die and writing the number 3 more times each.
5. Each player then uses the 4 numbers on his or her blanks to build a number.
   - The numbers on the first 3 blanks are the first 3 digits of the number the player builds.
   - The number on the last blank tells the number of zeros that come after the first 3 digits.
6. Each player reads his or her number. (See the place-value chart below.) The player with the larger number wins the round. The first player to win 4 rounds wins the game.

Note
If you don't have a die, you can use a deck of number cards. Use all cards with the numbers 1 through 6. Instead of rolling the die, draw the top card from the facedown deck.

Hundred Millions	Ten Millions	Millions	,	Hundred Thousands	Ten Thousands	Thousands	,	Hundreds	Tens	Ones

Example

First three digits — Number of zeros

Player 1: 1 3 2 | 6 = 132,000,000 (132 million)

Player 2: 3 5 6 | 4 = 3,560,000 (3 million, 560 thousand)

Player 1 wins.

Student Reference Book, p. 320

Game Master

Name ______ Date ______ Time ______

High-Number Toss Record Sheet

Hundred Millions	Ten Millions	Millions	,	Hundred Thousands	Ten Thousands	Thousands	,	Hundreds	Tens	Ones

Round	Player 1	>, <, =	Player 2
Sample	1 3 2, 6 132,000,000	>	3 5 6, 4 3,560,000
1	___ ___ ___ | ___		___ ___ ___ | ___
2	___ ___ ___ | ___		___ ___ ___ | ___
3	___ ___ ___ | ___		___ ___ ___ | ___
4	___ ___ ___ | ___		___ ___ ___ | ___
5	___ ___ ___ | ___		___ ___ ___ | ___

Math Masters, p. 487

record their responses on the journal page. Conduct a quick survey of the class for their responses.

Discuss the difference between a *guess* and an *estimate*. Use the discussion to clarify for students that a guess is an opinion that you might state without the support of other information. An estimate is based on some knowledge about the subject and is often called an educated guess. Students can only guess the amount of time it would take to tap 1 million times until they collect additional information with which to make an estimate.

Encourage students to think about what information they would need to make a more educated guess, and then ask volunteers to explain strategies that could be used to gather additional information.

Ongoing Assessment: Informing Instruction

Watch for students who are having difficulty developing a strategy. Explain that this is another situation for which obtaining the exact answer is impossible, such as the Estimation Challenge from Lesson 2-1. Recall the strategies students used in that lesson and have them use similar approaches here.

Students might suggest strategies such as the following:

▷ Count how many times you can tap your desk in a set amount of time, such as 10 seconds.

▷ Time how long it takes you to tap a certain number of times, such as 100 times.

▷ Pick a reasonable number of taps for a set amount of time, and make an estimate based on that rate, such as 3 taps per second.

When the class found and used the median step length, they were using a **sample.** Ask whether students know of any other situations where samples are used.

NOTE A sample of anything is a small piece or part that is intended to give information about the whole thing. Consumers use product samples to decide whether products suit their needs. Pollsters use population samples to estimate information for the whole population. The finger-tapping samples here are time samples: The count of taps in a 10-second period is a sample used to determine a tapping rate, and the rate is then used to estimate how long it would take to make large numbers of taps.

Each student will take a 10-second sample count of their own finger tapping. Practice taking sample counts by timing students as they tap and count for 10 seconds.

▶ Using Sampling to Make an Estimate

PARTNER ACTIVITY

(*Math Journal 1,* p. 57)

Have partners complete the journal page. They begin by finding their individual sample counts. Partners take turns. While one partner taps and counts the taps for 10 seconds, the second partner keeps time for 10 seconds, signaling when to start and stop.

Partners then use their 10-second sample counts to estimate the number of taps they could make in 1 minute; in 1 hour; and in 1 day. Encourage students to use their calculators, as needed.

Next students use their estimates to calculate the approximate number of days it would take to tap 1 million times. Encourage students to devise their own solution strategies. One possible approach is to divide 1 million by the number of taps per day.

▶ Making Time Estimates for 1 Billion and 1 Trillion Taps

PARTNER ACTIVITY

(*Math Journal 1,* p. 57)

In Problem 3 on journal page 57, students estimate the time it would take to tap 1 billion and 1 trillion times. Remind students that they can use the relationships between 1 million, 1 billion, and 1 trillion found in the Useful Information chart to help them estimate. They will also need to decide whether to report their estimates for 1 billion and 1 trillion taps as days or years.

NOTE Expect that the tapping rate for most students will be about 40 times in 10 seconds. At this rate they will tap about 250 times in 1 minute (6 * 40, rounded up); 15,000 times in 1 hour (60 * 250); 350,000 times in 1 day (24 * 15,000; rounded down), and about 3 days, without interruptions, to tap 1 million times.

▶ Sharing and Discussing the Results

SMALL-GROUP DISCUSSION

(*Math Journal 1,* p. 57)

When most students have completed the problems, have partners form small groups to discuss their strategies. Then have the groups report on the similarities and differences of the strategies used as well as any notable experiences they encountered. Use the following questions as a guide:

- How does your estimate of the time for 1 million taps compare with your initial guess?
- Did you use your estimate for the number of taps in 1 day to estimate how long it would take to tap 1 million times?
- Did you use the time for 1 million taps to estimate the time for 1 billion and 1 trillion taps?

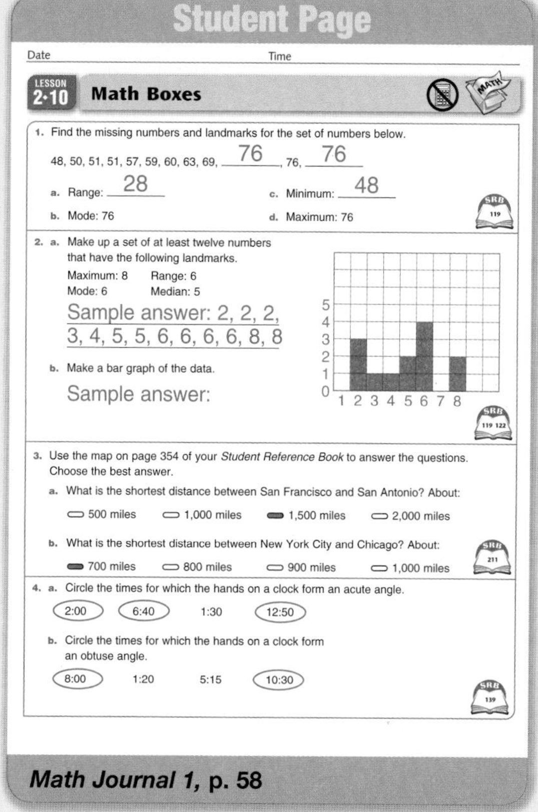

Student Page

Date Time

LESSON 2·10 **Math Boxes**

1. Find the missing numbers and landmarks for the set of numbers below.

48, 50, 51, 51, 57, 59, 60, 63, 69, 76, 76, 76

a. Range: 28 c. Minimum: 48

b. Mode: 76 d. Maximum: 76

2. a. Make up a set of at least twelve numbers that have the following landmarks.

Maximum: 8 Range: 6
Mode: 6 Median: 5

Sample answer: 2, 2, 2, 3, 4, 5, 5, 6, 6, 6, 6, 8, 8

b. Make a bar graph of the data.

Sample answer:

3. Use the map on page 354 of your *Student Reference Book* to answer the questions. Choose the best answer.

a. What is the shortest distance between San Francisco and San Antonio? About:

500 miles 1,000 miles 1,500 miles 2,000 miles

b. What is the shortest distance between New York City and Chicago? About:

700 miles 800 miles 900 miles 1,000 miles

4. a. Circle the times for which the hands on a clock form an acute angle.

2:00 6:40 1:30 12:50

b. Circle the times for which the hands on a clock form an obtuse angle.

8:00 1:20 5:15 10:30

Math Journal 1, p. 58

Study Link Master

STUDY LINK 2·10 **Place-Value Puzzles**

Millions			Thousands			Ones		
Hundred-millions	Ten-millions	Millions	Hundred-thousands	Ten-thousands	Thousands	Hundreds	Tens	Ones

Use the clues to solve the puzzles.

Puzzle 1

- The value of the digit in the **thousandths** place is equal to the sum of the measures of the angles in a triangle (180°) divided by 30.
- If you multiply the digit in the **tens** place by 1,000; the answer will be 9,000.
- Double 35. Divide the result by 10. Write the answer in the **tenths** place.
- The **hundreds**-place digit is $\frac{1}{2}$ the value of the digit in the thousandths place.
- When you multiply the digit in the **ones** place by itself, the answer is 0.
- Write a digit in the **hundredths** place so that the sum of all six digits in this number is 30.

What is the number? 3 9 0 . 7 5 6

Puzzle 2

- Double 12. Divide the result by 8. Write the answer in the **thousands** place.
- If you multiply the digit in the **hundredths** place by 10, your answer will be 40.
- The **tens**-place digit is a prime number. If you multiply it by itself, the answer is 49.
- Multiply 7 and 3. Subtract 12. Write the answer in the **thousandths** place.
- Multiply the digit in the hundredths place by the digit in the thousands place. Subtract 7 from the result. Write the digit in the **tenths** place.
- The digit in the **ones** place is an odd digit that has not been used yet.
- The value of the digit in the **hundreds** place is the same as the number of sides of a quadrilateral.

What is the number? 3 4 7 1 . 5 4 9

Check: The sum of the answers to both puzzles is 3,862.305.

Practice

3. 7,772 + 1,568 = 9,340 **4.** 472 − 228 = 244

5. 826 ∗ 54 = 44,604 **6.** 59 / 3 → 19 R2

61

Math Masters, **p. 61**

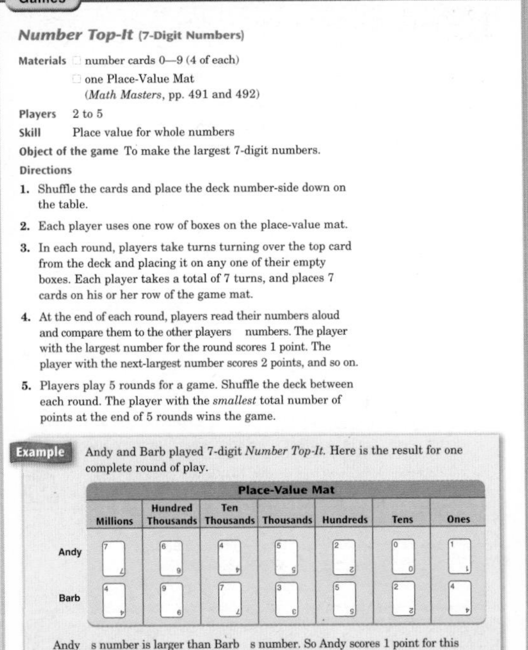

Student Page

Games

Number Top-It **(7-Digit Numbers)**

Materials □ number cards 0–9 (4 of each)
□ one Place-Value Mat (*Math Masters,* pp. 491 and 492)

Players 2 to 5

Skill Place value for whole numbers

Object of the game To make the largest 7-digit numbers.

Directions

1. Shuffle the cards and place the deck number-side down on the table.
2. Each player uses one row of boxes on the place-value mat.
3. In each round, players take turns turning over the top card from the deck and placing it on any one of their empty boxes. Each player takes a total of 7 turns, and places 7 cards on his or her row of the game mat.
4. At the end of each round, players read their numbers aloud and compare them to the other players numbers. The player with the largest number for the round scores 1 point. The player with the next-largest number scores 2 points, and so on.
5. Players play 5 rounds for a game. Shuffle the deck between each round. The player with the *smallest* total number of points at the end of 5 rounds wins the game.

Example Andy and Barb played 7-digit *Number Top-It.* Here is the result for one complete round of play.

Place-Value Mat

	Millions	Hundred Thousands	Ten Thousands	Thousands	Hundreds	Tens	Ones
Andy	7	6	4	5	2	0	1
Barb	4	9	7	3	5	2	4

Andy s number is larger than Barb s number. So Andy scores 1 point for this round, and Barb scores 2 points.

Student Reference Book, **p. 326**

To conclude Part 1 ask students: *If one person could tap 24 hours per day without stopping, would it be possible to tap 1 trillion times?* No Aim follow-up questions at getting students to support their responses. They would still need many more years than are in a normal lifetime. An exit question might be: *Do you feel that your informed estimate was more reasonable than your guess?*

2 Ongoing Learning & Practice

▶ Playing *High-Number Toss*

(*Student Reference Book,* p. 320; *Math Masters,* p. 487)

High-Number Toss provides students with the opportunity to apply their knowledge of place value and standard notation to create, write, read, and compare large numbers. Provide students with a reminder box on the board noting that < means *less than* and > means *greater than.*

Ongoing Assessment: Recognizing Student Achievement

Math Masters Page 487

Use the Record Sheet for *High-Number Toss* (*Math Masters,* page 487) to assess students' knowledge of place value and comparing numbers. Students are making adequate progress if they correctly insert the relational symbols between the two numbers in five rounds of the game.

[Numbers and Numeration Goals 1 and 6]

▶ Math Boxes 2·10

(*Math Journal 1,* p. 58)

Mixed Practice Math Boxes in this lesson are paired with Math Boxes in Lesson 2-8. The skill in Problem 4 previews Unit 3 content.

▶ Study Link 2·10

(*Math Masters,* p. 61)

Home Connection Students use their knowledge of place value and number relationships to solve number puzzles.

3 Differentiation Options

READINESS

PARTNER ACTIVITY

15–30 Min

▶ Playing *Number Top-It* (7-Digit Numbers)

(*Student Reference Book,* p.326; *Math Masters,* pp. 491 and 492)

To review place-value concepts, have students play *Number Top-It* (7-Digit Numbers).

EXTRA PRACTICE

SMALL-GROUP ACTIVITY

5–15 Min

▶ Comparing Powers of 10 Using Place Value

(*Math Masters,* p. 66B)

To provide additional practice with place value and understanding the relationships between powers of 10, have students complete *Math Masters,* page 66B.

ENRICHMENT

INDEPENDENT ACTIVITY

5–15 Min

▶ Applying Estimation Strategies

(*Math Masters,* p. 62)

To apply students' ability to use estimation strategies, have them solve problems that involve converting situational information into open number sentences. Direct students to focus on making informed estimates.

Teaching Master

Name Date Time

LESSON 2·10 **Number Stories and Estimation**

- Read each number story carefully.
- Write an open number sentence to use in estimating.
- Answer the question.

Example:

It is said that the Aztec king, Montezuma, drank about 50 cups of chocolate per day. Did he drink *more* or *less* than 10 gallons of chocolate in a week? (Hint: 16 cups = 1 gallon)

Open number sentence: $10 * 16$ = Number of cups in 10 gallons

Answer: more

1. Certain varieties of seahorses can move 10.5 inches per minute. At this rate, could these seahorses be able to travel 6 yards in 1 hour?
   a. Open number sentence: Sample answer: $10.5 * 60 \div 36$ = yards traveled in 1 hour
   b. Answer: Yes
2. Orville Wright completed the first airplane flight on December 17, 1903. He traveled 120 feet in 12 seconds. If he had been able to stay in the air for a full minute, would he have traveled 1 mile? (Hint: 1 mile = 5,280 feet)
   a. Open number sentence: Sample answer: $120 * 5$ = feet traveled in 1 minute
   b. Answer: No
3. In 1960, the Triton became the first submarine to circumnavigate the world. It covered 36,014 miles in 76 days. Is that more or less than 100 miles per day?
   a. Open number sentence: Sample answer: $100 * 76$ = total miles for 76 days at 100 miles per day
   b. Answer: more

Source: *The Kids' World Almanac of Records and Facts*

Math Masters, p. 62

Teaching Master

Name Date Time

LESSON 2·10 **Using Place Value to Compare Powers of 10**

1 meter	10 decimeters	100 centimeters	1,000 millimeters
1 centimeter	0.01 meter	0.1 decimeter	10 millimeters

Use the information in the conversion table to respond to each statement below. Complete each statement with one of the following phrases:

10 times, 100 times, $\frac{1}{10}$ of, $\frac{1}{100}$ of

1. 1 meter is 10 times the size of a decimeter.
2. 1 centimeter is $\frac{1}{100}$ of the size of a meter.
3. 1 centimeter is 10 times the size of a millimeter.
4. 1 decimeter is $\frac{1}{10}$ of the size of a meter.
5. 1 millimeter is $\frac{1}{100}$ of the size of a decimeter.

Write two of your own statements using the information in the table.

6. Answers vary.
7.

Complete the table below by making the appropriate conversions.

	millimeters	centimeters	decimeters	meters
8.	9,743	974.3	97.43	9.743
9.	3,000	300	30	3
10.	1,750	175	17.5	1.75

11. In Problem 10, explain what happens to the value of the digit 5 when you go from millimeters to centimeters, and then from decimeters to meters.
Sample answer: You divide by 10 with each conversion; so each time, you move the decimal point one position to the left. So with each move, the digit 5 is worth $\frac{1}{10}$ as much as before.

Math Master, p. 66B

2•11 Progress Check 2

Objective To assess students' progress on mathematical content through the end of Unit 2.

1 Looking Back: Cumulative Assessment

Input student data from Progress Check 2 into the **Assessment Management Spreadsheets**.

Materials
- Study Link 2•10
- *Assessment Handbook,* pp. 60–67, 158–163, 217, and 250–253
- slate

CONTENT ASSESSED	LESSON(S)	ASSESSMENT ITEMS				
		SELF	ORAL/SLATE	WRITTEN PART A	WRITTEN PART B	OPEN RESPONSE
Identify place value of digits. [Number and Numeration Goal 1]	2•2, 2•5, 2•7, 2•10	3	4, 5	9		
Write numbers in expanded notation. [Number and Numeration Goal 1]	2•2	8			16, 17	
Add and subtract whole numbers and decimals. [Operations and Computation Goal 1]	2•2–2•4	1		1–6		
Multiply whole numbers and decimals. [Operations and Computation Goal 3]	2•7–2•9	4		10, 11, 13, 14		✔
Describe and explain strategies used for multi-digit multiplication and division problems. [Operations and Computation Goal 3]	2•7–2•9					✔
Make reasonable estimates. [Operations and Computation Goal 6]	2•2–2•4, 2•7– 2•10	5	1–3	12–14		
Use scaling to model multiplication and division. [Operations and Computation Goal 7]				7		✔
Find landmarks for a data set. [Data and Chance Goal 2]	2•1, 2•5, 2•6	9			18	
Describe probabilities using words or phrases. [Data and Chance Goal 3]	2•6	7		15		
Convert between U.S. customary units of length. [Measurement and Reference Frame Goal 3]	2•1	2		8		
Write and solve number sentences that model addition and subtraction number stories. [Patterns, Functions, and Algebra Goal 2]	2•4, 2•8	6			19	

2 Looking Ahead: Preparing for Unit 3

Math Boxes 2•11

Study Link 2•11: Unit 3 Family Letter

Materials
- *Math Journal 1,* p. 59
- *Math Masters,* pp. 63–66

Getting Started

Math Message • Self Assessment

Complete the Self Assessment (Assessment Handbook, p. 158).

Study Link 2•10 Follow-Up

Allow students five minutes to work together to compare their answers and correct any errors.

1 Looking Back: Cumulative Assessment

Math Message Follow-Up

(Self Assessment, Assessment Handbook, p. 158)

The Self Assessment offers students the opportunity to reflect upon their progress.

Oral and Slate Assessments

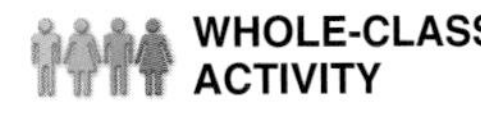

Problems 1 through 5 provide summative information and can be used for grading purposes.

Oral Assessment

1. Is the solution to 24 ∗ 15 in the tens, hundreds, or thousands? hundreds
2. Is the solution to 24 ∗ 1.5 in the tens, hundreds, or thousands? tens
3. Is the solution to 240 ∗ 15 in the tens, hundreds, or thousands? thousands

Slate Assessment

Dictate the following numbers, and have students identify the digits in given places.

4. 543,607: Circle the ten-thousands digit. 4 Underline the hundred-thousands digit. 5
5. 204.39: Circle the tenths digit. 3 Underline the tens digit. 0

Assessment Master

Name Date Time

LESSON 2•11 **Self Assessment** Progress Check 2

Think about each skill listed below. Assess your own progress by checking the most appropriate box.

Skills	I can do this on my own and explain how to do this.	I can do this on my own.	I can do this if I get help or look at an example.
1. Add and subtract whole numbers and decimals.			
2. Convert between U.S. customary units of length.			
3. Identify the place value of digits.			
4. Multiply whole numbers and decimals.			
5. Make reasonable estimates.			
6. Write and solve number sentences.			
7. Describe probabilities using words or phrases.			
8. Write numbers in expanded notation.			
9. Find the landmarks for a data set.			

Assessment Handbook, p. 158

Assessment Master

Name Date Time

LESSON 2•11 **Written Assessment** Progress Check 2

Part A

Solve at least one problem using the partial-sums addition method and at least one problem using the trade-first subtraction method. Use any method you want to solve the rest of the problems. Show your work.

1. 734 + 893 = 1,627
2. 24.7 + 103.9 = 128.6
3. 134.28 = 58.2 + 76.08
4. 692 − 348 = 344
5. 150.4 − 63.7 = 86.7
6. 14.59 = 28.3 − 13.71

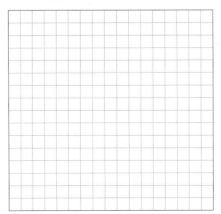

Assessment Handbook, p. 159

Assessment Master

Name ______ Date ______ Time ______

LESSON 2•11 Written Assessment *continued*

7. Students were studying a map of New Zealand. The map legend stated that 1 inch = 400 miles. They measured the distance between two cities. It was $1\frac{1}{2}$ inches. About how many miles apart were the two cities?
About 600 miles

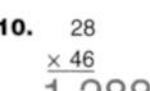

Fill in the blanks.

8. Demetrius walked 1,500 feet to the corner store in the rain. He wanted his friend to feel sorry for him. He said, "I just walked 18,000 inches to the store. And that was just one way!" His friend said, "That's not very far. It's only 500 yards."

9. Write the number that has
6 in the ones place,
4 in the thousands place,
7 in the ten-thousands place,
2 in the tenths place,
and 5 in all of the remaining places. 7 4, 5 5 6. 2 5 5

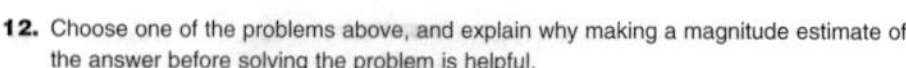

Solve the following problems using a paper-and-pencil algorithm. Show your work.

10. 28 × 46
1,288

11. 365 × 47
17,155

12. Choose one of the problems above, and explain why making a magnitude estimate of the answer before solving the problem is helpful.
Sample answer: A magnitude estimate is a rough estimate that helps to determine if the answer is in the ones, tens, hundreds, etc. The estimate can then be used to determine whether your answer seems reasonable.

Assessment Handbook, p. 160

Use the checklists on pages 251 and 253 of the *Assessment Handbook* to record results. Then input the data into the **Assessment Management Spreadsheets** to keep an ongoing record of students' progress toward Grade-Level Goals.

Assessment Master

Name ______ Date ______ Time ______

LESSON 2•11 Written Assessment *continued*

For Problems 13 and 14, make a magnitude estimate. Circle the appropriate box. Then solve each problem using the algorithm of your choice. Show your work.

13. 6.4 ∗ 8.3 = 53.12

10s (circled)	100s	1,000s	10,000s

14. 12.2 ∗ 1.56 = 19.032

10s (circled)	100s	1,000s	10,000s

Fill in the blank with the phrase from the word bank that describes the chance the event will happen.

Word Bank

certain	very likely	likely	50-50 chance	unlikely	very unlikely	impossible

15. a. A 10% chance of rain very unlikely or unlikely
b. Tossing a coin which lands heads up 50-50 chance
c. A $\frac{3}{4}$ chance of having pizza for dinner likely or very likely
d. Landing on red on a spinner that has 25% each of blue, red, yellow, and green unlikely or very unlikely

Assessment Handbook, p. 161

▶ Written Assessment

INDEPENDENT ACTIVITY

(*Assessment Handbook*, pp. 159–162)

Part A Recognizing Student Achievement

Problems 1–15 provide summative information and may be used for grading purposes.

Problem(s)	Description
1–6	Addition and subtraction of whole numbers and decimals.
7	Use scaling to model multiplication and division.
8	Convert between U.S. customary units of length.
9	Identify place value of digits.
10, 11, 13, 14	Multiply whole numbers and decimals.
12–14	Make reasonable estimates.
15	Describe given numerical probabilities using words or phrases.

Part B Informing Instruction

Problems 16–19 provide formative information that can be useful in planning future instruction.

Problem(s)	Description
16, 17	Write numbers in expanded notation.
18	Find landmarks for a data set.
19	Write and solve number sentences.

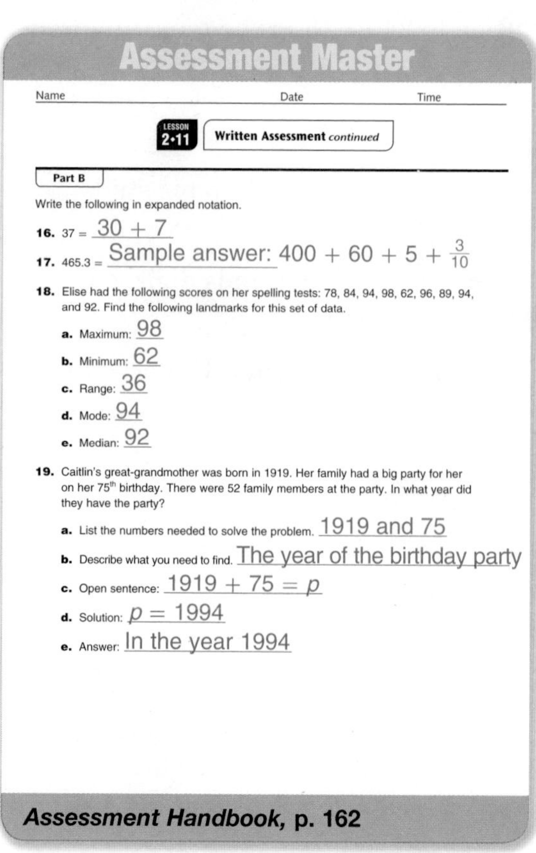

Assessment Master

Name ______ Date ______ Time ______

LESSON 2•11 Written Assessment *continued*

Part B

Write the following in expanded notation.

16. 37 = 30 + 7

17. 465.3 = Sample answer: $400 + 60 + 5 + \frac{3}{10}$

18. Elise had the following scores on her spelling tests: 78, 84, 94, 98, 62, 96, 89, 94, and 92. Find the following landmarks for this set of data.
a. Maximum: 98
b. Minimum: 62
c. Range: 36
d. Mode: 94
e. Median: 92

19. Caitlin's great-grandmother was born in 1919. Her family had a big party for her on her 75th birthday. There were 52 family members at the party. In what year did they have the party?
a. List the numbers needed to solve the problem. 1919 and 75
b. Describe what you need to find. The year of the birthday party
c. Open sentence: $1919 + 75 = p$
d. Solution: $p = 1994$
e. Answer: In the year 1994

Assessment Handbook, p. 162

▶ Open-Response Problem

INDEPENDENT ACTIVITY

(*Assessment Handbook*, p. 163)

Fund Raising

The open-response item requires students to apply skills and concepts from Unit 2 to solve a multistep problem. See *Assessment Handbook,* pages 63–67 for rubrics and students' work samples for this problem.

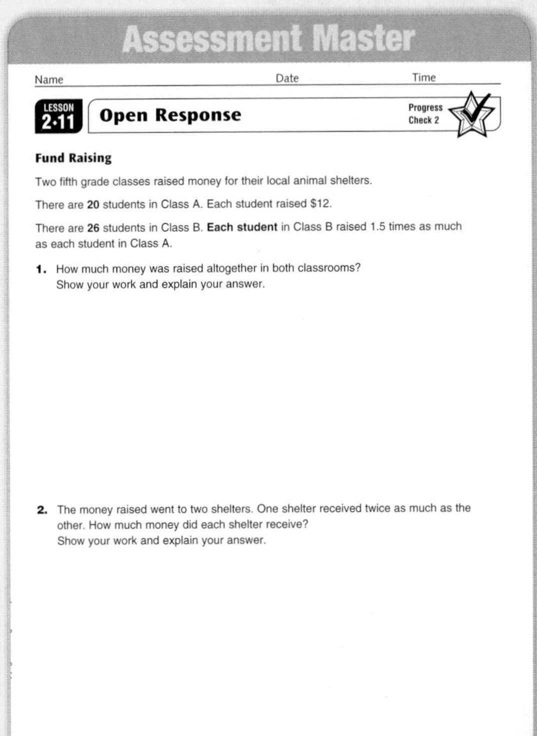

Assessment Master

Name | Date | Time

LESSON 2•11 **Open Response** Progress Check 2

Fund Raising

Two fifth grade classes raised money for their local animal shelters.

There are **20** students in Class A. Each student raised $12.

There are **26** students in Class B. **Each student** in Class B raised 1.5 times as much as each student in Class A.

1. How much money was raised altogether in both classrooms?
Show your work and explain your answer.

2. The money raised went to two shelters. One shelter received twice as much as the other. How much money did each shelter receive?
Show your work and explain your answer.

Assessment Handbook, **p. 163**

2 Looking Ahead: Preparing for Unit 3

▶ Math Boxes 2•11

INDEPENDENT ACTIVITY

(*Math Journal 1,* p. 59)

Mixed Practice This Math Boxes page previews Unit 3 content.

▶ Study Link 2•11: Unit 3 Family Letter

(*Math Masters*, pp. 63–66)

Home Connection The Unit 3 Family Letter provides parents and guardians with information and activities related to Unit 3 topics.

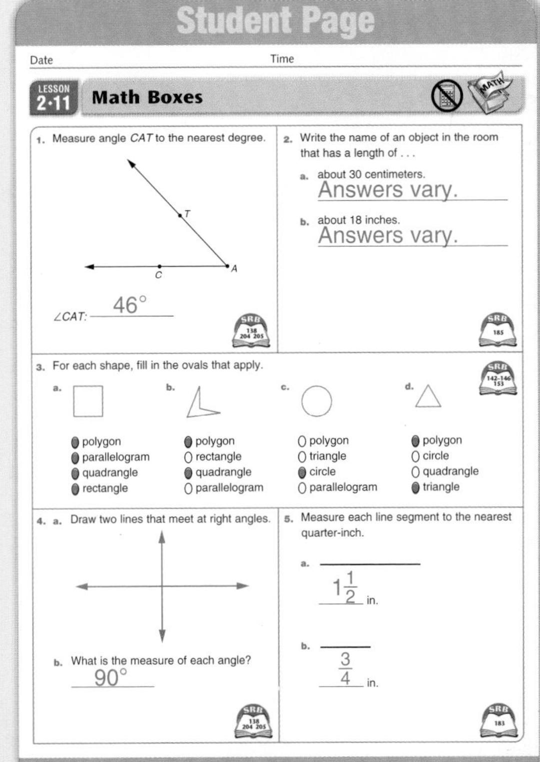

Student Page

Date | Time

LESSON 2•11 **Math Boxes**

1. Measure angle *CAT* to the nearest degree.
∠*CAT*: 46°

2. Write the name of an object in the room that has a length of . . .
a. about 30 centimeters. Answers vary.
b. about 18 inches. Answers vary.

3. For each shape, fill in the ovals that apply.
a. ● polygon ● parallelogram ● quadrangle ● rectangle
b. ● polygon ○ rectangle ● quadrangle ○ parallelogram
c. ○ polygon ○ triangle ● circle ○ parallelogram
d. ● polygon ○ circle ○ quadrangle ● triangle

4. a. Draw two lines that meet at right angles.
b. What is the measure of each angle? 90°

5. Measure each line segment to the nearest quarter-inch.
a. $1\frac{1}{2}$ in.
b. $\frac{3}{4}$ in.

Math Journal, **p. 59**

Unit 3 Organizer

Geometry Explorations and the American Tour

Overview

Unit 3 introduces students to the American Tour, a yearlong project that uses information from the *Student Reference Book.* This unit also examines properties of basic plane figures and the use of the tools of geometry. Students will use compasses, rulers, protractors, and the Geometry Template. Students will also explore tessellations made with polygons. Unit 3 has four main areas of focus:

- To explore data collection, organization, and interpretation,
- To review types of angles, geometric figures, and the use of geometry tools,
- To explore the geometric properties of polygons, and
- To explore side and angle relationships in regular tessellations.

Linking to the Common Core State Standards

The content of Unit 3 addresses the Common Core State Standards for Mathematics in *Geometry.* The correlation of the Common Core State Standards to the *Everyday Mathematics* Grade 5 lessons begins on page CS1.

Contents

Learning In Perspective

	Lesson Objectives	Links to the Past	Links to the Future
3·1	To explore data collection, organization, and interpretation.	In fourth grade, students organize and display data with a tally chart.	In sixth grade, students continue to study how sample size affects results in real-world situations.
3·2	To provide experiences with interpreting data.	In fourth grade, students interpret data using the World Tour Project.	In sixth grade, students analyze a real-world situation by constructing and using a data table and a graph.
3·3	To relate circles and relationships among angles to the degree measures of angles.	In fourth grade, students define a circle and use a protractor to draw and measure angles.	In sixth grade, students explore the relationship between angles formed by intersecting lines and by parallel lines cut by a transversal.
3·4	To review types of angles, geometric figures, and the use of the Geometry Template to measure and draw angles.	In fourth grade, students define acute, right, obtuse, straight, and reflex angles.	In sixth grade, students investigate angles of a parallelogram.
3·5	To review compass skills and explore angles formed by intersecting lines.	In fourth grade, students are introduced to tools for geometry, including a compass, a full-circle protractor, and a half-circle protractor.	In sixth grade, students construct figures with a straightedge and compass.
3·6	To explore triangle types and introduce methods for copying triangles.	In fourth grade, students construct angles, triangles, and quadrangles with a straightedge and compass.	In sixth grade, students explore the meaning of congruence and use drawing tools to construct congruent figures.
3·7	To explore the geometric properties of polygons.	In fourth grade, students practice naming polygons.	In sixth grade, students apply the properties of a polygon.
3·8	To explore side and angle relationships in regular tessellations and compare and classify quadrangles.	In fourth grade, students tessellate polygons using a ruler and the Geometry Template.	In sixth grade, students review regular tessellations; identify semi-regular tessellations; and create nonpolygonal Escher-type tessellations.
3·9	To develop an approach for finding the angle measurement sum for any polygon.	In fourth grade, students discover that the sum of the measures of the angles of a triangle is 180°.	In sixth grade, students find angle measures by reasoning with angle definitions and with sums of angle measures in triangles and quadrangles.
3·10	To review polygon attributes and vocabulary using the Geometry Template.	In fourth grade, students complete patterns using dot paper and pattern blocks and tessellate pattern blocks to make large polygons.	In sixth grade, students explore relationships between polygons and solve problems with polygons on a coordinate grid.

	Key Concepts and Skills	Grade 5 Goals*
3·1	Use collected data to make predictions.	Data and Chance Goal 2
	Use census data to estimate percentages.	Data and Chance Goal 2
	Express probability as a percent, decimal, or fraction.	Data and Chance Goal 4
3·2	Read and write large numbers.	Number and Numeration Goal 1
	Evaluate exact numbers versus estimates for population data.	Operations and Computation Goal 6
	Use table data to answer questions.	Data and Chance Goal 2
3·3	Determine the measure of angles by using known measures.	Geometry Goal 1
	Review naming conventions for angles.	Geometry Goal 1
	Use angle relationships to determine angle measures.	Geometry Goal 1
3·4	Define and classify angles according to their measures.	Geometry Goal 1
	Explore angle types and relationships.	Geometry Goal 1
	Use a full-circle and a half-circle protractor to measure and draw angles.	Measurement and Reference Frames Goal 1
3·5	Investigate vertical, opposite, and adjacent angles.	Geometry Goal 1
	Use angle relationships to determine angle measures.	Geometry Goal 1
	Copy, measure, and construct line segments using a compass, straightedge, and ruler.	Measurement and Reference Frames Goal 1
	Explore the relationship between radius and diameter measurements.	Measurement and Reference Frames Goal 2
3·6	Classify triangles as isosceles, equilateral, or scalene.	Geometry Goal 2
	Use a compass and straightedge to construct congruent triangles.	Geometry Goal 2
	Measure angles with a protractor.	Measurement and Reference Frames Goal 1
3·7	Identify the types of angles formed by polygons.	Geometry Goal 1
	Compare and classify polygons.	Geometry Goal 2
	Use relationships and properties to sort polygons.	Geometry Goal 2
3·8	Use angle relationships to determine angle measures.	Geometry Goal 1
	Describe the properties of regular polygons.	Geometry Goal 2
	Compare and classify quadrangles.	Geometry Goal 2
	Identify, describe, and create tessellations.	Geometry Goal 3
3·9	Investigate and compare the measurement sums of interior angles of polygons.	Geometry Goal 1
	Measure angles with a protractor.	Measurement and Reference Frames Goal 1
	Find maximum, minimum, and median for a data set.	Data and Chance Goal 2
	Draw conclusions based on collected data.	Data and Chance Goal 2
3·10	Identify and draw polygons according to angle type.	Geometry Goal 1
	Identify and draw polygons according to given properties.	Geometry Goal 2
	Draw circles of a given radius or diameter.	Measurement and Reference Frames Goal 1

*See the Appendix for a complete list of Grade 5 Goals.

A Balanced Curriculum

Ongoing Practice

Everyday Mathematics provides numerous opportunities for ongoing practice. These activities are embedded throughout the lessons:

Mental Math and Reflexes activities promote speed and accuracy in mental computation.

Math Boxes offer mixed practice and are paired across lessons as shown in the brackets below. This makes them useful as assessment tools. The last one or two boxes on each page preview the next unit's content.

Mixed practice	[3•1, 3•3], [3•2, 3•4], [3•5, 3•7], [3•6, 3•9], [3•8, 3•10]
Mixed practice with multiple choice	3•1, 3•3, 3•8, 3•10
Mixed practice with writing/reasoning opportunity	3•3, 3•5, 3•6, 3•7, 3•8, 3•9

Study Links are daily homework assignments that review the content of the lesson and often contain ongoing facts practice or computation practice.

5-Minute Math problems are offered for additional practice in Lessons 3•2 and 3•10.

EM Facts Workshop Game provides online practice of basic facts and computation.

EXTRA PRACTICE **Extra Practice** activities are included in Lessons 3•2, 3•3, 3•6, 3•9, and 3•10.

Practice through Games

Games are an essential component of practice in the *Everyday Mathematics* program. Games offer skills practice and promote strategic thinking. See the *Differentiation Handbook* for ways to adapt games to meet students' needs.

Lesson	Game	Skill Practiced
3•1, 3•5	*High-Number Toss: Decimal Version*	Writing, reading, and comparing numbers [NN Goals 1 and 6]
3•3	*Multiplication Top-It*	Multiplying multidigit numbers [OC Goal 3]
3•6, 3•8	*Angle Tangle*	Measuring and estimating angle measures [MRF Goal 1]
3•6	*Triangle Sort*	Exploring properties of triangles [GEO Goal 2]
3•6	*Sides and Angles: Triangles*	Exploring properties of triangles [GEO Goal 2]
3•6	*Where Do I Fit In?*	Exploring properties of triangles [GEO Goal 2]
3•7, 3•10	*Polygon Capture*	Identifying geometric properties of polygons [GEO Goal 2]
3•7	*What's My Attribute Rule?*	Sorting shapes according to their attributes [GEO Goal 2]

[NN] Number and Numeration
[MRF] Measurement and Reference Frames
[OC] Operations and Computation
[GEO] Geometry
[DC] Data and Chance
[PFA] Patterns, Functions, and Algebra

Problem Solving 

Experts at problem solving and mathematical modeling generally do these things:

- Identify the problem.
- Decide what information is needed to solve the problem.
- Play with and study the data to find patterns and meaning.
- Identify and use mathematical procedures to solve the problem.
- Decide whether the solution makes sense and whether it can be applied to other problems.

The table below lists some of the opportunities in this unit for students to practice these strategies.

Lessons that teach *through* problem solving, not just *about* problem solving

Lesson	Activity
3•1	Compare the 1790 Census with the 2000 Census.
3•2	Estimate colonial populations.
3•3	Find pattern-block angle measures.
3•6	Copy triangles.
3•8	Find out which regular polygons tessellate.
3•9	Find the sums of angles in polygons.
3•10	Solve geometry problems involving attributes and the Geometry Template.

See Chapter 18: Problem Solving in the *Teacher's Reference Manual* for more information.

The Language of Mathematics

Everyday Mathematics provides lesson-specific suggestions to help all students acquire, process, and express mathematical ideas. Throughout Unit 3, there are lesson-specific language development notes that address the needs of English language learners, indicated by ELL.

ELL SUPPORT Activities to support English language learners are in Part 3 of Lessons 3•4, 3•5, 3•7, and 3•9.

The *English Learners Handbook* and the *Differentiation Handbook* have suggestions for promoting language development and acquisition of mathematics vocabulary. See Unit 3 in each handbook.

Literacy Connection

A Cloak for the Dreamer, by Aileen Friedman, Scholastic Inc., 1995

The Greedy Triangle, by Marilyn Burns, Scholastic Inc., 1994

G Is for Googol, by David M. Schwartz, Tricycle Press, 1998

What's Your Angle, Pythagoras? by Julie Ellis, Charlesbridge, 2004

For more literacy connections, see the *Home Connection Handbook,* Grades 4–6.

Unit 3 Vocabulary

acute angle
adjacent angles
arc
census
congruent
diameter
equilateral triangle
Geometry Template
isosceles triangle
obtuse angle
pentagon
perimeter
polygon
quadrangle
radius
reflex angle
regular polygon
regular tessellation
right angle
scalene triangle
straight angle
tessellate
tessellation
tessellation vertex
vertical (or opposite) angles

Cross-Curricular Links 

Social Studies – Lesson 3•1

Art – Lessons 3•5, 3•8

Balanced Assessment

Daily Assessments

- **Recognizing Student Achievement** – A daily assessment that is included in every lesson to evaluate students' progress toward the Grade 5 Grade-Level Goals.
- **Informing Instruction** – Notes that appear throughout the unit to help anticipate students' common errors and suggest appropriate problem-solving strategies.

Lesson	Recognizing Student Achievement	Informing Instruction
3•1	Read and write large whole numbers. [NN Goal 1]	
3•2	Add and subtract whole numbers and decimals. [OC Goal 1]	
3•3	Identify angle measures using the relationship between circles and polygons. [GEO Goal 1]	
3•4	Understand how to use full-circle and half-circle protractors. [MRF Goal 1]	Align the protractor correctly when the Geometry Template spans two pages. Measure angles of small shapes accurately. Find the mean accurately.
3•5	Solve extended multiplication facts mentally. [OC Goal 2]	Use rulers correctly.
3•6	Compare decimals. [NN Goal 6]	
3•7	Recognize the relationship between sides and angles in polygons. [GEO Goal 2]	Interpret properties of polygons correctly.
3•8	Classify quadrangles. [GEO Goal 2]	
3•9	Understand angle measures and relationships in polygons. [GEO Goal 1]	
3•10	Make magnitude estimates for division with large numbers. [OC Goal 6]	Use extra paper to provide answers when the journal is difficult to write in.

[NN] Number and Numeration
[MRF] Measurement and Reference Frames
[OC] Operations and Computation
[GEO] Geometry
[DC] Data and Chance
[PFA] Patterns, Functions, and Algebra

Portfolio Opportunities

The following lessons provide opportunities to gather samples of students' mathematical writings, drawings, and creations to add balance to the assessment process: Lessons 3•3, 3•5, 3•6, 3•7, 3•8, 3•9, 3•10, and 3•11.

See pages 16 and 17 in the *Assessment Handbook* for more information about portfolios and how to use them.

Unit Assessment

Progress Check 3 – A cumulative assessment of concepts and skills taught in Unit 3 and in previous units, providing information for evaluating students' progress and planning for future instruction. These assessments include oral/slate, written, and open-response activities, as shown below in the sample Progress Check lesson opener.

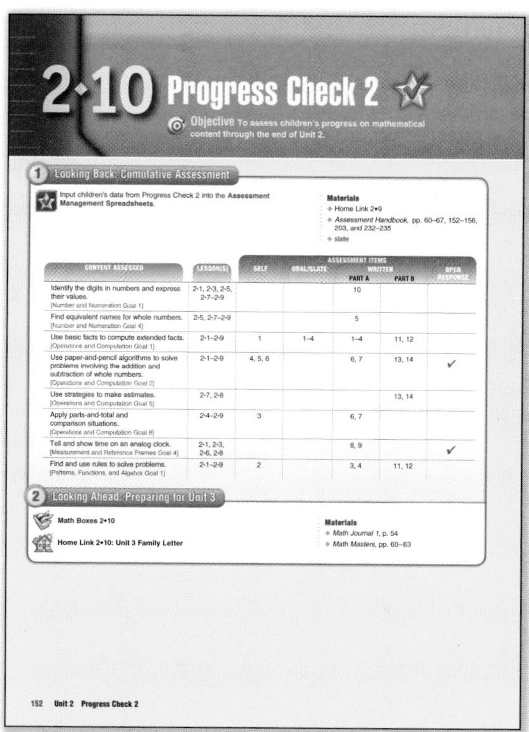

2·10 Progress Check 2

Objective To assess children's progress on mathematical content through the end of Unit 2.

1 Looking Back: Cumulative Assessment

Input children's data from Progress Check 2 into the **Assessment Management Spreadsheets.**

Materials
- Home Link 2•9
- *Assessment Handbook*, pp. 60–67, 152–156, 203, and 232–235
- slate

CONTENT ASSESSED	LESSON(S)	ASSESSMENT ITEMS				
		SELF	ORAL/SLATE	WRITTEN PART A	WRITTEN PART B	OPEN RESPONSE
Identify the digits in numbers and express their values. [Number and Numeration Goal 1]	2·1, 2·3, 2·5, 2·7–2·9			10		
Find equivalent names for whole numbers. [Number and Numeration Goal 4]	2·5, 2·7–2·9			5		
Use basic facts to compute extended facts. [Operations and Computation Goal 1]	2·1–2·9	1	1–4	1–4	11, 12	
Use paper-and-pencil algorithms to solve problems involving the addition and subtraction of whole numbers. [Operations and Computation Goal 2]	2·1–2·9	4, 5, 6		6, 7	13, 14	✓
Use strategies to make estimates. [Operations and Computation Goal 5]	2·7, 2·8				13, 14	
Apply parts-and-total and comparison situations. [Operations and Computation Goal 6]	2·4–2·9	3		6, 7		
Tell and show time on an analog clock. [Measurement and Reference Frames Goal 4]	2·1, 2·3, 2·6, 2·8			8, 9		✓
Find and use rules to solve problems. [Patterns, Functions, and Algebra Goal 1]	2·1–2·9	2		3, 4	11, 12	

2 Looking Ahead: Preparing for Unit 3

Math Boxes 2•10

Home Link 2•10: Unit 3 Family Letter

Materials
- *Math Journal 1*, p. 54
- *Math Masters*, pp. 60–63

152 Unit 2 Progress Check 2

Core Assessment Resources

Assessment Handbook

- **Unit 3 Assessment Overview,** pages 68–75
- **Unit 3 Assessment Masters,** pages 164–169
- **Unit 3 Individual Profiles of Progress,** pages 254, 255, and 302
- **Unit 3 Class Checklists,** pages 256, 257, and 303
- **Quarterly Checklist: Quarter 1,** pages 294 and 295
- **Math Logs,** pages 306–308
- **Exit Slip,** page 311
- **Other Student Assessment Forms,** pages 304, 305, 309, and 310

Assessment Management Spreadsheets

The Assessment Management Spreadsheets consist of the Digital Class Checklists and Individual Profile of Progress Checklists. Use them to monitor, record, and report student progress.

Addressing All Needs

Differentiated Instruction

Adjusting the Activity – suggests adaptations that target advanced learners, English language learners, or learners who need additional instructional support.

ELL SUPPORT / **ELL** – provides lesson-specific suggestions to help English language learners understand and process the mathematical content.

READINESS – accesses students' prior knowledge or previews content that prepares students to engage in the lesson's Part 1 activities.

EXTRA PRACTICE – provides additional opportunities to apply the mathematical content of the lesson.

ENRICHMENT – enables students to apply or further explore the mathematical content of the lesson.

Lesson	Adjusting the Activity	ELL Support/ ELL	Readiness	Extra Practice	Enrichment
3•1		•	•		•
3•2	•	•	•	•	•
3•3	•	•	•	•	•
3•4	•	•	•		•
3•5	•	•	•		•
3•6	•		•	•	•
3•7		•	•		•
3•8	•	•	•		•
3•9		•		•	•
3•10			•	•	•

Additional Resources

Differentiation Handbook
Provides ideas and strategies for differentiating instruction.
Pages 64–70

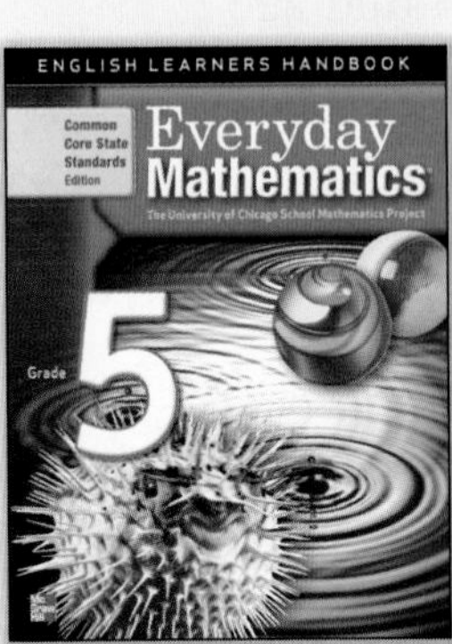

English Learners Handbook
Contains lesson-specific comprehension strategies.
Pages 20–29

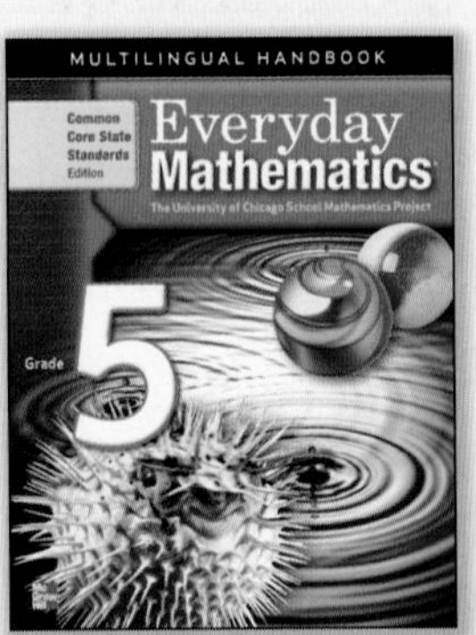

Multilingual Handbook
Previews concepts and vocabulary. It is written in six languages.
Pages 39–58

Planning Tips

Multiage Classroom

Companion Lessons from Grades 4 and 6 can help you meet instructional needs of a multiage classroom. The full Scope and Sequence can be found in the Appendix.

Grade 4	2•1		1•3	1•2, 1•3, 6•6, 6•7	1•2, 1•3, 1•6	1•3	1•3, 1•5		1•5	
Grade 5	**3•1**	**3•2**	**3•3**	**3•4**	**3•5**	**3•6**	**3•7**	**3•8**	**3•9**	**3•10**
Grade 6			5•1,5•2, 5•9	5•3	5•7, 5•8			10•1, 10•2		

Pacing for Success

Pacing depends on a number of factors, such as students' individual needs and how long your school has been using *Everyday Mathematics*. At the beginning of Unit 3, you may want to use tools available at www.everydaymathonline.com to help you set your pace.

Home Support

Unit 3 Family Letter (English/Spanish) provides families with an overview, Do-Anytime Activities, Building Skills through Games, a list of vocabulary, and answers to the daily homework (Study Links). Family Letters in English, Spanish, and seven other languages are also available online.

Study Links are the daily homework assignments. They consist of active projects and ongoing review problems.

Home Support Resources

Home Connection Handbook
Offers ideas and reproducible masters for communicating with families. See Table of Contents for unit information.

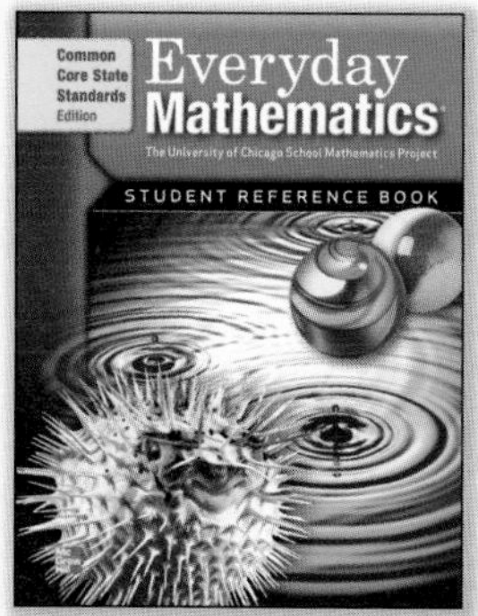

Student Reference Book
Provides a resource for students and parents.

Pages 32, 33, 121, 139, 141, 142, 144–146, 160–168, 171, 172, 296, 321, 328, 334, 338–396

Technology Resources

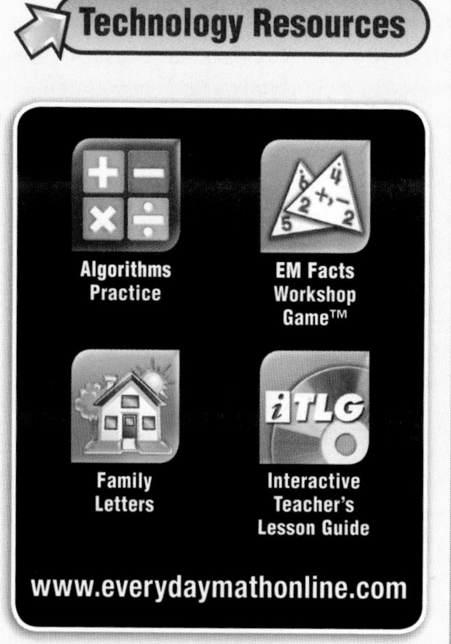

Materials

www.everydaymathonline.com

ePresentations

eToolkit

Algorithms Practice

EM Facts Workshop Game™

Family Letters

Assessment Management

Common Core State Standards

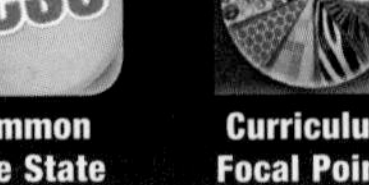

Curriculum Focal Points

Interactive Teacher's Lesson Guide

Lesson	Masters	Manipulative Kit	Other Items
3•1	Teaching Masters, pp. 67, 69, 70, and 71 Study Link Master, p. 68 Game Master, p. 511	per partnership: 4 each of number cards 0–9	Probability Meter; stick-on notes
3•2	Study Link Master, p. 72 Teaching Masters, pp. 73 and 74		
3•3	Study Link Master, p. 75 Teaching Masters, pp. 76 and 77	pattern blocks; per group: 4 each of number cards 1–10	straightedge
3•4	Teaching Masters, pp. 78*, 79*, 81, and 82 Teaching Aid Masters, pp. 414* and 419* Study Link Master, p. 80 *Differentiation Handbook,* p. 143		Geometry Template
3•5	Study Link Master, p. 83 Teaching Masters, pp. 84 and 85 *Differentiation Handbook,* p. 142 Game Master, p. 511	per partnership: 4 each of number cards 0–9; compass	Geometry Template; 1 sheet of paper 2 ft by 2 ft (for demonstration purposes); chalk; per partnership: string or rope at least 5 ft in length; ruler; straightedge; crayons or colored pencils
3•6	Study Link Master, p. 86 Game Masters, pp. 502, 504, and 510	meterstick; straws and connectors (or card stock strips and masking tape); compass; per partnership: 2 dice	Class Data Pad; Geometry Template; demonstration compass and protractor; straightedge; scissors
3•7	Game Masters, pp. 494–496, 508, and 509 Study Link Master, p. 87 Teaching Masters, pp. 87A, 87B, and 88	six-sided die	attribute blocks; scissors; 3" by 5" index card; ruler or Geometry Template
3•8	Teaching Masters, pp. 87A, 87B, 89, and 91 Study Link Master, p. 90 Game Master, p. 444	pattern blocks	Geometry Template; scissors
3•9	Transparency of *Math Masters,* p. 420* Teaching Aid Master, p. 414 Study Link Master, p. 92 Teaching Masters, pp. 93 and 94		Geometry Template; paper ($8\frac{1}{2}$" by 11"); cardstock*; scissors; tape
3•10	Study Link Master, p. 95 Teaching Masters, pp. 96 and 97		Geometry Template; overhead projector; 2 sharp pencils; drawing paper; straightedge; marker; paper
3•11	Assessment Masters, pp. 164–169 Study Link Masters, pp. 98–101	slate	Geometry Template

*Denotes optional materials

Mathematical Background

The discussion below highlights the major content ideas presented in Unit 3 and helps establish instructional priorities.

The American Tour (Lessons 3•1 and 3•2)

Students begin a yearlong American Tour, on which they will visit mathematical aspects of the history, demographics, politics, and environment of the United States. The American Tour will also provide connections to other subjects and the world outside the classroom.

To learn more about the American Tour Project, see Sections 1.2.7 and 12.2.4 of the *Teacher's Reference Manual.*

Tools for Measuring and Drawing (Lessons 3•4–3•6 and 3•10)

Students use the Geometry Template to explore geometry concepts. In Lesson 3-4, they use the half-circle and full-circle protractors to draw and measure angles. In Lesson 3-5, students practice drawing circles and copying line segments using a compass and then apply these skills to measuring lengths with a compass and the Geometry Template. There are additional activities involving the Geometry Template in Lesson 3-10.

Students review the terms for various kinds of angles, along with conventions for naming angles. In Lesson 3-6, although not presented explicitly, students explore concepts related to the classic congruence theorems of plane geometry (such as Side-Side-Side) and use measuring and drawing tools to copy triangles.

See the *Teacher's Reference Manual,* Section 3.2.5, for additional information about the tools used in this unit.

Polygons (Lessons 3•7 and 3•9)

Students consider the properties of a variety of polygons. They find the sum of the angle measures for triangles, quadrangles, and pentagons, and then for polygons in general.

See Section 13.4.2 of the *Teacher's Reference Manual* for additional information about polygons.

Tessellations (Lesson 3•8)

Students examine and create patterns with figures that cover a surface without gaps or overlaps. They discover criteria that determine whether a figure will tessellate, and they identify the regular polygons that will tessellate.

To learn more about tessellations, see Section 13.10 of the *Teacher's Reference Manual.*

3·1 Introduction to the American Tour

Objective To explore data collection, organization, and interpretation.

Technology Resources www.everydaymathonline.com

ePresentations

eToolkit

Algorithms Practice

EM Facts Workshop Game™

Family Letters

Assessment Management

Common Core State Standards

Curriculum Focal Points

Interactive Teacher's Lesson Guide

1 Teaching the Lesson

Key Concepts and Skills

- Use collected data to make predictions.
  [Data and Chance Goal 2]
- Use census data to estimate percentages.
  [Data and Chance Goal 2]
- Express probability as a percent, decimal, or fraction.
  [Data and Chance Goal 4]

Key Activities

Students identify data organized in text, tables, maps, and graphs for the American Tour. Students read and answer questions about the U.S. Census; complete abbreviated forms for a classroom census; and post the results on the Probability Meter.

Ongoing Assessment: Recognizing Student Achievement
Use Mental Math and Reflexes.
[Number and Numeration Goal 1]

Key Vocabulary

census

Materials

Math Journal 1, p. 60
Student Reference Book, pp. 338–395
Math Masters, p. 67
Probability Meter Poster ◆ stick-on notes

2 Ongoing Learning & Practice

Playing *High Number Toss: Decimal Version*
Student Reference Book, pp. 32, 33, and 321
Math Masters, p. 511
per partnership: 4 each of number cards 0–9 (from the Everything Math Deck, if available)
Students practice reading, writing, and comparing decimals.

Math Boxes 3·1
Math Journal 1, p. 61
Students practice and maintain skills through Math Box problems.

Study Link 3·1
Math Masters, p. 68
Students practice and maintain skills through Study Link activities.

3 Differentiation Options

READINESS

Reading for Information
Student Reference Book, p. 361
Math Masters, p. 69
Students practice reading text, tables, charts, and graphs.

ENRICHMENT

Analyzing Data
Math Masters, pp. 70 and 71
Students interpret a table of data taken from the U.S. Census.

Advance Preparation

Set up a display area for the American Tour project and other data, particularly those that relate to, or are from, your social studies curriculum. If possible, provide additional reference materials, such as almanacs, maps, and historical atlases. For the activity in Part 1, provide a collection box or other receptacle for the completed census forms.

***Teacher's Reference Manual,* Grades 4–6** pp. 13, 14

Ask: *Why do you think the census has a question about telephones?* Sample answers: Government agencies use this data to assess whether people have access to emergency medical or crime prevention services and as an indicator of the possible social isolation of older people.

Conclude the discussion by explaining that the data from census questions is interpreted and used by various government and community agencies in a variety of ways.

▶ Taking a Classroom Census

INDEPENDENT ACTIVITY

(*Math Masters*, p. 67)

Distribute the copies of *Math Masters,* page 67. Students will count and collect information about every student in the class. The U.S. Census has two forms—a short form that every household completes and a long form that only a sample of households completes. Point out that the class census form contains questions from the short and long U.S. Census forms. (Questions 1 and 2 are on both forms; Questions 3 to 5 are on the long form only.) Tell students that they do not need to write their names on the forms. Have students deposit completed forms in the collection box.

NOTE Provide a time for any absent students to complete the form when they return.

2 Ongoing Learning & Practice

▶ Playing *High Number Toss: Decimal Version*

PARTNER ACTIVITY

(*Student Reference Book,* pp. 32, 33, and 321; *Math Masters,* p. 511)

High Number Toss: Decimal Version provides students the opportunity to apply their knowledge of place value and standard notation to form, write, read, and compare decimals. Provide students with a reminder box on the board noting that < means *is less than* and > means *is greater than.*

After each round, ask students to record the decimals they formed on *Math Masters,* page 511, and use <, >, and = to compare them. If necessary, refer students to *Student Reference Book,* pages 32 and 33 to review comparing decimals.

Teaching Master

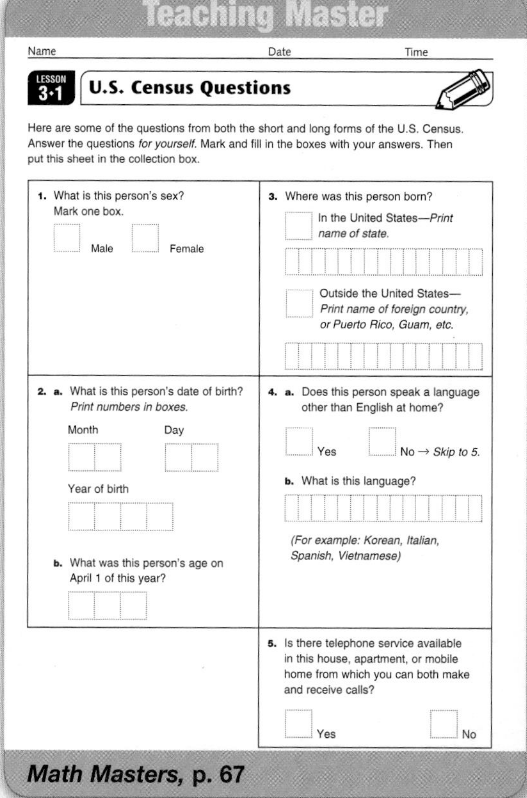

Name _______ Date _______ Time _______

LESSON 3•1 **U.S. Census Questions**

Here are some of the questions from both the short and long forms of the U.S. Census. Answer the questions *for yourself.* Mark and fill in the boxes with your answers. Then put this sheet in the collection box.

1. What is this person's sex? Mark one box.
   □ Male □ Female

2. a. What is this person's date of birth? *Print numbers in boxes.*
   Month □□ Day □□
   Year of birth □□□□
   b. What was this person's age on April 1 of this year? □□□

3. Where was this person born?
   □ In the United States—*Print name of state.*
   □ Outside the United States—*Print name of foreign country, or Puerto Rico, Guam, etc.*

4. a. Does this person speak a language other than English at home?
   □ Yes □ No → *Skip to 5.*
   b. What is this language?
   (For example: Korean, Italian, Spanish, Vietnamese)

5. Is there telephone service available in this house, apartment, or mobile home from which you can both make and receive calls?
   □ Yes □ No

Math Masters, p. 67

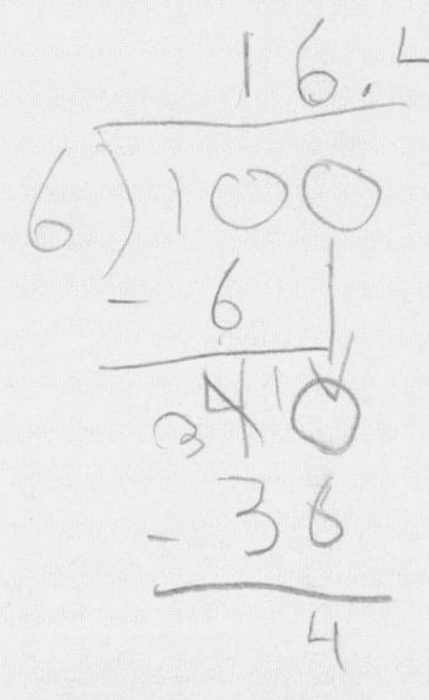

Student Page

Games

High-Number Toss: Decimal Version

Materials □ number cards 0–9 (4 of each)
□ scorecard for each player

Players 2

Skill Decimal place value, subtraction, and addition

Object of the game To make the largest decimal numbers possible.

Directions

1. Each player makes a scorecard like the one at the right. Players fill out their own scorecards at each turn.
2. Shuffle the cards and place them number-side down on the table.
3. In each round:
   - Player 1 draws the top card from the deck and writes the number on any of the 3 blanks on the scorecard. It need not be the first blank—it can be any of them.
   - Player 2 draws the next card from the deck and writes the number on one of his or her blanks.
   - Players take turns doing this 2 more times. The player with the larger number wins the round.
4. The winner's score for a round is the difference between the two players' numbers. (Subtract the smaller number from the larger number.) The loser scores 0 points for the round.

Scorecard

Game 1	
Round 1	**Score**
0. ___ ___ ___	______
Round 2	
0. ___ ___ ___	______
Round 3	
0. ___ ___ ___	______
Round 4	
0. ___ ___ ___	______
Total:	______

Example
Player 1: 0 . 6 5 4
Player 2: 0 . 7 5 3
Player 2 has the larger number and wins the round.
Since 0.753 − 0.654 = 0.099, Player 2 scores 0.099 point for the round. Player 1 scores 0 points.

5. Players take turns starting a round. At the end of 4 rounds, they find their total scores. The player with the larger total score wins the game.

Student Reference Book, p. 321

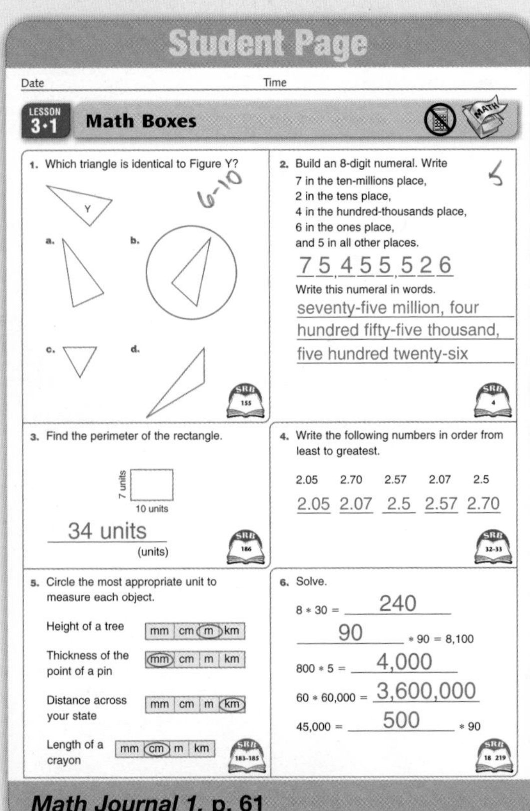

Student Page

Date Time

LESSON 3·1 **Math Boxes**

1. Which triangle is identical to Figure Y?

a. b. c. d.

2. Build an 8-digit numeral. Write
7 in the ten-millions place,
2 in the tens place,
4 in the hundred-thousands place,
6 in the ones place,
and 5 in all other places.

75,455,526

Write this numeral in words.

seventy-five million, four hundred fifty-five thousand, five hundred twenty-six

3. Find the perimeter of the rectangle.

7 units, 10 units

34 units (units)

4. Write the following numbers in order from least to greatest.

2.05 2.70 2.57 2.07 2.5

2.05 2.07 2.5 2.57 2.70

5. Circle the most appropriate unit to measure each object.

Height of a tree	mm	cm	(m)	km
Thickness of the point of a pin	(mm)	cm	m	km
Distance across your state	mm	cm	m	(km)
Length of a crayon	mm	(cm)	m	km

6. Solve.

8 ∗ 30 = 240

90 ∗ 90 = 8,100

800 ∗ 5 = 4,000

60 ∗ 60,000 = 3,600,000

45,000 = 500 ∗ 90

Math Journal 1, p. 61

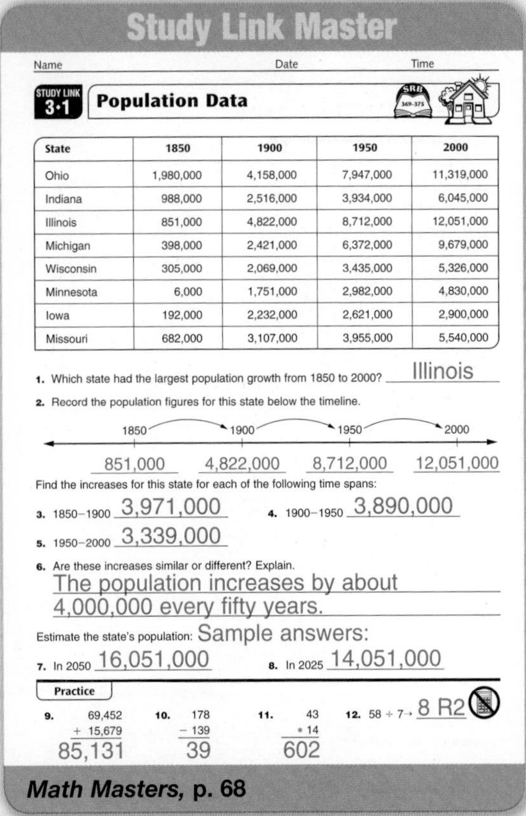

Study Link Master

Name Date Time

STUDY LINK 3·1 **Population Data**

State	1850	1900	1950	2000
Ohio	1,980,000	4,158,000	7,947,000	11,319,000
Indiana	988,000	2,516,000	3,934,000	6,045,000
Illinois	851,000	4,822,000	8,712,000	12,051,000
Michigan	398,000	2,421,000	6,372,000	9,679,000
Wisconsin	305,000	2,069,000	3,435,000	5,326,000
Minnesota	6,000	1,751,000	2,982,000	4,830,000
Iowa	192,000	2,232,000	2,621,000	2,900,000
Missouri	682,000	3,107,000	3,955,000	5,540,000

1. Which state had the largest population growth from 1850 to 2000? Illinois

2. Record the population figures for this state below the timeline.

1850 1900 1950 2000

851,000 4,822,000 8,712,000 12,051,000

Find the increases for this state for each of the following time spans:

3. 1850–1900 3,971,000

4. 1900–1950 3,890,000

5. 1950–2000 3,339,000

6. Are these increases similar or different? Explain.

The population increases by about 4,000,000 every fifty years.

Estimate the state's population: Sample answers:

7. In 2050 16,051,000

8. In 2025 14,051,000

Practice

9. 69,452 + 15,679 = 85,131

10. 178 − 139 = 39

11. 43 ∗ 14 = 602

12. 58 ÷ 7 → 8 R2

Math Masters, p. 68

▶ Math Boxes 3·1

INDEPENDENT ACTIVITY

(*Math Journal 1,* p. 61)

Mixed Practice Math Boxes in this lesson are paired with Math Boxes in Lesson 3-3. The skill in Problem 6 previews Unit 4 content.

▶ Study Link 3·1

INDEPENDENT ACTIVITY

(*Math Masters,* p. 68)

Home Connection Students use a table of census information about state populations to answer questions.

3 Differentiation Options

READINESS

WHOLE-CLASS ACTIVITY

▶ Reading for Information

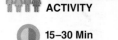

15–30 Min

(*Student Reference Book,* p. 361; *Math Masters,* p. 69)

To explore reading for information, have students answer questions about *Student Reference Book,* page 361. Have students complete this activity as part of the Examining the American Tour section of this lesson. Alternatively, complete the activity prior to the lesson during a class language arts or reading period.

Review the following elements on the *Student Reference Book* page: heading, American Tour; page title, How Much Schooling Did Students Receive in 1900?; table, stem-and-leaf display, and graph titles. You might also review topic sentences using the two paragraphs at the top of the page. Encourage students to look up words that they do not remember; for example, *mean* or *median.* When students have finished the page, have them share the questions they wrote.

ENRICHMENT

Analyzing Data

(*Math Masters*, pp. 70 and 71)

To explore analyzing data, have students answer questions using a census table about income and education levels. Remind students that although they can identify the changes between the data for 1980 and 1990, they cannot consider the pattern of change to be a trend without more data.

Planning Ahead

The results from the classroom census should be posted in your American Tour display. Make, or have students make, a table for the display like the one shown below. When all census forms have been collected, have students tabulate and record the results. Only the Number column should be filled in at this time. The Fraction, Decimal, and Percent columns will be filled in later.

Classroom Census Results

	Number	Fraction	Decimal	Percent
Total students in class				100%
Female				
Male				
Age 9 10 11				
Born in this state				
Born in another state				
Born in another country				
Speak a language other than English at home				
Have telephone at home				

Teaching Master

Name Date Time

LESSON 3•1 **Reading for Information**

1. Turn to page 361 in your *Student Reference Book*.
   What is the title of this page?
   How Much Schooling Did Students Receive in 1900?
2. Take a minute to look at this page. Based on the title, the tables, and the graphs, describe the information you expect to find on this page.
   Sample answer: The average number of days students went to school, by region and by state, in the year 1900
3. Look at the tables and graphs on the page. Which table or graph would you use to find the mean number of days in school per student, by region?
   The table that lists the states by region
   Explain why.
   The table shows the average attendance for each state, by region.
4. Look at the tables and graphs on the page. What graph would you use to find the median days in school for all states?
   The stem-and-leaf display
5. Write three questions that you could answer by reading this page, or by using the tables and charts on this page.
   Sample answers: Which region had the highest number of days in school? Which region had the fewest number of states? How many states had 90 to 99 days in school?

Math Masters, p. 69

Teaching Master

Name Date Time

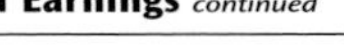

LESSON 3•1 **Education and Earnings** *continued*

Use the Education and Earnings table to answer the following questions.

1. Describe the relationship between number of years of education and income.
   Sample answer: The more years of school completed, the higher the median income
2. Compare the number of householders who did not graduate from high school in 1980 with the number in 1990. Describe any changes that occurred.
   Sample answer: In 1980, more householders did not graduate from high school. The number of householders who did not graduate from high school in 1990 decreased by about 4,400,000.
3. What would you expect to be the number of householders who do not graduate from high school in 2010?
   Sample answer: The number of householders who do not graduate from high school will be about 11,353,000 in 2010.
4. How does the number of householders who did not graduate from high school in 1990 compare to the number of householders who graduated from college?
   Sample answer: In 1990, about half as many householders did not graduate from high school as the number who did graduate from college.

Math Masters, p. 71

3•2 American Tour Population Data

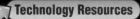

Objective To provide experiences with interpreting data.

www.everydaymathonline.com

ePresentations

eToolkit

Algorithms Practice

EM Facts Workshop Game™

Family Letters

Assessment Management

Common Core State Standards

Curriculum Focal Points

Interactive Teacher's Lesson Guide

1 Teaching the Lesson

Key Concepts and Skills

- Read and write large numbers. [Number and Numeration Goal 1]
- Evaluate exact numbers versus estimates for population data. [Operations and Computation Goal 6]
- Use table data to answer questions. [Data and Chance Goal 2]

Key Activities

Students use the official record of the 1790 U.S. Census and a table of state population estimates for the years 1610 to 1790 to discuss data organization and answer questions. Students practice reading large numbers and review place value.

Materials

Math Journal 1, pp. 62 and 63
Student Reference Book, pp. 370 and 371
Study Link 3•1
Class Data Pad

2 Ongoing Learning & Practice

Estimating and Calculating Sums and Differences

Math Journal 1, p. 64
Students solve number stories by writing open number sentences and calculating sums and differences.

Math Boxes 3•2

Math Journal 1, p. 65
Students practice and maintain skills through Math Box problems.

Ongoing Assessment: Recognizing Student Achievement

Use Math Boxes, Problems 1 and 4. [Operations and Computation Goal 1]

Study Link 3•2

Math Masters, p. 72
Students practice and maintain skills through Study Link activities.

3 Differentiation Options

READINESS

Solving Place-Value Puzzles

Math Masters, p. 73
Students use a place-value chart to practice reading large numbers.

ENRICHMENT

Interpreting Patterns from Data

Student Reference Book, p. 349
Math Masters, p. 74
Students use map data to compare and interpret exploration, settlement, and/or statehood patterns.

EXTRA PRACTICE

5-Minute Math

5-Minute Math™, pp. 39 and 117
Students read a bar graph.

Advance Preparation

***Teacher's Reference Manual,* Grades 4–6** pp. 168, 169

Getting Started

Mental Math and Reflexes

Write all problems on the board or Class Data Pad so students can visually recognize the patterns. Ask students to describe the patterns they notice in the moving of the decimal point in each set.

●○○	●●○	●●●
3.4 * 10 34	2.41 * 100 241	54 * 1,000 54,000
3.4 * 100 340	2.41 * 1,000 2,410	5,400 / 1,000 5.4
3.4 * 1,000 3,400	0.241 * 100 24.1	5,400 / 10,000 0.54

Math Message

What is the largest number in the table on page 371 of the Student Reference Book?

Study Link 3·1 Follow-Up

Ask volunteers to share their strategies. Explain that changes in data over time can be thought of as a trend. If students estimated using the population increases, they were estimating based on their identified trend. Ask whether they see any trends in the populations for other states.

1 Teaching the Lesson

▶ Math Message Follow-Up

(*Student Reference Book*, p. 371)

Ask students whether they needed to read the entire table in order to answer the Math Message question. No; the largest number in the table is 3,929,000. This was the total U.S. population in 1790. Remind them that it is always important to read any headings, labels, notes, and/or captions.

▶ Estimating Colonial Populations

(*Student Reference Book*, pp. 370 and 371)

Ask students to compare the totals in the official report of the 1790 Census on page 370 with the TOTAL column in the table on page 371 of the *Student Reference Book.* Survey the class for the differences they found. Sample answers: One gives the exact census count, and the other gives estimates; the numbers in the table are rounded. *Do the numbers in the table represent everyone in these areas?* Sample answers: No, estimates are not the same as exact counts; the estimates probably did not include the Native Americans in these areas. Explain that the table data is organized to give magnitude estimates of the population. The 1790 Census Report organized the data to show the categories used at that time for the people within the population being counted. The 1790 Census counted only European settlers and African Americans living in the original 13 colonies and in the four regions that later became separate states. There were Native Americans living throughout this area who were not included in the census count or the earlier estimates. It would be easy to use the table to find trends in the data for the total population that was counted, but it could not be used to answer questions about only the women, for instance.

Student Page

Date Time

LESSON 3·2 State Populations, 1610–1790

Use the population table on *Student Reference Book,* page 371, to answer the following.

1. What was the population of Pennsylvania in 1780? 335,000
2. What was the total population of all states in 1760? 1,610,000
3. a. Which colony started with the smallest population?
   Name of colony Massachusetts
   Year 1620
   Population 100
   b. What was the population of this state in the census of 1790? 379,000
4. Which colony was the first to have a population of more than 100,000?
   Name of colony Virginia
   Year 1720
   Population 116,000
5. a. In what year was the total population of all states greater than 1 million for the first time? 1750
   b. In what year was the total population of all states greater than 2 million for the first time? 1770
6. In 1790, which state had the largest population?
   Name of state Virginia
   Population 748,000

Math Journal 1, p. 62

Student Page

Date Time

LESSON 3·2 State Populations, 1610–1790 *continued*

7. In 1790, which states had smaller populations than Rhode Island?
Delaware and Tennessee

8. Below, fill in the total U.S. populations for 1780 and 1790. Then find how much the population increased during that 10-year period.
Population in 1790 3,929,000
Population in 1780 2,781,000
Increase 1,148,000

Try This

9. The table gives the population of Connecticut in 1750 as 100,000. Make a mark in front of the statement below that best describes the population of Connecticut in 1750.
_____ It was exactly 100,000.
✓ It was most likely between 99,000 and 101,000.
_____ It was most likely between 95,000 and 105,000.

Explain your answer.
The population was most likely between 99,000 and 101,000 because the table indicates that the estimates were rounded to the nearest thousand.

Math Journal 1, p. 63

Student Page

Date Time

LESSON 3·2 Addition and Subtraction Number Stories

For each problem, fill in the blanks and solve the problem.

1. Jeanne practiced her multiplication facts for 3 weeks. The first week she practiced for 45 minutes, the second week for 37 minutes, and the third week for 32 minutes. How many minutes did she practice in all?
   a. List the numbers needed to solve the problem. 45, 37, and 32
   b. Describe what you want to find. How many minutes Jeanne practiced in 3 weeks
   c. Open sentence: $45 + 37 + 32 = m$
   d. Solution: 114 e. Answer: 114 minutes (unit)

2. The shortest book Martha read one summer was 57 pages. The longest book was 243 pages. She read a total of 36 books. How many pages longer was the longest book than the shortest book?
   a. List the numbers needed to solve the problem. 57 and 243
   b. Describe what you want to find. How many more pages in the longer book than the shorter book
   c. Open sentence: $243 - 57 = p$
   d. Solution: 186 e. Answer: 186 pages (unit)

3. Cezar collects marbles. He had 347 marbles. Then he played in two tournaments. He lost 34 marbles in the first tournament. He won 23 marbles in the second tournament. How many marbles did he have after playing in both tournaments?
   a. List the numbers needed to solve the problem. 347, 34, and 23
   b. Describe what you want to find. The number of marbles Cezar had left after the two tournaments
   c. Open sentence: $347 - 34 + 23 = m$
   d. Solution: 336 e. Answer: 336 marbles (unit)

Math Journal 1, p. 64

▶ Using the Population Table to Answer Questions

PARTNER ACTIVITY

(*Math Journal 1*, pp. 62 and 63; *Student Reference Book*, p. 371)

Have students work with partners to answer the questions on the journal pages. Circulate and assist.

Adjusting the Activity

ELL

Remind students that it is easier to read tables like the one on page 371 if they lay a ruler or sheet of paper across the table, just beneath the row they are studying.

AUDITORY ◆ KINESTHETIC ◆ TACTILE ◆ VISUAL

2 Ongoing Learning & Practice

▶ Estimating and Calculating Sums and Differences

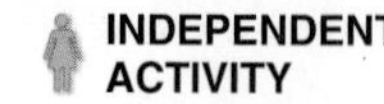
INDEPENDENT ACTIVITY

(*Math Journal 1*, p. 64)

Algebraic Thinking Students write open number sentences for addition and subtraction number stories, find the solutions, and calculate the answers.

Links to the Future

This activity provides another opportunity for students to solve number stories. Students first used the number stories practice page format in Lesson 2-4 on journal page 37. Writing open number sentences to model and solve number stories is a Grade 5 Goal.

▶ Math Boxes 3·2

INDEPENDENT ACTIVITY

(*Math Journal 1*, p. 65)

Mixed Practice Math Boxes in this lesson are paired with Math Boxes in Lesson 3-4. The skill in Problem 6 previews Unit 4 content.

Ongoing Assessment: Recognizing Student Achievement

Math Boxes Problems 1 and 4

Use **Math Boxes, Problems 1 and 4** to assess students' ability to add and subtract whole numbers and decimals. Students are making adequate progress if they correctly subtract the whole numbers in Problem 1 and correctly add the decimals in Problem 4.

[Operations and Computation Goal 1]

Study Link 3·2

(*Math Masters*, p. 72)

Home Connection Students use information from an unofficial census showing the number of people who believe that different sayings are true.

3 Differentiation Options

READINESS

Solving Place-Value Puzzles

(*Math Masters,* p. 73)

To explore place-value patterns, have students use a place-value chart to identify and write large numbers. Ask students to complete *Math Masters,* page 73. When students have finished, ask them to describe the patterns they see in the place-value chart. Sample answers: The chart divides place-value columns into sections with 3 columns each. Each column holds one digit. The 3 columns in a section represent the 1s, 10s, and 100s for that section.

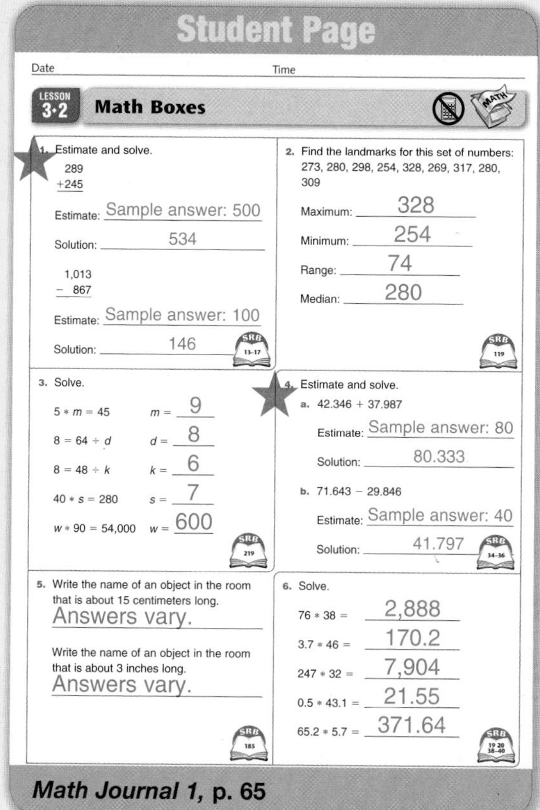

Student Page

Date Time

LESSON 3·2 **Math Boxes**

1. Estimate and solve.

289 + 245

Estimate: Sample answer: 500

Solution: 534

1,013 − 867

Estimate: Sample answer: 100

Solution: 146

2. Find the landmarks for this set of numbers: 273, 280, 298, 254, 328, 269, 317, 280, 309

Maximum: 328

Minimum: 254

Range: 74

Median: 280

3. Solve.

5 ∗ m = 45 m = 9

8 = 64 ÷ d d = 8

8 = 48 ÷ k k = 6

40 ∗ s = 280 s = 7

w ∗ 90 = 54,000 w = 600

4. Estimate and solve.

a. 42.346 + 37.987

Estimate: Sample answer: 80

Solution: 80.333

b. 71.643 − 29.846

Estimate: Sample answer: 40

Solution: 41.797

5. Write the name of an object in the room that is about 15 centimeters long. Answers vary.

Write the name of an object in the room that is about 3 inches long. Answers vary.

6. Solve.

76 ∗ 38 = 2,888

3.7 ∗ 46 = 170.2

247 ∗ 32 = 7,904

0.5 ∗ 43.1 = 21.55

65.2 ∗ 5.7 = 371.64

Math Journal 1, p. 65

#5 on test

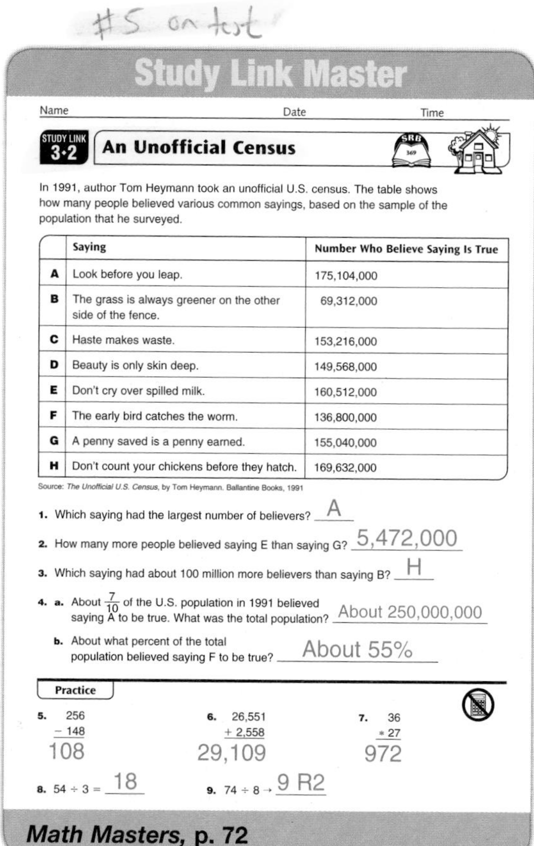

Study Link Master

Name Date Time

STUDY LINK 3·2 **An Unofficial Census**

In 1991, author Tom Heymann took an unofficial U.S. census. The table shows how many people believed various common sayings, based on the sample of the population that he surveyed.

	Saying	Number Who Believe Saying Is True
A	Look before you leap.	175,104,000
B	The grass is always greener on the other side of the fence.	69,312,000
C	Haste makes waste.	153,216,000
D	Beauty is only skin deep.	149,568,000
E	Don't cry over spilled milk.	160,512,000
F	The early bird catches the worm.	136,800,000
G	A penny saved is a penny earned.	155,040,000
H	Don't count your chickens before they hatch.	169,632,000

Source: *The Unofficial U.S. Census*, by Tom Heymann. Ballantine Books, 1991

1. Which saying had the largest number of believers? A

2. How many more people believed saying E than saying G? 5,472,000

3. Which saying had about 100 million more believers than saying B? H

4. a. About $\frac{7}{10}$ of the U.S. population in 1991 believed saying A to be true. What was the total population? About 250,000,000

b. About what percent of the total population believed saying F to be true? About 55%

Practice

5. 256 − 148 = 108

6. 26,551 + 2,558 = 29,109

7. 36 ∗ 27 = 972

8. 54 ÷ 3 = 18

9. 74 ÷ 8 → 9 R2

Math Masters, p. 72

#5 on test

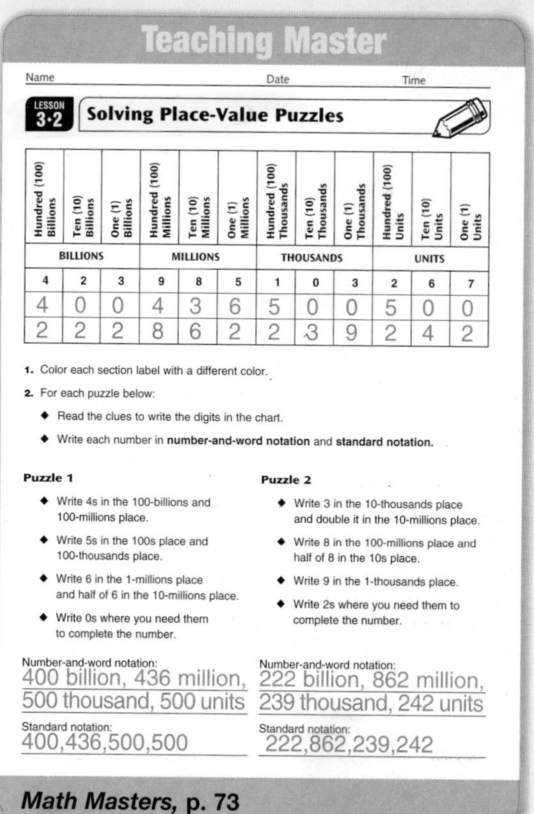

Teaching Master

Name Date Time

LESSON 3·2 **Solving Place-Value Puzzles**

Hundred (100) Billions	Ten (10) Billions	One (1) Billions	Hundred (100) Millions	Ten (10) Millions	One (1) Millions	Hundred (100) Thousands	Ten (10) Thousands	One (1) Thousands	Hundred (100) Units	Ten (10) Units	One (1) Units
BILLIONS			MILLIONS			THOUSANDS			UNITS		
4	2	3	9	8	5	1	0	3	2	6	7
4	0	0	4	3	6	5	0	0	5	0	0
2	2	2	8	6	2	2	3	9	2	4	2

1. Color each section label with a different color.

2. For each puzzle below:

- Read the clues to write the digits in the chart.
- Write each number in **number-and-word notation** and **standard notation.**

Puzzle 1

- Write 4s in the 100-billions and 100-millions place.
- Write 5s in the 100s place and 100-thousands place.
- Write 6 in the 1-millions place and half of 6 in the 10-millions place.
- Write 0s where you need them to complete the number.

Number-and-word notation: 400 billion, 436 million, 500 thousand, 500 units

Standard notation: 400,436,500,500

Puzzle 2

- Write 3 in the 10-thousands place and double it in the 10-millions place.
- Write 8 in the 100-millions place and half of 8 in the 10s place.
- Write 9 in the 1-thousands place.
- Write 2s where you need them to complete the number.

Number-and-word notation: 222 billion, 862 million, 239 thousand, 242 units

Standard notation: 222,862,239,242

Math Masters, p. 73

Study Link Master

Name Date Time

LESSON 3·2 **Interpreting Patterns from Data**

Use the map on page 349 of the *Student Reference Book.*

1. Choose a region and record the region name. ______

The dates for exploration, settlement, and statehood can be thought of as three data sets. Identify and record the minimum, maximum, median, and range for each data set.

Sample answers:

2.

Region: Midwest		Data Set: Exploration Dates	
Data: 1742, 1738, 1683, 1679, 1673, 1660, 1634, 1618, 1600, 1541, 1541			
Minimum	1541	Median	1660
Maximum	1742	Range	201

3.

Region: ______		Data Set: Settlement Dates	
Data: Answers vary.			
Minimum		Median	
Maximum		Range	

4.

Region: ______		Data Set: Statehood Dates	
Data: Answers vary.			
Minimum		Median	
Maximum		Range	

On the back of this page, use the information represented by the landmarks to write one true statement about each data set.

Math Masters, p. 74

ENRICHMENT

▶ Interpreting Patterns from Data

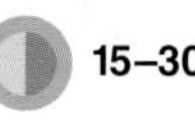

(*Student Reference Book*, p. 349, *Math Masters*, p. 74)

To apply students' understanding of data, have them interpret sets of data displayed on a map. Students use map data from *Student Reference Book,* page 349 to identify statistical landmarks and exploration, settlement, and/or statehood patterns. Assign groups to specific regions on the map so data is available for all regions. Then combine groups or bring the class together to discuss questions such as the following:

- Is there a relationship between exploration or settlement in a region and its geographical location? Areas along the coasts, rivers, and other waterways were the earliest to be explored and settled.
- Does the amount of time from exploration to settlement follow a pattern? From settlement to statehood? Are these patterns similar or different between regions? Sample answers: Most states had European or American settlements within 100 years after being explored; in most of the eastern regions, statehood followed more than 50 years after settlement; this time frame was shorter in the western regions.

NOTE You may wish to remind students that the dates given for settlement refer to European and American settlers moving into the areas indicated on the map. Native Americans already had settlements throughout North America before 1500.

EXTRA PRACTICE

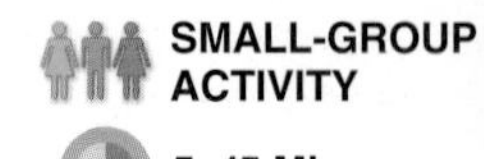

▶ *5-Minute Math*

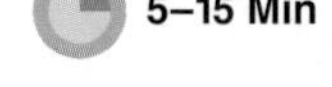

To offer students more experience reading a bar graph, see *5-Minute Math,* pages 39 and 117.

3•3 Exploring Angle Measures

Objective To relate circles and relationships among angles to the degree measures of angles.

Technology Resources www.everydaymathonline.com

ePresentations

eToolkit

Algorithms Practice

EM Facts Workshop Game™

Family Letters

Assessment Management

Common Core State Standards

Curriculum Focal Points

Interactive Teacher's Lesson Guide

1 Teaching the Lesson

Key Concepts and Skills

- Determine the measure of angles by using known measures.
  [Geometry Goal 1]
- Review naming conventions for angles.
  [Geometry Goal 1]
- Use angle relationships to determine angle measures.
  [Geometry Goal 1]

Key Activities

Students use what they know about the total number of degrees in a circle and the relationships among angles to determine the size of various angles.

Ongoing Assessment: Recognizing Student Achievement
Use journal page 66.
[Geometry Goal 1]

Materials

Math Journal 1, p. 66
Study Link 3•2
pattern blocks

2 Ongoing Learning & Practice

Playing a Variation of *Multiplication Top-It*
Student Reference Book, p. 334
per group: 4 each of number cards 1–10 (from the Everything Math Deck, if available)
Students practice and apply multiplication facts by multiplying 2-digit numbers by 1-digit numbers.

Math Boxes 3•3
Math Journal 1, p. 67
Students practice and maintain skills through Math Box problems.

Study Link 3•3
Math Masters, p. 75
Students practice and maintain skills through Study Link activities.

3 Differentiation Options

READINESS
Reviewing Ways to Name Angles
straightedge
Students draw and name an angle in different ways.

ENRICHMENT
Naming Segments, Lengths, and Collinear Points
Student Reference Book, p. 141
Math Masters, p. 76
Students explore notations used with lines and collinear points and the concepts they represent.

ELL SUPPORT
Measuring the Parts
Math Masters, p. 77
Students determine angle measures by using the total degrees in a circle.

Advance Preparation

For Part 1, students will need a supply of pattern blocks. Arrange students in small groups and provide a collection of pattern blocks for each group.

***Teacher's Reference Manual,* Grades 4–6** pp. 178–180, 194, 195

Getting Started

Mental Math and Reflexes

Use your established slate procedures and dictate problems like the following. *Suggestions:*

●○○ Write 345,082. Circle the digit in the tens place. Put an X through the digit in the hundreds place. 345,082

Write 140.7. Circle the digit in the hundreds place. Put an X through the digit in the tenths place. 140.7

●●○ Write 7,803,596. Circle the digit in the hundred-thousands place. Underline the digit in the thousands place. 7,803,596

Write 24.06. Circle the digit in the tenths place. Underline the digit in the tens place. 24.06

●●● Write 604,394,076. Circle the digit in the ten-millions place. Put an X through the digit in the ten-thousands place. 604,394,076

Write 478,062.077. Circle the digit in the tens place. Put an X through the digit in the thousandths place. 478,062.077

Math Message

How might you use this figure to prove that the measure of each angle of a square is 90°? Be prepared to explain your answer.

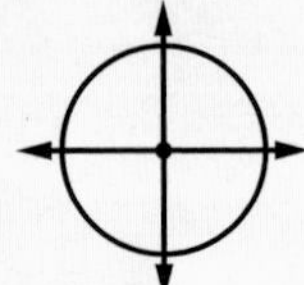

Study Link 3·2 Follow-Up

Ask volunteers to share their solution strategies for Problems 4a and 4b. Survey the class for the reason why all the numbers in the table end in zeros.

1 Teaching the Lesson

▶ Math Message Follow-Up

WHOLE-CLASS ACTIVITY

Ask volunteers to share their explanations. Expect that students will recognize the right angles in the figure as 90°. Ask how they could show that the angles are 90° if they didn't know the degree measure of a right angle. Use these responses to demonstrate the relationship between right angles and the degree measure of quarter circles (360° ÷ 4 = 90°). Each quarter of the circle represents an angle from the square, so each angle of the square measures 90°.

Adjusting the Activity

Have students trace a square onto a piece of paper (they could use a pattern-block square) and draw an arc in each angle; label the angles as *A, B, C,* and *D* inside of the arcs; and cut out each angle by cutting along the arcs. Ask students to match up the angles so that their arcs make a circle.

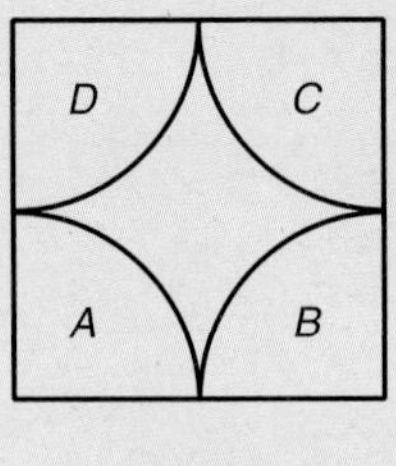

square

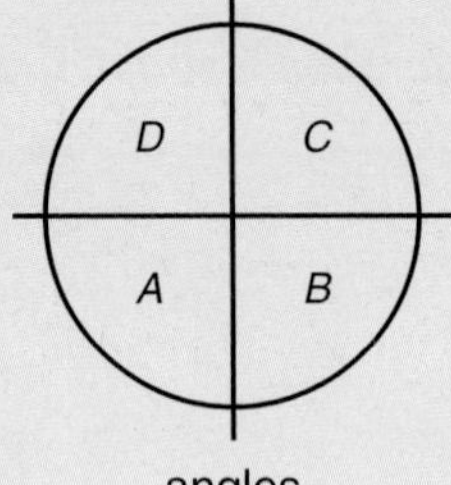

angles

AUDITORY ♦ KINESTHETIC ♦ TACTILE ♦ VISUAL

1-4

Student Page

Date Time

LESSON 3·3 **Pattern-Block Angles**

For each pattern block below, tell the degree measure of the angle and explain how you found the measure. Do not use a protractor.

1. measure of ∠A = 60°
Explain. Sample answer: Six triangles fit together at a point. The circle around that point has 360°. So each angle measures 360° / 6, or 60°.

2. m∠B = 120° (m∠B means measure of angle B.)

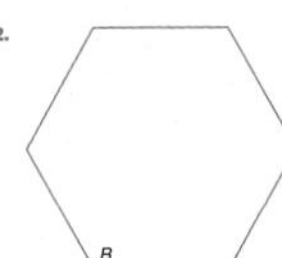

Explain. Sample answer: Two triangles fit together and exactly cover angle B. Each angle of the triangle measures 60°. So angle B measures 2 ∗ 60°, or 120°.

3. m∠C = 60° m∠D = 120°

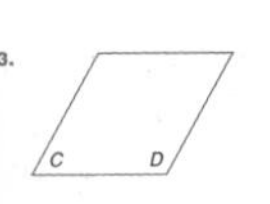

Explain. Sample answer: Angle C has the same measure as angle A of the triangle in Problem 1, or 60°. Angle D has the same measure as angle B of the hexagon in Problem 2, or 120°.

4. m∠E = 60° m∠F = 120°

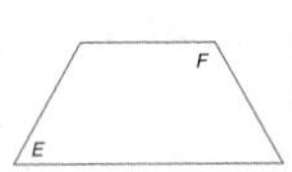

Explain. Sample answer: Angle E has the same measure as angle A of the triangle in Problem 1, or 60°. Angle F has the same measure as angle B of the hexagon in Problem 2, or 120°.

Math Journal 1, p. 66

▶ Finding Pattern-Block Angle Measures

PARTNER ACTIVITY

PROBLEM SOLVING

(*Math Journal 1,* p. 66)

Explain that because we accept that the total number of degrees in a circle is 360°, and that a circle can be drawn around any given point, we can find the measure of the angles in a polygon. Have students place four square pattern blocks together to form a larger square. Ask: *How many squares are around the point in the center?* 4 squares *What is the measure of each angle meeting at this point?* Each angle measures 90°.

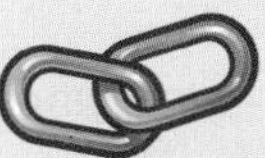

Links to the Future

This activity provides an opportunity for students to develop skill with identifying angle measures using relationships between angles. Using relationships between angles is a Grades 5 and 6 Goal.

Have students complete journal page 66. Remind them of the following:

- ▷ The symbol ∠ means *angle.*
- ▷ Sometimes an angle is named with a single capital letter, which also names the vertex of the angle. Sometimes an angle is named with three letters: The middle letter names the vertex, and the other two letters name points, one on each side of the angle.
- ▷ Point out symbols on the page, such as m∠*B* is an abbreviation for *the measure of angle B*. Remind students that the symbol ° means *degrees*.

Adjusting the Activity

Have students find all angle measurements for the small pattern-block rhombus. 30°, 150°, 30°, and 150° Ask: *What is the sum of the measure of the angles in a rhombus?* 360°

AUDITORY ◆ KINESTHETIC ◆ TACTILE ◆ VISUAL

Ongoing Assessment: Recognizing Student Achievement

Journal Page 66 

Use **journal page 66** to assess students' ability to use the relationship between circles and polygons to identify angle measures. Students are making adequate progress if they correctly identify the angle measures. Some students may use the relationships between pattern blocks and their angles to identify the angle measures.

[Geometry Goal 1]

Student Page

Games

Example A 4, an 8, and a 3 are turned over. There are three ways to form the numbers. Always subtract the smaller number from the larger one.

4 + 8 = 12 or 3 + 8 = 11 or 3 + 4 = 7
12 − 3 = 9 11 − 4 = 7 8 − 7 = 1

Advanced Version
Use only the number cards 1—9. Each player turns over 4 cards, forms two 2-digit numbers, and finds their difference. Players should carefully consider how they form their numbers. For example, 75 − 24 has a greater difference than 57 − 42 or 74 − 25.

Multiplication Top-It
Directions
1. The rules are the same as for *Addition Top-It*, except that players find the product of the numbers instead of the sum.
2. The player with the largest product takes all the cards. Answers can be checked with a Multiplication Table or a calculator.

Variation
Use only the number cards 1—9. Each player turns over 3 cards, forms a 2-digit number, then multiplies the 2-digit number by the remaining number.

Division Top-It
Directions
1. Use only the number cards 1—9. Each player turns over 3 cards and uses them to generate a division problem as follows:
   - ♦ Choose 2 cards to form the dividend.
   - ♦ Use the remaining card as the divisor.
   - ♦ Divide and drop any remainder.
2. The player with the largest quotient takes all the cards.

Advanced Version
Use only the number cards 1—9. Each player turns over 4 cards, chooses 3 of them to form a 3-digit number, then divides the 3-digit number by the remaining number. Players should carefully consider how they form their 3-digit numbers. For example, 462/5 is greater than 256/4.

Student Reference Book, p. 334

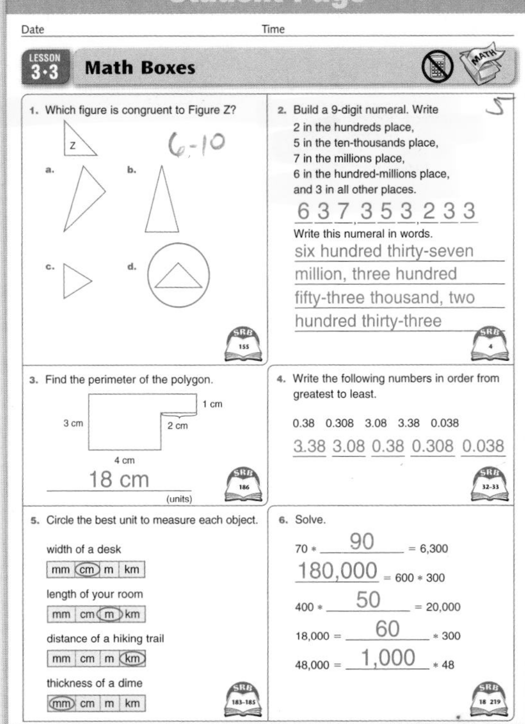

Student Page

Date Time

LESSON 3·3 **Math Boxes**

1. Which figure is congruent to Figure Z?
a. b. c. d.

2. Build a 9-digit numeral. Write 2 in the hundreds place, 5 in the ten-thousands place, 7 in the millions place, 6 in the hundred-millions place, and 3 in all other places.
637,353,233
Write this numeral in words.
six hundred thirty-seven million, three hundred fifty-three thousand, two hundred thirty-three

3. Find the perimeter of the polygon.
18 cm (units)

4. Write the following numbers in order from greatest to least.
0.38 0.308 3.08 3.38 0.038
3.38 3.08 0.38 0.308 0.038

5. Circle the best unit to measure each object.
width of a desk: mm cm m km
length of your room: mm cm m km
distance of a hiking trail: mm cm m km
thickness of a dime: mm cm m km

6. Solve.
70 ∗ 90 = 6,300
180,000 = 600 ∗ 300
400 ∗ 50 = 20,000
18,000 = 60 ∗ 300
48,000 = 1,000 ∗ 48

Math Journal 1, p. 67

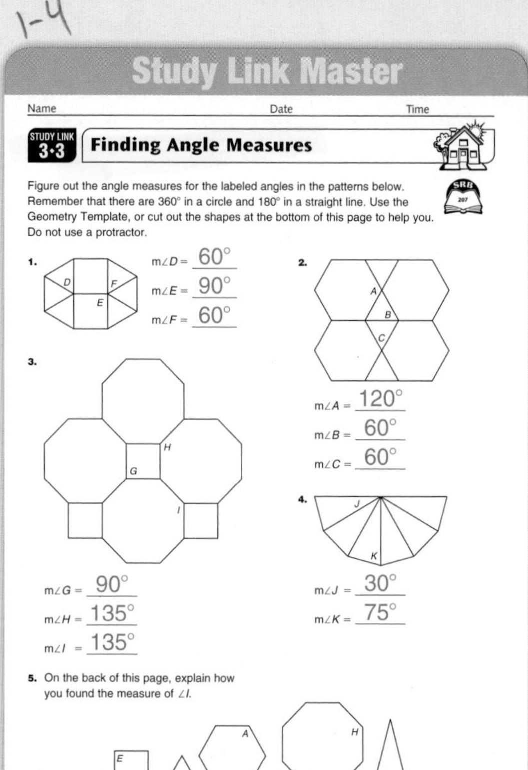
Study Link Master

Name Date Time

STUDY LINK 3·3 **Finding Angle Measures**

Figure out the angle measures for the labeled angles in the patterns below. Remember that there are 360° in a circle and 180° in a straight line. Use the Geometry Template, or cut out the shapes at the bottom of this page to help you. Do not use a protractor.

1. m∠D = 60° m∠E = 90° m∠F = 60°
2. m∠A = 120° m∠B = 60° m∠C = 60°
3. m∠G = 90° m∠H = 135° m∠I = 135°
4. m∠J = 30° m∠K = 75°
5. On the back of this page, explain how you found the measure of ∠I.

Math Masters, p. 75

Teaching Master

Name Date Time

LESSON 3·3 **Segments, Lengths, and Collinear Points**

In geometry, there are conventions used to name a figure and to name the measure of that figure. For example, ∠N names an angle with the vertex N, while the notation m∠N represents the measure of that angle. For line segments, the notation $\overline{NM}$ names the line segment with the endpoints N and M, and the notation NM represents the length of that line segment.

The notation NM = 4 inches means *line segment $\overline{NM}$ is 4 inches long.* Use the points and measures shown on the line below to answer Problems 1 and 2.

1. Which of the following statements show the correct use of these naming conventions for line segments and the measures of line segments? Circle your answer.
   a. PQ + QR + RS = PS
   b. $\overline{OP}$ + $\overline{PQ}$ = OQ
   c. OP ∗ 2 = $\overline{PQ}$
   d. $\overline{OP}$ + $\overline{QR}$ + $\overline{RS}$ = 35
2. For each statement with errors, write the corrections.
   b. OP + PQ = OQ; c. OP ∗ 2 = PQ; d. OP + QR + RS = 40
3. Points that lie on the same line are called **collinear points.** The points H, S, D, K, L, and B are collinear. Use the following information to locate them on the line and label the points accordingly.

   KS + SB = KB

   DH + HS = DS

   DH + HK = DK

   Points L and B are not between any other labeled points on the line.

   L D H K S B

Math Masters, p. 76

2 Ongoing Learning & Practice

Playing a Variation of *Multiplication Top-It*

PARTNER ACTIVITY

COMPUTATION PRACTICE

(*Student Reference Book*, p. 334)

Students practice and apply multiplication facts by playing the variation of *Multiplication Top-It* to multiply 2-digit numbers by 1-digit numbers. Consider having students multiply 3-digit numbers by 1-digit numbers.

Math Boxes 3·3

INDEPENDENT ACTIVITY

(*Math Journal 1,* p. 67)

Mixed Practice Math Boxes in this lesson are paired with Math Boxes in Lesson 3-1. The skill in Problem 6 previews Unit 4 content.

Writing/Reasoning Have students write a response to the following: *Explain how you solved Problem 1. Include reasons why your answer is correct.* Sample answer: Congruent triangles are the same size and shape. Because triangle Z is a right triangle, I considered triangles a and d. Because triangle d is a right triangle, and it is the same size as triangle Z, triangles d and Z are congruent.

NOTE Students' use of vocabulary (congruent) and explanation of the concepts in their solution (comparing angle measures and/or length of sides) will provide information about how students are integrating these geometry concepts.

Study Link 3·3

INDEPENDENT ACTIVITY

(*Math Masters*, p. 75)

Home Connection Students find the angle measures of tessellated polygons using the relationship between the angles and a circle.

3 Differentiation Options

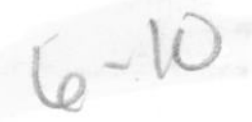

Reviewing Ways to Name Angles

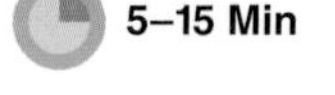

To explore ways to name angles, have students draw and name an angle in different ways.

Suggestions:
Draw ∠BAC. Sample answer:

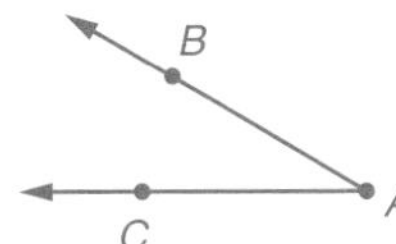

Pose the following questions:

- What are two other ways to name this angle? ∠*CAB* and ∠*A*
- What is the vertex of the angle? Point *A*

Draw the angle below on the board.

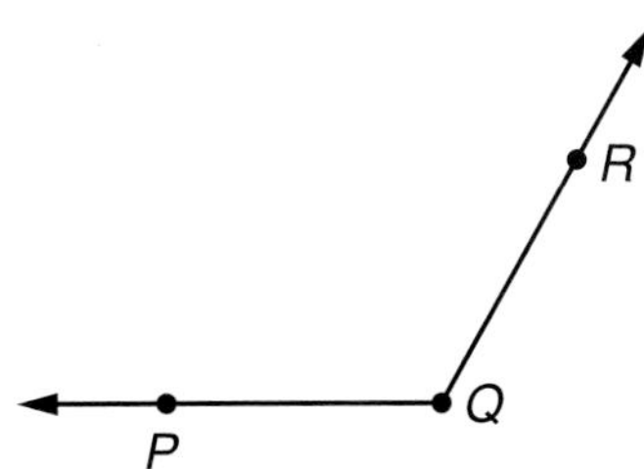

Ask students whether they agree with the following statement. *The name of this angle is ∠QRP.* Have them explain their reasoning. Disagree, because when using three points to name an angle, the vertex is named between the points on the sides of the angle

Have students trace the angles with a finger, and name the angle by saying the letters in order as they trace.

ENRICHMENT

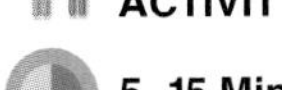

▶ Naming Segments, Lengths, and Collinear Points

(*Student Reference Book,* p. 141; *Math Masters,* p. 76)

To explore naming conventions for points and line segments, have students use clues to determine the order of collinear points.

EXTRA PRACTICE

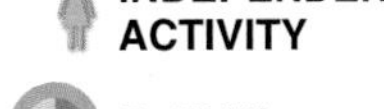

5–15 Min

▶ Measuring the Parts

(*Math Masters,* p. 77)

Students solve problems to establish the degree measure when a circle is divided into different parts.

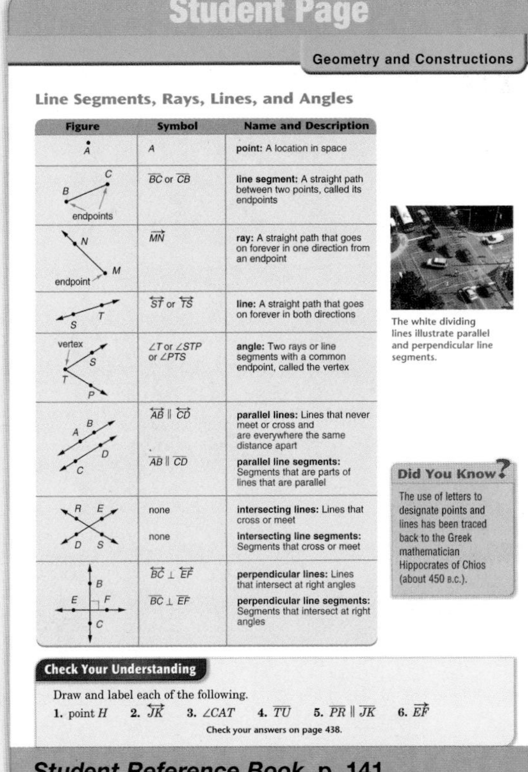

Student Page

Geometry and Constructions

Line Segments, Rays, Lines, and Angles

Figure	Symbol	Name and Description
A	*A*	**point:** A location in space
B, C, endpoints	$\overline{BC}$ or $\overline{CB}$	**line segment:** A straight path between two points, called its endpoints
N, M, endpoint	$\overrightarrow{MN}$	**ray:** A straight path that goes on forever in one direction from an endpoint
S, T	$\overleftrightarrow{ST}$ or $\overleftrightarrow{TS}$	**line:** A straight path that goes on forever in both directions
vertex, T, S, P	∠*T* or ∠*STP* or ∠*PTS*	**angle:** Two rays or line segments with a common endpoint, called the vertex
A, B, C, D	$\overleftrightarrow{AB} \parallel \overleftrightarrow{CD}$ $\overline{AB} \parallel \overline{CD}$	**parallel lines:** Lines that never meet or cross and are everywhere the same distance apart **parallel line segments:** Segments that are parts of lines that are parallel
R, E, D, S	none none	**intersecting lines:** Lines that cross or meet **intersecting line segments:** Segments that cross or meet
B, E, F, C	$\overleftrightarrow{BC} \perp \overleftrightarrow{EF}$ $\overline{BC} \perp \overline{EF}$	**perpendicular lines:** Lines that intersect at right angles **perpendicular line segments:** Segments that intersect at right angles

The white dividing lines illustrate parallel and perpendicular line segments.

Did You Know?
The use of letters to designate points and lines has been traced back to the Greek mathematician Hippocrates of Chios (about 450 B.C.).

Check Your Understanding

Draw and label each of the following.

1. point *H* 2. $\overleftrightarrow{JK}$ 3. ∠*CAT* 4. $\overline{TU}$ 5. $\overline{PR} \parallel \overline{JK}$ 6. $\overrightarrow{EF}$

Check your answers on page 438.

***Student Reference Book,* p. 141**

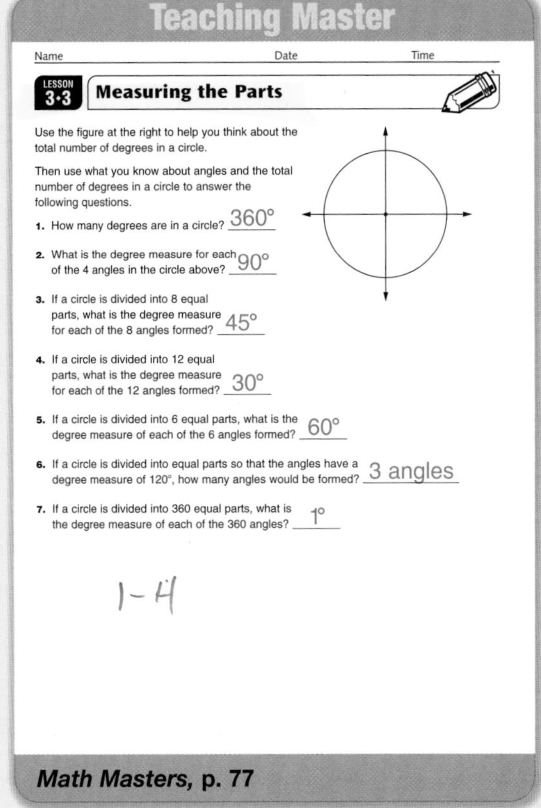

Teaching Master

Name Date Time

LESSON 3·3 **Measuring the Parts**

Use the figure at the right to help you think about the total number of degrees in a circle.

Then use what you know about angles and the total number of degrees in a circle to answer the following questions.

1. How many degrees are in a circle? 360°
2. What is the degree measure for each of the 4 angles in the circle above? 90°
3. If a circle is divided into 8 equal parts, what is the degree measure for each of the 8 angles formed? 45°
4. If a circle is divided into 12 equal parts, what is the degree measure for each of the 12 angles formed? 30°
5. If a circle is divided into 6 equal parts, what is the degree measure of each of the 6 angles formed? 60°
6. If a circle is divided into equal parts so that the angles have a degree measure of 120°, how many angles would be formed? 3 angles
7. If a circle is divided into 360 equal parts, what is the degree measure of each of the 360 angles? 1°

***Math Masters,* p. 77**

3•4 Using a Protractor

Objectives To review types of angles, geometric figures, and the use of the Geometry Template to measure and draw angles.

www.everydaymathonline.com

ePresentations

eToolkit

Algorithms Practice

EM Facts Workshop Game™

Family Letters

Assessment Management

Common Core State Standards

Curriculum Focal Points

Interactive Teacher's Lesson Guide

1 Teaching the Lesson

Key Concepts and Skills

- Define and classify angles according to their measures. [Geometry Goal 1]
- Explore angle types and relationships. [Geometry Goal 1]
- Use a full-circle and a half-circle protractor to measure and draw angles. [Measurement and Reference Frames Goal 1]

Key Activities

Students write definitions for acute and obtuse angles and review other types of angles. They use the Geometry Template to measure and draw angles.

Ongoing Assessment: Informing Instruction See pages 173 and 174.

Ongoing Assessment: Recognizing Student Achievement Use an Exit Slip (*Math Masters,* page 414). [Measurement and Reference Frames Goal 1]

Key Vocabulary

acute angle ◆ obtuse angle ◆ right angle ◆ straight angle ◆ reflex angle ◆ Geometry Template ◆ arc

Materials

Math Journal 1, pp. 68 and 69
Student Reference Book, pp. 145, 146, 162, and 163 ◆ Study Link 3•3
Math Masters, p. 414
transparencies of *Math Masters,* pp. 78, 79, and 419 (optional) ◆ Geometry Template

2 Ongoing Learning & Practice

Interpreting a Bar Graph
Math Journal 1, p. 70
Student Reference Book, p. 121
Students find the landmarks of data represented by a bar graph.

Ongoing Assessment: Informing Instruction See page 175.

Math Boxes 3•4
Math Journal 1, p. 71
Students practice and maintain skills through Math Box problems.

Study Link 3•4
Math Masters, p. 80
Students practice and maintain skills through Study Link activities.

3 Differentiation Options

READINESS

Identifying Points, Lines, and Angles
Student Reference Book, p. 141
Math Masters, p. 81
Students review the vocabulary of angles and their relationships.

ENRICHMENT

Measuring Baseball Angles
Math Masters, p. 82
Students use their knowledge of angle measures to solve a baseball challenge problem.

ELL SUPPORT

Building a Math Word Bank
Differentiation Handbook, p. 143
Students define and illustrate angle terms.

Advance Preparation

To help manage the Geometry Templates, experienced *Everyday Mathematics* teachers suggest writing student ID numbers on them with a permanent marker. For a mathematics and literacy connection, obtain a copy of ***G Is for Googol*** by David M. Schwartz (Tricycle Press, 1998). This book may be used throughout the unit.

***Teacher's Reference Manual,* Grades 4–6** pp. 44, 45

Getting Started

Mental Math and Reflexes

Students stand, facing the same direction, and follow directions related to angle measures or fractions of a turn. Direct students to focus on the degree equivalents for quarter (90°) and half turns (180°).

- Rotate 180° to the right.
- Make a half turn to the left.
- Make a quarter turn to the right.
- Make a 90° turn to the left.
- Turn 360° to the left.

Math Message

Use only the information given on journal page 68 to complete Problems 1 and 2.

Study Link 3·3 Follow-Up

Allow students five minutes to compare their answers. Ask volunteers to describe their strategies for estimating and finding the angle measures. Record strategies on the Class Data Pad for display.

1 Teaching the Lesson

▶ Math Message Follow-Up

WHOLE-CLASS DISCUSSION

(*Math Journal 1,* p. 68)

Survey the class for their definitions of **acute angle,** An angle whose measure is greater than 0° and less than 90° and **obtuse angle.** An angle whose measure is greater than 90° and less than 180° For each type of angle, compare the similarities and differences of students' definitions. Ask students to agree on a common definition for each type of angle and record these definitions on the Class Data Pad. Emphasize the importance of definitions in mathematics. For example, discuss why *narrow* and *wide* are not specific enough to be acceptable definitions for *acute* and *obtuse.* Ask whether an angle can be both acute and obtuse and why or why not.

NOTE Working with mathematical definitions helps students build logical thinking skills that are critical to success in higher mathematics. Definitions are closely related to classification schemes. The types of angles defined in this lesson, for example, make up a classification scheme for all angles. Every angle with a measure greater than 0° is either an acute angle, right angle, obtuse angle, straight angle, or reflex angle.

Adjusting the Activity

Consider assigning groups to combine their individual definitions into a group proposal for the class definition.

AUDITORY ◆ KINESTHETIC ◆ TACTILE ◆ VISUAL

Draw a **right,** a **straight,** and a **reflex angle** on the Class Data Pad. Ask students to name these angles. A 90° angle is called a *right angle*; a 180° angle is called a *straight angle*; an angle whose measure is greater than 180° and less than 360° is called a *reflex angle.* Draw a small square in the corner of the right angle and explain that the symbol represents the square corner formed by perpendicular lines. The symbol indicates that the measure of the angle is 90°.

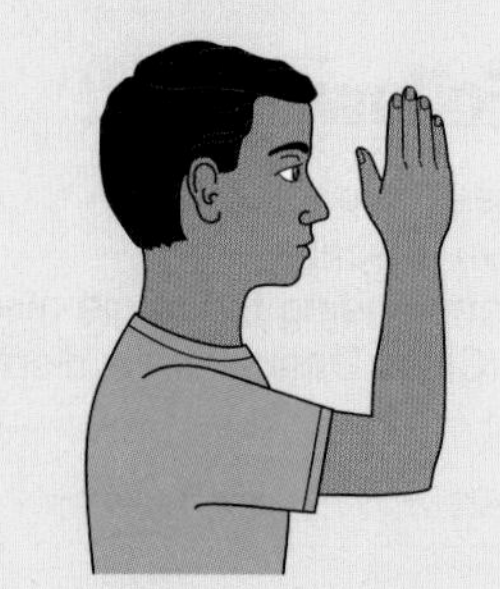

Demonstrating a right angle

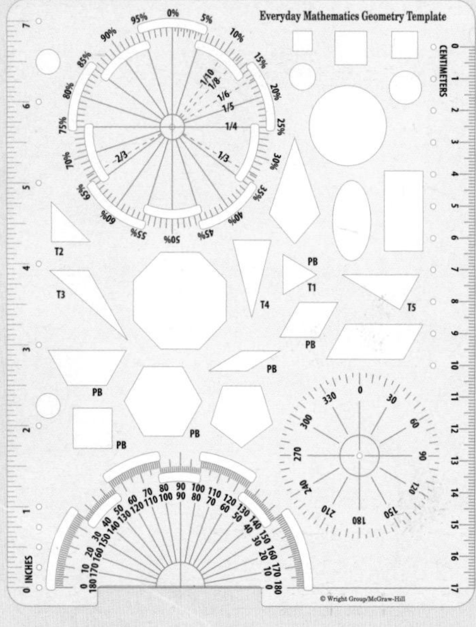

The Geometry Template appears on both *Math Masters,* page 419 and *Student Reference Book,* page 163.

Ask: *Why do you think the 180° angle is called a straight angle?* Sample answer: Because the two sides of the angle form a straight line Assign volunteers to label the angles on the Class Data Pad.

Ask partners to demonstrate angle types (right, straight, acute, and obtuse) using their arms as physical models. Sample answers: Think of the elbow as the vertex of the angle and bend one arm to form a 90° angle, an angle smaller than 90°, an angle between 90° and 180°, and a 180° angle. Students should name each modeled angle in turn. (*See margin.*)

Ask partners to illustrate each of the following terms using their arms: parallel, perpendicular, and intersecting. Assign volunteers to add these examples to the Class Data Pad. To summarize, review the concepts and objects from this lesson listed on the Class Data Pad with a focus on the vocabulary.

▶ Introducing the Geometry Template

(*Student Reference Book,* pp. 145, 146, 162, and 163; *Math Masters,* p. 419)

Transition to this activity by displaying the **Geometry Template,** either by placing the template on the overhead or by using a transparency of *Math Masters,* page 419.

Ask students to turn to pages 162 and 163 of the *Student Reference Book.* Consider assigning groups one each of the paragraph topics on page 162. Groups should read their assigned paragraph(s), identify the important information, and present it to the class. As groups present their information, make sure that the following features of the Geometry Template are noted:

- ▷ There is an inch ruler along the left edge and a centimeter ruler along the right edge.
- ▷ As part of the geometric figures, there are six pattern-block shapes—equilateral triangle, square, trapezoid, two rhombuses, and regular hexagon—labeled PB. The regular pentagon and octagon are not pattern-block shapes.
- ▷ Some of the other shapes have sides that are the same length as the pattern-block shapes.
- ▷ The squares and circles of various sizes can be used to draw figures quickly.

To review properties of quadrangles, or quadrilaterals, have students trace all of the quadrangles on the Geometry Template and sort them by various categories. Have students determine if some fit into more than one category. Use *Student Reference Book,* pages 145 and 146 as a resource.

Ask students to find the relationship between the template shapes and actual pattern blocks. The sides of the template shapes are half as long as the edges of the pattern blocks.

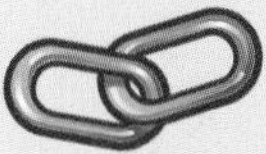

Links to the Future

The triangles on the Geometry Template will be discussed in Lesson 3-6. The Percent Circle is used to read and make circle (pie) graphs and will be discussed in Lessons 5-10 and 5-11.

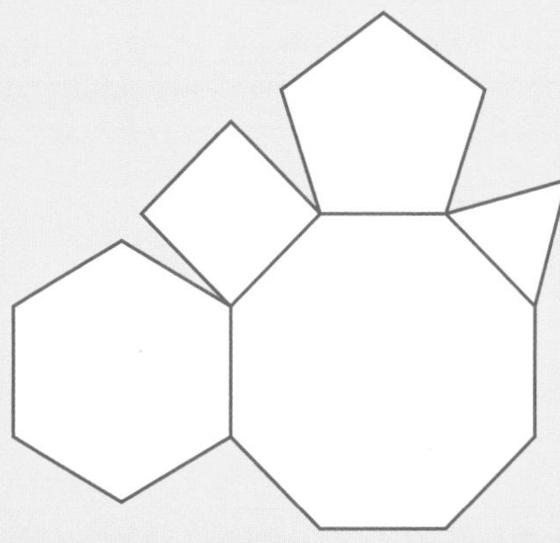

Comparing each figure with the octagon shows that all regular polygons on the Geometry Template have sides of the same length. Other shapes can be compared in the same way.

Ask students to use their templates to make tracings that identify different figures on the Geometry Template that have sides of the same length. Have volunteers record this list of figures on the Class Data Pad. The sides of the pentagon, octagon, five pattern-block shapes, and three sides of the pattern-block trapezoid are the same length; the fourth side of the trapezoid is twice as long.

Adjusting the Activity

Remind students that any two figures can be compared by tracing them so they are adjacent; that is, they share a common side. (See margin.)

AUDITORY ◆ KINESTHETIC ◆ TACTILE ◆ VISUAL

Ask students to identify the half-circle protractor and the full-circle protractor on the Geometry Template. Then ask a volunteer how they would measure one of the angles from Problem 1 on journal page 68. Ask another volunteer to use the full-circle protractor to measure one of the angles in Problem 2.

NOTE The key to using the half-circle protractor is knowing which scale to read. The key to using the full-circle protractor is knowing that the scale runs clockwise. The 0° mark must be aligned with one side of the angle. Students measure from 0° in the clockwise direction to find the answers. One way to reinforce this habit is for students to estimate whether the angle is more or less than 90° before measuring it.

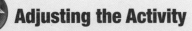

Ongoing Assessment: Informing Instruction

Watch for students who find it difficult to align the protractor when the Geometry Template spans across two pages. Have students try turning the page and/or aligning a different leg of the angle with the 0° mark on the protractor.

Measuring Angles

PARTNER ACTIVITY

(*Math Journal 1,* p. 68)

Partners work on Problem 3 at the bottom of the journal page. Remind students to estimate the angle measures before they use a protractor. (*See margin note.*) Explain that estimating first will help them confirm whether they're reading the correct scale or moving in the correct direction on the protractor. Allow 5 to 10 minutes, then discuss students' answers. Theresa's and Devon's answers are incorrect. Devon interpreted the angle to be a reflex angle (the angle larger than 180°). Theresa used the wrong scale on her half-circle protractor.

Student Page

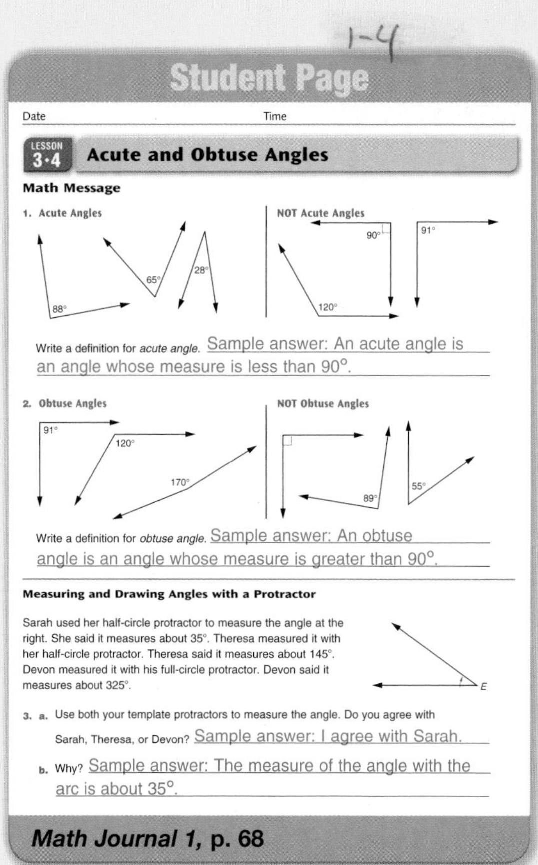

Date Time

LESSON 3·4 **Acute and Obtuse Angles**

Math Message

1. Acute Angles — NOT Acute Angles

Write a definition for *acute angle.* Sample answer: An acute angle is an angle whose measure is less than 90°.

2. Obtuse Angles — NOT Obtuse Angles

Write a definition for *obtuse angle.* Sample answer: An obtuse angle is an angle whose measure is greater than 90°.

Measuring and Drawing Angles with a Protractor

Sarah used her half-circle protractor to measure the angle at the right. She said it measures about 35°. Theresa measured it with her half-circle protractor. Theresa said it measures about 145°. Devon measured it with his full-circle protractor. Devon said it measures about 325°.

3. a. Use both your template protractors to measure the angle. Do you agree with Sarah, Theresa, or Devon? Sample answer: I agree with Sarah.

b. Why? Sample answer: The measure of the angle with the arc is about 35°.

Math Journal 1, p. 68

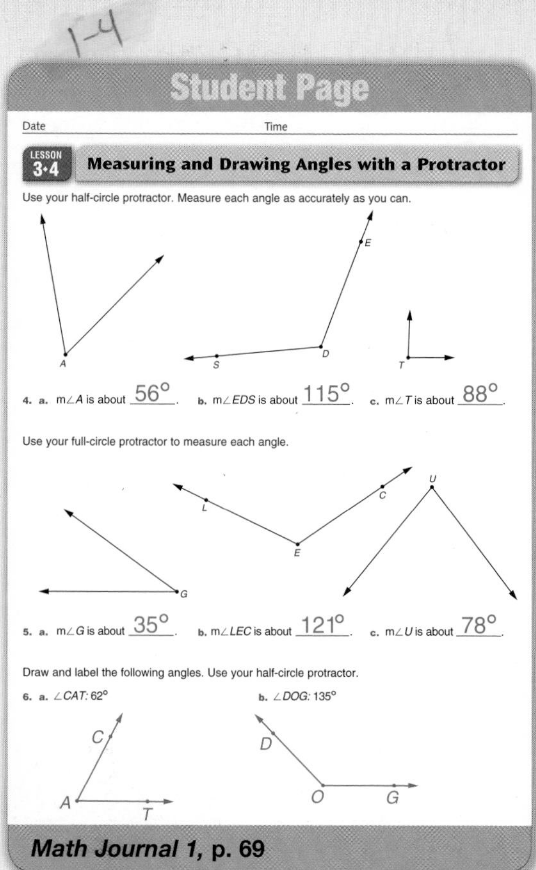
Student Page

Date Time

LESSON 3·4 **Measuring and Drawing Angles with a Protractor**

Use your half-circle protractor. Measure each angle as accurately as you can.

4. a. m∠A is about 56°. b. m∠EDS is about 115°. c. m∠T is about 88°.

Use your full-circle protractor to measure each angle.

5. a. m∠G is about 35°. b. m∠LEC is about 121°. c. m∠U is about 78°.

Draw and label the following angles. Use your half-circle protractor.

6. a. ∠CAT: 62° b. ∠DOG: 135°

Math Journal 1, p. 69

> **NOTE** Students used the full-circle and the half-circle protractors in *Fourth Grade Everyday Mathematics*. With half-circle protractors expect students to be able to measure to within about 2° of the measured approximation. With full-circle protractors, expect that students might be less precise, measuring to within about 5° of the approximation.

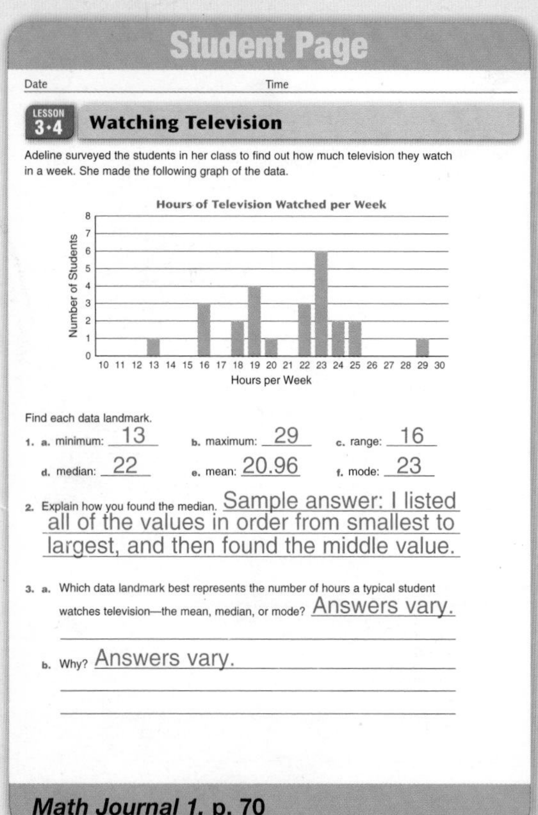
Student Page

Date Time

LESSON 3·4 **Watching Television**

Adeline surveyed the students in her class to find out how much television they watch in a week. She made the following graph of the data.

Find each data landmark.

1. a. minimum: 13 b. maximum: 29 c. range: 16
   d. median: 22 e. mean: 20.96 f. mode: 23
2. Explain how you found the median. Sample answer: I listed all of the values in order from smallest to largest, and then found the middle value.
3. a. Which data landmark best represents the number of hours a typical student watches television—the mean, median, or mode? Answers vary.
   b. Why? Answers vary.

Math Journal 1, p. 70

Explain that in *Everyday Mathematics* when students measure an angle, they will normally measure the smaller angle, not the reflex angle. When they are supposed to measure the reflex angle, it is indicated with an **arc.**

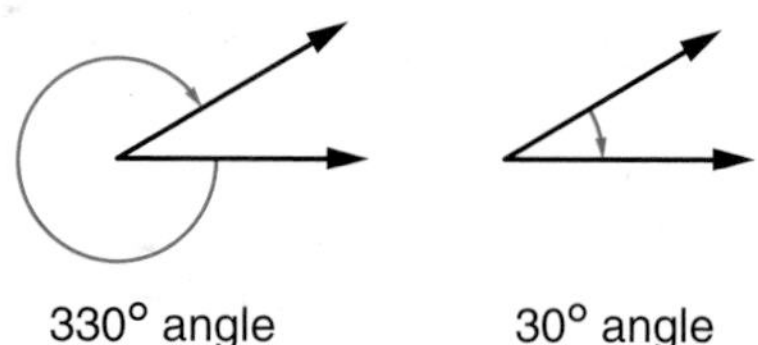

330° angle 30° angle

Students will practice measuring angles throughout the year in Math Boxes problems and in Ongoing Learning & Practice activities.

▶ Practicing Measuring and Drawing Angles

PARTNER ACTIVITY

(*Math Journal 1,* p. 69; *Math Masters*, pp. 419, 78, and 79)

Remind students that all measurements are approximations. They should always measure carefully but recognize that a measure obtained with a measuring tool does not give an exact size for the object being measured. The goal is to be as precise as possible, but the degree of precision is dependent on the accuracy of the measuring tool and how effectively it is used.

Assign journal page 69. Remind students to use the half-circle protractor to complete Problems 4 and 6, and the full-circle protractor to complete Problem 5. Ask them to estimate each angle before measuring. It is important that students practice with both types of protractors. You might want to display or use overhead transparencies of the Geometry Template and journal pages (*Math Masters,* pp. 419, 78, and 79). Circulate and assist.

Ongoing Assessment: Informing Instruction

Watch for students who have difficulty measuring Angle *T* because the figure is so small. Suggest that students extend the angle's sides with a straightedge before measuring the angle with a protractor. Demonstrate this approach and illustrate the pitfalls of extending the sides without using a straightedge.

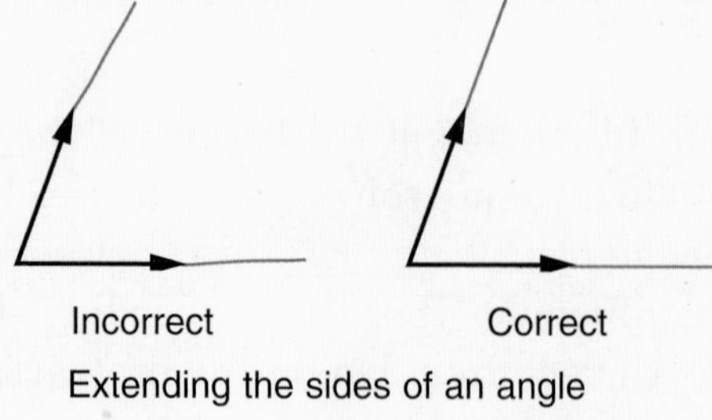

Extending the sides of an angle

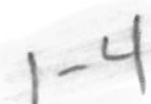

Ongoing Assessment: Recognizing Student Achievement

Exit Slip

Ask students to respond to the following question on an **Exit Slip** (*Math Masters,* page 414) or half-sheet of paper. *Which is easier to use—the full-circle protractor or the half-circle protractor? Why?* Students are making adequate progress if their answers demonstrate an understanding of how to use both protractor types.

[Measurement and Reference Frames Goal 1]

2 Ongoing Learning & Practice

▶ Interpreting a Bar Graph

INDEPENDENT ACTIVITY

(*Math Journal 1,* p. 70; *Student Reference Book,* p. 121)

Students find landmarks for data represented by the bar graph on journal page 70. They describe how to find the median, and tell whether the mean, median, or mode best represents the data for a typical student.

Ongoing Assessment: Informing Instruction

Watch for students who have difficulty finding the mean. It might be helpful to review the steps on *Student Reference Book,* page 121. Ask students to summarize the process for finding the mean in their own words and have them list the steps on an index card. For example: *1.* ***Count*** *the numbers in the data set; 2.* ***Add*** *the numbers in the data set; and 3.* ***Divide*** *the sum by the count.* Students should check their steps by using them to solve the Check Your Understanding problem at the bottom of the *Student Reference Book* page.

▶ Math Boxes 3•4

INDEPENDENT ACTIVITY

(*Math Journal 1,* p. 71)

Mixed Practice Math Boxes in this lesson are paired with Math Boxes in Lesson 3-2. The skill in Problem 6 previews Unit 4 content.

▶ Study Link 3•4

INDEPENDENT ACTIVITY

(*Math Masters,* p. 80)

Home Connection Students practice measuring angles with half-circle and full-circle protractors.

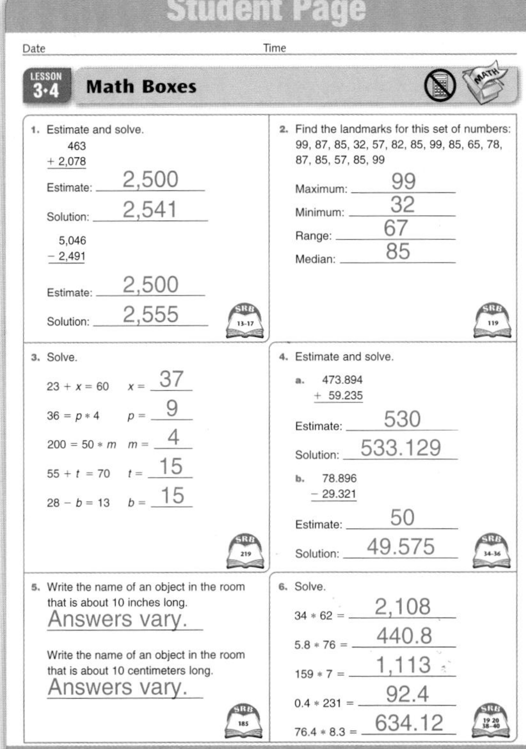

Student Page

Date Time

LESSON 3•4 **Math Boxes**

1. Estimate and solve.
463 + 2,078
Estimate: 2,500
Solution: 2,541
5,046 − 2,491
Estimate: 2,500
Solution: 2,555

2. Find the landmarks for this set of numbers: 99, 87, 85, 32, 57, 82, 85, 99, 85, 65, 78, 87, 85, 57, 85, 99
Maximum: 99
Minimum: 32
Range: 67
Median: 85

3. Solve.
23 + x = 60 x = 37
36 = p ∗ 4 p = 9
200 = 50 ∗ m m = 4
55 + t = 70 t = 15
28 − b = 13 b = 15

4. Estimate and solve.
a. 473.894 + 59.235
Estimate: 530
Solution: 533.129
b. 78.896 − 29.321
Estimate: 50
Solution: 49.575

5. Write the name of an object in the room that is about 10 inches long.
Answers vary.
Write the name of an object in the room that is about 10 centimeters long.
Answers vary.

6. Solve.
34 ∗ 62 = 2,108
5.8 ∗ 76 = 440.8
159 ∗ 7 = 1,113
0.4 ∗ 231 = 92.4
76.4 ∗ 8.3 = 634.12

Math Journal 1, p. 71

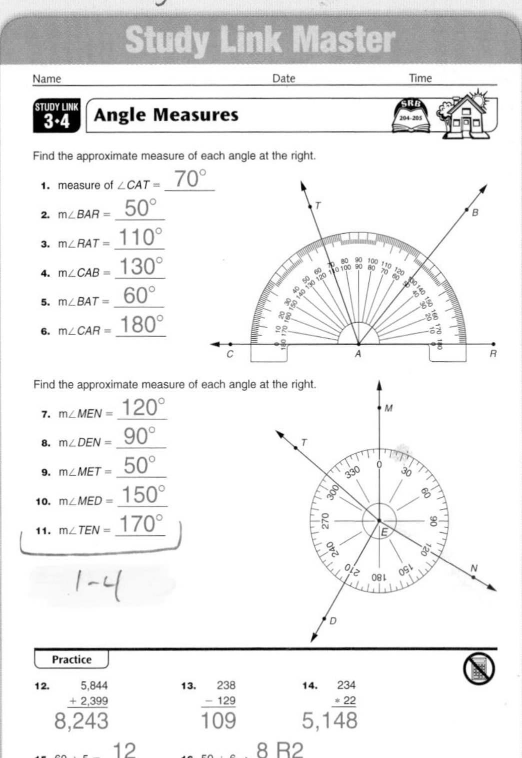

Study Link Master

Name Date Time

STUDY LINK 3•4 **Angle Measures**

Find the approximate measure of each angle at the right.
1. measure of ∠CAT = 70°
2. m∠BAR = 50°
3. m∠RAT = 110°
4. m∠CAB = 130°
5. m∠BAT = 60°
6. m∠CAR = 180°

Find the approximate measure of each angle at the right.
7. m∠MEN = 120°
8. m∠DEN = 90°
9. m∠MET = 50°
10. m∠MED = 150°
11. m∠TEN = 170°

Practice
12. 5,844 + 2,399 = 8,243
13. 238 − 129 = 109
14. 234 ∗ 22 = 5,148
15. 60 ÷ 5 = 12
16. 50 ÷ 6 → 8 R2

Math Masters, p. 80

Teaching Master

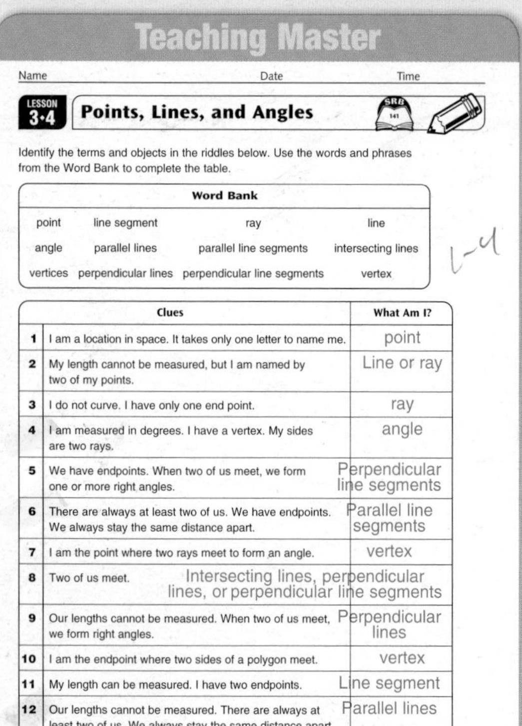
Name Date Time

LESSON 3·4 **Points, Lines, and Angles**

SRB 141

Identify the terms and objects in the riddles below. Use the words and phrases from the Word Bank to complete the table.

Word Bank

point	line segment	ray	line
angle	parallel lines	parallel line segments	intersecting lines
vertices	perpendicular lines	perpendicular line segments	vertex

	Clues	What Am I?
1	I am a location in space. It takes only one letter to name me.	point
2	My length cannot be measured, but I am named by two of my points.	Line or ray
3	I do not curve. I have only one end point.	ray
4	I am measured in degrees. I have a vertex. My sides are two rays.	angle
5	We have endpoints. When two of us meet, we form one or more right angles.	Perpendicular line segments
6	There are always at least two of us. We have endpoints. We always stay the same distance apart.	Parallel line segments
7	I am the point where two rays meet to form an angle.	vertex
8	Two of us meet.	Intersecting lines, perpendicular lines, or perpendicular line segments
9	Our lengths cannot be measured. When two of us meet, we form right angles.	Perpendicular lines
10	I am the endpoint where two sides of a polygon meet.	vertex
11	My length can be measured. I have two endpoints.	Line segment
12	Our lengths cannot be measured. There are always at least two of us. We always stay the same distance apart.	Parallel lines

Math Masters, p. 81

Teaching Master

Name Date Time

LESSON 3·4 **Baseball Angles**

The playing field for baseball lies between the foul lines, which form a 90° angle. Suppose that each of the four infielders can cover an angle of about 13° on a hard-hit ground ball, and that the pitcher can cover about 6°. (See the diagram above.)

Source: *Applying Arithmetic*, Usiskin, Z. and Bell, M. © 1983 University of Chicago

1. How many degrees are left for the batter to hit through? 32°

Math Masters, p. 82

3 Differentiation Options

READINESS

SMALL-GROUP ACTIVITY

5–15 Min

▶ Identifying Points, Lines, and Angles

(*Student Reference Book*, p. 141; *Math Masters*, p. 81)

To review vocabulary and concepts related to angles, have students solve riddles about points, lines, line segments, and angles.

ENRICHMENT

INDEPENDENT ACTIVITY

15–30 Min

▶ Measuring Baseball Angles

(*Math Masters*, p. 82)

To apply students' understanding of angle properties and angle measurements, have students solve a baseball problem that involves addition and subtraction of angle measures.

As students complete the assignment, discuss answers and strategies. The field has a 90° angle within which a batted ball is put in play. Each of the four infielders covers 13°, for a total of $4 * 13°$, or 52° and the pitcher covers 6°. That leaves $90° - 52° - 6°$, or 32°, uncovered, which suggests that on average a little more than one-third of hard-hit ground balls should get past the infield. Ask the baseball players and fans in the class whether that conclusion is consistent with their experiences.

ELL SUPPORT

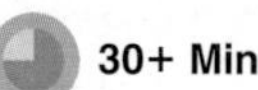
SMALL-GROUP ACTIVITY

30+ Min

▶ Building a Math Word Bank

(*Differentiation Handbook*, p. 143)

To provide language support for *angles,* have students use the Word Bank Template found on *Differentiation Handbook,* page 143. Ask students to write the terms *acute angle, right angle, obtuse angle, straight angle,* and *reflex angle,* draw pictures relating to each term, and write other related words. See the *Differentiation Handbook* for more information.

3•5 Using a Compass

Objectives To review compass skills and explore angles formed by intersecting lines.

Technology Resources www.everydaymathonline.com

ePresentations

eToolkit

Algorithms Practice

EM Facts Workshop Game™

Family Letters

Assessment Management

Common Core State Standards

Curriculum Focal Points

Interactive Teacher's Lesson Guide

1 Teaching the Lesson

Key Concepts and Skills

- Investigate vertical, opposite, and adjacent angles. [Geometry Goal 1]
- Use angle relationships to determine angle measures. [Geometry Goal 1]
- Copy, measure, and construct line segments using a compass, straightedge, and ruler. [Measurement and Reference Frames Goal 1]
- Explore the relationship between radius and diameter measurements. [Measurement and Reference Frames Goal 2]

Key Activities

Students use a compass to draw circles, copy line segments, and estimate lengths. They measure vertical and adjacent angles formed by intersecting lines.

Ongoing Assessment: Recognizing Student Achievement Use Mental Math and Reflexes. [Operations and Computation Goal 2]

Ongoing Assessment: Informing Instruction See page 180.

Key Vocabulary

radius ♦ diameter ♦ vertical (or opposite) angles ♦ adjacent angles

Materials

Math Journal 1, pp. 72 and 73
Student Reference Book, pp. 139, 164, and 165 (optional)
Study Link 3•4
Geometry Template ♦ compass ♦ one 2 ft by 2 ft sheet of paper ♦ chalk ♦ per partnership: 5 ft length of string or rope ♦ ruler

2 Ongoing Learning & Practice

Playing *High Number Toss: Decimal Version*
Student Reference Book, pp. 32, 33, and 321
Math Masters, p. 511
per partnership: 4 each of number cards 0–9 (from the Everything Math Deck, if available)
Students practice reading, writing, and comparing decimals.

Math Boxes 3•5
Math Journal 1, p. 74
Students practice and maintain skills through Math Box problems.

Study Link 3•5
Math Masters, p. 83
Students practice and maintain skills through Study Link activities.

3 Differentiation Options

READINESS

Reading a Ruler
Math Masters, p. 84
ruler
Students review the divisions and marks on an inch ruler and measure line segments.

ENRICHMENT

Inscribing a Regular Hexagon in a Circle
Student Reference Book, p. 168
Math Masters, p. 85
compass ♦ straightedge ♦ crayons or colored pencils
Students inscribe a regular hexagon in a circle, reproduce a design, and make their own designs.

ELL SUPPORT

Building a Math Word Bank
Differentiation Handbook, p. 142
Students add the terms *radius* and *diameter* to their Math Word Banks.

Advance Preparation

For Part 1, prepare a 2 ft by 2 ft square of paper and prearrange playground use for the students' large compass drawings.

***Teacher's Reference Manual,* Grades 4–6** pp. 43, 209–211

Getting Started

Mental Math and Reflexes ★

Use slate procedures and write all problems on the board or Class Data Pad so students can visually recognize the patterns.

●○○ 7 * 8 56
70 * 8 560
70 * 80 5,600
700 * 80 56,000

●●○ 42 ÷ 7 6
420 ÷ 7 60
4,200 ÷ 7 600
42,000 ÷ 7 6,000

●●● 560 ÷ 70 8
5,600 ÷ 700 8
56,000 ÷ 7,000 8

Math Message

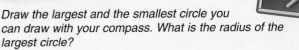

Draw the largest and the smallest circle you can draw with your compass. What is the radius of the largest circle?

Study Link 3·4 Follow-Up

Allow students five minutes to compare their answers and resolve any differences.
Survey students for important things to remember when measuring with the half-circle or full-circle protractors.

Ongoing Assessment: Recognizing Student Achievement

Mental Math and Reflexes ★

Use the **Mental Math and Reflexes problem sets** to assess students' ability to solve extended multiplication facts mentally. Students are making adequate progress if they correctly respond to the multiplication problems. Some students may also be successful with the division problems.

[Operations and Computation Goal 2]

1 Teaching the Lesson

▶ Math Message Follow-Up

Review the following definitions. To support English language learners, write the definitions along with labeled drawings on the board or Class Data Pad.

▷ The **radius** of a circle is any line segment from the center of the circle to any point on the circle.

▷ The **diameter** of a circle is any line segment that passes through the center of the circle and has its endpoints on the circle.

▷ In any circle, the length of a diameter is twice the length of a radius.

▷ *Radius* and *diameter* are also used to name length. For example, the radius of the circle is 2 inches and the diameter is 4 inches. Ask volunteers to use these terms to explain their solution strategies.

Adjusting the Activity

Have students review and practice the two methods for drawing circles explained on *Student Reference Book,* page 164.

AUDITORY ◆ KINESTHETIC ◆ TACTILE ◆ VISUAL

Demonstrate how to obtain a larger separation by adjusting the compass pencil. Clamp a full-length pencil in the compass with the eraser as close to the clamp as possible. (*See below.*) Then open the compass to its largest separation, and draw a very large circle on the 2 ft by 2 ft sheet of paper. This adjustment allows you to draw a circle with an 8-inch radius (16-inch diameter), even with a small compass.

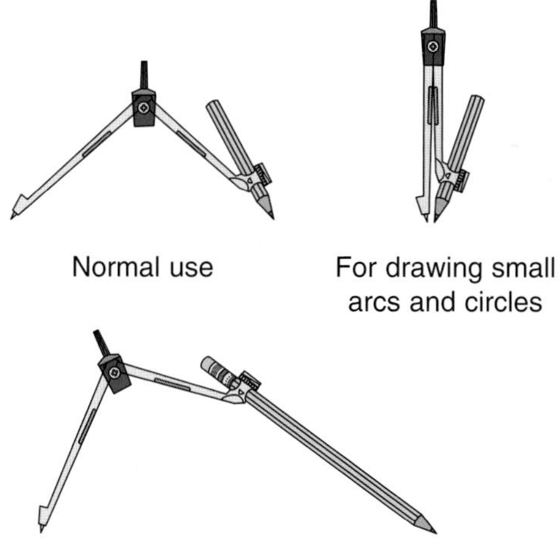

Normal use

For drawing small arcs and circles

For drawing large arcs and circles

Adjusting the Activity

ELL

Ask partners to explore drawing large and small circles on the school playground or sidewalk using string and chalk. This activity provides an opportunity for students to physically experience the roles of the compass anchor and the pencil point and reinforces the importance of keeping the anchor and the clamped pencil in set positions as students draw.

AUDITORY ◆ KINESTHETIC ◆ TACTILE ◆ VISUAL

▶ Copying Line Segments

PARTNER ACTIVITY

(*Math Journal 1,* p. 72)

Ask volunteers to explain the difference between a ruler and a straightedge.

- ▷ A ruler has a scale along at least one edge and is used to measure lengths.
- ▷ A straightedge is a tool for drawing straight lines but is not used for measuring.
- ▷ A ruler can be used as a straightedge, even when you're not using it to measure something.

Assign partners to complete Problems 1 and 2 on the journal page. Circulate and assist.

Student Page

Date Time

LESSON 3·5 **Copying Line Segments and Finding Lengths**

1. Use your compass and straightedge to copy line segment $\overline{AB}$. Do not measure the line segment with a ruler. Label the endpoints of the new line segment as points *M* and *N*. Line segment $\overline{MN}$ should be the same length as line segment $\overline{AB}$.

A B

M N

2. Three line segments are shown below:

A B C D E F

Use your compass and straightedge. Construct one line segment that is as long as the three segments joined together end to end. Label the two endpoints of the long line segment *X* and *Y*.

X Y

Use your compass to find the lengths of different parts of the Geometry Template.

Example: Find the length of the longer side of the rectangle on the Geometry Template.

Step 1 Open the compass to the length of the longer side.

Step 2 Don't change the opening on your compass. Hold the compass against the inch ruler with the anchor at 0. Read the length. The length is about 1 inch.

INCHES 1

3. The length of the longer side of the trapezoid is about 1 inch(es).
4. The diameter of the full-circle protractor is about 2 inch(es).
5. The distance between the center of the full-circle protractor and the center of the Percent Circle is about $4\frac{3}{4}$ inch(es).
6. Use your compass and a ruler to find two other lengths. Be sure to include units.

Part Measured	Length

Math Journal 1, p. 72

Student Page

Date   Time

LESSON 3•5 Adjacent and Vertical Angles

Angles that are "next to" each other are called **adjacent angles.** Adjacent angles have the same vertex and a common side.

When two lines intersect, four angles are formed. The angles opposite each other are called **vertical angles** or **opposite angles.**

1. a. Angles *ABD* and *CBE* are vertical angles. Name another pair of vertical angles.
   ∠*ABC* and ∠*DBE*

   b. Angles *ABC* and *CBE* are adjacent angles. Name two other pairs of adjacent angles.
   Sample answers: ∠*CBE* and ∠*EBD*; ∠*DBA* and ∠*ABC*

2. The two lines at the right intersect to form four angles. One angle has been measured. Use your full-circle protractor to measure the other three angles. Record your measurements on the drawing.

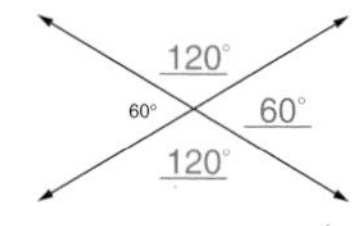

3. On a blank sheet of paper, draw two lines that intersect. Measure the four angles. Record the measures on your drawing. Answers vary.

4. What do you notice about the measures of pairs of vertical angles?
   Sample answer: They are the same.

5. What do you notice about the measures of pairs of adjacent angles?
   Sample answer: They total 180°.

Try This

6. For any pair of adjacent angles formed by two intersecting lines, the sum of the measures is always 180°. Explain why. Sample answer: The adjacent angles form a straight angle, which always measures 180°.

***Math Journal 1*, p. 73**

Students might benefit from reviewing the procedure for copying a line segment on page 165 of the *Student Reference Book.* The construction for Problem 2 can be done by following two steps. Draw a line segment that is longer than the three line segments arranged end to end. Then copy each of the three line segments onto the longer line segment, end to end.

▶ Finding Lengths with a Compass

PARTNER ACTIVITY

(*Math Journal 1,* p. 72)

For Problems 3–6 on the journal page, students measure lengths and distances with a compass and a ruler. Work through the example with the class and make sure students understand what they are to do. Each measurement is a two-step operation.

1. Set the compass opening to the length that will be measured.
2. Hold the compass against the inch ruler with the anchor at 0. Measure the length of the compass opening. This is the desired length.

Circulate and assist.

Ongoing Assessment: Informing Instruction

Watch for students who solve the problems by measuring. Emphasize that they should use their rulers only as straightedges for these problems.

▶ Measuring Angles Formed by Intersecting Lines

PARTNER ACTIVITY

(*Math Journal 1,* p. 73)

Have students work with partners to complete the journal page. Circulate and assist.

Bring the class together to share results. Survey the class for true statements about the angles formed by two intersecting lines. When two lines intersect, the measures of the angles opposite each other are equal and are called **vertical** or **opposite angles** (*See Figure 1*); angles that are next to each other and have a common side are called **adjacent angles.** (*See Figure 2.*)

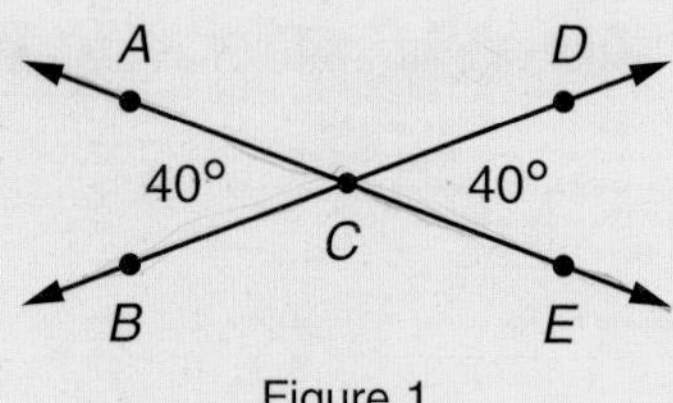

Figure 1

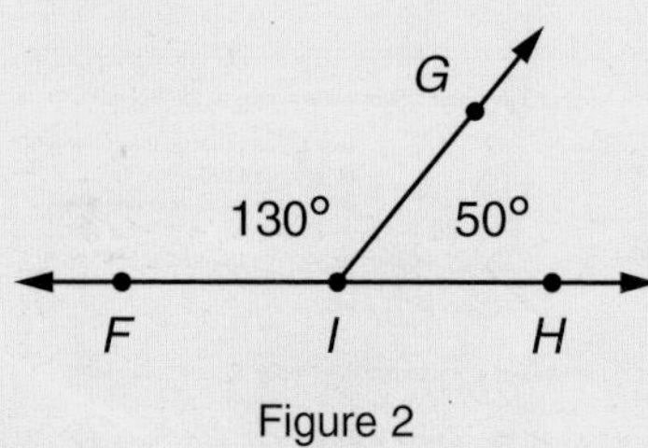

Figure 2

For Problem 6, point out that when two lines intersect, the sum of the measures of two adjacent angles is 180°. Ask students how they might confirm this without measuring the angles. When two lines intersect, two adjacent angles form a straight angle, and the measure of a straight angle is 180°.

To review *parallel* and *perpendicular lines,* ask students to identify examples of parallel and perpendicular lines found in the classroom. Write students' responses on the board.

Adjusting the Activity

Discuss the example of angles formed by intersecting lines on page 139 of the *Student Reference Book* and the Check Your Understanding problems.

AUDITORY ◆ KINESTHETIC ◆ TACTILE ◆ VISUAL

2 Ongoing Learning & Practice

▶ Playing *High Number Toss: Decimal Version*

PARTNER ACTIVITY

(*Student Reference Book,* pp. 32, 33, and 321; *Math Masters,* p. 511)

High Number Toss: Decimal Version provides students with the opportunity to apply their knowledge of place value and standard notation to form, write, read, and compare decimals. Provide students with a reminder box on the board noting that < means *is less than* and > means *is greater than.*

After each round, ask students to record the decimals they formed on *Math Masters,* page 511, and use <, >, and = to compare them. If necessary, refer students to *Student Reference Book,* pages 32 and 33 to review comparing decimals.

▶ Math Boxes 3•5

INDEPENDENT ACTIVITY

(*Math Journal 1,* p. 74)

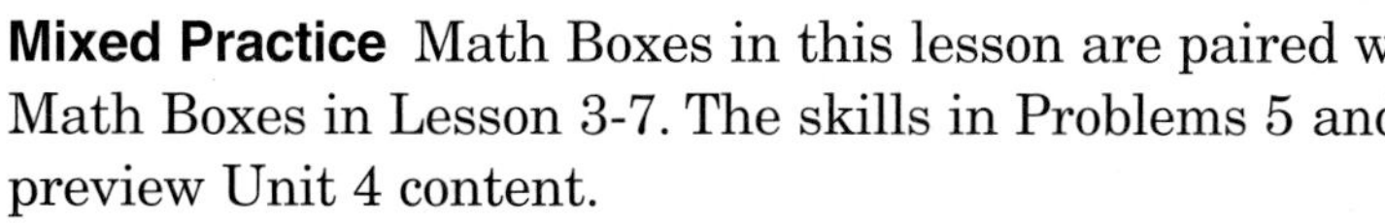

Mixed Practice Math Boxes in this lesson are paired with Math Boxes in Lesson 3-7. The skills in Problems 5 and 6 preview Unit 4 content.

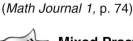

Writing/Reasoning Have students write a response to the following: *In Problem 5, will there be an even or an odd number of factors?* Sample answer: There will be an even number of factors because 48 is not a square number.

▶ Study Link 3•5

INDEPENDENT ACTIVITY

(*Math Masters,* p. 83)

Home Connection Students identify acute, obtuse, right, vertical (or opposite), and adjacent angles. They measure the angles in a triangle.

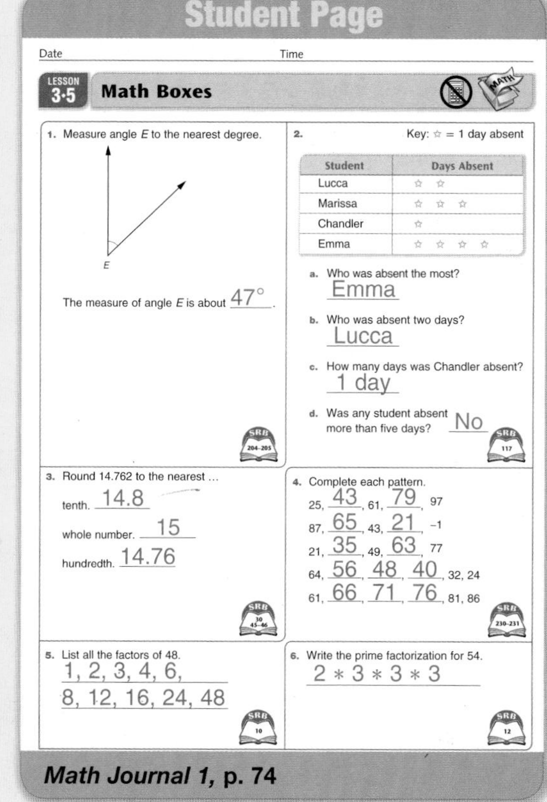

Student Page

Date Time

LESSON 3•5 **Math Boxes**

1. Measure angle *E* to the nearest degree.

The measure of angle *E* is about 47°.

2. Key: ☆ = 1 day absent

Student	Days Absent
Lucca	☆ ☆
Marissa	☆ ☆ ☆
Chandler	☆
Emma	☆ ☆ ☆ ☆

a. Who was absent the most? Emma

b. Who was absent two days? Lucca

c. How many days was Chandler absent? 1 day

d. Was any student absent more than five days? No

3. Round 14.762 to the nearest ...

tenth. 14.8

whole number. 15

hundredth. 14.76

4. Complete each pattern.

25, 43, 61, 79, 97

87, 65, 43, 21, −1

21, 35, 49, 63, 77

64, 56, 48, 40, 32, 24

61, 66, 71, 76, 81, 86

5. List all the factors of 48.

1, 2, 3, 4, 6, 8, 12, 16, 24, 48

6. Write the prime factorization for 54.

2 ∗ 3 ∗ 3 ∗ 3

Math Journal 1, p. 74

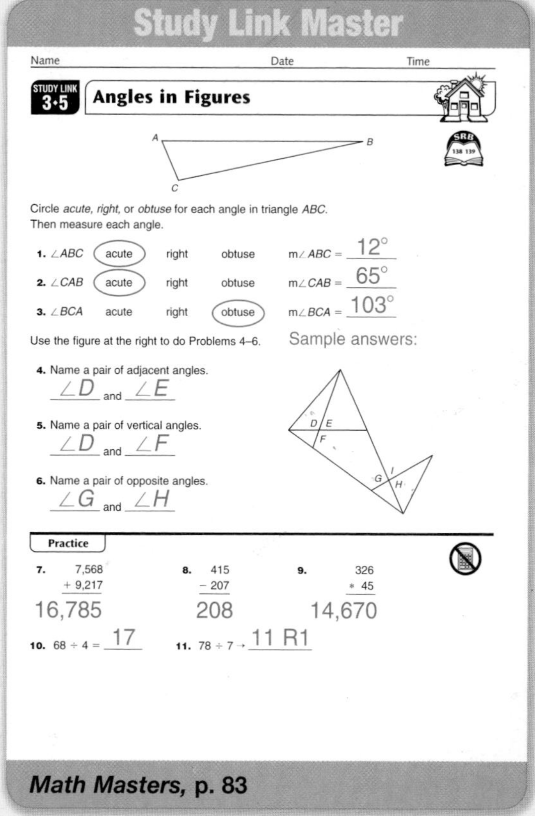

Study Link Master

Name Date Time

STUDY LINK 3•5 **Angles in Figures**

Circle *acute, right,* or *obtuse* for each angle in triangle *ABC.* Then measure each angle.

1. ∠*ABC* (acute) right obtuse m∠*ABC* = 12°
2. ∠*CAB* (acute) right obtuse m∠*CAB* = 65°
3. ∠*BCA* acute right (obtuse) m∠*BCA* = 103°

Use the figure at the right to do Problems 4–6. Sample answers:

4. Name a pair of adjacent angles. ∠*D* and ∠*E*
5. Name a pair of vertical angles. ∠*D* and ∠*F*
6. Name a pair of opposite angles. ∠*G* and ∠*H*

Practice

7. 7,568 + 9,217 = 16,785
8. 415 − 207 = 208
9. 326 ∗ 45 = 14,670
10. 68 ÷ 4 = 17
11. 78 ÷ 7 → 11 R1

Math Masters, p. 83

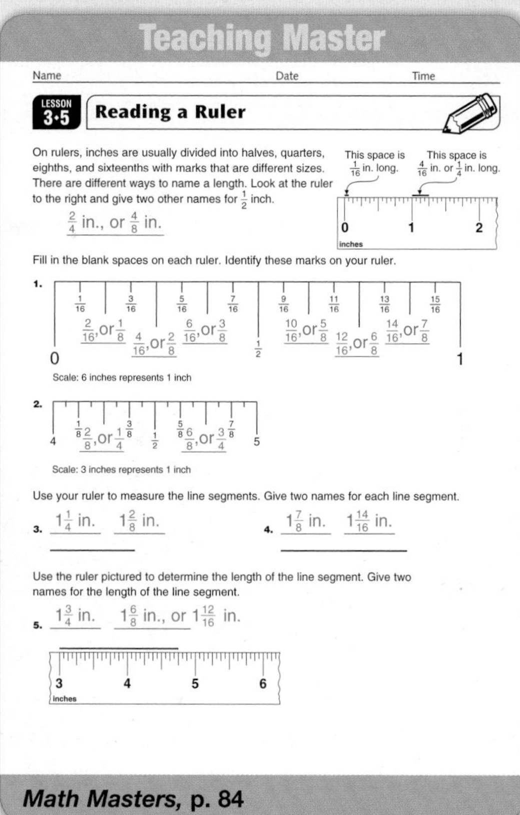
Teaching Master

Name ____ Date ____ Time ____

LESSON 3·5 **Reading a Ruler**

On rulers, inches are usually divided into halves, quarters, eighths, and sixteenths with marks that are different sizes. There are different ways to name a length. Look at the ruler to the right and give two other names for $\frac{1}{2}$ inch.

$\frac{2}{4}$ in., or $\frac{4}{8}$ in.

This space is $\frac{1}{16}$ in. long. This space is $\frac{4}{16}$ in. or $\frac{1}{4}$ in. long.

Fill in the blank spaces on each ruler. Identify these marks on your ruler.

1. $\frac{2}{16}$, or $\frac{1}{8}$; $\frac{4}{16}$, or $\frac{2}{8}$; $\frac{6}{16}$, or $\frac{3}{8}$; $\frac{10}{16}$, or $\frac{5}{8}$; $\frac{12}{16}$, or $\frac{6}{8}$; $\frac{14}{16}$, or $\frac{7}{8}$

Scale: 6 inches represents 1 inch

2. $\frac{2}{8}$, or $\frac{1}{4}$; $\frac{6}{8}$, or $\frac{3}{4}$

Scale: 3 inches represents 1 inch

Use your ruler to measure the line segments. Give two names for each line segment.

3. $1\frac{1}{4}$ in. $1\frac{2}{8}$ in.
4. $1\frac{7}{8}$ in. $1\frac{14}{16}$ in.

Use the ruler pictured to determine the length of the line segment. Give two names for the length of the line segment.

5. $1\frac{3}{4}$ in. $1\frac{6}{8}$ in., or $1\frac{12}{16}$ in.

Math Masters, p. 84

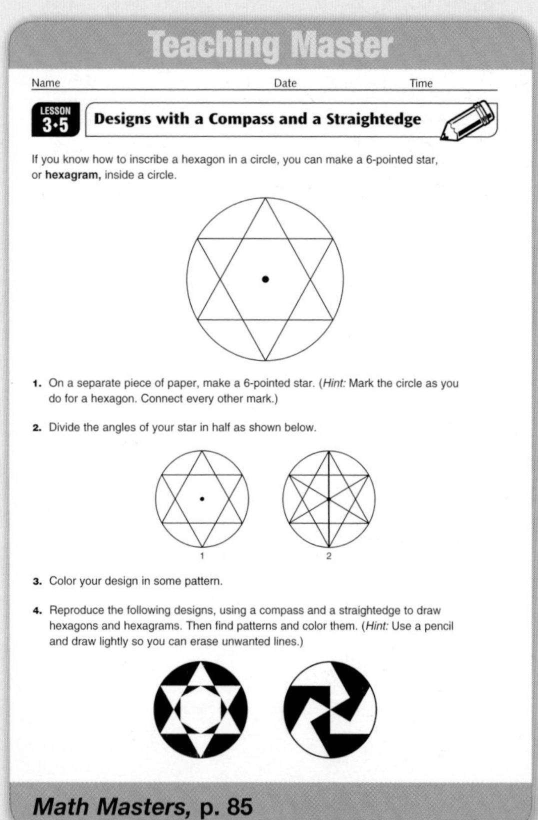
Teaching Master

Name ____ Date ____ Time ____

LESSON 3·5 **Designs with a Compass and a Straightedge**

If you know how to inscribe a hexagon in a circle, you can make a 6-pointed star, or **hexagram,** inside a circle.

1. On a separate piece of paper, make a 6-pointed star. (*Hint:* Mark the circle as you do for a hexagon. Connect every other mark.)
2. Divide the angles of your star in half as shown below.
3. Color your design in some pattern.
4. Reproduce the following designs, using a compass and a straightedge to draw hexagons and hexagrams. Then find patterns and color them. (*Hint:* Use a pencil and draw lightly so you can erase unwanted lines.)

Math Masters, p. 85

3 Differentiation Options

READINESS

INDEPENDENT ACTIVITY

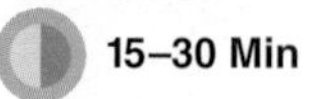

▶ Reading a Ruler

15–30 Min

(*Math Masters,* p. 84)

To explore measuring with a ruler, have students find equivalent measures and measure line segments in different ways. When students have finished the page, discuss how they solved Problem 5.

ENRICHMENT

INDEPENDENT ACTIVITY

▶ Inscribing a Regular Hexagon in a Circle

15–30 Min

(*Student Reference Book,* p. 168; *Math Masters,* p. 85)

Art Link To further explore straight-edge constructions, have students follow the steps on page 168 of the *Student Reference Book* to inscribe a regular hexagon in a circle. Then follow the directions to complete *Math Masters,* page 85. Invite students to create their own designs with inscribed hexagons, hexagrams, and coloring patterns for display in the classroom.

ELL SUPPORT

SMALL-GROUP ACTIVITY

▶ Building a Math Word Bank

30+ Min

(*Differentiation Handbook,* p. 142)

To provide language support for properties of circles, have students use the Word Bank Template found on *Differentiation Handbook,* page 142. Ask students to write the terms *diameter* and *radius,* draw pictures relating to each term, and write other related words. See the *Differentiation Handbook* for more information.

3•6 Congruent Triangles

Objectives To explore triangle types and introduce methods for copying triangles.

www.everydaymathonline.com

ePresentations

eToolkit

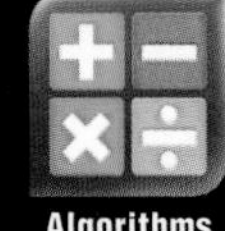
Algorithms Practice

EM Facts Workshop Game™

Family Letters

Assessment Management

Common Core State Standards

Curriculum Focal Points

Interactive Teacher's Lesson Guide

1 Teaching the Lesson

Key Concepts and Skills

- Classify triangles as isosceles, equilateral, or scalene. [Geometry Goal 2]
- Use a compass and straightedge to construct congruent triangles. [Geometry Goal 2]
- Measure angles with a protractor. [Measurement and Reference Frames Goal 1]

Key Activities

Students define equilateral, isosceles, and scalene triangles; they copy a triangle with a compass, ruler, and protractor and then with a compass and straightedge only.

Key Vocabulary

equilateral triangle ◆ isosceles triangle ◆ scalene triangle ◆ congruent

Materials

Math Journal 1, pp. 75–78
Student Reference Book, p. 166; pp. 165, 167, 171, and 172 (optional)
Study Link 3•5
Class Data Pad ◆ Geometry Template ◆ demonstration compass and protractor ◆ meterstick ◆ straws and connectors (or card stock strips and masking tape) ◆ compass

2 Ongoing Learning & Practice

Playing *Angle Tangle*
Student Reference Book, p. 296
Geometry Template (or straightedge and protractor)
Students practice estimating and measuring angles.

Math Boxes 3•6
Math Journal 1, p. 79
Students practice and maintain skills through Math Box problems.

Ongoing Assessment: Recognizing Student Achievement
Use Math Boxes, Problem 3.
[Number and Numeration Goal 6]

Study Link 3•6
Math Masters, p. 86
Students practice and maintain skills through Study Link activities.

3 Differentiation Options

READINESS

Playing *Triangle Sort*
Math Masters, p. 504
scissors
Students explore triangle properties by sorting pictures of triangles into categories.

ENRICHMENT

Playing *Sides and Angles: Triangles*
Math Masters, p. 502
scissors ◆ protractor ◆ straightedge
Students play a game to reinforce the relationship between the length of the sides in triangle types and their angle measures.

EXTRA PRACTICE

Playing *Where Do I Fit In?*
Student Reference Book, p. 144
Math Masters, p. 510
per partnership: 2 dice, scissors
Students identify types of triangles by the properties of their sides and angles.

Advance Preparation

For Part 1, students will need straws in three sizes—full length (about 8"), 6", and 4"—and connectors for the straws. If straws and connectors are not available, use card stock cut in 8", 6", and 4" strips, connected with masking tape.

For a mathematics and literacy connection, obtain a copy of ***What's Your Angle, Pythagoras?*** by Julie Ellis (Charlesbridge, 2004).

***Teacher's Reference Manual,* Grades 4–6** pp. 193, 194

Getting Started

Mental Math and Reflexes

Have students round each number to the nearest whole number.

●○○ 209.82 210
32.06 32

Have students round to the nearest tenth.

●●○ 81.39 81.4
376.14 376.1
546.96 547.0

Math Message

Use only the information given on the page and complete the problems on page 75 in your journal.

Study Link 3·5 Follow-Up

Allow partners five minutes to share their answers and resolve any differences.

1 Teaching the Lesson

▶ Math Message Follow-Up

WHOLE-CLASS ACTIVITY

(*Math Journal 1,* p. 75)

Clarify the use of the marks on the sides of some figures on the journal page. Ask students what the marks represent. The marks indicate sides of the same length in the given figure. Expect a variety of responses. The marks can simply be called *marks*. Other names are hatch marks, slash marks, and tick marks. The number of marks has nothing to do with length. If a side has two marks, this does not mean it is longer than a side with one mark.

Survey the class for their definitions. For each type of triangle, compare the students' definitions with the definitions below. Ask students to agree on a common definition for each type of triangle and record these on the Class Data Pad.

▷ An **equilateral** (ee-kwi-LAT-er-el) **triangle** has three sides that are the same length.

▷ An **isosceles** (eye-SOS-e-leez) **triangle** has at least two sides that are the same length.

▷ A **scalene** (SKAY-leen) **triangle** has no sides that are the same length.

Assign partners to examine the triangles on their Geometry Templates and classify them as equilateral, isosceles, or scalene. Ask volunteers to use their templates on the overhead projector to share answers. Encourage students to use the terminology of the definitions as they support their answers.

▶ Copying a Triangle Using Any Available Tools

PARTNER ACTIVITY

(*Math Journal 1,* p. 76)

Ask volunteers for the name given to figures that are exact copies (the same size and shape). Congruent figures

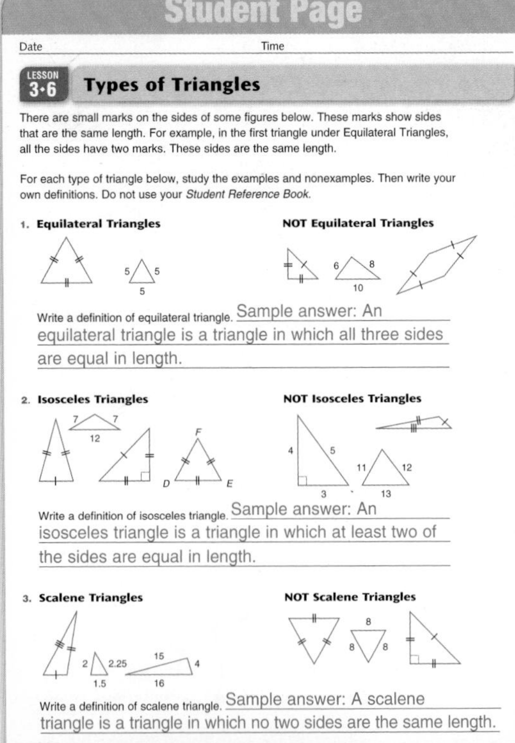

Student Page

Date Time

LESSON 3·6 Types of Triangles

There are small marks on the sides of some figures below. These marks show sides that are the same length. For example, in the first triangle under Equilateral Triangles, all the sides have two marks. These sides are the same length.

For each type of triangle below, study the examples and nonexamples. Then write your own definitions. Do not use your *Student Reference Book.*

1. Equilateral Triangles — NOT Equilateral Triangles

Write a definition of equilateral triangle. Sample answer: An equilateral triangle is a triangle in which all three sides are equal in length.

2. Isosceles Triangles — NOT Isosceles Triangles

Write a definition of isosceles triangle. Sample answer: An isosceles triangle is a triangle in which at least two of the sides are equal in length.

3. Scalene Triangles — NOT Scalene Triangles

Write a definition of scalene triangle. Sample answer: A scalene triangle is a triangle in which no two sides are the same length.

Math Journal 1, p. 75

Explain that in this lesson students will construct **congruent** triangles. Ask students to copy triangle *BIG* on a blank sheet of paper. They can make the copy using any of their drawing and measuring tools, such as a protractor, ruler, straightedge, or compass. Remind students that they used a compass to copy line segments in Lesson 3-5 (covered on *Student Reference Book*, page 165) and that in *Fourth Grade Everyday Mathematics* they copied a triangle using a compass and straightedge (covered on *Student Reference Book*, page 166). Students are not allowed to trace the figure.

If a student copies triangle *BIG* correctly, the sides and angles of the copy should have the same measures as the sides and angles of the original triangle. Advise students to verify that triangle *BIG* and triangle *PAL* are congruent by laying the cutout triangle *PAL* on top of the original and confirming that the two figures match, *before* taping triangle *PAL* to the journal page. Circulate and assist.

NOTE The vertices of congruent triangles cannot be labeled arbitrarily. They must match. For example, the vertices *PAL* must match the vertices *BIG*.

After about 10 minutes, bring students together to share results. Expect that students will have devised a variety of methods. Provide a meterstick, a demonstration compass, and a protractor for volunteers to show different methods.

Here are some common solutions.

▷ Use a protractor to copy angle *B*. Label the vertex of the new angle as point *P*. Next use a ruler to copy sides $\overline{BI}$ and $\overline{BG}$ onto the sides of the new angle, using *P* as one endpoint for each segment. Label the two new endpoints *A* and *L*. Finally connect points *A* and *L*.

▷ Use a ruler to draw a line segment the length of side $\overline{BG}$. Label its endpoints *P* and *L*. Use a protractor to draw angles at points *P* and *L* that are the same size as angles *B* and *G*. Extend the sides of the angles at *P* and *L* so they intersect. Label the point of intersection *A*.

▷ Use a ruler to draw a line segment that is the length of side $\overline{BG}$. Label its endpoints *P* and *L*. Use a protractor to draw an angle at point *P* that is the same size as angle *B*. Use a ruler to measure side $\overline{BI}$. Extend the line segment at *P* so it is the same length as side $\overline{BI}$. Label the endpoint of that segment *A*. Draw line segment $\overline{AL}$.

▷ Draw a 6 cm line segment and label the endpoints *P* and *L*. Draw a 71° angle at *P*. Extend the side of angle *P* 4.9 cm to point A. Draw a 63° angle at *A* and extend the side of angle *A* 6.3 cm to point *L*. After the construction is complete, verify that angle *L* is 46°.

Advise students that regardless of the solution they used, all sides and angles of both triangles should be measured to ensure that they have been copied correctly.

Adjusting the Activity

Have students identify objects in the room that are congruent. For example, two identical desktops, books, windows, and so on.

AUDITORY ◆ KINESTHETIC ◆ TACTILE ◆ VISUAL

Adjusting the Activity

When copying triangle BIG, suggest that students begin by using a protractor to copy one angle. Then they can use their ruler to measure the two sides adjacent to that angle. Connecting the endpoints of the two sides will complete the triangle.

AUDITORY ◆ KINESTHETIC ◆ TACTILE ◆ VISUAL

NOTE For board demonstrations, draw the triangle sides 10 times the given length—that is, 60 cm instead of 6 cm, 50 cm instead of 5 cm, and so on.

Student Page

Date Time

LESSON 3·6 **Copying a Triangle**

If two triangles are identical—exactly the same size and shape—they are **congruent** to each other. Congruent triangles would match perfectly if you could move one on top of the other.

1. a. Make a copy of triangle *BIG* on a blank sheet of paper. Use any of your drawing and measuring tools, but DO NOT trace triangle *BIG*. The sides of your copy should be the same length as the sides of triangle *BIG*. The angles also should be the same size as the angles of triangle *BIG*.

I

B G

b. When you are satisfied with your work, cut it out and tape it in the space below. Label the vertices *P*, *A*, and *L*. Triangle *PAL* should be congruent to triangle *BIG*.

A

P L

Math Journal 1, p. 76

NOTE Students are not expected to know the triangle congruence theorems from plane geometry (such as Side-Angle-Side and Side-Side-Side). But as you circulate and assist, where it is appropriate, point out that when some angle and side information is copied, the remainder of the construction is determined automatically.

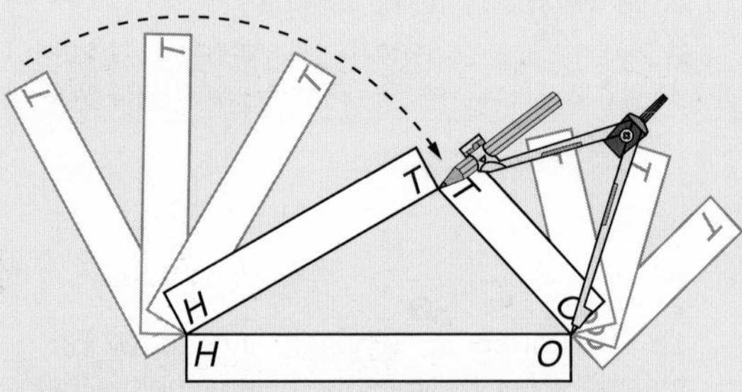

Putting three straws or strips together to make a triangle resembles the compass and straightedge procedure illustrated on page 166 of the *Student Reference Book.*

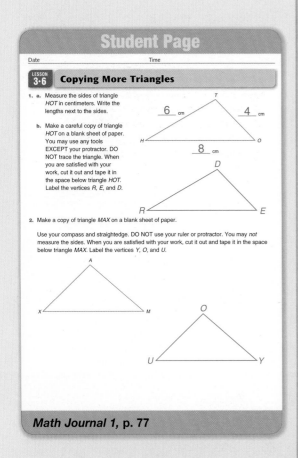

Student Page

Date Time

LESSON 3·6 **Copying More Triangles**

1. a. Measure the sides of triangle *HOT* in centimeters. Write the lengths next to the sides.

   6 cm 4 cm 8 cm

   b. Make a careful copy of triangle *HOT* on a blank sheet of paper. You may use any tools EXCEPT your protractor. DO NOT trace the triangle. When you are satisfied with your work, cut it out and tape it in the space below triangle *HOT*. Label the vertices *R, E,* and *D.*

2. Make a copy of triangle *MAX* on a blank sheet of paper.

   Use your compass and straightedge. DO NOT use your ruler or protractor. You may *not* measure the sides. When you are satisfied with your work, cut it out and tape it in the space below triangle *MAX*. Label the vertices *Y, O,* and *U.*

Math Journal 1, p. 77

▶ Copying a Triangle without a Protractor

PARTNER ACTIVITY

(*Math Journal 1,* p. 77)

Assign Problem 1 on the journal page. Explain that this problem is similar to the previous one except that this time students will use only a compass and a ruler or straightedge. They are not allowed to trace or to use a protractor.

Allow partners 5 to 10 minutes as an exploration period. Distribute several straws and connectors (or card stock strips and masking tape) to each partnership. Students may cut the straws to create three pieces that have the same lengths as the sides of triangle *HOT*. These pieces will serve as a physical model for the problem and will help students develop a copying method. Circulate and assist.

▶ Modeling a Triangle

(*Math Journal 1,* p. 77)

Bring the class together to share results. Ask volunteers to demonstrate their copying methods. Bring closure to this discussion by explaining that the straws or card stock strips have the same relative sizes as the sides of triangle *HOT*. Use the board to demonstrate how they can be used to copy triangle *HOT*.

1. Tape one of the straws or strips onto the board as the first side.
2. Hold or fasten the other two straws or strips to the first, one at each end.
3. Swing these two until their ends meet, and fasten the ends together.

Explain to students that this demonstration illustrates the principle that two triangles are congruent if the sides of one are the same length as the sides of the other. This is the Side-Side-Side or SSS triangle congruence theorem.

▶ Copying a Triangle with Compass and Straightedge Only

(*Math Journal 1,* pp. 77–78; *Student Reference Book*, p. 166)

Make a transition to this activity by drawing a triangle labeled *MOP* on the board. Assign volunteers to read aloud the method for copying a triangle on *Student Reference Book,* page 166. Assign other volunteers to make a copy of triangle *MOP* using a demonstration compass and meterstick to do each step on the board as it is read.

Assign partners Problem 2 on journal page 77. Circulate and assist. Remind students to verify that the triangles are congruent by laying the cutout triangle *YOU* on top of the original and confirming that the two figures match before taping triangle *YOU* to the journal page.

As students finish, assign journal page 78. Partners draw triangles, exchange drawings, and then practice the compass-and-straightedge method further by copying their partner's drawings.

As time permits, assign students to use the directions on *Student Reference Book* page 167 to construct a parallelogram. They should use the directions on pages 171 and 172 to construct perpendicular line segments.

2 Ongoing Learning & Practice

▶ Playing *Angle Tangle*

PARTNER ACTIVITY

(*Student Reference Book,* p. 296)

Playing *Angle Tangle* provides students with practice measuring angles with a protractor and estimating angle measures.

▶ Math Boxes 3·6

INDEPENDENT ACTIVITY

(*Math Journal 1,* p. 79)

Mixed Practice Math Boxes in this lesson are paired with Math Boxes in Lesson 3-9. The skill in Problem 6 previews Unit 4 content.

Writing/Reasoning Have students write a response to the following: *Maddie did Problem 4 by drawing and naming a trapezoid. What's wrong with that answer? How would you help Maddie know the correct figure to draw and name?* Sample answer: Both a quadrangle and a trapezoid have four angles and four sides. The only polygon with fewer than four sides is a triangle.

Ongoing Assessment: Recognizing Student Achievement

Math Boxes Problem 3 ★

Use **Math Boxes, Problem 3** to assess students' ability to compare decimals. Students are making adequate progress if they correctly solve the first three problems. Some students may correctly solve the last two problems.

[Number and Numeration Goal 6]

▶ Study Link 3·6

INDEPENDENT ACTIVITY

(*Math Masters,* p. 86)

Home Connection Students classify triangles. Students find three angles at home, draw those angles, and identify each angle by type.

Student Page

Date Time

LESSON 3·6 **Copying a Partner's Triangle**

1. Use a ruler to draw two triangles on a blank sheet of paper. Make your triangles fairly large, but leave enough room to draw a copy of each one. Then exchange drawings with your partner.
2. Copy your partner's triangles using only your compass and straightedge. Don't erase the arcs you make—they show how you made your copies. Measure the sides of the triangles and your copies of the triangles. Write the lengths next to the sides.
3. Cut out one of the triangles your partner drew, and cut out the copy you made. Tape them in the space below.

Math Journal 1, p. 78

Adjusting the Activity

Review and/or have available the steps used to copy a line segment with only a compass and straightedge from page 165 of the *Student Reference Book.*

AUDITORY ◆ KINESTHETIC ◆ TACTILE ◆ VISUAL

NOTE Assess student's use of vocabulary (quadrangle, quadrilateral, trapezoid, triangle, sides, angles) and their explanation of the concepts in their solutions (a quadrangle is a figure with 4 vertices, 4 sides, and 4 angles; a polygon is a closed figure; the only polygon with fewer sides than a quadrangle is a triangle) to provide information about how students are integrating these geometry concepts.

Student Page

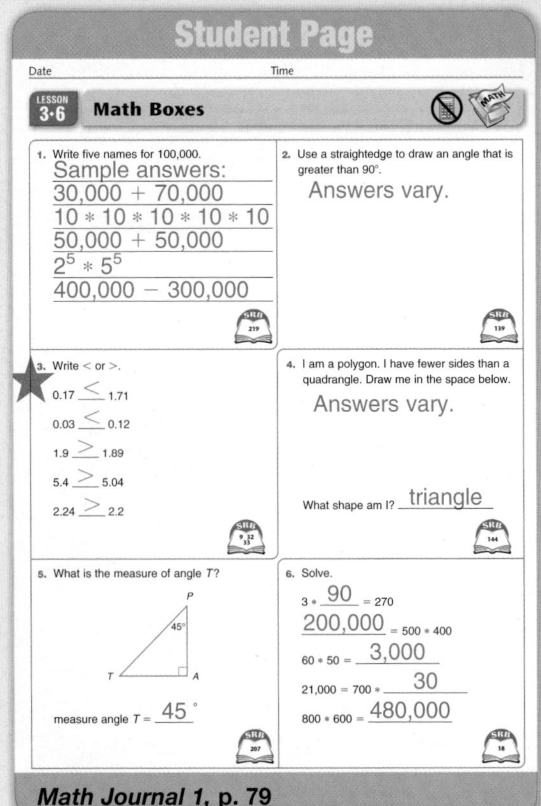
Date Time

LESSON 3·6 **Math Boxes**

1. Write five names for 100,000.
Sample answers:
30,000 + 70,000
10 * 10 * 10 * 10 * 10
50,000 + 50,000
$2^5 * 5^5$
400,000 − 300,000
SRB 219

2. Use a straightedge to draw an angle that is greater than 90°.
Answers vary.
SRB 139

3. Write < or >.
0.17 < 1.71
0.03 < 0.12
1.9 > 1.89
5.4 > 5.04
2.24 > 2.2
SRB 9 32 33

4. I am a polygon. I have fewer sides than a quadrangle. Draw me in the space below.
Answers vary.
What shape am I? triangle
SRB 144

5. What is the measure of angle *T*?
measure angle *T* = 45°
SRB 207

6. Solve.
3 * 90 = 270
200,000 = 500 * 400
60 * 50 = 3,000
21,000 = 700 * 30
800 * 600 = 480,000
SRB 18

Math Journal 1, p. 79

3 Differentiation Options

READINESS

PARTNER ACTIVITY

15–30 Min

▶ Playing *Triangle Sort*

(*Math Masters,* p. 504)

To explore properties of triangles, have students sort pictures of triangles into categories and explain how they sorted. First students sort the collection of triangles into two categories. Sample answer: Right triangles and triangles that are not right triangles Then they sort them into three categories. Sample answer: Triangles that have the same angles, triangles that have two matching angles, triangles that do not have any matching angles Students describe in words how they organized the triangles.

ENRICHMENT

PARTNER ACTIVITY

15–30 Min

▶ Playing *Sides and Angles: Triangles*

(*Math Masters,* p. 502)

To apply students' understanding of the properties of triangles, have them identify the side and angle relationships that form different types of triangles.

EXTRA PRACTICE

PARTNER ACTIVITY

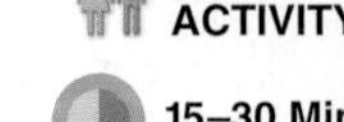
15–30 Min

▶ Playing *Where Do I Fit In?*

(*Student Reference Book,* p. 144; *Math Masters,* p. 510)

Students identify the sides and angles properties for specific triangles by sorting cards. Have partners make posters of their sorted cards and label the triangles.

You might consider making a larger chart for display.

Planning Ahead

Before Lesson 3-7, students need to remove Activity Sheets 3 and 4 from their journals and cut out the pieces and cards. Make a transparency of *Math Masters*, page 494 and cut out the polygons.

Study Link Master

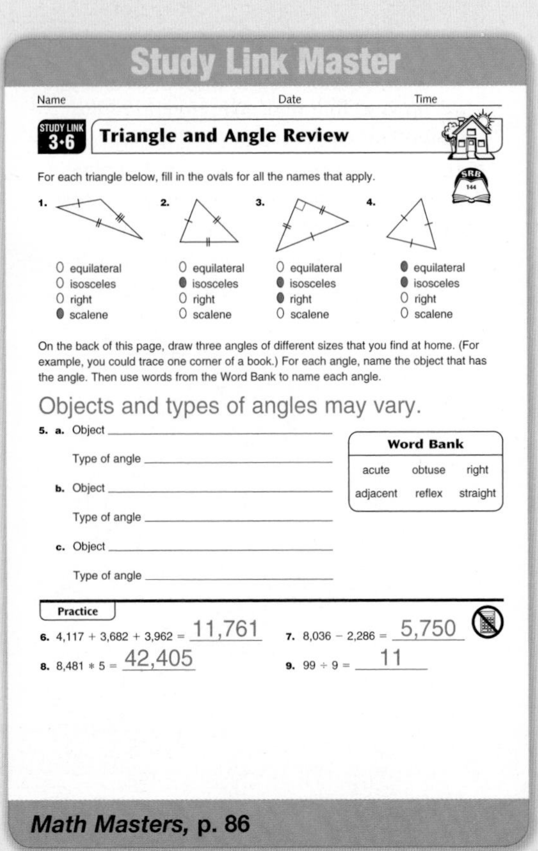
Name Date Time

STUDY LINK 3·6 **Triangle and Angle Review**

For each triangle below, fill in the ovals for all the names that apply.

SRB 144

1. ○ equilateral ○ isosceles ○ right ● scalene
2. ○ equilateral ● isosceles ○ right ○ scalene
3. ○ equilateral ● isosceles ● right ○ scalene
4. ● equilateral ● isosceles ○ right ○ scalene

On the back of this page, draw three angles of different sizes that you find at home. (For example, you could trace one corner of a book.) For each angle, name the object that has the angle. Then use words from the Word Bank to name each angle.

Objects and types of angles may vary.

5. a. Object ______
Type of angle ______
b. Object ______
Type of angle ______
c. Object ______
Type of angle ______

Word Bank		
acute	obtuse	right
adjacent	reflex	straight

Practice

6. 4,117 + 3,682 + 3,962 = 11,761
7. 8,036 − 2,286 = 5,750
8. 8,481 * 5 = 42,405
9. 99 ÷ 9 = 11

Math Masters, p. 86

3•7 Properties of Polygons

Objective To explore the geometric properties of polygons.

Technology Resources www.everydaymathonline.com

ePresentations

eToolkit

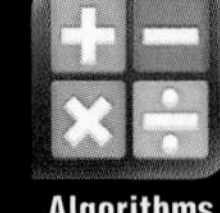
Algorithms Practice

EM Facts Workshop Game™

Family Letters

Assessment Management

Common Core State Standards

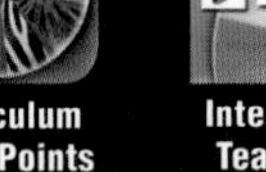
Curriculum Focal Points

Interactive Teacher's Lesson Guide

1 Teaching the Lesson

Key Concepts and Skills

- Identify the types of angles formed by polygons. [Geometry Goal 1]
- Compare and classify polygons; use relationships and properties to sort polygons. [Geometry Goal 2]

Key Activities

Students sort geometric shapes into sets according to various rules. They identify geometric properties of polygons by playing *Polygon Capture.* They compare and classify quadrangles according to their properties.

Ongoing Assessment: Recognizing Student Achievement Use journal page 80. [Geometry Goal 2]

Ongoing Assessment: Informing Instruction See page 191.

Key Vocabulary

polygon ◆ quadrangle

Materials

Math Journal 1, p. 80
Math Journal 1, Activity Sheets 3 and 4
Student Reference Book, pp. 142, 145, 146, and 328
Study Link 3•6
Math Masters, pp. 87A, 87B, 495, and 496 (optional)
transparency of *Math Masters,* p. 494 ◆ scissors ◆ 3" by 5" index card ◆ ruler or Geometry Template

2 Ongoing Learning & Practice

Math Boxes 3•7
Math Journal 1, p. 81
Students practice and maintain skills through Math Box problems.

Study Link 3•7
Math Masters, p. 87
Students practice and maintain skills through Study Link activities.

3 Differentiation Options

READINESS

Sorting Attribute Blocks by Two Properties
attribute blocks
Students sort attribute blocks by two properties at a time.

ENRICHMENT

Connecting Vertices
Math Masters, p. 88
Students describe the polygons that are formed when diagonals are drawn in polygonal regions.

ELL SUPPORT

Playing *What's My Attribute Rule?*
Math Masters, pp. 508 and 509
per partnership: 1 six-sided die
Students sort shapes according to their attributes.

Advance Preparation

For Part 1, have students cut out the polygons and Property Cards from Activity Sheets 3 and 4 in the journal and place in envelopes or baggies. Copy and cut apart the shapes on a transparency of *Math Masters,* page 494. These are the same shapes that are on Activity Sheet 3. For a mathematics and literacy connection, obtain a copy of ***The Greedy Triangle*** by Marilyn Burns (Scholastic Inc., 1994).

***Teacher's Reference Manual,* Grades 4–6** pp. 180–185

Getting Started

Mental Math and Reflexes

Survey the class for their definitions of *parallel* and *perpendicular.* Then ask them to stand beside their desks or in an area where there is enough room for them to stretch out their arms. Use the following instructions, alternating between degree measures and names for angles.

- Hold your arms so they are parallel to each other.
- Form a right angle (a 90° angle) with your arms.
- Form an acute angle (an angle between 0° and 90°) with your arms.
- Hold your arms so they are perpendicular to the floor.
- Hold your arms so they form a right angle and are parallel to each other. This cannot be done. Ask students to explain why this is impossible.

Math Message

Solve the problem on journal page 80.

Study Link 3·6 Follow-Up

Have students share where they found their angles. Discuss why there might be more (or fewer) of a given angle type.

NOTE Strictly speaking, a polygon consists of line segments. The interior (inside) of a polygon is not a part of the polygon. If the drawing of a polygon is cut out along its sides, the resulting shape consists of a polygon and its interior. This is a polygonal region, not a polygon. However, the distinction does not need to be stressed.

Student Page

Date Time

LESSON 3·7 Completing Partial Drawings of Polygons

Gina drew four shapes: equilateral triangle, square, rhombus, and hexagon.

She covered up most of each figure, as shown below.

Can you tell which figure is which? Write the name below each figure. Then try to draw the rest of the figure.

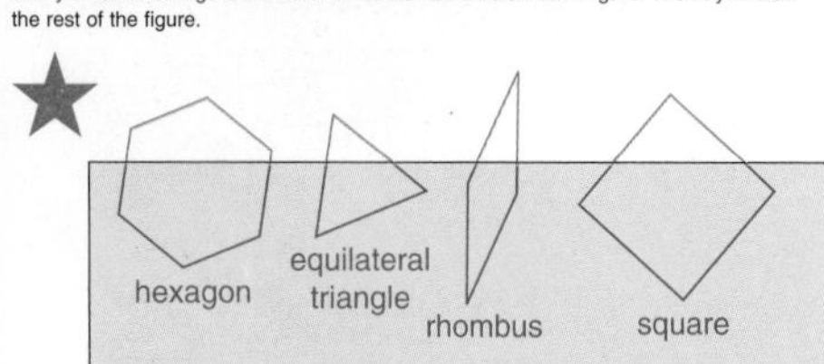

Explain how you solved this problem.
Sample answer: The first shape has more than 4 sides, so it could not be a square, rhombus, or triangle; the second and third shapes could not be a square because the angle shown was not 90°.

Math Journal 1, p. 80

1 Teaching the Lesson

▶ Math Message Follow-Up

WHOLE-CLASS DISCUSSION

(*Math Journal 1,* p. 80)

For each of the shapes, ask students how they eliminated options. For example, the first shape has more than 4 sides, so it could not be a square, rhombus, or triangle, and the third shape could not be a square because the angle shown was not 90 degrees. Encourage students to use the terminology from the class definitions in their explanations. You can model this by restating student remarks, where necessary, without interrupting the flow of the discussion.

Ongoing Assessment: Recognizing Student Achievement

***Math Journal* Page 80**

Use **journal page 80** to assess students' ability to recognize the relationships between sides and angles in polygons. Students are making adequate progress if they correctly draw and name the shapes and if their explanations refer to the angle and/or side attributes of the polygons.

[Geometry Goal 2]

▶ Sorting Polygons by Their Properties

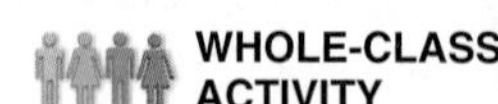

WHOLE-CLASS ACTIVITY

(*Math Journal 1,* Activity Sheet 3; *Student Reference Book*, p. 142; *Math Masters*, p. 494)

Spread the figures that you made from *Math Masters*, page 494 on the overhead projector. Ask students what these shapes are called. polygons Use follow-up questions to ask students how they know that these shapes are **polygons,** or simply ask why. Expect a variety of responses.

Refer students to page 142 of the *Student Reference Book.* Have partners develop a definition for the term *polygon.* Circulate and assist.

Survey partners for their ideas and ask students to agree on a common definition for *polygon.* Record the class definition on the Class Data Pad.

Explain that students will work individually to sort the sixteen polygons into two or three different sets according to any rule that they choose. Demonstrate the activity by sorting the polygons on the overhead projector according to an unstated rule. Ask students to identify the rule. *Suggestions:*

▷ At least two sides are parallel.

▷ The polygons are convex.

▷ The polygons are nonconvex.

▷ At least one angle is greater than 90 degrees.

Allow students several minutes to formulate their rules and sort their polygons. Ask volunteers to show their sorting results on the overhead projector, and survey the class for the rules being demonstrated.

▶ Playing *Polygon Capture*

PARTNER ACTIVITY

(*Math Journal 1,* Activity Sheets 3 and 4; *Student Reference Book,* p. 328)

Students identify geometric properties of polygons by playing *Polygon Capture*. The game is played with two players or two teams of two players each.

Play a game or two against the class to help students learn the rules. Consider displaying a set of polygons on the overhead projector while students lay their polygons on their desks.

Ongoing Assessment: Informing Instruction

Watch for students who might not be correctly interpreting the properties. Show these students one of the following variations.

- During each turn, the player draws one Property Card and takes all polygons with this property. If no polygons match, the player loses the turn. Play continues until fewer than three polygons are left.
- During each turn, the player draws one Property Card and takes all the polygons with this property. Then the player draws another Property Card and puts back all the polygons he or she just captured that DO NOT have the property on the second card.

NOTE Use your established procedures to store the polygons and *Polygon Capture* Property Cards.

Student Page

Games

Polygon Capture

Materials ☐ 1 set of *Polygon Capture* Pieces (*Math Journal 1,* Activity Sheet 3)
☐ 1 set of *Polygon Capture* Property Cards (*Math Journal 1,* Activity Sheet 4)

Players 2, or two teams of 2

Skill Properties of polygons

Object of the game To collect more polygons.

Directions

1. Spread the polygons out on the table. Shuffle the Property Cards and sort them writing-side down into ANGLE-card and SIDE-card piles. (The cards are labeled on the back.)
2. Players take turns. When it is your turn:
   - ♦ Draw the top card from each pile of Property Cards.
   - ♦ Take all of the polygons that have **both** of the properties shown on the Property Cards in your hand.
   - ♦ If there are no polygons with both properties, draw one additional Property Card—either an ANGLE- or a SIDE-card. Look for polygons that have this new property and one of the properties already drawn. Take these polygons.
   - ♦ At the end of a turn, if you have not captured a polygon that you could have taken, the other player may name and capture it.
3. When all the Property Cards in either pile have been drawn, shuffle *all* of the Property Cards. Sort them writing-side down into ANGLE-card and SIDE-card piles. Continue play.
4. The game ends when there are fewer than 3 polygons left.
5. The winner is the player who has captured more polygons.

Example Liz has these Property Cards: "All angles are right angles," and "All sides are the same length." She can take all the squares (polygons A and H). Liz has "captured" these polygons.

***Polygon Capture* Pieces**

***Polygon Capture* Property Cards (writing-side up)**

There is only one right angle.	There are one or more right angles.	All angles are right angles.	There are no right angles.
There is at least one acute angle.	At least one angle is more than 90°.	All angles are right angles.	There are no right angles.
All opposite sides are parallel.	Only one pair of sides is parallel.	There are no parallel sides.	All sides are the same length.
All opposite sides are parallel.	Some sides have the same length.	All opposite sides have the same length.	**Wild Card:** Pick your own side property.

***Student Reference Book,* p. 328**

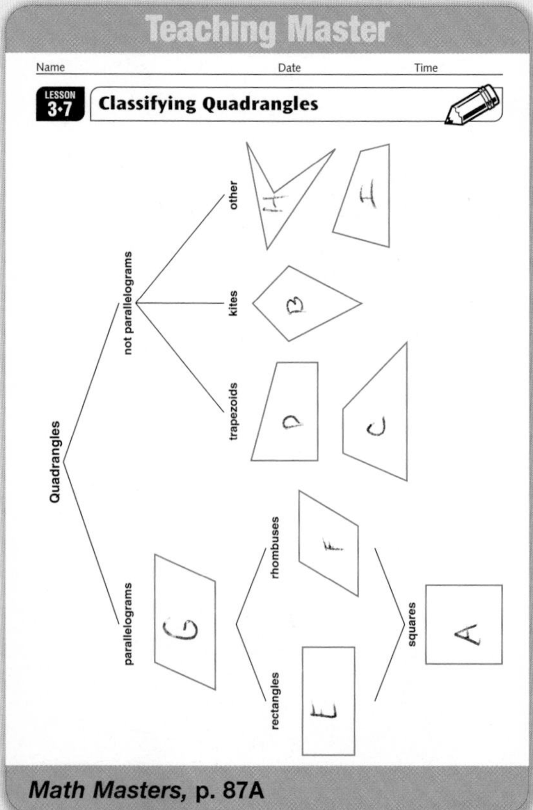

Math Masters, p. 87A

NOTE *Math Masters,* page 87A will also be used in Lesson 3-8. Collect the page at the end of the lesson.

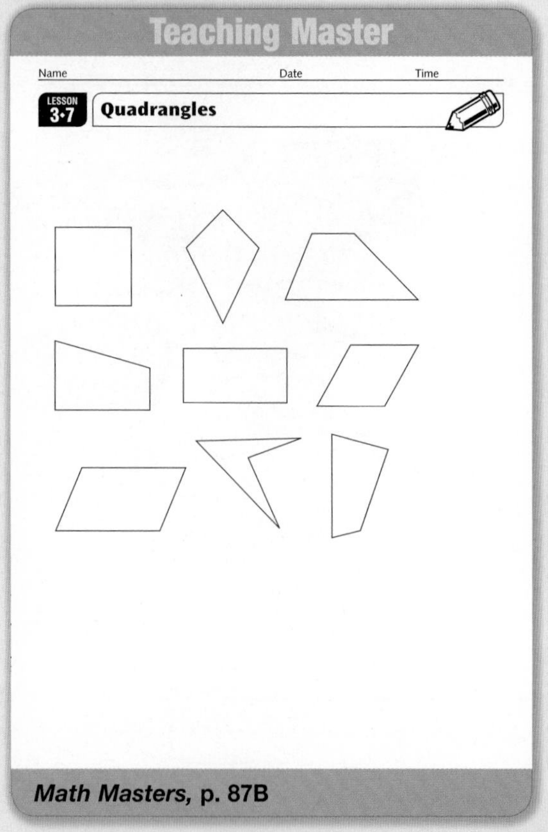

Teaching Master
Name
Date
Time
LESSON 3·7
Quadrangles

Math Masters, p. 87B

▶ Classifying Quadrangles

(*Math Masters*, pp. 87A and 87B; *Student Reference Book*, pp. 145 and 146)

Distribute *Math Masters,* page 87B and have students cut out the nine shapes on the page. Ask: *What do all of the shapes on your desk have in common?* Sample answers: All of the shapes have four sides; all have four angles; all are called quadrangles (or quadrilaterals); all of them are polygons.

Review the names and properties of each **quadrangle.** Ask students to work with a partner to place the eight quadrangles under the appropriate categories on *Math Masters,* page 87A. Students may use *Student Reference Book,* pages 145 and 146 as a reference, if necessary.

NOTE *Everyday Mathematics* uses the term *quadrangle,* although the term *quadrilateral* is also used. The polygons on *Math Masters,* page 87B are generic examples from each category. In the diagram students created on *Math Masters,* page 87A, each polygon may also be classified as the shape listed in the tiers of the diagram above it. For example, a square is also a rhombus, and a rhombus is also a parallelogram.

Remind students to be prepared to share their thinking and to give logical arguments explaining how they organized or classified the shapes. Once they have placed the shapes on the tree diagram, students check their work with their partner and then glue the shapes to the page. Circulate and assist.

Draw a graphic organizer, like the one shown below, on the board. Allow room for shapes to be placed under each category.

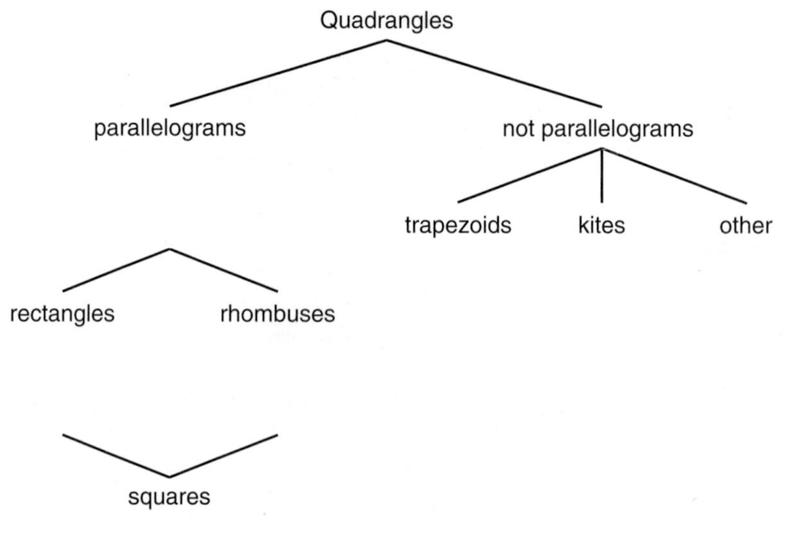

Ask questions like the following, and record students' responses on the board.

- What properties did you consider when you placed the shapes in the diagram? Sample answers: I considered whether the shapes had parallel lines or right angles. I also considered the length of the sides, whether they were the same or different.
- What logical arguments can you make from the organization of the quadrangles in the tree diagram? Answers vary.

Be sure the following ideas are shared in the discussion:

▷ Some four-sided figures are not parallelograms because they do not have two pairs of parallel sides.

▷ Kites, trapezoids and shapes classified as "other" are not parallelograms because they do not have two pairs of parallel sides.

▷ All squares are parallelograms because they have two pairs of parallel sides.

▷ All squares are rectangles because they have two pairs of parallel sides and all of the angles are right angles.

▷ All squares are rhombuses because they have two sets of parallel sides and all sides are the same length.

▷ Rectangles, rhombuses, and squares are all parallelograms because they have two sets of parallel sides.

▷ All squares are rectangles, but not all rectangles are squares because not all rectangles have four sides of equal length.

▷ All squares are rhombuses, but not all rhombuses are squares because some rhombuses do not have right angles.

Distribute a 3 in. by 5 in. index card to each student. Ask students to draw a quadrangle on their card, using a ruler or Geometry Template as a straightedge, and then cut out the shape. Encourage students to fill most of the card. As students finish creating their quadrangles, ask them to trace the shapes on the board or tape them under the appropriate category. Circulate and assist.

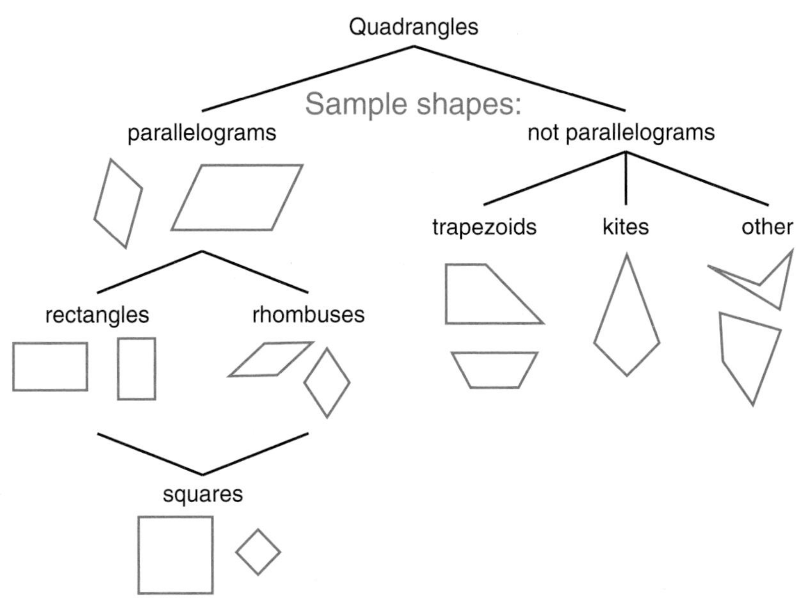

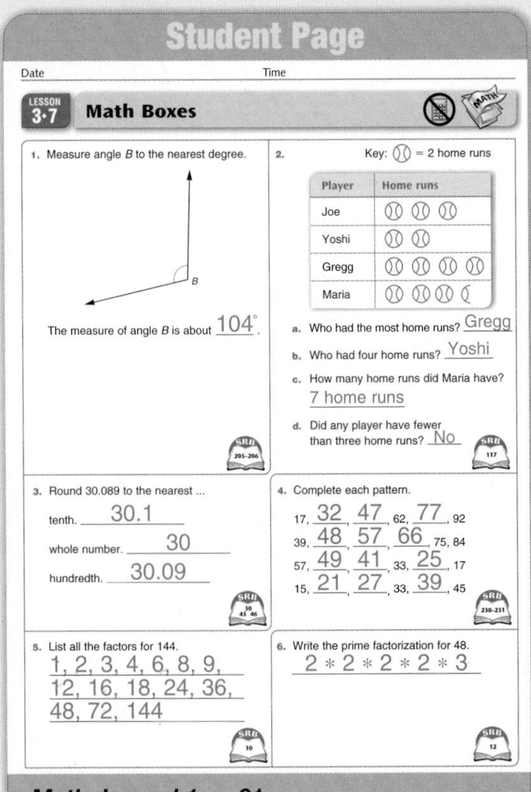
Student Page

Date Time

LESSON 3·7 **Math Boxes**

1. Measure angle *B* to the nearest degree.

The measure of angle *B* is about 104°.

2. Key: ⚾ = 2 home runs

Player	Home runs
Joe	⚾ ⚾ ⚾
Yoshi	⚾ ⚾
Gregg	⚾ ⚾ ⚾ ⚾
Maria	⚾ ⚾ ⚾ ◖

a. Who had the most home runs? Gregg

b. Who had four home runs? Yoshi

c. How many home runs did Maria have? 7 home runs

d. Did any player have fewer than three home runs? No

3. Round 30.089 to the nearest ...

tenth. 30.1

whole number. 30

hundredth. 30.09

4. Complete each pattern.

17, 32, 47, 62, 77, 92

39, 48, 57, 66, 75, 84

57, 49, 41, 33, 25, 17

15, 21, 27, 33, 39, 45

5. List all the factors for 144.

1, 2, 3, 4, 6, 8, 9, 12, 16, 18, 24, 36, 48, 72, 144

6. Write the prime factorization for 48.

2 ∗ 2 ∗ 2 ∗ 2 ∗ 3

Math Journal 1, p. 81

2 Ongoing Learning & Practice

▶ Math Boxes 3·7

INDEPENDENT ACTIVITY

(*Math Journal 1,* p. 81)

Mixed Practice Math Boxes in this lesson are paired with Math Boxes in Lesson 3-5. The skills in Problems 5 and 6 preview Unit 4 content.

Writing/Reasoning Have students write a response to the following: *Explain how you determined the first number pattern in Problem 4.* Sample answer: Subtract 17 from 62. There are 3 intervals between 17 and 62, so 62 − 17 = 45 and 45 ÷ 3 = 15; 17 + 15 = 32; 32 + 15 = 47; 62 + 15 = 77.

▶ Study Link 3·7

INDEPENDENT ACTIVITY

(*Math Masters,* p. 87)

Home Connection Students solve Odd Shape Out problems, in which they identify one shape that is different from others in a set and tell why it is different. Students then write their own Odd Shape Out problem.

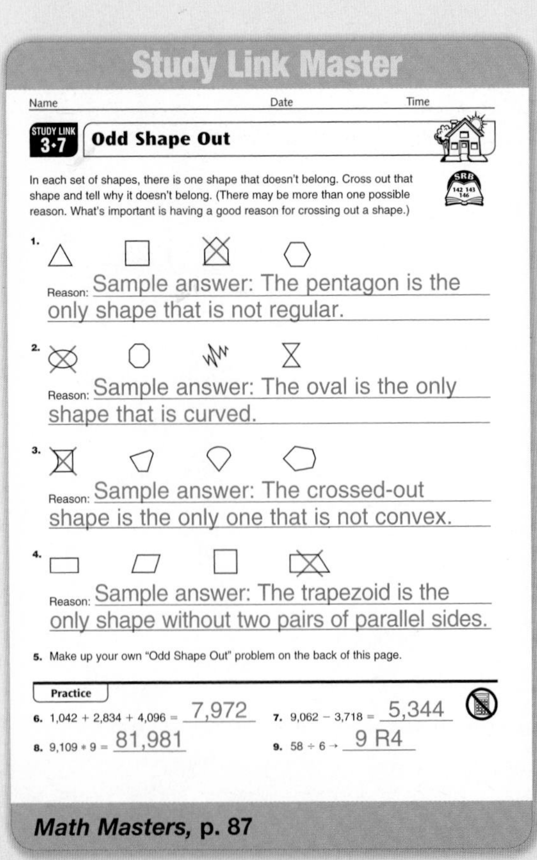
Study Link Master

Name Date Time

STUDY LINK 3·7 **Odd Shape Out**

In each set of shapes, there is one shape that doesn't belong. Cross out that shape and tell why it doesn't belong. (There may be more than one possible reason. What's important is having a good reason for crossing out a shape.)

1. Reason: Sample answer: The pentagon is the only shape that is not regular.

2. Reason: Sample answer: The oval is the only shape that is curved.

3. Reason: Sample answer: The crossed-out shape is the only one that is not convex.

4. Reason: Sample answer: The trapezoid is the only shape without two pairs of parallel sides.

5. Make up your own "Odd Shape Out" problem on the back of this page.

Practice

6. 1,042 + 2,834 + 4,096 = 7,972

7. 9,062 − 3,718 = 5,344

8. 9,109 ∗ 9 = 81,981

9. 58 ÷ 6 → 9 R4

Math Masters, p. 87

3 Differentiation Options

READINESS

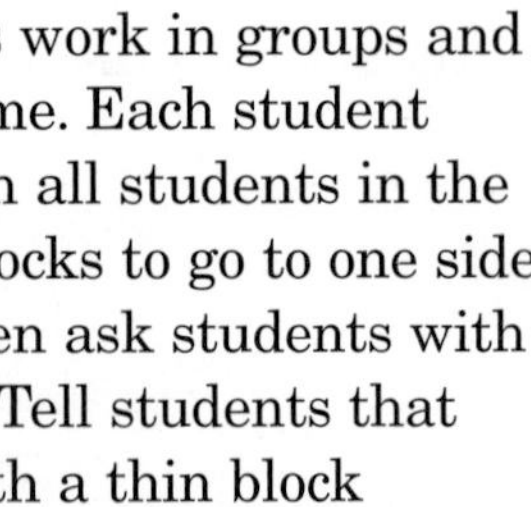
SMALL-GROUP ACTIVITY

15–30 Min

▶ Sorting Attribute Blocks by Two Properties

To review geometric properties, have students work in groups and sort attribute blocks by two properties at a time. Each student takes an attribute block at random. Start with all students in the middle of the classroom. Ask students with blocks to go to one side of the room. (Every student should move.) Then ask students with a circle to go to the opposite side of the room. Tell students that when you say, *"Spread Out!"*, the students with a thin block should move to one corner on their side of the room and the students with a thick block should move to the other corner on their side of the room. Students will need to negotiate to decide which corner is for thick and which is for the thin figures. If there is overwhelming confusion, answer questions and start over. A successful division of students will end up in four groups—thin polygons, thick polygons, thin circles, and thick circles.

Each group should discuss the characteristics of their blocks and then share these characteristics with the class. Repeat the exercise, sorting the blocks by other properties (Attributes are polygons, circles, thick, thin, big, small, and colors.)

ENRICHMENT

PARTNER ACTIVITY

15–30 Min

▶ Connecting Vertices

(*Math Masters,* p. 88)

To apply students' understanding of the properties of polygons, have them draw and describe the properties of polygons within polygonal regions. Encourage students to use vocabulary from this unit. Have students read aloud the names of the new shapes and the properties for those shapes.

ELL SUPPORT

PARTNER ACTIVITY

15–30 Min

▶ Playing *What's My Attribute Rule?*

(*Math Masters,* pp. 508 and 509)

To explore sorting shapes according to their attributes, have students play *What's My Attribute Rule?* When students have finished the game, have them discuss some of the difficult rules in the game. Encourage students to say the rules in more than one way. For example: *All Red Shapes* could also be *No Blue or Yellow Shapes.*

Teaching Master

Name Date Time

LESSON 3•7 **Vertex Connection**

If you draw a line segment from one vertex of a polygon to any other vertex that does not share a common side, new shapes will be formed inside the polygon. Connect pairs of vertices in these polygons. Name the new shapes as they are formed.

Sample answers:

Write the name of each new polygon and as many true statements as you can about the polygons. Be sure to use what you know about the definitions of angles and lines.

kite pentagon hexagon

kite	
New Polygon	**Properties**
Right triangle, or isosceles triangle	Right angle, 2 acute angles, 2 equal sides and angles, congruent to adjacent isosceles triangle
Scalene triangle	Right angle, 2 acute angles, 3 sides of different lengths, congruent to adjacent scalene triangle
Right triangle, or isosceles triangle	Right angle, 2 acute angles, 2 equal sides and angles, congruent to adjacent isosceles triangle

pentagon	
New Polygon	**Properties**
Obtuse triangle, or isosceles triangle	Obtuse angle, 2 acute angles, 2 equal sides and angles, congruent to the isosceles triangle that is not adjacent
Acute triangle, or isosceles triangle	3 acute angles, 2 equal sides and angles, adjacent to 2 isosceles triangles

hexagon	
New Polygon	**Properties**
Obtuse triangle, or isosceles triangle	Obtuse angle, 2 acute angles, 2 equal sides and angles, adjacent to right triangle
Right triangle, or scalene triangle	1 right angle, 2 acute angles, scalene, right triangle, adjacent to obtuse triangle and trapezoid
trapezoid	1 pair of parallel sides, 2 equal sides, 2 pairs of equal angles, adjacent to right triangle

Math Masters, p. 88

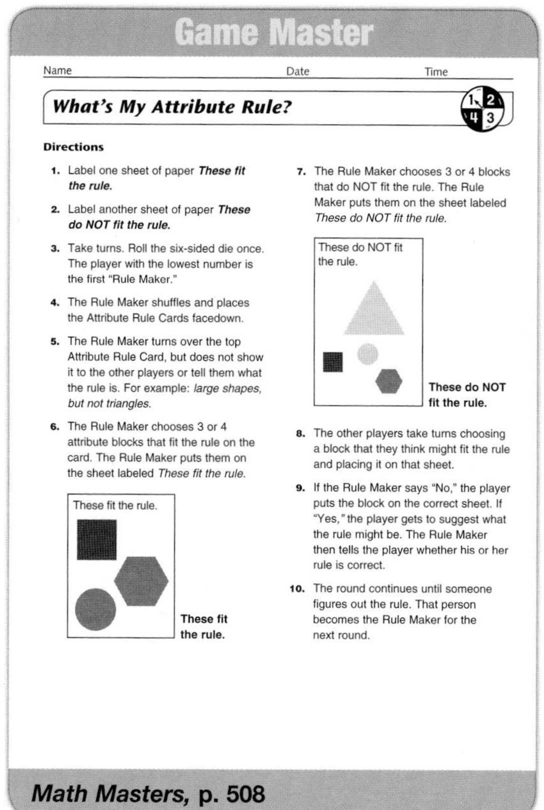

Game Master

Name Date Time

What's My Attribute Rule?

Directions

1. Label one sheet of paper ***These fit the rule.***
2. Label another sheet of paper ***These do NOT fit the rule.***
3. Take turns. Roll the six-sided die once. The player with the lowest number is the first "Rule Maker."
4. The Rule Maker shuffles and places the Attribute Rule Cards facedown.
5. The Rule Maker turns over the top Attribute Rule Card, but does not show it to the other players or tell them what the rule is. For example: *large shapes, but not triangles.*
6. The Rule Maker chooses 3 or 4 attribute blocks that fit the rule on the card. The Rule Maker puts them on the sheet labeled *These fit the rule.*

7. The Rule Maker chooses 3 or 4 blocks that do NOT fit the rule. The Rule Maker puts them on the sheet labeled *These do NOT fit the rule.*

8. The other players take turns choosing a block that they think might fit the rule and placing it on that sheet.
9. If the Rule Maker says "No," the player puts the block on the correct sheet. If "Yes," the player gets to suggest what the rule might be. The Rule Maker then tells the player whether his or her rule is correct.
10. The round continues until someone figures out the rule. That person becomes the Rule Maker for the next round.

Math Masters, p. 508

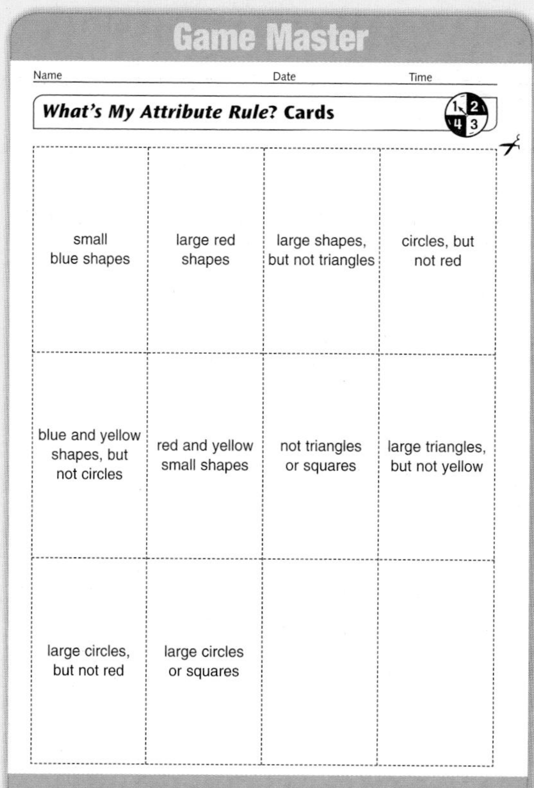

Game Master

Name Date Time

***What's My Attribute Rule?* Cards**

small blue shapes	large red shapes	large shapes, but not triangles	circles, but not red
blue and yellow shapes, but not circles	red and yellow small shapes	not triangles or squares	large triangles, but not yellow
large circles, but not red	large circles or squares		

Math Masters, p. 509

3•8 Regular Tessellations

Objective To explore side and angle relationships in regular tessellations and compare and classify quadrangles.

Technology Resources www.everydaymathonline.com

ePresentations

eToolkit

Algorithms Practice

EM Facts Workshop Game™
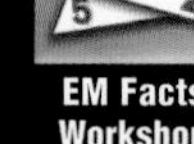
Family Letters

Assessment Management

Common Core State Standards

Curriculum Focal Points

Interactive Teacher's Lesson Guide

1 Teaching the Lesson

Key Concepts and Skills

- Use angle relationships to determine angle measures. [Geometry Goal 1]
- Describe the properties of regular polygons. [Geometry Goal 2]
- Compare and classify quadrangles. [Geometry Goal 2]
- Identify, describe, and create tessellations. [Geometry Goal 3]

Key Activities

Students are introduced to the history and concept of tessellations; they explore regular tessellations and decide which regular polygons tessellate and which ones do not, based on the sum of the angle measures around a single point. They compare and classify quadrangles.

Ongoing Assessment: Recognizing Student Achievement
Use an Exit Slip (*Math Masters,* page 414). [Geometry Goal 2]

Key Vocabulary

regular polygon ◆ tessellation ◆ regular tessellation ◆ tessellate ◆ tessellation vertex

Materials

Math Journal 1, pp. 82 and 83
Student Reference Book, pp. 146, 160, and 161
Study Link 3•7
Math Masters, pp. 87A, 89 and 414
Geometry Template ◆ scissors

2 Ongoing Learning & Practice

Playing *Angle Tangle*
Student Reference Book, p. 296
Math Masters, p. 444
Geometry Template (or straightedge and protractor)
Students practice estimating and measuring angles.

Math Boxes 3•8
Math Journal 1, p. 84
Students practice and maintain skills through Math Box problems.

Study Link 3•8
Math Masters, p. 90
Students practice and maintain skills through Study Link activities.

3 Differentiation Options

READINESS

Making Tessellations with Pattern Blocks
pattern blocks or Geometry Template
Students explore tessellations using a concrete model.

ENRICHMENT

Naming Tessellations
Math Masters, p. 91
Students create regular tessellations to explore the naming conventions for tessellations.

Advance Preparation

For Part 1, make copies of *Math Masters,* page 89 and place them near the Math Message. The Study Link for this lesson asks students to collect examples for a Tessellation Museum. Prepare a space in your classroom for this display. For a mathematics and literacy connection, obtain a copy of ***A Cloak for the Dreamer*** by Aileen Friedman (Scholastic Inc., 1995).

***Teacher's Reference Manual,* Grades 4–6** pp. 201–206

Getting Started

Mental Math and Reflexes

Use your established slate procedures. Pose the following problems. Students respond by writing their magnitude estimate—placing their solution in the 1,000s; 10,000s; 100,000s; or 1,000,000s.

●○○ 18 ∗ 200 1,000s
300 ∗ 12 1,000s
200 ∗ 19 1,000s

●●○ 5 ∗ 48,000 100,000s
13 ∗ 500,000 1,000,000s
60 ∗ 5,000 100,000s

●●● 28 ∗ 3,020 10,000s
39 ∗ 5,130 100,000s
4,000 ∗ 527 1,000,000s

Math Message

Follow the directions on Math Masters, *page 89.*

Study Link 3·7 Follow-Up

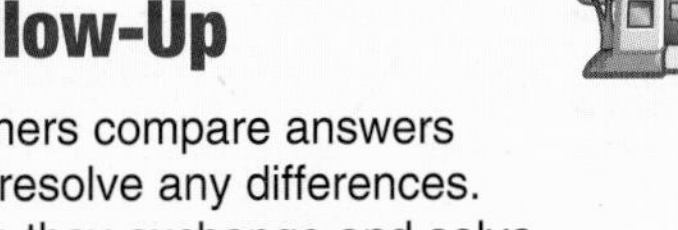

Partners compare answers and resolve any differences. Then they exchange and solve Odd Shape Out problems.

1 Teaching the Lesson

▶ Math Message Follow-Up

WHOLE-CLASS DISCUSSION

ELL

(*Math Masters*, p. 89)

Allow time for students to finish cutting out the polygons on *Math Masters*, page 89. Review the names of the polygons. Ask students to verify that each polygon's sides are the same length and their angle measures are equal. Tell students that such polygons are called **regular polygons.** To support English language learners, write *regular polygons* on the board along with some examples.

These cut-out polygons may be discarded at the end of this lesson.

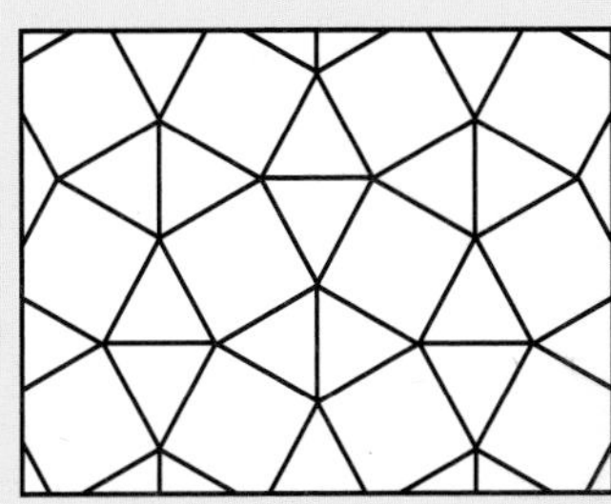

A tessellation

▶ Exploring Tessellations

WHOLE-CLASS DISCUSSION

(*Student Reference Book*, pp. 160 and 161)

As a class read and discuss pages 160 and 161 of the *Student Reference Book*. Highlight the following points.

▷ A **tessellation** is an arrangement of repeated, closed shapes that cover a surface so no shapes overlap and no gaps exist between shapes. (*See margin.*)

▷ Some tessellations repeat only one shape. Others combine two or more shapes.

▷ A tessellation with shapes that are congruent regular polygons is called a **regular tessellation.**

Teaching Master

Name Date Time

LESSON 3·8 **Regular Polygons**

Cut along the dashed lines. Fold the page like this along the solid lines.

Cut out the polygons. You will be cutting out four of each shape at once.

Math Masters, p. 89

Student Page

Date Time

LESSON 3·8 **Regular Tessellations**

1. A **regular polygon** is a polygon in which all sides are the same length and all angles have the same measure. Circle the regular polygons below.

2. In the table below, write the name of each regular polygon under its picture. Then, using the polygons that you cut out from Activity Sheet 3, decide whether each polygon can be used to create a regular tessellation. Record your answers in the middle column. In the last column, use your Geometry Template to draw examples showing how the polygons tessellate or don't tessellate. Record any gaps or overlaps.

Polygon	Tessellates? (yes or no)	Draw an Example
triangle	Yes	
square	Yes	
pentagon	No	gap

Math Journal 1, **p. 82**

Student Page

Date Time

LESSON 3·8 **Regular Tessellations** *continued*

Polygon	Tessellates? (yes or no)	Draw an Example
hexagon	Yes	
octagon	No	overlap

3. Which of the polygons can be used to create regular tessellations? Triangles, squares, and hexagons

4. Explain how you know that these are the only ones. Three pentagons leave a gap, and 4 pentagons create an overlap. For regular polygons that have 7 or more sides, 2 shapes leave a gap, and 3 shapes create an overlap.

Math Journal 1, **p. 83**

Adjusting the Activity

ELL

Have students identify tessellations that they see around them—in ceiling tiles, floor tiles, carpet designs, clothing designs, and so on. Ask which of these tessellations use only one shape and whether any are made with regular polygons. For example, the floor or ceiling might be tiled with squares. Remind students that in a regular polygon, all the sides are the same length and all the angles have the same measure.

AUDITORY ◆ KINESTHETIC ◆ TACTILE ◆ VISUAL

▶ Exploring Regular Tessellations

PARTNER ACTIVITY

(*Math Journal 1,* pp. 82 and 83; *Math Masters,* p. 89)

Have students use the regular polygons that they cut from *Math Masters*, page 89 to help them complete the tables on journal pages 82 and 83 and answer the questions on journal page 83.

For each of the given regular polygons, partners must decide whether the polygon can be used to create a regular tessellation. Ask students to use their Geometry Templates to draw an example of each tessellation. For polygons that do not **tessellate**, the drawing should show an overlap or a gap in the design.

Ask volunteers to share their results from the journal page with the class. Then survey the class: *Which regular polygons will tessellate and which ones will not?* The triangle, square, and hexagon tessellate; the pentagon and octagon do not.

Ask students to examine their drawings on journal page 82. What true statements can they make about the angles in the drawings? For the triangle and the square, the sum of the measures of the angles around a single point is 360°; for the pentagon, the sum of the angle measures around a single point is not 360°. Note that the point where vertices meet in a tessellation is called the **tessellation vertex.** Ask students what true statements they can make about their drawings on journal page 83. For the hexagon, the sum of the angle measures around a tessellation vertex is 360°; for the octagon, the sum of the angle measures is not 360°.

Conclude the discussion by asking students to use what they know about the total number of degrees in a circle and the measure of the angles in regular polygons to determine which regular polygons will tessellate and which ones will not. A regular polygon can be tessellated if a multiple of the measure of its angles equals 360°. Each angle in a regular pentagon is 108°. No multiple of 108° equals 360°, so there will be overlaps or gaps if pentagons are arranged around a point.

▶ Quadrangles

(*Math Masters,* p. 87A)

INDEPENDENT ACTIVITY

NOTE For this activity, students will need the completed *Math Masters,* page 87A from Lesson 3-7.

Distribute *Math Masters,* page 87A. Remind students of the work they did when they classified quadrangles in Lesson 3-7. Draw a tree diagram, like the one below, on the board. Ask volunteers to draw shapes on the board for each category.

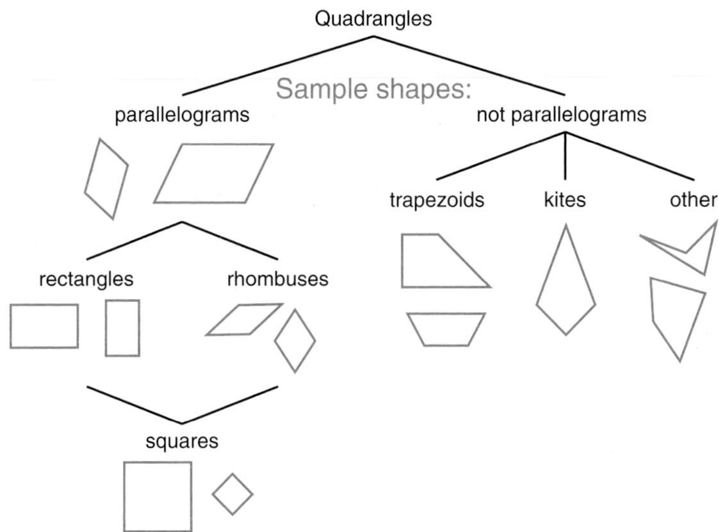

Record the following statements on the board. Ask students to identify each statement as true or false. Students defend their thinking using logical arguments. Refer students to their tree diagrams as a resource, if necessary.

- ▷ All squares are parallelograms. true
- ▷ All rhombuses are rectangles. false
- ▷ A kite is a rhombus. false
- ▷ All quadrangles are parallelograms. false
- ▷ Trapezoids are not parallelograms. true
- ▷ All rhombuses are parallelograms. true

Record the following sentences on the board, along with the words *always, sometimes,* and *never.* Ask students to make each sentence true by using the word *always, sometimes,* or *never.*

- ▷ Squares are ________ rectangles. always
- ▷ Rhombuses are ________ rectangles. sometimes
- ▷ Trapezoids are ________ rectangles. never
- ▷ A kite is ________ a parallelogram. never
- ▷ Rectangles are ________ squares. sometimes

Ask students to explain why each of the above statements is always, sometimes, or never true. Encourage students to use what they know about the properties of quadrangles in their explanations and to refer to the tree diagram as needed.

Teaching Master

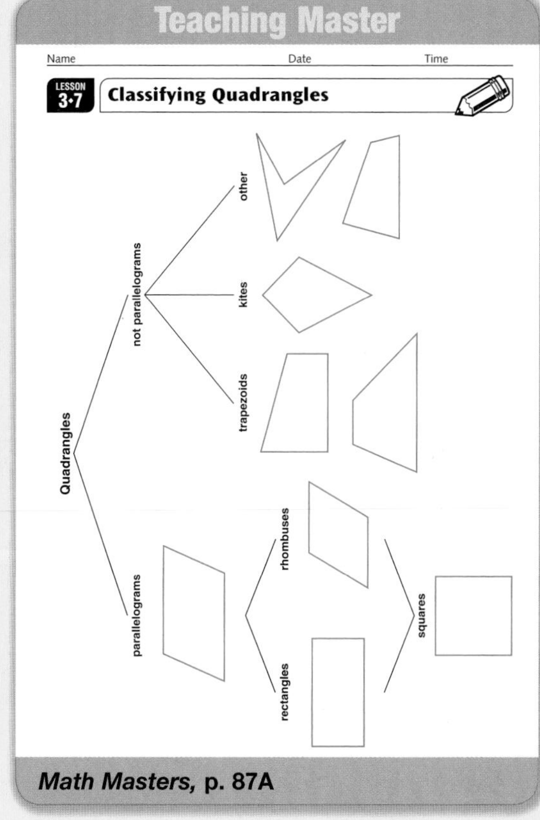

Math Masters, p. 87A

Ask students to use their knowledge of the relationships among quadrangles to generate three statements similar to those discussed in the second group of statements on page 196A. Have students record the statements on an Exit Slip, *Math Masters,* page 414. The statements should include one of each type of response—*always, sometimes,* or *never*—to make it true. Have students share their statements with a partner. Circulate and assist.

Ongoing Assessment: Recognizing Student Achievement

***Math Masters* Page 414**

Use the statements on **Exit Slip,** *Math Masters,* page 414 to assess students' abilities to classify quadrangles according to a hierarchy of properties. Students are making adequate progress if their statements include a basic understanding of the classification of quadrangles. Some students may demonstrate a more sophisticated understanding. For example, a square is *always* a rhombus, a rectangle, and a parallelogram.

[Geometry Goal 2]

Write the three statements listed below on the board. To extend students' understanding of the properties of quadrangles, ask them to work with a partner to write each of the statements on a sheet of paper, inserting the names of quadrangles in the blanks and then indicating if the statement is true or false. An example has been given for each.

▷ If it is a ________, then it is also a ________.
Example: If it is a rectangle, then it is also a parallelogram. true

▷ All ________ are ________.
Example: All trapezoids are parallelograms. false

▷ Some ________ are ________.
Example: Some squares are rhombuses. false

Circulate and assist.

2 Ongoing Learning & Practice

▶ Playing *Angle Tangle*

PARTNER ACTIVITY

(*Student Reference Book*, p. 296; *Math Masters*, p. 444)

Students practice estimating angle measures and measuring angles with a protractor by playing *Angle Tangle*. Students draw angles and record their answers and points on the *Angle Tangle* Record Sheet.

▶ Math Boxes 3•8

INDEPENDENT ACTIVITY

(*Math Journal 1*, p. 84)

Mixed Practice Math Boxes in this lesson are paired with Math Boxes in Lesson 3-10. The skill in Problem 6 previews Unit 4 content.

Writing/Reasoning Have students write a response to the following: *Blaire wrote the following true statement based on the questions for Problem 6:* 450 is 90 times as great as 5. *Write similar statements for the question "How many 5s are in 35,000?"* Sample answer: 35,000 is 7,000 times as great as 5.

▶ Study Link 3•8

INDEPENDENT ACTIVITY

(*Math Masters*, p. 90)

Home Connection Students collect tessellations that they can bring to class. Students can draw tessellations that they find if they cannot cut them out.

Student Page

Games

Angle Tangle

Materials
- 1 protractor
- 1 straightedge
- several blank sheets of paper

Players 2

Skill Estimating and measuring angle size

Object of the game To estimate angle sizes accurately and have the lower total score.

Directions

In each round:

1. Player 1 uses a straightedge to draw an angle on a sheet of paper.
2. Player 2 estimates the degree measure of the angle.
3. Player 1 measures the angle with a protractor. Players agree on the measure.
4. Player 2's score is the difference between the estimate and the actual measure of the angle. (The difference will be 0 or a positive number.)
5. Players trade roles and repeat Steps 1–4.

Players add their scores at the end of five rounds. The player with the lower total score wins the game.

Example

	Player 1			Player 2		
	Estimate	Actual	Score	Estimate	Actual	Score
Round 1	120°	108°	12	50°	37°	13
Round 2	75°	86°	11	85°	87°	2
Round 3	40°	44°	4	15°	19°	4
Round 4	60°	69°	9	40°	56°	16
Round 5	135°	123°	12	150°	141°	9
Total score			48			44

Player 2 has the lower total score. Player 2 wins the game.

Student Reference Book, p. 296

NOTE Several math supply catalogs offer paper pattern blocks. These are already cut to the correct shapes and colors. They only need to be separated and glued down. Tessellations can also be explored using computer software or online sites such as the Tessellation Creator provided by the National Council of Teachers of Mathematics at http://illuminations.nctm.org/ActivityDetail.aspx?ID=202.

Game Master

Name Date Time

***Angle Tangle* Record Sheet**

Round	Angle	Estimated measure	Actual measure	Score
1		____°	____°	
2		____°	____°	
3		____°	____°	
4		____°	____°	
5		____°	____°	
			Total Score	

Math Masters, p. 444

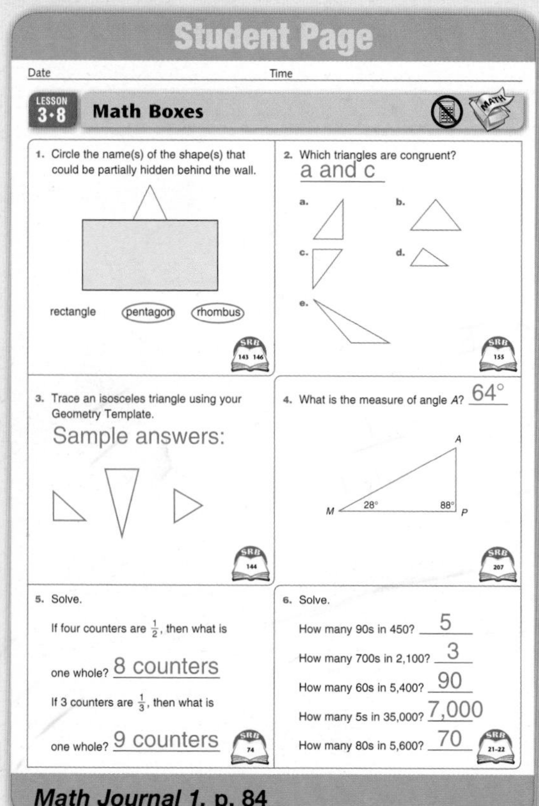
Student Page

Date Time

LESSON 3·8 **Math Boxes**

1. Circle the name(s) of the shape(s) that could be partially hidden behind the wall.

rectangle (pentagon) (rhombus)

SRB 143 146

2. Which triangles are congruent? a and c

a. b. c. d. e.

SRB 155

3. Trace an isosceles triangle using your Geometry Template.

Sample answers:

SRB 144

4. What is the measure of angle *A*? 64°

M 28° 88° *P* *A*

SRB 207

5. Solve.

If four counters are $\frac{1}{2}$, then what is one whole? 8 counters

If 3 counters are $\frac{1}{3}$, then what is one whole? 9 counters

SRB 74

6. Solve.

How many 90s in 450? 5

How many 700s in 2,100? 3

How many 60s in 5,400? 90

How many 5s in 35,000? 7,000

How many 80s in 5,600? 70

SRB 21-22

Math Journal 1, p. 84

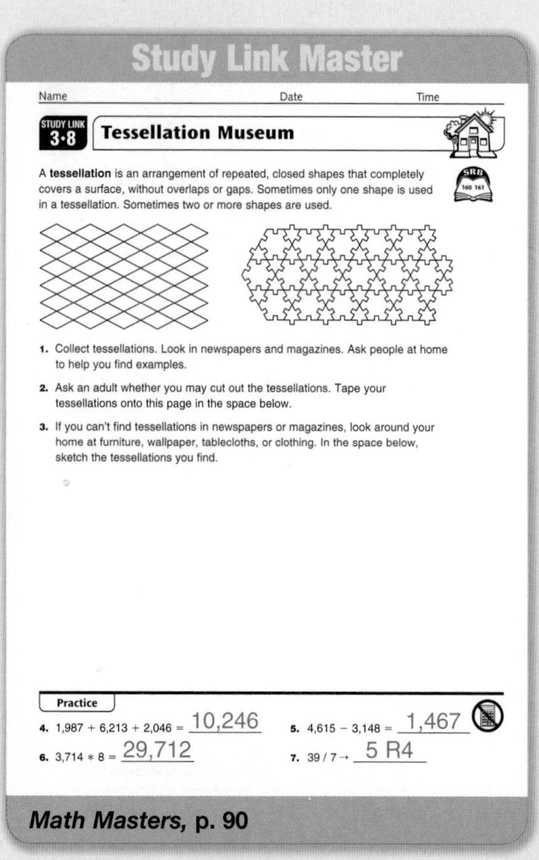
Study Link Master

Name Date Time

STUDY LINK 3·8 **Tessellation Museum**

A **tessellation** is an arrangement of repeated, closed shapes that completely covers a surface, without overlaps or gaps. Sometimes only one shape is used in a tessellation. Sometimes two or more shapes are used.

SRB 160 161

1. Collect tessellations. Look in newspapers and magazines. Ask people at home to help you find examples.
2. Ask an adult whether you may cut out the tessellations. Tape your tessellations onto this page in the space below.
3. If you can't find tessellations in newspapers or magazines, look around your home at furniture, wallpaper, tablecloths, or clothing. In the space below, sketch the tessellations you find.

Practice

4. 1,987 + 6,213 + 2,046 = 10,246
5. 4,615 − 3,148 = 1,467
6. 3,714 ∗ 8 = 29,712
7. 39 / 7 → 5 R4

Math Masters, p. 90

3 Differentiation Options

READINESS

INDEPENDENT ACTIVITY

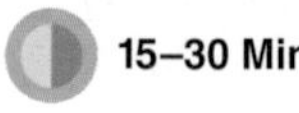
15–30 Min

▶ Making Tessellations with Pattern Blocks

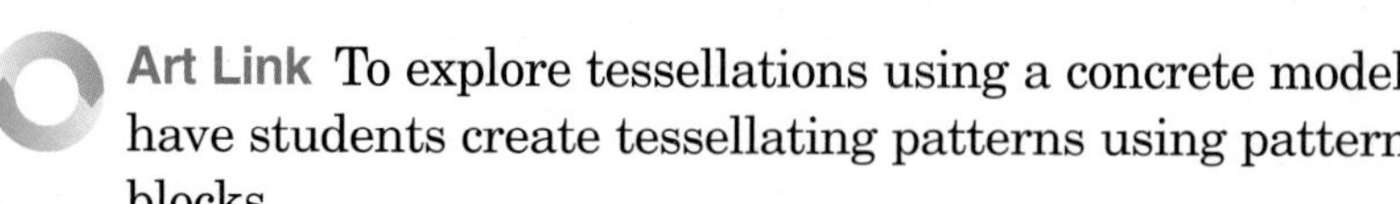
Art Link To explore tessellations using a concrete model, have students create tessellating patterns using pattern blocks.

They should trace their patterns onto a piece of paper, either by tracing around the blocks or by using the Geometry Template. Suggest that students color their patterns in a way that emphasizes repeating elements.

ENRICHMENT

INDEPENDENT ACTIVITY

15–30 Min

▶ Naming Tessellations

(*Math Masters,* p. 91)

To explore naming conventions for tessellations, have students create and label tessellations using Geometry Template polygons. Students focus on the vertex points of tessellations and the number of polygons that are arranged around a tessellation vertex.

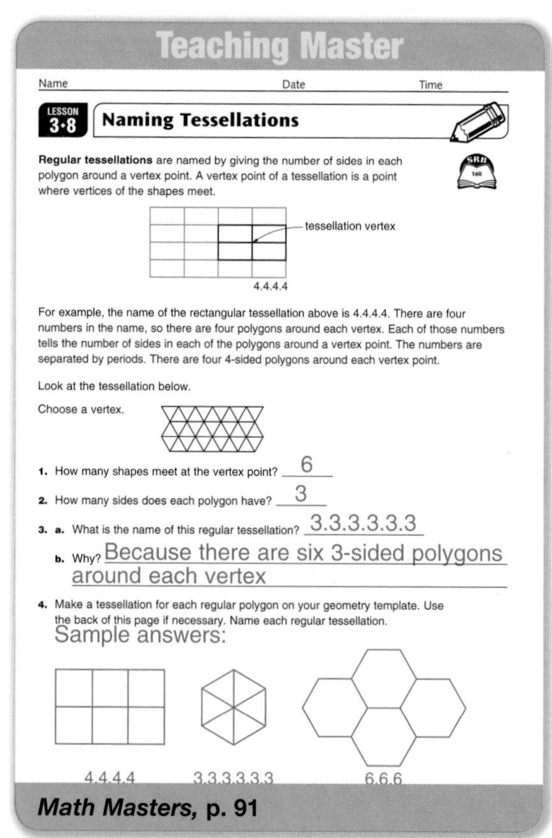
Teaching Master

Name Date Time

LESSON 3·8 **Naming Tessellations**

Regular tessellations are named by giving the number of sides in each polygon around a vertex point. A vertex point of a tessellation is a point where vertices of the shapes meet.

SRB 160

tessellation vertex

4.4.4.4

For example, the name of the rectangular tessellation above is 4.4.4.4. There are four numbers in the name, so there are four polygons around each vertex. Each of those numbers tells the number of sides in each of the polygons around a vertex point. The numbers are separated by periods. There are four 4-sided polygons around each vertex point.

Look at the tessellation below.

Choose a vertex.

1. How many shapes meet at the vertex point? 6
2. How many sides does each polygon have? 3
3. a. What is the name of this regular tessellation? 3.3.3.3.3.3

   b. Why? Because there are six 3-sided polygons around each vertex
4. Make a tessellation for each regular polygon on your geometry template. Use the back of this page if necessary. Name each regular tessellation.

Sample answers:

4.4.4.4 3.3.3.3.3.3 6.6.6

Math Masters, p. 91

3•9 Angles of Polygons

Objective To develop an approach for finding the angle measurement sum for any polygon.

www.everydaymathonline.com

ePresentations

eToolkit

Algorithms Practice

EM Facts Workshop Game™

Family Letters

Assessment Management

Common Core State Standards

Curriculum Focal Points

Interactive Teacher's Lesson Guide

1 Teaching the Lesson

Key Concepts and Skills

- Investigate and compare the measurement sums of interior angles of polygons. [Geometry Goal 1]
- Measure angles with a protractor. [Measurement and Reference Frames Goal 1]
- Find maximum, minimum, and median for a data set. [Data and Chance Goal 2]
- Draw conclusions based on collected data. [Data and Chance Goal 2]

Key Activities

Students measure to find angle sums for triangles, quadrangles, pentagons, and hexagons. They use the pattern in these sums to devise a method for finding the angle sum for any polygon.

Ongoing Assessment: Recognizing Student Achievement
Use an Exit Slip (*Math Masters,* page 414).
[Geometry Goal 1]

Materials

Math Journal 1, pp. 85–89
Study Link 3•8
Math Masters, p. 414
transparency of *Math Masters,* p. 420 (optional) ◆ Class Data Pad ◆ Geometry Template (or protractor and straightedge)

2 Ongoing Learning & Practice

Practicing Expanded Notation

Math Journal 1, p. 90
Student Reference Book, p. 396
Students practice place-value concepts by reading and writing large numbers and decimals in standard and expanded notation.

Math Boxes 3•9

Math Journal 1, p. 91
Students practice and maintain skills through Math Box problems.

Study Link 3•9

Math Masters, p. 92
Students practice and maintain skills through Study Link activities.

3 Differentiation Options

ENRICHMENT

Tessellating Quadrangles

Math Masters, p. 93
paper ($8\frac{1}{2}$" by 11") ◆ scissors ◆ tape ◆ cardstock (optional)
Students investigate whether all quadrangles will tessellate.

EXTRA PRACTICE

Finding Angle Measures in Polygons

Math Masters, p. 94
Students find the sums of the interior angles of polygons.

ELL SUPPORT

Describing Tessellations

Students describe the tessellations in the Tessellation Museum.

Advance Preparation

This 2-day lesson begins with the Math Message on Day 1 and Dividing Polygons into Triangles on Day 2. For the Math Message, draw a line plot on the board for students to record the sums of the angles they find. Label it from about 175° to 185°. The Lesson 3•8 Study Link asks students to collect tessellations. These will be displayed in the Tessellation Museum. Include the class definitions for angles and triangles in this display. For the optional Enrichment activity in Part 3, do the tessellation activity yourself in advance, with convex and nonconvex quadrangles, so you can help students see how the angles fit.

***Teacher's Reference Manual,* Grades 4–6** p. 203

Getting Started

Mental Math and Reflexes

FACTS PRACTICE

Use your slate procedures for problems such as the following:

●○○	●●○	●●●
47 * 10,000 470,000	356 * 1,000 356,000	0.109 * 1,000 109
4.7 * 1,000 4,700	42.6 * 100 4,260	7.08 * 10,000 70,800
0.47 * 100 47	0.862 * 100 86.2	0.084 * 100 8.4
0.047 * 10 0.47	0.009 * 1,000 9	79.04 * 1,000 79,040

Math Message

Use a straightedge to draw a big triangle on a sheet of paper. Measure its angles and find the sum. Record the sum on the class line plot.

Study Link 3·8 Follow-Up

Ask volunteers to share their tessellation examples. Encourage them to include the names of polygons and to explain how they identified the patterns as tessellations.

- On **Day 1** of this lesson, students should complete the Math Message, the Study Link 3-8 Follow-Up, and explore finding the sums of the angle measures.
- On **Day 2** of this lesson, students begin with Dividing Polygons into Triangles and explore further how to find the sums of the angle measures in any polygon. Then have students complete Part 2 activities.

1 Teaching the Lesson

▶ Math Message Follow-Up

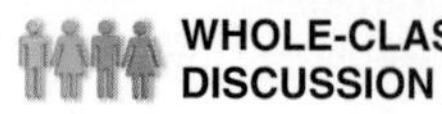

Survey the class to complete the line plot and identify the following landmarks.

- What is the maximum sum of the angle measures?
- What is the minimum sum of the angle measures?
- What is the median sum of the angle measures?

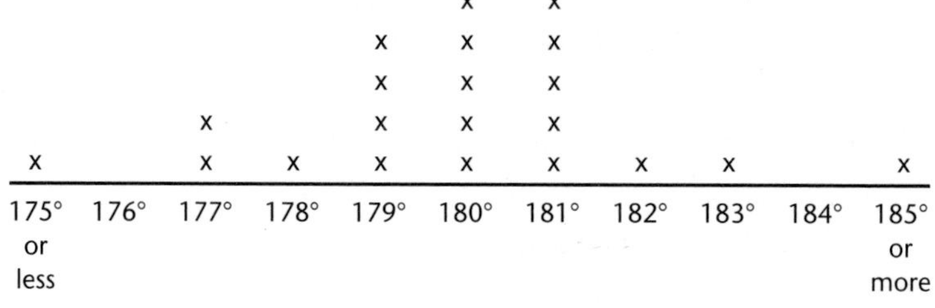

Sample data

Expect a range of sums, because measurements are never exact, and because some of the sides of students' drawings may not be straight or meet exactly. Explain that if a triangle is accurately drawn, and its angles are measured with precision, the sum of the angle measures will always be 180°.

Explain that students can prove this statement using their triangles as models. Ask students to tear the three angles off their triangles as shown below.

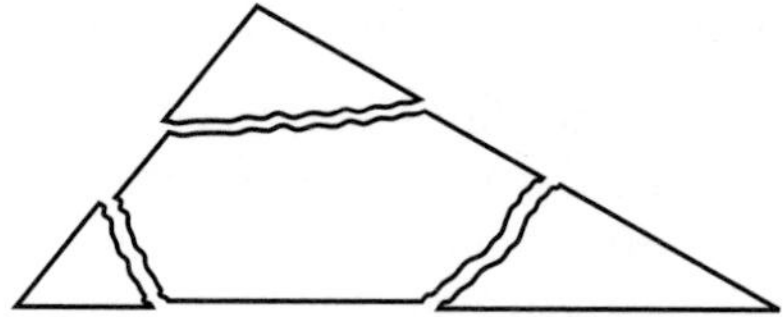

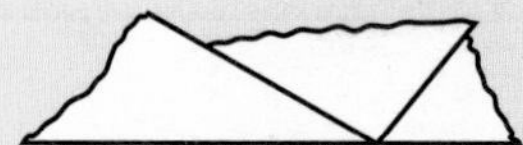

Students' angle measures might seem to total slightly more or less than 180° because their original triangles might not be accurate.

Next have students arrange their three angles next to each other so they line up. (*See margin.*) Ask students what type of angle they have formed, A straight angle and what the measure of a straight angle is. 180° This shows that the sum of the three angles of the triangle is 180°. Ask students to leave their angles arranged in a straight angle on their desks, and then check each other's triangles. When students return to their desks, ask what they observed about the angles in triangles. All the angles will form straight angles; the sum of the angle measures in a triangle will always total 180°. Record this property on the Class Data Pad.

NOTE Precise language would call for writing and saying: *the sum of the measures of the angles* instead of *the sum of the angles*. But it is common in mathematics to use the shorter phrase.

▶ Finding the Sums of Angles in Polygons

SMALL-GROUP ACTIVITY

(*Math Journal 1,* pp. 85 and 86)

Draw an example of a convex polygon and a concave polygon on the board.

NOTE These figures will be used later in the lesson.

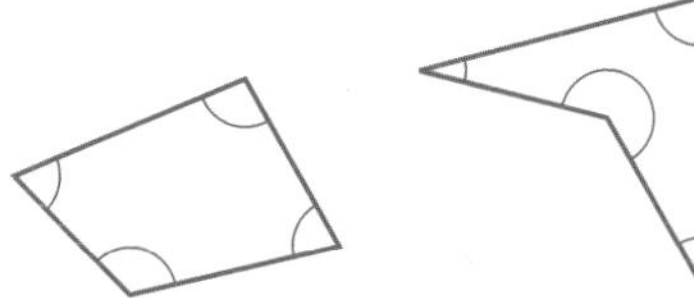

Ask students what true statements they can make about the interior angles in the two figures. Expect responses to vary, but structure your follow-up questions to guide students to recognize that the concave polygon has one angle that is a reflex angle. Remind students that the names for angles refer to the angles' measures, not to whether the angle is or is not an interior angle.

Ask students to fold a blank sheet of paper into fourths. Open it and label each box in the top row *Polygons* and *Not Polygons*. Label the boxes in the bottom row *Convex Polygons* and *Concave Polygons*. Assign small groups of three to five students to work together to draw at least two examples of each figure. As groups finish, they should examine other students' examples. Circulate and assist.

Transition to the journal activity by first surveying the class for questions or observations about their drawings. Then assign groups to work on quadrangles or pentagons. Ask students to circle the name of the figure they are going to work on, listed at the top of journal page 85.

Ask students to complete Problems 1–7 on journal pages 85 and 86. Problem 7 provides data on hexagons for the next activity. As you circulate, consider asking students, who are waiting for the group to finish Problem 5, to go on to Problem 7 until the others are done.

Student Page

Date Time

LESSON 3·9 **Angles in Quadrangles and Pentagons**

1. Circle the kind of polygon your group is working on: quadrangle pentagon

2. Below, use a straightedge to carefully draw the kind of polygon your group is working on. Your polygon should look different from the ones drawn by others in your group, but it should have the same number of sides.

Drawings vary.

3. Measure the angles in your polygon. Write each measure for each angle.

Answers vary for individual angle measurements.

4. Find the sum of the angles in your polygon.

The total sum of the angles should be close to 360° for quadrangles and 540° for pentagons.

Math Journal 1, p. 85

Student Page

Date Time

LESSON 3·9 **Angles in Quadrangles and Pentagons** *cont.*

5. Record your group's data below.

Group Member's Name	Sketch of Polygon	Sum of Angles
	Drawings of polygons vary. The sum of the angles varies but should be close to 360° for quadrangles and 540° for pentagons.	

6. Find the median of the angle sums for your group.

The total sum of the angles should be close to 360° for quadrangles and 540° for pentagons.

7. If you have time, draw a hexagon. Measure its angles with a protractor. Find the sum.

Drawings vary.

Sum of the angles in a hexagon = 720°

Math Journal 1, p. 86

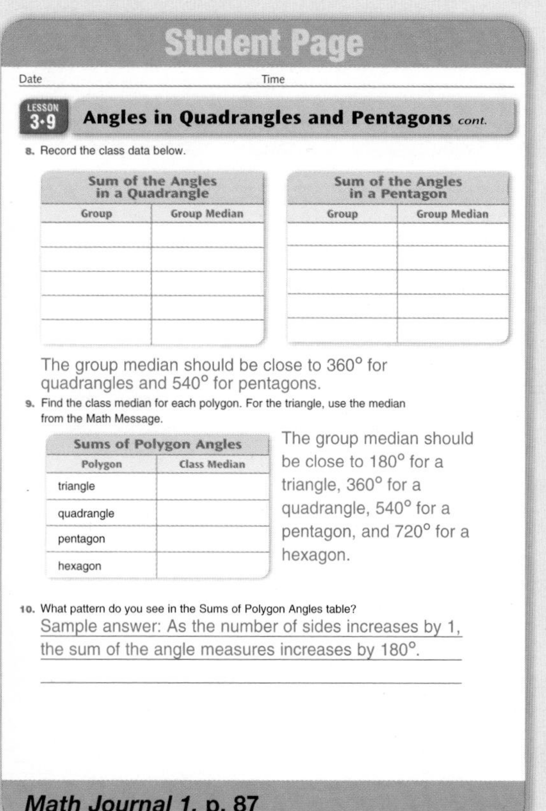
Student Page

Date Time

LESSON 3·9 **Angles in Quadrangles and Pentagons** *cont.*

8. Record the class data below.

Sum of the Angles in a Quadrangle	
Group	Group Median

Sum of the Angles in a Pentagon	
Group	Group Median

The group median should be close to 360° for quadrangles and 540° for pentagons.

9. Find the class median for each polygon. For the triangle, use the median from the Math Message.

Sums of Polygon Angles	
Polygon	Class Median
triangle	
quadrangle	
pentagon	
hexagon	

The group median should be close to 180° for a triangle, 360° for a quadrangle, 540° for a pentagon, and 720° for a hexagon.

10. What pattern do you see in the Sums of Polygon Angles table?
Sample answer: As the number of sides increases by 1, the sum of the angle measures increases by 180°.

Math Journal 1, p. 87

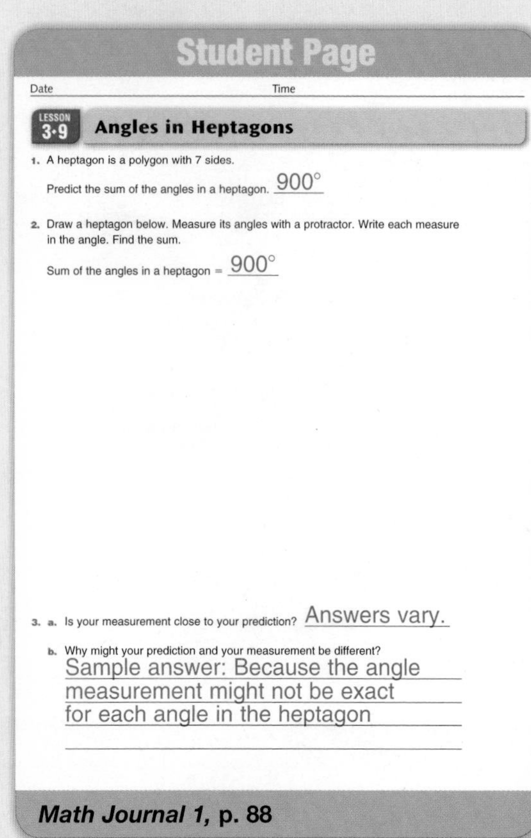
Student Page

Date Time

LESSON 3·9 **Angles in Heptagons**

1. A heptagon is a polygon with 7 sides.
Predict the sum of the angles in a heptagon. 900°

2. Draw a heptagon below. Measure its angles with a protractor. Write each measure in the angle. Find the sum.
Sum of the angles in a heptagon = 900°

3. a. Is your measurement close to your prediction? Answers vary.
b. Why might your prediction and your measurement be different?
Sample answer: Because the angle measurement might not be exact for each angle in the heptagon

Math Journal 1, p. 88

▶ Finding the Median for the Sums of Angles

WHOLE-CLASS DISCUSSION

(*Math Journal 1,* p. 87)

Bring the class together and use the board or a transparency of *Math Masters*, page 420 to collect the group's median angle sums; first from the quadrangle group and then from the pentagon group. Ask students to record this data in the tables for Problem 8 on journal page 87.

Next ask students to use the group medians to find the class median for quadrangles and pentagons. Then record this data in the table for Problem 9. For the triangle row, enter the class median from the Math Message line plot.

Collect data from students who did Problem 7 on journal page 86, listing the sums on the Class Data Pad or the overhead projector. Ask students to find the median of these sums and record it in the table for Problem 9.

The class medians should be close to 180° for a triangle, 360° for a quadrangle, 540° for a pentagon, and 720° for a hexagon.

Ask students to complete Problem 10 on the journal page. As they look for patterns in the Sums of Polygon Angles table, ask them to think about how the contents of each column in the table are related. Ask: *What are the differences between a triangle and a quadrangle? Do the numbers in the class median column increase or decrease and by how much?* The quadrangle has one more side than the triangle; the median sum of their angles increases by about 180°. Circulate and assist.

▶ Dividing Polygons into Triangles

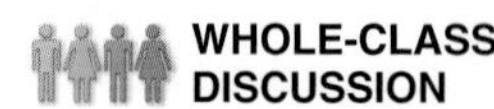

(*Math Journal 1,* pp. 87 and 88)

Survey the class for the patterns that students found in the Sums of Polygon Angles table. Ask: *Why do you think the medians for the sums of polygon angles increase by 180°?* Use the following points to guide the discussion.

▷ The sum of the angles of a triangle equals 180°.

▷ Quadrangles divide into 2 triangles. The sum of the angles of the quadrangle equals $2 * 180$, or 360°.

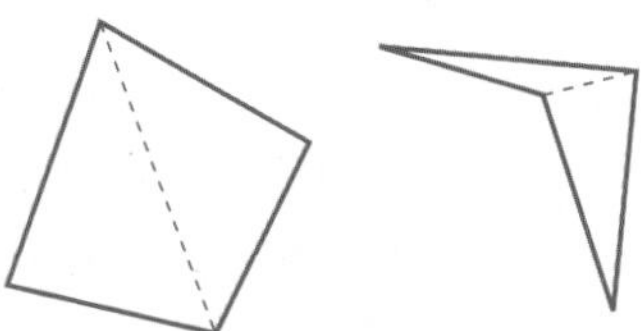

Use dotted lines to divide the polygons on the board from the earlier discussion so the two triangles can be seen. (*See above.*) Ask: *How many triangles do you think could be drawn in a pentagon?* 3 *What would be the sum of angles?* $3 * 180°$ is 540°.

In a hexagon? 4; 4 ∗ 180° is 720°. Summarize by stating that as the number of sides in a polygon increases by 1, the sum of the angle measures increases by 180°.

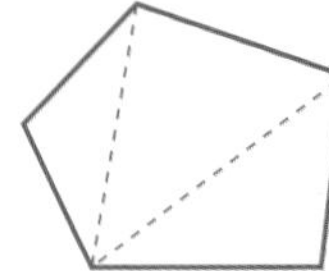

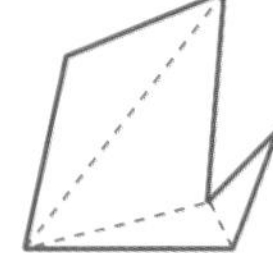

Ask partners to work together to solve Problems 1–3 on journal page 88. They can use the pattern in the table or try dividing a heptagon into triangles to make their prediction. Circulate and assist.

Bring the class together to discuss results. Ask: *Do your predictions match your measurements? Why might they be different?* The angle measurement(s) may not be exact for each angle in the heptagon.

▶ Finding Angle Sums for Any Polygon

PARTNER ACTIVITY

(*Math Journal 1,* p. 89; *Math Masters,* p. 414)

Ask students to state the relationship between the number of sides of a polygon and the number of triangles that the polygon can be divided into. The number of triangles is 2 less than the number of sides. Explain that some polygons are impractical to draw because they have so many sides that it's hard to draw them accurately. In these instances, the number of triangles can be determined by subtracting 2 from that polygon's number of sides. Ask partners to work together to complete journal page 89.

Ongoing Assessment: Recognizing Student Achievement

Exit Slip

Use an **Exit Slip** (*Math Masters,* page 414) to assess students' understanding of angle measures and relationships in polygons. Have students write a response to the following: *Explain how to find the sum of the measures of the angles in polygons without using a protractor.* Students are making adequate progress if they indicate that they are able to use the sum of the measures of the angles in a triangle to calculate the angle sums for at least one other polygon. Some students may generalize finding the sum of angles for all polygons.

[Geometry Goal 1]

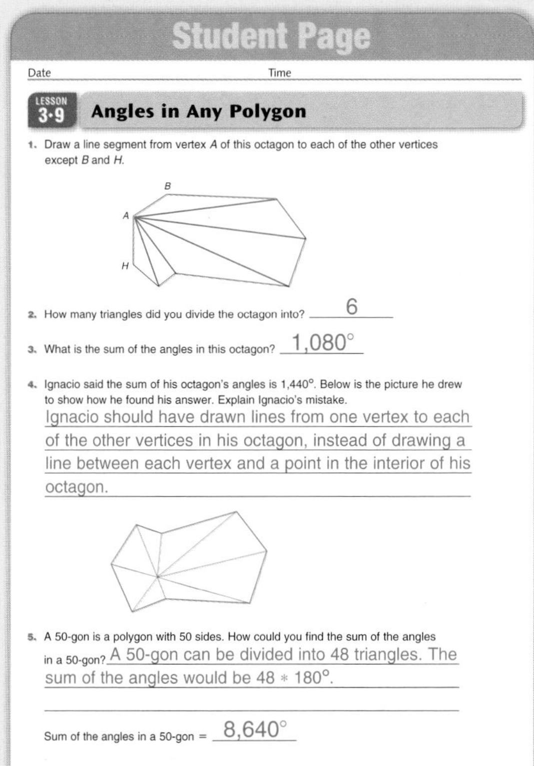

Student Page

Date Time

LESSON 3·9 **Angles in Any Polygon**

1. Draw a line segment from vertex *A* of this octagon to each of the other vertices except *B* and *H*.

2. How many triangles did you divide the octagon into? 6

3. What is the sum of the angles in this octagon? 1,080°

4. Ignacio said the sum of his octagon's angles is 1,440°. Below is the picture he drew to show how he found his answer. Explain Ignacio's mistake.
Ignacio should have drawn lines from one vertex to each of the other vertices in his octagon, instead of drawing a line between each vertex and a point in the interior of his octagon.

5. A 50-gon is a polygon with 50 sides. How could you find the sum of the angles in a 50-gon? A 50-gon can be divided into 48 triangles. The sum of the angles would be 48 ∗ 180°.

Sum of the angles in a 50-gon = 8,640°

Math Journal 1, p. 89

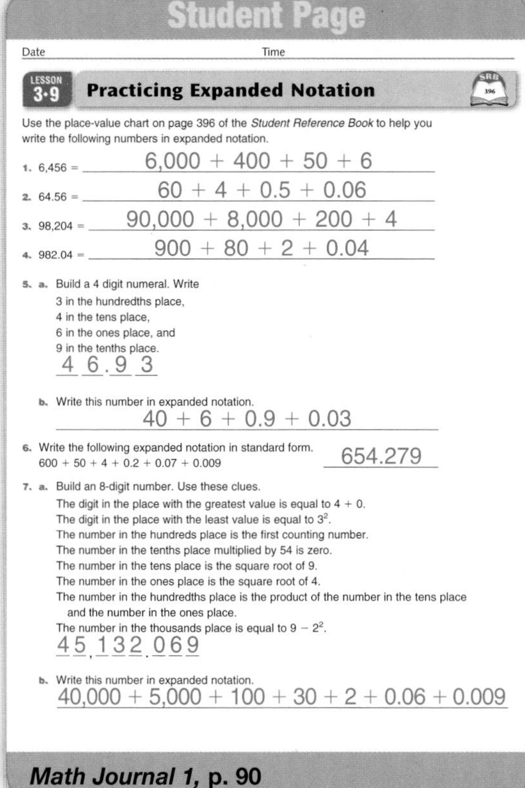

Student Page

Date Time

LESSON 3·9 **Practicing Expanded Notation**

Use the place-value chart on page 396 of the *Student Reference Book* to help you write the following numbers in expanded notation.

1. 6,456 = 6,000 + 400 + 50 + 6

2. 64.56 = 60 + 4 + 0.5 + 0.06

3. 98,204 = 90,000 + 8,000 + 200 + 4

4. 982.04 = 900 + 80 + 2 + 0.04

5. a. Build a 4 digit numeral. Write
3 in the hundredths place,
4 in the tens place,
6 in the ones place, and
9 in the tenths place.
4 6 . 9 3

b. Write this number in expanded notation.
40 + 6 + 0.9 + 0.03

6. Write the following expanded notation in standard form.
600 + 50 + 4 + 0.2 + 0.07 + 0.009 654.279

7. a. Build an 8-digit number. Use these clues.
The digit in the place with the greatest value is equal to 4 ÷ 0.
The digit in the place with the least value is equal to 3^2.
The number in the hundreds place is the first counting number.
The number in the tenths place multiplied by 54 is zero.
The number in the tens place is the square root of 9.
The number in the ones place is the square root of 4.
The number in the hundredths place is the product of the number in the tens place and the number in the ones place.
The number in the thousands place is equal to $9 - 2^2$.
4 5 , 1 3 2 . 0 6 9

b. Write this number in expanded notation.
40,000 + 5,000 + 100 + 30 + 2 + 0.06 + 0.009

Math Journal 1, p. 90

Student Page

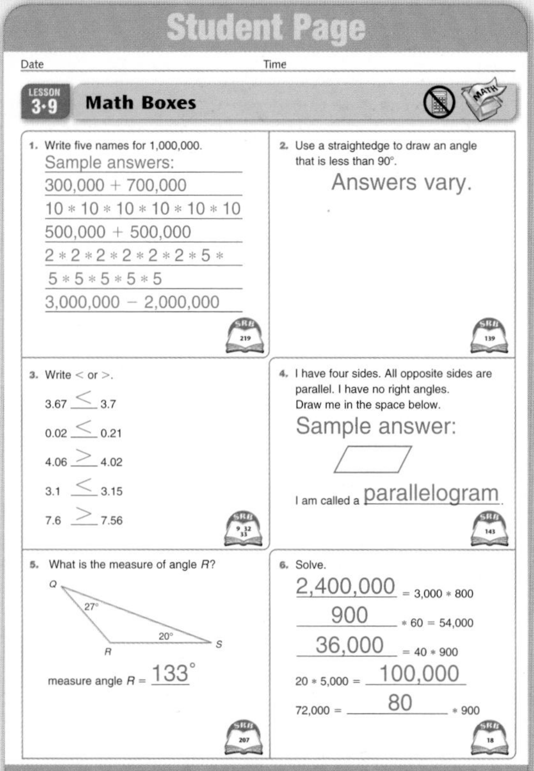

Date Time

LESSON 3·9 **Math Boxes**

1. Write five names for 1,000,000.
Sample answers:
300,000 + 700,000
10 * 10 * 10 * 10 * 10 * 10
500,000 + 500,000
2 * 2 * 2 * 2 * 2 * 2 * 5 * 5 * 5 * 5 * 5 * 5
3,000,000 − 2,000,000

2. Use a straightedge to draw an angle that is less than 90°.
Answers vary.

3. Write < or >.
3.67 < 3.7
0.02 < 0.21
4.06 > 4.02
3.1 < 3.15
7.6 > 7.56

4. I have four sides. All opposite sides are parallel. I have no right angles. Draw me in the space below.
Sample answer:
I am called a parallelogram.

5. What is the measure of angle *R*?
Q 27° R 20° S
measure angle *R* = 133°

6. Solve.
2,400,000 = 3,000 * 800
900 * 60 = 54,000
36,000 = 40 * 900
20 * 5,000 = 100,000
72,000 = 80 * 900

Math Journal 1, p. 91

2 Ongoing Learning & Practice

▶ Practicing Expanded Notation

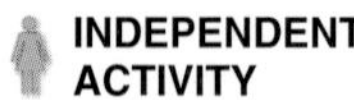
INDEPENDENT ACTIVITY

(*Math Journal 1,* p. 90; *Student Reference Book,* p. 396)

Students practice place-value concepts by reading and writing large numbers and decimals in standard notation and in expanded notation. Students can refer to the place-value chart in the *Student Reference Book,* page 396. Remind students that decimals may also be written as fractions. For example, in Problem 2, the expanded notation for 64.56 may be written as $60 + 4 + \frac{5}{10} + \frac{6}{100}$.

▶ Math Boxes 3·9

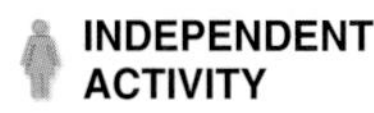
INDEPENDENT ACTIVITY

(*Math Journal 1,* p. 91)

Mixed Practice Math Boxes in this lesson are paired with Math Boxes in Lesson 3-6. The skill in Problem 6 previews Unit 4 content.

Writing/Reasoning Have students write a response to the following: *John called his drawing in Problem 4 a parallelogram, and Jack called his drawing a rhombus. Who was correct?* Sample answer: A rhombus is a parallelogram with 4 equal sides. Both are correct.

NOTE Student use of vocabulary (quadrangle, quadrilateral, parallel sides, congruent sides, and/or opposite sides) and explanation of the concepts in their solution will provide information about how students are integrating these geometry concepts.

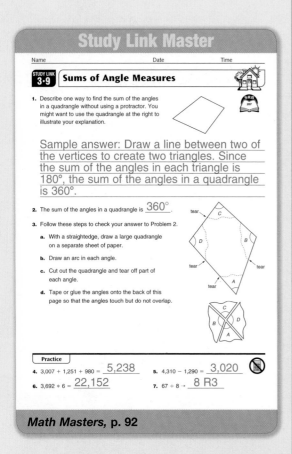

Study Link Master

Name Date Time

STUDY LINK 3·9 **Sums of Angle Measures**

1. Describe one way to find the sum of the angles in a quadrangle without using a protractor. You might want to use the quadrangle at the right to illustrate your explanation.

Sample answer: Draw a line between two of the vertices to create two triangles. Since the sum of the angles in each triangle is 180°, the sum of the angles in a quadrangle is 360°.

2. The sum of the angles in a quadrangle is 360°.

3. Follow these steps to check your answer to Problem 2.
   a. With a straightedge, draw a large quadrangle on a separate sheet of paper.
   b. Draw an arc in each angle.
   c. Cut out the quadrangle and tear off part of each angle.
   d. Tape or glue the angles onto the back of this page so that the angles touch but do not overlap.

tear C B D A

Practice

4. 3,007 + 1,251 + 980 = 5,238
5. 4,310 − 1,290 = 3,020
6. 3,692 * 6 = 22,152
7. 67 ÷ 8 → 8 R3

Math Masters, p. 92

▶ Study Link 3·9

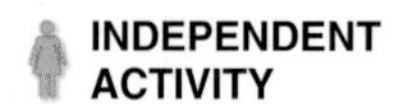
INDEPENDENT ACTIVITY

(*Math Masters,* p. 92)

Home Connection Students describe one way to find the sum of the angles of a quadrangle without using a protractor. They investigate finding the sum by tearing off the angles and putting them together around a point.

3 Differentiation Options

ENRICHMENT

INDEPENDENT ACTIVITY

15–30 Min

▶ Tessellating Quadrangles

(*Math Masters,* p. 93)

Portfolio Ideas

To apply their understanding of interior angle measures of polygons, have students investigate whether all quadrangles will tessellate. Ask students whether they think the following statement is true. *Because the sum of the angles in a quadrangle is equal to the number of degrees in a circle, all quadrangles should tessellate.* Answers vary. Explain that in this activity, students will investigate whether the statement is true.

Ask students to tape their results onto a separate piece of paper. Challenge students to tessellate concave (nonconvex) quadrangles. Concave quadrangles will tessellate, but it is more difficult to place the pieces so all four angles meet. Make sure all angles are correctly labeled to facilitate the process.

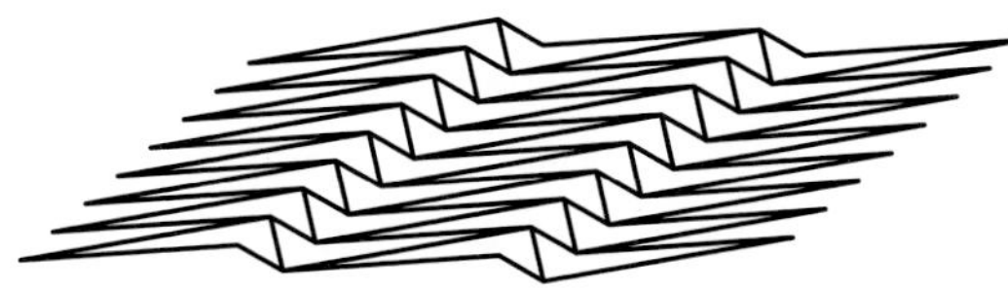

Tessellations with concave (nonconvex) quadrangles

EXTRA PRACTICE

INDEPENDENT ACTIVITY

5–15 Min

▶ Finding Angle Measures in Polygons

(*Math Masters,* p. 94)

Algebraic Thinking Students complete a table that shows the relationship between the number of the sides of a polygon and the number of interior triangles. Then they summarize the pattern by writing numerical expressions.

ELL SUPPORT

PARTNER ACTIVITY

5–15 Min

▶ Describing Tessellations

To provide language support for polygon angles, have students look at the Tessellations Museum and describe some of the tessellations in the museum to a partner. Encourage them to use mathematical terminology (for example, *polygons*) and to describe components such as colors, shapes, and patterns.

Teaching Master

Name Date Time

LESSON 3·9 **A Quadrangle Investigation**

The sum of the angles in a quadrangle is equal to 360°. Since there are 360° in a circle, you might predict that every quadrangle will tessellate. Follow the procedure below to investigate this prediction.

1. Fold a piece of paper ($8\frac{1}{2}$" by 11") into six parts by first folding it into thirds and then into halves.

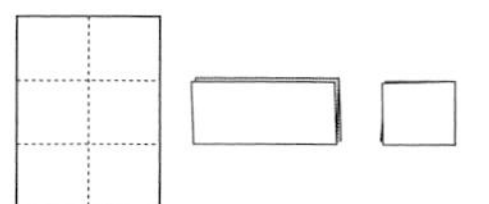

2. Using a straightedge, draw a quadrangle on the top layer of the folded paper. Label each of the four vertices with a letter *inside the figure*—for example, *A, B, C,* and *D.*
3. Cut through all six layers so that you have six identical quadrangles. Label the vertices of each quadrangle in the same manner as the quadrangle on top.

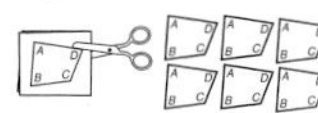

4. Arrange the quadrangles so that they tessellate.
5. When you have a tessellating pattern, tape the final pattern onto a separate piece of paper. Color it if you want to.
6. Talk with other students who did this investigation. Were their quadrangles a different shape than yours? Do you think that any quadrangle will tessellate?

Option To make a pattern that has more than six quadrangles, draw your original quadrangle on a piece of cardstock, cut it out, and use it as a stencil. By tracing around your quadrangle, you can easily cover a half-sheet of paper with your pattern. Label the angles on your stencil so you can be sure you are placing all four angles around points in the tessellation. Color your finished pattern.

***Math Masters,* p. 93**

Teaching Master

Name Date Time

LESSON 3·9 **Angle Measures in Polygons**

The measure of the interior angles of a triangle is 180°. The number of triangles within a polygon is 2 less than the number of sides of the polygon.

1. Fill in the chart below using this pattern.

Polygons		
Number of Sides	Number of Triangles	Sum of Angles
4	2	2 ∗ 180° = 360°
5	3	3 ∗ 180° = 540°
6	4	4 ∗ 180° = 720°
7	5	5 ∗ 180° = 900°
13	11	11 ∗ 180° = 1,980°
26	24	24 ∗ 180° = 4,320°
51	49	49 ∗ 180° = 8,820°
63	61	61 ∗ 180° = 10,980°
85	83	83 ∗ 180° = 14,940°

2. Use expressions to complete the statement.

If *n* equals the number of sides in a polygon, $n - 2$ equals the number of triangles within the polygon, and $(n - 2) * 180°$ equals the sum of the angles in the polygon.

***Math Masters,* p. 94**

3•10 Solving Problems Using the Geometry Template

Objective To review polygon attributes and vocabulary using the Geometry Template.

www.everydaymathonline.com

ePresentations

eToolkit

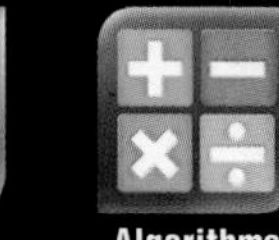
Algorithms Practice

EM Facts Workshop Game™

Family Letters

Assessment Management

Common Core State Standards

Curriculum Focal Points

Interactive Teacher's Lesson Guide

1 Teaching the Lesson

Key Concepts and Skills

- Identify and draw polygons according to angle type. [Geometry Goal 1]
- Identify and draw polygons according to given properties. [Geometry Goal 2]
- Draw circles of a given radius or diameter. [Measurement and Reference Frames Goal 1]

Key Activities

Students use their Geometry Templates to draw circles and investigate geometric concepts by solving a variety of problems.

Ongoing Assessment: Recognizing Student Achievement Use Mental Math and Reflexes. [Operations and Computation Goal 6]

Ongoing Assessment: Informing Instruction See page 208.

Key Vocabulary

radius ◆ diameter ◆ pentagon ◆ perimeter

Materials

Math Journal 1, pp. 92–96
Study Link 3•9
Geometry Template ◆ overhead projector ◆ 2 sharp pencils ◆ drawing paper

2 Ongoing Learning & Practice

Playing *Polygon Capture*
Math Journal 1, Activity Sheets 3 and 4
Student Reference Book, p. 328
Students practice identifying attributes of polygons.

Math Boxes 3•10
Math Journal 1, p. 97
Students practice and maintain skills through Math Box problems.

Study Link 3•10
Math Masters, p. 95
Students practice and maintain skills through Study Link activities.

3 Differentiation Options

READINESS

Reviewing Geometry Vocabulary
straightedge ◆ marker ◆ paper
Students create vocabulary posters to provide a visual reference for geometry words.

ENRICHMENT

Solving Geometry Template Challenges
Math Masters, pp. 96 and 97
Geometry Template
Students solve challenging problems by using the Geometry Template.

EXTRA PRACTICE

5-Minute Math
5-Minute Math™, p. 53
Students practice measuring angles.

Advance Preparation

Many teachers have found that this lesson can extend over two or more class periods. Consider revisiting problems over the next several weeks.

***Teacher's Reference Manual,* Grades 4–6** pp. 178–186

Getting Started

Mental Math and Reflexes

Students write a magnitude estimate to predict whether the solution is in the 1,000s; 10,000s; 100,000s; or 1,000,000s.

●○○ 350,000 ÷ 7 10,000s
64,000,000 ÷ 8 1,000,000s
250,000 ÷ 5 10,000s

●●○ 24,578,297 ÷ 6 1,000,000s
54,197 ÷ 9 1,000s
99,654 ÷ 3 10,000s

●●● 350,000 ÷ 70 1,000s
64,000,000 ÷ 80 100,000s
250,000 ÷ 50 1,000s

Math Message

Answer the three questions on the top of journal page 92.

Study Link 3·9 Follow-Up

Survey the class for their strategies to find the sum of the angles of quadrangles without using a protractor. Poll students for those who answered that the sum of the angles of a quadrangle is 360°. Resolve any differences.

Ongoing Assessment: Recognizing Student Achievement

Mental Math and Reflexes ★

Use the **Mental Math and Reflexes problems in level** ●○○ to assess students' ability to make magnitude estimates for division with large numbers. Students are making adequate progress if they correctly estimate the magnitude of the problems. Some students may be successful with the problems in levels ●●○ and ●●●. Ask these students to explain their estimation strategies.

[Operations and Computation Goal 6]

1 Teaching the Lesson

▶ Math Message Follow-Up

WHOLE-CLASS DISCUSSION

(*Math Journal 1,* p. 92)

Survey the class for their responses to the three questions on journal page 92. The Geometry Template has a total of 24 shapes, not counting the protractors, Percent Circle, and little holes next to the rulers; $\frac{18}{24}$ or $\frac{3}{4}$ of the shapes are polygons; $\frac{10}{24}$ or $\frac{5}{12}$ of the shapes are quadrangles.

▶ Drawing Circles with the Geometry Template

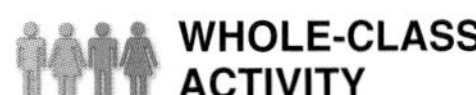

WHOLE-CLASS ACTIVITY

Demonstrate on the overhead projector how to use circle guides on the Geometry Template to draw a circle of a specific **radius,** and have students mirror you step-by-step. Draw a circle with a radius of 3 inches by following the steps shown on the next page.

Student Page

Date Time

LESSON 3·10 **The Geometry Template**

Math Message

Answer the following questions about your Geometry Template. DO NOT count the protractors, Percent Circle, and little holes next to the rulers.

1. How many shapes are on the Geometry Template? 24
2. What fraction of these shapes are polygons? $\frac{3}{4}$
3. What fraction of the shapes are quadrangles? $\frac{10}{24}$

Problems for the Geometry Template

The problems on journal pages 93 and 95 are labeled Easy and Moderate. Each problem has been assigned a number of points according to its difficulty.

Complete as many of these problems as you can. Your Geometry Template and a sharp pencil are the only tools you may use. Record and label your answers on the page opposite the problems.

Some of the problems might seem confusing at first. Before asking your teacher for help, try the following:

- Look at the examples on the journal page. Do they help you understand what the problem is asking you to do?
- If you are not sure what a word means, look it up in the Glossary in your *Student Reference Book.* You might also look for help in the geometry section of the *Student Reference Book.*
- Find a classmate who is working on the same problem. Can the two of you work together to find a solution?
- Find a classmate who has completed the problem. Can she or he give you hints about how to solve it?

When the time for this activity has ended, total the number of points that you have scored. If you didn't have time to complete all these pages, you can continue working on them when you have free time.

Good luck and have fun!

Math Journal 1, p. 92

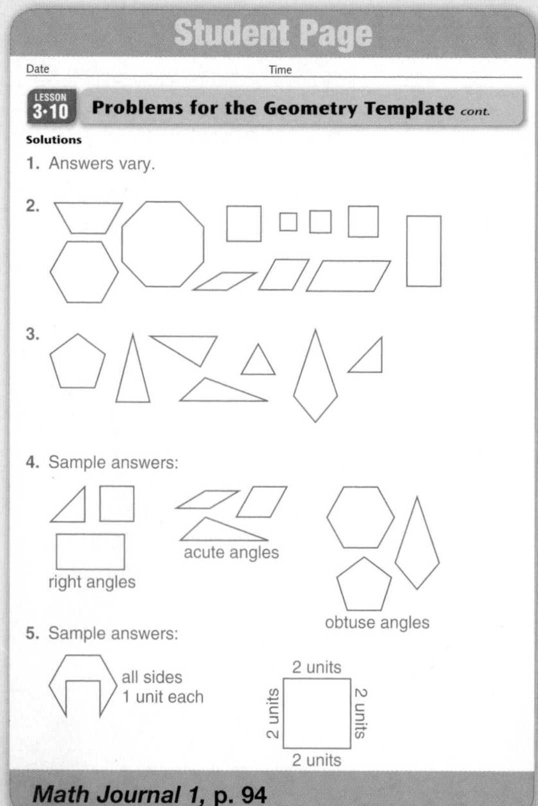
Student Page

Date Time

LESSON 3·10 **Problems for the Geometry Template** *cont.*

Solutions

1. Answers vary.
2.
3.
4. Sample answers:

right angles

acute angles

obtuse angles

5. Sample answers:

all sides 1 unit each

2 units

2 units

2 units

2 units

Math Journal 1, p. 94

NOTE As students devise solutions, ask them to copy their solutions for a classroom display. Consider having the students add a description of the method they used to obtain their solutions.

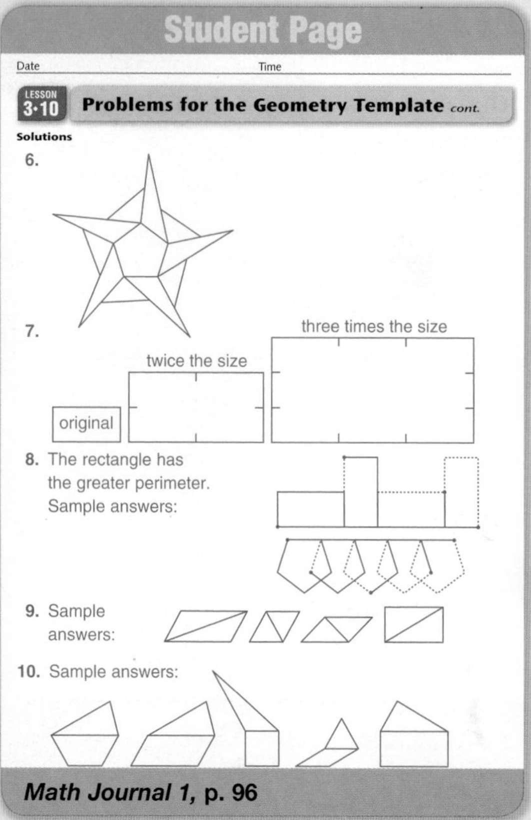
Student Page

Date Time

LESSON 3·10 **Problems for the Geometry Template** *cont.*

Solutions

6.
7.

three times the size

twice the size

original

8. The rectangle has the greater perimeter. Sample answers:
9. Sample answers:
10. Sample answers:

Math Journal 1, p. 96

1. Place the Geometry Template on a piece of paper.

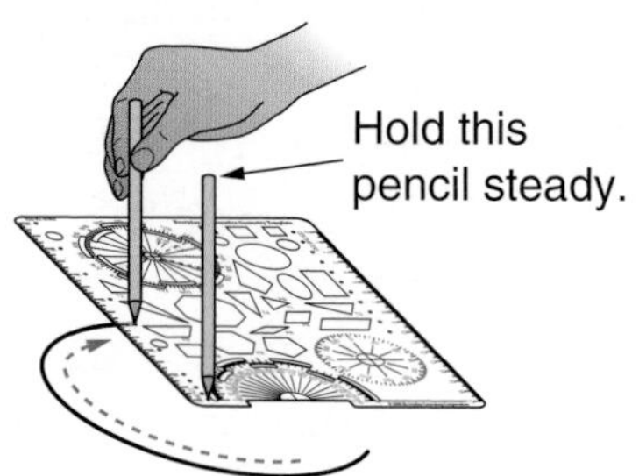

2. Put one pencil in the circle guide at 0 inches and another pencil in the circle guide at 3 inches.
3. Use the pencil at the 0-inch mark as an anchor (like the anchor on a compass) while you scribe a circle around it with the pencil at the 3-inch mark.
4. This circle has a **diameter** of 6 inches.

Give students a few minutes to experiment with drawing circles of different diameters. Circulate and assist.

▶ Solving Problems Using the Geometry Template

(*Math Journal 1*, pp. 92–96)

Bring the class back together. Introduce this activity by reading the information on journal page 92 under Problems for the Geometry Template. Then ask students to look over the problems on journal pages 93 and 95. Explain that students may choose which problems they want to solve on those pages, but they must solve at least three on each page. They may do the problems alone or with a partner. Circulate and assist.

Ongoing Assessment: Informing Instruction

Watch for students who find that the binding makes it difficult to work directly on the journal. Provide extra paper and allow students to tape their examples to the journal page.

Encourage students to try problems that they think might be a challenge and to make note of any additional discoveries that they make while using the Geometry Template. As students work, look for opportunities to bring the class together to poll for suggestions or to share discoveries about specific problems. This type of sharing encourages students to try problems that they might have avoided otherwise. The following comments are methods for approaching two of the problems.

Problem 7: One method is to trace a side of the rectangle, slide the Geometry Template along the tracing, trace the same side again, and then trace the other sides in the same way. In this way the length and the width are doubled. To draw a rectangle 3 times as large, trace each side 3 times.

Problem 8: One method is to first trace the five sides of the **pentagon** end to end, forming a line segment equal in length to the **perimeter** of the pentagon. Then trace the four sides of the rectangle in the same manner, above the line segment for the pentagon. It should be simple to determine which segment is longer and therefore which figure has the greater perimeter.

Bring closure to this activity by asking volunteers to share their favorite strategy, solution, or discovery from the problems.

2 Ongoing Learning & Practice

▶ Playing *Polygon Capture*

PARTNER ACTIVITY

(*Math Journal 1*, Activity Sheets 3 and 4; *Student Reference Book,* p. 328)

Students practice identifying attributes of polygons by playing *Polygon Capture*. The game is played with two players or two teams of two players each.

▶ Math Boxes 3•10

INDEPENDENT ACTIVITY

(*Math Journal 1,* p. 97)

Mixed Practice Math Boxes in this lesson are paired with Math Boxes in Lesson 3-8. The skill in Problem 6 previews Unit 4 content.

▶ Study Link 3•10

INDEPENDENT ACTIVITY

(*Math Masters,* p. 95)

Home Connection Students review some of the major concepts of the unit. They draw polygons with specific attributes, find missing angle measurements in two figures, measure a line segment, add angles, and identify a type of polygon.

3 Differentiation Options

READINESS

▶ Reviewing Geometry Vocabulary

INDEPENDENT ACTIVITY

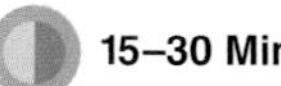
15–30 Min

To provide a visual reference for geometry words, have students create small vocabulary posters. Assign students the ten vocabulary words or phrases listed below. They write each word or phrase on a separate piece of paper and create a visual to

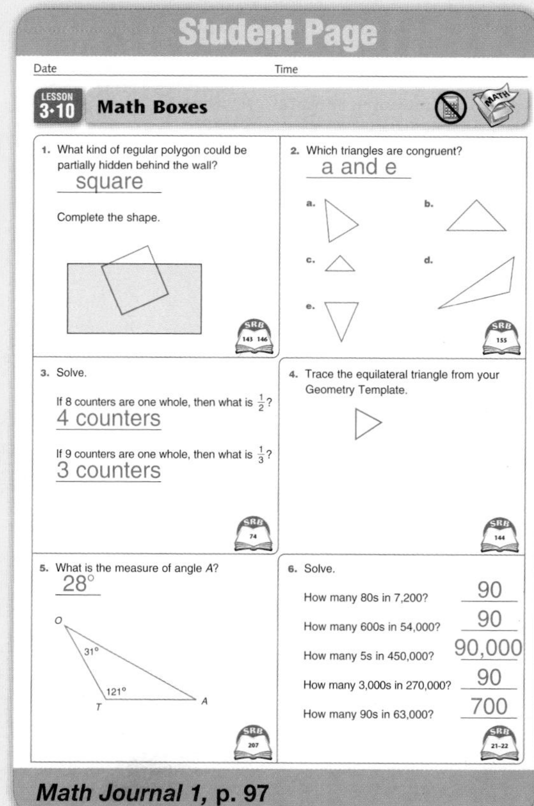

Student Page

Date Time

LESSON 3•10 **Math Boxes**

1. What kind of regular polygon could be partially hidden behind the wall? square
Complete the shape.

2. Which triangles are congruent? a and e

3. Solve.
If 8 counters are one whole, then what is $\frac{1}{2}$? 4 counters
If 9 counters are one whole, then what is $\frac{1}{3}$? 3 counters

4. Trace the equilateral triangle from your Geometry Template.

5. What is the measure of angle *A*? 28°

6. Solve.
How many 80s in 7,200? 90
How many 600s in 54,000? 90
How many 5s in 450,000? 90,000
How many 3,000s in 270,000? 90
How many 90s in 63,000? 700

Math Journal 1, p. 97

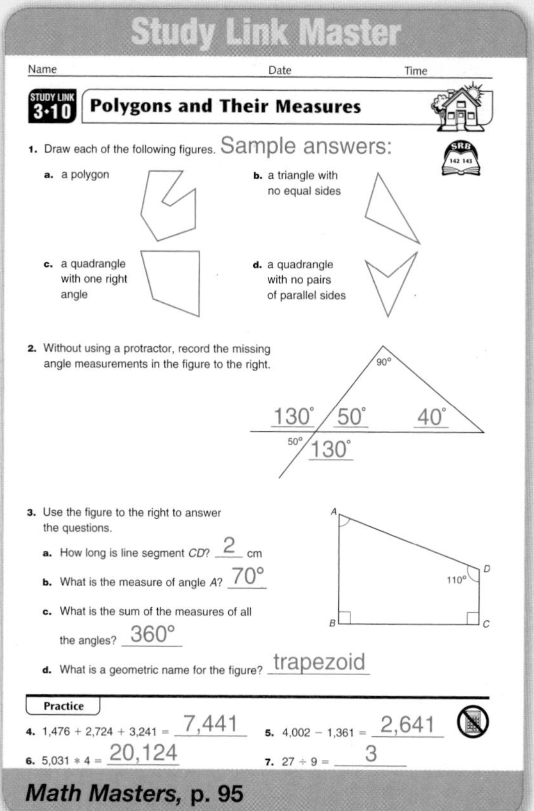

Study Link Master

Name Date Time

STUDY LINK 3•10 **Polygons and Their Measures**

1. Draw each of the following figures. Sample answers:
a. a polygon
b. a triangle with no equal sides
c. a quadrangle with one right angle
d. a quadrangle with no pairs of parallel sides

2. Without using a protractor, record the missing angle measurements in the figure to the right.

3. Use the figure to the right to answer the questions.
a. How long is line segment *CD*? 2 cm
b. What is the measure of angle *A*? 70°
c. What is the sum of the measures of all the angles? 360°
d. What is a geometric name for the figure? trapezoid

Practice
4. 1,476 + 2,724 + 3,241 = 7,441
5. 4,002 − 1,361 = 2,641
6. 5,031 ∗ 4 = 20,124
7. 27 ÷ 9 = 3

Math Masters, p. 95

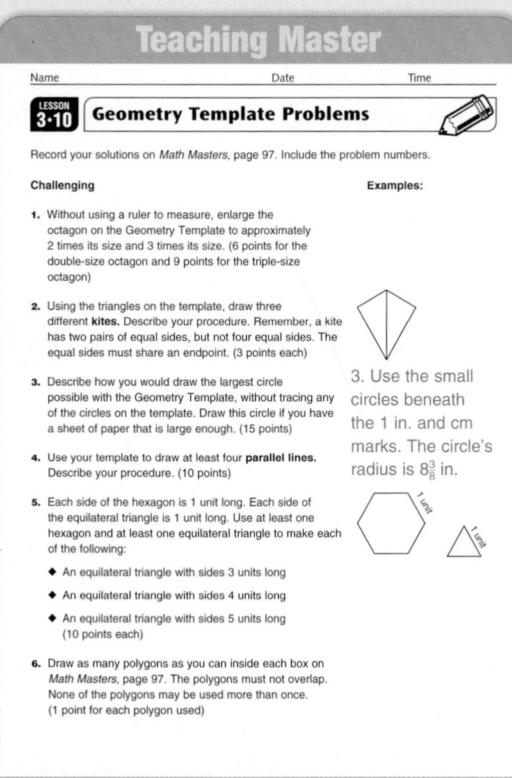
Teaching Master

Name Date Time

LESSON 3•10 **Geometry Template Problems**

Record your solutions on *Math Masters,* page 97. Include the problem numbers.

Challenging **Examples:**

1. Without using a ruler to measure, enlarge the octagon on the Geometry Template to approximately 2 times its size and 3 times its size. (6 points for the double-size octagon and 9 points for the triple-size octagon)
2. Using the triangles on the template, draw three different **kites.** Describe your procedure. Remember, a kite has two pairs of equal sides, but not four equal sides. The equal sides must share an endpoint. (3 points each)
3. Describe how you would draw the largest circle possible with the Geometry Template, without tracing any of the circles on the template. Draw this circle if you have a sheet of paper that is large enough. (15 points)
4. Use your template to draw at least four **parallel lines.** Describe your procedure. (10 points)
5. Each side of the hexagon is 1 unit long. Each side of the equilateral triangle is 1 unit long. Use at least one hexagon and at least one equilateral triangle to make each of the following:
   - An equilateral triangle with sides 3 units long
   - An equilateral triangle with sides 4 units long
   - An equilateral triangle with sides 5 units long (10 points each)
6. Draw as many polygons as you can inside each box on *Math Masters,* page 97. The polygons must not overlap. None of the polygons may be used more than once. (1 point for each polygon used)

3. Use the small circles beneath the 1 in. and cm marks. The circle's radius is $8\frac{3}{8}$ in.

1 unit

1 unit

Math Masters, p. 96

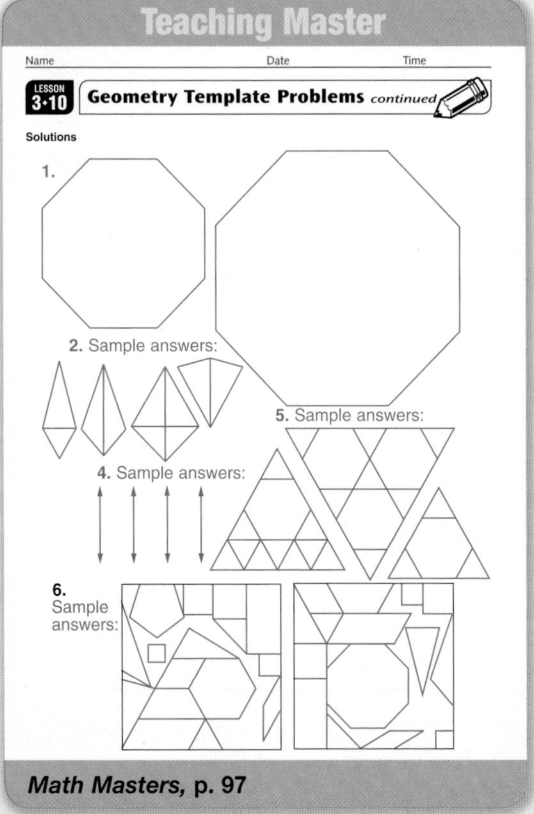
Teaching Master

Name Date Time

LESSON 3•10 **Geometry Template Problems** *continued*

Solutions

1.

2. Sample answers:

5. Sample answers:

4. Sample answers:

6. Sample answers:

Math Masters, p. 97

remind everyone what the word or phrase means. The visuals should be drawn with marker and a straightedge when appropriate. These words can be posted during the lesson.

Words and phrases: *radius, diameter, parallel, right angle, acute angle, obtuse angle, perimeter, parallelogram, pentagon, kite*

ENRICHMENT

15–30 Min

▶ Solving Geometry Template Challenges

(*Math Masters,* pp. 96 and 97)

To further explore polygons on the Geometry Template, have students use what they know about polygons and angle relationships to solve the problems on *Math Masters*, pages 96 and 97.

Problem 1: This problem is similar to Problem 7 on journal page 95, except that there are eight sides instead of four.

Problem 2: To draw a kite using one of the triangles on the Geometry Template, trace the triangle, flip the template over, and trace the triangle again to get a mirror image of the first tracing.

Problem 3: Use the circle guides at the 0-centimeter and 0-inch marks (diagonally across from each other) to draw the largest possible circle.

Problem 4: Use a side of the Geometry Template to draw a line segment. Place a side of one of the template triangles on this segment. Trace one of the other sides of the triangle. Slide the triangle along the first line segment that you drew and trace the same side of the triangle as before. The two tracings should be parallel.

Continue in this manner to create a series of parallel tracings. Put arrowheads on the ends of the tracings, to represent parallel lines.

EXTRA PRACTICE

SMALL-GROUP ACTIVITY

5–15 Min

▶ *5-Minute Math*

To offer students more experience with measuring angles, see *5-Minute Math,* page 53.

3•11 Progress Check 3

Objective To assess students' progress on mathematical content through the end of Unit 3.

1 Looking Back: Cumulative Assessment

Input student data from Progress Check 3 into the **Assessment Management Spreadsheets**.

Materials
- ◆ Study Link 3•10
- ◆ *Assessment Handbook,* pp. 68–75, 164–169, 218, and 254–257
- ◆ slate; Geometry Template

CONTENT ASSESSED	LESSON(S)	ASSESSMENT ITEMS				
		SELF	ORAL/SLATE	WRITTEN PART A	WRITTEN PART B	OPEN RESPONSE
Identify place value in numbers to billions. [Number and Numeration Goal 1]	3•1, 3•2	1	1, 3	5		
Use rules of divisibility. [Number and Numeration Goal 3]			2			
Use mental arithmetic and paper-and-pencil algorithms to solve problems involving the addition and subtraction of whole numbers. [Operations and Computation Goal 1]						✓
Solve multiplication fact extensions. [Operations and Computation Goal 2]			4			
Use table data to answer questions. [Data and Chance Goal 2]	3•1, 3•2				18	
Use tools to estimate and measure angles. [Measurement and Reference Frames Goal 1]	3•4–3•6, 3•9, 3•10	3		1–4	17	
Identify types of angles. [Geometry Goal 1]	3•3–3•5, 3•7, 3•9, 3•10	2		1–4	16, 17	✓
Determine angle measures based on relationships between angles. [Geometry Goal 1]	3•3–3•5, 3•9	5			13–15	
Draw and identify types of triangles. [Geometry Goal 2]	3•6, 3•10	4		6–10		
Compare and contrast the properties of polygons. [Geometry Goal 2]	3•7, 3•8, 3•10	6		11, 12		
Create and define tessellations. [Geometry Goal 3]	3•8	7			19, 20	

2 Looking Ahead: Preparing for Unit 4

Math Boxes 3•11

Study Link 3•11: Unit 4 Family Letter

Materials
- ◆ *Math Journal 1,* p. 98
- ◆ *Math Masters,* pp. 98–101

Getting Started

Math Message • Self Assessment

Complete the Self Assessment (Assessment Handbook, *page 164*).

Study Link 3•10 Follow-Up

Allow students five minutes to work together to compare their answers and resolve any differences.

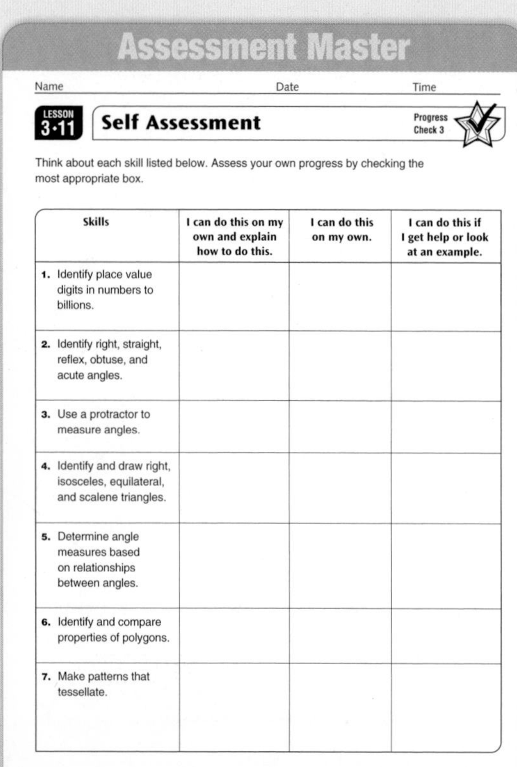

Assessment Master

Name Date Time

LESSON 3•11 Self Assessment Progress Check 3

Think about each skill listed below. Assess your own progress by checking the most appropriate box.

Skills	I can do this on my own and explain how to do this.	I can do this on my own.	I can do this if I get help or look at an example.
1. Identify place value digits in numbers to billions.			
2. Identify right, straight, reflex, obtuse, and acute angles.			
3. Use a protractor to measure angles.			
4. Identify and draw right, isosceles, equilateral, and scalene triangles.			
5. Determine angle measures based on relationships between angles.			
6. Identify and compare properties of polygons.			
7. Make patterns that tessellate.			

Assessment Handbook, p. 164

1 Looking Back: Cumulative Assessment

▶ Math Message Follow-Up

INDEPENDENT ACTIVITY

(Self Assessment, *Assessment Handbook,* p. 164)

The Self Assessment offers students the opportunity to reflect upon their progress.

▶ Oral and Slate Assessment

WHOLE-CLASS ACTIVITY

Problems 1, 3, and 4 provide summative information and may be used for grading purposes. Problem 2 provides formative information that can be useful in planning future instruction.

Oral Assessment

1. Rounding numbers.
   - 472 to the nearest ten 470
   - 3,804 to the nearest ten 3,800
   - 76.7 to the nearest whole number 77
   - 29.08 to the nearest tenth 29.1
   - 140.23 to the nearest tenth 140.2
   - 653.09 to the nearest whole number 653
2. Write numbers on the board. Students show thumbs up if the number is divisible by the stated divisor and thumbs down if it is not divisible.
   - Is 1,263 divisible by 2? down By 3? up By 5? down By 9? down
   - Is 476 divisible by 2? up By 3? down By 4? up By 6? down
   - Is 750 divisible by 2? up By 3? up By 5? up By 6? up By 9? down By 10? up

Slate Assessment

3. Use your slate procedures. Dictate the problems for students to write and mark on their slates.

- Write 5,008,724. Circle the digit in the ten-thousands place. Underline the digit in the hundred-thousands place. 5,008,724
- Write 19,430,201,155. Circle the digit in the thousands place. Underline the digit in the hundred-thousands place. 19,430,201,155
- Write 628.07. Circle the digit in the tenths place. Underline the digit in the tens place. 628.07
- Write 523.19. Circle the hundredths digit. Underline the tenths digit. 523.19

4. Complete. Ask students to explain the patterns in the products for each set.

- 4 [50s] = ? 200 40 [50s] = ? 2,000 400 [50s] = ? 20,000
- 90 [6s] = ? 540 90 [60s] = ? 5,400 900 [60s] = ? 54,000
- 7 [80s] = ? 560 70 [80s] = ? 5,600 700 [80s] = ? 56,000

▶ Written Assessment

INDEPENDENT ACTIVITY

(*Assessment Handbook*, pp. 165–168)

Part A Recognizing Student Achievement

Problems 1–12 provide summative information and may be used for grading purposes.

Problem(s)	Description
1–4	Measure angles.
1–4	Identify types of angles.
5	Identify place value in numbers to billions.
6–8	Draw types of triangles.
9, 10	Identify types of triangles and compare properties.
11, 12	Compare the properties of polygons.

Part B Informing Instruction

Problems 13–20 provide formative information that can be useful in planning future instruction.

Problem(s)	Description
13–15	Determine angle measures based on relationships between angles.
17	Estimate angle measures.
16, 17	Identify types of angles.
18	Read a chart.
19, 20	Create and define tessellations.

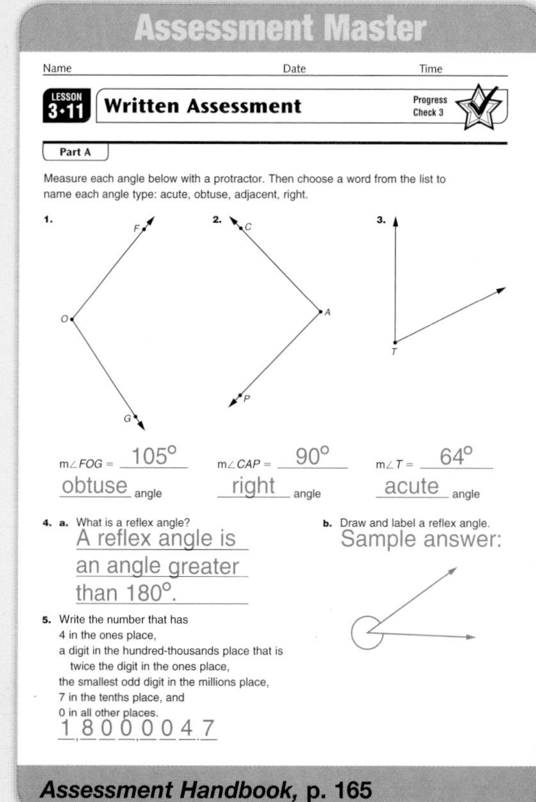
Assessment Master

Name Date Time

LESSON 3·11 Written Assessment Progress Check 3

Part A

Measure each angle below with a protractor. Then choose a word from the list to name each angle type: acute, obtuse, adjacent, right.

1. m∠FOG = 105° obtuse angle
2. m∠CAP = 90° right angle
3. m∠T = 64° acute angle

4. a. What is a reflex angle? A reflex angle is an angle greater than 180°.
b. Draw and label a reflex angle. Sample answer:

5. Write the number that has
4 in the ones place,
a digit in the hundred-thousands place that is twice the digit in the ones place,
the smallest odd digit in the millions place,
7 in the tenths place, and
0 in all other places.
1,800,004.7

Assessment Handbook, p. 165

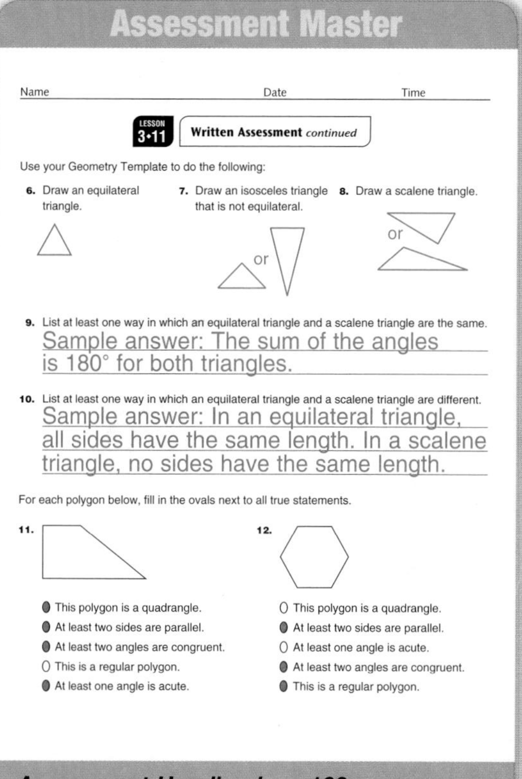
Assessment Master

Name Date Time

LESSON 3·11 Written Assessment *continued*

Use your Geometry Template to do the following:

6. Draw an equilateral triangle.
7. Draw an isosceles triangle that is not equilateral.
8. Draw a scalene triangle.

9. List at least one way in which an equilateral triangle and a scalene triangle are the same.
Sample answer: The sum of the angles is 180° for both triangles.

10. List at least one way in which an equilateral triangle and a scalene triangle are different.
Sample answer: In an equilateral triangle, all sides have the same length. In a scalene triangle, no sides have the same length.

For each polygon below, fill in the ovals next to all true statements.

11.
- ● This polygon is a quadrangle.
- ● At least two sides are parallel.
- ● At least two angles are congruent.
- ○ This is a regular polygon.
- ● At least one angle is acute.

12.
- ○ This polygon is a quadrangle.
- ● At least two sides are parallel.
- ○ At least one angle is acute.
- ● At least two angles are congruent.
- ● This is a regular polygon.

Assessment Handbook, p. 166

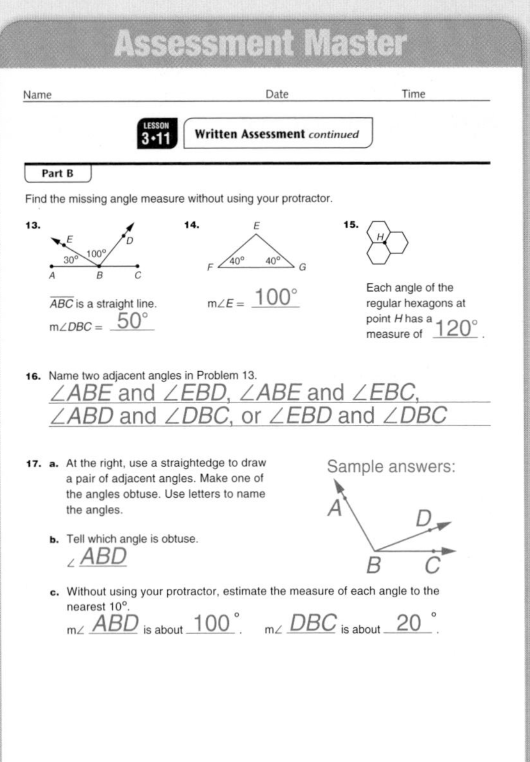
Assessment Master

Name ____ Date ____ Time ____

LESSON 3•11 **Written Assessment** *continued*

Part B

Find the missing angle measure without using your protractor.

13. $\overline{ABC}$ is a straight line.
m∠DBC = 50°

14. m∠E = 100°

15. Each angle of the regular hexagons at point *H* has a measure of 120°.

16. Name two adjacent angles in Problem 13.
∠ABE and ∠EBD, ∠ABE and ∠EBC, ∠ABD and ∠DBC, or ∠EBD and ∠DBC

17. a. At the right, use a straightedge to draw a pair of adjacent angles. Make one of the angles obtuse. Use letters to name the angles.
Sample answers:

b. Tell which angle is obtuse.
∠ABD

c. Without using your protractor, estimate the measure of each angle to the nearest 10°.
m∠ABD is about 100°. m∠DBC is about 20°.

Assessment Handbook, p. 167

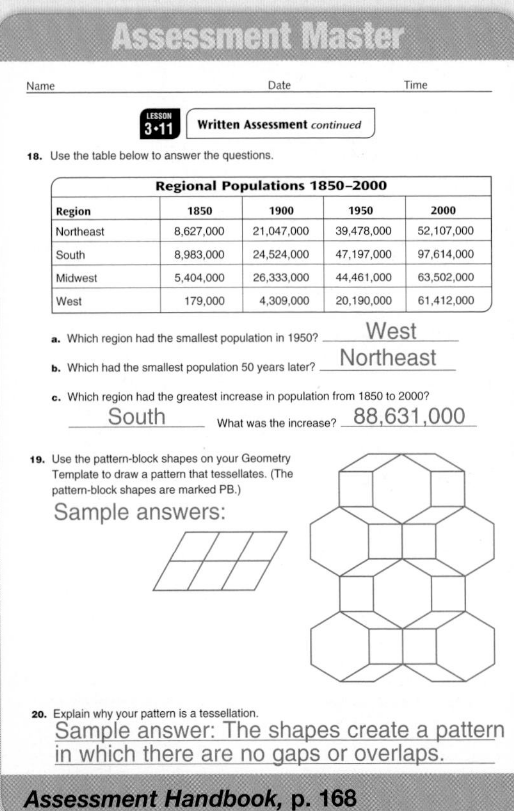
Assessment Master

Name ____ Date ____ Time ____

LESSON 3•11 **Written Assessment** *continued*

18. Use the table below to answer the questions.

Regional Populations 1850–2000				
Region	**1850**	**1900**	**1950**	**2000**
Northeast	8,627,000	21,047,000	39,478,000	52,107,000
South	8,983,000	24,524,000	47,197,000	97,614,000
Midwest	5,404,000	26,333,000	44,461,000	63,502,000
West	179,000	4,309,000	20,190,000	61,412,000

a. Which region had the smallest population in 1950? West

b. Which had the smallest population 50 years later? Northeast

c. Which region had the greatest increase in population from 1850 to 2000?
South What was the increase? 88,631,000

19. Use the pattern-block shapes on your Geometry Template to draw a pattern that tessellates. (The pattern-block shapes are marked PB.)
Sample answers:

20. Explain why your pattern is a tessellation.
Sample answer: The shapes create a pattern in which there are no gaps or overlaps.

Assessment Handbook, p. 168

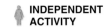

Use the checklists on pages 255 and 257 of the *Assessment Handbook* to record results. Then input the data into the **Assessment Management Spreadsheets** to keep an ongoing record of students' progress toward Grade-Level Goals.

▶ Open Response

INDEPENDENT ACTIVITY

(*Assessment Handbook,* p. 169)

Adding Angles

The open-response item requires students to apply skills and concepts from Unit 3 to solve a multistep problem. See *Assessment Handbook,* pages 71 through 75 for rubrics and students' work samples for this problem.

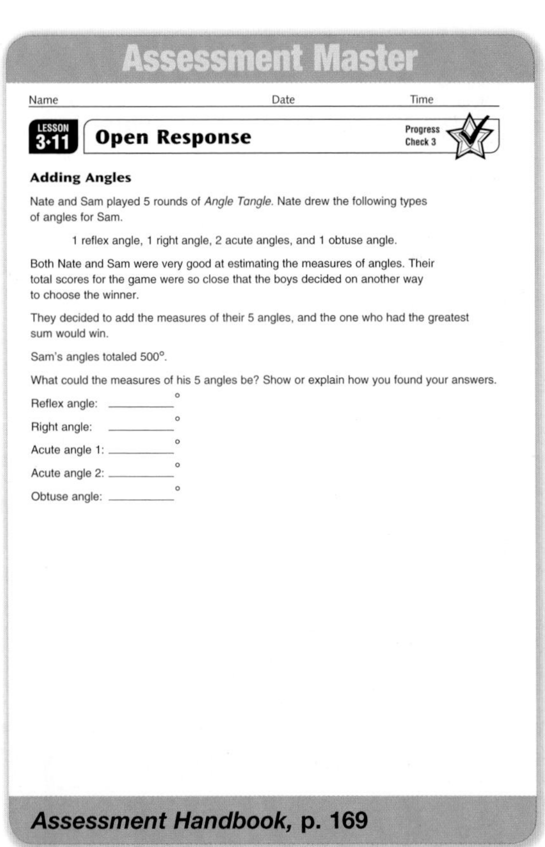
Assessment Master

Name ____ Date ____ Time ____

LESSON 3•11 **Open Response** Progress Check 3

Adding Angles

Nate and Sam played 5 rounds of *Angle Tangle.* Nate drew the following types of angles for Sam.

1 reflex angle, 1 right angle, 2 acute angles, and 1 obtuse angle.

Both Nate and Sam were very good at estimating the measures of angles. Their total scores for the game were so close that the boys decided on another way to choose the winner.

They decided to add the measures of their 5 angles, and the one who had the greatest sum would win.

Sam's angles totaled 500°.

What could the measures of his 5 angles be? Show or explain how you found your answers.

Reflex angle: ____°

Right angle: ____°

Acute angle 1: ____°

Acute angle 2: ____°

Obtuse angle: ____°

Assessment Handbook, p. 169

2 Looking Ahead: Preparing for Unit 4

Math Boxes 3•11

INDEPENDENT ACTIVITY

(*Math Journal 1,* p. 98)

Mixed Practice This Math Boxes page previews Unit 4 content.

Study Link 3•11: Unit 4 Family Letter

INDEPENDENT ACTIVITY

(*Math Masters*, pp. 98–101)

Home Connection The Unit 4 Family Letter provides parents and guardians with information and activities related to Unit 4 topics.

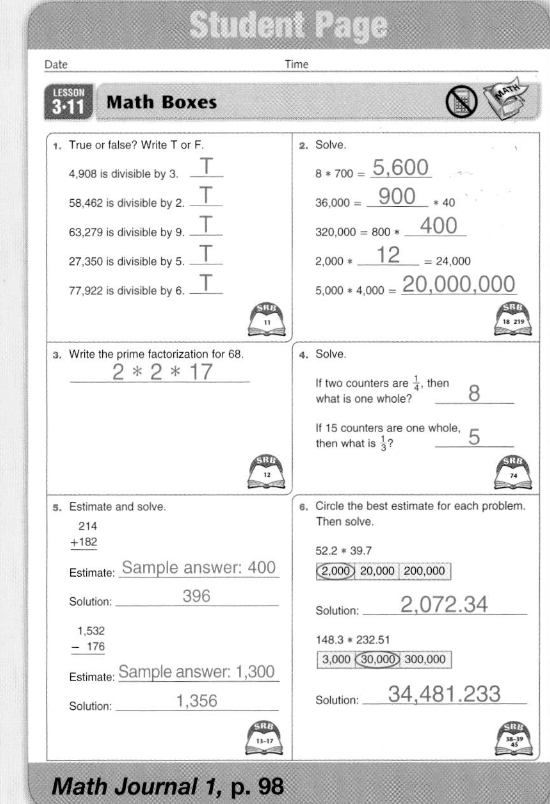

Student Page

Date Time

LESSON 3•11 **Math Boxes**

1. True or false? Write T or F.
   - 4,908 is divisible by 3. T
   - 58,462 is divisible by 2. T
   - 63,279 is divisible by 9. T
   - 27,350 is divisible by 5. T
   - 77,922 is divisible by 6. T

2. Solve.
   - 8 * 700 = 5,600
   - 36,000 = 900 * 40
   - 320,000 = 800 * 400
   - 2,000 * 12 = 24,000
   - 5,000 * 4,000 = 20,000,000

3. Write the prime factorization for 68.
   2 * 2 * 17

4. Solve.
   - If two counters are $\frac{1}{4}$, then what is one whole? 8
   - If 15 counters are one whole, then what is $\frac{1}{3}$? 5

5. Estimate and solve.
   - 214 + 182
     Estimate: Sample answer: 400
     Solution: 396
   - 1,532 − 176
     Estimate: Sample answer: 1,300
     Solution: 1,356

6. Circle the best estimate for each problem. Then solve.
   - 52.2 * 39.7
     (2,000) 20,000 200,000
     Solution: 2,072.34
   - 148.3 * 232.51
     3,000 (30,000) 300,000
     Solution: 34,481.233

Math Journal 1, p. 98

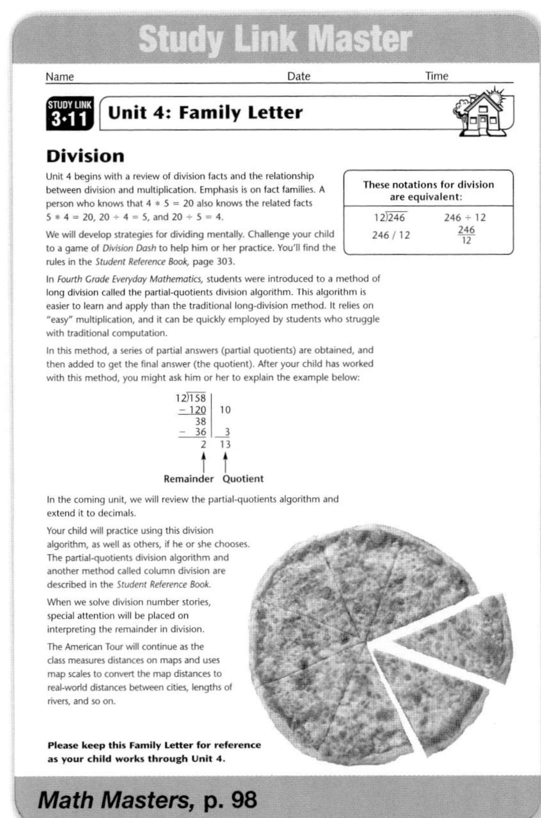

Study Link Master

Name Date Time

STUDY LINK 3•11 **Unit 4: Family Letter**

Division

Unit 4 begins with a review of division facts and the relationship between division and multiplication. Emphasis is on fact families. A person who knows that 4 * 5 = 20 also knows the related facts 5 * 4 = 20, 20 ÷ 4 = 5, and 20 ÷ 5 = 4.

These notations for division are equivalent:	
12)246	246 ÷ 12
246 / 12	$\frac{246}{12}$

We will develop strategies for dividing mentally. Challenge your child to a game of *Division Dash* to help him or her practice. You'll find the rules in the *Student Reference Book,* page 303.

In *Fourth Grade Everyday Mathematics,* students were introduced to a method of long division called the partial-quotients division algorithm. This algorithm is easier to learn and apply than the traditional long-division method. It relies on "easy" multiplication, and it can be quickly employed by students who struggle with traditional computation.

In this method, a series of partial answers (partial quotients) are obtained, and then added to get the final answer (the quotient). After your child has worked with this method, you might ask him or her to explain the example below:

```
12)158 |
 - 120 | 10
    38 |
 -  36 |  3
     2   13
     ↑    ↑
Remainder Quotient
```

In the coming unit, we will review the partial-quotients algorithm and extend it to decimals.

Your child will practice using this division algorithm, as well as others, if he or she chooses. The partial-quotients division algorithm and another method called column division are described in the *Student Reference Book.*

When we solve division number stories, special attention will be placed on interpreting the remainder in division.

The American Tour will continue as the class measures distances on maps and uses map scales to convert the map distances to real-world distances between cities, lengths of rivers, and so on.

Please keep this Family Letter for reference as your child works through Unit 4.

Math Masters, p. 98

Unit 4 Organizer

Division

Overview

The main purpose of Unit 4 is to develop division concepts. The unit begins by reviewing basic division facts and the partial-quotients division algorithm. The algorithm, which was introduced in fourth grade, is then extended to include division of a decimal by a whole number. The American Tour Project lesson in this unit focuses on map scales. Unit 4 has four main areas of focus:

- To review multiplication and division facts and to apply basic facts to division with 1-digit divisors,
- To review and practice the partial-quotients division algorithm with whole numbers,
- To use the partial-quotients algorithm to divide decimals by whole numbers, and
- To practice solving division number stories and interpreting the remainder.

Linking to the Common Core State Standards

The content of Unit 4 addresses the Common Core State Standards for Mathematics in *Number and Operations in Base Ten.* The correlation of the Common Core State Standards to the *Everyday Mathematics* Grade 5 lessons begins on page CS1.

Contents

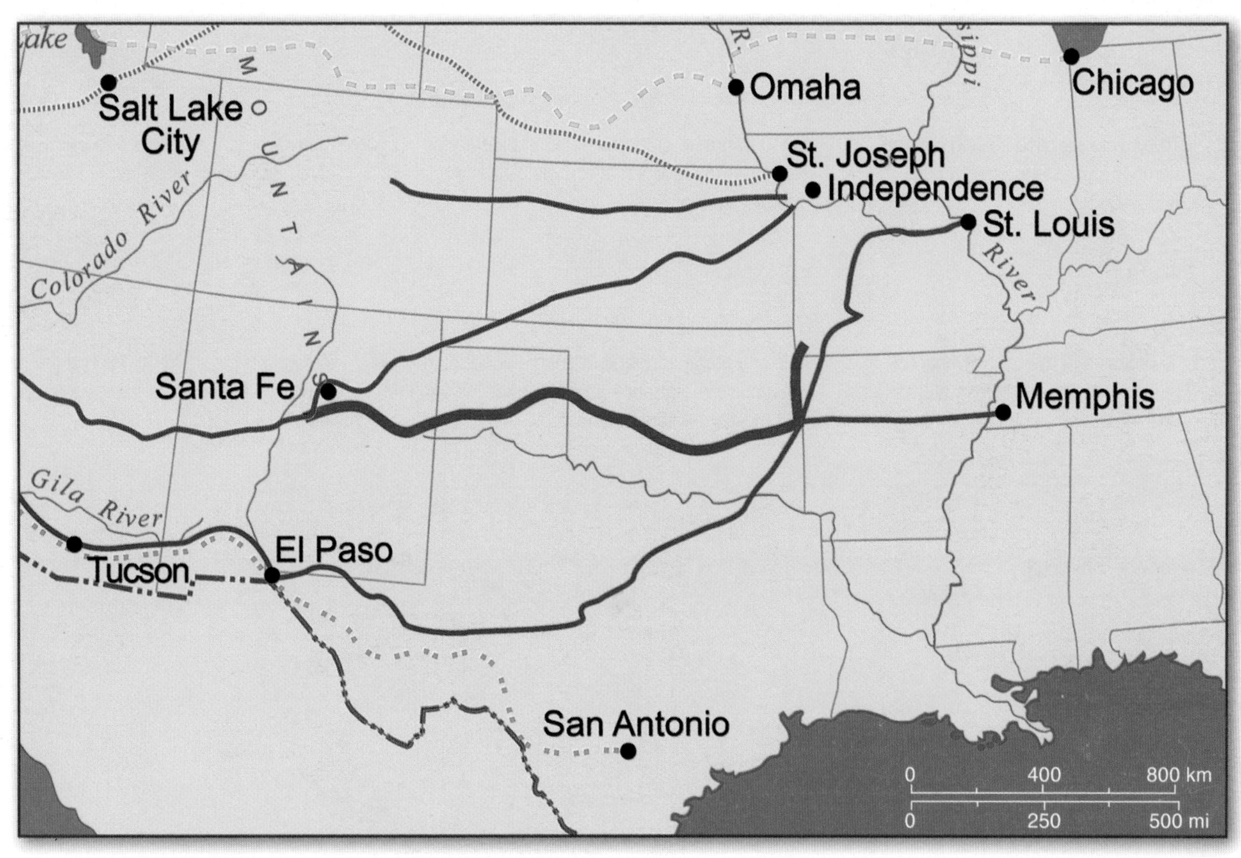

Salt Lake City
Omaha
Chicago
St. Joseph
Independence
St. Louis
Colorado River
Santa Fe
Memphis
Gila River
Tucson
El Paso
San Antonio
0 400 800 km
0 250 500 mi

Unit 4 Organizer

Learning In Perspective

	Lesson Objectives	Links to the Past	Links to the Future
4•1	To review multiplication and division facts and apply basic facts to division with 1-digit divisors.	In fourth grade, students work toward automatic recall of multiplication facts and explore the relationship between multiplication and division.	In sixth grade, students maintain and apply skills to develop proficiency with partial-quotients for whole number and decimal division.
4•2	To review the partial-quotients division algorithm with whole numbers.	In fourth grade, students are introduced to the partial-quotient division algorithm.	In sixth grade, students use estimation and algorithms to divide whole numbers.
4•3	To develop strategies for estimating straight-path distances using a map scale.	In fourth grade, students practice measuring and using a map scale.	In sixth grade, students explore the use of ratios to describe size changes.
4•4	To provide practice with strategies for the partial-quotients algorithm.	In fourth grade, students are introduced to the partial-quotient division algorithm.	In sixth grade, students extend the partial-quotients method to decimal divisors.
4•5	To provide experience with making magnitude estimates for quotients and using the partial-quotients algorithm with decimals.	In fourth grade, students are introduced to the partial-quotients method to divide decimals by whole numbers and the use of magnitude estimates to place decimal points in quotients.	In sixth grade, students use the partial-quotients method to find quotients to any given number of decimal places and to rename fractions as decimals.
4•6	To provide practice solving division number stories and interpreting remainders.	In fourth grade, students explore a variety of strategies to solve equal-grouping division number stories.	In sixth grade, students find quotients to a given number of decimal places.
4•7	To investigate the use of variables, review a variety of mathematics skills, and explore division concepts.	In fourth grade, students identify the solution of an open number sentence as a value for the variable that makes the sentence true.	In sixth grade, students extend the pan-balance approach to more complex equations.

	Key Concepts and Skills	Grade 5 Goals*
4·1	Generate equivalent names for whole numbers.	Number and Numeration Goal 4
	Apply multiplication facts, related division facts, or extended facts to identify friendly numbers.	Operations and Computation Goal 2
	Use friendly numbers to divide 2-digit by 1-digit numbers.	Operations and Computation Goal 3
4·2	Use the partial-quotients algorithm for problems.	Operations and Computation Goal 3
	Apply friendly numbers to identify partial quotients.	Operations and Computation Goal 3
	Factor numbers to identify partial quotients.	Operations and Computation Goal 3
4·3	Use a map scale.	Operations and Computation Goal 7
	Measure to the nearest half-inch.	Measurement and Reference Frames Goal 1
	Estimate distances on a map.	Measurement and Reference Frames Goal 1
4·4	Use divisibility rules to identify multiples.	Number and Numeration Goal 3
	Apply division facts and extended facts to identify partial quotients.	Operations and Computation Goal 2
	Use the partial-quotients algorithm for problems.	Operations and Computation Goal 3
4·5	Use vocabulary (dividend, divisor, quotient, and remainder) to discuss magnitude estimates.	Operations and Computation Goal 3
	Use the partial-quotients algorithm to solve problems.	Operations and Computation Goal 3
	Make magnitude estimates for quotients.	Operations and Computation Goal 6
4·6	Interpret the remainder in number story solutions.	Operations and Computation Goal 3
	Make magnitude estimates for quotients.	Operations and Computation Goal 6
	Write and solve number sentences that model division number stories.	Patterns, Functions, and Algebra Goal 2
4·7	Find the value of an algebraic expression.	Patterns, Functions, and Algebra Goal 2
	Write number sentences that model given situations.	Patterns, Functions, and Algebra Goal 2

*See the Appendix for a complete list of Grade 5 Goals.

A Balanced Curriculum

Ongoing Practice

Everyday Mathematics provides numerous opportunities for ongoing practice. These activities are embedded throughout the lessons:

Mental Math and Reflexes activities promote speed and accuracy in mental computation.

Math Boxes offer mixed practice and are paired across lessons as shown in the brackets below. This makes them useful as assessment tools. The last one or two boxes on each page preview the next unit's content.

Mixed practice	[4•1, 4•3], [4•2, 4•4, 4•6], [4•5, 4•7]
Mixed practice with multiple choice	4•1, 4•2, 4•3, 4•4, 4•5, 4•6, 4•7
Mixed practice with writing/reasoning opportunity	4•1, 4•2, 4•5, 4•6, 4•7

Study Links are daily homework assignments that review the content of the lesson and often contain ongoing facts practice or computation practice.

5-Minute Math problems are offered for additional practice in Lessons 4•1 and 4•6.

EM Facts Workshop Game provides online practice of basic facts and computation.

EXTRA PRACTICE **Extra Practice** activities are included in Lessons 4•1, 4•3, 4•4, 4•6, and 4•7.

Practice through Games

Games are an essential component of practice in the *Everyday Mathematics* program. Games offer skills practice and promote strategic thinking. See the *Differentiation Handbook* for ways to adapt games to meet students' needs.

Lesson	Game	Skill Practiced
4•1	*Name That Number*	Generate equivalent names for whole numbers [NN Goal 4]
4•2	*Division Dash*	Mentally calculate division problems [OC Goal 3]
4•4	*Divisibility Dash*	Recognize multiples and use divisibility rules [NN Goal 3]
4•5	*Division Top-It* (3-Digit Dividends)	Apply multiples and practice division facts and extended facts [OC Goal 3]
4•7	*First to 100*	Review various mathematics skills [PFA Goal 2]
4•7	*Algebra Election*	Review various mathematics skills [PFA Goal 2]

[NN] Number and Numeration
[MRF] Measurement and Reference Frames
[OC] Operations and Computation
[GEO] Geometry
[DC] Data and Chance
[PFA] Patterns, Functions, and Algebra

Problem Solving 

Experts at problem solving and mathematical modeling generally do these things:

- Identify the problem.
- Decide what information is needed to solve the problem.
- Play with and study the data to find patterns and meaning.
- Identify and use mathematical procedures to solve the problem.
- Decide whether the solution makes sense and whether it can be applied to other problems.

The table below lists some of the opportunities in this unit for students to practice these strategies.

Lessons that teach *through* problem solving, not just *about* problem solving

Lesson	Activity
4•1	Find equivalent names for a number using multiples of a given number.
4•3	Find distances on a map using the map scale.
4•6	Use division to solve number stories; and interpret the quotient and remainder in context.
4•7	Replace variables with randomly generated numbers, then solve.

See Chapter 18: Problem Solving in the *Teacher's Reference Manual* for more information.

The Language of Mathematics

Everyday Mathematics provides lesson-specific suggestions to help all students acquire, process, and express mathematical ideas. Throughout Unit 4, there are lesson-specific language development notes that address the needs of English language learners, indicated by ELL.

ELL SUPPORT Activities to support English language learners are in Part 3 of Lessons 4•2, 4•5, and 4•7.

The *English Learners Handbook* and the *Differentiation Handbook* have suggestions for promoting language development and acquisition of mathematics vocabulary. See Unit 4 in each handbook.

Unit 4 Vocabulary

decimal point
dividend
divisor
magnitude estimate
map legend, or map key
map scale
multiples
partial quotient
quotient
remainder
variable

Literacy Connection

A Remainder of One, by Elinor J. Pinczes, Houghton Mifflin Harcourt, 2002

One Hundred Hungry Ants, by Elinor J. Pinczes, Houghton Mifflin Harcourt, 1999

For more literacy connections, see the *Home Connection Handbook,* Grades 4–6.

Cross-Curricular Links 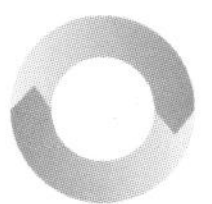

Social Studies

Lesson 4•3 Students explore the physical geography of the United States using a landform map.

Lesson 4•7 Students play a variation of *First to 100* using electoral votes as points.

Balanced Assessment

Daily Assessments

- **Recognizing Student Achievement** – A daily assessment that is included in every lesson to evaluate students' progress toward the Grade 5 Grade-Level Goals.
- **Informing Instruction** – Notes that appear throughout the unit to help anticipate students' common errors and suggest appropriate problem-solving strategies.

Lesson	Recognizing Student Achievement	Informing Instruction
4•1	Use multiplication and division facts for division with 1-digit divisors. [OC Goal 3]	Use visualization to support mental math.
4•2	Understand the partial-quotients algorithm. [OC Goal 3]	Use mental strategies.
4•3	Recognize decimal places to the thousandths. [NN Goal 1]	Locate and measure endpoints for map distances.
4•4	Write a division number story. [OC Goal 3]	Use multiples other than multiples of 10.
4•5	Make magnitude estimates for division. [OC Goal 6]	
4•6	Interpret the remainder. [OC Goal 3]	
4•7	Find the value of an algebraic expression. [PFA Goal 2]	

[NN] Number and Numeration
[MRF] Measurement and Reference Frames
[OC] Operations and Computation
[GEO] Geometry
[DC] Data and Chance
[PFA] Patterns, Functions, and Algebra

Portfolio Opportunities

The following lessons provide opportunities to gather samples of students' mathematical writings, drawings, and creations to add balance to the assessment process: Lessons 4•1, 4•2, 4•3, 4•4, 4•5, 4•6, 4•7, and 4•8.

See pages 16 and 17 in the *Assessment Handbook* for more information about portfolios and how to use them.

Unit Assessment

Progress Check 4 – A cumulative assessment of concepts and skills taught in Unit 4 and in previous units, providing information for evaluating students' progress and planning for future instruction. These assessments include oral/slate, written, and open-response activities, as shown below in the sample Progress Check lesson opener.

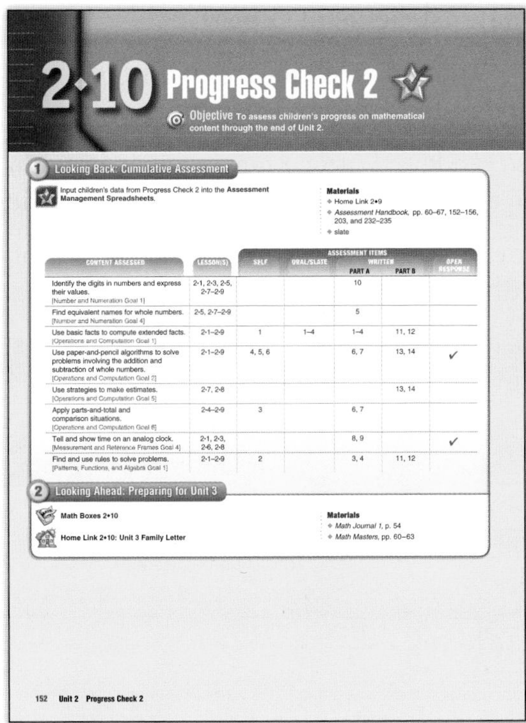

2·10 Progress Check 2

Objective To assess children's progress on mathematical content through the end of Unit 2.

1 Looking Back: Cumulative Assessment

Input children's data from Progress Check 2 into the **Assessment Management Spreadsheets.**

Materials
- Home Link 2•9
- *Assessment Handbook,* pp. 60–67, 152–156, 203, and 232–235
- slate

Content Assessed	Lesson(s)	Assessment Items: Self	Oral/Slate	Written: Part A	Written: Part B	Open Response
Identify the digits in numbers and express their values. [Number and Numeration Goal 1]	2·1, 2·3, 2·5, 2·7–2·9			10		
Find equivalent names for whole numbers. [Number and Numeration Goal 4]	2·5, 2·7–2·9			5		
Use basic facts to compute extended facts. [Operations and Computation Goal 1]	2·1–2·9	1	1–4	1–4	11, 12	
Use paper-and-pencil algorithms to solve problems involving the addition and subtraction of whole numbers. [Operations and Computation Goal 2]	2·1–2·9	4, 5, 6		6, 7	13, 14	✓
Use strategies to make estimates. [Operations and Computation Goal 5]	2·7, 2·8				13, 14	
Apply parts-and-total and comparison situations. [Operations and Computation Goal 6]	2·4–2·9	3		6, 7		
Tell and show time on an analog clock. [Measurement and Reference Frames Goal 4]	2·1, 2·3, 2·6, 2·8			8, 9		✓
Find and use rules to solve problems. [Patterns, Functions, and Algebra Goal 1]	2·1–2·9	2		3, 4	11, 12	

2 Looking Ahead: Preparing for Unit 3

Math Boxes 2•10

Home Link 2•10: Unit 3 Family Letter

Materials
- *Math Journal 1,* p. 54
- *Math Masters,* pp. 60–63

152 Unit 2 Progress Check 2

Core Assessment Resources

Assessment Handbook

- **Unit 4 Assessment Overview,** pages 76–83
- **Unit 4 Assessment Masters,** pages 170–174
- **Unit 4 Individual Profiles of Progress,** pages 258, 259, and 302
- **Unit 4 Class Checklists,** pages 260, 261, and 303
- **Math Logs,** pages 306–308
- **Exit Slip,** page 311
- **Other Student Assessment Forms,** pages 304, 305, 309, 310, and 312

Assessment Management Spreadsheets

The Assessment Management Spreadsheets consist of the Digital Class Checklists and Individual Profile of Progress Checklists. Use them to monitor, record, and report student progress.

Addressing All Needs

Differentiated Instruction

Adjusting the Activity – suggests adaptations that target advanced learners, English language learners, or learners who need additional instructional support.

ELL SUPPORT / ELL – provides lesson-specific suggestions to help English language learners understand and process the mathematical content.

READINESS – accesses students' prior knowledge or previews content that prepares students to engage in the lesson's Part 1 activities.

EXTRA PRACTICE – provides additional opportunities to apply the mathematical content of the lesson.

ENRICHMENT – enables students to apply or further explore the mathematical content of the lesson.

Lesson	Adjusting the Activity	ELL Support/ ELL	Readiness	Extra Practice	Enrichment
4•1	•		•	•	•
4•2	•	•	•		•
4•3	•	•	•	•	•
4•4			•	•	
4•5		•	•		•
4•6			•	•	•
4•7	•	•	•	•	•

Additional Resources

Differentiation Handbook
Provides ideas and strategies for differentiating instruction.

Pages 71–77

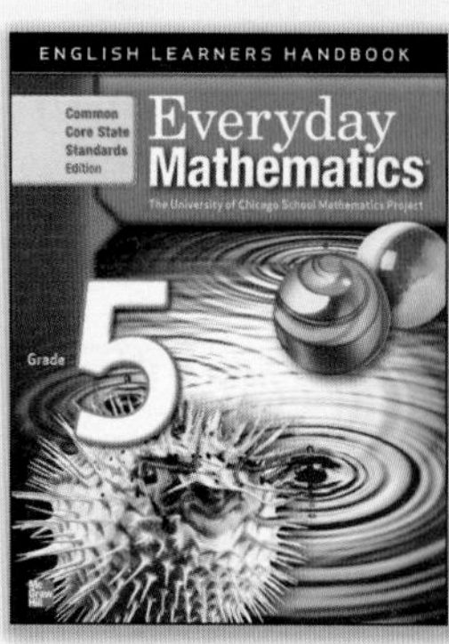

English Learners Handbook
Contains lesson-specific comprehension strategies.

Pages 30–36

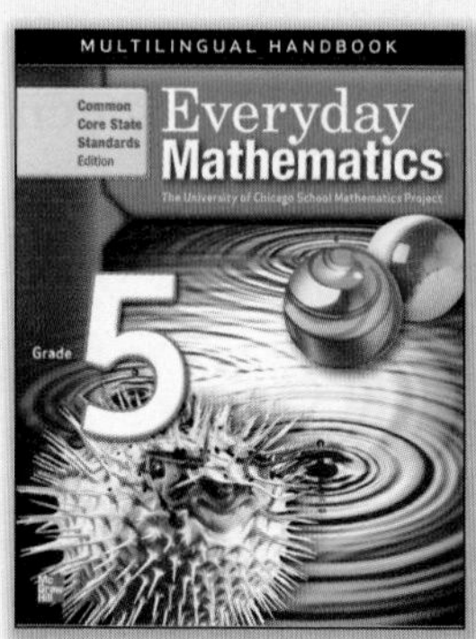

Multilingual Handbook
Previews concepts and vocabulary. It is written in six languages.

Pages 59–72

Planning Tips

Multiage Classroom

Companion Lessons from Grades 4 and 6 can help you meet instructional needs of a multiage classroom. The full Scope and Sequence can be found in the Appendix.

Grade 4	3•5, 4•7	6•3	3•7	6•3, 6•10	9•9	6•4	
Grade 5	4•1	4•2	4•3	4•4	4•5	4•6	4•7
Grade 6	2•7	2•7			2•8		

Pacing for Success

Pacing depends on a number of factors, such as students' individual needs and how long your school has been using *Everyday Mathematics*. At the beginning of Unit 4, you may want to use tools available at www.everydaymathonline.com to help you set your pace.

Home Support

Unit 4 Family Letter (English/Spanish) provides families with an overview, Do-Anytime Activities, Building Skills through Games, a list of vocabulary, and answers to the daily homework (Study Links). Family Letters in English, Spanish, and seven other languages are also available online.

Study Links are the daily homework assignments. They consist of active projects and ongoing review problems.

Home Support Resources

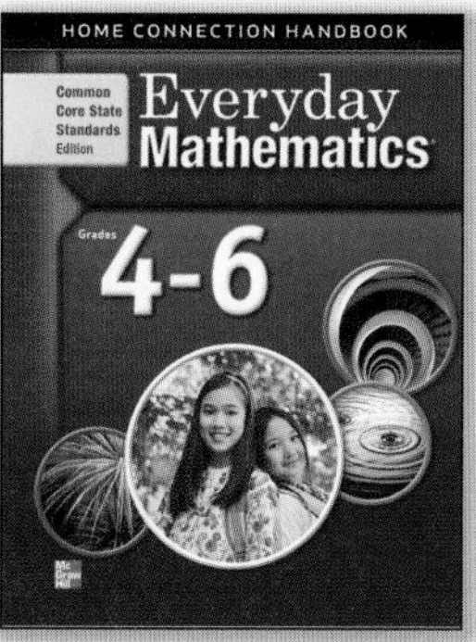

Home Connection Handbook
Offers ideas and reproducible masters for communicating with families. See Table of Contents for unit information.

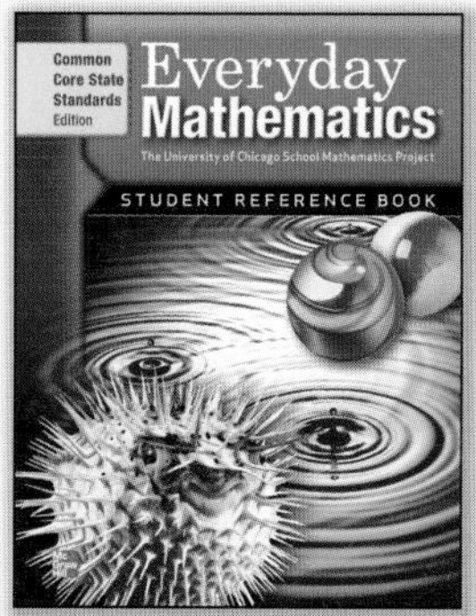

Student Reference Book
Provides a resource for students and parents.

Pages 11, 22–24, 38–44, 211, 212, 242, 302, 303, 308, 325, 334, 339, 381, 386, 387

Technology Resources

Unit 4 Organizer

Materials

Technology Resources www.everydaymathonline.com

ePresentations

eToolkit

Algorithms Practice

EM Facts Workshop Game™

Family Letters

Assessment Management

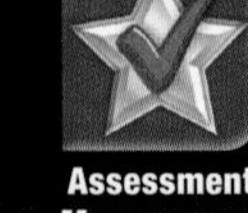
Common Core State Standards

Curriculum Focal Points

Interactive Teacher's Lesson Guide

Lesson	Masters	Manipulative Kit	Other Items
4•1	Study Link Master, p. 102 Teaching Master, p. 103 Teaching Aid Masters, pp. 421 and 440A	per partnership: 4 each of number cards 1–9; per group: 1 deck of number cards; slate	Geometry Template or protractor
4•2	Teaching Aid Masters, pp. 414 and 415 Study Link Master, p. 104 Teaching Master, p. 105	per partnership: 4 each of number cards 1–9; slate	Class Data Pad
4•3	Study Link Master, p. 106 Teaching Masters, pp. 107 and 108 Teaching Aid Master, p. 422	slate; compass	Geometry Template; ruler; string; calculator
4•4	Teaching Masters, pp. 109*, 111, and 112 Teaching Aid Masters, pp. 414 and 415 Study Link Master, p. 110	per partnership: 4 each of number cards 0–9 from one deck of cards and 2 each of number cards 2, 3, 5, 6, 9, and 10 from another deck of cards	Class Data Pad; calculator
4•5	Teaching Aid Master, p. 415 Study Link Master, p. 113 Teaching Masters, pp. 114 and 115	base-10 blocks (6 flats, 22 longs, 40 cubes); slate	bills and coins*; chart paper or posterboard; calculator
4•6	Teaching Aid Masters, pp. 414* and 423 Study Link Master, p. 116 Teaching Master, p. 117		Class Data Pad; calculator
4•7	Teaching Masters, pp. 118 and 120 Study Link Master, p. 119 Game Masters, pp. 442, 443, 456–458 *Differentiation Handbook,* p. 142	per partnership: 4 each of number cards 1–9; 2 six-sided dice; slate*	envelopes or reusable plastic bags; 4 pennies or other counters; 3" × 5" index cards cut in half*; transparent tape; scissors; calculator; Geometry Template
4•8	Assessment Masters, pp. 170–174 Teaching Aid Master, p. 415 Study Link Masters, pp. 121–124	slate	ruler

*Denotes optional materials

Mathematical Background

The discussion below highlights the major content ideas presented in Unit 4 and helps establish instructional priorities.

Division Facts and Extensions

(Lesson 4◆1)

In *Everyday Mathematics,* instant recall of basic addition and multiplication facts is emphasized and then used in strategies for getting answers to basic subtraction and division facts and "extended facts." For example, a student who knows by reflex that $7 \times 8 = 56$ can use fact-family knowledge to find $56 \div 7$ and $56 \div 8$, and can apply extended-fact strategies to find 70×80 and to tell how many 7s are in 560.

Lesson 4-1 provides students with an opportunity to refresh their division-fact and extended-fact knowledge and use it to solve division problems in a variety of contexts. A strategy for mental division is introduced, in which the dividend is broken into two or more "friendly" parts that are easy to divide.

For more information about division facts and extensions, see the *Teacher's Reference Manual,* Chapter 16.

Note

Having instant recall of all the basic addition and multiplication facts is very helpful and important. For a few otherwise capable students, however, this may be unrealistic. For these students, possible alternatives include using tables, calculators, or mental-arithmetic strategies that rely on remembering only a few key facts rather than all the basic facts.

A Division Algorithm (Lessons 4◆2 and 4◆4)

In the adult world, the usual procedure used to solve any moderately complicated division problem is to reach for a calculator. Students, however, need to know how to solve some division problems without calculators. Students gain an understanding of the meanings of division by considering paper-and-pencil computation procedures.

Lesson 4-2 reteaches a method for division, the partial-quotients division algorithm, that was introduced in *Fourth Grade Everyday Mathematics.* This "low-stress algorithm" takes much of the mystery out of long division. It is a conceptually revealing alternative to the traditional U.S. long-division algorithm, which research has shown to be difficult for many students to learn and apply.

Division is a way of answering the question, "How many of these are in that?" or "How many n's are in m?" The algorithm taught in this unit encourages students to ask a series of "How many . . ." questions. Using multiples of the divisor, they build up a series of interim answers, or partial quotients. At each step, if not enough n's have been taken from the m's, more are taken. When all possible n's have been taken, the partial quotients are added.

Strategies for the partial-quotients division algorithm are described in detail in the teacher's commentary for Lessons 4-2 and 4-4 and on pages 22 and 23 of the *Student Reference Book.* For example, $158 \div 12 = ?$ can be thought of as "How many 12s are in 158?" The dividend and divisor are first written in the traditional way. Then multiples of the divisor, 12, are subtracted from the dividend, 158. When the difference is less than the divisor, the process stops. The partial quotients are added. (See the margin.)

Project Note

To teach U.S. traditional long division, see Algorithm Project 7.

12)158	
−120	10
38	
−36	3
2	13
↑ Remainder	↑ Quotient

It is important to note that students can use different partial quotients to obtain the correct answer. For example, a student could use 2 [12s] in the second step ($2 \times 12 = 24$), leaving 14. Then the student would take away another 12, leaving a remainder of 2. Thus the student would reach the final answer in three steps rather than two. One way is not better than another.

One advantage of this algorithm is that students can use numbers that are easy to work with. Students who are confident with their extended multiplication facts and/or renaming numbers will need only a few multiples of the divisor to arrive at the quotient, while others will be more comfortable taking smaller steps. More important than the course a student follows is that he or she understands how and why this algorithm works and can use it to get an accurate answer.

The authors consider the partial-quotients division algorithm as a focus algorithm, to be learned by all students. If, however, students know another algorithm and prefer it to the one taught in the lesson, they should feel free to use it.

See the *Teacher's Reference Manual,* Section 11.2.4, for more information about the partial-quotients division algorithm.

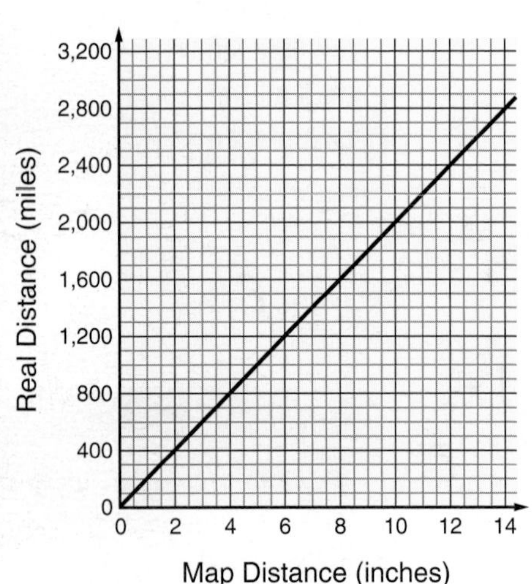

American Tour: Finding Distances on a Map (Lesson 4◆3)

The American Tour section of the *Student Reference Book* allows teachers to integrate mathematics into other disciplines, as well as incorporate other subjects into mathematics. It provides links among social studies, United States history, and mathematics. In this unit, students use maps in the American Tour to develop their skills of measuring distances and, using map scales, convert these measurements into real-world distances.

Additional information about the American Tour Project can be found in Section 1.2.7 of the *Teacher's Reference Manual.*

Division of Decimal Numbers (Lesson 4◆5)

Project Note

To teach U.S. traditional division with decimals, see Algorithm Projects 8 and 9.

In Lesson 4-5, the partial-quotients division algorithm is extended to division of a decimal number by a whole number. The strategy is first to make a magnitude estimate of the quotient. Will it be in the 0.1s, 1s, 10s, or 100s? For example, estimate the quotient of $67.2 \div 3$ by rounding the dividend to an "easy" number—for example, 60. $60 \div 3 = 20$, so the quotient is in the 10s. Then ignore the decimal point and use the algorithm to divide, getting 224. Use the magnitude estimate to insert the decimal point: 22.4.

To learn more about division of decimal numbers, see Section 11.2.4 of the *Teacher's Reference Manual.*

Interpreting the Remainder

(Lesson 4•6)

Students use the division algorithm that was reviewed in Lessons 4-2 and 4-4 and focus on interpreting remainders within problem contexts. Depending on the situation, a remainder is handled in different ways:

The remainder might represent a "leftover" amount that cannot be further split up. For example, leftover people or cars can't easily be split up.

The remainder might be regarded as a fractional or decimal part of the whole. For example, leftover parts of a dollar can be converted into cents.

The remainder might indicate that the quotient should be rounded up to the next larger whole number to obtain the answer. For example, if 30 people need to be transported in vans that hold 8 people each, it makes sense to order 4 vans rather than 3.75 vans.

The remainder might be ignored, and the answer is the quotient. If CDs are $9 and I have $50, I can only buy 5 CDs.

More information on interpreting the remainder of a division problem can be found in Section 11.2.4 of the *Teacher's Reference Manual.*

Skills Review with *First to 100* and Calculators (Lesson 4•7)

Students play the game *First to 100,* which exercises a variety of skills and develops the mathematical concept of a variable (a letter or other symbol whose value can vary). Players take turns drawing cards containing problems such as $(3x + 4) - 8 = ?$ At each turn, the player rolls two dice and finds the product of the numbers on the top faces. The player substitutes the product just calculated for the x or x's in the problem(s) on the card. The player solves the problem(s) mentally or with paper and pencil, and offers the answer(s). The other player checks the answer(s) with a calculator.

Students explore generating random numbers on their calculators to practice division with 1-digit divisors and comparing magnitudes for the squares of 3-, 4-, and 5-digit numbers.

See Section 1.2.2 of the *Teacher's Reference Manual* for more information about the game *First to 100.*

4•1 Division Facts and Extensions

Objectives To review multiplication and division facts and apply basic facts to division with 1-digit divisors.

Technology Resources www.everydaymathonline.com

ePresentations

eToolkit

Algorithms Practice

EM Facts Workshop Game™

Family Letters

Assessment Management

Common Core State Standards

Curriculum Focal Points

Interactive Teacher's Lesson Guide

1 Teaching the Lesson

Key Concepts and Skills

- Generate equivalent names for whole numbers.
  [Number and Numeration Goal 4]
- Apply multiplication facts, related division facts, or extended facts to identify friendly numbers.
  [Operations and Computation Goal 2]
- Use friendly numbers to divide 2-digit by 1-digit numbers.
  [Operations and Computation Goal 3]

Key Activities

Students practice division facts and extended facts. They use multiples of a given number to rename numbers. They use friendly numbers to solve problems with 1-digit divisors.

Ongoing Assessment: Informing Instruction See page 233.

Ongoing Assessment: Recognizing Student Achievement Use journal page 99.
[Operations and Computation Goal 3]

Key Vocabulary

dividend ◆ divisor ◆ quotient ◆ multiples

Materials

Math Journal 1, p. 99
slates ◆ per partnership: 4 each of number cards 1–9 (from the Everything Math Deck, if available)

2 Ongoing Learning & Practice

Playing *Name That Number*
Student Reference Book, p. 325
per partnership: 1 complete deck of number cards (from the Everything Math Deck, if available)
Students apply number properties, equivalent names, arithmetic operations, and basic facts.

Quadrangle Relationships
Math Masters, p. 440A
Students practice classifying and comparing relationships among quadrangles.

Math Boxes 4•1
Math Journal 1, p. 100
Geometry Template
Students practice and maintain skills through Math Box problems.

Study Link 4•1
Math Masters, p. 102
Students practice and maintain skills through Study Link activities.

3 Differentiation Options

READINESS
Using Equivalent Names for Numbers
Math Masters, p. 421
per partnership: 4 each of number cards 1–9 (from the Everything Math Deck, if available)
Students complete name-collection boxes focusing on number properties to make equivalent names for numbers.

ENRICHMENT
Exploring More Divisibility Rules
Math Masters, p. 103
Students apply divisibility rules to 5-, 6-, and 7-digit numbers.

EXTRA PRACTICE
5-Minute Math
5-Minute Math™, pp. 25, 28, and 183
Students solve division problems.

Advance Preparation

For Part 1, make classroom posters showing the names of multiplication and division problem parts and relating those names to the three numbers of a fact family.

***Teacher's Reference Manual,* Grades 4–6** pp. 16, 269–271

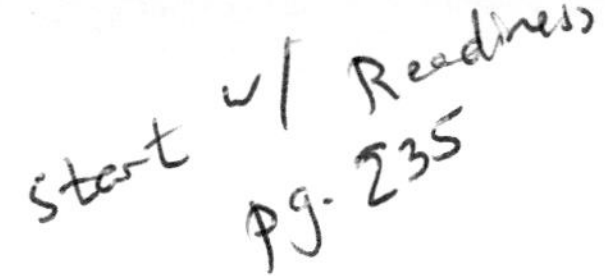

Getting Started

Mental Math and Reflexes

Use your slate procedures. Remind students to think of missing factors.
Example: How many 9s are in 72? Think: *9 times what number equals 72?*

●○○ How many 3s are in 21? 7 How many 30s are in 210? 7 How many 3s are in 210? 70

●●○ How many 7s are in 49? 7 How many 70s are in 490? 7 How many 7s are in 490? 70

●●● *Estimate:* About how many 4s are in 21? About 5 About how many 40s are in 210? About 5 About how many 4s are in 210? About 50

Math Message

For each problem below, write two related division facts.

$6 * 7 = 42$

$9 * 6 = x$

1 Teaching the Lesson

▶ Math Message Follow-Up

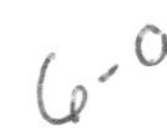

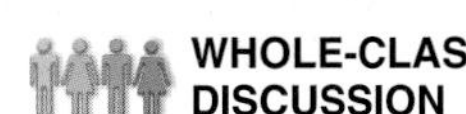

Algebraic Thinking Ask volunteers which 3 numbers are in the fact family for $6 * 7 = 42$. 6, 7, and 42 Ask: *Is this an addition / subtraction or multiplication / division fact family?* Multiplication/division *How do you know?* Sample answers: The numbers come from a multiplication fact; it can't be addition/subtraction because $6 + 7$ is not equal to 42. Fact families have opposite operations; division is the opposite of multiplication. Pose questions such as the following:

- Use the related multiplication and division facts for 6, 7, and 42 to write a statement similar to the following: 42 is 7 times as great as 6. Sample answer: 42 is 6 times as great as 7.
- In a related division fact, which number is the **dividend?** 42 Ask volunteers to state the related division facts, naming the **divisor** and the **quotient.** In $42 / 7 = 6$, 7 is the divisor and 6 is the quotient. In $42 / 6 = 7$, 6 is the divisor and 7 is the quotient.
- Which 3 numbers are in the fact family for $9 * 6 = x$? 9, 6, and x Expect that some students might respond 9, 6, and 54. In this case, ask students whether they think x can be used as a member of the fact family. Yes, because x is a variable and represents a number. Ask volunteers to give the related division facts. $x / 6 = 9$; $x / 9 = 6$
- Use the related multiplication and division facts for 6, 9, and x to write a statement similar to the following: x is 9 times as great as 6. Sample answer: x is 6 times as great as 9.
- What number is in the multiplication/division fact family with 20 and 5? 4 How do you know? $5 * 4 = 20$; $20 / 5 = 4$; there are 4 [5s] in 20.

Conclude the discussion by summarizing that knowing one multiplication fact leads to knowing 2 division facts. Ask students to compare the size of a product to one of its factors, based on the other factor. Tell them, for example: *Using the numbers 4, 5, and 20,*

Interactive whiteboard-ready ePresentations are available at www.everydaymathonline.com to help you teach the lesson.

NOTE *Everyday Mathematics* reinforces students' understanding of the link between multiplication and division. It is expected that students who have automatic recall of the multiplication facts will be able to state related division facts.

you could say that 20 (the product) is 4 (one of the factors) times as great as 5 (the other factor). Ask: *What other comparisons can you make using the product and the factors?* Sample answers: 20 is 5 times as great as 4. Using 5: 4 times is 20. Using 4: 5 times is 20.

Pose questions to have students compare the size of a product to one of its factors:

- 20 is how many times as great as one of its factors, 4? 5 times as great
- $x / 9 = 6$ means that x is how many times as great as its quotient, 6? 9 times as great
- $2 * (4 + 5)$ is how many times as great as one of its factors, $(4 + 5)$? 2 times as great

▶ Practicing Division Facts and Extended Division Facts

Use your slate procedures to practice division facts and their extensions. Dictate problems like the following, varying your language. For example, ask: *What is 63 divided by 7? How many 7s are in 63?* If necessary, give a clue, such as, *Think: 7 times what number equals 63?*

63 / 7 9	64 / 8 8	240 / 30 8
630 / 7 90	1,000 / 10 100	2,000 / 50 40
27 / 3 9	200 / 20 10	360 / 9 40
270 / 30 9	120 / 10 12	4,900 / 70 70

What number is 7 times as great as 6? 42
What number is 90 times as great as 7? 630
What number is one-fourth the size of 48? 12
What number is 1,000 times as great as 5? 5,000

▶ Renaming Numbers

Use the following activity to prepare students for the mental division strategy on journal page 99. On a transparency, or the board, draw a name-collection box.

▷ Shuffle the cards (4 each of number cards 1 through 9).

▷ Turn over 2 cards and make a 2-digit number.

▷ Write the number in the collection box tag. Ask volunteers what they think you should do next. Most students will recognize the name-collection box format and will respond that you should write equivalent names for the number in the box. Explain that for this activity, students will look for equivalent names that contain **multiples** of another number.

▷ Turn over a third card. Survey the class for equivalent names that contain multiples of the number from the third card.

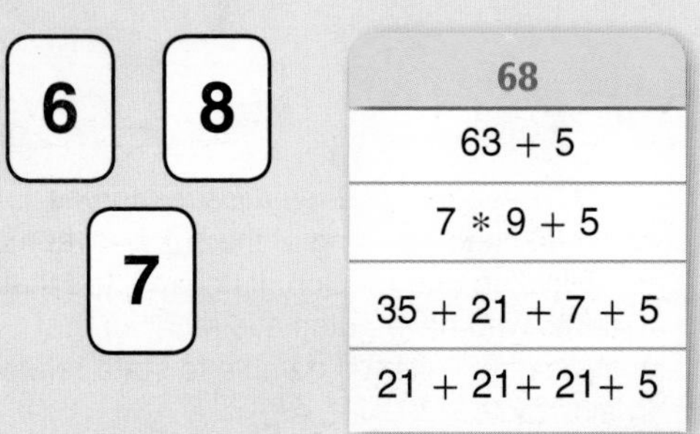

Use follow-up questions to guide students to see that the largest multiple can be broken into smaller parts to make other equivalent names. Allow partners time to try at least three different name-collection boxes, drawing them on scrap paper or using slates. Circulate and assist.

Using a Mental Division Strategy

WHOLE-CLASS ACTIVITY

(*Math Journal 1,* p. 99)

Explain that using equivalent names for numbers, knowing multiplication and division facts, and recognizing fact extensions in order to break numbers into friendly parts will simplify calculations.

Refer students to journal page 99. As a class, discuss the presented division strategy.

Have students complete Problems 1–6. Remind them to use multiplication to check their results. Circulate and assist.

Ongoing Assessment: Informing Instruction

Watch for students who use paper-and-pencil exclusively, rather than mental arithmetic. Encourage these students to try to visualize what they might write before they actually write anything.

Survey the class for methods of breaking numbers into friendly parts. Use follow-up questions to help students recognize how to use a multiple of the divisor.

Adjusting the Activity

Have students break the dividend into two friendly numbers so that one number is the divisor times 10 and the other is the remaining part. For 42 divided by 3, use 3 * 10, or 30, as the first friendly number, and 12 as the second. For larger dividends, it might be necessary to use the divisor times a multiple of 10. For 132 divided by 3, use 3 * 40, or 120, as the first friendly number and 12 as the second.

AUDITORY ◆ KINESTHETIC ◆ TACTILE ◆ VISUAL

Ongoing Assessment: Recognizing Student Achievement

Journal Page 99 Problems 1–4

Use **journal page 99, Problems 1–4** to assess students' facility using multiplication and division facts for division with 1-digit divisors. Students are making adequate progress if they successfully identify friendly numbers and use these to solve the problems.

[Operations and Computation Goal 3]

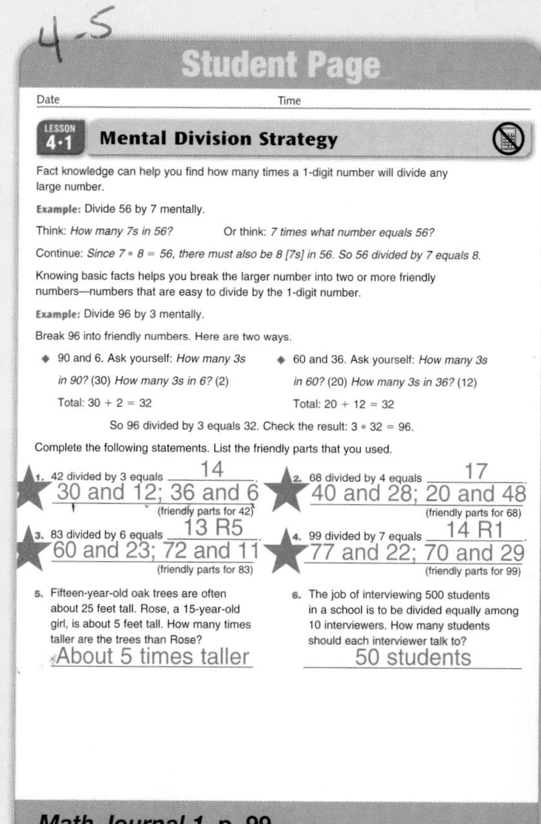

Student Page

Date Time

LESSON 4·1 **Mental Division Strategy**

Fact knowledge can help you find how many times a 1-digit number will divide any large number.

Example: Divide 56 by 7 mentally.

Think: *How many 7s in 56?* Or think: *7 times what number equals 56?*

Continue: *Since 7 * 8 = 56, there must also be 8 [7s] in 56. So 56 divided by 7 equals 8.*

Knowing basic facts helps you break the larger number into two or more friendly numbers—numbers that are easy to divide by the 1-digit number.

Example: Divide 96 by 3 mentally.

Break 96 into friendly numbers. Here are two ways.

- 90 and 6. Ask yourself: *How many 3s in 90?* (30) *How many 3s in 6?* (2) Total: 30 + 2 = 32
- 60 and 36. Ask yourself: *How many 3s in 60?* (20) *How many 3s in 36?* (12) Total: 20 + 12 = 32

So 96 divided by 3 equals 32. Check the result: 3 * 32 = 96.

Complete the following statements. List the friendly parts that you used.

1. 42 divided by 3 equals 14
30 and 12; 36 and 6 (friendly parts for 42)
2. 68 divided by 4 equals 17
40 and 28; 20 and 48 (friendly parts for 68)
3. 83 divided by 6 equals 13 R5
60 and 23; 72 and 11 (friendly parts for 83)
4. 99 divided by 7 equals 14 R1
77 and 22; 70 and 29 (friendly parts for 99)
5. Fifteen-year-old oak trees are often about 25 feet tall. Rose, a 15-year-old girl, is about 5 feet tall. How many times taller are the trees than Rose?
About 5 times taller
6. The job of interviewing 500 students in a school is to be divided equally among 10 interviewers. How many students should each interviewer talk to?
50 students

Math Journal 1, p. 99

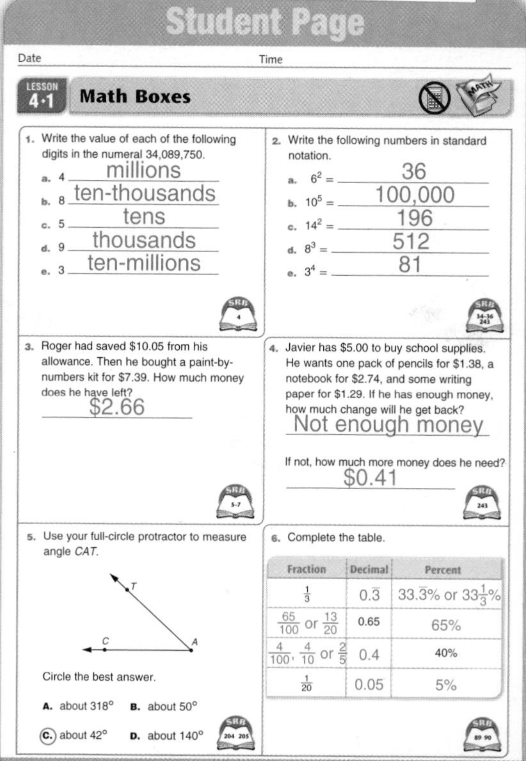

Student Page

Date Time

LESSON 4·1 **Math Boxes**

1. Write the value of each of the following digits in the numeral 34,089,750.
   a. 4 millions
   b. 8 ten-thousands
   c. 5 tens
   d. 9 thousands
   e. 3 ten-millions
2. Write the following numbers in standard notation.
   a. 6^2 = 36
   b. 10^5 = 100,000
   c. 14^2 = 196
   d. 8^3 = 512
   e. 3^4 = 81
3. Roger had saved $10.05 from his allowance. Then he bought a paint-by-numbers kit for $7.39. How much money does he have left?
$2.66
4. Javier has $5.00 to buy school supplies. He wants one pack of pencils for $1.38, a notebook for $2.74, and some writing paper for $1.29. If he has enough money, how much change will he get back?
Not enough money
If not, how much more money does he need?
$0.41
5. Use your full-circle protractor to measure angle *CAT*.
Circle the best answer.
A. about 318° B. about 50° (C.) about 42° D. about 140°
6. Complete the table.

Fraction	Decimal	Percent
$\frac{1}{3}$	$0.\overline{3}$	$33.\overline{3}\%$ or $33\frac{1}{3}\%$
$\frac{65}{100}$ or $\frac{13}{20}$	0.65	65%
$\frac{4}{100}$, $\frac{4}{10}$ or $\frac{2}{5}$	0.4	40%
$\frac{1}{20}$	0.05	5%

Math Journal 1, p. 100

Teaching Aid Master

Name Date Time

Venn Diagram

Properties of Parallelograms | Properties of Kites

- exactly 2 pairs of parallel sides
- sides of equal length opposite each other
- 2 pairs of sides are the same length
- quadrangle
- no pairs of parallel sides
- sides of equal length next to each other

Math Masters, **p. 440A**

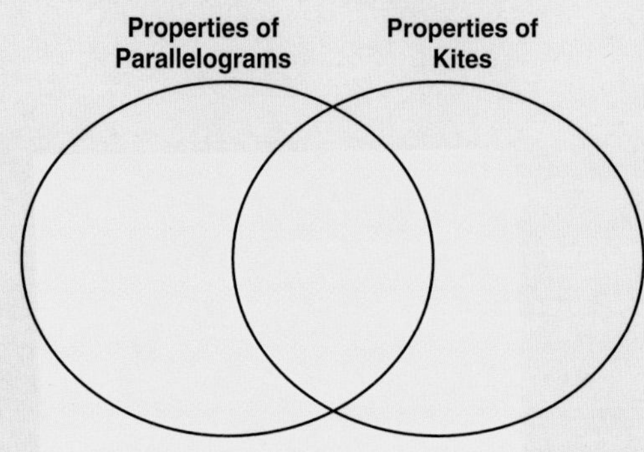

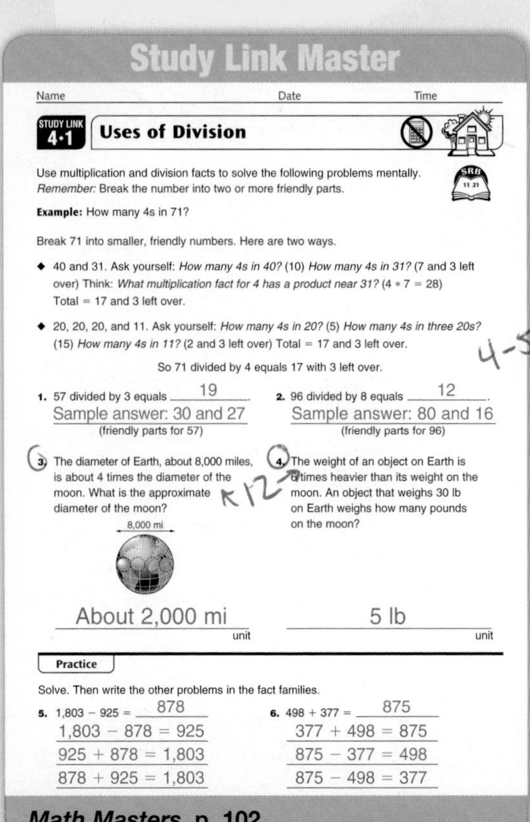

Study Link Master

Name Date Time

STUDY LINK 4•1 **Uses of Division**

Use multiplication and division facts to solve the following problems mentally. *Remember:* Break the number into two or more friendly parts.

Example: How many 4s in 71?

Break 71 into smaller, friendly numbers. Here are two ways.

- 40 and 31. Ask yourself: *How many 4s in 40?* (10) *How many 4s in 31?* (7 and 3 left over) Think: *What multiplication fact for 4 has a product near 31?* (4 ∗ 7 = 28) Total = 17 and 3 left over.
- 20, 20, 20, and 11. Ask yourself: *How many 4s in 20?* (5) *How many 4s in three 20s?* (15) *How many 4s in 11?* (2 and 3 left over) Total = 17 and 3 left over.

So 71 divided by 4 equals 17 with 3 left over.

1. 57 divided by 3 equals 19. Sample answer: 30 and 27 (friendly parts for 57)
2. 96 divided by 8 equals 12. Sample answer: 80 and 16 (friendly parts for 96)
3. The diameter of Earth, about 8,000 miles, is about 4 times the diameter of the moon. What is the approximate diameter of the moon? (8,000 mi) About 2,000 mi unit
4. The weight of an object on Earth is 6 times heavier than its weight on the moon. An object that weighs 30 lb on Earth weighs how many pounds on the moon? 5 lb unit

Practice

Solve. Then write the other problems in the fact families.

5. 1,803 − 925 = 878
   1,803 − 878 = 925
   925 + 878 = 1,803
   878 + 925 = 1,803
6. 498 + 377 = 875
   377 + 498 = 875
   875 − 377 = 498
   875 − 498 = 377

Math Masters, **p. 102**

2 Ongoing Learning & Practice

▶ Playing *Name That Number*

PARTNER ACTIVITY

(*Student Reference Book,* p. 325)

Students practice applying number properties, equivalent names, arithmetic operations, and basic facts by playing *Name That Number.*

▶ Quadrangle (Quadrilateral) Relationships

PARTNER ACTIVITY

(*Math Masters,* p. 440A)

Students practice and extend their thinking about classifying and comparing relationships among quadrangles. Draw a Venn diagram on the board with the headings Properties of Parallelograms and Properties of Kites. (*See margin.*)

Briefly review how to use a Venn diagram. The properties unique to parallelograms are listed below the label Properties of Parallelograms, and properties unique to kites are listed below Properties of Kites. The properties the two shapes have in common are listed in the intersection of the two ovals. Students complete *Math Masters,* page 440A with a partner. Assign additional pairings for additional practice.

Possible pairings include square and rectangle, trapezoid and parallelogram, kite and rhombus, square and rhombus, and parallelogram and rhombus.

▶ Math Boxes 4•1

INDEPENDENT ACTIVITY

(*Math Journal 1,* p. 100)

Mixed Review Math Boxes in this lesson are paired with Math Boxes in Lesson 4-3. The skill in Problem 6 previews Unit 5 content.

Writing/Reasoning Have students write a response to the following: *Explain your answer to Problem 4.* Sample answer: I added to find the total cost for the supplies Javier wanted. It was more than $5.00, so I subtracted $5.00 from the total cost to see how much more money he needed.

▶ Study Link 4•1

INDEPENDENT ACTIVITY

(*Math Masters,* p. 102)

Home Connection Students use friendly numbers, division facts, and related multiplication facts to solve division problems and number stories.

3 Differentiation Options

READINESS

▶ Using Equivalent Names for Numbers

Start w/ this

PARTNER ACTIVITY

5–15 Min

(*Math Masters,* p. 421)

To provide experience with finding equivalent names for numbers, have students use name-collection boxes, focusing on number properties and relationships. For example, they might use multiples of ten, add 0, or multiply by 1 to make equivalent names.

Partners take turns dealing two cards from a deck comprised of 4 each of the numbers 1–9. Each partner uses the numbers on the cards to form a 2-digit number. Their numbers can be the same or different. Partners write their numbers in one of the name-collection box tags on *Math Masters,* page 421 and find as many different equivalent names for the number as they can.

NOTE In Part 1, students rename numbers using multiples of given numbers. However, do not restrict the forms of the equivalent names students collect for this activity.

Teaching Aid Master

Name Date Time

Equivalent Names for Numbers

Math Masters, p. 421

ENRICHMENT

▶ Exploring More Divisibility Rules

PARTNER ACTIVITY

15–30 Min

(*Math Masters,* p. 103)

To apply students' understanding of divisibility, have them solve problems using divisibility rules for prime numbers. Partners complete *Math Masters,* page 103.

After partners finish, have them create and exchange 6-digit numbers to test for divisibility by 7, 11, or 13. They might also find numbers that are divisible by more than one of these primes. Products of multiples of primes are easy to find.
Example: $(65 * 7)(89 * 13) = 526,435$

EXTRA PRACTICE

▶ *5-Minute Math*

SMALL-GROUP ACTIVITY

5–15 Min

To offer students more experience with whole-number division, see *5-Minute Math,* pages 25, 28, and 183.

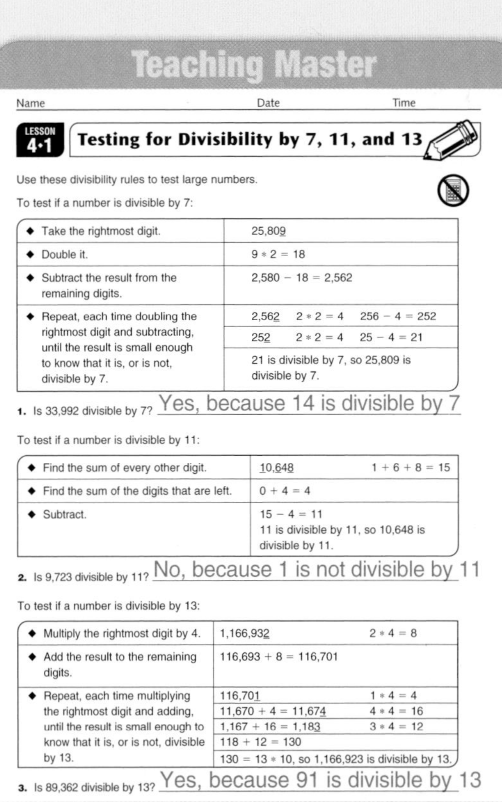

Teaching Master

Name Date Time

LESSON 4•1 **Testing for Divisibility by 7, 11, and 13**

Use these divisibility rules to test large numbers.

To test if a number is divisible by 7:

◆ Take the rightmost digit.	25,809		
◆ Double it.	9 * 2 = 18		
◆ Subtract the result from the remaining digits.	2,580 − 18 = 2,562		
◆ Repeat, each time doubling the rightmost digit and subtracting, until the result is small enough to know that it is, or is not, divisible by 7.	2,562	2 * 2 = 4	256 − 4 = 252
	252	2 * 2 = 4	25 − 4 = 21
	21 is divisible by 7, so 25,809 is divisible by 7.		

1. Is 33,992 divisible by 7? Yes, because 14 is divisible by 7

To test if a number is divisible by 11:

◆ Find the sum of every other digit.	10,648	1 + 6 + 8 = 15
◆ Find the sum of the digits that are left.	0 + 4 = 4	
◆ Subtract.	15 − 4 = 11 11 is divisible by 11, so 10,648 is divisible by 11.	

2. Is 9,723 divisible by 11? No, because 1 is not divisible by 11

To test if a number is divisible by 13:

◆ Multiply the rightmost digit by 4.	1,166,932	2 * 4 = 8
◆ Add the result to the remaining digits.	116,693 + 8 = 116,701	
◆ Repeat, each time multiplying the rightmost digit and adding, until the result is small enough to know that it is, or is not, divisible by 13.	116,701	1 * 4 = 4
	11,670 + 4 = 11,674	4 * 4 = 16
	1,167 + 16 = 1,183	3 * 4 = 12
	118 + 12 = 130	
	130 = 13 * 10, so 1,166,923 is divisible by 13.	

3. Is 89,362 divisible by 13? Yes, because 91 is divisible by 13

Math Masters, p. 103

4•2 The Partial-Quotients Division Algorithm

Objective To review the partial-quotients division algorithm with whole numbers.

Technology Resources www.everydaymathonline.com

ePresentations

eToolkit

Algorithms Practice

EM Facts Workshop Game™

Family Letters

Assessment Management

Common Core State Standards

Curriculum Focal Points

Interactive Teacher's Lesson Guide

1 Teaching the Lesson

Key Concepts and Skills

- Use the partial-quotients algorithm for problems.
  [Operations and Computation Goal 3]
- Apply friendly numbers to identify partial quotients.
  [Operations and Computation Goal 3]
- Factor numbers to identify partial quotients.
  [Operations and Computation Goal 3]

Key Activities

Students review and practice the use of a friendly number paper-and-pencil division algorithm strategy. They play *Division Dash* to practice mental division with 1-digit divisors.

Ongoing Assessment: Recognizing Student Achievement Use journal page 101.
[Operations and Computation Goal 3]

Ongoing Assessment: Informing Instruction See page 240.

Key Vocabulary

dividend ◆ divisor ◆ partial quotient ◆ quotient ◆ remainder

Materials

Math Journal 1, p. 101
Student Reference Book, pp. 22, 23, and 303
Study Link 4•1
Math Masters, pp. 414 and 415
Class Data Pad ◆ slate ◆ per partnership: 4 each of number cards 1–9 (from the Everything Math Deck, if available)

2 Ongoing Learning & Practice

Math Boxes 4•2
Math Journal 1, p. 102
Students practice and maintain skills through Math Box problems.

Study Link 4•2
Math Masters, p. 104
Students practice and maintain skills through Study Link activities.

3 Differentiation Options

READINESS

Reviewing Divisibility Rules
Student Reference Book, p. 11
Students review divisibility rules for 1-digit divisors.

ENRICHMENT

Exploring Divisibility by the Digits
Math Masters, p. 105
Students apply their understanding of factors by finding numbers that meet divisibility criteria.

ELL SUPPORT

Supporting Math Vocabulary Development
Class Data Pad or chart paper
Students review vocabulary for the parts of a division problem.

Advance Preparation

For Part 1, you will need 2 copies of the computation grid (*Math Masters,* page 415) for each student.

***Teacher's Reference Manual,* Grades 4–6** pp. 132–140

Getting Started

Mental Math and Reflexes

Pose multiplication and division problems like the following.

●○○ How many 5s are in 45? 9

What number times 9 equals 27? 3

What is 3 times 120? 360

●●○ How many 4s are in 32? 8

What number times 8 equals 40? 5

Multiply 5 times 80. 400

●●● What number times 7 equals 35? 5

Multiply 12 by 7. 84

Multiply 55 by 3. 165

Math Message

Amy is 127 days older than Bob. How many weeks is that?

Study Link 4·1 Follow-Up

Have partners compare answers. Explain that fact family relationships can be used to check computations. Write 605 − 67 = 528 on the board or a transparency. An addition problem from this fact family will check the subtraction. Write 528 + 67 = 605. Ask: *Are there any problems with this approach?* Most students will recognize either the subtraction or the addition error. It is important to calculate the check problem, not just rewrite the numbers. 528 + 67 = 595, not 605, so the subtraction was incorrect in the initial number sentence. Change the equal sign to not equal, and then write 605 − 67 = 538. Encourage students to use number relationships to check their calculations.

1 Teaching the Lesson

▶ Math Message Follow-Up

Ask volunteers to share their solution strategies. Solution strategies should indicate that 127 days is about 18 weeks or 18 weeks and 1 day. Expect that some students will suggest breaking 127 into friendly numbers.

Survey the class for clues that the Math Message was a division problem. The problem gave the whole (127 days) and asked how many groups (weeks); because there are 7 days in a week, the problem was to figure out how many 7s are in 127. Ask volunteers to write a number model for this problem. 127 / 7; $\frac{127}{7}$; 127 ÷ 7; and 7)127

▶ Reviewing the Partial-Quotients Algorithm

(*Math Masters*, p. 415)

Given a **dividend** and a **divisor,** the partial-quotients algorithm is one pencil-and-paper strategy for division. Model the following steps on the Class Data Pad:

1. Write the problem in traditional form: 7)127.
2. Draw a vertical line to the right of the problem to separate the subtraction part of the algorithm from the partial quotients.

7)127 |

Algorithm Project The focus of this lesson is the partial-quotients algorithm. To teach U.S. traditional long division, see Algorithm Project 7 on page A32.

NOTE The partial-quotients algorithm was first introduced in *Fourth Grade Everyday Mathematics.*

Explain that with this notation, students will list their **partial quotients** on the right of the vertical line and then subtract the related multiples on the left of the vertical line, until the remaining dividend is smaller than the divisor.

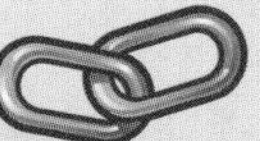

Links to the Future

Students will practice the partial-quotients algorithm in Lesson 4-4, using an easy-multiples strategy to find partial quotients, and in Lesson 4-5 with decimal dividends.

One strategy for finding partial quotients is to use friendly numbers. Rename the dividend as an expression that contains multiples of the divisor. Make a name-collection box for 127, and add the expression 70 + 57. Use this expression to model the algorithm.

3. Ask: *How many 7s are in 70?* 10, because $10 * 7 = 70$. Write 70 under 127 and 10 next to it, to the right of the vertical line. Subtract, saying: *127 minus 70 equals 57.* Explain that 10 is the first partial quotient and 57 is what remains to be divided.

7)127	127 = 70 + 57
− 70	10
57	57 is left to divide.

4. Ask: *How many 7s are in 57?* 8, because $8 * 7 = 56$. Write 56 under 57 and 8 next to it, to the right of the vertical line. Subtract, saying: *57 minus 56 equals 1.* Explain that 8 is the second partial quotient, and 1 is what remains to be divided.

7)127	
− 70	10
57	
− 56	8
1	1 is left to divide.

5. Explain that they can stop this process when the number left to be divided is smaller than the divisor. This number can be written in the **quotient** as a whole-number **remainder.**

6. Combine the partial quotients, saying: *10 + 8 equals 18.* Write 18 above the dividend. Circle the 1 and write R1 next to 18. There are 18 [7s] in 127, with a remainder of 1. So Amy is how many weeks older than Bob? About 18 weeks older, or 18 weeks and 1 day older

18	R1
7)127	
− 70	10
57	
− 56	8
(1)	18

$127 \div 7 \rightarrow 18$ R1

Ask: *How could you write the remainder as a fraction?* $18\frac{1}{7}$ *What does the 1 represent?* The remainder *What does the 7 represent?* The number of days in the week; it is the divisor in the division problem.

NOTE When the result of division is expressed as a quotient and a nonzero remainder, *Everyday Mathematics* uses an arrow rather than an equal sign, as in $246 \div 12 \rightarrow 20$ R6. *Everyday Mathematics* prefers this notation because $246 \div 12 = 20$ R6 is not a proper number sentence. The arrow is read as *is, yields,* or *results in.* Model this expression for students in your examples of the partial-quotients algorithm. Label the arrow on the Class Data Pad for display throughout this unit.

Adjusting the Activity

ELL

The arrow as a mathematical symbol is used to represent several different concepts. To support English language learners, remind students of the relationship between multiplication and division. Explain that when a quotient is written to show a whole number remainder, the remainder is not part of the multiplication expression for that fact family. So we need a different way, the arrow, to show that the division results in the quotient and the whole-number remainder.

AUDITORY ◆ KINESTHETIC ◆ TACTILE ◆ VISUAL

Ask students for other ways to rename 127 using multiples of 7. Add these to the name-collection box. Sample answers: 105 + 22; 70 + 49 + 7 + 1; 35 + 35 + 35 + 21 + 1 Have students choose one of these expressions to use with the partial-quotients algorithm. Remind them to write the problem and draw the vertical line, using the problem on the Class Data Pad as a model. To help students remember place value as they write digits, have them use a computation grid. Circulate and assist.

▶ Using the Partial-Quotients Algorithm

(*Math Journal 1,* p. 101; *Student Reference Book,* pp. 22 and 23)

Remind students that pages 22 and 23 in the *Student Reference Book* and the samples on the Class Data Pad can be used to verify correct usage of the steps in this algorithm. Have students complete the page. Circulate and assist.

Links to the Future

Problem 5 on journal page 101 will provide some information about students' ability to interpret remainders. Interpreting remainders will be covered in Lesson 4-6.

Ongoing Assessment: Recognizing Student Achievement

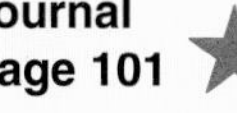

Use **journal page 101** to assess students' understanding of the partial-quotients algorithm. Students are making adequate progress if they demonstrate accurate use of the notation for the algorithm.

[Operations and Computation Goal 3]

Ask students to select one of the problems on *Math Journal 1,* page 101 and then explain and illustrate their strategy for solving the problem on an Exit Slip (*Math Masters,* page 414).

Student Page

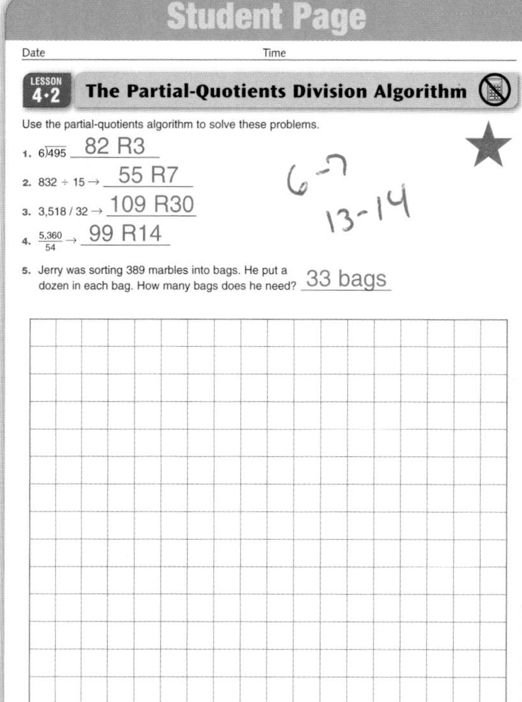

Date Time

LESSON 4•2 **The Partial-Quotients Division Algorithm**

Use the partial-quotients algorithm to solve these problems.

1. 6)495 82 R3
2. 832 ÷ 15 → 55 R7
3. 3,518 / 32 → 109 R30
4. $\frac{5,360}{54}$ → 99 R14
5. Jerry was sorting 389 marbles into bags. He put a dozen in each bag. How many bags does he need? 33 bags

Math Journal 1, p. 101

Student Page

Whole Numbers

Division Algorithms

Different symbols may be used to indicate division. For example, "94 divided by 6" may be written as 94 ÷ 6, 6)94, 94 / 6, or $\frac{94}{6}$.

- The number that is being divided is called the **dividend.**
- The number that divides the dividend is called the **divisor.**
- The answer to a division problem is called the **quotient.**
- Some numbers cannot be divided evenly. When this happens, the answer includes a quotient and a **remainder.**

Four ways to show "123 divided by 4"

123 ÷ 4 123 / 4 4)123 $\frac{123}{4}$

123 is the dividend. 4 is the divisor.

Partial-Quotients Method

In the **partial-quotients method,** it takes several steps to find the quotient. At each step, you find a partial answer (called a **partial quotient**). These partial answers are then added to find the quotient.

Study the example below. To find the number of 6s in 1,010 first find partial quotients and then add them. Record the partial quotients in a column to the right of the original problem.

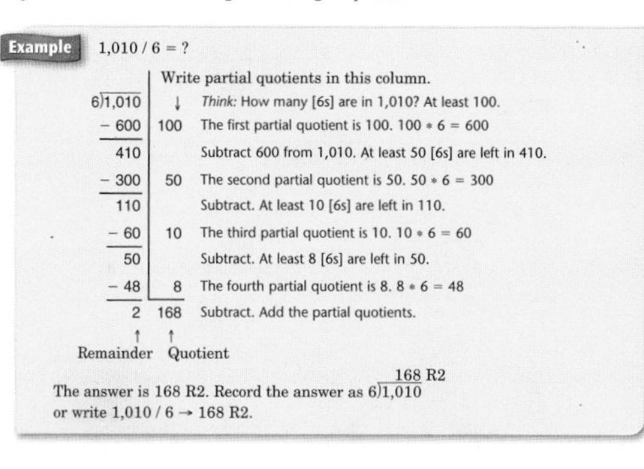

Example 1,010 / 6 = ?

Write partial quotients in this column.

6)1,010	↓	*Think:* How many [6s] are in 1,010? At least 100.
− 600	100	The first partial quotient is 100. 100 ∗ 6 = 600
410		Subtract 600 from 1,010. At least 50 [6s] are left in 410.
− 300	50	The second partial quotient is 50. 50 ∗ 6 = 300
110		Subtract. At least 10 [6s] are left in 110.
− 60	10	The third partial quotient is 10. 10 ∗ 6 = 60
50		Subtract. At least 8 [6s] are left in 50.
− 48	8	The fourth partial quotient is 8. 8 ∗ 6 = 48
2	168	Subtract. Add the partial quotients.
↑ Remainder	↑ Quotient	

The answer is 168 R2. Record the answer as 6)1,010 (168 R2) or write 1,010 / 6 → 168 R2.

Student Reference Book, p. 22

Student Page

Games

Division Dash

Materials ☐ number cards 1–9 (4 of each)
☐ 1 score sheet

Players 1 or 2

Skill Division of 2-digit by 1-digit numbers

Object of the game To reach 100 in the fewest divisions possible.

Directions

1. Prepare a score sheet like the one shown at the right.
2. Shuffle the cards and place the deck number-side down on the table.
3. Each player follows the instructions below:
   - ♦ Turn over 3 cards and lay them down in a row, from left to right. Use the 3 cards to generate a division problem. The 2 cards on the left form a 2-digit number. This is the *dividend.* The number on the card at the right is the *divisor.*
   - ♦ Divide the 2-digit number by the 1-digit number and record the result. This result is your quotient. Remainders are ignored. Calculate mentally or on paper.
   - ♦ Add your quotient to your previous score and record your new score. (If this is your first turn, your previous score was 0.)
4. Players repeat Step 3 until one player's score is 100 or more. The first player to reach at least 100 wins. If there is only one player, the Object of the game is to reach 100 in as few turns as possible.

Player 1		Player 2	
Quotient	Score	Quotient	Score

Example

Turn 1: Bob draws 6, 4, and 5. He divides 64 by 5. Quotient = 12. Remainder is ignored. The score is 12 + 0 = 12.

Turn 2: Bob then draws 8, 2, and 1. He divides 82 by 1. Quotient = 82. The score is 82 + 12 = 94.

Turn 3: Bob then draws 5, 7, and 8. He divides 57 by 8. Quotient = 7. Remainder is ignored. The score is 7 + 94 = 101.

Bob has reached 100 in 3 turns and the game ends.

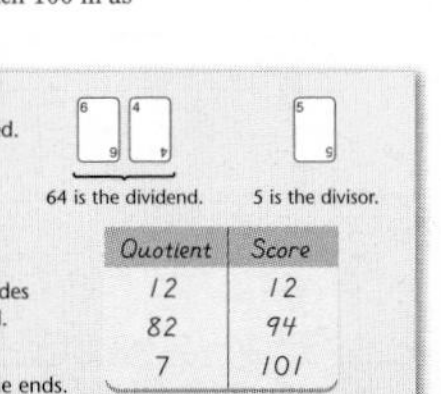

Quotient	Score
12	12
82	94
7	101

Student Reference Book, **p. 303**

▶ Introducing *Division Dash*

(*Student Reference Book,* p. 303)

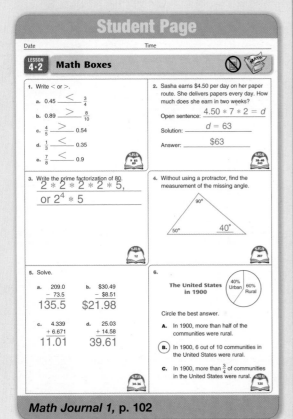

Division Dash uses randomly generated numbers to obtain values for 1-digit divisors and 2-digit dividends. Encourage students to calculate mentally, but do not restrict paper-and-pencil use.

Discuss the example on the *Student Reference Book* page. Then have the class play a round of *Division Dash* together. The whole class mentally calculates the division. Remind students that only the whole-number part of the quotient is recorded. If the dividend is less than the divisor, the quotient should be recorded as 0.

After students understand the rules, have partners play the game. Circulate and assist.

Ongoing Assessment: Informing Instruction

Watch for students who use paper-and-pencil, rather than mental strategies, to calculate the division. To help them bridge into mental math, ask them to write the division expression 4)49 but then use multiplication facts and friendly parts to calculate mentally.

2 Ongoing Learning & Practice

▶ Math Boxes 4·2

(*Math Journal 1,* p. 102)

Mixed Review Math Boxes in this lesson are paired with Math Boxes in Lesson 4-4 and 4-6. The skills in Problems 5 and 6 preview Unit 5 content.

Writing/Reasoning Have students write a response to the following: *Explain why your answer to Problem 4 is correct.* Sample answer: The sum of the measures of the angles equals 180°. My answer is correct because 50 + 90 = 140, and the missing angle measure is 40 because 50 + 90 + 40 = 180.

Student Page

Date Time

LESSON 4·2 Math Boxes

1. Write < or >.
   a. 0.45 < $\frac{3}{4}$
   b. 0.89 > $\frac{8}{10}$
   c. $\frac{4}{5}$ > 0.54
   d. $\frac{1}{3}$ < 0.35
   e. $\frac{7}{8}$ < 0.9

   SRB 9 83 89

2. Sasha earns \$4.50 per day on her paper route. She delivers papers every day. How much does she earn in two weeks?

   Open sentence: $4.50 * 7 * 2 = d$

   Solution: $d = 63$

   Answer: \$63

   SRB 38–40 243

3. Write the prime factorization of 80.
   2 ∗ 2 ∗ 2 ∗ 2 ∗ 5,
   or $2^4 * 5$

   SRB 12

4. Without using a protractor, find the measurement of the missing angle.

   90° 50° 40°

   SRB 207

5. Solve.
   a. 209.0 − 73.5 = 135.5
   b. \$30.49 − \$8.51 = \$21.98
   c. 4.339 + 6.671 = 11.01
   d. 25.03 + 14.58 = 39.61

   SRB 34–36

6. The United States in 1900 (40% Urban, 60% Rural)

   Circle the best answer.

   A. In 1900, more than half of the communities were rural.

   (B.) In 1900, 6 out of 10 communities in the United States were rural.

   C. In 1900, more than $\frac{3}{4}$ of communities in the United States were rural.

   SRB 125

Math Journal 1, **p. 102**

▶ Study Link 4·2

(*Math Masters,* p. 104)

Home Connection Students practice the partial-quotients division algorithm.

3 Differentiation Options

READINESS

PARTNER ACTIVITY

5–15 Min

Reviewing Divisibility Rules

(*Student Reference Book,* p. 11)

To provide experience identifying factors, have partners read about divisibility on page 11 of the *Student Reference Book* and complete the Check Your Understanding problems.

ENRICHMENT

PARTNER ACTIVITY

5–15 Min

Exploring Divisibility by the Digits

(*Math Masters,* p. 105)

To apply students' understanding of factors, have them explore divisibility from another perspective. Students examine 3-digit numbers that meet certain divisibility criteria. Then they use the same criteria to identify larger numbers.

ELL SUPPORT

SMALL-GROUP ACTIVITY

15–30 Min

Supporting Math Vocabulary Development

To provide language support for division, have volunteers write a division number model on chart paper in several different formats.

$127 / 7 \rightarrow 18 \text{ R1}$

$\frac{127}{7} \rightarrow 18 \text{ R1}$

$127 \div 7 \rightarrow 18 \text{ R1}$

$7\overline{)127}$ → 18 R1

For each number model, have students label and underline the dividend in red (the number being divided); label and underline the divisor in blue (the number the dividend is being divided by); label and circle the quotient in a third color; label and circle the remainder in a fourth color. Emphasize that both the quotient and the remainder are part of the answer. Display this chart throughout all the division lessons.

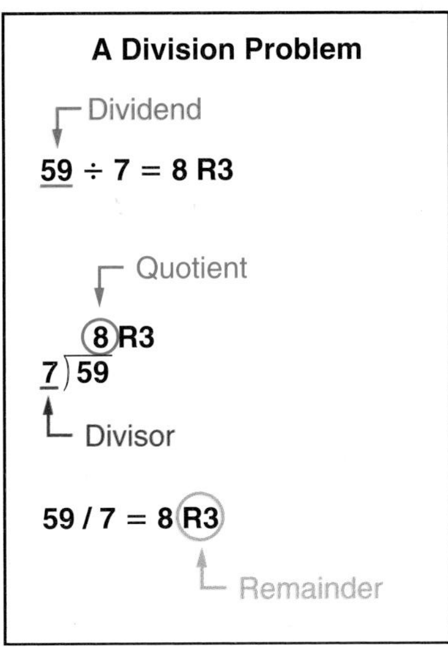

A Division Problem
Dividend
59 ÷ 7 = 8 R3
Quotient
8 R3
7)59
Divisor
59 / 7 = 8 R3
Remainder

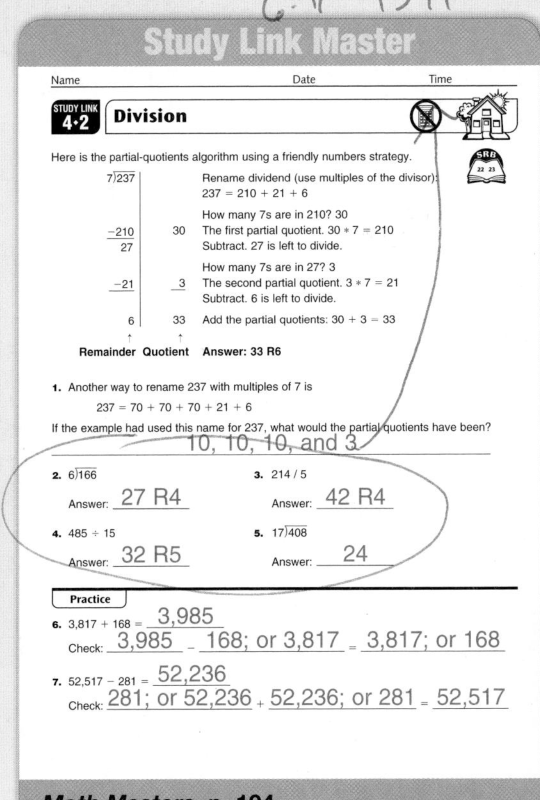

Study Link Master

Name Date Time

STUDY LINK 4•2 **Division**

Here is the partial-quotients algorithm using a friendly numbers strategy.

7)237 — Rename dividend (use multiples of the divisor): 237 = 210 + 21 + 6

How many 7s are in 210? 30

−210 | 30 — The first partial quotient. 30 ∗ 7 = 210

27 — Subtract. 27 is left to divide.

How many 7s are in 27? 3

−21 | 3 — The second partial quotient. 3 ∗ 7 = 21

Subtract. 6 is left to divide.

6 | 33 — Add the partial quotients: 30 + 3 = 33

Remainder Quotient **Answer: 33 R6**

1. Another way to rename 237 with multiples of 7 is
237 = 70 + 70 + 70 + 21 + 6
If the example had used this name for 237, what would the partial quotients have been? 10, 10, 10, and 3

2. 6)166 Answer: 27 R4

3. 214 / 5 Answer: 42 R4

4. 485 ÷ 15 Answer: 32 R5

5. 17)408 Answer: 24

Practice

6. 3,817 + 168 = 3,985
Check: 3,985 − 168; or 3,817 = 3,817; or 168

7. 52,517 − 281 = 52,236
Check: 281; or 52,236 + 52,236; or 281 = 52,517

Math Masters, p. 104

Teaching Master

Name Date Time

LESSON 4•2 **Divisibility by the Digits**

Ms. Winters asked Vito and Jacob to make answer cards for a division puzzle. They had to find numbers that met all of the following characteristics.

	Example:
◆ The first digit is divisible by 1.	1
◆ The first two digits are divisible by 2.	12
◆ The first three digits are divisible by 3.	120
◆ The first four digits are divisible by 4.	1,204
◆ The first five digits are divisible by 5.	12,040
◆ The first six digits are divisible by 6.	120,402
◆ The first seven digits are divisible by 7.	1,204,021
◆ The first eight digits are divisible by 8.	12,049,216
◆ The first nine digits are divisible by 9.	120,402,162

1. Jacob knew that with divisibility rules, it should be easy. The boys started with 3-digit numbers and found 123 and 242. Latoya checked their work. What should she tell them?
123 is correct because 1 is divisible by 1; 12 is correct because it is an even number; and 123 is correct because 1 + 2 + 3 = 6, which is divisible by 3.
242 is not correct because 2 + 4 + 2 = 8, which is not divisible by 3.

2. Use the characteristics listed above to find as many puzzle numbers as you can. Record them in the boxes below. Sample answers:

Puzzle Numbers					
4-digit	5-digit	6-digit	7-digit	8-digit	9-digit
1,472	14,725	147,252	1,472,527	14,725,272	147,252,726
1,624	16,240	162,408	1,624,084	16,240,840	162,408,402

Math Masters, p. 105

4•3 American Tour: Finding Distances on a Map

Objective To develop strategies for estimating straight-path distances using a map scale.

www.everydaymathonline.com

ePresentations

eToolkit

Algorithms Practice

EM Facts Workshop Game™

Family Letters

Assessment Management

Common Core State Standards

Curriculum Focal Points

Interactive Teacher's Lesson Guide

1 Teaching the Lesson

Key Concepts and Skills

- Use a map scale. [Operations and Computation Goal 7]
- Measure to the nearest $\frac{1}{2}$ inch. [Measurement and Reference Frames Goal 1]
- Estimate distances on a map. [Measurement and Reference Frames Goal 1]

Key Activities

Students discuss parts of a map. They use map scales to estimate real distances along straight paths.

Ongoing Assessment: Informing Instruction See page 245.

Key Vocabulary

map legend, or map key ◆ map scale

Materials

Math Journal 1, p. 103
Student Reference Book, pp. 211, 381, 386, and 387
Study Link 4•2
calculator ◆ ruler ◆ slate

2 Ongoing Learning & Practice

Finding Factors

Math Journal 1, p. 104
Students practice factoring numbers and finding the prime factorization.

Math Boxes 4•3

Math Journal 1, p. 105
Geometry Template
Students practice and maintain skills through Math Box problems.

Ongoing Assessment: Recognizing Student Achievement
Use Math Boxes, Problem 1a, b, and e.
[Number and Numeration Goal 1]

Study Link 4•3

Math Masters, p. 106
ruler
Students practice and maintain skills through Study Link activities.

3 Differentiation Options

READINESS

Reviewing Measurement and Rounding

Math Masters, p. 422
Students practice ruler measurements and rounding to the nearest fraction of an inch.

ENRICHMENT

Estimating Curved-Path Distances

Student Reference Book, pp. 212, 386, and 387
Math Masters, p. 107
Students use map scales to estimate real distances.

EXTRA PRACTICE

Estimating a Route Length

Student Reference Book, pp. 211 and 212
Math Masters, p. 108
ruler, compass, or string
Students estimate distances using a map scale.

Advance Preparation

***Teacher's Reference Manual,* Grades 4–6** pp. 29–35, 148–154, 230, 251–253

Getting Started

Mental Math and Reflexes

Have students use calculators to evaluate these expressions. Remind them to clear first and to press [=] only at the end of each expression.

●○○ $(15 * 47) + 330 - (607 \div 4)$ 883.25

●●○ $600 + 5{,}000 - (768 * 3 \div 36)$ 5,536

●●● $(\sqrt{16} * 4^2) + (6^2) - (8^2 \div 10^2)$ 99.36

Slate practice

●○○ If 1 in. represents 200 mi, 2 in. represents ____; 3 in. represents ____; 10 in. represents ____. 400 mi; 600 mi; 2,000 mi

●●○ If 2 in. represents 400 mi, 4 in. represents ____; 6 in. represents ____; 8 in. represents ____. 800 mi; 1,200 mi; 1,600 mi

●●● If $\frac{1}{2}$ in. represents 100 mi, 10 in. represents ____. 2,000 mi

Math Message

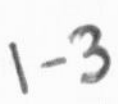

Complete Problem 1 on journal page 103.

Study Link 4·2 Follow-Up

Allow students 5 minutes to compare answers. Survey the class for any unresolved questions or concerns.

1 Teaching the Lesson

▶ Math Message Follow-Up

WHOLE-CLASS DISCUSSION

ELL

(*Student Reference Book*, pp. 211 and 381)

Survey the class for questions they recorded. Ask volunteers to respond with the answers. Ask students to read the section(s) in the *Student Reference Book* on page 211 that supports their answers.

Social Studies Link Refer students to the map at the top of page 381. Ask volunteers to make true statements about what the map shows. Encourage general and specific comments. Highlight the map title and labels. Then summarize the function of the map legend and the map scale.

▷ A **map legend,** or **map key,** explains the symbols, markings, and colors on the map.

▷ A **map scale** compares distances on the map with real distances.

Emphasize that to read a map correctly, it is important first to locate and interpret the information in the map legend. To support English language learners, discuss the meanings of *map legend* or *map key* in this context.

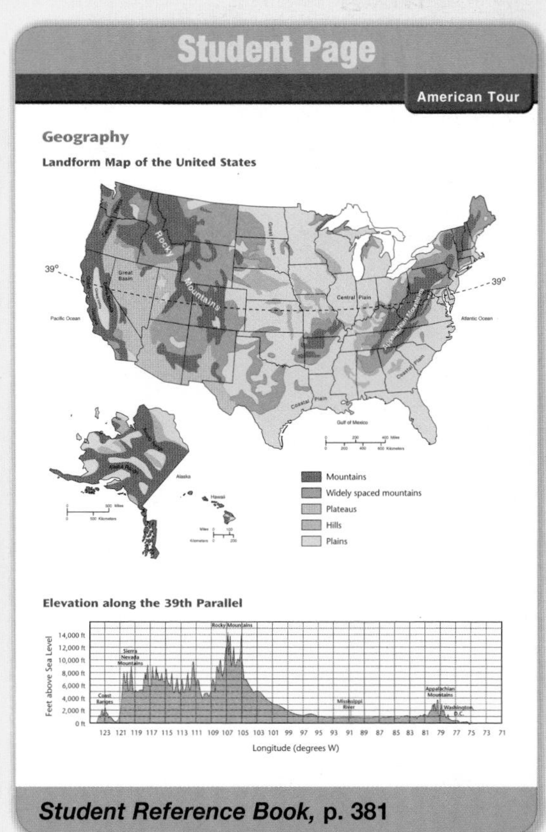

Student Reference Book, p. 381

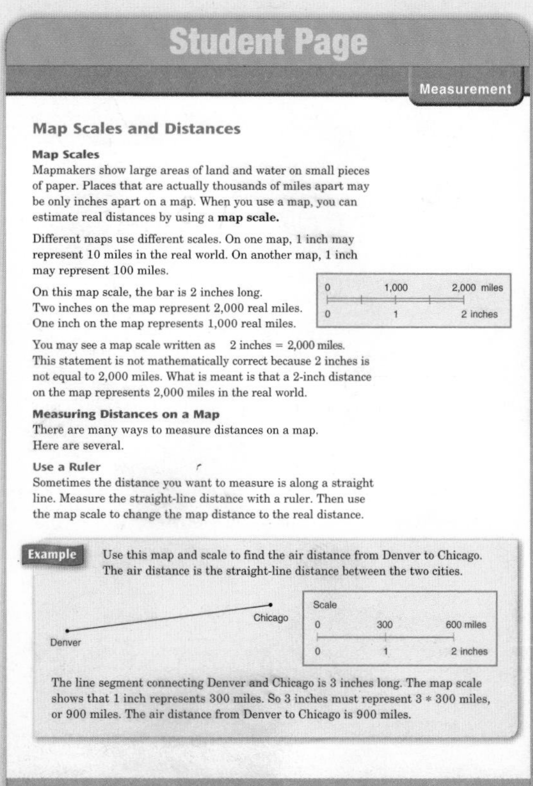

Student Page

Measurement

Map Scales and Distances

Map Scales
Mapmakers show large areas of land and water on small pieces of paper. Places that are actually thousands of miles apart may be only inches apart on a map. When you use a map, you can estimate real distances by using a **map scale.**

Different maps use different scales. On one map, 1 inch may represent 10 miles in the real world. On another map, 1 inch may represent 100 miles.

On this map scale, the bar is 2 inches long. Two inches on the map represent 2,000 real miles. One inch on the map represents 1,000 real miles.

You may see a map scale written as 2 inches = 2,000 miles. This statement is not mathematically correct because 2 inches is not equal to 2,000 miles. What is meant is that a 2-inch distance on the map represents 2,000 miles in the real world.

Measuring Distances on a Map
There are many ways to measure distances on a map. Here are several.

Use a Ruler
Sometimes the distance you want to measure is along a straight line. Measure the straight-line distance with a ruler. Then use the map scale to change the map distance to the real distance.

Example Use this map and scale to find the air distance from Denver to Chicago. The air distance is the straight-line distance between the two cities.

The line segment connecting Denver and Chicago is 3 inches long. The map scale shows that 1 inch represents 300 miles. So 3 inches must represent 3 * 300 miles, or 900 miles. The air distance from Denver to Chicago is 900 miles.

Student Reference Book, p. 211

Adjusting the Activity

ELL

The arrow as a mathematical symbol is used to represent several different concepts. To support English language learners, explain that the arrow is used in this context to indicate that 1 inch represents 200 miles since 1 inch is not the same as 200 miles.

AUDITORY ◆ KINESTHETIC ◆ TACTILE ◆ VISUAL

▶ Using a Map Scale for Straight-Path Distances

(*Student Reference Book,* pp. 211, 386, and 387)

Have students locate the legend for the map of the United States on pages 386 and 387 of the *Student Reference Book.* Some students might be confused by the insets on page 386 showing Alaska and Hawaii. Explain that a legend defines the symbols used on the map, and the scale applies to the area within the borders of the two pages. However, Alaska and Hawaii are located outside of this area; therefore, they are shown in boxes (insets) placed outside of the main area of the map.

Ask volunteers why there are 3 different scales. Depending on student response, you might follow-up with questions about the relative size of the inset areas in comparison with the main map. Sample answers: The scale for Hawaii is $\frac{1}{4}$ smaller, and the scale for Alaska is 3.5 times smaller than the main map.

Ask the class to suggest several distance problems. For example: *How far is it from Chicago to New York?* Write the students' problems on the board.

Discuss how to use a map to estimate straight-path distances. The scale for the map on page 387 can be written:

1 inch represents 200 miles
or
1 in. → 200 mi

If map distances are in whole numbers of inches, then the real distances are easier to find. *For example,* the map straight-path distance from Chicago to Pittsburgh is about 2 inches. Think: *If 1 inch represents 200 miles, 2 inches represents 2 * 200 miles. The real distance is approximately 2 * 200 miles, or 400 miles.*

Discuss the students' suggested problems on the board. For each distance, ask students to measure the straight-path distance on the map, rounding to the nearest whole number of inches. Then have them give the real distance. Use the following to supplement student problems, if needed.

- ▷ Dallas, TX, to Nashville, TN 3 in., 600 mi
- ▷ Lansing, MI, to Columbus, OH 1 in., 200 mi
- ▷ Salt Lake City, UT, to Raleigh, NC 9 in., 1,800 mi
- ▷ Boston, MA, to Washington, D.C. 2 in., 400 mi
- ▷ Helena, MT, to Kansas City, MO 5 in., 1,000 mi

Explain that the estimates of straight-path distances on maps become more accurate if they are rounded to the nearest fraction of an inch. As an example, use the distance from Chicago, IL, to New York, NY. Students might have already measured it. This time, tell them not to round their measurement to the whole inch. Instead they will want to round to the nearest fraction of an inch that simplifies the calculation. The straight-path distance on the map is about $3\frac{1}{2}$ inches. Since 1 inch represents 200 miles,

3 inches represents 3 * 200 miles, or 600 miles. An additional $\frac{1}{2}$ inch represents another 100 miles, for a total of 700 miles. The distance from Chicago to New York is a little more than 700 miles.

Adjusting the Activity

Ask: *What fraction of an inch would you use if the map scale reads 1 inch represents 160 miles?* Some students will recognize that they wouldn't have to round their measurement to simplify the calculation. Because 1 inch represents 160 miles, $\frac{1}{16}$ inch represents 10 miles, and $\frac{9}{16}$ inch represents 90 miles; 160 * 3 + 90 = 570. With this scale, the distance from Chicago to New York is about 570 miles.

AUDITORY ◆ KINESTHETIC ◆ TACTILE ◆ VISUAL

Student Page

Date Time

LESSON 4·3 **Distances between U.S. Cities**

1. Write 2 questions about map scales that can be answered using page 211 of your *Student Reference Book.*
Sample answers: How is distance measured on a map? Does every map use the same map scale?

2. Use the map of the United States on pages 386 and 387 of your *Student Reference Book* to estimate the distances between the following cities. Measure each map distance in inches. Complete the table.
(Scale: 1 inch represents 200 miles) 1-3

Cities	Map Distance (inches)	Real Distance (miles)
Chicago, IL, to Pittsburgh, PA	2 in.	400 mi
Little Rock, AR, to Jackson, MS	1 in.	200 mi
San Francisco, CA, to Salt Lake City, UT	3 in.	600 mi
Indianapolis, IN, to Raleigh, NC	$2\frac{1}{2}$ in.	500 mi
Chicago, IL, to Boston, MA	$4\frac{1}{4}$ in.	850 mi
San Antonio, TX, to Buffalo, NY	$7\frac{1}{4}$ in.	1,450 mi
Salt Lake City, UT, to Pierre, SD	$3\frac{1}{4}$ in.	650 mi

3. Explain how you found the real distance from Salt Lake City, UT, to Pierre, SD.
1-3 I measured the distance from Salt Lake City to Pierre. The distance was $3\frac{1}{4}$ in., to the nearest $\frac{1}{4}$ in. 3 in. represents 600 mi, and $\frac{1}{4}$ in. represents 50 mi. So the distance is about 650 mi.

Math Journal 1, p. 103

Finding Distances in the United States with a Map Scale 1-3

PARTNER ACTIVITY

PROBLEM SOLVING

(*Math Journal 1,* p. 103; *Student Reference Book,* pp. 386 and 387)

Ask partners to complete the journal page. Remind them that they should use the fractions in their measurements to make as accurate an estimate as possible. Circulate and assist.

Ongoing Assessment: Informing Instruction

Watch for students who have difficulty locating and measuring the endpoints for map distances. Direct these students to use a sheet of paper to measure the distance. Have them line up the edge of a piece of paper to connect two cities and mark the edge of the paper for each city's location. Then they measure the distance between the two marks on the paper.

2 Ongoing Learning & Practice

Finding Factors

INDEPENDENT ACTIVITY

(*Math Journal 1,* p. 104)

Students use factor rainbows, factor trees, and factor strings to practice factoring numbers and finding the prime factorization of numbers.

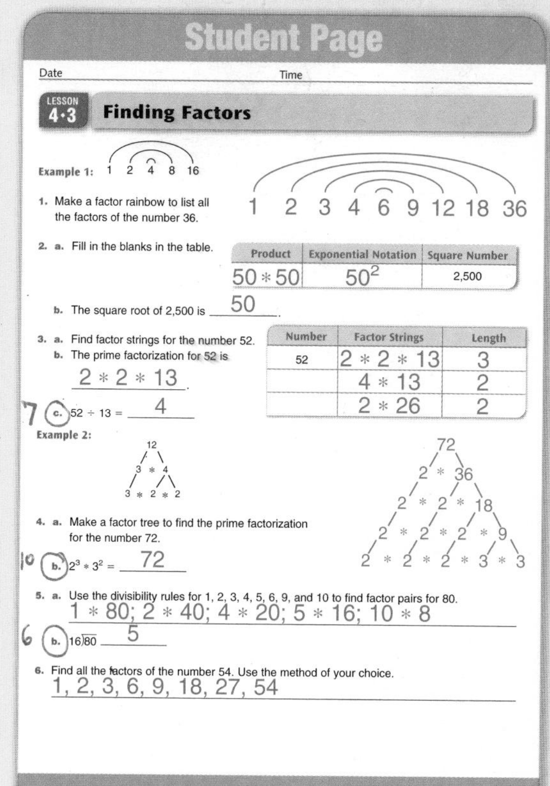

Student Page

Date Time

LESSON 4·3 **Finding Factors**

Example 1: 1 2 4 8 16

1. Make a factor rainbow to list all the factors of the number 36.
1 2 3 4 6 9 12 18 36

2. a. Fill in the blanks in the table.

Product	Exponential Notation	Square Number
50 * 50	50^2	2,500

b. The square root of 2,500 is 50.

3. a. Find factor strings for the number 52.
b. The prime factorization for 52 is 2 * 2 * 13.

Number	Factor Strings	Length
52	2 * 2 * 13	3
	4 * 13	2
	2 * 26	2

7 c. 52 ÷ 13 = 4

Example 2:
12
3 * 4
3 * 2 * 2

4. a. Make a factor tree to find the prime factorization for the number 72.
72
2 * 36
2 * 2 * 18
2 * 2 * 2 * 9
2 * 2 * 2 * 3 * 3

10 b. $2^3 * 3^2$ = 72

5. a. Use the divisibility rules for 1, 2, 3, 4, 5, 6, 9, and 10 to find factor pairs for 80.
1 * 80; 2 * 40; 4 * 20; 5 * 16; 10 * 8

6 b. 16)80 5

6. Find all the factors of the number 54. Use the method of your choice.
1, 2, 3, 6, 9, 18, 27, 54

Math Journal 1, p. 104

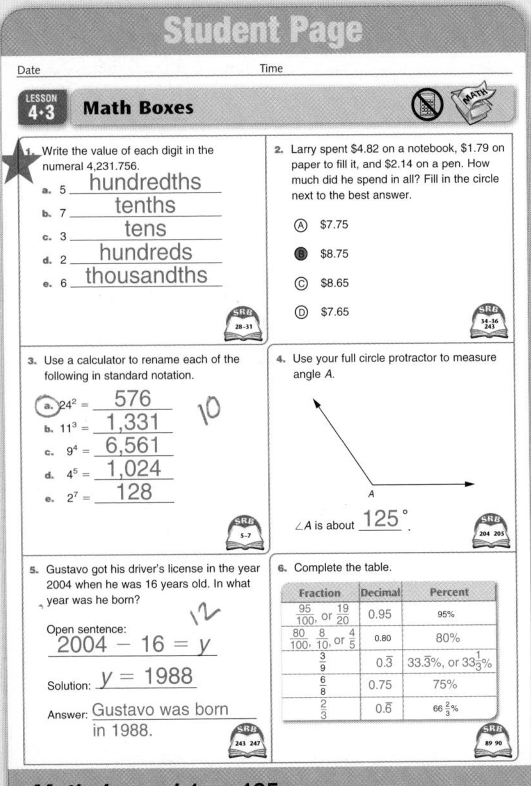

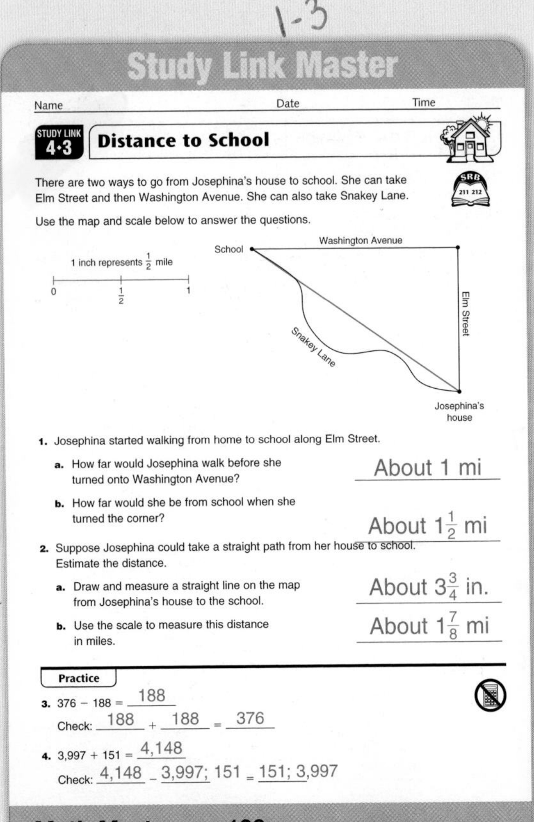

Math Boxes 4·3

(*Math Journal 1,* p. 105)

Mixed Review Math Boxes in this lesson are paired with Math Boxes in Lesson 4-1. The skill in Problem 6 previews Unit 5 content.

Ongoing Assessment: Recognizing Student Achievement

Math Boxes Problem 1

Use **Math Boxes, Problem 1a, b,** and **e** to assess students' recognition of decimal places. Students are making adequate progress if they correctly identify decimal places to the thousandths.

[Number and Numeration Goal 1]

Study Link 4·3

(*Math Masters*, p. 106)

Home Connection Students use a map scale to approximate distances.

3 Differentiation Options

READINESS

Reviewing Measurement and Rounding

(*Math Masters*, p. 422)

To explore strategies for measuring and rounding to the nearest fraction of an inch with designated easy fractions, have students complete the following activity.

Ask students to look at the ruler close-up on *Math Masters,* page 422 and count by half-inches from 4 to 6 inches, marking the points with their index fingers as they go along. 4 in., $4\frac{1}{2}$ in., 5 in., $5\frac{1}{2}$ in., 6 in. Repeat for quarter-inches 4 in., $4\frac{1}{4}$ in., $4\frac{1}{2}$ in., $4\frac{3}{4}$ in., 5 in., and so on and again for eighth-inches and sixteenth-inches. 4 in., $4\frac{1}{8}$ in., $4\frac{1}{4}$ in., $4\frac{3}{8}$ in., $4\frac{1}{2}$ in., $4\frac{5}{8}$ in., and so on; 4 in., $4\frac{1}{16}$ in., $4\frac{1}{8}$ in., $4\frac{3}{16}$ in., $4\frac{1}{4}$ in., and so on

Ask students to use their rulers to draw line segments on the page. Then have them write a rounded measure under each line, to the nearest half-inch. *Suggestions*: $5\frac{5}{8}$ in.; $5\frac{1}{2}$ in. $4\frac{1}{16}$ in.; 4 in. $4\frac{7}{8}$ in.; 5 in. $4\frac{7}{16}$ in. $4\frac{1}{2}$ in.

ENRICHMENT

PARTNER ACTIVITY

15–30 Min

Estimating Curved-Path Distances

(*Student Reference Book*, pp. 212, 386, and 387; *Math Masters*, p. 107)

To apply students' understanding of calculating distances on a map using a map scale, have them find distances on curved paths.

▷ Partners read and discuss page 212 in the *Student Reference Book*. This page explains several methods for estimating map distances that don't follow a straight path.

▷ Partners use each method to estimate the length of the U.S./Mexico border.

▷ Partners then use the method(s) of their choice to complete *Math Masters,* page 107.

NOTE In the compass method, straight-line segments are used to measure a curved path. Advise students that shorter segments will produce a more accurate answer.

EXTRA PRACTICE

INDEPENDENT ACTIVITY

5–15 Min

Estimating a Route Length

(*Student Reference Book,* pp. 211 and 212;
Math Masters, p. 108)

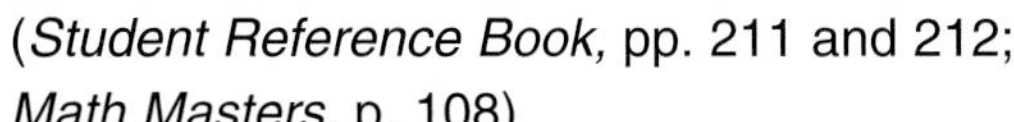

Students designate, draw, and measure a route from New York, through the Panama Canal, to Los Angeles.

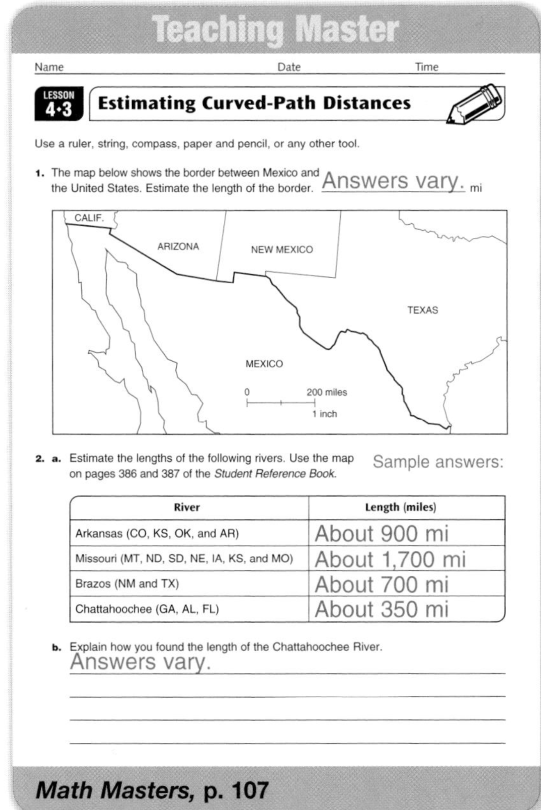

Teaching Master

Name Date Time

LESSON 4·3 **Estimating Curved-Path Distances**

Use a ruler, string, compass, paper and pencil, or any other tool.

1. The map below shows the border between Mexico and the United States. Estimate the length of the border. Answers vary. mi

2. a. Estimate the lengths of the following rivers. Use the map on pages 386 and 387 of the *Student Reference Book.* Sample answers:

River	Length (miles)
Arkansas (CO, KS, OK, and AR)	About 900 mi
Missouri (MT, ND, SD, NE, IA, KS, and MO)	About 1,700 mi
Brazos (NM and TX)	About 700 mi
Chattahoochee (GA, AL, FL)	About 350 mi

b. Explain how you found the length of the Chattahoochee River.
Answers vary.

Math Masters, p. 107

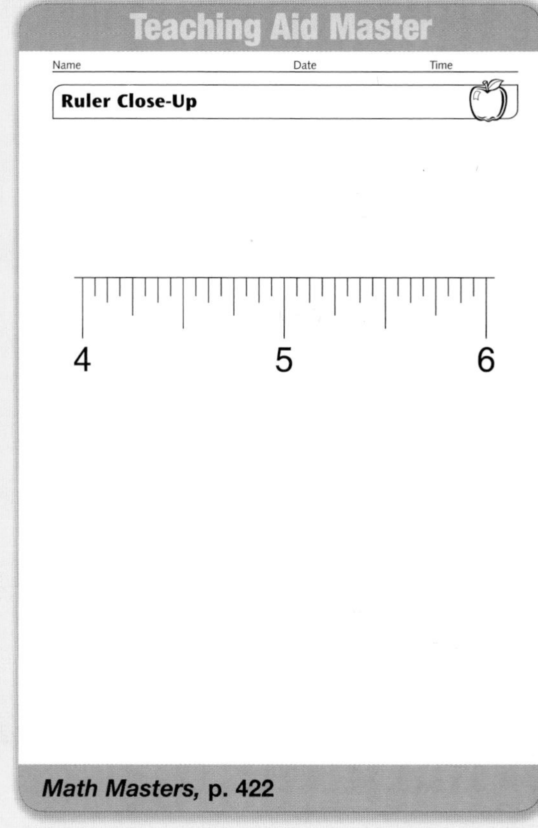

Teaching Aid Master

Name Date Time

Ruler Close-Up

Math Masters, p. 422

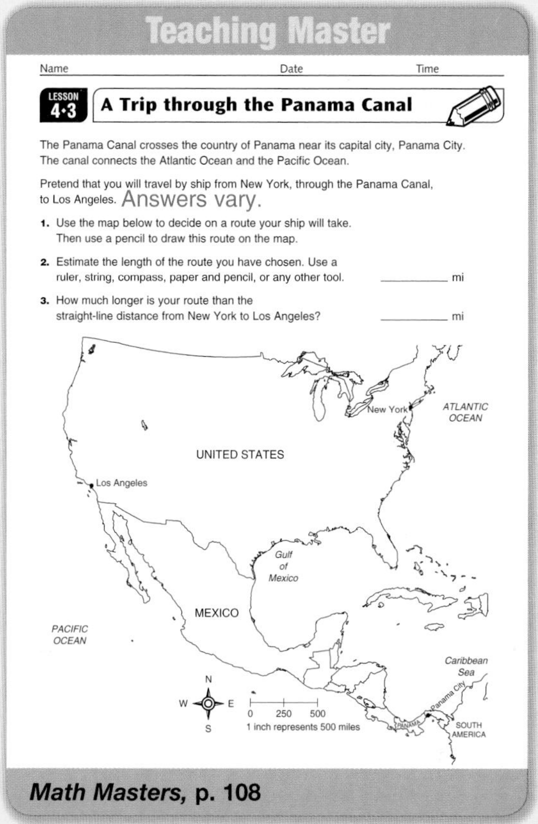

Teaching Master

Name Date Time

LESSON 4·3 **A Trip through the Panama Canal**

The Panama Canal crosses the country of Panama near its capital city, Panama City. The canal connects the Atlantic Ocean and the Pacific Ocean.

Pretend that you will travel by ship from New York, through the Panama Canal, to Los Angeles. Answers vary.

1. Use the map below to decide on a route your ship will take. Then use a pencil to draw this route on the map.
2. Estimate the length of the route you have chosen. Use a ruler, string, compass, paper and pencil, or any other tool. ______ mi
3. How much longer is your route than the straight-line distance from New York to Los Angeles? ______ mi

Math Masters, p. 108

4•4 Partial-Quotients Algorithm Strategies

 **Objective** To provide practice with strategies for the partial-quotients algorithm.

 www.everydaymathonline.com

ePresentations

eToolkit

Algorithms Practice

EM Facts Workshop Game™

Family Letters

Assessment Management

Common Core State Standards

Curriculum Focal Points

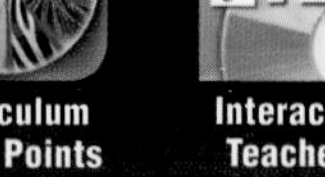
Interactive Teacher's Lesson Guide

1 Teaching the Lesson

Key Concepts and Skills

- Use divisibility rules to identify multiples. [Number and Numeration Goal 3]
- Apply division facts and extended facts to identify partial quotients. [Operations and Computation Goal 2]
- Use the partial-quotients algorithm for problems. [Operations and Computation Goal 3]

Key Activities

Students play *Divisibility Dash* to practice recognizing multiples and using divisibility rules. They practice finding partial quotients by using easy multiples of the divisor.

 **Ongoing Assessment: Informing Instruction** See page 251.

 **Ongoing Assessment: Recognizing Student Achievement** Use journal page 107. [Operations and Computation Goal 3]

Key Vocabulary

multiple ◆ divisor ◆ partial quotient ◆ dividend

Materials

Math Journal 1, pp. 106 and 107
Student Reference Book, pp. 22, 23, and 302
Study Link 4•3
Math Masters, p. 109 (optional); pp. 414 and 415
Class Data Pad ◆ calculator ◆ per partnership: 4 each of number cards 0–9 from one deck and 2 each of number cards 2, 3, 5, 6, 9, and 10 from a second deck

2 Ongoing Learning & Practice

Math Boxes 4•4
Math Journal 1, p. 108
Students practice and maintain skills through Math Box problems.

Study Link 4•4
Math Masters, p. 110
Students practice and maintain skills through Study Link activities.

3 Differentiation Options

READINESS

Using Expanded Notation to Find Multiples
Math Masters, p. 112
per partnership: 4 each of number cards 1–9 (from the Everything Math Deck, if available)
Students write numbers in expanded notation to explore using extended facts.

EXTRA PRACTICE

Practicing Division
Math Masters, p. 111
Students use lists of multiples of the divisor to solve division problems.

Advance Preparation

For Part 1, you will need a coin for the calculator practice in the Mental Math and Reflexes and 2 copies of the computation grid (*Math Masters,* page 415) for each student. For the game *Divisibility Dash,* each partnership will need two decks of cards. For the optional Extra Practice activity in Part 3, prepare *Math Masters,* page 111 to provide individualized practice as needed.

 ***Teacher's Reference Manual,* Grades 4–6** pp. 132–140

Getting Started

Mental Math and Reflexes

For calculator practice, write each problem on the board or a transparency. Use a coin toss to determine whether students express the answer with a whole-number remainder or a fraction remainder.

●○○ $5\overline{)36}$ 7 R1; $7\frac{1}{5}$

$11 \div 4$ 2 R3; $2\frac{3}{4}$

$34 / 8$ 4 R2; $4\frac{2}{8}$ or $4\frac{1}{4}$

●●○ $6\overline{)75}$ 12 R3; $12\frac{3}{6}$ or $12\frac{1}{2}$

$78 \div 8$ 9 R6; $9\frac{6}{8}$ or $9\frac{3}{4}$

$99 / 8$ 12 R3; $12\frac{3}{8}$

●●● $11\overline{)102}$ 9 R3; $9\frac{3}{9}$ or $9\frac{1}{3}$

$25\overline{)230}$ 9 R5; $9\frac{5}{25}$ or $9\frac{1}{5}$

$680 / 50$ 13 R30; $13\frac{30}{50}$ or $13\frac{3}{5}$

Ask volunteers to explain the meaning of the fraction remainder. The divisor represents how many are needed in a group or how many groups. The divisor is the denominator. The remainder is the numerator; how many you have. The fraction represents division—the remainder, $\frac{1}{5}$, is one divided by 5.

Math Message

Write a 3-digit number that is divisible by 6.

Study Link 4·3 Follow-Up

Allow students five minutes to compare their answers and resolve any differences. Circulate and assist.

1 Teaching the Lesson

Math Message Follow-Up

WHOLE-CLASS DISCUSSION

Survey the class for their 3-digit numbers that are divisible by 6. Write student responses on the Class Data Pad. Ask students how they might check these numbers without actually dividing by 6. Most students will refer to the divisibility rule for 6: A number is divisible by 6 if it is divisible by 2 and 3. Check the numbers as a class, and discuss students' strategies for finding their numbers.

Introducing *Divisibility Dash*

WHOLE-CLASS ACTIVITY

(*Student Reference Book*, p. 302)

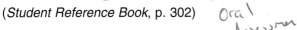

Playing *Divisibility Dash* provides students with practice recognizing **multiples** and using divisibility rules in a context that also develops speed. The variation is for 3-digit numbers. Discuss the variation example on *Student Reference Book,* page 302, and demonstrate a turn by playing one hand as a class. Then allow partners time to play at least 3 rounds of *Divisibility Dash.*

Reviewing the Partial-Quotients Algorithm

WHOLE-CLASS ACTIVITY

(*Math Masters*, p. 415)

Explain that another approach to finding partial quotients is to use a series of at least...not more than multiples of the **divisor.** A good strategy is to start with easy numbers, such as 100 times the divisor or 10 times the divisor.

Student Page

Games

Divisibility Dash

Materials number cards 0–9 (4 of each)
number cards: 2, 3, 5, 6, 9, and 10 (2 of each)

Players 2 or 3

Skill Recognizing multiples, using divisibility tests

Object of the game To discard all cards.

Directions

1. Shuffle the divisor cards and place them number-side down on the table. Shuffle the draw cards and deal 8 to each player. Place the remaining draw cards number-side down next to the divisor cards.
2. For each round, turn the top divisor card number-side up. Players take turns. When it is your turn:
   - Use the cards in your hand to make 2-digit numbers that are multiples of the divisor card. Make as many 2-digit numbers that are multiples as you can. A card used to make one 2-digit number may not be used again to make another number.
   - Place all the cards you used to make 2-digit numbers in a discard pile.
   - If you cannot make a 2-digit number that is a multiple of the divisor card, you must take a card from the draw pile. Your turn is over.
3. If a player disagrees that a 2-digit number is a multiple of the divisor card, that player may challenge. Players use the divisibility test for the divisor card value to check the number in question. Any numbers that are not multiples of the divisor card must be returned to the player's hand.
4. If the draw pile or divisor cards have all been used, they can be reshuffled and put back into play.
5. The first player to discard all of his or her cards is the winner.

Note

The number cards 0–9 (4 of each) are the **draw cards.** This set of draw cards is also called the **draw pile.**

The number cards 2, 3, 5, 6, 9, and 10 (2 of each) are the **divisor cards.**

Example Andrew's cards: 1 2 5 5 7 8 Divisor card: 3

Andrew uses his cards to make 2 numbers that are multiples of 3: 1 5 5 7

He discards these 4 cards and holds the 2 and 8 for the next round of play.

Student Reference Book, p. 302

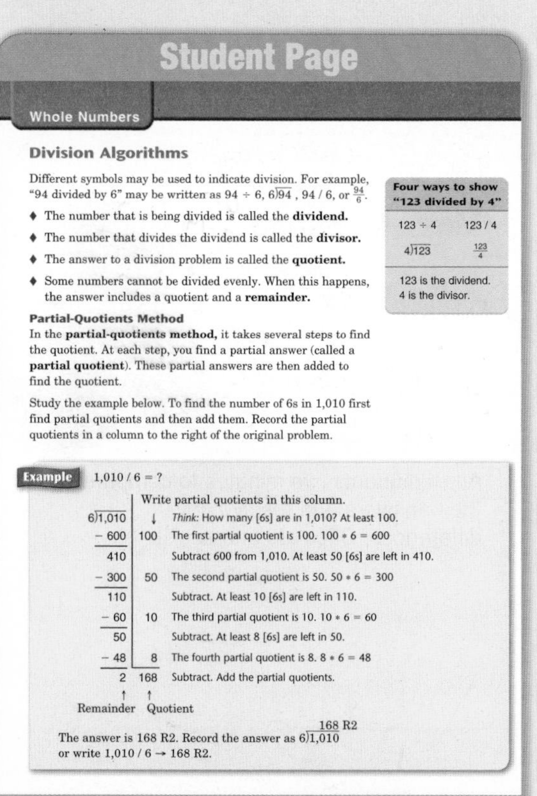
Student Page

Whole Numbers

Division Algorithms

Different symbols may be used to indicate division. For example, "94 divided by 6" may be written as $94 \div 6$, $6\overline{)94}$, 94 / 6, or $\frac{94}{6}$.

- The number that is being divided is called the **dividend.**
- The number that divides the dividend is called the **divisor.**
- The answer to a division problem is called the **quotient.**
- Some numbers cannot be divided evenly. When this happens, the answer includes a quotient and a **remainder.**

Four ways to show "123 divided by 4"	
$123 \div 4$	123 / 4
$4\overline{)123}$	$\frac{123}{4}$

123 is the dividend.
4 is the divisor.

Partial-Quotients Method
In the **partial-quotients method,** it takes several steps to find the quotient. At each step, you find a partial answer (called a **partial quotient**). These partial answers are then added to find the quotient.

Study the example below. To find the number of 6s in 1,010 first find partial quotients and then add them. Record the partial quotients in a column to the right of the original problem.

Example 1,010 / 6 = ?

	Write partial quotients in this column.	
$6\overline{)1,010}$	↓	*Think:* How many [6s] are in 1,010? At least 100.
− 600	100	The first partial quotient is 100. 100 ∗ 6 = 600
410		Subtract 600 from 1,010. At least 50 [6s] are left in 410.
− 300	50	The second partial quotient is 50. 50 ∗ 6 = 300
110		Subtract. At least 10 [6s] are left in 110.
− 60	10	The third partial quotient is 10. 10 ∗ 6 = 60
50		Subtract. At least 8 [6s] are left in 50.
− 48	8	The fourth partial quotient is 8. 8 ∗ 6 = 48
2	168	Subtract. Add the partial quotients.
↑ Remainder	↑ Quotient	

The answer is 168 R2. Record the answer as $6\overline{)1,010}$ with 168 R2 above, or write 1,010 / 6 → 168 R2.

Student Reference Book, p. 22

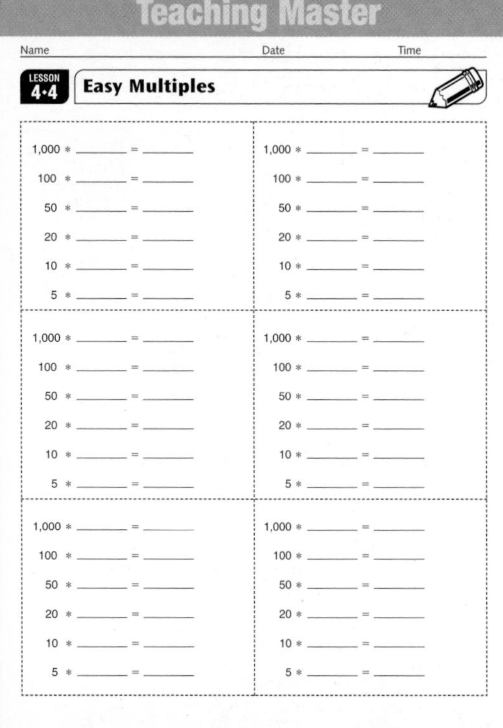
Teaching Master

Name Date Time

LESSON 4•4 **Easy Multiples**

1,000 ∗ ______ = ______	1,000 ∗ ______ = ______
100 ∗ ______ = ______	100 ∗ ______ = ______
50 ∗ ______ = ______	50 ∗ ______ = ______
20 ∗ ______ = ______	20 ∗ ______ = ______
10 ∗ ______ = ______	10 ∗ ______ = ______
5 ∗ ______ = ______	5 ∗ ______ = ______
1,000 ∗ ______ = ______	1,000 ∗ ______ = ______
100 ∗ ______ = ______	100 ∗ ______ = ______
50 ∗ ______ = ______	50 ∗ ______ = ______
20 ∗ ______ = ______	20 ∗ ______ = ______
10 ∗ ______ = ______	10 ∗ ______ = ______
5 ∗ ______ = ______	5 ∗ ______ = ______
1,000 ∗ ______ = ______	1,000 ∗ ______ = ______
100 ∗ ______ = ______	100 ∗ ______ = ______
50 ∗ ______ = ______	50 ∗ ______ = ______
20 ∗ ______ = ______	20 ∗ ______ = ______
10 ∗ ______ = ______	10 ∗ ______ = ______
5 ∗ ______ = ______	5 ∗ ______ = ______

Math Masters, p. 109

1. Write the problem $6\overline{)1,010}$, drawing a vertical line to the right of the problem.

   - Are there at least 100 [6s] in 1,010? Yes, because 100 ∗ 6 = 600, which is less than 1,010. Are there at least 200 [6s] in 1,010? No, because 200 ∗ 6 = 1,200, which is more than 1,010.
   - So there are at least 100 [6s] but not more than 200 [6s]. Try 100.

   Write 600 under 1,010. Write 100 to the right. 100 is the first **partial quotient.**

$6\overline{)1,010}$		
− 600	100	The first partial quotient, 100 ∗ 6 = 600.

2. Next find out how much is left to be divided. Subtract 600 from 1,010.

$6\overline{)1,010}$		
− 600	100	The first partial quotient, 100 ∗ 6 = 600.
410		410 is left to divide.

3. Now find the number of 6s in 410. There are several ways to do this:

   ▷ Use a fact family and extended facts. 6 ∗ 6 = 36; 60 ∗ 6 = 360, so there are at least 60 [6s] in 410.

$6\overline{)1,010}$		
− 600	100	The first partial quotient, 100 ∗ 6 = 600.
410		410 is left to divide.
− 360	60	The second partial quotient, 60 ∗ 6 = 360.
50		50 is left to divide.
− 48	8	The third partial quotient, 8 ∗ 6 = 48.
2		2 is left to divide.

   ▷ Or continue to use at least...not more than multiples with easy numbers. For example, ask: *Are there at least 100 [6s] in 410?* No, because 100 ∗ 6 = 600. *Are there at least 50 [6s]?* Yes, because 50 ∗ 6 = 300.

$6\overline{)1,010}$		
− 600	100	The first partial quotient, 100 ∗ 6 = 600.
410		410 is left to divide.
− 300	50	The second partial quotient, 50 ∗ 6 = 300.
110		110 is left to divide.

Algorithm Project The focus of this lesson is the partial-quotients algorithm. To teach U.S. traditional long division, see Algorithm Project 7 on page A32.

Subtract 300 from 410, and continue by asking: *Are there 10 [6s] in 110?* Yes, because 10 ∗ 6 = 60. *Are there 20 [6s] in 110?* No, because 20 ∗ 6 = 120.

6)1,010		
– 600	100	The first partial quotient, 100 ∗ 6 = 600.
410		410 is left to divide.
– 300	50	The second partial quotient, 50 ∗ 6 = 300.
110		110 is left to divide.
– 60	10	The third partial quotient, 10 ∗ 6 = 60.
50		50 is left to divide.
– 48	8	The fourth partial quotient, 8 ∗ 6 = 48.
2		2 is left to divide.

4. When the subtraction leaves a number less than the divisor (2 in this example), students should move to the final step and add the partial quotients.

168 R2	
6)1,010	
– 600	100
410	
– 360	60
50	
– 48	8
2	168

168 R2	
6)1,010	
– 600	100
410	
– 300	50
110	
– 60	10
50	
– 48	8
2	168

1,010 ÷ 6 → 168 R2

Ask: *How would you record the remainder as a fraction?* $\frac{2}{6}$ or $\frac{1}{3}$

Ongoing Assessment: Informing Instruction

Watch for students who use only multiples of 10. Encourage them to look for larger multiples of the divisor, as appropriate. Suggest they first compile a list of easy multiples of the divisor.

Example: If the divisor is 6, students might make the following list:

200 ∗ 6 = 1,200
100 ∗ 6 = 600
50 ∗ 6 = 300
20 ∗ 6 = 120
10 ∗ 6 = 60
5 ∗ 6 = 30

Remind students that listing the easy multiples in advance allows them to focus on solving the division problem, rather than looking for multiples. *Math Masters,* page 109 provides an optional form for writing multiples.

Use number cards 1 through 9 (4 of each) to generate random 3- or 4-digit **dividends** and 1- or 2-digit divisors for the class. Ask partners to use the partial-quotients algorithm to solve these problems. Circulate and assist.

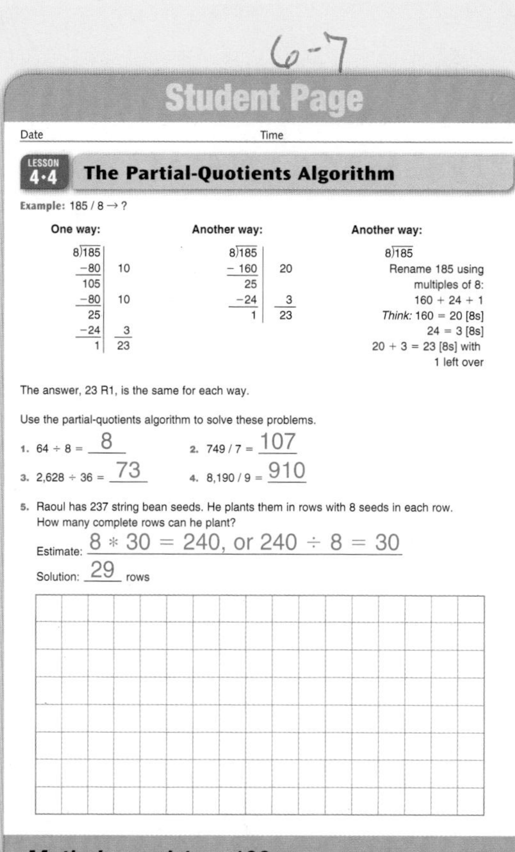
6-7

Student Page

Date Time

LESSON 4•4 **The Partial-Quotients Algorithm**

Example: 185 / 8 → ?

One way:

8)185	
–80	10
105	
–80	10
25	
–24	3
1	23

Another way:

8)185	
– 160	20
25	
–24	3
1	23

Another way:

8)185
Rename 185 using multiples of 8:
160 + 24 + 1
Think: 160 = 20 [8s]
24 = 3 [8s]
20 + 3 = 23 [8s] with 1 left over

The answer, 23 R1, is the same for each way.

Use the partial-quotients algorithm to solve these problems.

1. 64 ÷ 8 = 8
2. 749 / 7 = 107
3. 2,628 ÷ 36 = 73
4. 8,190 / 9 = 910
5. Raoul has 237 string bean seeds. He plants them in rows with 8 seeds in each row. How many complete rows can he plant?

Estimate: 8 ∗ 30 = 240, or 240 ÷ 8 = 30

Solution: 29 rows

Math Journal 1, p. 106

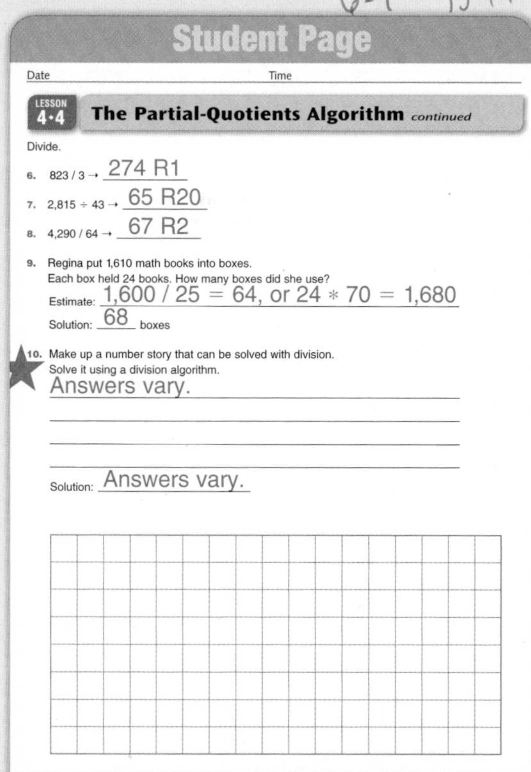

Student Page

Date ______ Time ______

LESSON 4·4 **The Partial-Quotients Algorithm** *continued*

Divide.

6. 823 / 3 → 274 R1
7. 2,815 ÷ 43 → 65 R20
8. 4,290 / 64 → 67 R2
9. Regina put 1,610 math books into boxes. Each box held 24 books. How many boxes did she use?
   Estimate: 1,600 / 25 = 64, or 24 ∗ 70 = 1,680
   Solution: 68 boxes
10. Make up a number story that can be solved with division. Solve it using a division algorithm.
   Answers vary.
   Solution: Answers vary.

Math Journal 1, p. 107

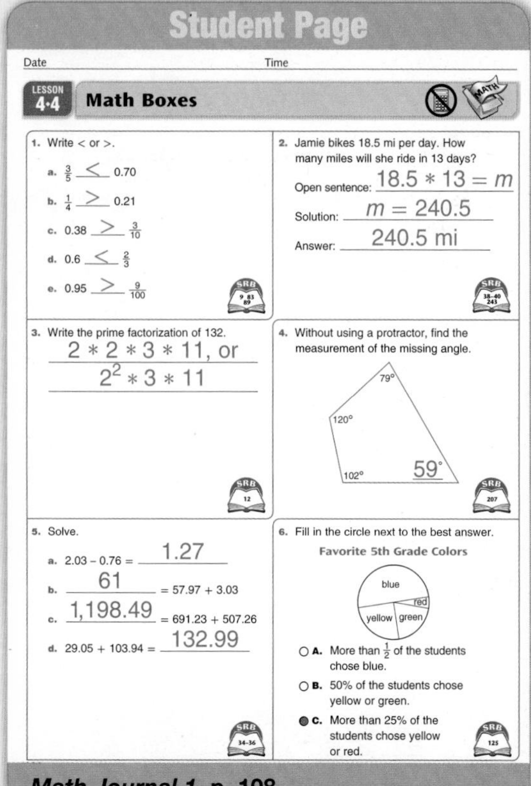

Student Page

Date ______ Time ______

LESSON 4·4 **Math Boxes**

1. Write < or >.
   a. $\frac{3}{5}$ < 0.70
   b. $\frac{1}{4}$ > 0.21
   c. 0.38 > $\frac{3}{10}$
   d. 0.6 < $\frac{2}{3}$
   e. 0.95 > $\frac{9}{100}$
2. Jamie bikes 18.5 mi per day. How many miles will she ride in 13 days?
   Open sentence: 18.5 ∗ 13 = m
   Solution: m = 240.5
   Answer: 240.5 mi
3. Write the prime factorization of 132.
   2 ∗ 2 ∗ 3 ∗ 11, or
   2^2 ∗ 3 ∗ 11
4. Without using a protractor, find the measurement of the missing angle.
   79°, 120°, 102°, 59°
5. Solve.
   a. 2.03 − 0.76 = 1.27
   b. 61 = 57.97 + 3.03
   c. 1,198.49 = 691.23 + 507.26
   d. 29.05 + 103.94 = 132.99
6. Fill in the circle next to the best answer.
   Favorite 5th Grade Colors
   (blue, red, yellow, green)
   ○ A. More than $\frac{1}{2}$ of the students chose blue.
   ○ B. 50% of the students chose yellow or green.
   ● C. More than 25% of the students chose yellow or red.

Math Journal 1, p. 108

After students have worked for a few minutes, look for partnerships with solutions that have different partial-quotients lists, and ask them to share their solutions with the class. Emphasize the following:

▷ Students should use the multiples that are easy for them. This might sometimes require more steps, but it will make the work go faster.

▷ Students should not be concerned if they pick a multiple that is too large. If that happens, they will quickly realize that they have a subtraction problem with a larger number being subtracted from a smaller number. Students can use this information to revise the multiple they used.

▶ Using the Partial-Quotients Algorithm

INDEPENDENT ACTIVITY

(*Math Journal 1,* pp. 106 and 107; *Student Reference Book*, pp. 22 and 23)

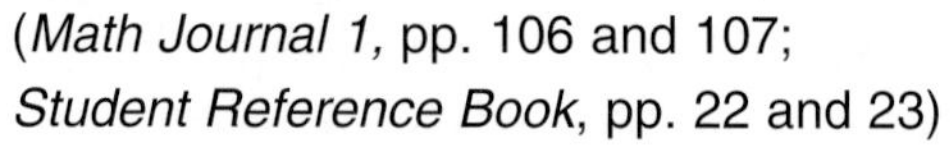

Have students solve the problems on the journal pages, showing their work on the computation grids. Encourage students to use the *Student Reference Book* as needed. Circulate and assist.

Ongoing Assessment: Recognizing Student Achievement

Journal Page 107 Problem 10

Use **journal page 107, Problem 10** to assess students' understanding of division. Students are making adequate progress if they have written a number story that can be solved using division.

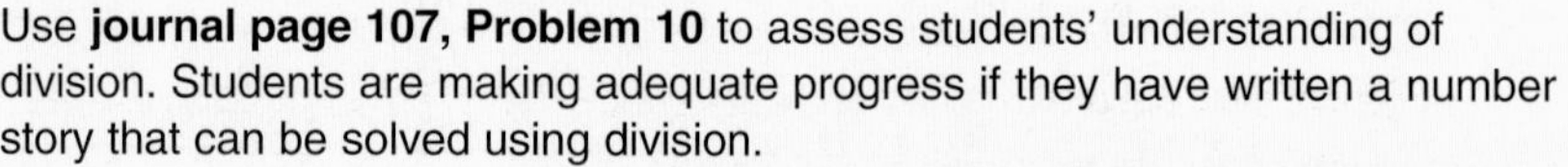

[Operations and Computation Goal 3]

Ask students to select from Problems 1–4 on *Math Journal 1,* page 106 and then explain and illustrate their strategy for solving one of the problems on an Exit Slip (*Math Masters,* page 414).

2 Ongoing Learning & Practice

▶ Math Boxes 4·4

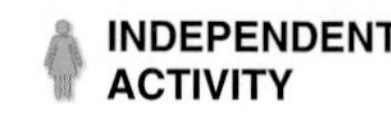

INDEPENDENT ACTIVITY

(*Math Journal 1,* p. 108)

Mixed Review Math Boxes in this lesson are paired with Math Boxes in Lessons 4-2 and 4-6. The skills in Problems 5 and 6 preview Unit 5 content.

6-7 13

Study Link 4•4

(*Math Masters*, p. 110)

INDEPENDENT ACTIVITY

Home Connection Students practice the partial-quotients division algorithm.

3 Differentiation Options

READINESS

Using Expanded Notation to Find Multiples

PARTNER ACTIVITY

15–30 Min

(*Math Masters,* p. 112)

To explore using extended facts, have students write numbers in expanded notation. Students then complete *Math Masters,* page 112 using the expanded notation to find equivalent names.

EXTRA PRACTICE

INDEPENDENT ACTIVITY

5–15 Min

Practicing Division

(*Math Masters,* p. 111)

Use *Math Masters,* page 111 to create division problems for individualized extra practice. Encourage students to list the multiples of the divisor. Have students create problems for partners to solve.

Teaching Master

Name Date Time

LESSON 4•4 **Division Practice**

For each division problem, complete the list of multiples of the divisor. Then divide.

1. ____)‾‾‾‾

Answer: ____

200 ∗ ____ = ____
100 ∗ ____ = ____
50 ∗ ____ = ____
20 ∗ ____ = ____
10 ∗ ____ = ____
5 ∗ ____ = ____

2. ____ ÷ ____

Answer: ____

200 ∗ ____ = ____
100 ∗ ____ = ____
50 ∗ ____ = ____
20 ∗ ____ = ____
10 ∗ ____ = ____
5 ∗ ____ = ____

3. ____ / ____

Answer: ____

200 ∗ ____ = ____
100 ∗ ____ = ____
50 ∗ ____ = ____
20 ∗ ____ = ____
10 ∗ ____ = ____
5 ∗ ____ = ____

4. ____ ÷ ____

Answer: ____

200 ∗ ____ = ____
100 ∗ ____ = ____
50 ∗ ____ = ____
20 ∗ ____ = ____
10 ∗ ____ = ____
5 ∗ ____ = ____

***Math Masters,* p. 111**

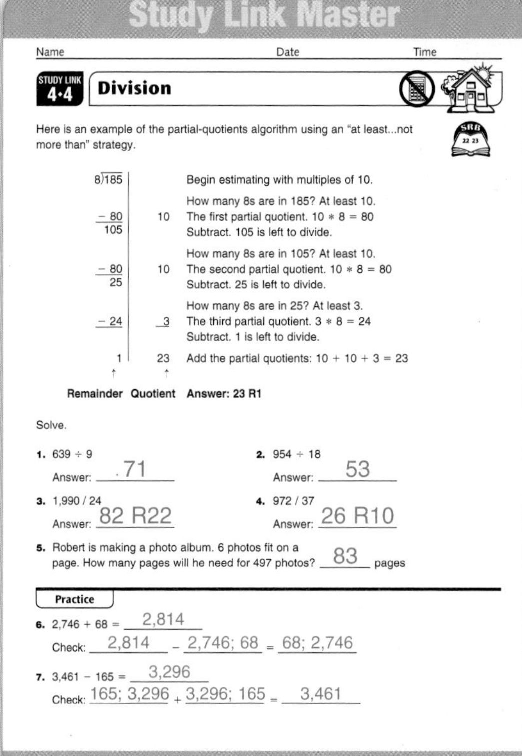

Study Link Master

Name Date Time

STUDY LINK 4•4 **Division**

Here is an example of the partial-quotients algorithm using an "at least...not more than" strategy.

8)185		Begin estimating with multiples of 10.
		How many 8s are in 185? At least 10.
− 80	10	The first partial quotient. 10 ∗ 8 = 80
105		Subtract. 105 is left to divide.
		How many 8s are in 105? At least 10.
− 80	10	The second partial quotient. 10 ∗ 8 = 80
25		Subtract. 25 is left to divide.
		How many 8s are in 25? At least 3.
− 24	3	The third partial quotient. 3 ∗ 8 = 24
		Subtract. 1 is left to divide.
1	23	Add the partial quotients: 10 + 10 + 3 = 23
↑ Remainder	↑ Quotient	**Answer: 23 R1**

Solve.

1. 639 ÷ 9 Answer: 71
2. 954 ÷ 18 Answer: 53
3. 1,990 / 24 Answer: 82 R22
4. 972 / 37 Answer: 26 R10
5. Robert is making a photo album. 6 photos fit on a page. How many pages will he need for 497 photos? 83 pages

Practice

6. 2,746 + 68 = 2,814
Check: 2,814 − 2,746; 68 = 68; 2,746
7. 3,461 − 165 = 3,296
Check: 165; 3,296 + 3,296; 165 = 3,461

***Math Masters,* p. 110**

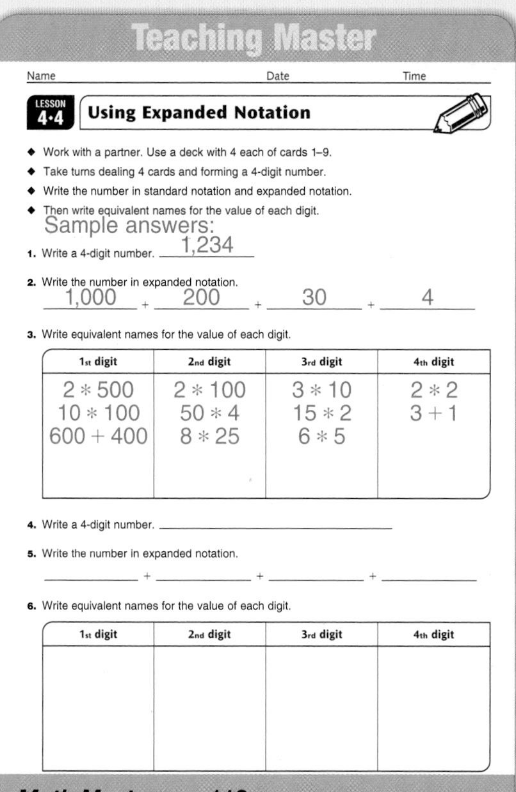

Teaching Master

Name Date Time

LESSON 4•4 **Using Expanded Notation**

- Work with a partner. Use a deck with 4 each of cards 1–9.
- Take turns dealing 4 cards and forming a 4-digit number.
- Write the number in standard notation and expanded notation.
- Then write equivalent names for the value of each digit.

Sample answers:

1. Write a 4-digit number. 1,234
2. Write the number in expanded notation. 1,000 + 200 + 30 + 4
3. Write equivalent names for the value of each digit.

1st digit	2nd digit	3rd digit	4th digit
2 ∗ 500 10 ∗ 100 600 + 400	2 ∗ 100 50 ∗ 4 8 ∗ 25	3 ∗ 10 15 ∗ 2 6 ∗ 5	2 ∗ 2 3 + 1

4. Write a 4-digit number. ____
5. Write the number in expanded notation. ____ + ____ + ____ + ____
6. Write equivalent names for the value of each digit.

1st digit	2nd digit	3rd digit	4th digit

***Math Masters,* p. 112**

4•5 Division of Decimal Numbers

Objectives To provide experience with making magnitude estimates for quotients and using the partial-quotients algorithm with decimals.

Technology Resources www.everydaymathonline.com

ePresentations

eToolkit

Algorithms Practice

EM Facts Workshop Game™

Family Letters

Assessment Management

Common Core State Standards

Curriculum Focal Points

Interactive Teacher's Lesson Guide

1 Teaching the Lesson

Key Concepts and Skills

- Use vocabulary (dividend, divisor, quotient, and remainder) to discuss magnitude estimates. [Operations and Computation Goal 3]
- Use the partial-quotients algorithm to solve problems. [Operations and Computation Goal 3]
- Make magnitude estimates for quotients. [Operations and Computation Goal 6]

Key Activities

Students make and record magnitude estimates for quotients. They divide decimals by whole numbers and use magnitude estimates to insert the decimal point in their answers.

Ongoing Assessment: Recognizing Student Achievement Use journal page 109. [Operations and Computation Goal 6]

Key Vocabulary

decimal point ◆ magnitude estimate

Materials

Math Journal 1, p. 109
Study Link 4•4
Math Masters, p. 415
calculator ◆ slate

2 Ongoing Learning & Practice

Playing *Division Top-It* (3-Digit Dividends)

Student Reference Book, p. 334
Students practice recognizing multiples and applying division facts and extended facts.

Math Boxes 4•5

Math Journal 1, p. 110
Students practice and maintain skills through Math Box problems.

Study Link 4•5

Math Masters, p. 113
Students practice and maintain skills through Study Link activities.

3 Differentiation Options

READINESS

Modeling Division with Base-10 Blocks

Math Masters, p. 114
base-10 blocks (6 flats, 22 longs, 40 cubes)
Students solve division problems using a concrete model.

ENRICHMENT

Exploring an Alternative Division Algorithm

Student Reference Book, pp. 24 and 44
Math Masters, p. 115
bills and coins (optional)
Students explore the column-division algorithm for decimal division.

ELL SUPPORT

Illustrating Division Algorithms

chart paper or posterboard
Students make posters for different versions of division algorithms.

Advance Preparation

For the optional Enrichment activity in Part 3, review the column-division algorithm on *Math Masters,* page 115 and on *Student Reference Book,* pages 24 and 44.

***Teacher's Reference Manual,* Grades 4–6** pp. 19, 132–140, 260–263

Getting Started

Mental Math and Reflexes

Calculator Practice:

●○○ Square 364 132,496

●●○ Find the square root of 4,761 69

●●● Square the sum of 34^2 and 78 1,522,756

Have students use slates for the following problems:

●○○ Write 18.09. Circle the digit in the tenths place. Underline the digit in the ones place. 18.⓪9

●●○ Write 305.72. Circle the digit in the tens place. Underline the digit in the tenths place. 3⓪5.72

●●● Write 7,019.33. Circle the digit in the hundreds place. Underline the digit in the tenths place. 7,⓪19.33

Math Message

A rope measuring 87.6 m long is cut into 12 equal pieces. Estimate the length of each piece. Be prepared to explain your estimation strategy.

Study Link 4·4 Follow-Up

Have partners compare their answers. Survey the class for any unresolved questions or concerns.

1 Teaching the Lesson

Math Message Follow-Up

(*Math Masters,* p. 415)

Ask partners to discuss which situation diagram they would use to model the Math Message problem. Allow partners time to make a decision, and then ask volunteers to explain their choices. Rate Multiplication situation diagram with labeled pieces (12), length per piece (unknown), and total length (87.6)

pieces	length per piece	total length
12	?	87.6

Explain that if the total length had been unknown, a multiplication number model would find the total length. In this situation, the length of the pieces is unknown. Ask volunteers which number model they would use to find the exact solution. $87.6 \div 12$ Understanding how to find the exact solution helps students find an estimate for the solution.

Discuss students' strategies for estimating the quotient. **Examples:**

▷ Using a multiple-of-10 strategy, the rope would need to be 120 meters long; each piece would be 120 meters $\div$ 12 = 10 meters long. So the answer is less than 10 meters.

▷ $2 * 12 = 24$. Double this: $4 * 12 = 48$. Double again: $8 * 12 = 96$, which is more than 87.6. So the answer is less than 8 meters.

▷ $5 * 12 = 60$; $2 * 12 = 24$; $60 + 24$, or $7 * 12 = 84$, which is a little less than 87.6. So each piece is between 7 and 8 meters long.

Explain that the partial-quotients algorithm can be used to divide a decimal dividend by initially ignoring the **decimal point** and

Algorithm Project The focus of this lesson is using the partial-quotients algorithm with decimals. To teach U.S. traditional long division with decimals, see Algorithm Projects 8 and 9 on pages A40 and A43.

12)876		Using easy multiples of 12
		100 * 12 = 1,200
− 600	50	50 * 12 = 600
276		20 * 12 = 240
− 240	20	3 * 12 = 36
36		Estimate: 1s
− 36	3	
0	73	Answer: 7.3

Links to the Future

Problems in this lesson use whole or decimal numbers divided by whole numbers. Interpreting decimal remainders will be introduced in Lesson 4-6. Remainders as fractions will be developed in Unit 5.

Ongoing Assessment: Recognizing Student Achievement

Journal Page 109 Problems 2–6

Use **journal page 109, Problems 2–6** to assess students' ability to make magnitude estimates for division. Students are making adequate progress if they write appropriate number sentences.

[Operations and Computation Goal 6]

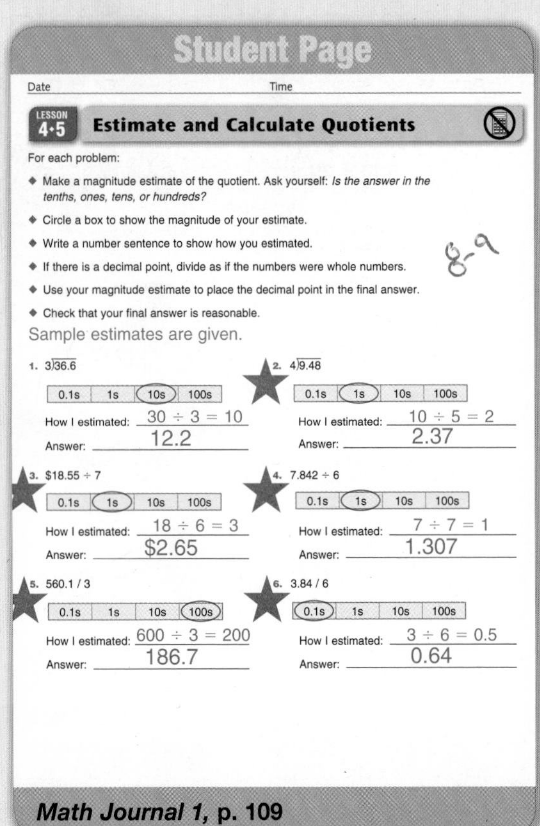

Student Page

Date Time

LESSON 4•5 **Estimate and Calculate Quotients**

For each problem:

- Make a magnitude estimate of the quotient. Ask yourself: *Is the answer in the tenths, ones, tens, or hundreds?*
- Circle a box to show the magnitude of your estimate.
- Write a number sentence to show how you estimated.
- If there is a decimal point, divide as if the numbers were whole numbers.
- Use your magnitude estimate to place the decimal point in the final answer.
- Check that your final answer is reasonable.

Sample estimates are given.

1. 3)36.6
   0.1s | 1s | (10s) | 100s
   How I estimated: 30 ÷ 3 = 10
   Answer: 12.2

2. 4)9.48
   0.1s | (1s) | 10s | 100s
   How I estimated: 10 ÷ 5 = 2
   Answer: 2.37

3. \$18.55 ÷ 7
   0.1s | (1s) | 10s | 100s
   How I estimated: 18 ÷ 6 = 3
   Answer: \$2.65

4. 7.842 ÷ 6
   0.1s | (1s) | 10s | 100s
   How I estimated: 7 ÷ 7 = 1
   Answer: 1.307

5. 560.1 / 3
   0.1s | 1s | 10s | (100s)
   How I estimated: 600 ÷ 3 = 200
   Answer: 186.7

6. 3.84 / 6
   (0.1s) | 1s | 10s | 100s
   How I estimated: 3 ÷ 6 = 0.5
   Answer: 0.64

Math Journal 1, p. 109

proper place of the quotient. To support English language learners, discuss the meaning of magnitude estimates by using some examples.

Ask students to show their work on a computation grid and divide by 12, treating 87.6 as though it was the whole number 876. (*See margin.*)

Ask: *Is it reasonable for 73 to be the answer to the problem?* Sample answer: No, because the estimated answer was between 7 and 8 meters.

Ask students to use their previous estimates to insert a decimal point in the quotient for the correct solution to the division problem. 7.3 Each piece of rope is 7.3 meters in length.

Have students multiply the quotient by the divisor to check the answer. 7.3 * 12 = 87.6

▶ Making Magnitude Estimates before Calculating Quotients

(*Math Journal 1,* p. 109; *Math Masters,* p. 415)

Remind students that they should first make a magnitude estimate when they work on a multiplication or division problem, whether they are using a calculator or a paper-and-pencil algorithm. A magnitude estimate answers questions such as: *Is the answer in the tenths? Tens? Ones? Hundreds?* By using a magnitude estimate to place the decimal point, students are checking that the result is reasonable.

NOTE Students made magnitude estimates for multiplication in Lesson 2-7.

Ask the class to estimate the quotient for Problem 1 on journal page 109. Remind students to make use of friendly numbers and to estimate before finding the exact answer.

For example, students might estimate the quotient for 3)36.6 by thinking of multiples of the divisor. There are 10 [3s] in 30, so there are a few more than 10 [3s] in 36.6. Some students might recognize that there are 12 [3s] in 36. In either case, the quotient is in the 10s. Ask students to record their answers on the magnitude bar and show the number model they used to make their estimates.

Ask students to complete Problem 1 by calculating the exact quotient. Remind them to use the partial-quotients algorithm and to initially ignore the decimal point, dividing 366 by 3. Then have students use their estimates to insert the decimal point in the proper place in the quotient for the correct answer. 366 ÷ 3 = 122; estimated answer is in the tens; 12.2 is the correct answer.

Ask students to use this same procedure to solve the rest of the problems on their own. Circulate and assist.

When most students have completed the page, write some of the problems on the board. Ask students to share their solution strategies, and record them on the board or Class Data Pad.

2 Ongoing Learning & Practice

▶ Playing *Division Top-It* (3-Digit Dividends)

PARTNER ACTIVITY

(*Student Reference Book,* p. 334)

Students practice recognizing multiples and applying division facts and extended facts by playing *Division Top-It.*

▶ Math Boxes 4•5

INDEPENDENT ACTIVITY

(*Math Journal 1,* p. 110)

Mixed Review Math Boxes in this lesson are paired with Math Boxes in Lesson 4-7. The skill in Problem 6 previews Unit 5 content.

Writing/Reasoning Have students write a response to the following: *Explain how you used the table data in Problem 1 to make your prediction. Include the number models for your calculations.* Sample answer: I added the population growth from 1900–1950 and from 1950–2000 to find the total population growth for the 100 years from 1900–2000. Then I divided the total by 10 and added the quotient to the population for 2000. The sum was about 1,300,000, so I predicted 1,400,000. (914,000 – 694,000) + (1,259,000 – 914,000) = 565,000; 565,000 / 10 = 56,500; 1,259,000 + 56,500 = 1,315,500.

▶ Study Link 4•5

INDEPENDENT ACTIVITY

(*Math Masters,* p. 113)

Home Connection Students make magnitude estimates. Then they solve the problems using their estimates to place the decimal point.

3 Differentiation Options

READINESS

▶ Modeling Division with Base-10 Blocks

SMALL-GROUP ACTIVITY

15–30 Min

(*Math Masters,* p. 114)

To provide experience with division using a concrete model, have students explore a long division algorithm using base-10 blocks. Pose the problem $4\overline{)623}$. Have

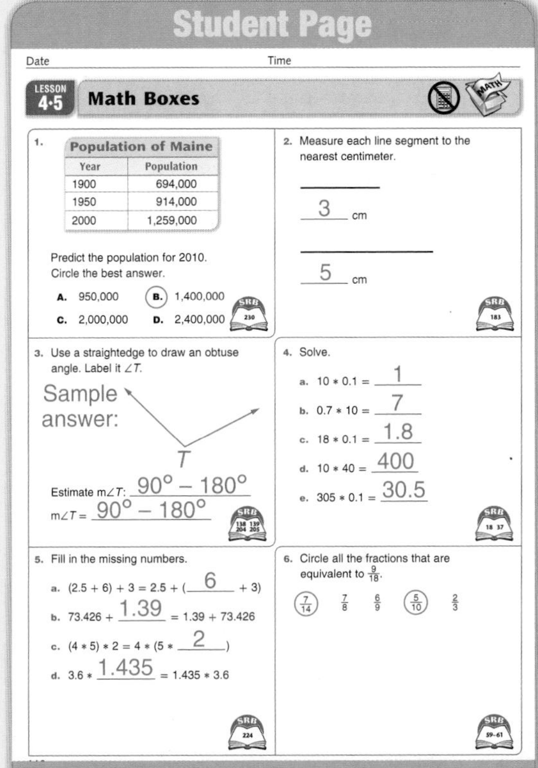

Student Page

Date Time

LESSON 4•5 **Math Boxes**

1.

Population of Maine	
Year	Population
1900	694,000
1950	914,000
2000	1,259,000

Predict the population for 2010. Circle the best answer.

A. 950,000 (B.) 1,400,000
C. 2,000,000 D. 2,400,000

SRB 230

2. Measure each line segment to the nearest centimeter.

3 cm

5 cm

SRB 183

3. Use a straightedge to draw an obtuse angle. Label it ∠T.

Sample answer:

T

Estimate m∠T: 90° – 180°
m∠T = 90° – 180°

SRB 138 139 204 205

4. Solve.

a. 10 ∗ 0.1 = 1
b. 0.7 ∗ 10 = 7
c. 18 ∗ 0.1 = 1.8
d. 10 ∗ 40 = 400
e. 305 ∗ 0.1 = 30.5

SRB 18 37

5. Fill in the missing numbers.

a. (2.5 + 6) + 3 = 2.5 + (6 + 3)
b. 73.426 + 1.39 = 1.39 + 73.426
c. (4 ∗ 5) ∗ 2 = 4 ∗ (5 ∗ 2)
d. 3.6 ∗ 1.435 = 1.435 ∗ 3.6

SRB 224

6. Circle all the fractions that are equivalent to $\frac{9}{18}$.

($\frac{7}{14}$) $\frac{7}{8}$ $\frac{6}{9}$ ($\frac{5}{10}$) $\frac{2}{3}$

SRB 59–61

Math Journal 1, p. 110

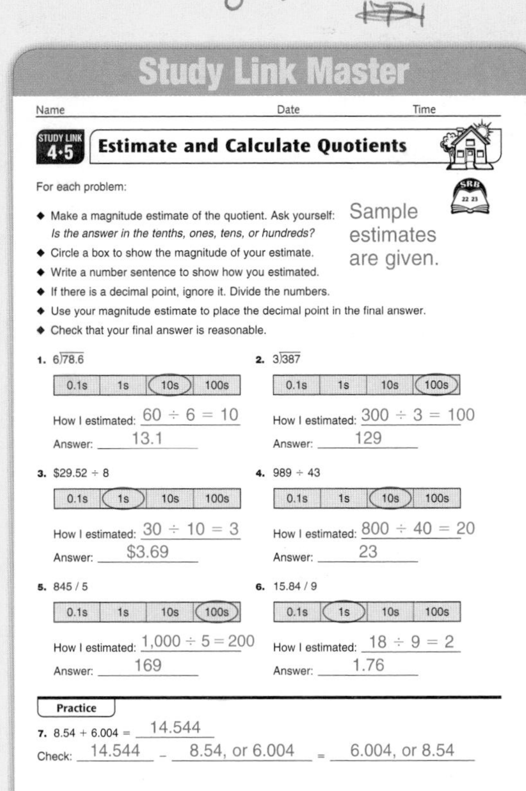

Study Link Master

Name Date Time

STUDY LINK 4•5 **Estimate and Calculate Quotients**

SRB 22 23

For each problem:

- Make a magnitude estimate of the quotient. Ask yourself: *Is the answer in the tenths, ones, tens, or hundreds?*
- Circle a box to show the magnitude of your estimate.
- Write a number sentence to show how you estimated.
- If there is a decimal point, ignore it. Divide the numbers.
- Use your magnitude estimate to place the decimal point in the final answer.
- Check that your final answer is reasonable.

Sample estimates are given.

1. $6\overline{)78.6}$
0.1s | 1s | (10s) | 100s
How I estimated: 60 ÷ 6 = 10
Answer: 13.1

2. $3\overline{)387}$
0.1s | 1s | 10s | (100s)
How I estimated: 300 ÷ 3 = 100
Answer: 129

3. $29.52 ÷ 8
0.1s | (1s) | 10s | 100s
How I estimated: 30 ÷ 10 = 3
Answer: $3.69

4. 989 ÷ 43
0.1s | 1s | (10s) | 100s
How I estimated: 800 ÷ 40 = 20
Answer: 23

5. 845 / 5
0.1s | 1s | 10s | (100s)
How I estimated: 1,000 ÷ 5 = 200
Answer: 169

6. 15.84 / 9
0.1s | (1s) | 10s | 100s
How I estimated: 18 ÷ 9 = 2
Answer: 1.76

Practice

7. 8.54 + 6.004 = 14.544
Check: 14.544 – 8.54, or 6.004 = 6.004, or 8.54

Math Masters, p. 113

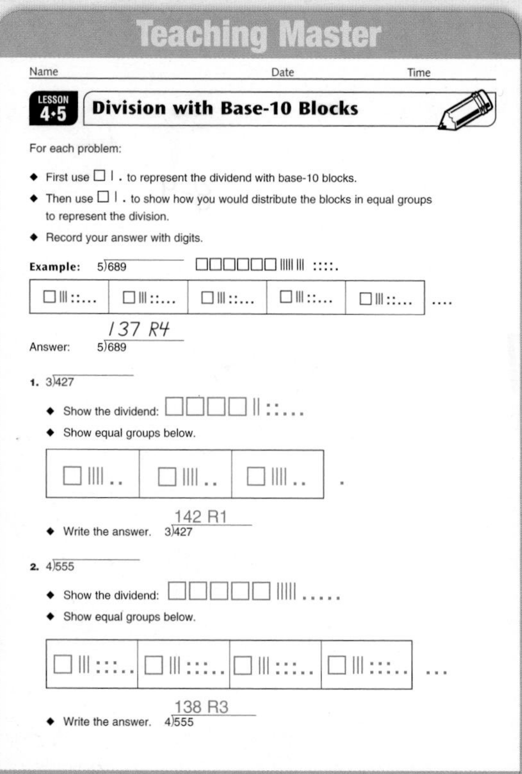
Teaching Master

Name ______ Date ______ Time ______

LESSON 4·5 **Division with Base-10 Blocks**

For each problem:

- First use □ | . to represent the dividend with base-10 blocks.
- Then use □ | . to show how you would distribute the blocks in equal groups to represent the division.
- Record your answer with digits.

Example: 5)689 □□□□□□ |||||||| ::::.

□|||::...	□|||::...	□|||::...	□|||::...	□|||::...	....

Answer: 5)689 137 R4

1. 3)427
   - Show the dividend: □□□□ || ::...
   - Show equal groups below.

□|||| ..	□|||| ..	□|||| ..	.

   - Write the answer. 3)427 142 R1

2. 4)555
   - Show the dividend: □□□□□ ||||| .....
   - Show equal groups below.

□|||:::..	□|||:::..	□|||:::..	□|||:::..	...

   - Write the answer. 4)555 138 R3

Math Masters, p. 114

Teaching Master

Name ______ Date ______ Time ______

LESSON 4·5 **A Division Challenge**

Judy and two friends bought a raffle ticket at the school fund-raiser. They agreed that if they won, they would share the winnings equally. They won $145! They received one $100 bill, four $10 bills, and five $1 bills. Judy used this division algorithm to calculate how much money each person should get. Can you figure out how the algorithm works?

(*Hint:* There were 3 people in all. Judy realized that in order to share the $100 bill, they needed to trade it for ten $10 bills. Then they would have fourteen $10 bills and five $1 bills.)

	100s	10s	1s	10ths	100ths
		4	8	3	3
3	1	4	5	0	0
		14	25	10	10
		−12	−24	−9	−9
		2	1	1	1

1. Explain how you think the algorithm works. Sample answer: Trade the 1 $100 bill for 10 $10 bills. Think of the 4 in the tens column as 4 $10 bills. That makes 10 + 4, or 14 $10 bills in all. If 3 people share 14 $10 bills, each person gets 4 $10 bills, and 2 $10 bills are left over. Trade the 2 $10 bills for 20 $1 bills. Think of the 5 in the ones column as 5 $1 bills. That makes 20 + 5, or 25 $1 bills in all. Continue sharing and trading in the same manner.
2. Explain what Judy did when she had $1 left. Sample answer: Judy traded $1 for 10 tenths and wrote 10 in that column.
3. How much money did each person get? $48.33
4. Use the algorithm to divide: 4)51.6 12.9

Math Masters, p. 115

students model the dividend (623) with base-10 blocks. Ask a volunteer to explain what it means to divide 623 blocks by 4. Sample answer: It means that the 623 blocks are to be grouped into 4 equal piles. Have each small group of students take four pieces of paper and distribute the blocks equally among the four pieces of paper.

Students will need to make trades. For example, each of the four groups of blocks gets 1 flat, and there will be 2 flats left over. Students trade these 2 flats for 20 longs. Then they distribute the 22 longs among the 4 groups of blocks. Each of the four groups gets 5 longs, and 2 longs are left over. Students trade these 2 longs for 20 cubes. They distribute 20 of the 23 cubes evenly among the four groups. There are 3 cubes left over.

Have a volunteer interpret the model. Each group has 155 cubes. There are 3 left over. So 623 divided by 4 is 155 with a remainder of 3.

Students work alone or with a partner to complete *Math Masters*, page 114. They represent base-10 blocks with the symbols, □, |, and ▪.

ENRICHMENT

INDEPENDENT ACTIVITY

5–15 Min

▶ Exploring an Alternative Division Algorithm

(*Student Reference Book*, pp. 24 and 44; *Math Masters*, p. 115)

To further explore division algorithms, have students try the column-division algorithm for decimal division. Ask students to examine the steps of the column-division algorithm presented on pages 24 and 44 of the *Student Reference Book*. Students then complete *Math Masters*, page 115 and include an explanation of the algorithm using the problem on the master as an example. Invite them to model the problems using bills and coins.

ELL SUPPORT

SMALL-GROUP ACTIVITY

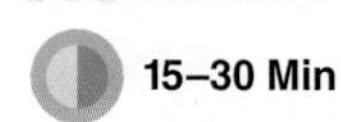
15–30 Min

▶ Illustrating Division Algorithms

To support language development for division, have students make posters for different versions of division algorithms. Possibilities include a basic partial-quotients algorithm with a 1-digit divisor, a partial-quotients algorithm with a 2-digit divisor (including a short-cut sheet), a partial-quotients algorithm with decimals (including the estimate first), and finally a poster of the column-division algorithm. Have them annotate the posters to explain steps. Display the posters during lessons that include division.

4•6 Interpreting the Reminder

Remainder

Objective To provide practice solving division number stories and interpreting remainders.

www.everydaymathonline.com

ePresentations

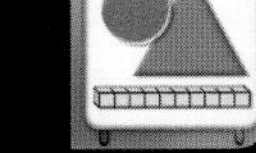

eToolkit

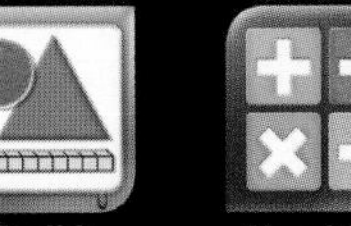

Algorithms Practice

EM Facts Workshop Game™

Family Letters

Assessment Management

Common Core State Standards

Curriculum Focal Points

Interactive Teacher's Lesson Guide

1 Teaching the Lesson

Key Concepts and Skills

- Interpret the remainder in number story solutions.
[Operations and Computation Goal 3]
- Make magnitude estimates for quotients.
[Operations and Computation Goal 6]
- Write and solve number sentences that model division number stories.
[Patterns, Functions, and Algebra Goal 2]

Key Activities

Students review magnitude estimates for whole number division. They make models for division number stories, and they use a division algorithm to solve number stories and interpret the remainders.

Ongoing Assessment: Recognizing Student Achievement
Use journal pages 111 and 112.
[Operations and Computation Goal 3]

Materials

Math Journal 1, pp. 111 and 112
Student Reference Book, p. 242
Study Link 4•5
Math Masters, p. 414
Class Data Pad ◆ calculator

2 Ongoing Learning & Practice

Solving Place-Value Puzzles
Math Journal 1, p. 113
Students practice place-value skills by solving place-value puzzles.

Math Boxes 4•6
Math Journal 1, p. 114
Students practice and maintain skills through Math Box problems.

Study Link 4•6
Math Masters, p. 116
Students practice and maintain skills through Study Link activities.

3 Differentiation Options

READINESS

Finding Number Story Information
Math Masters, p. 117
Students identify required information in number stories.

ENRICHMENT

Writing Division Number Stories
Math Masters, p. 423
Students apply their knowledge of mathematical models by writing and solving their own division number stories.

EXTRA PRACTICE

5-Minute Math
5-Minute Math™, pp. 20, 96, and 97
Students write and solve division number stories.

Advance Preparation

For Parts 1 and 2, students will need copies of the computation grid (*Math Masters,* page 415).

***Teacher's Reference Manual,* Grades 4–6** pp. 94, 132–140

Getting Started

Mental Math and Reflexes

Draw a magnitude bar on the Class Data Pad.

0.1s	1s	10s	100s	1,000s

Ask students to make magnitude estimates for division by thinking of multiplication models. 4,789 ÷ 16 Think: *16 times what* = 4,789? 16 ∗ 100 = 1,600; 16 ∗ 200 = 3,200; 16 ∗ 300 = 4,800; quotient is in the 100s.

Then students use calculators to check that their estimate number models are close to the dividend.

Key sequence: 16 (×) 300 (Enter); 4,800 is close to 4,789.

●○○ 326 ÷ 7 10s 897 ÷ 4 100s 8,760 ÷ 5 1,000s

●●○ 6,420 ÷ 12 100s 76.15 ÷ 15 1s 925 ÷ 7 100s

●●● 254 ÷ 0.5 100s 36.5 ÷ 6 1s 7.2 ÷ 8 0.1s

Math Message

There are 100 minutes of computer time for 8 students to share equally. How many minutes should each student get?

Study Link 4·5 Follow-Up

Briefly review answers. Have volunteers share their strategies for placing the decimal point in Problem 3.

100 minutes

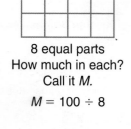

8 equal parts
How much in each?
Call it *M*.

M = 100 ÷ 8

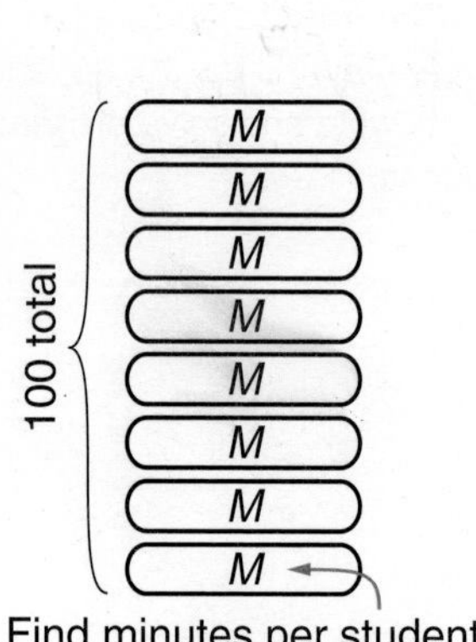

Find minutes per student.

8 ∗ *M* = 100

1 Teaching the Lesson

▶ Math Message Follow-Up

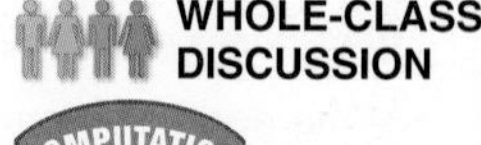

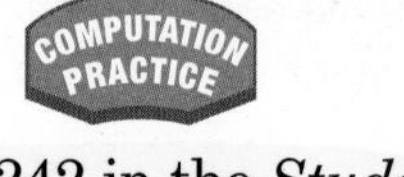

(*Student Reference Book*, p. 242)

Algebraic Thinking Ask partners to read page 242 in the *Student Reference Book.* Explain that the class will solve the Math Message problem by using simple pictures as mathematical models.

1. Read the problem. Use symbols to draw a picture that organizes the given information. Have several volunteers draw their pictures on the board. Students' pictures should show 8 equal parts in some way. (*See margin.*)
2. Read the problem again, and decide what you want to find. Write this in a word or short phrase, and represent it with a letter variable, such as *M*, for number of minutes.
3. Write a number sentence showing how the letter variable and other numbers in the problem are related.
4. Solve the number sentence.

NOTE Students may view the problem as division by 8 (*M* = 100 ÷ 8) or as multiplication by 8 (8 ∗ *M* = 100). If students wrote the multiplication sentence, they might need a prompt to recognize the related fact that will let them use division to solve the problem.

8)100		*How many 8s are in 100?* At least 10.
− 80	10	The first partial quotient, 10 ∗ 8 = 80.
20		Subtract. At least 2 [8s] are left.
− 16	2	The second partial quotient, 2 ∗ 8 = 16.
4	12	Subtract. Add the partial quotients.
↑ Remainder	↑ Quotient	

Algorithm Project To teach U.S. traditional long division with whole numbers and decimals, see Algorithm Projects 7, 8, and 9 on pages A32, A40, and A43.

5. Interpret the quotient and remainder. Decide what to do about the remainder. Ask: *What do the quotient 12 and remainder 4 mean?* Each student can have 12 minutes of computer time, and 4 minutes will remain to be shared or left unused. Ask: *Should the 4 minutes be ignored?* No In this case, students would want as much computer time as possible; therefore, the remainder should be included as part of the answer.

   ▷ One way to do this is to change 4 minutes into 240 seconds. 240 seconds ÷ 8 = 30 seconds per student.

   ▷ Another way is to divide the remainder among the 8 students. The remainder is then reported as a fraction, $\frac{4}{8}$ or $\frac{1}{2}$ or as a decimal, 0.5, of a minute per student.

   The solution is $12\frac{1}{2}$ minutes, 12.5 minutes, or 12 minutes 30 seconds.

6. Check the solution by substituting 12.5 for M in students' number sentences and dividing or multiplying. $100 \div 8 = 12.5$, and $8 * 12.5 = 100$ are true number sentences.

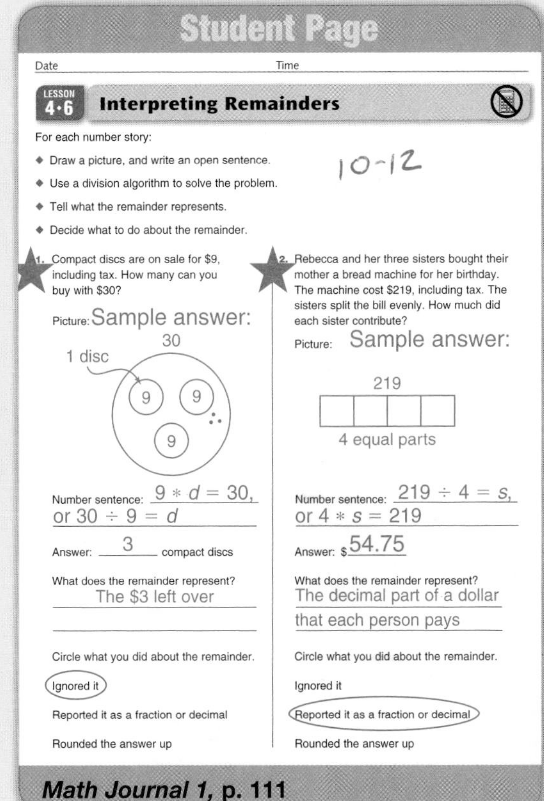

Student Page

Date ____ Time ____

LESSON 4·6 **Interpreting Remainders**

For each number story:

- Draw a picture, and write an open sentence.
- Use a division algorithm to solve the problem.
- Tell what the remainder represents.
- Decide what to do about the remainder.

10-12

1. Compact discs are on sale for $9, including tax. How many can you buy with $30?

Picture: Sample answer: 30, 1 disc, 9, 9, 9

Number sentence: 9 ∗ d = 30, or 30 ÷ 9 = d

Answer: 3 compact discs

What does the remainder represent? The $3 left over

Circle what you did about the remainder.
(Ignored it)
Reported it as a fraction or decimal
Rounded the answer up

2. Rebecca and her three sisters bought their mother a bread machine for her birthday. The machine cost $219, including tax. The sisters split the bill evenly. How much did each sister contribute?

Picture: Sample answer: 219, 4 equal parts

Number sentence: 219 ÷ 4 = s, or 4 ∗ s = 219

Answer: $54.75

What does the remainder represent? The decimal part of a dollar that each person pays

Circle what you did about the remainder.
Ignored it
(Reported it as a fraction or decimal)
Rounded the answer up

Math Journal 1, p. 111

▶ Solving Division Number Stories and Interpreting Remainders

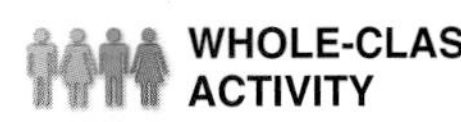

10-12

Algebraic Thinking Students should follow the same steps used to solve the Math Message problem for these examples.

Example 1:
A roller coaster holds 30 people. There are 252 people waiting for a ride. How many times will the roller coaster need to run so all 252 people get a ride?

Expect that most students will think: *How many 30s in 252?* They will write a number sentence like $252 \div 30 = r$ (where r is the number of runs). Some might draw an array with 30 objects per row and write a number sentence like $r * 30 = 252$. (*See margin.*)

30)252	
− 150	5
102	
− 90	3
12	8
↑ Remainder	↑ Quotient

Ask: *What do the quotient 8 and remainder 12 mean?* Students should explain that in 8 runs, 240 of the 252 people could ride. This would leave 12 people. The ride will need to run 9 times to take all 252 people.

For this problem the answer should be rounded up to the next whole number because the extra people would not realistically be discarded.

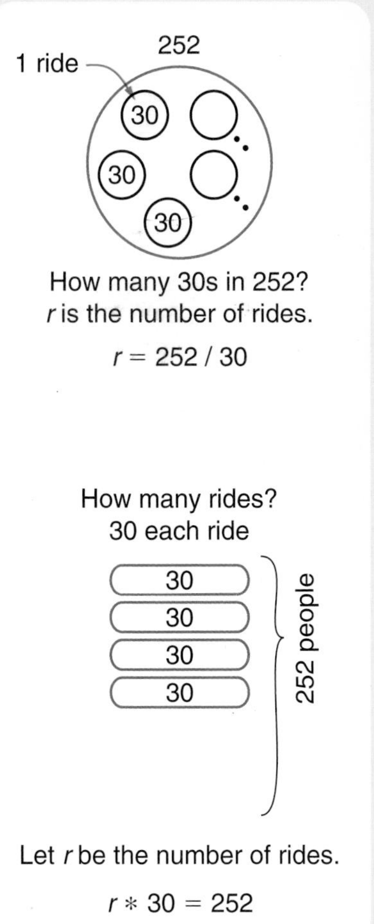

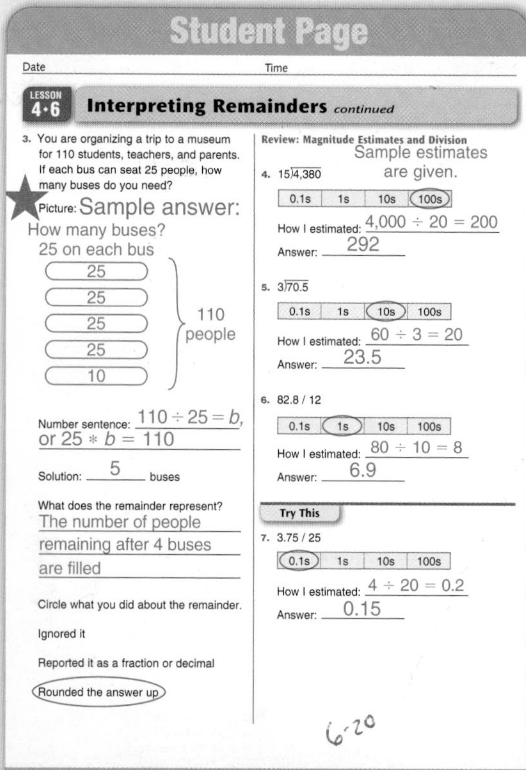

Student Page

Date Time

LESSON 4·6 **Interpreting Remainders** *continued*

3. You are organizing a trip to a museum for 110 students, teachers, and parents. If each bus can seat 25 people, how many buses do you need?

Picture: Sample answer: How many buses? 25 on each bus

25, 25, 25, 25, 10 — 110 people

Number sentence: $110 \div 25 = b$, or $25 * b = 110$

Solution: 5 buses

What does the remainder represent? The number of people remaining after 4 buses are filled

Circle what you did about the remainder.

Ignored it

Reported it as a fraction or decimal

(Rounded the answer up)

Review: Magnitude Estimates and Division

Sample estimates are given.

4. $15\overline{)4,380}$

0.1s	1s	10s	(100s)

How I estimated: $4,000 \div 20 = 200$

Answer: 292

5. $3\overline{)70.5}$

0.1s	1s	(10s)	100s

How I estimated: $60 \div 3 = 20$

Answer: 23.5

6. 82.8 / 12

0.1s	(1s)	10s	100s

How I estimated: $80 \div 10 = 8$

Answer: 6.9

Try This

7. 3.75 / 25

(0.1s)	1s	10s	100s

How I estimated: $4 \div 20 = 0.2$

Answer: 0.15

Math Journal 1, p. 112

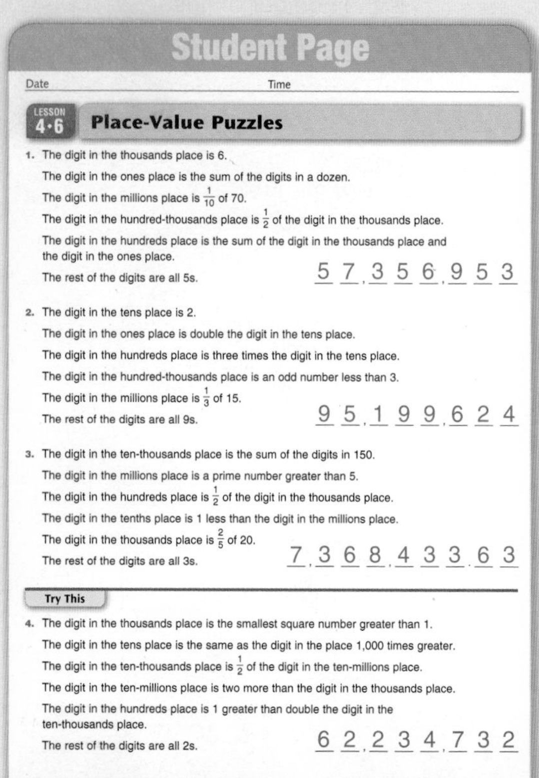

Student Page

Date Time

LESSON 4·6 **Place-Value Puzzles**

1. The digit in the thousands place is 6.
   The digit in the ones place is the sum of the digits in a dozen.
   The digit in the millions place is $\frac{1}{10}$ of 70.
   The digit in the hundred-thousands place is $\frac{1}{2}$ of the digit in the thousands place.
   The digit in the hundreds place is the sum of the digit in the thousands place and the digit in the ones place.
   The rest of the digits are all 5s. 5 7, 3 5 6, 9 5 3
2. The digit in the tens place is 2.
   The digit in the ones place is double the digit in the tens place.
   The digit in the hundreds place is three times the digit in the tens place.
   The digit in the hundred-thousands place is an odd number less than 3.
   The digit in the millions place is $\frac{1}{3}$ of 15.
   The rest of the digits are all 9s. 9 5, 1 9 9, 6 2 4
3. The digit in the ten-thousands place is the sum of the digits in 150.
   The digit in the millions place is a prime number greater than 5.
   The digit in the hundreds place is $\frac{1}{2}$ of the digit in the thousands place.
   The digit in the tenths place is 1 less than the digit in the millions place.
   The digit in the thousands place is $\frac{2}{5}$ of 20.
   The rest of the digits are all 3s. 7, 3 6 8, 4 3 3. 6 3

Try This

4. The digit in the thousands place is the smallest square number greater than 1.
   The digit in the tens place is the same as the digit in the place 1,000 times greater.
   The digit in the ten-thousands place is $\frac{1}{2}$ of the digit in the ten-millions place.
   The digit in the ten-millions place is two more than the digit in the thousands place.
   The digit in the hundreds place is 1 greater than double the digit in the ten-thousands place.
   The rest of the digits are all 2s. 6 2, 2 3 4, 7 3 2

Math Journal 1, p. 113

Example 2:
It costs $3 to rent a video. Bonita has $14. How many videos can she rent?

The partial-quotients algorithm is shown below. Some students, however, might just use pictures, count by 3s, or use the fact, $4 * 3 = 12$, to find that there are 4 [3s] in 14 with 2 left over.

$3\overline{)14}$	
$-\ 12$	$\underline{4}$
2	4
↑ Remainder	↑ Quotient

Encourage students to focus on interpreting the remainder within the context of the problem. Ask for a volunteer to share the solution. Bonita can rent 4 videos. She will have $2 left, but she won't be able to rent another video. In this situation, the remainder is ignored. Students can check their answers by multiplying $3 * 4$ and adding the remainder of 2.

Summary:

- ▷ In the Math Message problem, the remainder is treated as a fraction of the whole and becomes part of the answer. The remainder is divided among the 8 students in order not to waste time.
- ▷ In Example 1, the answer is rounded up. Otherwise, 12 people do not get a ride.
- ▷ In Example 2, the remainder is ignored because the remaining money is not enough to rent another video.

▶ Interpreting Remainders in Division Number Stories

INDEPENDENT ACTIVITY

(*Math Journal 1,* pp. 111 and 112)

Algebraic Thinking Have students complete journal pages 111 and 112. Remind students to think about each remainder and the different ways it can be interpreted. Summarize briefly how the interpretation of the remainder determines how students should answer the question in the problem. Circulate and assist. When a majority of students have completed the pages, discuss their solutions and the models they used.

Ongoing Assessment: Recognizing Student Achievement

Journal pages 111 and 112 Problems 1–3

Portfolio Ideas

Use **journal pages 111 and 112, Problems 1–3** to assess students' ability to interpret the remainder. Ask students to choose one of the problems to illustrate and explain their solution on an Exit Slip (*Math Masters,* page 414). They should also describe how they used the remainder to answer the question. Students are making adequate progress if their answers demonstrate an understanding of how the remainder affects the solution.

[Operations and Computation Goal 3]

2 Ongoing Learning & Practice

▶ Solving Place-Value Puzzles

INDEPENDENT ACTIVITY

(*Math Journal 1,* p. 113)

Students practice place-value skills by using clues to find each digit in a number. Remind students that they will need information from more than one clue to find the digits in some of the places (Problems 3 and 4).

▶ Math Boxes 4•6

INDEPENDENT ACTIVITY

(*Math Journal 1,* p. 114)

Mixed Review Math Boxes in this lesson are paired with Math Boxes in Lessons 4-2 and 4-4. The skills in Problems 5 and 6 preview Unit 5 content.

Writing/Reasoning Have students write a response to the following: *Compare the prime factorization for 200 in Problem 3 with the prime factorization for 400.* The prime factorization for 400 has an additional factor of 2 because it is twice as big as 200.

▶ Study Link 4•6

INDEPENDENT ACTIVITY

(*Math Masters,* p. 116)

Home Connection Students use a division algorithm and interpret remainders to solve division number stories. Remind students that a remainder can be used in three ways—as a fraction of the whole, ignored, or used to round up the quotient—depending on how the remainder is interpreted for each problem.

3 Differentiation Options

READINESS

▶ Finding Number Story Information

INDEPENDENT ACTIVITY

5–15 Min

(*Math Masters,* p. 117)

Algebraic Thinking To focus on the relevant information in a number story, have students complete *Math Masters,* page 117. If you choose, students can solve the problems.

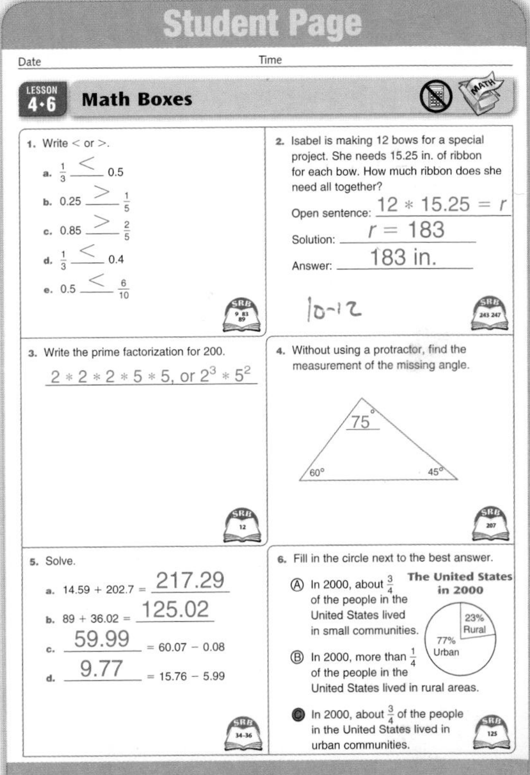

Student Page

Date Time

LESSON 4•6 **Math Boxes**

1. Write < or >.
   a. $\frac{1}{3}$ < 0.5
   b. 0.25 > $\frac{1}{5}$
   c. 0.85 > $\frac{2}{5}$
   d. $\frac{1}{3}$ < 0.4
   e. 0.5 < $\frac{6}{10}$

2. Isabel is making 12 bows for a special project. She needs 15.25 in. of ribbon for each bow. How much ribbon does she need all together?
   Open sentence: $12 * 15.25 = r$
   Solution: $r = 183$
   Answer: 183 in.

   10-12

3. Write the prime factorization for 200.
   $2 * 2 * 2 * 5 * 5$, or $2^3 * 5^2$

4. Without using a protractor, find the measurement of the missing angle.
   75°, 60°, 45°

5. Solve.
   a. 14.59 + 202.7 = 217.29
   b. 89 + 36.02 = 125.02
   c. 59.99 = 60.07 − 0.08
   d. 9.77 = 15.76 − 5.99

6. Fill in the circle next to the best answer.
   Ⓐ In 2000, about $\frac{3}{4}$ of the people in the United States lived in small communities.
   Ⓑ In 2000, more than $\frac{1}{4}$ of the people in the United States lived in rural areas.
   ● In 2000, about $\frac{3}{4}$ of the people in the United States lived in urban communities.

   The United States in 2000: 23% Rural, 77% Urban

Math Journal 1, p. 114

10-16 14-20

Study Link Master

Name Date Time

STUDY LINK 4•6 **Division Number Stories with Remainders**

For each number story draw a picture or write a number sentence on the back of this page. Then divide to solve the problem. Decide what to do about the remainder. Explain what you did.

Example:

You need to set up benches for a picnic. Each bench seats 7 people. You expect 25 people to attend. How many benches do you need?

How many benches? 7 seats per bench: 7, 7, 7, 4 } 25 people

$25 \div 7 = b$

Circle what you did with the remainder. 4 benches

Ignored it Reported it as a fraction or decimal (Rounded the answer up)

Why? *3 benches seat 21 people. One more bench is needed.*

1. It costs $50.00 to be a member of a soccer team. The team plays 8 games during the season. What is the cost per game? $ 6.25

   Circle what you did with the remainder.

   Ignored it (Reported it as a fraction or decimal) Rounded the answer up

   Why? The cost per game is exact, so the answer needs to be exact.

2. Lynn is having a party. Pizzas cost $8.00 each. How many pizzas can she buy with $60.00? 7 pizzas

   Circle what you did with the remainder.

   (Ignored it) Reported it as a fraction or decimal Rounded the answer up

   Why? The remaining $4.00 won't buy another pizza

Practice

3. 31 ÷ 2 → 15 R1
4. 629 * 84 = 52,836

Math Masters, p. 116

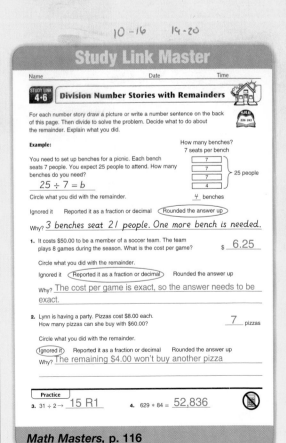

Teaching Master

Name Date Time

LESSON 4·6 **Finding Number Story Information** 

For each problem, write the number of the sentence that has the information for each part of the situation diagram. Then complete the situation diagram.

Problem 1

1. Ms. Haag is rearranging her classroom.
2. There are 32 students.
3. The students sit at tables.
4. Four students can sit at each table.
5. How many tables does she need?

Sentence(s): 2, 4, and 5

tables	students per table	total students
?	4	32

Problem 2

1. Marc needs 3 yards of fabric to make a cape for a costume party.
2. His friends want capes that match his.
3. If Marc has 15 yards of fabric, how many capes can he make?

Sentence(s): 1 and 3

capes	yards per cape	yards of fabric in all
?	3	15

Math Masters, **p. 117**

ENRICHMENT

INDEPENDENT ACTIVITY

5–15 Min

▶ Writing Division Number Stories

(*Math Masters,* p. 423)

To apply students' knowledge of mathematical models, have students write and solve their own division number stories. Remind students to use picture and number models as they solve their problems. These can be collected into a class book, before students solve them, and used as an additional practice resource for division number stories.

EXTRA PRACTICE

COMPUTATION PRACTICE

SMALL-GROUP ACTIVITY

5–15 Min

▶ *5-Minute Math*

To offer students more experience with division and remainders, see *5-Minute Math,* pages 20, 96, and 97.

Teaching Aid Master

Name Date Time

A Number Story

Title:

Mathematical Number Model:

Solution:

Math Masters, **p. 423**

4•7 Skills Review with *First to 100*

6)9476 1579R2 42)8975 213R29

Objectives To investigate the use of variables, review a variety of mathematics skills, and explore division concepts.

Technology Resources www.everydaymathonline.com

ePresentations

eToolkit

Algorithms Practice

EM Facts Workshop Game™

Family Letters

Assessment Management

Common Core State Standards

Curriculum Focal Points

Interactive Teacher's Lesson Guide

1 Teaching the Lesson

Key Concepts and Skills

- Find the value of an algebraic expression. [Patterns, Functions, and Algebra Goal 2]
- Write number sentences that model given situations. [Patterns, Functions, and Algebra Goal 2]

Key Activities

Students play *First to 100* to write open number sentences and evaluate expressions for given variables.

Ongoing Assessment: Recognizing Student Achievement
Use the Math Message.
[Patterns, Functions, and Algebra Goal 2]

Key Vocabulary

variable

Materials

Math Journal 1, p. 115
Student Reference Book, pp. 303 and 308
Study Link 4•6
Math Masters, pp. 118 and 456–458
calculator ◆ per partnership: 2 six-sided dice, envelope or reuseable plastic bag, scissors

2 Ongoing Learning & Practice

Playing *Division Dash*
Student Reference Book, p. 303
per partnership: 4 each of number cards 1–9 (from the Everything Math Deck, if available)
Students solve division problems with 1-digit divisors and 2-digit dividends.

Reviewing Magnitude Estimates with Decimals
Math Journal 1, p. 115
Student Reference Book, pp. 38–43
Students make magnitude estimates for multiplication and division problems.

Reviewing Types of Triangles
Math Journal 1, p. 116
Geometry Template
Students identify triangles and draw polygons.

Math Boxes 4•7
Math Journal 1, p. 117
Students practice and maintain skills through Math Box problems.

Study Link 4•7
Math Masters, p. 119
Students practice and maintain skills through Study Link activities.

3 Differentiation Options

READINESS

Solving for Unknown Quantities
Math Masters, p. 120
Students explore the connection between situation diagrams and open number sentences.

ENRICHMENT

Playing *Algebra Election*
Math Journal 1, pp. 118 and 119
Math Masters, pp. 442, 443, 456, and 457
per group: 1 six-sided die, calculator, transparent tape, 4 pennies or other counters, 3" by 5" index cards cut in half (optional)
Students solve open number sentences by playing *Algebra Election.*

EXTRA PRACTICE

Solving Open Number Sentences
slate or paper
Students practice writing and solving open number sentences.

ELL SUPPORT

Building a Math Word Bank
Differentiation Handbook, p. 142
Students define and illustrate the term *variable.*

Advance Preparation

For Part 1, copy and cut apart *Math Masters,* page 118. Familiarize yourself with the rules, scoring, and Problem Cards (*Math Masters,* pages 456 and 457) for *First to 100.* For the optional Enrichment activity in Part 3, copy and tape together 1 set of *Math Masters,* pages 442 and 443 for each group. Additional Problem Cards can be made using 3" by 5" index cards, cut in half.

***Teacher's Reference Manual,* Grades 4–6** pp. 285–287, 291–297

Getting Started

Mental Math and Reflexes

Ask students to round the following decimals…

to the nearest whole number.	to the nearest tenth.	to the nearest hundredth.
●○○ 24.2 24	●●○ 17.63 17.6	●●● 89.064 89.06
308.56 309	109.14 109.1	2.327 2.33
77.09 77	239.86 239.9	645.009 645.01

Math Message 

Take a Math Message slip of paper. Roll 2 six-sided dice. Multiply the 2 numbers that come up. Let the letter P *represent this product. Then find the product of 20 ∗* P*. Record your work on the Math Message slip.*

Study Link 4·5 Follow-Up

Briefly review answers. Have volunteers tell how they decided what to do with the remainders.

1 Teaching the Lesson

▶ Math Message Follow-Up

(*Math Masters*, p. 118)

Algebraic Thinking The Math Message problem previews the game *First to 100* in which students generate and solve problems by substituting numbers for letter **variables.**

Draw a table on the board to record students' answers. Write *P* and 20 ∗ *P* as the column headings. Record the responses of about 10 students in the table. (*See margin.*)

Briefly discuss the Math Message problem, asking questions such as the following:

- Is there any right or wrong choice for a number to use in place of *P*? After rolling the 2 dice, for example, if Bob's product is 18 and Maria's product is 4, is one of these values the correct value for *P* and the other the wrong value for *P*? No. The letter *P* represents 18 when we talk about Bob's result after rolling the dice. The letter *P* represents 4 when we talk about Maria's result after rolling the dice.
- What different numbers can the letter *P* represent? Any product of the top numbers on 2 dice
- What do we call a letter that is used to represent numbers? A variable

NOTE In Lessons 2-4 and 4-6, letter variables were used differently from their use in this lesson. Previously, the variable represented one specific missing number that would make a number sentence true. In this lesson, the variable is assigned a value to be used in a calculation from a range of possible values.

P	20 ∗ *P*
18	20 ∗ 18 = 360
12	20 ∗ 12 = 240
30	20 ∗ 30 = 600
16	20 ∗ 16 = 320
9	20 ∗ 9 = 180
15	20 ∗ 15 = 300
12	20 ∗ 12 = 240
4	20 ∗ 4 = 80
20	20 ∗ 20 = 400
24	20 ∗ 24 = 480

Ongoing Assessment: Recognizing Student Achievement

Math Message 

Use the **Math Message** to assess students' ability to find the value of an algebraic expression. Students are making adequate progress if they have correctly assigned a value to *P* and found the product of 20 ∗ *P*.

[Patterns, Functions, and Algebra Goal 2]

▶ Introducing *First to 100*

PARTNER ACTIVITY

(*Student Reference Book*, p. 308; *Math Masters*, pp. 456 and 457)

Ask students to cut apart the Problem Cards on *Math Masters*, pages 456 and 457. There are 32 cards numbered 1–32. Cards numbered 25 through 32 will not be used in this lesson. Students should store these for later use. Briefly review the directions and the example problem at the bottom of *Student Reference Book*, page 308.

▶ Playing *First to 100*

PARTNER ACTIVITY

(*Student Reference Book,* p. 308; *Math Masters,* pp. 456–458)

Portfolio Ideas

Algebraic Thinking A player will typically need between 6 and 10 turns to accumulate 100 points. Players record points on a sheet of paper, or *Math Masters,* page 458, updating their total as they win new points. It is wise to agree on a time limit for answering questions.

Encourage students to play *First to 100* during their free time. This game reviews a variety of skills and can address any skills you want to review (including skills covered on standardized tests) by writing a new set of Problem Cards.

Adjusting the Activity

Play a variation. Increase the number of solved problems needed to accumulate 100 points by having players roll 2 six-sided dice and find the *sum* of the numbers on the top faces. This sum is then substituted for the *x* or *x*'s in the problem(s) on the card.

AUDITORY ◆ KINESTHETIC ◆ TACTILE ◆ VISUAL

Student Page

Games

First to 100

Materials □ one set of *First to 100* Problem Cards (*Math Masters*, pp. 456 and 457)

□ 2 six-sided dice

□ 1 calculator

Players 2 to 4

Skill Variable substitution, solving equations

Object of the game To collect 100 points by solving problems.

Directions

1. Shuffle the Problem Cards and place them word-side down on the table.
2. Players take turns. When it is your turn:
   - Roll 2 dice and find the product of the numbers.
   - Turn over the top Problem Card and substitute the product for the variable *x* in the problem on the card.
   - Solve the problem mentally or use paper and pencil. Give the answer. (You have 3 chances to use a calculator to solve difficult problems during a game.) Other players check the answer with a calculator.
   - If the answer is correct, you win the number of points equal to the product that was substituted for the variable *x*. Some Problem Cards require 2 or more answers. In order to win any points, you must answer all parts of the problem correctly.
   - Put the used Problem Card at the bottom of the deck.
3. The first player to get at least 100 points wins the game.

First to 100 Problem Cards

Example Alice rolls a 3 and a 4. The product is 12. She turns over a Problem Card: $20 * x = ?$ She substitutes 12 for *x* and answers 240. The answer is correct. Alice wins 12 points.

Student Reference Book, p. 308

Game Master

Name Date Time

***First to 100* Record Sheet**

Example: A student rolls a 5 and a 6. The product is 30. So *x* = 30. The student draws card number 29.

x	Card Number	Number Model/ Response	Score
30	29	$(3 * 30 + 4) - 8 = 86$	30

x	Card Number	Number Model/ Response	Score

Math Masters, p. 458

Student Page

Games

Division Dash

Materials □ number cards 1–9 (4 of each)
□ 1 score sheet

Players 1 or 2

Skill Division of 2-digit by 1-digit numbers

Object of the game To reach 100 in the fewest divisions possible.

Player 1		Player 2	
Quotient	Score	Quotient	Score

Directions

1. Prepare a score sheet like the one shown at the right.
2. Shuffle the cards and place the deck number-side down on the table.
3. Each player follows the instructions below:
   - Turn over 3 cards and lay them down in a row, from left to right. Use the 3 cards to generate a division problem. The 2 cards on the left form a 2-digit number. This is the *dividend.* The number on the card at the right is the *divisor.*
   - Divide the 2-digit number by the 1-digit number and record the result. This result is your quotient. Remainders are ignored. Calculate mentally or on paper.
   - Add your quotient to your previous score and record your new score. (If this is your first turn, your previous score was 0.)
4. Players repeat Step 3 until one player's score is 100 or more. The first player to reach at least 100 wins. If there is only one player, the Object of the game is to reach 100 in as few turns as possible.

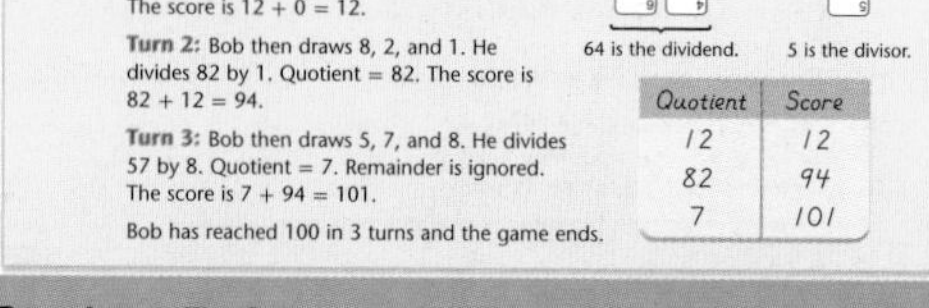
Example

Turn 1: Bob draws 6, 4, and 5. He divides 64 by 5. Quotient = 12. Remainder is ignored. The score is 12 + 0 = 12.

Turn 2: Bob then draws 8, 2, and 1. He divides 82 by 1. Quotient = 82. The score is 82 + 12 = 94.

Turn 3: Bob then draws 5, 7, and 8. He divides 57 by 8. Quotient = 7. Remainder is ignored. The score is 7 + 94 = 101.

Bob has reached 100 in 3 turns and the game ends.

64 is the dividend. 5 is the divisor.

Quotient	Score
12	12
82	94
7	101

***Student Reference Book,* p. 303**

Student Page

Date Time

LESSON 4·7 Making Magnitude Estimates with Multiplication and Division

For each problem make a magnitude estimate. Circle the appropriate box. Then solve Problems 1 and 4.

Sample estimates are given.

1. 45.7 * 38.3

10s	100s	(1,000s)	10,000s

How I estimated: 50 * 40 = 2,000

Solve: 45.7 * 38.3 = 1,750.31

2. 5.4 * 0.6

0.1s	(1s)	10s	100s

How I estimated: 5 * 1 = 5

3. 0.8 * 0.9

(0.1s)	1s	10s	100s

How I estimated: 1 * 1 = 1

4. 707.3 / 9

0.1s	1s	(10s)	100s

How I estimated: 700 ÷ 10 = 70

Solve: 707.3 / 9 = 78.58

5. 6.34 ÷ 12w

0.01s	(0.1s)	1s	10s

How I estimated: 6 ÷ 12 = 0.5

Try This

6. 0.5 ÷ 9

(0.01s)	0.1s	1s	10s

How I estimated: 0.5 ÷ 10 = 0.05

***Math Journal 1,* p. 115**

2 Ongoing Learning & Practice

▶ Playing *Division Dash*

PARTNER ACTIVITY

COMPUTATION PRACTICE

(*Student Reference Book,* p. 303)

Students practice dividing with 1-digit divisors and 2-digit dividends by playing *Division Dash.* Encourage students to calculate the quotient mentally.

Adjusting the Activity

Play a variation. Have players draw four cards. Place 3 cards on the left as the dividend and place 1 card on the right as the divisor. The object of the game is to reach 500 in the fewest divisions possible.

AUDITORY ◆ KINESTHETIC ◆ TACTILE ◆ VISUAL

NOTE Review the terms *dividend, divisor, quotient,* and *remainder* prior to playing *Division Dash.*

▶ Reviewing Magnitude Estimates with Decimals

8-9

INDEPENDENT ACTIVITY

COMPUTATION PRACTICE

(*Math Journal 1,* p. 115; *Student Reference Book,* pp. 38–43)

Students practice making magnitude estimates for multiplication and division problems with decimals. Encourage them to refer to *Student Reference Book,* pages 38–43 as needed. For each problem,

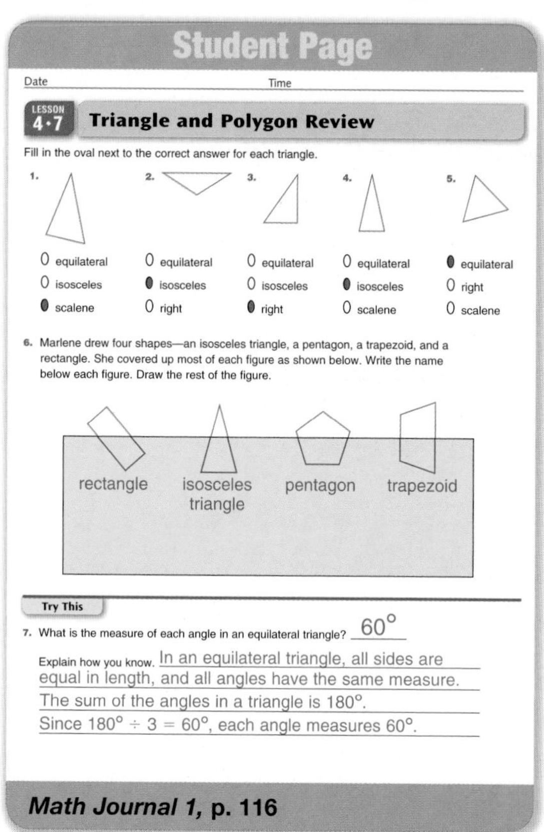
Student Page

Date Time

LESSON 4·7 Triangle and Polygon Review

Fill in the oval next to the correct answer for each triangle.

1.	2.	3.	4.	5.
○ equilateral	○ equilateral	○ equilateral	○ equilateral	● equilateral
○ isosceles	● isosceles	○ isosceles	● isosceles	○ right
● scalene	○ right	● right	○ scalene	○ scalene

6. Marlene drew four shapes—an isosceles triangle, a pentagon, a trapezoid, and a rectangle. She covered up most of each figure as shown below. Write the name below each figure. Draw the rest of the figure.

rectangle isosceles triangle pentagon trapezoid

Try This

7. What is the measure of each angle in an equilateral triangle? 60°

Explain how you know. In an equilateral triangle, all sides are equal in length, and all angles have the same measure. The sum of the angles in a triangle is 180°. Since 180° ÷ 3 = 60°, each angle measures 60°.

***Math Journal 1,* p. 116**

students make a magnitude estimate. They circle the appropriate box in the estimation bar to identify whether the answer is in the hundredths, tenths, ones, tens, hundreds, and so on. Students should then record a number sentence to reflect how they estimated for each problem. For Problems 1 and 4, they should also solve the problems, using their magnitude estimates to help them appropriately place the decimal point. When most have finished, write some of the problems on the board and have students describe how they estimated. For example, ask: *How did you make a magnitude estimate for Problem 6?* Sample answer: I rounded the divisor to 10. I thought of 0.5 being equivalent to $0.50. If I divide $0.50 among 10 people, each person would get about $0.05. So my magnitude estimate would be in the 0.01s.

Reviewing Types of Triangles

INDEPENDENT ACTIVITY

(*Math Journal 1,* p. 116)

Students identify equilateral, isosceles, right, and scalene triangles. They identify and complete drawings of polygons.

Math Boxes 4•7

INDEPENDENT ACTIVITY

(*Math Journal 1,* p. 117)

Mixed Review Math Boxes in this lesson are paired with Math Boxes in Lesson 4-5. The skill in Problem 6 previews Unit 5 content.

Writing/Reasoning Have students write a response to the following: *Explain how you determined the placement of the decimal point for Problem 4f.* Sample answer: When you multiply 234 by 0.1, the value of 234 becomes $\frac{1}{10}$ of its original value. To show a number being decreased by a factor of 10, you move the decimal point one place to the left. So for 234 ∗ 0.1, you move the decimal point one place to the left to get 23.4. This is $\frac{1}{10}$ of 234.

Study Link 4•7

INDEPENDENT ACTIVITY

(*Math Masters,* p. 119)

Home Connection Students find the values of variables. They use these values to complete open number sentences and solve other problems.

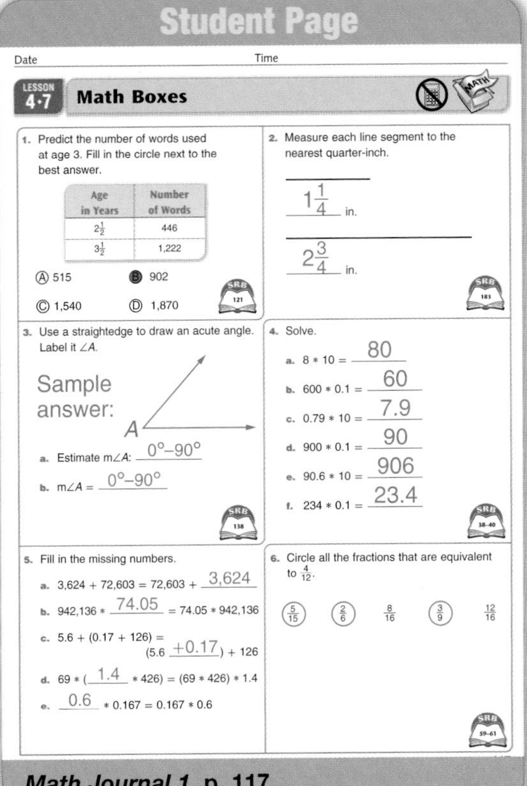

Student Page

Date Time

LESSON 4•7 **Math Boxes**

1. Predict the number of words used at age 3. Fill in the circle next to the best answer.

Age in Years	Number of Words
$2\frac{1}{2}$	446
$3\frac{1}{2}$	1,222

Ⓐ 515 Ⓑ 902 (filled)
Ⓒ 1,540 Ⓓ 1,870

2. Measure each line segment to the nearest quarter-inch.

$1\frac{1}{4}$ in.

$2\frac{3}{4}$ in.

3. Use a straightedge to draw an acute angle. Label it ∠A.

Sample answer:

a. Estimate m∠A: 0°–90°

b. m∠A = 0°–90°

4. Solve.

a. 8 ∗ 10 = 80
b. 600 ∗ 0.1 = 60
c. 0.79 ∗ 10 = 7.9
d. 900 ∗ 0.1 = 90
e. 90.6 ∗ 10 = 906
f. 234 ∗ 0.1 = 23.4

5. Fill in the missing numbers.

a. 3,624 + 72,603 = 72,603 + 3,624
b. 942,136 ∗ 74.05 = 74.05 ∗ 942,136
c. 5.6 + (0.17 + 126) = (5.6 + 0.17) + 126
d. 69 ∗ (1.4 ∗ 426) = (69 ∗ 426) ∗ 1.4
e. 0.6 ∗ 0.167 = 0.167 ∗ 0.6

6. Circle all the fractions that are equivalent to $\frac{4}{12}$.

$\frac{5}{15}$ $\frac{2}{6}$ $\frac{8}{16}$ $\frac{3}{9}$ $\frac{12}{16}$

Math Journal 1, p. 117

10-11

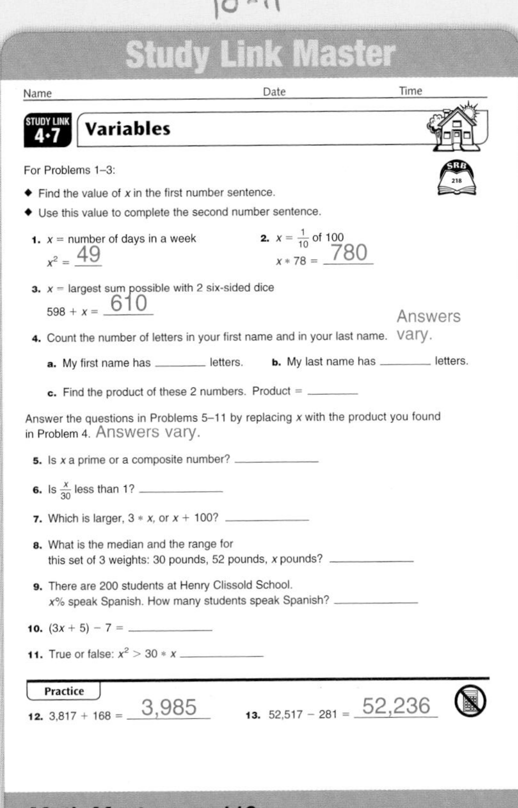

Study Link Master

Name Date Time

STUDY LINK 4•7 **Variables**

For Problems 1–3:

- Find the value of x in the first number sentence.
- Use this value to complete the second number sentence.

1. x = number of days in a week
x^2 = 49

2. $x = \frac{1}{10}$ of 100
$x ∗ 78$ = 780

3. x = largest sum possible with 2 six-sided dice
598 + x = 610

4. Count the number of letters in your first name and in your last name. Answers vary.

a. My first name has ______ letters. b. My last name has ______ letters.

c. Find the product of these 2 numbers. Product = ______

Answer the questions in Problems 5–11 by replacing x with the product you found in Problem 4. Answers vary.

5. Is x a prime or a composite number? ______

6. Is $\frac{x}{30}$ less than 1? ______

7. Which is larger, $3 ∗ x$, or $x + 100$? ______

8. What is the median and the range for this set of 3 weights: 30 pounds, 52 pounds, x pounds? ______

9. There are 200 students at Henry Clissold School. x% speak Spanish. How many students speak Spanish? ______

10. $(3x + 5) - 7$ = ______

11. True or false: $x^2 > 30 ∗ x$ ______

Practice

12. 3,817 + 168 = 3,985

13. 52,517 − 281 = 52,236

Math Masters, p. 119

Teaching Master

Name Date Time

LESSON 4·7 **Solving for Unknown Quantities**

For each number story:

- Draw a situation diagram.
- Fill in the numbers. Write a ? for the unknown quantity.
- Write a number sentence with □ for the unknown.
- Solve the problem.

Example:

Fran bought a bag of 14 marbles from a game store. She added them to her collection. She now has 47 marbles. How many marbles did she have before she bought more?

Number sentence: 14 + □ = 47

Solution: □ = 33

Total	
47	
Part	Part
14	?

Diagram

1. It was 68° when Nadine left for school. By lunchtime, it was 75°. By how many degrees had the temperature gone up?
   Number sentence: 68° + □ = 75°
   Solution: □ = 7°
2. Michael wants to buy a milkshake. With tax, it costs $3.92, and he has $3.43. How much more money does he need?
   Number sentence: $3.92 − $3.43 = □
   Solution: □ = $0.49
3. Lora bought 5 packages of pencils. Each package had 12 pencils in it. How many pencils did she buy in all?
   Number sentence: 5 × 12 = □
   Solution: □ = 60 pencils
4. Make up a problem of your own on the back of this page.

Math Masters, p. 120

Student Page

Date Time

LESSON 4·7 ***Algebra Election***

Materials
- □ 32 *First to 100* Problem Cards (*Math Masters,* pp. 456 and 457)
- □ Electoral Vote Map (*Math Masters,* pp. 442 and 443)
- □ 1 six-sided die
- □ 4 pennies or other small counters
- □ calculator

Players 2 teams, each with 2 players

Object of the game Players move their counters on a map of the United States. For each state, or the District of Columbia (D.C.), that a player lands on, the player tries to win that state's electoral votes by solving a problem. The first team to collect 270 or more votes wins the election. Winning-team members become President and Vice President.

Directions

1. Each player puts a counter on Iowa.
2. One member of each team rolls the die. The team with the higher roll goes first.
3. Alternate turns between teams and partners: Team 1, Player 1; Team 2, Player 1; Team 1, Player 2; Team 2, Player 2.
4. Shuffle the Problem Cards. Place them facedown in a pile.
5. The first player rolls the die. The result tells how many moves the player must make from the current state. Each new state counts as one move. Moves can be in any direction as long as they pass between states that share a common border. *Exceptions:* Players can get to and from Alaska by way of Washington state, and to and from Hawaii by way of California. Once a player has been in a state, the player may not return to that state on the same turn.
6. The player makes the indicated number of moves and puts the counter on the last state moved to. The map names how many electoral votes the state has.

Math Journal 1, p. 118

3 Differentiation Options

READINESS

PARTNER ACTIVITY

5–15 Min

▶ Solving for Unknown Quantities

(*Math Masters,* p. 120)

Algebraic Thinking To explore situation diagrams and their connection to open number sentences, have students make situation diagrams and use the diagrams to write open number sentences.

When students have finished, have them share the problems they wrote for Problem 4. Discuss any incorrect problem structures. Have volunteers draw the related situation diagrams on the board.

ENRICHMENT

SMALL-GROUP ACTIVITY

30+ Min

▶ Playing *Algebra Election*

(*Math Journal 1,* pp. 118 and 119; *Math Masters,* pp. 442, 443, 456, and 457)

Algebraic Thinking

Social Studies Link To apply students' understanding of solving open number sentences, have them play *Algebra Election,* which is a variation of *First to 100.* In *Algebra Election*, students travel through the United States, capturing electoral votes by using algebraic thinking to solve the problems on the *First to 100* cards.

EXTRA PRACTICE

▶ Solving Open Number Sentences

Algebraic Thinking To focus on strategies for solving open number sentences, write open sentences on the board or a transparency. Have students write the solutions on their slates or on sheets of paper. Remind students to think of fact family relationships to find the missing values.

Suggestions:

- ▷ $22 + a = 74$ 52
- ▷ $105 = 99 + n$ 6
- ▷ $30 * f = 360$ 12
- ▷ $7 * (4 + k) = 70$ 6
- ▷ $546 / w = 6$ 91
- ▷ $y - 36 = 58$ 94

ELL SUPPORT

SMALL-GROUP ACTIVITY

Building a Math Word Bank

5–15 Min

(*Differentiation Handbook,* p. 142)

To provide language support for number sentences, have students use the Word Bank Template found on *Differentiation Handbook,* page 142. Ask students to write the term *variable,* draw pictures relating to the term, and write other related words. See the *Differentiation Handbook* for more information.

4•8 Progress Check 4

Objective To assess students' progress on mathematical content through the end of Unit 4.

1 Looking Back: Cumulative Assessment

Input student data from Progress Check 3 into the **Assessment Management Spreadsheets**.

Materials
- Study Link 4•7
- *Assessment Handbook,* pp. 76–83, 170–174, 219, and 258–261
- *Math Masters,* p. 415
- slate; ruler

CONTENT ASSESSED	LESSON(S)	ASSESSMENT ITEMS				
		SELF	ORAL/SLATE	WRITTEN PART A	WRITTEN PART B	OPEN RESPONSE
Use rules of divisibility. [Number and Numeration Goal 3]			2			✓
Generate equivalent names for wholes numbers. [Number and Numeration Goal 4]	4•1, 4•2	1		4, 5		
Know and apply multiplication facts, related division facts, and extended facts. [Operations and Computation Goal 2]	4•1, 4•4, 4•7	2	1, 3	4–7, 13, 14		
Use partial-quotients algorithm to divide. [Operations and Computation Goal 3]	4•1, 4•2, 4•4–4•6	3, 4		4–7, 13, 14	15–20	
Interpret remainders in a division problem. [Operations and Computation Goal 3]	4•6	9	4		19, 20	
Make magnitude estimates. [Operations and Computation Goal 6]	4•5–4•7	5		8, 9	17, 18	
Use scaling to model multiplication. [Operations and Computation Goal 7]	4•3	7		1–3		
Measure to the nearest $\frac{1}{2}$ inch. [Measurement and Reference Frames Goal 1]	4•3	6		1–3		
Estimate distances on a map. Measurement and Reference Frames Goal 1]	4•3	7		1–3		
Write and solve number sentences. [Patterns, Functions, and Algebra Goal 2]	4•6, 4•7	8		10–12	19, 20	

2 Looking Ahead: Preparing for Unit 5

Math Boxes 4•8

Study Link 4•8: Unit 5 Family Letter

Materials
- *Math Journal 1,* p. 120
- *Math Masters,* pp. 121–124

Getting Started

Math Message • Self Assessment

Complete the Self Assessment (Assessment Handbook, page 170).

Study Link 4•7 Follow-Up

Review Problems 5–11 using the number of letters in your school principal's first and last names to form the product to substitute for x.

1 Looking Back: Cumulative Assessment

Math Message Follow-Up

INDEPENDENT ACTIVITY

(Self Assessment, *Assessment Handbook*, p. 170)

The Self Assessment offers students the opportunity to reflect upon their progress.

Oral and Slate Assessments

WHOLE-CLASS ACTIVITY

Problems 1 and 3 provide summative information and can be used for grading purposes. Problems 2 and 4 provide formative information that can be useful in planning future instruction.

Oral Assessment

1. Pose problems like the following:
   - How many 5s are in 35? 7 What number times 7 equals 63? 9 Multiply 400 by 9. 3,600
   - How many 6s are in 36? 6 What number times 6 equals 60? 10 Multiply 10 by 4.5. 45
   - What number times 8 equals 56? 7 How many 7s are in 77? 11 Multiply 11 by 5. 55
2. Pose problems like the following:
   - Is 4,492 divisible by 2? Yes by 3? No by 9? No
   - Is 228 divisible by 3? Yes by 4? Yes by 6? Yes
   - Is 6,237 divisible by 2? No by 5? No by 9? Yes

Slate Assessment

3. Pose problems like the following. Then ask students to explain the patterns they notice in the number of zeros in the products.
   - 8 [50s] = ? 400; 80 [50s] = ? 4,000; 800 [50s] = ? 40,000
   - 90 [7s] = ? 630; 90 [70s] = ? 6,300; 900 [70s] = ? 63,000
   - 7 [60s] = ? 420; 70 [60s] = ? 4,200; 700 [60s] = ? 42,000

Assessment Master

Name Date Time

LESSON 4•8 **Self Assessment** Progress Check 4

Think about each skill listed below. Assess your own progress by checking the most appropriate box.

Skills	I can do this on my own and explain how to do it.	I can do this on my own.	I can do this if I get help or look at an example.
1. Find multiples, and use them to rename numbers.			
2. Know and use multiplication facts, related division facts, and extended facts.			
3. Divide using a friendly number strategy with the partial-quotients algorithm.			
4. Divide using an "at least...not more than strategy" with the partial-quotients algorithm.			
5. Make magnitude estimates to correctly place the decimal point in quotients.			
6. Measure and draw line segments to the nearest $\frac{1}{2}$ inch.			
7. Estimate distances using a map scale.			
8. Write an open number sentence for number stories.			
9. Determine what to do with a remainder.			

***Assessment Handbook*, p. 170**

Assessment Master

Name Date Time

LESSON 4•8 **Written Assessment** Progress Check 4

Part A

Use the map to answer the questions.

1. Estimate the distance from New Delhi to Mumbai (Bombay).
   Map distance: 1 in.
   Real distance: 750 mi
2. Estimate the distance from Mumbai (Bombay) to Mt. Everest.
   Map distance: $1\frac{1}{2}$ in.
   Real distance: 1,125 mi
3. About how many miles from the northern tip of Sri Lanka is K2? 1,875 mi

Use a friendly number strategy to solve these problems mentally.

4. 84 divided by 6 equals 14.
   Sample answer: 60 and 24
   (friendly parts for 84)
5. 104 divided by 8 equals 13.
   Sample answer: 80 and 24
   (friendly parts for 104)

Solve.

6. $3\overline{)141}$ 47
   Check: $3 * 47 = 141$
7. $624 \div 8 =$ 78
   Check: $78 * 8 = 624$

***Assessment Handbook*, p. 171**

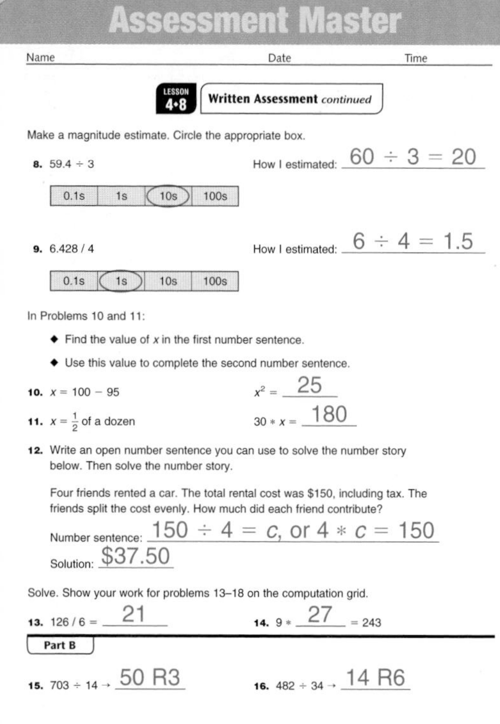
Assessment Master

Name Date Time

LESSON 4•8 Written Assessment *continued*

Make a magnitude estimate. Circle the appropriate box.

8. 59.4 ÷ 3 How I estimated: $60 \div 3 = 20$

0.1s	1s	(10s)	100s

9. 6.428 / 4 How I estimated: $6 \div 4 = 1.5$

0.1s	(1s)	10s	100s

In Problems 10 and 11:

- Find the value of x in the first number sentence.
- Use this value to complete the second number sentence.

10. $x = 100 - 95$ $x^2 =$ 25

11. $x = \frac{1}{2}$ of a dozen $30 * x =$ 180

12. Write an open number sentence you can use to solve the number story below. Then solve the number story.

Four friends rented a car. The total rental cost was $150, including tax. The friends split the cost evenly. How much did each friend contribute?

Number sentence: $150 \div 4 = c$, or $4 * c = 150$

Solution: $37.50

Solve. Show your work for problems 13–18 on the computation grid.

13. 126 / 6 = 21 **14.** 9 * 27 = 243

Part B

15. 703 ÷ 14 → 50 R3 **16.** 482 ÷ 34 → 14 R6

Assessment Handbook, p. 172

Use the checklists on pages 259 and 261 of the *Assessment Handbook* to record results. Then input the data into the **Assessment Management Spreadsheets** to keep an ongoing record of students' progress toward Grade-Level Goals.

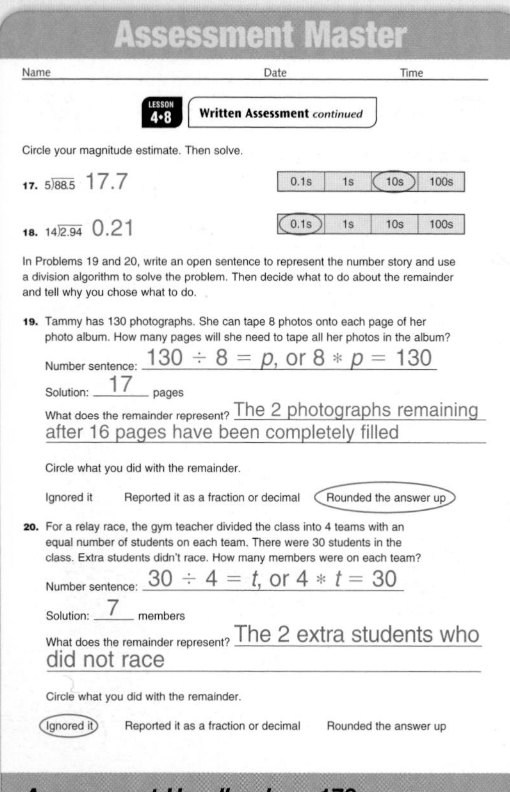
Assessment Master

Name Date Time

LESSON 4•8 Written Assessment *continued*

Circle your magnitude estimate. Then solve.

17. $5\overline{)88.5}$ 17.7

0.1s	1s	(10s)	100s

18. $14\overline{)2.94}$ 0.21

(0.1s)	1s	10s	100s

In Problems 19 and 20, write an open sentence to represent the number story and use a division algorithm to solve the problem. Then decide what to do about the remainder and tell why you chose what to do.

19. Tammy has 130 photographs. She can tape 8 photos onto each page of her photo album. How many pages will she need to tape all her photos in the album?

Number sentence: $130 \div 8 = p$, or $8 * p = 130$

Solution: 17 pages

What does the remainder represent? The 2 photographs remaining after 16 pages have been completely filled

Circle what you did with the remainder.

Ignored it Reported it as a fraction or decimal (Rounded the answer up)

20. For a relay race, the gym teacher divided the class into 4 teams with an equal number of students on each team. There were 30 students in the class. Extra students didn't race. How many members were on each team?

Number sentence: $30 \div 4 = t$, or $4 * t = 30$

Solution: 7 members

What does the remainder represent? The 2 extra students who did not race

Circle what you did with the remainder.

(Ignored it) Reported it as a fraction or decimal Rounded the answer up

Assessment Handbook, p. 173

4. Have students express the remainders as whole numbers, fractions, and as decimals. *Suggestions:*

- $94 \div 5 = ?$ 18 R4, $18\frac{4}{5}$, 18.8
- $73 \div 3 = ?$ 24 R1, $24\frac{1}{3}$, $24.\overline{3}$
- $863 \div 7 = ?$ 123 R2, $123\frac{2}{7}$, 123.29
- $2{,}948 \div 6 = ?$ 491 R2, $491\frac{2}{6}$ or $\frac{1}{3}$, $491.3\overline{3}$

Written Assessment

INDEPENDENT ACTIVITY

(*Assessment Handbook,* p. 171–173; *Math Masters,* p. 415)

Part A Recognizing Student Achievement

Problems 1–14 provide summative information and may be used for grading purposes.

Problem(s)	Description
1–3	Use a map scale to estimate distance.
4, 5	Use a friendly-number strategy to divide.
6, 7, 13, 14	Use the partial-quotients algorithm.
8, 9	Make magnitude estimates to place decimal point.
10, 11	Solve number sentences for given variables.
12	Write number sentences that model number stories.

Part B Informing Instruction

Problems 15–20 provide formative information that can be useful in planning future instruction.

Problem(s)	Description
15–18	Use the partial-quotients algorithm.
17, 18	Divide decimals.
19, 20	Write number sentences that model number stories.
19, 20	Interpret remainders.

Open Response

INDEPENDENT ACTIVITY

(*Assessment Handbook,* p. 174)

Missing Digits

The open-response item requires students to apply skills and concepts from Unit 4 to solve a multistep problem. See *Assessment Handbook*, pages 79–83 for rubrics and student work samples for this problem.

2 Looking Ahead: Preparing for Unit 5

▶ Math Boxes 4·8

INDEPENDENT ACTIVITY

(*Math Journal 1,* p. 120)

Mixed Review This Math Boxes page previews Unit 5 content.

▶ Study Link 4·8: Unit 5 Family Letter

INDEPENDENT ACTIVITY

(*Math Masters,* pp. 121–124)

Home Connection The Unit 5 Family Letter provides parents and guardians with information and activities related to Unit 5 topics.

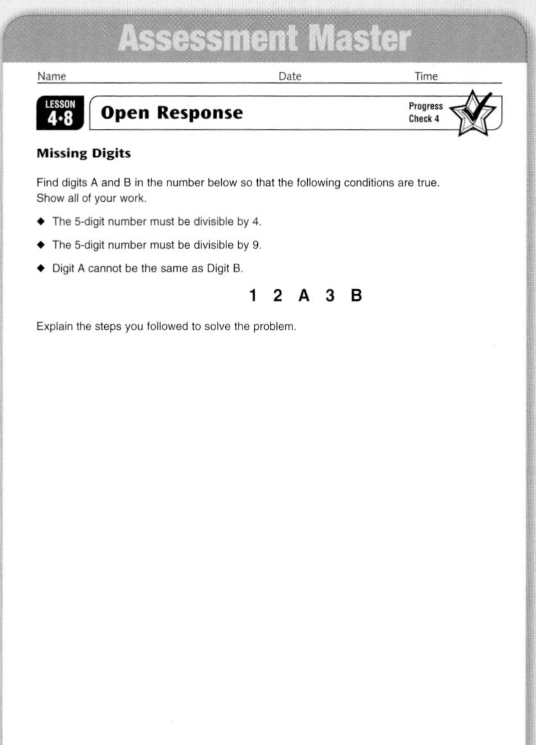

Assessment Master

Name Date Time

LESSON 4·8 **Open Response** Progress Check 4

Missing Digits

Find digits A and B in the number below so that the following conditions are true. Show all of your work.

- The 5-digit number must be divisible by 4.
- The 5-digit number must be divisible by 9.
- Digit A cannot be the same as Digit B.

1 2 A 3 B

Explain the steps you followed to solve the problem.

Assessment Handbook, p. 174

Student Page

Date Time

LESSON 4·8 **Math Boxes**

1. Complete the table.

Fraction	Decimal	Percent
$\frac{1}{5}$	0.2	20%
$\frac{38}{100}$, or $\frac{19}{50}$	0.38	38%
$\frac{75}{100}$, or $\frac{3}{4}$	0.75	75%
$\frac{4}{6}$	0.67, or $0.\overline{6}$	$66.\overline{6}\%$, or $66\frac{2}{3}\%$
$\frac{625}{1,000}$, $\frac{25}{40}$, or $\frac{5}{8}$	0.625	62.5%

SRB 89 90

2. Make up a set of at least 12 numbers that have the following landmarks.

minimum: 3

maximum: 9

median: 7

mode: 7

Sample answer: 3, 4, 5, 6, 6, 7, 7, 7, 8, 8, 9, 9

SRB 119

3. Label these points on the number line.

0.9 0.56 0.25 0.1 0.7 0.4

0.1 0.25 0.4 0.56 0.7 0.9

0 0.5 1.0

SRB 32

4. Write 5 names for $\frac{1}{4}$.

Sample answers: $\frac{2}{8}$, $\frac{4}{16}$, 0.25, 0.20 + 0.05, $1 - \frac{3}{4}$

SRB 59-61

5. Tracy scored 95, 82, 90, and 83 on four tests. After the fifth test, the mode of her scores was 90. What did she score on the fifth test?

Score: 90

What was the mean of her 5 tests? 88

SRB 119-121

Math Journal 1, p. 120

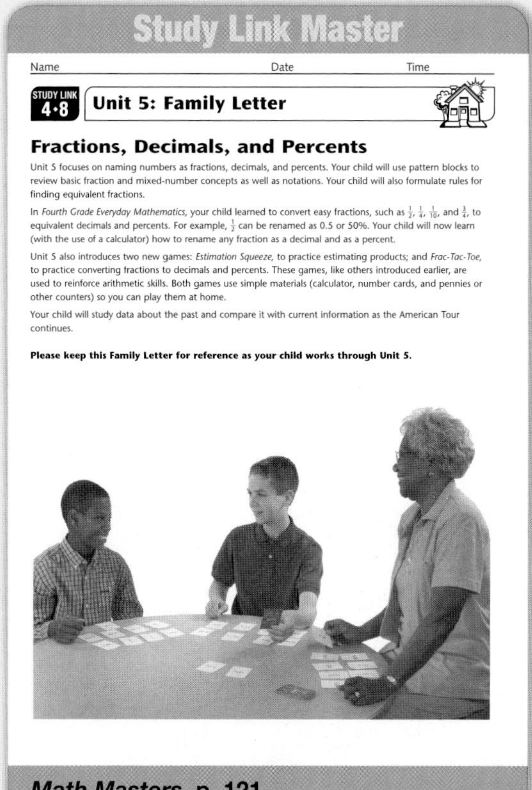

Study Link Master

Name Date Time

STUDY LINK 4·8 **Unit 5: Family Letter**

Fractions, Decimals, and Percents

Unit 5 focuses on naming numbers as fractions, decimals, and percents. Your child will use pattern blocks to review basic fraction and mixed-number concepts as well as notations. Your child will also formulate rules for finding equivalent fractions.

In *Fourth Grade Everyday Mathematics,* your child learned to convert easy fractions, such as $\frac{1}{2}$, $\frac{1}{4}$, $\frac{1}{10}$, and $\frac{3}{4}$, to equivalent decimals and percents. For example, $\frac{1}{2}$ can be renamed as 0.5 or 50%. Your child will now learn (with the use of a calculator) how to rename any fraction as a decimal and as a percent.

Unit 5 also introduces two new games: *Estimation Squeeze,* to practice estimating products; and *Frac-Tac-Toe,* to practice converting fractions to decimals and percents. These games, like others introduced earlier, are used to reinforce arithmetic skills. Both games use simple materials (calculator, number cards, and pennies or other counters) so you can play them at home.

Your child will study data about the past and compare it with current information as the American Tour continues.

Please keep this Family Letter for reference as your child works through Unit 5.

Math Masters, p. 121

Unit 5 Organizer

Fractions, Decimals, and Percents

Overview

The main purpose of Unit 5 is to review the meanings of fraction, decimal, and percent notations for rational numbers. Another objective is to concentrate on conversion among these notations, often emphasizing the fact that embedded in every fraction is a division problem. This freedom to convert among these notations is often important in solving problems in everyday life and in the occupations of many people. Unit 5 has three main areas of focus:

- To review fraction concepts, such as exploring mixed numbers, comparing and ordering fractions, and finding equivalent fractions,
- To practice turning fractions into decimals and percents, and
- To review the properties and construction of bar and circle graphs.

CCSS Linking to the Common Core State Standards

The content of Unit 5 addresses the Common Core State Standards for Mathematics in *Number and Operations–Fractions.* The correlation of the Common Core State Standards to the *Everyday Mathematics* Grade 5 lessons begins on page CS1.

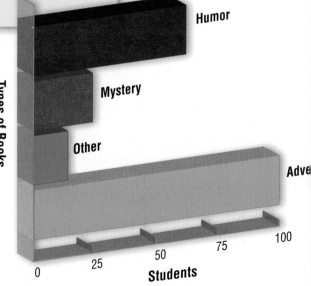

Humor
Mystery
Other
Adve
Types of Books
0
25
50
75
100
Students

Contents

Learning In Perspective

	Lesson Objectives	Links to the Past	Links to the Future
5•1	To review key fraction concepts; to provide practice with solving parts-and-whole problems and finding fractional parts of whole numbers; and to interpret a fraction as division.	In fourth grade, students review fractions as parts of a whole, and they find the whole for given fractions.	In sixth grade, students represent the fraction multiplication algorithm as a general statement.
5•2	To review the whole; and to provide experience with mixed-number and improper fraction concepts.	In fourth grade, students use improper fractions and mixed numbers to name numbers greater than or equal to 1.	In sixth grade, students rename fractions and mixed numbers in simplest form and find equivalent fractions.
5•3	To review equivalent fractions; to compare and order fractions; and to explore fraction addition.	In fourth grade, students compare and order fractions with like numerators, with like denominators, and with unlike numerators and denominators.	In sixth grade, students add and subtract fractions with like and unlike denominators.
5•4	To introduce multiplication and division rules for finding equivalent fractions.	In fourth grade, students develop and use a rule for generating equivalent fractions.	In sixth grade, students use cross multiplication to test equivalency of fractions.
5•5	To provide practice with renaming fractions as decimals; and to review rounding decimals.	In fourth grade, students rename fractions as decimals and decimals as fractions.	In sixth grade, students use division to convert fractions to decimals.
5•6	To provide experience with several graphic models for renaming fractions as decimals.	In fourth grade, students explore the relationship between fractions and division.	In sixth grade, students review converting between fractions and decimals.
5•7	To use a calculator to find decimal equivalents for fractions.	In fourth grade, students use a calculator to rename fractions as decimals and as percents.	In sixth grade, students use division to convert fractions to percents.
5•8	To discuss the meaning and uses of percents; and to introduce using a calculator to convert decimals to percents.	In fourth grade, students shade 10-by-10 grids to represent percents, then rename each percent as a fraction and as a decimal.	In sixth grade, students develop rules for converting between decimals and percents.
5•9	To review the properties and construction of bar graphs; and to discuss the properties of circle graphs.	In fourth grade, students make and use bar graphs for a set of collected data.	In sixth grade, students create, read, and interpret bar graphs.
5•10	To introduce the use of the Percent Circle to measure circle graph sectors.	In the primary grades, children compare circle sections equal to halves, fourths, and eighths.	Students measure, draw, and interpret circle graphs for more complicated contexts.
5•11	To introduce constructing circle graphs with the use of the Percent Circle.	In fourth grade, students use full- and half-circle protractors to measure and draw angles.	Students represent data on a circle graph.
5•12	[illegible] extend the American Tour with information about mathematics instruction and related historical problems.	In fourth grade, students interpret data using the World Tour project.	In sixth grade, students use the *Student Reference Book* to find information and solve problems.

Lesson	Key Concepts and Skills	Grade 5 Goals*
5·1	Find fractions of a set and find the whole based on a known fraction of a set.	Number and Numeration Goal 2
	Find equivalent names for a fraction of a set.	Number and Numeration Goal 5
	Interpret a fraction as division of the numerator by the denominator.	Operations and Computation Goal 3
	Identify and use unit fractions to solve problems.	Operations and Computation Goal 7
5·2	Find equivalent names for fractions and mixed numbers.	Number and Numeration Goal 5
	Compare fractions and mixed numbers.	Number and Numeration Goal 6
	Add fractions using an area model.	Operations and Computation Goal 4
	Explore the meaning of fractions using an area model to identify parts or the whole.	Operations and Computation Goal 7
5·3	Find equivalent fractions using a length model.	Number and Numeration Goal 5
	Compare fractions to the benchmarks 0, $\frac{1}{2}$, and 1.	Number and Numeration Goal 6
	Order fractions from least to greatest.	Number and Numeration Goal 6
	Solve fraction number stories using a number-line model.	Operations and Computation Goal 4
	Use fraction sticks to add fractions.	Operations and Computation Goal 4
5·4	Generate equivalent fractions using a length model.	Number and Numeration Goal 5
	Use and explain multiplication and division rules to find equivalent fractions.	Number and Numeration Goal 5
5·5	Rename fractions and mixed numbers as decimals.	Number and Numeration Goal 5
	Compare and order decimals.	Number and Numeration Goal 6
	Round decimals.	Operations and Computation Goal 6
5·6	Convert between fractions, mixed numbers, and decimals.	Number and Numeration Goal 5
	Order rational numbers.	Number and Numeration Goal 6
	Order fractions and decimals on a number line.	Number and Numeration Goal 6
5·7	Differentiate between repeating and terminating decimals.	Number and Numeration Goal 1
	Use a calculator to rename fractions as decimals.	Number and Numeration Goal 5
	Convert between fractions and decimals.	Number and Numeration Goal 5
	Compare fractions, whole numbers, and mixed numbers.	Number and Numeration Goal 6
5·8	Use correct notation to write terminating and repeating decimals.	Number and Numeration Goal 1
	Define the uses and meaning of percents.	Number and Numeration Goal 2
	Use a calculator to rename fractions as decimals.	Number and Numeration Goal 5
	Convert between fractions, decimals, and percents.	Number and Numeration Goal 5
5·9	Create a bar graph for a data set.	Data and Chance Goal 1
	Explore how circle graphs represent data.	Data and Chance Goal 2
5·10	Convert between fractions and percents.	Number and Numeration Goal 5
	Estimate circle-graph sector sizes.	Measurement and Reference Frames Goal 1
	Measure sectors of a circle-graph using the Percent Circle.	Measurement and Reference Frames Goal 1
	Interpret circle graph sectors.	Data and Chance Goal 2
5·11	Find fraction and percent equivalents.	Number and Numeration Goal 5
	Measure sectors of a circle graph using the Percent Circle.	Measurement and Reference Frames Goal 1
	Construct circle graphs from table data.	Data and Chance Goal 1
	Interpret data presented in various forms.	Data and Chance Goal 2
5·12	Convert between fractions, decimals, and percents.	Number and Numeration Goal 5
	Solve problems involving ratios.	Operations and Computation Goal 7
	Use graphs to ask and answer questions and draw conclusions.	Data and Chance Goal 2
	Answer questions based on tables.	Data and Chance Goal 2

*See the Appendix for a complete list of Grade 5 Goals.

A Balanced Curriculum

Ongoing Practice

Everyday Mathematics provides numerous opportunities for ongoing practice. These activities are embedded throughout the lessons:

Mental Math and Reflexes activities promote speed and accuracy in mental computation.

Math Boxes offer mixed practice and are paired across lessons as shown in the brackets below. This makes them useful as assessment tools. The last one or two boxes on each page preview the next unit's content.

Mixed practice	[5•1, 5•3], [5•2, 5•4], [5•5, 5•7], [5•6, 5•8], [5•9, 5•11], [5•10, 5•12]
Mixed practice with multiple choice	5•6, 5•8
Mixed practice with writing/reasoning opportunity	5•3, 5•7, 5•8, 5•9, 5•11, 5•12

Study Links are daily homework assignments that review the content of the lesson and often contain ongoing facts practice or computation practice.

5-Minute Math problems are offered for additional practice in Lessons 5•4, 5•6, and 5•10.

EM Facts Workshop Game provides online practice of basic facts and computation.

EXTRA PRACTICE **Extra Practice** activities are included in Lessons 5•2, 5•4, 5•5, 5•6, 5•8, 5•9, 5•10, and 5•12.

Practice through Games

Games are an essential component of practice in the *Everyday Mathematics* program. Games offer skills practice and promote strategic thinking. See the *Differentiation Handbook* for ways to adapt games to meet students' needs.

Lesson	Game	Skill Practiced
5•1, 5•3	*Fraction Top-It*	Comparing fractions [NN Goal 6]
5•4	*Factor Captor*	Finding factors [NN Goal 3 and OC Goal 2]
5•5	*Estimation Squeeze*	Finding decimals between two decimals [OC Goal 6]
5•6	*Number Top-It* (3-Place Decimals)	Ordering decimals [NN Goals 1 and 6]
5•7	*2-4-5-10 Frac-Tac-Toe* (Decimal Version)	Converting fractions to decimals [NN Goal 5]
5•8	*2-4-5-10 Frac-Tac-Toe* (Percent Version)	Converting fractions to percents [NN Goal 5]
5•8	*Fraction/Percent Concentration*	Converting between fractions and percents [NN Goal 5]
5•11	*Fraction Of*	Finding fractional parts of sets [NN Goal 2]
5•12	*Name That Number*	Finding equivalent names for numbers [NN Goal 4]

[NN] Number and Numeration
[MRF] Measurement and Reference Frames
[OC] Operations and Computation
[GEO] Geometry
[DC] Data and Chance
[PFA] Patterns, Functions, and Algebra

Problem Solving 

Experts at problem solving and mathematical modeling generally do these things:

- Identify the problem.
- Decide what information is needed to solve the problem.
- Play with and study the data to find patterns and meaning.
- Identify and use mathematical procedures to solve the problem.
- Decide whether the solution makes sense and whether it can be applied to other problems.

The table below lists some of the opportunities in this unit for students to practice these strategies.

Lessons that teach *through* problem solving, not just *about* problem solving

Lesson	Activity
5•1	Solve parts-and-whole problems with fractions.
5•2	Use pattern blocks to model mixed numbers.
5•3	Solve fraction number stories using addition.
5•8	Use a calculator to find decimal equivalents for fractions or to convert decimals to percents.
5•8	Solve number stories using percents.
5•9, 5•11	Construct a bar graph and circle graph of snack-survey data.
5•12	Interpret information from text and graphic displays.

See Chapter 18: Problem Solving in the *Teacher's Reference Manual* for more information.

The Language of Mathematics

Everyday Mathematics provides lesson-specific suggestions to help all students acquire, process, and express mathematical ideas. Throughout Unit 5, there are lesson-specific language development notes that address the needs of English language learners, indicated by ELL.

ELL SUPPORT Activities to support English language learners are in Part 3 of Lessons 5•1, 5•3, 5•8, and 5•9.

The *English Learners Handbook* and the *Differentiation Handbook* have suggestions for promoting language development and acquisition of mathematics vocabulary. See Unit 5 in each handbook.

Unit 5 Vocabulary

bar graph
benchmark
circle (pie) graph
denominator
equivalent fractions
fraction stick
improper fraction
mixed number
numerator
percent
Percent Circle
repeating decimal
round down
round to the nearest . . .
round up
sector
unit fraction
whole (ONE, or unit)

Literacy Connection

Tiger Math, by Ann Whitehead Nagda, Owlet Paperbacks, 2002

For more literacy connections, see the *Home Connection Handbook,* Grades 4–6.

Cross-Curricular Links

Language Arts

Lesson 5•1 Students review the meaning of *vinculum.*

Lesson 5•8 Students review the meaning of *percent.*

Social Studies

Lesson 5•12 Students explore historical texts.

Science

Lesson 5•10 Students conduct a test for eye dominance.

Balanced Assessment

Daily Assessments

- **Recognizing Student Achievement** – A daily assessment that is included in every lesson to evaluate students' progress toward the Grade 5 Grade-Level Goals.
- **Informing Instruction** – Notes that appear throughout the unit to help anticipate students' common errors and suggest appropriate problem-solving strategies.

Lesson	Recognizing Student Achievement	Informing Instruction
5•1	Demonstrate an appropriate strategy for finding the unit fraction of a set. [OC Goal 7]	Use counters to represent fractions.
5•2	Find the value of a region based on a defined unit fraction. [OC Goal 7]	Reference the names of pattern block shapes.
5•3	Explain the relationship between the numerator and denominator. [NN Goal 6]	Use a straightedge with the fraction-stick chart.
5•4	Find equivalent fractions. [NN Goal 5]	
5•5	Convert between equivalent number forms. [NN Goal 5]	
5•6	Compare fractions. [NN Goal 6]	
5•7	Understand fraction and decimal relationships. [NN Goal 5]	Separate the fraction part when renaming mixed numbers as decimals.
5•8	Recognize percent equivalents for fractions. [NN Goal 5]	Use a decimal place-value chart when interpreting a calculator display.
5•9	Demonstrate knowledge of bar and circle graphs. [DC Goal 1]	
5•10	Estimate and find the percent measure of circle graph sectors. [MRF Goal 1]	Use a Percent Circle properly when measuring.
5•11	Demonstrate understanding of how to use the data-set fractions to draw circle graph sectors. [DC Goal 1]	Construct a circle graph using a demonstrated method.
5•12	Estimate answers. [OC Goal 6]	

[NN] Number and Numeration [OC] Operations and Computation [DC] Data and Chance
[MRF] Measurement and Reference Frames [GEO] Geometry [PFA] Patterns, Functions, and Algebra

Portfolio Opportunities

The following lessons provide opportunities to gather samples of students' mathematical writings, drawings, and creations to add balance to the assessment process: Lessons 5•1, 5•2, 5•4, 5•6, 5•7, 5•11, 5•12, and 5•13.

See pages 16 and 17 in the *Assessment Handbook* for more information about portfolios and how to use them.

Unit Assessment

Progress Check 5 – A cumulative assessment of concepts and skills taught in Unit 5 and in previous units, providing information for evaluating students' progress and planning for future instruction. These assessments include oral/slate, written, and open-response activities.

Unit Assessment

Progress Check 5 – A cumulative assessment of concepts and skills taught in Unit 5 and in previous units, providing information for evaluating students' progress and planning for future instruction. These assessments include oral/slate, written, and open-response activities, as shown below in the sample Progress Check lesson opener.

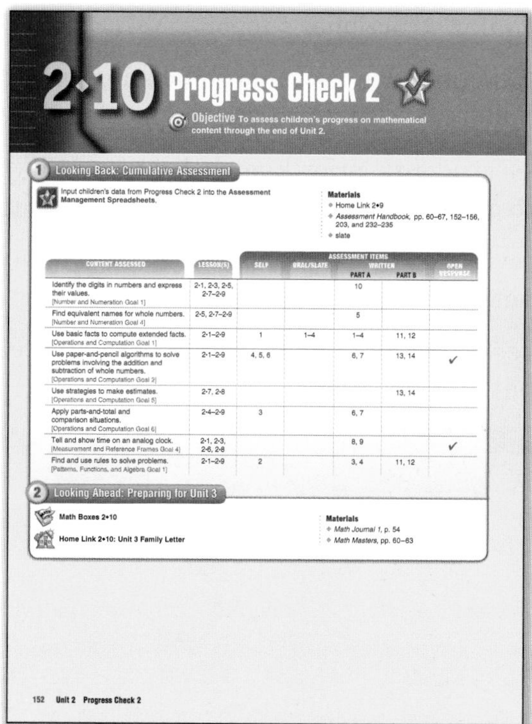

2·10 Progress Check 2

Objective To assess children's progress on mathematical content through the end of Unit 2.

1 Looking Back: Cumulative Assessment

Input children's data from Progress Check 2 into the **Assessment Management Spreadsheets.**

Materials
- Home Link 2•9
- *Assessment Handbook,* pp. 60–67, 152–156, 203, and 232–235
- slate

CONTENT ASSESSED	LESSON(S)	ASSESSMENT ITEMS				
		SELF	ORAL/SLATE	WRITTEN PART A	WRITTEN PART B	OPEN RESPONSE
Identify the digits in numbers and express their values. [Number and Numeration Goal 1]	2·1, 2·3, 2·5, 2·7–2·9			10		
Find equivalent names for whole numbers. [Number and Numeration Goal 4]	2·5, 2·7–2·9			5		
Use basic facts to compute extended facts. [Operations and Computation Goal 1]	2·1–2·9	1	1–4	1–4	11, 12	
Use paper-and-pencil algorithms to solve problems involving the addition and subtraction of whole numbers. [Operations and Computation Goal 2]	2·1–2·9	4, 5, 6		6, 7	13, 14	✓
Use strategies to make estimates. [Operations and Computation Goal 5]	2·7, 2·8				13, 14	
Apply parts-and-total and comparison situations. [Operations and Computation Goal 6]	2·4–2·9	3		6, 7		
Tell and show time on an analog clock. [Measurement and Reference Frames Goal 4]	2·1, 2·3, 2·6, 2·8			8, 9		✓
Find and use rules to solve problems. [Patterns, Functions, and Algebra Goal 1]	2·1–2·9	2		3, 4	11, 12	

2 Looking Ahead: Preparing for Unit 3

Math Boxes 2•10

Home Link 2•10: Unit 3 Family Letter

Materials
- *Math Journal 1,* p. 54
- *Math Masters,* pp. 60–63

152 Unit 2 Progress Check 2

Core Assessment Resources

Assessment Handbook

- **Unit 5 Assessment Overview,** pages 84–91
- **Unit 5 Assessment Masters,** pages 175–179
- **Unit 5 Individual Profiles of Progress,** pages 262, 263, and 302
- **Unit 5 Class Checklists,** pages 264, 265, and 303
- **Math Logs,** pages 306–308
- **Exit Slip,** page 311
- **Other Student Assessment Forms,** pages 304, 305, 309, and 310

Assessment Management Spreadsheets

The Assessment Management Spreadsheets consist of the Digital Class Checklists and Individual Profile of Progress Checklists. Use them to monitor, record, and report student progress.

Addressing All Needs

Differentiated Instruction

Adjusting the Activity – suggests adaptations that target advanced learners, English language learners, or learners who need additional instructional support.

ELL SUPPORT / **ELL** – provides lesson-specific suggestions to help English language learners understand and process the mathematical content.

READINESS – accesses students' prior knowledge or previews content that prepares students to engage in the lesson's Part 1 activities.

EXTRA PRACTICE – provides additional opportunities to apply the mathematical content of the lesson.

ENRICHMENT – enables students to apply or further explore the mathematical content of the lesson.

Lesson	Adjusting the Activity	ELL Support/ ELL	Readiness	Extra Practice	Enrichment
5•1	•	•	•		•
5•2	•	•	•	•	•
5•3		•	•		•
5•4		•	•	•	•
5•5	•	•	•	•	
5•6			•	•	•
5•7	•		•		•
5•8		•	•	•	•
5•9		•	•	•	
5•10			•	•	•
5•11	•		•		•
5•12				•	•

Additional Resources

Differentiation Handbook
Provides ideas and strategies for differentiating instruction.
Pages 78–84

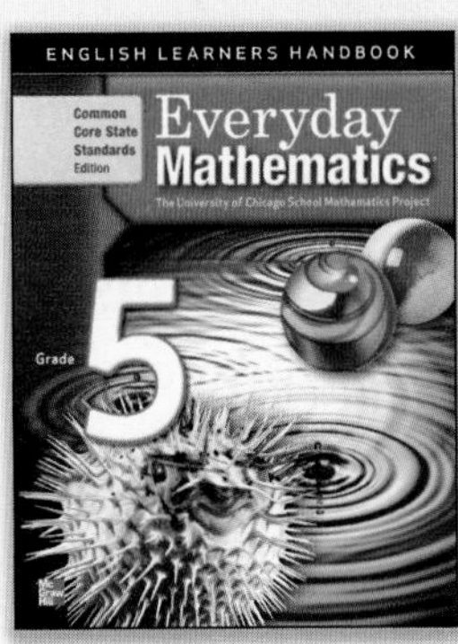

English Learners Handbook
Contains lesson-specific comprehension strategies.
Pages 37–48

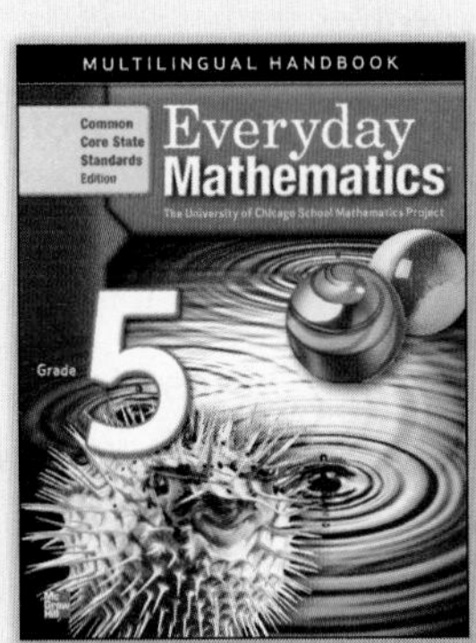

Multilingual Handbook
Previews concepts and vocabulary. It is written in six languages.
Pages 73–96

Planning Tips

Multiage Classroom

Companion Lessons from Grades 4 and 6 can help you meet instructional needs of a multiage classroom. The full Scope and Sequence can be found in the Appendix.

Grade 4	7•1	7•1	4•3, 7•1	7•7	4•2, 7•8	4•3, 7•8	4•4, 7•8	9•4, 9•5		1•7	1•7	
Grade 5	**5•1**	**5•2**	**5•3**	**5•4**	**5•5**	**5•6**	**5•7**	**5•8**	**5•9**	**5•10**	**5•11**	**5•12**
Grade 6	4•1		4•4, 4•5	4•1				4•9		3•9	3•9	

Pacing for Success

Pacing depends on a number of factors, such as students' individual needs and how long your school has been using *Everyday Mathematics*. At the beginning of Unit 5, you may want to use tools available at www.everydaymathonline.com to help you set your pace.

Home Support

Unit 5 Family Letter (English/Spanish) provides families with an overview, Do-Anytime Activities, Building Skills through Games, a list of vocabulary, and answers to the daily homework (Study Links). Family Letters in English, Spanish, and seven other languages are also available online.

Study Links are the daily homework assignments. They consist of active projects and ongoing review problems.

Home Support Resources

Home Connection Handbook
Offers ideas and reproducible masters for communicating with families. See Table of Contents for unit information.

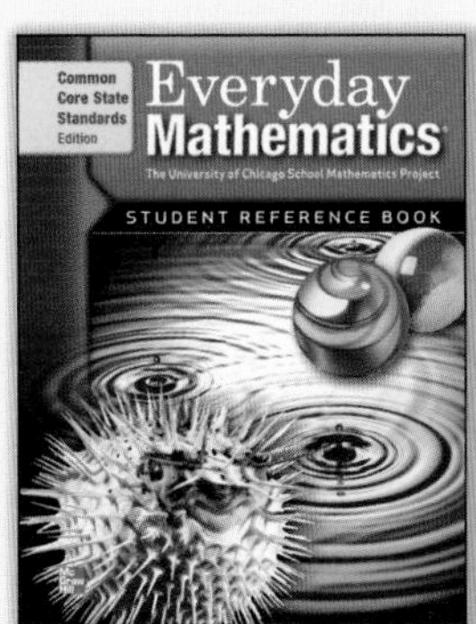

Student Reference Book
Provides a resource for students and parents.

Pages 57, 58, 78C, 78D, 88, 102–105, 259–262, 266, 304, 306, 309–311, 313, 316, 325, 327, 360–362

Technology Resources

Materials

www.everydaymathonline.com

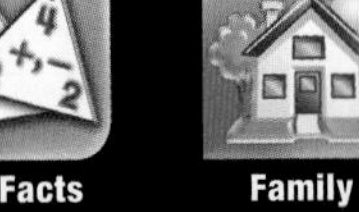

ePresentations | eToolkit | Algorithms Practice | EM Facts Workshop Game™ | Family Letters | Assessment Management | Common Core State Standards | Curriculum Focal Points | Interactive Teacher's Lesson Guide

Lesson	Masters	Manipulative Kit	Other Items
5•1	Teaching Aid Master, p. 414 Study Link Master, p. 125 Teaching Master, p. 126	slate	Class Data Pad; per group: 20 counters; scissors; envelope*
5•2	Study Link Master, p. 127 Teaching Masters, pp. 128 and 129	pattern blocks; slate	Geometry Template*; Class Data Pad; per group: 24 counters; yellow, red, blue, and green colored pencils, crayons, or markers*
5•3	Transparency of *Math Masters,* p. 137 Study Link Master, p. 131 Teaching Master, p. 130 *Differentiation Handbook*, p. 142	slate	Geometry Template or ruler; Fraction Cards; 6 strips of colored paper, each 2" by $8\frac{1}{2}$"
5•4	Teaching Aid Master, p. 414 Study Link Master, p. 132 Game Master, p. 454 or 455 Teaching Master, p. 133	Everything Math Deck	Geometry Template; Class Data Pad; per group: 70 counters; calculator
5•5	Transparency of *Math Masters,* p. 424* Study Link Master, p. 134 Teaching Masters, pp. 135 and 136	base-10 blocks*; slate	calculator
5•6	Transparencies of *Math Masters,* pp. 137, 138, and 141 Study Link Master, p. 139 Game Master, p. 493 Teaching Masters, pp. 140 and 141	4 each of number cards 0–9; slate	straightedge
5•7	Game Masters, pp. 472, 474, 478*, and 482* Transparency of *Math Masters,* p. 472* Study Link Master, p. 142	per group: 4 each of number cards 0–10; slate	per group: counters (2 colors or pennies); calculator
5•8	Study Link Master, p. 143 Game Masters, pp. 467, 468, 472, and 476 Teaching Master, p. 144 Teaching Aid Master, p. 425 *Differentiation Handbook,* p. 142	per group: 4 each of number cards 0–10	overhead calculator*; per group: counters; calculator
5•9	Study Link Master, p. 145 Teaching Master, p. 146 *Differentiation Handbook,* p. 149	4 each of number cards 0–10; slate	Class Data Pad; poster board*; string; masking tape; ruler; paper circles; calculator
5•10	Teaching Master, p. 147 Teaching Aid Masters, pp. 426 and 427* Transparencies of *Math Masters,* pp. 147 and 426 Study Link Masters, pp. 148 and 149		Geometry Template; Probability Meter; stick-on note; compass; calculator
5•11	Teaching Aid Masters, pp. 414*, 426*, 427, and 428 Game Masters, pp. 464–466, and 469 Study Link Master, p. 150		Geometry Template; Class Data Pad*; chalkboard; compass; counters; index cards; per group: masking tape, 12" by 12" paper square
5•12	Study Link Master, p. 151 Teaching Master, p. 152	number cards 0–9; slate	Geometry Template; Class Data Pad; sample bar graphs; calculator
5•13	Assessment Masters, pp. 175–179 Study Link Masters, pp. 153–156	slate	

*Denotes optional materials

Mathematical Background

The discussion below highlights the major content ideas presented in Unit 5 and helps establish instructional priorities.

Rational Numbers and Their Notations

(Lessons 5•1–5•4)

The emphasis of this program with respect to fractions, decimals, and percents may be different from that of other fifth-grade mathematics programs you may have used in the past. The emphasis is based on the fact that fractions, decimals, and percents have emerged as interchangeable notations for "rational numbers."

Every society throughout history has invented verbal counting, counting words, and counting systems. Many societies went beyond verbal counting to invent symbol systems for writing and calculating with whole numbers, including zero. As commerce and trade developed, many societies found that measures of length, capacity, and weight often needed numbers between whole numbers to express parts of whole measures. For this reason, people invented written notations for these "in-between numbers"—some with symbols that we recognize as precursors to fraction notation and some that we see as precursors to decimal notation. In the relatively recent development of mathematics, the rules for equivalence, order, and operations have been organized into what is called "the rational number system."

To find out more about rational numbers and their notations, refer to Sections 9.3 and 9.4 of the *Teacher's Reference Manual.*

1
2
3
4
5
6
7
8
9
10

In 3000 B.C., the Babylonians developed a base-60 positional system for numbers. Their notation used different combinations of a unit symbol and a ten symbol to represent the system's 59 "digits."

Equivalence and Conversions among Fractions, Decimals, and Percents (Lessons 5•5–5•8)

Fraction and decimal notation systems invented in ancient times had ways of expressing order and equivalence within systems, but equivalencies between fraction and decimal notation systems (including endlessly repeating decimals) have been fully understood only in modern times. We now know that the three modern notations for rational numbers—fractions, decimals, and percents—are interchangeable. Any rational number written in one of these ways can be written in the other two ways, often by considering a fraction as a division problem, which is easily done with a calculator (Lesson 5-8).

There are, however, practical difficulties in converting from one notation system to another, since many fractions written as decimals go on forever in a repeating pattern—such as $\frac{1}{3} = 0.333... = 0.\overline{3}$. This endless repetition poses no difficulty when going from fractions to decimals. We generally use a calculator for the division and then round the resulting decimal (which may be part of an endlessly repeating decimal) to however many significant figures we want. It is, however, more difficult to go from a repeating decimal such as $0.090909 = 0.\overline{09}$ to its fraction equivalent ($\frac{1}{11}$), and *Everyday Mathematics* does not address this problem in the fifth grade program.

Project Note

Use Project 5, How Would You Spend $1,000,000? to have students research and plan how to spend a million dollars and to practice converting between fractions, decimals, and percents, while analyzing and displaying data.

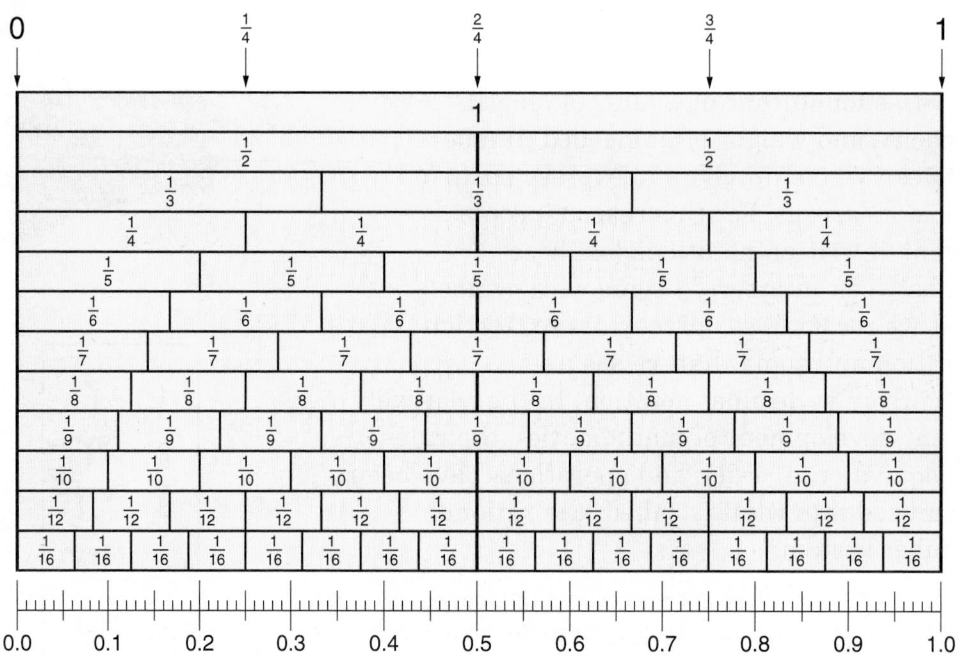

The Fraction-Stick Chart is one of the tools used to help students convert fractions to decimals.

Section 9.3 of the *Teacher's Reference Manual* contains more information on equivalence and conversions among fractions, decimals, and percents.

Circle Graphs and the Percent Circle

(Lessons 5•9–5•11)

Circle graphs are effective visual displays for certain kinds of information and are among the most common statistical displays encountered in newspapers and magazines. Circle graphs are often called "pie graphs" and are said to show how the "pie" is divided.

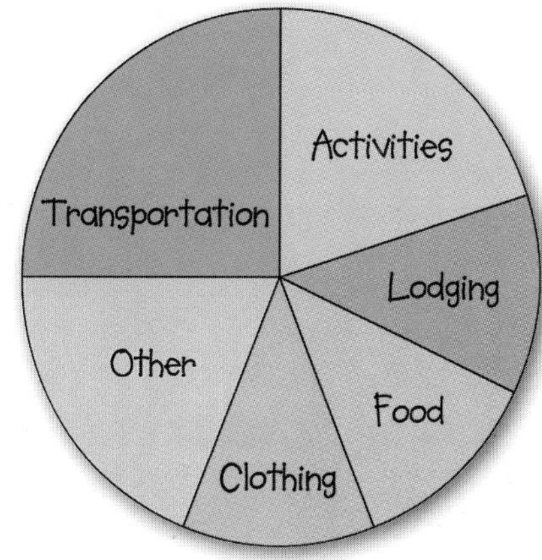

Preparing information for a circle graph involves expressing parts as fractions of a whole and then applying the fraction-to-percent conversion skills emphasized in these lessons. One then decides what part of 360° is needed to represent each part as a slice (sector) of the pie (circle) graph.

A protractor is used to draw angles that represent parts of a whole as parts of a full 360° rotation. Doing this over and over gets tedious (as does converting fractions to percents without a calculator), so the authors suggest using the Percent Circle, which is on the Geometry Template and also on *Math Masters,* pages 426 and 427 (ready to be cut out). The Percent Circle is like a full-circle protractor, except that the circumference is marked with percents instead of degrees. You might want to practice using the Percent Circle before the lessons in which students use it.

Refer to Section 14.11.2 of the *Teacher's Reference Manual* for more information about circle graphs and the Percent Circle.

American Tour: School Days

(Lesson 5•12)

The American Tour continues as students read the article "School" in the American Tour section of the *Student Reference Book.* They answer questions that require them to interpret information about school attendance over the past 200 years. They also compare their skills with those of previous generations by solving problems that illustrate the changing emphases in mathematics instruction.

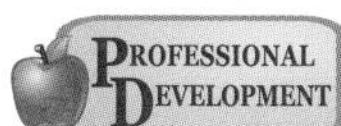

For more information about the American Tour, look in Section 1.2.7 of the *Teacher's Reference Manual.*

5•1 Fraction Review

Objectives To review key fraction concepts; to provide practice with solving parts-and-whole problems and finding fractional parts of whole numbers; and to interpret a fraction as division.

Technology Resources www.everydaymathonline.com

ePresentations

eToolkit

Algorithms Practice

EM Facts Workshop Game™

Family Letters

Assessment Management

Common Core State Standards

Curriculum Focal Points

Interactive Teacher's Lesson Guide

1 Teaching the Lesson

Key Concepts and Skills

- Find fractions of a set and find the whole based on a known fraction of a set. [Number and Numeration Goal 2]
- Find equivalent names for a fraction of a set. [Number and Numeration Goal 5]
- Interpret a fraction as division of the numerator by the denominator. [Operations and Computation Goal 3]
- Identify and use unit fractions to solve problems. [Operations and Computation Goal 7]

Key Activities

Students review the uses of and notations for fractions, solve parts-and-whole problems, and find fractional parts of whole numbers. They identify fractions around them in the classroom and create displays for the Fractions, Decimals, and Percents Museum.

Ongoing Assessment: Informing Instruction See page 293.

Ongoing Assessment: Recognizing Student Achievement Use Exit Slip (*Math Masters,* p. 414). [Operations and Computation Goal 7]

Key Vocabulary

whole (ONE, or unit) ◆ denominator ◆ numerator ◆ unit fraction

Materials

Math Journal 1, pp. 121–122
Student Reference Book, pp. 57, 58, 78C, 78D, and 102–105 ◆ *Math Masters,* p. 414
slate ◆ Class Data Pad ◆ per partnership: 20 counters

2 Ongoing Learning & Practice

Playing *Fraction Top-It*
Student Reference Book, p. 316
Math Journal 2, Activity Sheets 5–7
scissors ◆ envelope (optional)
Students practice comparing fractions.

Math Boxes 5•1
Math Journal 1, p. 123
Students practice and maintain skills through Math Box problems.

Study Link 5•1
Math Masters, p. 125
Students practice and maintain skills through Study Link activities.

3 Differentiation Options

READINESS
Reviewing Whole-Number Relationships in Number Stories
Math Masters, p. 126
Students explore relationships between fractions of a set and a whole to solve number stories.

ENRICHMENT
Exploring Relationships in Number Stories
Math Masters, p. 126
Students identify whole-number, fraction, and mixed-number relationships to solve a number story.

ELL SUPPORT
Discussing the Fractions, Decimals, and Percents Museum
Students select items from the display and describe what they represent or how they use numbers.

Advance Preparation

For Part 1, prepare a display area for the classroom Fractions, Decimals, and Percents Museum.
For Part 2, students will need to cut out and store the Fraction Cards from *Math Masters,* pages 462 and 463.

***Teacher's Reference Manual,* Grades 4–6** pp. 19, 52, 60–74

Getting Started

Mental Math and Reflexes

●○○ An hour is what fraction of a day? $\frac{1}{24}$

A minute is what fraction of an hour? $\frac{1}{60}$

A second is what fraction of a minute? $\frac{1}{60}$

●●○ $\frac{1}{2}$ hour is how many minutes? 30

$\frac{3}{4}$ of an hour is how many minutes? 45

$\frac{1}{3}$ of an hour is how many minutes? 20

●●● $\frac{1}{6}$ of an hour is how many minutes? 10

$\frac{1}{5}$ of an hour is how many minutes? 12

Four days is what fraction of a week? $\frac{4}{7}$

11 months is what fraction of a year? $\frac{11}{12}$

Math Message

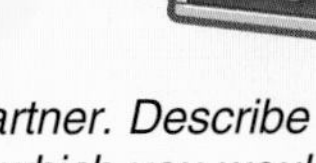

Work with a partner. Describe 2 situations in which you would use fractions.

1 Teaching the Lesson

Interactive whiteboard-ready ePresentations are available at www.everydaymathonline.com to help you teach the lesson.

Math Message Follow-Up

WHOLE-CLASS DISCUSSION

ELL

Partners share their situations. List them on the Class Data Pad. Use follow-up questions to highlight basic fraction ideas.

▷ Fractions were invented to express numbers that are between whole numbers.

▷ Fractions can show measures between whole numbers on rulers and scales.

▷ Fractions can name part of a whole object (for example, part of a cake or pizza).

▷ Fractions can name part of a collection of objects (for example, part of the eggs in a carton).

▷ Most fractions are fractions of something. That something is referred to as the **whole,** the **ONE,** or with measurements as the **unit.**

Pose the following situation to the class: *If I give you half of my CD collection, how many CDs will I have left?* Most students will recognize that there is not enough information to answer the question. Emphasize that when fractions name parts of something, their meaning depends on the whole. You can understand a fraction only if you can identify the whole. The answer to the question posed above depends on how many CDs are in the whole collection.

Use the "whole box" as a reminder of the whole, or the ONE, while students are working with fractions. To support English language learners, write *whole* on the board and provide some examples.

Whole

A "whole box" or "unit box"

▶ Reviewing Basic Fraction Ideas

(*Student Reference Book,* pp. 57 and 58)

Fractions can be written vertically as $\frac{a}{b}$, or horizontally as *a/b*. The number below (or to the right of) the fraction bar is called the **denominator.** The denominator names the number of equal parts into which the whole is divided. The number above (or to the left of) the fraction bar is called the **numerator.** The numerator names the number of parts under consideration.

Fractions in which the denominator and the numerator are the same number are equivalent to 1. Ask: *Why is this true?* The number of equal parts named by the numerator is the same as the number of equal parts named by the denominator that make the whole. Write these key ideas on the board to support English language learners.

Language Arts Link Students may be interested in knowing that the bar separating numerator from denominator is called a *vinculum*, from the Latin *vinci*, meaning *to bind.*

Refer students to pages 57 and 58 in the *Student Reference Book* and to any relevant situations on the Class Data Pad list to review additional uses of fractions.

- ▷ A fraction may represent division. For example, $\frac{3}{4}$ is another way of saying 3 divided by 4; 3 ÷ 4; $4\overline{)3}$; or 3/4.
- ▷ Fractions can express probability. For example, the chance that a die will land with 3 up is 1 out of 6, or $\frac{1}{6}$.
- ▷ Fractions are used to compare two quantities as ratios: 1 out of 2 students in the class is a boy, so $\frac{1}{2}$ of the students are boys; or rates, the car's gas mileage is $\frac{100 \text{ miles}}{4 \text{ gallons}}$.

Adjusting the Activity

Use the definitions and examples on pages 102–105 of the *Student Reference Book* to clarify the use of fractions to represent comparisons in ratios and rates.

AUDITORY ◆ KINESTHETIC ◆ TACTILE ◆ VISUAL

Links to the Future

Fraction concepts will continue to be developed and practiced throughout the year. Unit 8 further develops fractions and ratios. Unit 12 expands this work to rates and proportions.

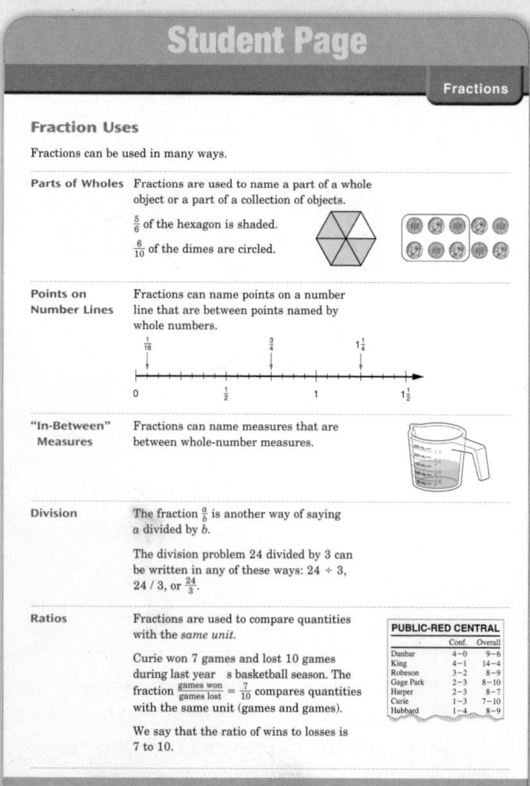

Student Page

Fractions

Fraction Uses

Fractions can be used in many ways.

Parts of Wholes Fractions are used to name a part of a whole object or a part of a collection of objects.

$\frac{5}{6}$ of the hexagon is shaded.

$\frac{6}{10}$ of the dimes are circled.

Points on Number Lines Fractions can name points on a number line that are between points named by whole numbers.

"In-Between" Measures Fractions can name measures that are between whole-number measures.

Division The fraction $\frac{a}{b}$ is another way of saying *a* divided by *b*.

The division problem 24 divided by 3 can be written in any of these ways: 24 ÷ 3, 24 / 3, or $\frac{24}{3}$.

Ratios Fractions are used to compare quantities with the *same unit.*

Curie won 7 games and lost 10 games during last year s basketball season. The fraction $\frac{\text{games won}}{\text{games lost}} = \frac{7}{10}$ compares quantities with the same unit (games and games).

We say that the ratio of wins to losses is 7 to 10.

PUBLIC-RED CENTRAL	Conf.	Overall
Dunbar	4–0	9–6
King	4–1	14–4
Robeson	3–2	8–9
Gage Park	2–3	8–10
Harper	2–3	8–7
Curie	1–3	7–10
Hubbard	1–4	8–9

Student Reference Book, p. 57

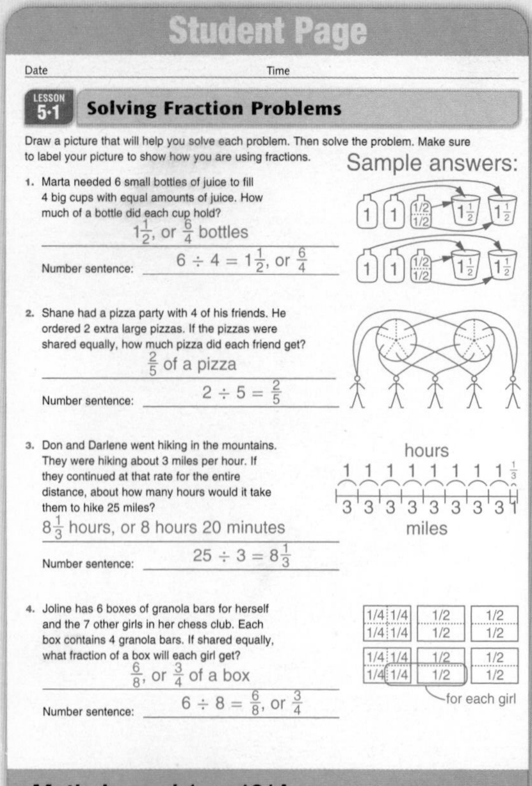

Student Page

Date Time

LESSON 5·1 **Solving Fraction Problems**

Draw a picture that will help you solve each problem. Then solve the problem. Make sure to label your picture to show how you are using fractions.

Sample answers:

1. Marta needed 6 small bottles of juice to fill 4 big cups with equal amounts of juice. How much of a bottle did each cup hold?
   $1\frac{1}{2}$, or $\frac{6}{4}$ bottles
   Number sentence: $6 \div 4 = 1\frac{1}{2}$, or $\frac{6}{4}$
2. Shane had a pizza party with 4 of his friends. He ordered 2 extra large pizzas. If the pizzas were shared equally, how much pizza did each friend get?
   $\frac{2}{5}$ of a pizza
   Number sentence: $2 \div 5 = \frac{2}{5}$
3. Don and Darlene went hiking in the mountains. They were hiking about 3 miles per hour. If they continued at that rate for the entire distance, about how many hours would it take them to hike 25 miles?
   $8\frac{1}{3}$ hours, or 8 hours 20 minutes
   Number sentence: $25 \div 3 = 8\frac{1}{3}$
4. Joline has 6 boxes of granola bars for herself and the 7 other girls in her chess club. Each box contains 4 granola bars. If shared equally, what fraction of a box will each girl get?
   $\frac{6}{8}$, or $\frac{3}{4}$ of a box
   Number sentence: $6 \div 8 = \frac{6}{8}$, or $\frac{3}{4}$

Math Journal 1, p. 121A

▶ Introducing Fractions as Division

WHOLE-CLASS ACTIVITY

Read the following problem to students, and ask them to think about how they might solve it.

> *Julia came home from school to find 3 fresh homemade lemon squares. She had 3 girlfriends with her. The 4 friends decided to share the 3 lemon squares equally. How much of a whole lemon square did each girl get to eat?*

Have partners discuss and solve the problem. Invite them to draw pictures to help them find a solution.

When most students have finished, have several volunteers show and describe the strategies they used and the pictures they drew. Have students recreate their drawings on the board. Expect that students may draw pictures like those shown in the margin.

As students share their drawings, encourage them to label the fractional parts of the lemon squares and to tell how much of a lemon square each friend will receive. $\frac{3}{4}$ of a lemon square After several drawings have been presented, if no one has done so, ask students to record a number sentence for the problem. $3 \div 4 = \frac{3}{4}$

▶ Using Fractions to Solve Division Problems

PARTNER ACTIVITY

(*Math Journal 1,* p. 121A; *Student Reference Book,* pp. 78C and 78D)

Have students work on journal page 121A. Emphasize that they should draw pictures to show how they are solving each problem. Have them label the fractional parts in their drawings and record number sentences.

When most of the students have finished, bring them together to discuss what they learned about fractions and division from doing the problems. First have students discuss with a partner, and then share with the class how they think fractions and division are related. Have students refer to *Student Reference Book,* pages 78C and 78D as needed.

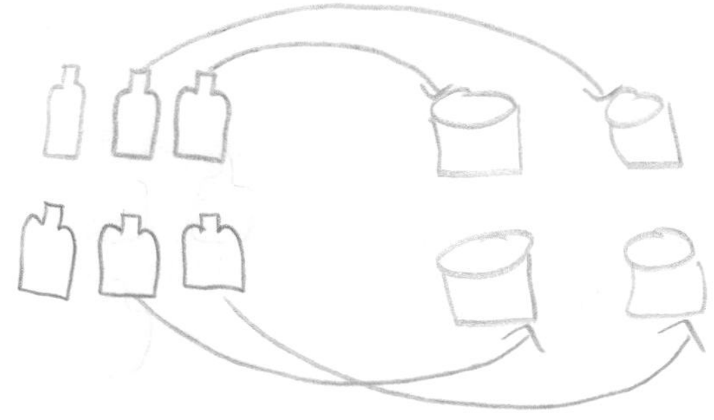

Each friend gets $\frac{1}{2}$ of one lemon square and $\frac{1}{4}$ of one lemon square. So each friend gets $\frac{1}{2} + \frac{1}{4}$, or $\frac{3}{4}$ of a whole lemon square.

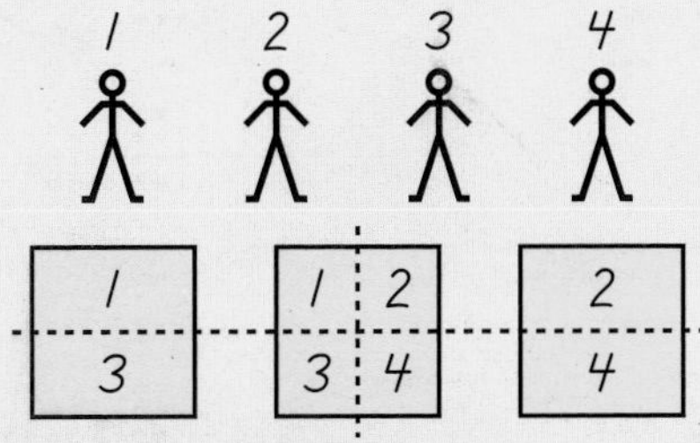

Each friend gets $\frac{1}{4}$ of the 3 lemon squares. This is equivalent to $\frac{3}{4}$ of a whole lemon square.

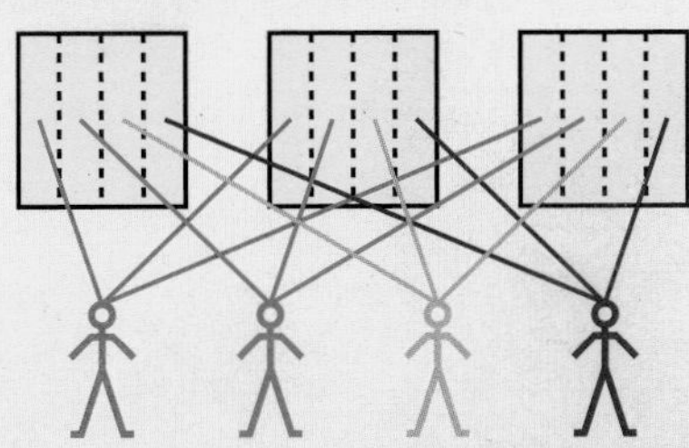

Each lemon square is cut into fourths because there are 4 friends. Each friend is dealt $\frac{1}{4}$ of each lemon square, or $\frac{1}{4} + \frac{1}{4} + \frac{1}{4} = \frac{3}{4}$ in all.

Student Page

Date　　　　Time

LESSON 5·1 Using Fraction Notation for Division

For each problem below:
- Write each division problem as a fraction.
- Solve the problem.
- Show your work.

Example: Ms. Sanders has 18 packages of paper to divide equally among 4 classes. How many packages will each class get?
Division sentence: $18 \div 4 = ?$　Fraction notation: $\frac{18}{4}$
Solution: $4\frac{2}{4}$, or $4\frac{1}{2}$ packages

$$\begin{array}{r} 4\frac{2}{4} \\ 4\overline{)18} \\ \underline{16} \\ 2 \end{array}$$

1. Jason made pan-sized pancakes for breakfast. Usually his 2 brothers each eat 5 pancakes. Because Jason made them so big, his 2 brothers equally split 5 pancakes. How many pancakes did each brother eat?
   Division sentence: $5 \div 2 = ?$　Fraction notation: $\frac{5}{2}$
   Solution: $2\frac{1}{2}$ pancakes

2. Rita was in charge of providing lemonade to sell at the fair. She supplied 19 large containers of lemonade to fill the empty pitchers at 5 lemonade booths. If each booth got the same amount, how many large containers of lemonade did each booth get?
   Division sentence: $19 \div 5 = ?$　Fraction notation: $\frac{19}{5}$
   Solution: $3\frac{4}{5}$ containers

3. Maurice bought a 3-pack of strawberry cakes. He decided to share them with his 3 best friends. How much strawberry cake did each of the 4 boys get?
   Division sentence: $3 \div 4 = ?$　Fraction notation: $\frac{3}{4}$
   Solution: $\frac{3}{4}$ of a strawberry cake

Try This

4. Daisy had 27 feet of ribbon to make 8 hair ties. If each one was the same length, and there was no ribbon left over, how long was each hair tie?
   Division sentence: $27 \div 8 = ?$　Fraction notation: $\frac{27}{8}$
   Solution: $3\frac{3}{8}$ feet

***Math Journal 1,* p. 121B**

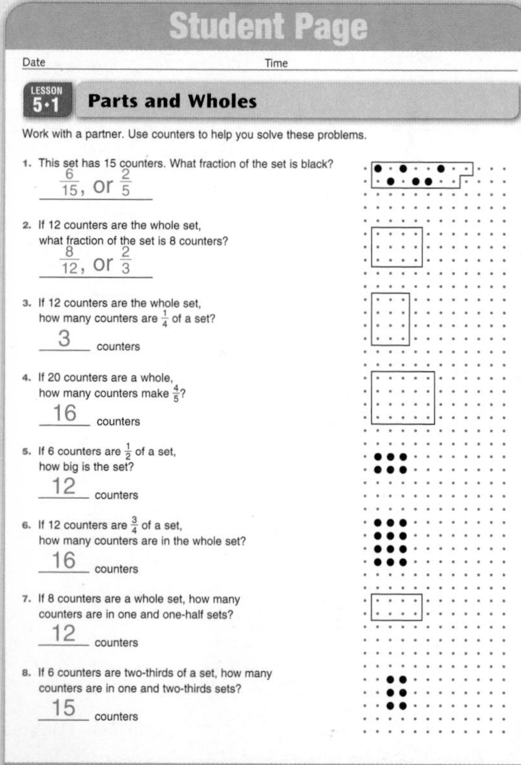

Student Page

Date Time

LESSON 5·1 **Parts and Wholes**

Work with a partner. Use counters to help you solve these problems.

1. This set has 15 counters. What fraction of the set is black? $\frac{6}{15}$, or $\frac{2}{5}$
2. If 12 counters are the whole set, what fraction of the set is 8 counters? $\frac{8}{12}$, or $\frac{2}{3}$
3. If 12 counters are the whole set, how many counters are $\frac{1}{4}$ of a set? 3 counters
4. If 20 counters are a whole, how many counters make $\frac{4}{5}$? 16 counters
5. If 6 counters are $\frac{1}{2}$ of a set, how big is the set? 12 counters
6. If 12 counters are $\frac{3}{4}$ of a set, how many counters are in the whole set? 16 counters
7. If 8 counters are a whole set, how many counters are in one and one-half sets? 12 counters
8. If 6 counters are two-thirds of a set, how many counters are in one and two-thirds sets? 15 counters

Math Journal 1, p. 121

Highlight some of the following points, and record number sentences on the board when appropriate:

- You can write a division problem as a fraction in which the dividend is the numerator and the divisor is the denominator. For example, $3 \div 4$ can also be written as $\frac{3}{4}$.
- You can write a division problem as an improper fraction. For example, $25 \div 3$ can be written as $\frac{25}{3}$.
- The answer to a division problem can be a fraction. For example, when 5 boys equally share 2 pizzas, they each get $\frac{2}{5}$.
- Sometimes it makes sense to answer a division problem with an improper fraction, but sometimes it does not. For example, we might say a cup can hold $\frac{6}{4}$ bottles of juice, but we would not say that it takes $\frac{25}{3}$ hours to hike a trail.
- When you solve division problems with fractions, different pictures can be used to solve the same problem, depending on how you divide or share. For example, 5 boys could equally share 2 pizzas by giving each boy $\frac{2}{5}$ of one of the two pizzas, or each boy could get $\frac{1}{5}$ of each pizza, for a total of $\frac{2}{5}$. (See the sample answer for Problem 2 on journal page 121A.)

▶ Using Fraction Notation for Division

PARTNER ACTIVITY

(*Math Journal 1,* p. 121B)

Remind students that, in the last unit, they used fractions to show the remainder in some division problems. On journal page 121B, students record division problems using fraction notation and then revisit solving the problems and recording the remainder as a fraction. Have partners compare their answers as they work on journal page 121B.

▶ Solving Parts-and-Whole Problems with Fractions

PARTNER ACTIVITY

ELL

PROBLEM SOLVING

(*Math Journal 1,* p. 121)

Distribute about 20 counters to each partnership and explain that there are three types of problems on this journal page.

▷ In Problems 1 and 2, the whole and a part are given; the fraction needs to be named.

▷ In Problems 3, 4, and 7, the whole is given, and the fraction is named; the part needs to be found.

▷ In Problems 5, 6, and 8, a part is given, and the fraction is named; the whole needs to be found.

Student Page

$\frac{9}{12}$	$\frac{0}{5}$	$\frac{2}{6}$	$\frac{1}{2}$
$\frac{3}{5}$	$\frac{3}{4}$	$\frac{4}{10}$	$\frac{2}{8}$
$\frac{10}{10}$	$\frac{4}{6}$	$\frac{3}{12}$	$\frac{5}{5}$
$\frac{2}{10}$	$\frac{8}{12}$	$\frac{1}{4}$	$\frac{5}{10}$

Math Journal 2, Activity Sheet 5 (back)

One important method for solving this third type of problem is to use the concept of **unit fractions.** When a whole is divided into equal parts, the unit fraction has a 1 as its numerator and names one of those equal parts. To support English language learners, write *unit fraction* on the board and list examples. Ask volunteers to name the unit fraction if the whole is divided into 10 parts; 12 parts; 75 parts. $\frac{1}{10}$; $\frac{1}{12}$; $\frac{1}{75}$

The whole (or some other amount) is a multiple of the unit fraction part. Use counters on the overhead to model this example: If $\frac{1}{10}$ of a set is 2 counters, $\frac{2}{10}$ is $2 * 2$, or 4 counters; $\frac{4}{10}$ is $4 * 2$, or 8 counters. Ask: *How many counters are in the whole set?* $10 * 2$, or 20 counters

Have partners complete journal page 121. Circulate and assist, noting which ideas need follow-up discussion.

Ongoing Assessment: Informing Instruction

Watch for students who experience difficulty arranging counters to find the whole from a given fraction. Model this concept using a unit box to organize the information. For example, in Problem 6 the given denominator is 4. Sketch a unit box divided into four sections. Because $\frac{3}{4}$ is 12, use 12 counters to fill three of the sections ($12 \div 3 = 4$). Filling in the fourth section shows that the whole set has 16 counters.

Ask volunteers to explain their answers for the problems. Use follow-up questions to reinforce identifying the unit fraction.

▶ Finding a Fraction of a Whole

PARTNER ACTIVITY

(*Math Journal 1,* p. 122)

Have partners work together to solve the journal page problems.

Ongoing Assessment: Recognizing Student Achievement

Exit Slip

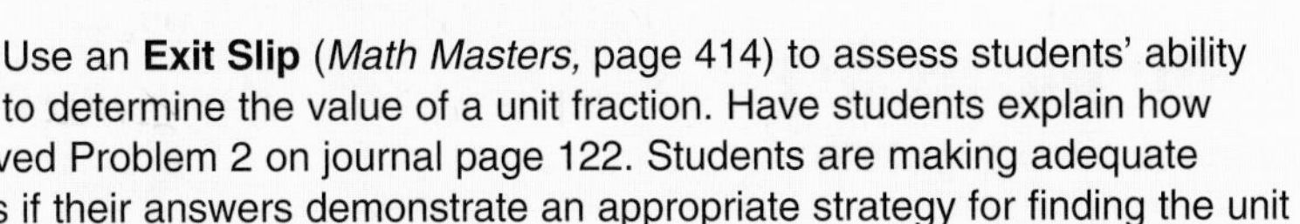

Portfolio Ideas

Use an **Exit Slip** (*Math Masters,* page 414) to assess students' ability to determine the value of a unit fraction. Have students explain how they solved Problem 2 on journal page 122. Students are making adequate progress if their answers demonstrate an appropriate strategy for finding the unit fraction of a set.

[Operations and Computation Goal 7]

Ask volunteers to explain their solutions. Use follow-up questions to reinforce vocabulary and key concepts.

Student Page

$\frac{4}{5}$	$\frac{2}{4}$	$\frac{6}{9}$	$\frac{1}{3}$
$\frac{2}{3}$	$\frac{4}{12}$	$\frac{3}{6}$	$\frac{0}{10}$
$\frac{6}{8}$	$\frac{8}{10}$	$\frac{1}{5}$	$\frac{4}{8}$
$\frac{6}{12}$	$\frac{6}{10}$	$\frac{3}{9}$	$\frac{2}{5}$

Math Journal 2, Activity Sheet 6 (back)

Student Page

$\frac{6}{16}$	$\frac{4}{4}$	$\frac{10}{16}$	$\frac{2}{2}$
$\frac{8}{8}$	$\frac{14}{16}$	$\frac{5}{8}$	$\frac{0}{16}$
$\frac{8}{16}$	$\frac{3}{8}$	$\frac{2}{16}$	$\frac{3}{3}$
$\frac{6}{6}$	$\frac{7}{8}$	$\frac{16}{16}$	$\frac{1}{8}$

Math Journal 2, Activity Sheet 7 (back)

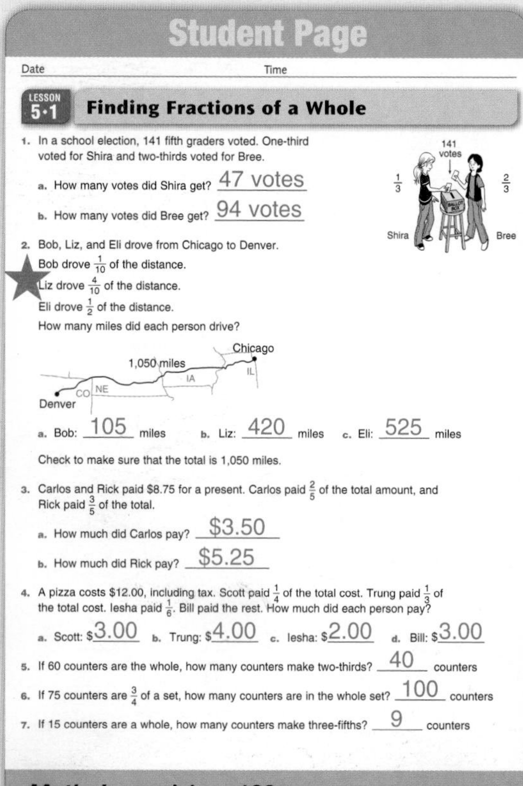
Student Page

Date Time

LESSON 5•1 **Finding Fractions of a Whole**

1. In a school election, 141 fifth graders voted. One-third voted for Shira and two-thirds voted for Bree.
   a. How many votes did Shira get? 47 votes
   b. How many votes did Bree get? 94 votes

2. Bob, Liz, and Eli drove from Chicago to Denver.
   Bob drove $\frac{1}{10}$ of the distance.
   Liz drove $\frac{4}{10}$ of the distance.
   Eli drove $\frac{1}{2}$ of the distance.
   How many miles did each person drive?

   a. Bob: 105 miles b. Liz: 420 miles c. Eli: 525 miles
   Check to make sure that the total is 1,050 miles.
3. Carlos and Rick paid $8.75 for a present. Carlos paid $\frac{2}{5}$ of the total amount, and Rick paid $\frac{3}{5}$ of the total.
   a. How much did Carlos pay? $3.50
   b. How much did Rick pay? $5.25
4. A pizza costs $12.00, including tax. Scott paid $\frac{1}{4}$ of the total cost. Trung paid $\frac{1}{3}$ of the total cost. Iesha paid $\frac{1}{6}$. Bill paid the rest. How much did each person pay?
   a. Scott: $3.00 b. Trung: $4.00 c. Iesha: $2.00 d. Bill: $3.00
5. If 60 counters are the whole, how many counters make two-thirds? 40 counters
6. If 75 counters are $\frac{3}{4}$ of a set, how many counters are in the whole set? 100 counters
7. If 15 counters are a whole, how many counters make three-fifths? 9 counters

Math Journal 1, p. 122

- ▷ In Problem 1, focus on the unit fraction $\frac{1}{3}$. A set of 141 (votes) must be divided into thirds. Conceptually, this is the same as dividing 15 counters into 3 equal parts.
- ▷ In Problem 3, $8.75 (or 875 cents) must be divided into fifths. Focus on finding the unit fraction $\frac{1}{5}$. Students divide $8.75 into 5 equal shares.
- ▷ Encourage students to use mental math and friendly numbers strategies to find fractional parts that are easy fractions, such as $\frac{1}{2}$, $\frac{1}{10}$, $\frac{1}{4}$, $\frac{1}{3}$, and $\frac{1}{6}$.

▶ Introducing the Fractions, Decimals, and Percents Museum

SMALL-GROUP ACTIVITY

Ask students to look for classroom examples of fractions. For example, a full box of crayons might represent $\frac{8}{8}$ and a partial box might represent $\frac{3}{8}$. As fractions or situations are identified, add them to the list on the Class Data Pad. Assign small groups to create displays with labels for the fractions section of the museum. Students might add objects to the museum or draw pictures. They might also create a fractions word wall by making posters of vocabulary words with illustrated examples. Display the fractions usage list from the Math Message Follow-up for student reference.

2 Ongoing Learning & Practice

▶ Playing *Fraction Top-It*

SMALL-GROUP ACTIVITY

(*Student Reference Book*, p. 316; *Math Journal 2*, Activity Sheets 5–7)

Students practice comparing fractions by playing *Fraction Top-It*. Students will need to cut out their set of Fraction Cards from *Math Journal 2*, Activity Sheets 5–7 and write in the missing numerator or denominator on each card for this game. Labeled envelopes can be used to store the cards for future use.

NOTE If available, the Everything Math Deck cards can be used instead of the Fraction Cards.

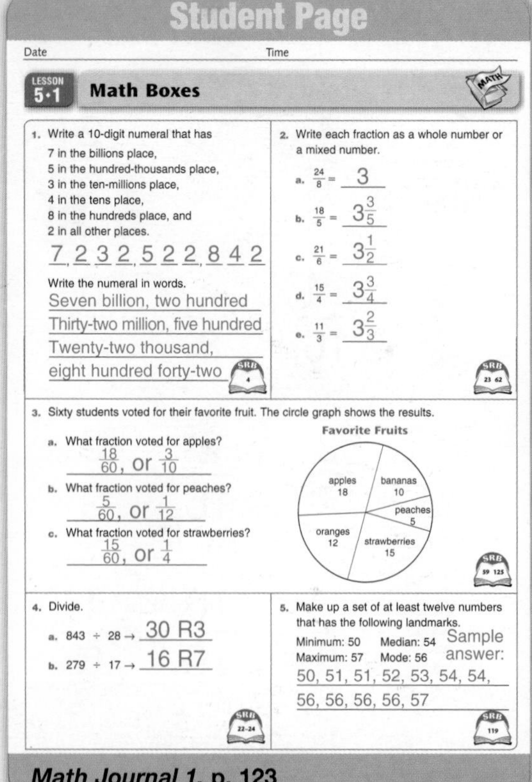
Student Page

Date Time

LESSON 5•1 **Math Boxes**

1. Write a 10-digit numeral that has
   7 in the billions place,
   5 in the hundred-thousands place,
   3 in the ten-millions place,
   4 in the tens place,
   8 in the hundreds place, and
   2 in all other places.
   7, 2 3 2, 5 2 2, 8 4 2
   Write the numeral in words.
   Seven billion, two hundred Thirty-two million, five hundred Twenty-two thousand, eight hundred forty-two
2. Write each fraction as a whole number or a mixed number.
   a. $\frac{24}{8}$ = 3
   b. $\frac{18}{5}$ = $3\frac{3}{5}$
   c. $\frac{21}{6}$ = $3\frac{1}{2}$
   d. $\frac{15}{4}$ = $3\frac{3}{4}$
   e. $\frac{11}{3}$ = $3\frac{2}{3}$
3. Sixty students voted for their favorite fruit. The circle graph shows the results.
   a. What fraction voted for apples? $\frac{18}{60}$, or $\frac{3}{10}$
   b. What fraction voted for peaches? $\frac{5}{60}$, or $\frac{1}{12}$
   c. What fraction voted for strawberries? $\frac{15}{60}$, or $\frac{1}{4}$

4. Divide.
   a. 843 ÷ 28 → 30 R3
   b. 279 ÷ 17 → 16 R7
5. Make up a set of at least twelve numbers that has the following landmarks.
   Minimum: 50 Median: 54
   Maximum: 57 Mode: 56
   Sample answer: 50, 51, 51, 52, 53, 54, 54, 56, 56, 56, 56, 57

Math Journal 1, p. 123

▶ Math Boxes 5•1

INDEPENDENT ACTIVITY

(*Math Journal 1*, p. 123)

Mixed Practice Math Boxes in this lesson are paired with Math Boxes in Lesson 5-3. The skill in Problem 5 previews Unit 6 content.

Study Link 5•1

INDEPENDENT ACTIVITY

(*Math Masters*, p. 125)

Home Connection Students use counters or draw pictures to solve parts-and-whole fraction problems.

Differentiation Options

READINESS

PARTNER ACTIVITY

5–15 Min

Reviewing Whole-Number Relationships in Number Stories

(*Math Masters*, p. 126)

To explore relationships between fractions of a set and a whole, have students solve number story problems. Students use the Data Bank: Whole Numbers to complete *Math Masters*, page 126. They share their solutions with a partner.

ENRICHMENT

PARTNER ACTIVITY

5–15 Min

Exploring Relationships in Number Stories

(*Math Masters*, p. 126)

To explore fraction, whole number, and mixed-number relationships and how these relationships can be used to solve number stories, have students use the Data Bank: Fractions and Mixed Numbers to complete *Math Masters,* page 126. They share their solutions with a partner. Discuss whether there might be more than one way to assign the numbers in this problem and how students decided on their selections.

ELL SUPPORT

SMALL-GROUP ACTIVITY

5–15 Min

Discussing the Fractions, Decimals, and Percents Museum

To provide language support for fractions, decimals, and percents, have students choose two displays from the Fractions, Decimals, and Percents Museum and describe what the numbers represent or how they are used.

Planning Ahead

Remind students to collect examples for the Fractions, Decimals, and Percents Museum.

Study Link Master

Name Date Time

STUDY LINK 5•1 **Parts-and-Whole Fraction Practice**

For the following problems, use counters or draw pictures to help you.

1. If 15 counters are the whole set, how many are $\frac{3}{5}$ of the set? 9 counters
2. If 18 counters are the whole set, how many are $\frac{7}{9}$ of the set? 14 counters
3. If 20 counters are the whole set, what fraction of the set is 16 counters? $\frac{16}{20}$, or $\frac{4}{5}$
4. If 50 counters are the whole set, what fraction of the set is 45 counters? $\frac{45}{50}$, or $\frac{9}{10}$
5. If 35 counters are half of a set, what is the whole set? 70 counters
6. If 12 counters are $\frac{3}{4}$ of a set, what is the whole set? 16 counters
7. Gerald and Michelle went on a 24-mile bike ride. By lunchtime, they had ridden $\frac{5}{8}$ of the total distance.
   How many miles did they have left to ride after lunch? 9 miles
8. Jen and Heather went to lunch. When the bill came, Jen discovered that she had only \$8. Luckily, Heather had enough money to pay the other part, or $\frac{3}{5}$, of the bill.
   a. How much did Heather pay? \$12 b. How much was the total bill? \$20
   c. Explain how you figured out Heather's portion of the bill.
   Sample answer: Jen paid $\frac{2}{5}$ of the bill: $8 \div 2 = 4$ so each fifth of the total was \$4. That means $\frac{3}{5}$ must be \$12, and \$12 + \$8 = \$20.

Practice

9. $3\overline{)42}$ 14
10. $3\overline{)420}$ 140
11. $30\overline{)420}$ 14
12. $30\overline{)4,200}$ 140

Math Masters, p. 125

Teaching Master

Name Date Time

LESSON 5•1 **Birthday Box**

Use only numbers from one data bank below to fill in the missing values for this number story.

Reminder: oz means ounce

For her birthday, Alisha got a box containing 36 or 24 pieces of candy that weighed 73 or $8\frac{3}{4}$ oz. Each piece of candy weighed 2 or $\frac{1}{3}$ oz. She ate 6 or 9 pieces of candy. The remaining 30 or 15 pieces of candy and the box weighed 61 or $5\frac{3}{4}$ oz. The weight of the box is 1 or $\frac{3}{4}$ oz.

1. Read the problem.
2. Think about how the missing values need to relate to each other. Which values should be greater than other values? Which should be less than other values? Are there multiples that can help you?
3. Fill in the missing values.
4. Read the problem again. Make sure the number relationships make sense.

Data Bank: Whole Numbers						
1	2	6	30	36	61	73

Data Bank: Fractions and Mixed Numbers						
$\frac{1}{3}$	$\frac{3}{4}$	$5\frac{3}{4}$	$8\frac{3}{4}$	9	15	24

Math Masters, p. 126

5•2 Mixed Numbers

Objectives To review the whole; and to provide experience with mixed-number and improper fraction concepts.

Technology Resources www.everydaymathonline.com

ePresentations

eToolkit

Algorithms Practice

EM Facts Workshop Game™

Family Letters

Assessment Management

Common Core State Standards

Curriculum Focal Points

Interactive Teacher's Lesson Guide

1 Teaching the Lesson

Key Concepts and Skills

- Find equivalent names for fractions and mixed numbers.
  [Number and Numeration Goal 5]
- Compare fractions and mixed numbers.
  [Number and Numeration Goal 6]
- Add fractions using an area model.
  [Operations and Computation Goal 4]
- Explore the meaning of fractions using an area model to identify parts or the whole.
  [Operations and Computation Goal 7]

Key Activities

Students use pattern blocks to review the role of ONE, and to explore mixed-number concepts. They name, and convert between, mixed numbers and improper fractions.

Ongoing Assessment: Informing Instruction See page 298.

Ongoing Assessment: Recognizing Student Achievement Use journal page 125.
[Operations and Computation Goal 7]

Key Vocabulary

improper fraction ◆ mixed number

Materials

Math Journal 1, pp. 124–126
Study Link 5•1
Class Data Pad ◆ Geometry Template ◆ pattern blocks: 2 yellow hexagons, 2 red trapezoids, 3 blue rhombuses, and 6 green triangles ◆ slate ◆ yellow, red, blue, and green colored pencils, markers, or crayons (optional)

2 Ongoing Learning & Practice

Reviewing Fractions on a Ruler

Math Journal 1, p. 127
Students locate and label fractions and mixed numbers on a ruler and analyze mistakes in the placement of fraction labels on a number line.

Math Boxes 5•2

Math Journal 1, p. 128
Students practice and maintain skills through Math Box problems.

Study Link 5•2

Math Masters, p. 127
Students practice and maintain skills through Study Link activities.

3 Differentiation Options

READINESS

Finding Fractions of a Whole with Pattern Blocks

Math Masters, p. 128
Geometry Template or pattern blocks
Students practice finding fractional parts of a whole using an area model.

ENRICHMENT

Solving Pattern-Block Puzzles

Math Masters, p. 129
Geometry Template or pattern blocks
Students solve puzzles by representing ONE, or a fraction of ONE, with a pattern block and by calculating the value of various designs.

EXTRA PRACTICE

Solving "Fraction-of" Problems

per partnership: 24 counters
Students practice strategies for solving "fraction-of" problems.

Advance Preparation

For Part 1, use overhead pattern blocks, the blocks themselves, or draw the shapes on the board to model the teaching activities. Draw and label examples of the pattern block shapes on the Class Data Pad.

***Teacher's Reference Manual,* Grades 4–6** pp. 60–74

Getting Started

Mental Math and Reflexes

Encourage students to express fractions using several equivalent names, including the simplest form.

What fraction of an hour is...

●○○ 30 minutes? $\frac{30}{60}$, $\frac{15}{30}$, or $\frac{1}{2}$

10 minutes? $\frac{10}{60}$, or $\frac{1}{6}$

15 minutes? $\frac{15}{60}$, or $\frac{1}{4}$

●●○ 45 minutes? $\frac{45}{60}$, or $\frac{3}{4}$

50 minutes? $\frac{50}{60}$, or $\frac{5}{6}$

40 minutes? $\frac{40}{60}$, or $\frac{2}{3}$

How many hours is...

●●● 120 minutes? 2 hours

150 minutes? $2\frac{1}{2}$ hours

90 minutes? $1\frac{1}{2}$ hours

75 minutes? $1\frac{1}{4}$ hours

Math Message

Take the following pattern blocks: 2 yellow hexagons, 2 red trapezoids, 3 blue rhombuses, and 6 green triangles. If a hexagon is worth 1, what are 5 trapezoids worth?

Study Link 5·1 Follow-Up

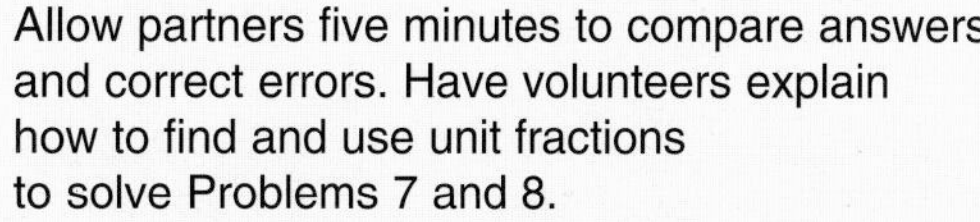

Allow partners five minutes to compare answers and correct errors. Have volunteers explain how to find and use unit fractions to solve Problems 7 and 8.

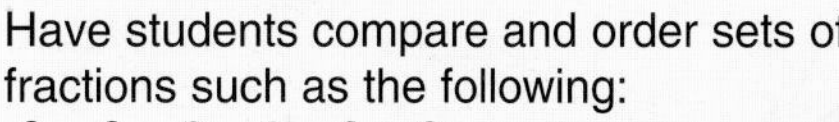

Have students compare and order sets of fractions such as the following: $\frac{9}{14}$, $\frac{8}{13}$, $\frac{2}{32}$ $\frac{2}{32}$, $\frac{8}{13}$, $\frac{9}{14}$

1 Teaching the Lesson

▶ Math Message Follow-Up

Discuss how students found the value of the 5 trapezoids. Probably the most common approach is to find the value of 1 trapezoid by finding how many trapezoids are worth 1 hexagon. 2 trapezoids cover 1 hexagon, so a trapezoid is worth $\frac{1}{2}$ and 5 trapezoids are worth 5 halves or $2\frac{1}{2}$.

Review the importance of the whole, or ONE. To understand a fraction, it is necessary to know what represents the ONE. Half of a personal pizza is not the same as half of an extra-large pizza. To support English language learners, highlight the ONE in each problem discussed.

Pose problems like the following to emphasize that the meaning of fractions depends on what is the whole, or ONE. Keep the pace brisk (these ideas are explored later in this lesson).

- If the triangle is $\frac{1}{3}$, what shape is ONE? trapezoid
- If the triangle is $\frac{1}{3}$, what is the rhombus? $\frac{2}{3}$
- If the rhombus is $\frac{1}{3}$, what shape is ONE? hexagon
- If the rhombus is $\frac{1}{3}$, what is the triangle? $\frac{1}{6}$
- If the triangle is $\frac{1}{2}$, what shape is ONE? rhombus
- If the triangle is $\frac{1}{2}$, what is the trapezoid? $1\frac{1}{2}$, or $\frac{3}{2}$

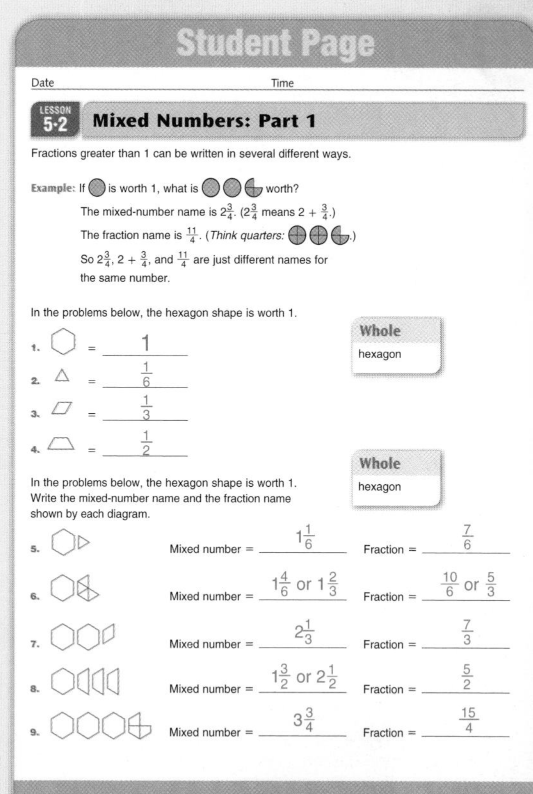

Student Page

Date Time

LESSON 5·2 **Mixed Numbers: Part 1**

Fractions greater than 1 can be written in several different ways.

Example: If ⬤ is worth 1, what is ⬤⬤◔ worth?

The mixed-number name is $2\frac{3}{4}$. ($2\frac{3}{4}$ means $2 + \frac{3}{4}$.)

The fraction name is $\frac{11}{4}$. (*Think quarters:* ⊕⊕◔.)

So $2\frac{3}{4}$, $2 + \frac{3}{4}$, and $\frac{11}{4}$ are just different names for the same number.

In the problems below, the hexagon shape is worth 1.

Whole: hexagon

1. ⬡ = 1
2. △ = $\frac{1}{6}$
3. ▱ = $\frac{1}{3}$
4. ⏢ = $\frac{1}{2}$

In the problems below, the hexagon shape is worth 1. Write the mixed-number name and the fraction name shown by each diagram.

Whole: hexagon

5. Mixed number = $1\frac{1}{6}$ Fraction = $\frac{7}{6}$
6. Mixed number = $1\frac{4}{6}$ or $1\frac{2}{3}$ Fraction = $\frac{10}{6}$ or $\frac{5}{3}$
7. Mixed number = $2\frac{1}{3}$ Fraction = $\frac{7}{3}$
8. Mixed number = $1\frac{3}{2}$ or $2\frac{1}{2}$ Fraction = $\frac{5}{2}$
9. Mixed number = $3\frac{3}{4}$ Fraction = $\frac{15}{4}$

Math Journal 1, p. 124

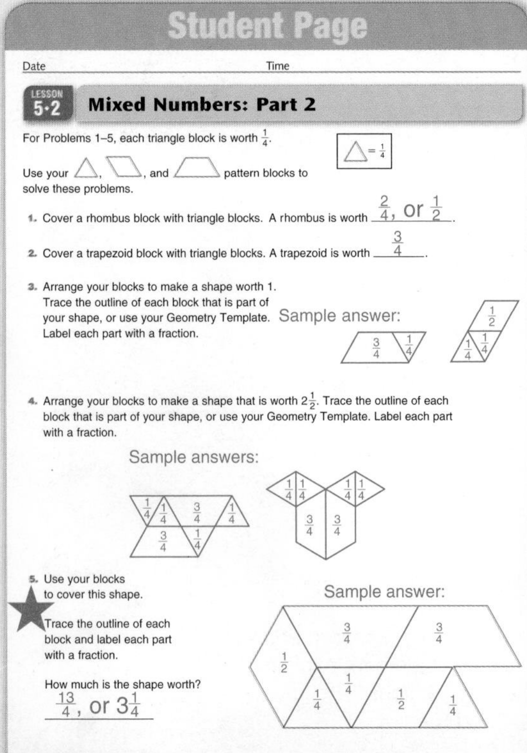

Student Page

Date Time

LESSON 5·2 **Mixed Numbers: Part 2**

For Problems 1–5, each triangle block is worth $\frac{1}{4}$.

Use your △, ▱, and ⏢ pattern blocks to solve these problems.

1. Cover a rhombus block with triangle blocks. A rhombus is worth $\frac{2}{4}$, or $\frac{1}{2}$.
2. Cover a trapezoid block with triangle blocks. A trapezoid is worth $\frac{3}{4}$.
3. Arrange your blocks to make a shape worth 1. Trace the outline of each block that is part of your shape, or use your Geometry Template. Label each part with a fraction. Sample answer:
4. Arrange your blocks to make a shape that is worth $2\frac{1}{2}$. Trace the outline of each block that is part of your shape, or use your Geometry Template. Label each part with a fraction. Sample answers:
5. Use your blocks to cover this shape. Trace the outline of each block and label each part with a fraction. Sample answer:

How much is the shape worth? $\frac{13}{4}$, or $3\frac{1}{4}$

Math Journal 1, p. 125

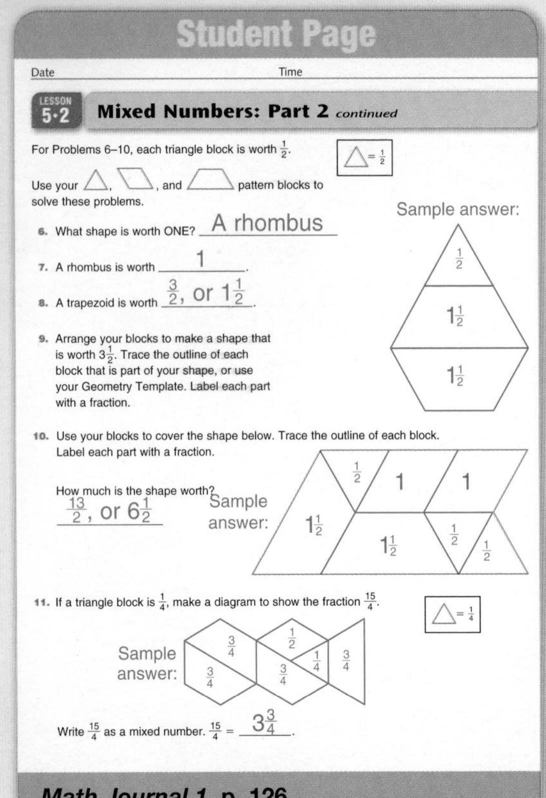

Student Page

Date Time

LESSON 5·2 **Mixed Numbers: Part 2** *continued*

For Problems 6–10, each triangle block is worth $\frac{1}{2}$.

Use your △, ▱, and ⏢ pattern blocks to solve these problems.

6. What shape is worth ONE? A rhombus
7. A rhombus is worth 1.
8. A trapezoid is worth $\frac{3}{2}$, or $1\frac{1}{2}$.
9. Arrange your blocks to make a shape that is worth $3\frac{1}{2}$. Trace the outline of each block that is part of your shape, or use your Geometry Template. Label each part with a fraction. Sample answer:
10. Use your blocks to cover the shape below. Trace the outline of each block. Label each part with a fraction.

How much is the shape worth? $\frac{13}{2}$, or $6\frac{1}{2}$ Sample answer:

11. If a triangle block is $\frac{1}{4}$, make a diagram to show the fraction $\frac{15}{4}$. Sample answer:

Write $\frac{15}{4}$ as a mixed number. $\frac{15}{4}$ = $3\frac{3}{4}$.

Math Journal 1, p. 126

Readiness Wkst.

▶ Using Pattern Blocks to Model Mixed Numbers

Complete a whole box on the Class Data Pad. Announce that for this activity, the hexagon is the whole, or ONE. Cover a hexagon with the remaining shapes, one at a time, on the overhead (or board). Ask volunteers to name the fractional value of each shape and record it on the Class Data Pad for reference.

Hexagon = 1; trapezoid = $\frac{1}{2}$; rhombus = $\frac{1}{3}$; triangle = $\frac{1}{6}$

Whole
hexagon

Ongoing Assessment: Informing Instruction

Watch for students who are unsure about the names of the pattern block shapes. Underline the shape names on the Class Data Pad and have students underline these words on their journal pages with markers, crayons, or pencils the same color as the blocks. For example, the word *trapezoid* would be underlined in red.

Display 8 rhombuses. Ask volunteers for true statements about the fraction $\frac{8}{3}$. Sample answers: The numerator is greater than the denominator; $\frac{8}{3}$ is greater than 1.

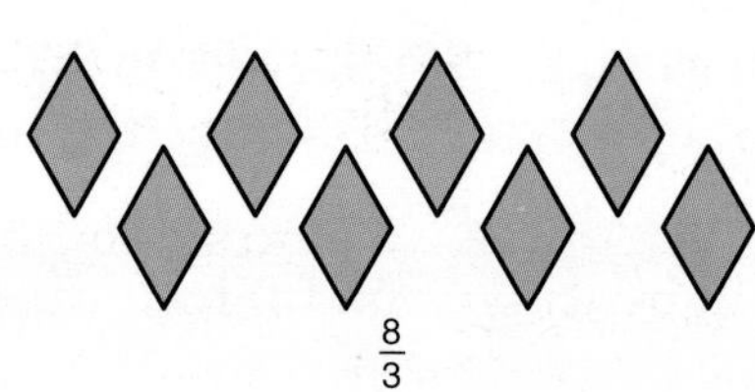

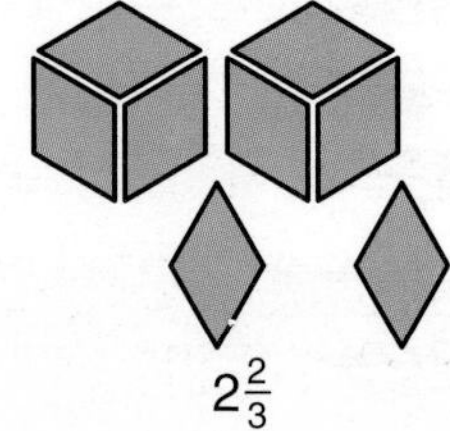

Explain that fractions that are equal to or greater than 1 are often called **improper fractions,** even though there is nothing improper about them. Improper fractions are an acceptable and sometimes preferable form. In algebra, students will often encounter and manipulate fractions written in this way. Write *improper fractions* on the board along with some examples.

Pose mixed numbers such as the following. Have students write equivalent improper fractions on their slates.

- $2\frac{3}{7}$ $\frac{17}{7}$
- $7\frac{3}{8}$ $\frac{59}{8}$
- $3\frac{8}{6}$ $\frac{26}{6}$
- $4\frac{1}{2}$ $\frac{9}{2}$
- $10\frac{4}{5}$ $\frac{54}{5}$

Ask students to name the rhombus display in different ways. Sample answers: $1\frac{5}{3}$, 2 and $\frac{2}{3}$, 2 + $\frac{2}{3}$, 2 wholes and $\frac{2}{3}$, and the mixed number 2 $\frac{2}{3}$ As students give various names for $\frac{8}{3}$, rearrange the rhombuses to model these names. Highlight that $\frac{8}{3} = \frac{3}{3} + \frac{3}{3} + \frac{2}{3} = 2 + \frac{2}{3} = 2\frac{2}{3}$, reinforcing that $\frac{3}{3}$ has a numerator and denominator that are the same number; $\frac{3}{3}$ = 1, or the whole.

Explain that the number $2\frac{2}{3}$ is read as *2 and 2 thirds.* It is called a **mixed number.** Write the term and the example on the board. It represents $2 + \frac{2}{3}$. Mixed numbers are understood to be addition expressions, but when they are written, the addition symbol (+) is not written.

Use other pattern-block displays to practice forming mixed numbers. Ask the class to read each display. For example, rearrange triangles to show $\frac{13}{6}$ and $2\frac{1}{6}$. Rearrange 7 trapezoids to show $\frac{7}{2}$ and $3\frac{1}{2}$. Write each mixed-number example on the board.

Display 3 hexagons and 5 triangles to show $3\frac{5}{6}$. Then discuss the model.

- How should the display be changed to show the same value with a fraction? Replace the 3 hexagons with 18 triangles.
- What is the name of this fraction? $\frac{23}{6}$

Rearrange the display to highlight that $3\frac{5}{6} = \frac{6}{6} + \frac{6}{6} + \frac{6}{6} + \frac{5}{6} = \frac{23}{6}$.

Continue to make other pattern-block displays of mixed numbers using the hexagon to represent the whole, or ONE. For example, display $\frac{9}{2}$ as 4 hexagons and 1 trapezoid.

▶ Modeling Mixed Numbers

PARTNER ACTIVITY

(*Math Journal 1,* p. 124)

Read the example at the top of the page as a class before students start the problems. Partners will need to share their pattern blocks in order to model the problems. Circulate and assist.

Ask volunteers to share their strategies. Highlight that in Problem 8, the display suggests $1\frac{3}{2}$, which can be written as $2\frac{1}{2}$.

The answers $1\frac{3}{2}$, $2\frac{1}{2}$, and $\frac{5}{2}$ are all correct. Encourage students to look for other equivalent mixed numbers.

▶ Changing ONE with Fractions and Mixed Numbers

PARTNER ACTIVITY

(*Math Journal 1,* pp. 125 and 126)

Point out that on these pages, the hexagon is not ONE. Instead, units other than the whole are given. Ask students what they will need to do first before they can begin the problems. Use the unit to establish the ONE and find the value for each pattern-block shape.

Assign partners to work together to complete the problems and questions on journal pages 125 and 126. Circulate and assist.

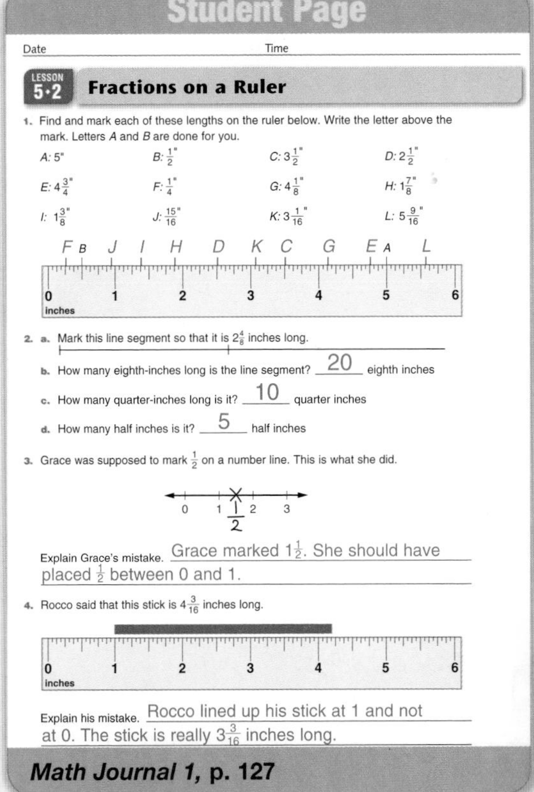
Student Page

Date Time

LESSON 5·2 **Fractions on a Ruler**

1. Find and mark each of these lengths on the ruler below. Write the letter above the mark. Letters *A* and *B* are done for you.

A: 5"	*B:* $\frac{1}{2}$"	*C:* $3\frac{1}{2}$"	*D:* $2\frac{1}{2}$"
E: $4\frac{3}{4}$"	*F:* $\frac{1}{4}$"	*G:* $4\frac{1}{8}$"	*H:* $1\frac{7}{8}$"
I: $1\frac{3}{8}$"	*J:* $\frac{15}{16}$"	*K:* $3\frac{1}{16}$"	*L:* $5\frac{9}{16}$"

2. a. Mark this line segment so that it is $2\frac{4}{8}$ inches long.
   b. How many eighth-inches long is the line segment? 20 eighth inches
   c. How many quarter-inches long is it? 10 quarter inches
   d. How many half inches is it? 5 half inches
3. Grace was supposed to mark $\frac{1}{2}$ on a number line. This is what she did.

Explain Grace's mistake. Grace marked $1\frac{1}{2}$. She should have placed $\frac{1}{2}$ between 0 and 1.

4. Rocco said that this stick is $4\frac{3}{16}$ inches long.

Explain his mistake. Rocco lined up his stick at 1 and not at 0. The stick is really $3\frac{3}{16}$ inches long.

Math Journal 1, p. 127

Adjusting the Activity

For additional practice, write various fractions or mixed numbers on the board or a transparency. Ask students how to represent each number with pattern blocks. For example, write $\frac{11}{6}$. Sample answers: 1 hexagon plus 5 triangles, 11 triangles, or 1 hexagon plus 1 trapezoid and 2 triangles

AUDITORY ◆ KINESTHETIC ◆ TACTILE ◆ VISUAL

Adjusting the Activity

ELL

If students seem uncertain how to begin, have partners make posters similar to the Class Data Pad display. Partners trace the pattern block shapes and show their values, first when a triangle is worth $\frac{1}{4}$ and again showing the triangle as $\frac{1}{2}$. Remind students to include the unit box.

AUDITORY ◆ KINESTHETIC ◆ TACTILE ◆ VISUAL

Student Page

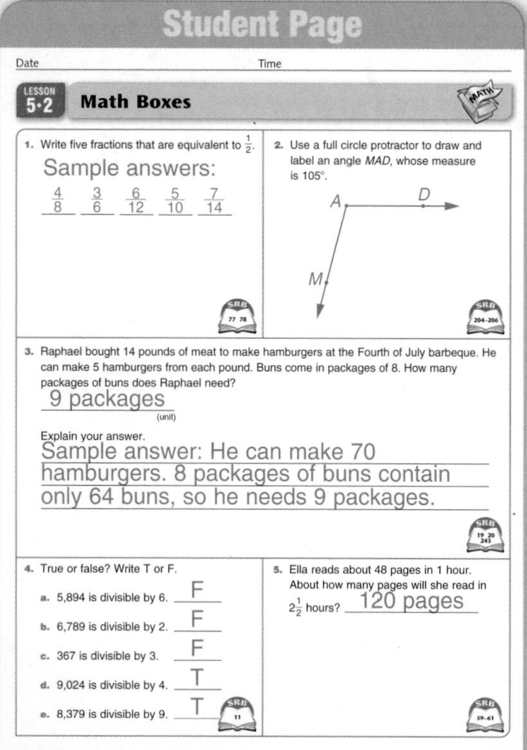
Date Time

LESSON 5·2 **Math Boxes**

1. Write five fractions that are equivalent to $\frac{1}{2}$.
Sample answers:
$\frac{4}{8}$ $\frac{3}{6}$ $\frac{6}{12}$ $\frac{5}{10}$ $\frac{7}{14}$

2. Use a full circle protractor to draw and label an angle *MAD*, whose measure is 105°.

3. Raphael bought 14 pounds of meat to make hamburgers at the Fourth of July barbeque. He can make 5 hamburgers from each pound. Buns come in packages of 8. How many packages of buns does Raphael need?
9 packages (unit)
Explain your answer.
Sample answer: He can make 70 hamburgers. 8 packages of buns contain only 64 buns, so he needs 9 packages.

4. True or false? Write T or F.
a. 5,894 is divisible by 6. F
b. 6,789 is divisible by 2. F
c. 367 is divisible by 3. F
d. 9,024 is divisible by 4. T
e. 8,379 is divisible by 9. T

5. Ella reads about 48 pages in 1 hour. About how many pages will she read in $2\frac{1}{2}$ hours? 120 pages

Math Journal 1, p. 128

Links to the Future

This lesson's informal exploration of fraction addition continues in the fraction-stick activity in Lesson 5-3. Algorithms for fraction operations will be developed in Units 6 and 8.

Study Link Master

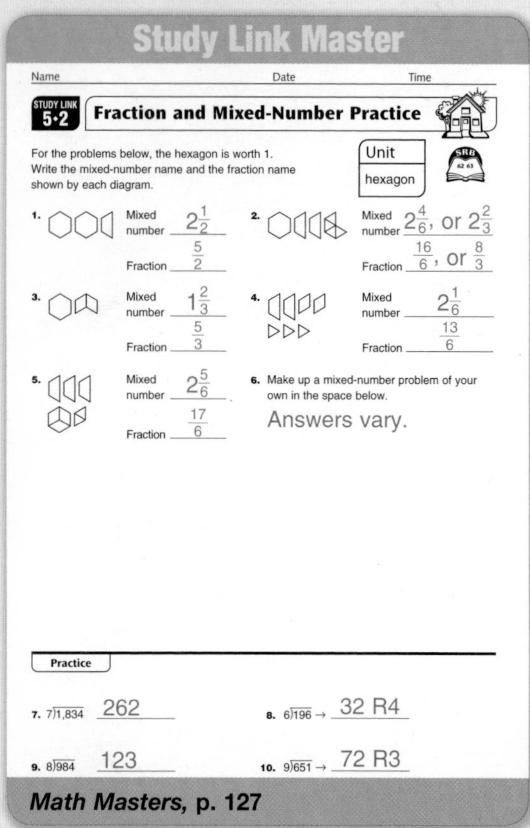
Name Date Time

STUDY LINK 5·2 **Fraction and Mixed-Number Practice**

For the problems below, the hexagon is worth 1. Write the mixed-number name and the fraction name shown by each diagram.

Unit: hexagon

1. Mixed number $2\frac{1}{2}$ Fraction $\frac{5}{2}$
2. Mixed number $2\frac{4}{6}$, or $2\frac{2}{3}$ Fraction $\frac{16}{6}$, or $\frac{8}{3}$
3. Mixed number $1\frac{2}{3}$ Fraction $\frac{5}{3}$
4. Mixed number $2\frac{1}{6}$ Fraction $\frac{13}{6}$
5. Mixed number $2\frac{5}{6}$ Fraction $\frac{17}{6}$
6. Make up a mixed-number problem of your own in the space below.
Answers vary.

Practice

7. 7)1,834 262
8. 6)196 → 32 R4
9. 8)984 123
10. 9)651 → 72 R3

Math Masters, p. 127

With all the problems on these pages, there are many possible combinations of blocks, and most of these combinations can be used to make a variety of shapes. Ask volunteers to share their solutions for Problems 3, 4, 9, and 11 and have them explain how they know their arrangements are correct.

Ongoing Assessment: Recognizing Student Achievement

Journal Page 125 Problem 5

Use **journal page 125, Problem 5** to assess students' ability to find the value of a region based on a defined unit fraction. Students are making adequate progress if they have correctly written the fractions that label each part of the shape.

[Operations and Computation Goal 7]

2 Ongoing Learning & Practice

▶ Reviewing Fractions on a Ruler

PARTNER ACTIVITY

(*Math Journal 1,* p. 127)

Students measure or locate and label fractions and mixed numbers on a ruler and analyze mistakes in the placement of fraction labels on a number line.

When most students have completed the journal page, conclude by asking what is the whole, or ONE, on a ruler. 1 inch Then briefly discuss students' explanations for Problems 3 and 4. Emphasize that remembering the whole helps to avoid errors. Grace would have known that her mark should be between 0 and 1, and Rocco would have counted the wholes and known that he had 3 inches, not 4.

▶ Math Boxes 5·2

INDEPENDENT ACTIVITY

(*Math Journal 1,* p. 128)

Mixed Practice Math Boxes in this lesson are paired with Math Boxes in Lesson 5-4. The skill in Problem 5 previews Unit 6 content.

▶ Study Link 5·2

INDEPENDENT ACTIVITY

(*Math Masters,* p. 127)

Home Connection Students write mixed numbers and improper fractions to represent the values of shapes made with pattern blocks.

3 Differentiation Options

READINESS

 PARTNER ACTIVITY

 15–30 Min

▶ Finding Fractions of a Whole with Pattern Blocks

(*Math Masters,* p. 128)

To explore relationships between fractions using an area model, have students model the relationship between pattern block fractions. Students complete *Math Masters,* page 128. They practice finding fractional parts of a whole with pattern-block shapes.

ENRICHMENT

 INDEPENDENT ACTIVITY

 15–30 Min

▶ Solving Pattern-Block Puzzles

(*Math Masters,* p. 129)

To apply students' understanding of fractions, have them calculate the value of shapes made with pattern blocks. Then they calculate the value of various shapes and designs made from these shapes.

When students have completed the page, discuss how the values of the shapes in their designs would change if they doubled the value of the pattern block representing ONE.

EXTRA PRACTICE

 PARTNER ACTIVITY

 15–30 Min

▶ Solving "Fraction-of" Problems

To practice strategies for solving fraction-of problems, have partners start with 24 counters and count out $\frac{3}{4}$ of them. Ask students to share their strategies and encourage them to try each other's strategies. Expect strategies like the following:

▷ First I separated the 24 counters into four equal groups. I put three of the groups together to get three-fourths.

▷ I organized the 24 counters into an array with four in each row. I pushed three of the four columns together and left the last column. The three columns are three-fourths of the total.

▷ I counted out three counters to the left and one counter to the right. I repeated this until I had counted out all the counters.

Continue to pose problems such as the following:

- Find $\frac{3}{5}$ of 20. 12
- Find $\frac{2}{3}$ of 18. 12
- Find $\frac{5}{6}$ of 30. 25

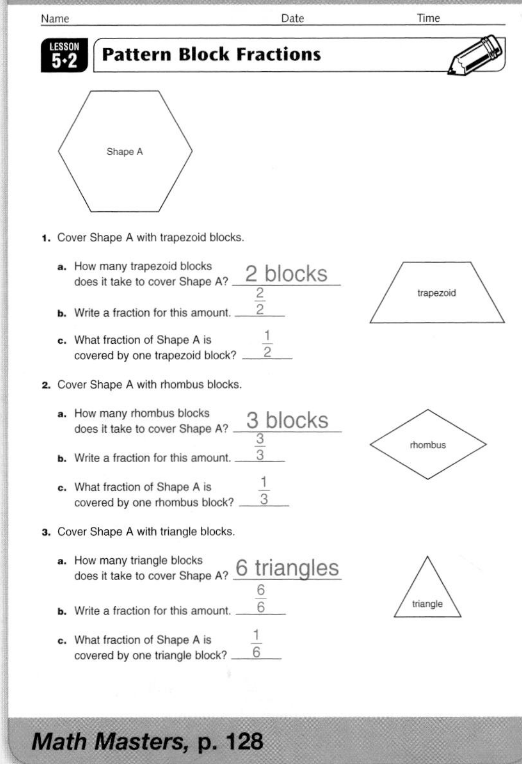

Teaching Master

Name Date Time

LESSON 5·2 **Pattern Block Fractions**

Shape A

1. Cover Shape A with trapezoid blocks.
   a. How many trapezoid blocks does it take to cover Shape A? 2 blocks
   b. Write a fraction for this amount. $\frac{2}{2}$
   c. What fraction of Shape A is covered by one trapezoid block? $\frac{1}{2}$

trapezoid

2. Cover Shape A with rhombus blocks.
   a. How many rhombus blocks does it take to cover Shape A? 3 blocks
   b. Write a fraction for this amount. $\frac{3}{3}$
   c. What fraction of Shape A is covered by one rhombus block? $\frac{1}{3}$

rhombus

3. Cover Shape A with triangle blocks.
   a. How many triangle blocks does it take to cover Shape A? 6 triangles
   b. Write a fraction for this amount. $\frac{6}{6}$
   c. What fraction of Shape A is covered by one triangle block? $\frac{1}{6}$

triangle

Math Masters, p. 128

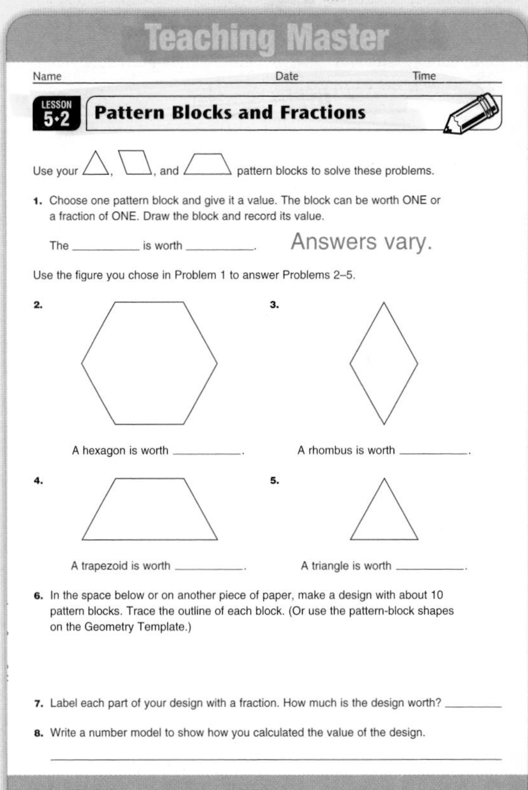

Teaching Master

Name Date Time

LESSON 5·2 **Pattern Blocks and Fractions**

Use your △, ▱, and ⏢ pattern blocks to solve these problems.

1. Choose one pattern block and give it a value. The block can be worth ONE or a fraction of ONE. Draw the block and record its value.

   The ________ is worth ________. Answers vary.

Use the figure you chose in Problem 1 to answer Problems 2–5.

2. A hexagon is worth ________.
3. A rhombus is worth ________.
4. A trapezoid is worth ________.
5. A triangle is worth ________.
6. In the space below or on another piece of paper, make a design with about 10 pattern blocks. Trace the outline of each block. (Or use the pattern-block shapes on the Geometry Template.)
7. Label each part of your design with a fraction. How much is the design worth? ________
8. Write a number model to show how you calculated the value of the design.

Math Masters, p. 129

5·3 Comparing and Ordering Fractions

Objectives To review equivalent fractions; and to provide experience with comparing and ordering fractions.

Technology Resources www.everydaymathonline.com

ePresentations

eToolkit

Algorithms Practice

EM Facts Workshop Game™

Family Letters

Assessment Management

Common Core State Standards

Curriculum Focal Points

Interactive Teacher's Lesson Guide

1 Teaching the Lesson

Key Concepts and Skills

- Find equivalent fractions using a length model. [Number and Numeration Goal 5]
- Compare fractions to the benchmarks 0, $\frac{1}{2}$, and 1. [Number and Numeration Goal 6]
- Order fractions from least to greatest. [Number and Numeration Goal 6]
- Solve fraction number stories using a number-line model. [Operations and Computation Goal 4]
- Use fraction sticks to add fractions. [Operations and Computation Goal 4]

Key Activities

Students use the Fraction-Stick Chart to find equivalent fractions and compare fractions to the benchmarks 0, $\frac{1}{2}$, 1, and $1\frac{1}{2}$. They use the fraction-stick model to compare pairs of fractions, find equivalent fractions, and continue their exploration of fraction addition.

Ongoing Assessment: Recognizing Student Achievement Use journal page 129. [Number and Numeration Goal 6]

Ongoing Assessment: Informing Instruction See page 305.

Key Vocabulary

benchmark ◆ fraction stick ◆ equivalent fractions

Materials

Math Journal 1, pp. 129–132
Study Link 5•2
transparency of *Math Masters,* p. 137 ◆ slate ◆ Geometry Template ◆ straightedge (optional)

2 Ongoing Learning & Practice

Playing *Fraction Top-It*
Student Reference Book, p. 316
Fraction Cards (*Math Journal 2,* Activity Sheets 5–7)
Students practice comparing fractions by playing *Fraction Top-It.*

Math Boxes 5•3
Math Journal 1, p. 133
Students practice and maintain skills through Math Box problems.

Study Link 5•3
Math Masters, p. 131
Students practice and maintain skills through Study Link activities.

3 Differentiation Options

READINESS
Making Fraction Strips
6 strips of colored paper, each 2" by $8\frac{1}{2}$"
Students use a length model to explore comparing and ordering fractions by making fraction strips.

ENRICHMENT
Exploring a Fraction-Stick Chart
Math Masters, p. 130
Students explore relationships between the numerators and denominators of equivalent fractions.

ELL SUPPORT
Building a Math Word Bank
Differentiation Handbook, p. 142
Students add the term *equivalent fractions* to their Math Word Banks.

Advance Preparation

For Part 1, make a transparency of the chart on *Math Masters,* page 137. For the optional Readiness activity in Part 3, each student will need 6 strips of colored paper, each 2" by $8\frac{1}{2}$". These can be prepared ahead of time or during the activity.

***Teacher's Reference Manual,* Grades 4–6** pp. 38, 44, 45, 60–74, 88, 89

Getting Started

Mental Math and Reflexes

Have students use the rulers on their Geometry Templates.

●○○ Find $2\frac{1}{2}$ inches on a ruler. How many half-inches is that? 5

Find 6 cm on a ruler. How many $\frac{1}{2}$ cm is that? 12

●●○ Find $2\frac{4}{8}$ inches on a ruler. How many quarter-inches is that? 10

Find $3\frac{1}{2}$ cm on a ruler. How many $\frac{1}{2}$ cm is that? 7

●●● $\frac{1}{2}$ inch is what fraction of $2\frac{1}{2}$ inches? $\frac{1}{5}$

$\frac{3}{4}$ inch is what fraction of $2\frac{1}{2}$ inches? $\frac{3}{10}$

Math Message

Use the benchmarks 0, $\frac{1}{2}$, and 1 to answer Problems 1–5 on journal page 129.

Study Link 5·2 Follow-Up

Allow students five minutes to compare answers and correct any errors. Have volunteers share their mixed-number problems.

1 Teaching the Lesson

▶ Math Message Follow-Up

WHOLE-CLASS DISCUSSION

(*Math Journal 1,* p. 129)

Remind students that a **benchmark** is a well-known count or measure that can serve as a reference point when estimating. When working with fractions, the benchmarks 0, $\frac{1}{2}$, and 1 are often used. Discuss how students applied their knowledge of numerators, denominators, and benchmarks to tell if each measurement is closest to 0, $\frac{1}{2}$, or 1.

Ongoing Assessment: Recognizing Student Achievement

Journal Page 129 Problem 5

Use **journal page 129, Problem 5** to assess students' understanding of the structure of fractions. Students are making adequate progress if their explanations correctly represent the relationship between the numerator and denominator and the use of benchmarks such as 0, $\frac{1}{2}$, and 1.

[Number and Numeration Goal 6]

▶ Ordering Fractions

PARTNER ACTIVITY

(*Math Journal 1,* p. 129)

On the board or a transparency, draw 4 horizontal lines in a row to order the fractions from Problems 1–4 of the journal page. Volunteers explain which of the Math Message fractions is least and which is greatest. $\frac{1}{8}$ is the least because it is the closest to 0; $\frac{15}{16}$ is the greatest because it is closest to 1. Write these fractions on the first and last lines, respectively. Ask: *Since $\frac{5}{8}$ and $\frac{3}{8}$ are equally close to $\frac{1}{2}$, how do we decide where to write them?* Both fractions are eighths, and 5 is more than 3, which means that $\frac{3}{8}$ is the smaller fraction so it is closer to 0.

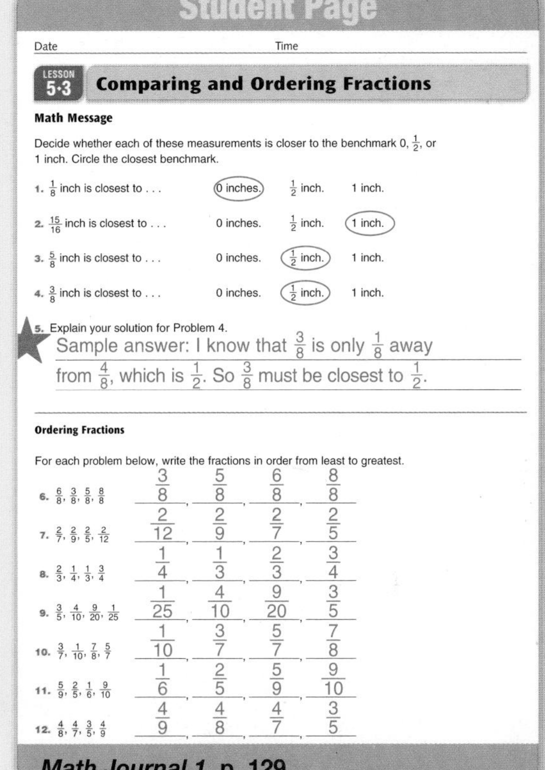

Student Page

Date Time

LESSON 5·3 **Comparing and Ordering Fractions**

Math Message

Decide whether each of these measurements is closer to the benchmark 0, $\frac{1}{2}$, or 1 inch. Circle the closest benchmark.

1. $\frac{1}{8}$ inch is closest to . . . (0 inches.) $\frac{1}{2}$ inch. 1 inch.
2. $\frac{15}{16}$ inch is closest to . . . 0 inches. $\frac{1}{2}$ inch. (1 inch.)
3. $\frac{5}{8}$ inch is closest to . . . 0 inches. ($\frac{1}{2}$ inch.) 1 inch.
4. $\frac{3}{8}$ inch is closest to . . . 0 inches. ($\frac{1}{2}$ inch.) 1 inch.
5. Explain your solution for Problem 4.
Sample answer: I know that $\frac{3}{8}$ is only $\frac{1}{8}$ away from $\frac{4}{8}$, which is $\frac{1}{2}$. So $\frac{3}{8}$ must be closest to $\frac{1}{2}$.

Ordering Fractions

For each problem below, write the fractions in order from least to greatest.

6. $\frac{6}{8}, \frac{3}{8}, \frac{5}{8}, \frac{8}{8}$ — $\frac{3}{8}$, $\frac{5}{8}$, $\frac{6}{8}$, $\frac{8}{8}$
7. $\frac{2}{7}, \frac{2}{9}, \frac{2}{5}, \frac{2}{12}$ — $\frac{2}{12}$, $\frac{2}{9}$, $\frac{2}{7}$, $\frac{2}{5}$
8. $\frac{2}{3}, \frac{1}{4}, \frac{1}{3}, \frac{3}{4}$ — $\frac{1}{4}$, $\frac{1}{3}$, $\frac{2}{3}$, $\frac{3}{4}$
9. $\frac{3}{5}, \frac{4}{10}, \frac{9}{20}, \frac{1}{25}$ — $\frac{1}{25}$, $\frac{4}{10}$, $\frac{9}{20}$, $\frac{3}{5}$
10. $\frac{3}{7}, \frac{1}{10}, \frac{7}{8}, \frac{5}{7}$ — $\frac{1}{10}$, $\frac{3}{7}$, $\frac{5}{7}$, $\frac{7}{8}$
11. $\frac{5}{9}, \frac{2}{5}, \frac{1}{6}, \frac{9}{10}$ — $\frac{1}{6}$, $\frac{2}{5}$, $\frac{5}{9}$, $\frac{9}{10}$
12. $\frac{4}{8}, \frac{4}{7}, \frac{3}{5}, \frac{4}{9}$ — $\frac{4}{9}$, $\frac{4}{8}$, $\frac{4}{7}$, $\frac{3}{5}$

Math Journal 1, p. 129

Student Page

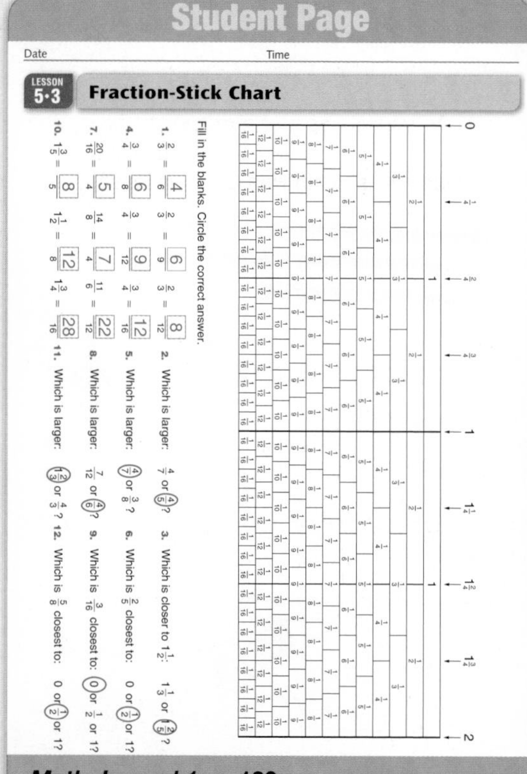
Date Time

LESSON 5·3 **Fraction-Stick Chart**

Fill in the blanks. Circle the correct answer.

Math Journal 1, p. 130

Student Page

Date Time

LESSON 5·3 **Adding with Fraction Sticks**

A whole stick is worth 1. = 1

= 2 halves = 8 eighths

= 4 quarters = 16 sixteenths

1. Use the fraction sticks to find equivalent fractions.

   a. $\frac{1}{8} = \frac{2}{16}$ b. $\frac{6}{8} = \frac{12}{16} = \frac{3}{4}$ c. $\frac{6}{8} = \frac{3}{4} = \frac{12}{16}$

   d. $\frac{1}{2} = \frac{2}{4} = \frac{4}{8} = \frac{8}{16}$ e. $\frac{2}{2} = \frac{4}{4} = \frac{8}{8} = \frac{16}{16}$

2. Use the fraction sticks to add fractions with the same denominator.

   Example: $\frac{1}{8} + \frac{2}{8} = \frac{3}{8}$

   a. $\frac{2}{4} + \frac{1}{4} = \frac{3}{4}$

   b. $\frac{3}{16} + \frac{9}{16} = \frac{12}{16}$, or $\frac{3}{4}$

   c. $\frac{1}{16} + \frac{5}{16} + \frac{8}{16} = \frac{14}{16}$, or $\frac{7}{8}$

3. Use the fraction sticks to add fractions with different denominators.

   a. $\frac{1}{2} + \frac{1}{4} = \frac{3}{4}$

   b. $\frac{1}{2} + \frac{3}{8} = \frac{7}{8}$

   c. $\frac{5}{8} + \frac{1}{4} = \frac{7}{8}$

   d. $\frac{1}{4} + \frac{7}{8} + \frac{2}{16} = \frac{20}{16}$, $1\frac{4}{16}$, or $1\frac{1}{4}$

Math Journal 1, p. 131

Explain that examining numerators and denominators is the first step when comparing and ordering fractions. Refer students to journal page 129.

Examples:

▷ Ask students to describe the fractions in Problem 6. The denominators are the same. So we know that all the unit fractions are the same size. Only the number of pieces (the numerators) need to be compared.

▷ Ask students to describe the fractions in Problem 7. The numerators are the same. Now what do we know? There are the same number of pieces for each fraction. So only the size of the pieces (the denominators) needs to be compared. Remind students that the smaller the denominator is, the larger the piece is.

▷ Ask students to describe the fractions in Problem 8. There are two different denominators; there are two unit fractions. First compare the unit fractions $\frac{1}{3}$ and $\frac{1}{4}$. The smaller denominator is the larger fraction. The remaining fractions are within one piece of 1—that is, $\frac{3}{4}$ is $\frac{1}{4}$ away from 1, and $\frac{2}{3}$ is $\frac{1}{3}$ away from 1. Since $\frac{1}{3}$ is greater than $\frac{1}{4}$, that makes $\frac{2}{3}$ farther away from 1.

Ask partners to complete the problems on the journal page. When most students are finished, discuss their strategies for Problems 9–12, including the following:

▷ Problem 9: The least fraction is $\frac{1}{25}$. That leaves the other three to compare. Change each to an equivalent fraction with a denominator of 20.

▷ Problem 10: One of these fractions is close to 0, one is close to 1, and the other two are close to $\frac{1}{2}$.

▷ Problem 11: One way to compare a fraction to $\frac{1}{2}$ is to see if the numerator is more or less than $\frac{1}{2}$ of the denominator. Two of the fractions are greater than $\frac{1}{2}$. Their order is determined because $\frac{5}{9}$ is close to $\frac{1}{2}$ and $\frac{9}{10}$ is close to 1. Of the two fractions that are less than $\frac{1}{2}$, the denominators are close to each other, and one numerator is 2 times the numerator of the other.

▷ Problem 12: One fraction equals $\frac{1}{2}$ (the numerator is $\frac{1}{2}$ of the denominator). The others are close to $\frac{1}{2}$, and $\frac{4}{9}$ is less than $\frac{1}{2}$. The other two are greater than $\frac{1}{2}$ but only by $\frac{1}{2}$ of a piece each—that is, $\frac{4}{7}$ is $\frac{1}{2}$ of a seventh greater than $\frac{1}{2}$, and $\frac{3}{5}$ is $\frac{1}{2}$ of a fifth greater than $\frac{1}{2}$. Because fifths are greater than sevenths, $\frac{3}{5}$ is greater than $\frac{4}{7}$.

▶ Introducing the Fraction-Stick Chart

(*Math Journal 1*, p. 130; *Math Masters*, p. 137)

Use a transparency of the chart from *Math Masters*, page 137 to demonstrate how to use the Fraction-Stick Chart.

1. Skip-Counting with Fractions

Please refer students to journal page 130. Explain that a **fraction stick** is a model for the whole, or the ONE, that shows unit fractions for the interval between 0 and 1. Each row of the Fraction-Stick Chart combines 2 fraction sticks to show the interval from 0 to 2, divided into unit fractions for a particular denominator.

Example: The third row shows two sticks, each divided into thirds. There are 6 pieces in this row, each labeled $\frac{1}{3}$. The pieces can be used to count by thirds.

2. Finding Equivalent Fractions

The Fraction-Stick Chart on *Math Masters,* page 137 can be used to find **equivalent fractions.** Survey the class for examples of pairs of fractions that name the same part of a whole. Emphasize that these are *equivalent fractions* and list the examples on the board. For example, $\frac{3}{6}$ is equivalent to $\frac{1}{2}$.

Example: Find equivalent fractions for $\frac{2}{3}$.

Step 1: The denominator is 3, so use the thirds stick to locate the fraction $\frac{2}{3}$. Count the pieces from left to right. The right edge of the second piece is $\frac{2}{3}$.

Step 2: Place one edge of a straightedge at $\frac{2}{3}$, that is, along the right edge of the second $\frac{1}{3}$ piece. The straightedge should be parallel to the sides of the Fraction-Stick Chart. Now look for other fraction sticks on the chart along the straightedge.

On the sixths stick, the straightedge touches the right edge of a piece. Count the sixths-stick pieces from left to right. The straightedge is at the end of the fourth piece, which is $\frac{4}{6}$. So $\frac{4}{6}$ is equivalent to $\frac{2}{3}$.

On the ninths stick, the straightedge touches the end of the sixth piece, which is $\frac{6}{9}$. So $\frac{6}{9} = \frac{2}{3}$.

On the twelfths stick, the straightedge touches the end of the eighth piece, which is $\frac{8}{12}$. So $\frac{8}{12} = \frac{2}{3}$. The fractions $\frac{2}{3}$, $\frac{4}{6}$, $\frac{6}{9}$, and $\frac{8}{12}$ are equivalent. They name the same distance on the Fraction-Stick Chart.

On the other sticks, the straightedge cuts through some of the pieces, so $\frac{2}{3}$ cannot be written as an equivalent fraction using the denominator on those sticks.

3. Comparing Fractions

The Fraction-Stick Chart on *Math Masters,* page 137 can be used to compare fractions, for example, compare $\frac{4}{9}$ and $\frac{3}{8}$. *(See margin.)*

Step 1: The denominator of the first fraction is 9, so use the ninths stick to locate $\frac{4}{9}$. Count the pieces from left to right. The right edge of the fourth piece is $\frac{4}{9}$. Place the straightedge along this edge.

NOTE A fraction stick is a narrow rectangle divided into pieces that represents fractions. Sometimes it is helpful to make physical fraction sticks, as in Part 3 of this lesson.

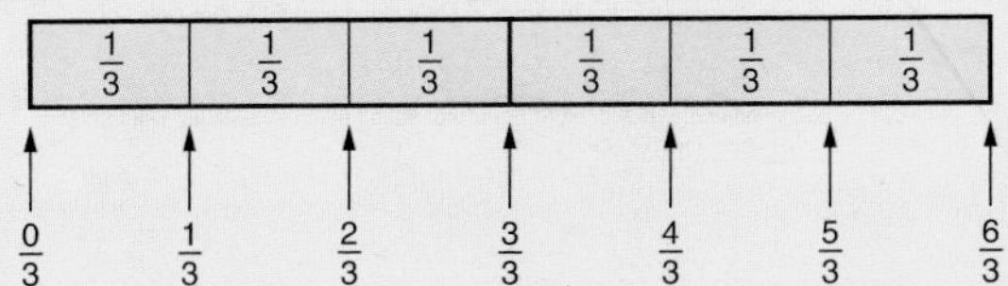

The third row of the Fraction-Stick Chart

Ongoing Assessment: Informing Instruction

Watch for students who confuse the fraction labels with the actual end of the fraction stick. Remind students that the labels are in the center of a portion, not at its end. Have students draw a light pencil line along the straightedge and use the line instead of the straightedge to identify equivalent portions.

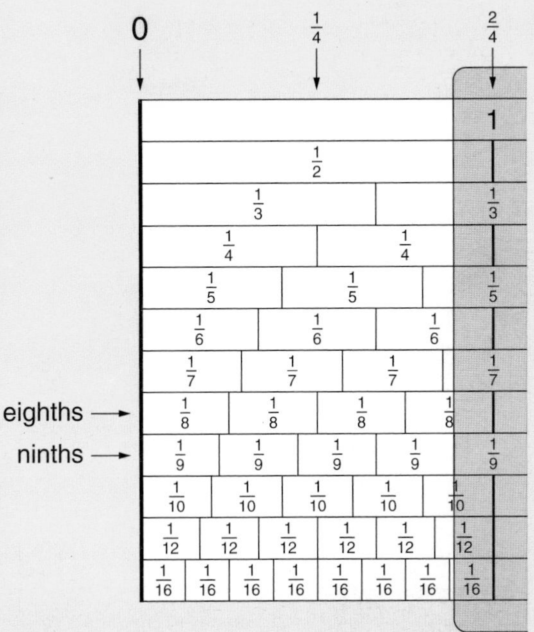

Student Page

Date Time

LESSON 5·3 **Fraction Number Stories**

Shade the fraction sticks to help you solve these fraction number stories.
Write a number model for each story.

1. Chris made pizza dough with $\frac{5}{8}$ cup of white flour and $\frac{1}{4}$ cup of whole wheat flour.
   a. How much flour did he use in all? $\frac{7}{8}$ cup
   b. Number model: $\frac{5}{8} + \frac{1}{4} = \frac{7}{8}$
2. Sheryl's puppy weighed $1\frac{1}{2}$ pounds when it was born. After two weeks, the puppy had gained $\frac{3}{8}$ pounds.
   a. How much did the puppy weigh after two weeks? $1\frac{7}{8}$ pounds
   b. Number model: $1\frac{1}{2} + \frac{3}{8} = 1\frac{7}{8}$
3. Shade the fraction sticks to solve the number model. Then write a fraction number story that fits the number model.
   a. $\frac{3}{4} + \frac{5}{8} =$ $1\frac{3}{8}$
   b. Number story: Answers vary.
4. Make up your own fraction number story. Draw and shade fraction sticks to solve it. Write a number model for your story.
   Answers vary.
   a. Number story: ______
   b. Number model: ______
   c. Solution: ______

Math Journal 1, p. 132

Student Page

Date Time

LESSON 5·3 **Math Boxes**

1. Write a 10-digit numeral that has
   9 in the tens place,
   3 in the millions place,
   5 in the billions place,
   7 in the hundred-millions place,
   1 in the thousands place, and
   6 in all other places.
   5, 7 6 3, 6 6 1, 6 9 6
   Write the numeral in words.
   Five billion, seven hundred sixty-three million, six hundred sixty-one thousand, six hundred ninety-six
2. Write each fraction as a whole number or a mixed number.
   a. $\frac{17}{4} = 4\frac{1}{4}$
   b. $\frac{24}{3} = 8$
   c. $\frac{5}{2} = 2\frac{1}{2}$
   d. $\frac{9}{8} = 1\frac{1}{8}$
   e. $\frac{32}{5} = 6\frac{2}{5}$
3. Where 32 students vacationed, ...
   a. what fraction of the students traveled within their state? $\frac{11}{32}$
   b. what fraction traveled to Europe? $\frac{4}{32}$, or $\frac{1}{8}$
   c. what fraction traveled to Canada or Mexico? $\frac{8}{32}$, or $\frac{1}{4}$

   Vacation Travel: within state 11; stayed home 3; another state 6; Europe 4; Canada or Mexico 8
4. Divide.
   a. $21\overline{)493} \rightarrow$ 23 R10
   b. $35\overline{)623} \rightarrow$ 17 R28
5. Find the following landmarks for this set of numbers: 929, 842, 986, 978, 869, 732, 898, 986, 900, 899, 986, 920, 842
   a. Minimum: 732
   b. Maximum: 986
   c. Mode: 986
   d. Range: 254
   e. Median: 900

Math Journal 1, p. 133

Step 2: Locate $\frac{3}{8}$ (the right edge of the third piece on the eighths stick). Since $\frac{3}{8}$ is to the left of $\frac{4}{9}$, it is less than $\frac{4}{9}$. Conversely, $\frac{4}{9}$ is to the right of $\frac{3}{8}$, so it is greater than $\frac{3}{8}$. Ask partners to complete journal page 130. Ask volunteers to explain their solutions.

▶ Adding with Fraction Sticks

PARTNER ACTIVITY

(*Math Journal 1,* p. 131)

The five fraction sticks at the top of journal page 131 provide a length model for fraction work. Note that the denominators are restricted to 1, 2, 4, 8, and 16. This model will be used to formally introduce the addition of fractions. All these problems can be solved visually. The correct amount of shading for any fraction can be decided by using the appropriate fraction stick at the top of the page.

▶ Solving Fraction Number Stories

INDEPENDENT ACTIVITY

PROBLEM SOLVING

(*Math Journal 1,* p. 132)

Students solve the fraction number stories on journal page 132. Circulate and assist. Encourage students to use the benchmarks 0, $\frac{1}{2}$, and 1 when explaining their solutions and assessing the reasonableness of answers. Discuss the answers and write the strategies on the board.

2 Ongoing Learning & Practice

▶ Playing *Fraction Top-It*

PARTNER ACTIVITY

(*Student Reference Book,* p. 316; *Math Journal 2,* Activity Sheets 5–7)

Students practice comparing fractions by playing *Fraction Top-It*. Students use the Fraction Cards that were stored in Lesson 5-1.

▶ Math Boxes 5·3

INDEPENDENT ACTIVITY

(*Math Journal 1,* p. 133)

Mixed Practice Math Boxes in this lesson are paired with Math Boxes in Lesson 5-1. The skill in Problem 5 previews Unit 6 content.

Writing/Reasoning Have students write a response to the following: *Explain how you converted the fractions to mixed numbers in Problem 2.* Sample answer: For the whole number part, I found how many groups of the denominator were in the numerator. The fraction part was what was left.

Study Link 5·3

INDEPENDENT ACTIVITY

(*Math Masters,* p. 131)

Home Connection Students find equivalent fractions, add fractions, and solve fraction number stories using fraction sticks.

3 Differentiation Options

READINESS

SMALL-GROUP ACTIVITY

15–30 Min

Making Fraction Strips

To explore comparing and ordering fractions using a length model, have students make fraction strips. Students cut 6 strips of paper, each 2" by $8\frac{1}{2}$" and then fold and label them to represent halves, thirds, fourths, fifths, sixths, and eighths. (*See margin.*)

- ▷ To fold into thirds, fold one end in so the doubled parts and the single part are the same size.
- ▷ To fold into sixths, fold a strip into thirds and then in half.
- ▷ For fifths, fold the two outside edges of the strip in toward the middle but not together. Fold them so the doubled parts and the space between them look like three equal parts. Now fold the doubled parts back the other way at the point where the folded ends first came down.

Have students label the fractions on the folds. As they finish, ask students to fold two strips so only the unit fraction shows and then make a comparison statement. *For example,* $\frac{1}{5}$ is less than $\frac{1}{3}$.

ENRICHMENT

PARTNER ACTIVITY

15–30 Min

Exploring a Fraction-Stick Chart

(*Math Masters,* p. 130)

To apply students' understanding of fractions, have them explore the relationships between the numerators and denominators of equivalent fractions. When they finish, have them share one of their discoveries.

ELL SUPPORT

SMALL-GROUP ACTIVITY

15–30 Min

Building a Math Word Bank

(*Differentiation Handbook,* p. 142)

To provide language support for fractions, have students use the Word Bank Template found on *Differentiation Handbook,* page 142. They write the term *equivalent fraction,* draw pictures related to the term, and write other related words. See the *Differentiation Handbook* for more information.

Study Link Master

Name Date Time

STUDY LINK 5·3 **Fraction-Stick Problems**

Shade the fraction sticks to help you find equivalent fractions.

1. $\frac{1}{2} = \frac{4}{8}$
2. $\frac{3}{4} = \frac{12}{16}$
3. $\frac{1}{4} = \frac{2}{8} = \frac{4}{16}$

Shade the fraction sticks to help you solve the addition problems.

4. $\frac{1}{4} + \frac{3}{4} = \frac{4}{4} = 1$
5. $\frac{1}{2} + \frac{2}{8} = \frac{6}{8} = \frac{3}{4}$
6. $\frac{1}{2} + \frac{3}{4} = \frac{5}{4} = 1\frac{1}{4}$

Shade the fraction sticks to help you solve the fraction number stories.

7. Joe was baking a cake. He added $\frac{3}{4}$ cup of white sugar and $\frac{3}{8}$ cup of brown sugar. How much sugar did he use in all?
   $\frac{9}{8}$, or $1\frac{1}{8}$ cups (unit)
8. On the back of this page, write a number story using fractions. Then write a number model to show how you solved it.

Practice

9. $3\overline{)891}$ 297
10. $6\overline{)891}$ → 148 R3
11. $12\overline{)891}$ → 74 R3
12. $24\overline{)891}$ → 37 R3

Math Masters, p. 131

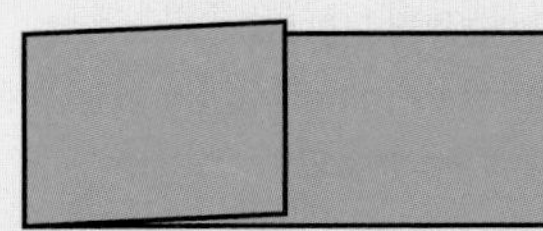

When folded into thirds, the edge of the folded end divides the rest into halves.

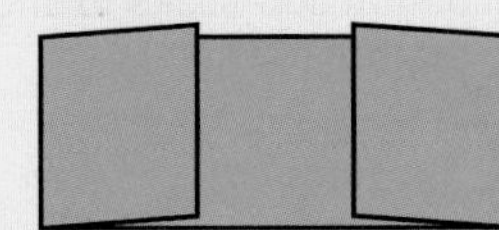

When folded into fifths, the two folded ends are equal in size to the space in the middle.

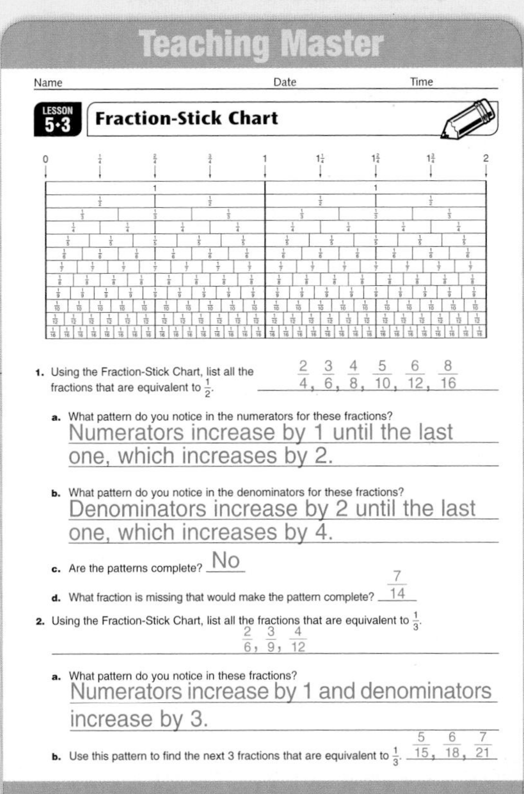

Teaching Master

Name Date Time

LESSON 5·3 **Fraction-Stick Chart**

1. Using the Fraction-Stick Chart, list all the fractions that are equivalent to $\frac{1}{2}$. $\frac{2}{4}, \frac{3}{6}, \frac{4}{8}, \frac{5}{10}, \frac{6}{12}, \frac{8}{16}$
   a. What pattern do you notice in the numerators for these fractions? Numerators increase by 1 until the last one, which increases by 2.
   b. What pattern do you notice in the denominators for these fractions? Denominators increase by 2 until the last one, which increases by 4.
   c. Are the patterns complete? No
   d. What fraction is missing that would make the pattern complete? $\frac{7}{14}$
2. Using the Fraction-Stick Chart, list all the fractions that are equivalent to $\frac{1}{3}$. $\frac{2}{6}, \frac{3}{9}, \frac{4}{12}$
   a. What pattern do you notice in these fractions? Numerators increase by 1 and denominators increase by 3.
   b. Use this pattern to find the next 3 fractions that are equivalent to $\frac{1}{3}$. $\frac{5}{15}, \frac{6}{18}, \frac{7}{21}$

Math Masters, p. 130

5•4 Two Rules for Finding Equivalent Fractions

Objective To introduce multiplication and division rules for finding equivalent fractions.

Technology Resources www.everydaymathonline.com

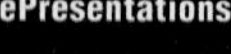
ePresentations

eToolkit

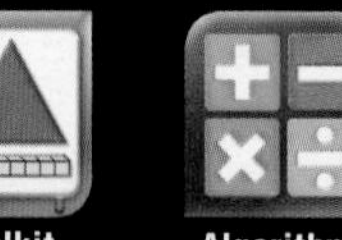

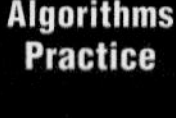
Algorithms Practice

EM Facts Workshop Game™

Family Letters

Assessment Management

Common Core State Standards

Curriculum Focal Points

Interactive Teacher's Lesson Guide

1 Teaching the Lesson

Key Concepts and Skills

- Generate equivalent fractions using a length model.
  [Number and Numeration Goal 5]
- Use and explain multiplication and division rules to find equivalent fractions.
  [Number and Numeration Goal 5]

Key Activities

Students partition fraction sticks to show equivalent fractions. They define a multiplication rule and a division rule for finding equivalent fractions.

Ongoing Assessment: Recognizing Student Achievement Use an Exit Slip (*Math Masters,* page 414).
[Number and Numeration Goal 5]

Key Vocabulary

equivalent fractions

Materials

Math Journal 1, pp. 134 and 135
Study Link 5•3
Math Masters, p. 414
calculator ◆ Class Data Pad

2 Ongoing Learning & Practice

Playing *Factor Captor*
Student Reference Book, p. 306
Math Masters, pp. 454 and 455
calculator ◆ paper and pencil ◆ per partnership: 70 counters
Students practice finding factors of numbers.

Math Boxes 5•4
Math Journal 1, p. 136
Geometry Template
Students practice and maintain skills through Math Box problems.

Study Link 5•4
Math Masters, p. 132
Students practice and maintain skills through Study Link activities.

3 Differentiation Options

READINESS

Exploring Equivalent Fractions
Everything Math Deck
Students explore equivalent fractions using a length model.

ENRICHMENT

Using the Division Rule to Explore Simplest Form
Math Masters, p. 133
Students use the division rule to find equivalent fractions and then identify the simplest form.

EXTRA PRACTICE

5-Minute Math
5-Minute Math™, p. 17
Students find equivalent fractions.

Advance Preparation

For the Mental Math and Reflexes calculator practice, refer to the *Student Reference Book,* pages 259–262 for the TI and Casio key sequences.

***Teacher's Reference Manual,* Grades 4–6** pp. 60–74, 141, 142

Getting Started

Mental Math and Reflexes

Have students practice entering fractions and mixed numbers on a calculator. The key sequences are similar on most calculators: Enter the whole number part and press a key to indicate that you are writing a mixed number. Then enter the numerator and press a key to indicate that you are writing a fraction, and enter the denominator. Then press a key to toggle between fractions and mixed numbers. (*See Advance Preparation.*)

Estimate first. Then display the fraction.

●○○ $2\frac{2}{3}$ $\frac{8}{3}$ ●●○ $1\frac{6}{9}$ $\frac{15}{9}$ ●●● $\frac{26}{3}$ $8\frac{2}{3}$

Estimate first. Then display the mixed number.

●○○ $\frac{41}{9}$ $4\frac{5}{9}$ ●●○ $\frac{203}{2}$ $101\frac{1}{2}$ ●●● $\frac{2,337}{85}$ $27\frac{42}{85}$

Math Message

Jamal has two quarters. Sam has five dimes. Hunter has ten nickels. Elliot has 50 pennies. Write a fraction to show what part of a dollar each person has. Who has the most money?

Study Link 5·3 Follow-Up

Allow students five minutes to compare answers and correct any errors. Have volunteers share their fraction number stories.

1 Teaching the Lesson

Math Message Follow-Up

Ask volunteers to share solutions. Jamal has $\frac{2}{4}$ dollar; Sam, $\frac{5}{10}$ dollar; Hunter, $\frac{10}{20}$ dollar; and Elliot, $\frac{50}{100}$ dollar. Because these fractions each name \$0.50, or $\frac{1}{2}$ of a dollar, everyone has the same amount. Survey the class to name the relationship between those fractions. They are equivalent. Confirm that **equivalent fractions** are defined as two or more fractions that represent the same amount.

Finding Equivalent Fractions

Draw a rectangle on the Class Data Pad to use as a model for fractions. Demonstrate the use of this model to find equivalent fractions. For example, start with a rectangle showing $\frac{2}{3}$.

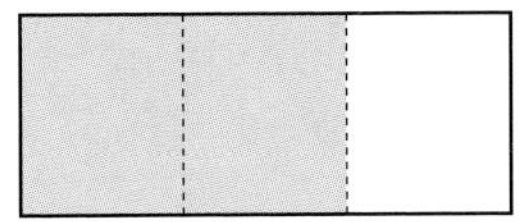

Write the fraction $\frac{2}{3}$ and point out that the whole consists of the 3 parts in the rectangle, and that 2 parts are shaded. Next, draw a horizontal line that divides each part of the rectangle into 2 parts.

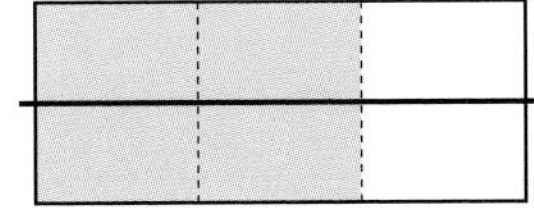

Point out that now the whole consists of the 6 parts in the rectangle and 4 are shaded. Write the fraction $\frac{4}{6}$. Ask: *Has the shaded amount of the rectangle changed?* No Explain that because

> **NOTE** *Everyday Mathematics* students are very familiar with the idea of equivalent names for numbers through their experiences with name-collection boxes and the game *Name That Number* that began in the primary grades.

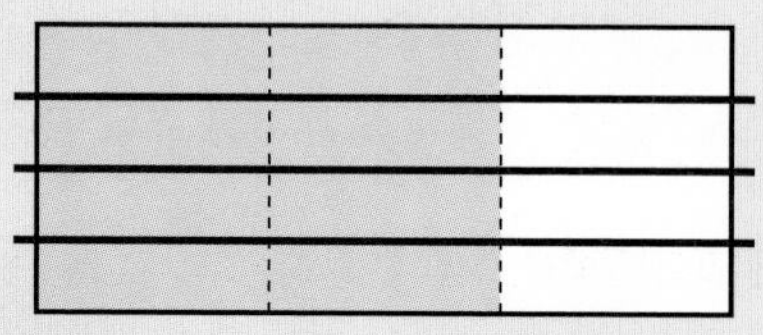

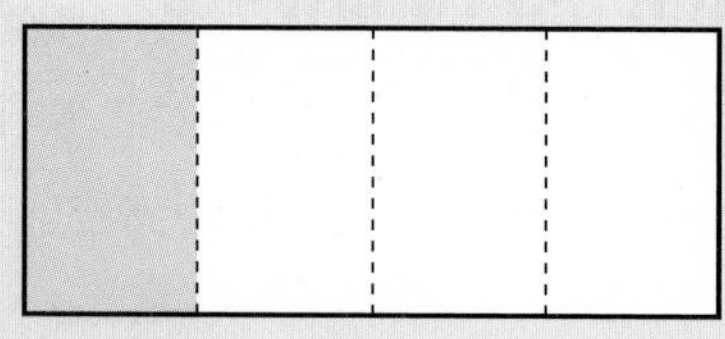

$\frac{1}{4} = \frac{3}{12}$

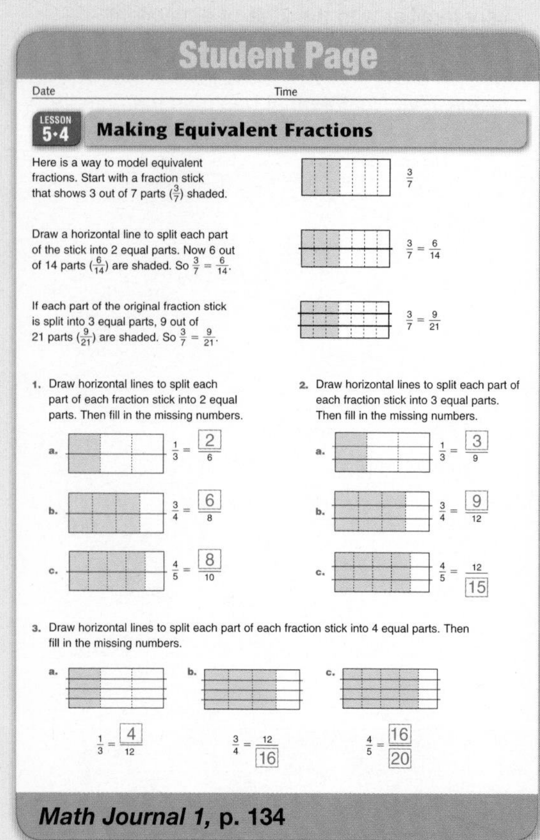

Student Page

Date Time

LESSON 5·4 **Making Equivalent Fractions**

Here is a way to model equivalent fractions. Start with a fraction stick that shows 3 out of 7 parts ($\frac{3}{7}$) shaded. $\frac{3}{7}$

Draw a horizontal line to split each part of the stick into 2 equal parts. Now 6 out of 14 parts ($\frac{6}{14}$) are shaded. So $\frac{3}{7} = \frac{6}{14}$. $\frac{3}{7} = \frac{6}{14}$

If each part of the original fraction stick is split into 3 equal parts, 9 out of 21 parts ($\frac{9}{21}$) are shaded. So $\frac{3}{7} = \frac{9}{21}$. $\frac{3}{7} = \frac{9}{21}$

1. Draw horizontal lines to split each part of each fraction stick into 2 equal parts. Then fill in the missing numbers.

a. $\frac{1}{3} = \frac{2}{6}$

b. $\frac{3}{4} = \frac{6}{8}$

c. $\frac{4}{5} = \frac{8}{10}$

2. Draw horizontal lines to split each part of each fraction stick into 3 equal parts. Then fill in the missing numbers.

a. $\frac{1}{3} = \frac{3}{9}$

b. $\frac{3}{4} = \frac{9}{12}$

c. $\frac{4}{5} = \frac{12}{15}$

3. Draw horizontal lines to split each part of each fraction stick into 4 equal parts. Then fill in the missing numbers.

a. $\frac{1}{3} = \frac{4}{12}$

b. $\frac{3}{4} = \frac{12}{16}$

c. $\frac{4}{5} = \frac{16}{20}$

Math Journal 1, p. 134

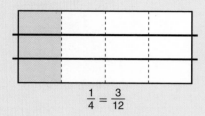

exactly the same amount of the rectangle is shaded, the fractions $\frac{2}{3}$ and $\frac{4}{6}$ are equivalent. Write $\frac{2}{3} = \frac{4}{6}$. Draw two more horizontal lines so that the rectangle is divided into 12 equal parts. (*See margin.*)

Now the whole consists of the 12 parts in the rectangle and 8 are shaded. Write $\frac{8}{12}$. What is the relationship between $\frac{2}{3}$, $\frac{4}{6}$, and $\frac{8}{12}$? They represent the same shaded amount of the rectangle. They are equivalent. Now ask students to draw a rectangle, divide it into fourths with vertical lines, and shade $\frac{1}{4}$ of it. *(See margin.)*

Explain that splitting the rectangle into more equal pieces will show another fraction equivalent to $\frac{1}{4}$. Ask students to draw one or more evenly spaced horizontal lines on the rectangle and identify the fraction of the shaded part. For example, two evenly spaced horizontal lines split the rectangle into 12 pieces and show that $\frac{1}{4} = \frac{3}{12}$. *(See margin.)*

Ask volunteers to draw their rectangles on the Class Data Pad and explain their solutions. Display the labeled drawings in the Fractions, Decimals, and Percents Museum for student reference.

▶ Splitting Fraction Sticks to Make Equivalent Fractions

PARTNER ACTIVITY

(*Math Journal 1,* p. 134)

Assign partners to read the examples at the top of journal page 134 and complete the problems. Circulate and assist. When most students have completed the page, briefly review the answers.

▶ Formulating Rules for Generating Equivalent Fractions

WHOLE-CLASS DISCUSSION

(*Math Journal 1,* p. 134)

Ask students for true statements describing the changes that occurred when they increased the number of parts in the whole. Use follow-up questions to guide students to notice that, for a given unit, whenever the total number of equal parts is doubled (or tripled, or quadrupled), the number of shaded parts is also doubled (or tripled, or quadrupled).

Model the following example on the board or a transparency. Start with a fraction stick representing $\frac{3}{4}$. When each part of the stick is split into two equal parts, the total number of parts is doubled ($4 * 2 = 8$), and the number of shaded parts is also doubled ($3 * 2 = 6$).

Write this as $\frac{3 \text{ shaded} * 2}{4 \text{ total} * 2} = \frac{6 \text{ shaded}}{8 \text{ total}}$ and then as $\frac{3 * 2}{4 * 2} = \frac{6}{8}$.

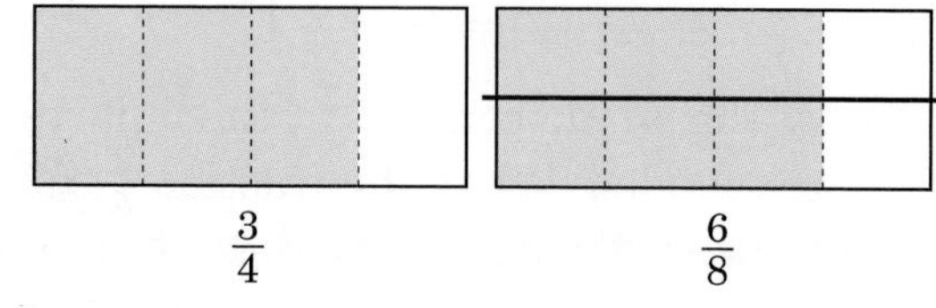

Repeat this strategy for the other fraction-stick models on journal page 134. Ask volunteers to record the fractions for the models on the board.

Models for $\frac{1}{3}$	Models for $\frac{3}{4}$	Models for $\frac{4}{5}$
$\frac{1*2}{3*2} = \frac{2}{6}$	$\frac{3*2}{4*2} = \frac{6}{8}$	$\frac{4*2}{5*2} = \frac{8}{10}$
$\frac{1*3}{3*3} = \frac{3}{9}$	$\frac{3*3}{4*3} = \frac{9}{12}$	$\frac{4*3}{5*3} = \frac{12}{15}$
$\frac{1*4}{3*4} = \frac{4}{12}$	$\frac{3*4}{4*4} = \frac{12}{16}$	$\frac{4*4}{5*4} = \frac{16}{20}$

Write the fractions $\frac{2}{2}$, $\frac{3}{3}$, $\frac{4}{4}$, $\frac{5}{5}$, and $\frac{6}{6}$ on the board or a transparency. Ask students what these fractions have in common and write the important ideas on the board. They have the same number for the numerator and the denominator, so they are equivalent to 1, or the whole. Point out that when students multiplied both the numerator and the denominator by the same number, they were multiplying by another name for 1. Ask: *What important idea do you know about multiplying by 1?* The product of any number and 1 is that number. Multiplying a fraction by another name for 1, renames the fraction, but its value does not change. $\frac{1}{3}$ represents the same amount as $\frac{2}{6}$, $\frac{3}{9}$, $\frac{4}{12}$, and many more fractions.

We can use these ideas to make a rule for finding equivalent fractions using multiplication. Guide students to a phrasing similar to the following.

Multiplication Rule

To find an equivalent fraction, multiply both the numerator and the denominator of the fraction by the same number.

Ask: *What important idea do you know about dividing by 1?* The quotient of any number divided by 1 is that number. Ask: *How might you use division to find equivalent fractions?* Reverse the multiplication and divide both the numerator and the denominator by the same number. Have volunteers demonstrate examples on the board that rename $\frac{3}{9}$, $\frac{6}{8}$, and $\frac{16}{20}$. $\frac{3 \div 3}{9 \div 3} = \frac{1}{3}$, $\frac{6 \div 2}{8 \div 2} = \frac{3}{4}$, $\frac{16 \div 4}{20 \div 4} = \frac{4}{5}$ or $\frac{16 \div 2}{20 \div 2} = \frac{8}{10}$

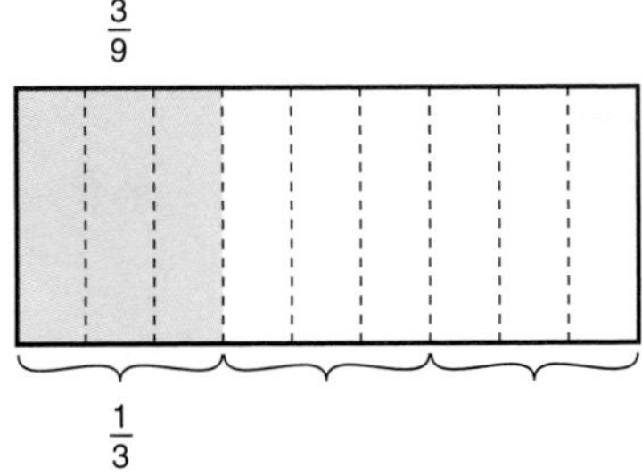

NOTE In general, Everyday Mathematics recommends using "/" to show division, because it reinforces the connection between division and fractions. In working with the division rule for finding equivalent fractions, however, use "÷" instead of "/ " to avoid confusion.

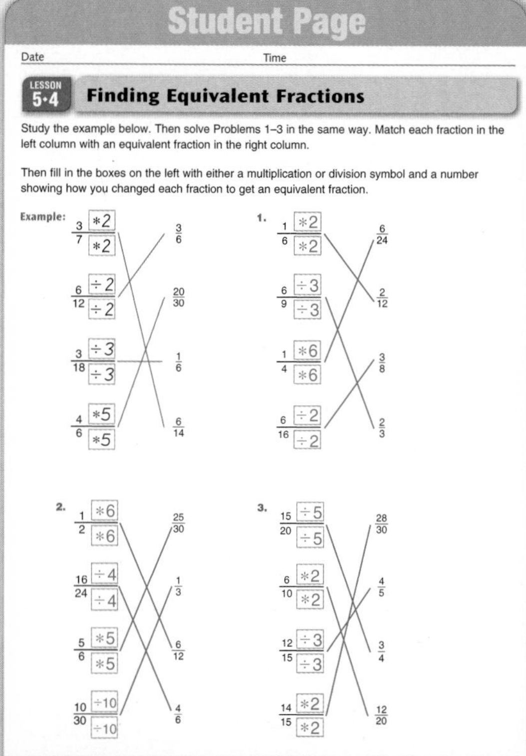
Student Page

Date Time

LESSON 5·4 **Finding Equivalent Fractions**

Study the example below. Then solve Problems 1–3 in the same way. Match each fraction in the left column with an equivalent fraction in the right column.

Then fill in the boxes on the left with either a multiplication or division symbol and a number showing how you changed each fraction to get an equivalent fraction.

Example:

$\frac{3}{7}$	*2	$\frac{3}{6}$
$\frac{6}{12}$	÷2	$\frac{20}{30}$
$\frac{3}{18}$	÷3	$\frac{1}{6}$
$\frac{4}{6}$	*5	$\frac{6}{14}$

1.

$\frac{1}{6}$	*2	$\frac{6}{24}$
$\frac{6}{9}$	÷3	$\frac{2}{12}$
$\frac{1}{4}$	*6	$\frac{3}{8}$
$\frac{6}{16}$	÷2	$\frac{2}{3}$

2.

$\frac{1}{2}$	*6	$\frac{25}{30}$
$\frac{16}{24}$	÷4	$\frac{1}{3}$
$\frac{5}{6}$	*5	$\frac{6}{12}$
$\frac{10}{30}$	÷10	$\frac{4}{6}$

3.

$\frac{15}{20}$	÷5	$\frac{28}{30}$
$\frac{6}{10}$	*2	$\frac{4}{5}$
$\frac{12}{15}$	÷3	$\frac{3}{4}$
$\frac{14}{15}$	*2	$\frac{12}{20}$

Math Journal 1, p. 135

Now we can make a rule for using division. Use follow-up questions to guide students toward a phrasing similar to the following:

Division Rule

To find an equivalent fraction, divide the numerator and the denominator of the fraction by the same number.

▶ Finding Equivalent Fractions

(*Math Journal 1,* p. 135)

Have partners study the example and then solve Problems 1–3 in the same way.

Each problem lists two columns of fractions. Students match each fraction in the first column with an equivalent fraction in the second column and fill in empty boxes to show how fractions were changed to find the equivalents.

NOTE A fraction is said to be in *simplest form* or *lowest terms* if the division rule can't be applied to get an equivalent fraction (with a whole number numerator and denominator). It is traditional to think that fractions in simplest form are preferable, but there is little mathematical justification for this. What is desirable is the ability to shift to whatever form is most convenient for the problem at hand.

Ongoing Assessment: Recognizing Student Achievement

Exit Slip

Portfolio Ideas

Use an **Exit Slip** (*Math Masters,* page 414) to assess students' ability to find equivalent fractions. Give the following prompt: *List three equivalent fractions for $\frac{4}{5}$, and explain how you found them.* Students are making adequate progress if they correctly identify equivalent fractions, and their explanations refer to multiplying the numerator and the denominator by the same number.

[Number and Numeration Goal 5]

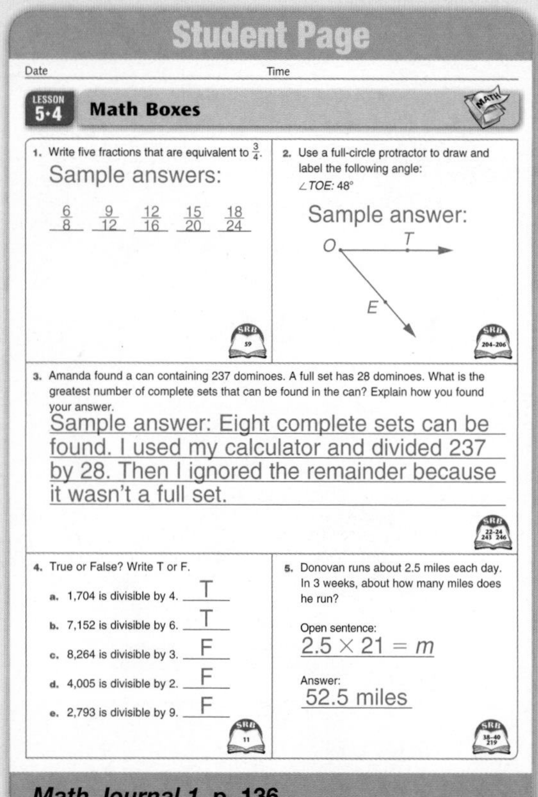
Student Page

Date Time

LESSON 5·4 **Math Boxes**

1. Write five fractions that are equivalent to $\frac{3}{4}$.
Sample answers:
$\frac{6}{8}$ $\frac{9}{12}$ $\frac{12}{16}$ $\frac{15}{20}$ $\frac{18}{24}$

2. Use a full-circle protractor to draw and label the following angle:
∠TOE: 48°
Sample answer:

3. Amanda found a can containing 237 dominoes. A full set has 28 dominoes. What is the greatest number of complete sets that can be found in the can? Explain how you found your answer.
Sample answer: Eight complete sets can be found. I used my calculator and divided 237 by 28. Then I ignored the remainder because it wasn't a full set.

4. True or False? Write T or F.
a. 1,704 is divisible by 4. T
b. 7,152 is divisible by 6. T
c. 8,264 is divisible by 3. F
d. 4,005 is divisible by 2. F
e. 2,793 is divisible by 9. F

5. Donovan runs about 2.5 miles each day. In 3 weeks, about how many miles does he run?
Open sentence: $2.5 \times 21 = m$
Answer: 52.5 miles

Math Journal 1, p. 136

2 Ongoing Learning & Practice

▶ Playing *Factor Captor*

(*Student Reference Book,* p. 306; *Math Masters,* pp. 454 and 455)

Students play *Factor Captor* using Grid 2 or using the 1–110 Grid to practice finding factors and improve fluency with multiplication facts.

▶ Math Boxes 5•4

INDEPENDENT ACTIVITY

(*Math Journal 1,* p. 136)

Mixed Practice Math Boxes in this lesson are paired with Math Boxes in Lesson 5-2. The skill in Problem 5 previews Unit 6 content.

▶ Study Link 5•4

INDEPENDENT ACTIVITY

(*Math Masters,* p. 132)

Home Connection Students calculate or identify equivalent fractions. They complete equivalent fraction pairs by calculating a missing numerator or denominator.

Study Link Master

Name Date Time

STUDY LINK 5•4 **Equivalent Fractions**

If the fractions are equivalent, write = in the answer blank.

If the fractions are not equivalent, write ≠ (not equal to) in the answer blank.

SRB 59

1. $\frac{3}{4}$ = $\frac{9}{12}$
2. $\frac{3}{10}$ ≠ $\frac{1}{5}$
3. $\frac{7}{14}$ ≠ $\frac{8}{15}$
4. $\frac{10}{12}$ = $\frac{5}{6}$
5. $\frac{16}{100}$ = $\frac{8}{50}$
6. $\frac{36}{72}$ = $\frac{1}{2}$
7. $\frac{7}{12}$ = $\frac{21}{36}$
8. $\frac{8}{3}$ = $\frac{16}{6}$

Fill in the boxes to complete and match the equivalent fractions.

Example: $\frac{2}{15} = \frac{6}{45}$

9. $\frac{3}{5} = \frac{6}{10}$
10. $\frac{2}{3} = \frac{14}{21}$
11. $\frac{44}{55} = \frac{4}{5}$
12. $\frac{12}{40} = \frac{3}{10}$
13. $\frac{35}{60} = \frac{7}{12}$
14. $\frac{9}{16} = \frac{45}{80}$
15. $\frac{9}{36} = \frac{27}{108}$
16. $\frac{7}{56} = \frac{1}{8}$
17. $\frac{30}{135} = \frac{6}{27}$
18. $\frac{10}{16} = \frac{70}{112}$

Practice

19. 7)$49.28 $7.04
20. 15)$300.45 $20.03
21. 21)367 → 17 R10
22. 8)644 → 80 R4

Math Masters, p. 132

3 Differentiation Options

READINESS

PARTNER ACTIVITY

▶ Exploring Equivalent Fractions

15–30 Min

To explore equivalent fractions using a length model, have students find equivalent fractions by using the fraction sides of the Everything Math Deck. For example, students take out the $\frac{1}{2}$ fraction card, then they find all other cards in the deck with a fraction equivalent to $\frac{1}{2}$. They order the cards by denominators, either least to greatest or greatest to least. Have students discuss the relationships they see between numerators and denominators.

ENRICHMENT

PARTNER ACTIVITY

▶ Using the Division Rule to Explore Simplest Form

15–30 Min

(*Math Masters,* p. 133)

To apply students' understanding of equivalent fractions, have students write fractions in simplest form on *Math Masters,* page 133. Students use the division rule to find equivalent fractions and then identify the simplest form. To support English language learners, provide examples of simplest form or lowest terms on the board, and emphasize that *lowest terms* does not mean smallest fraction.

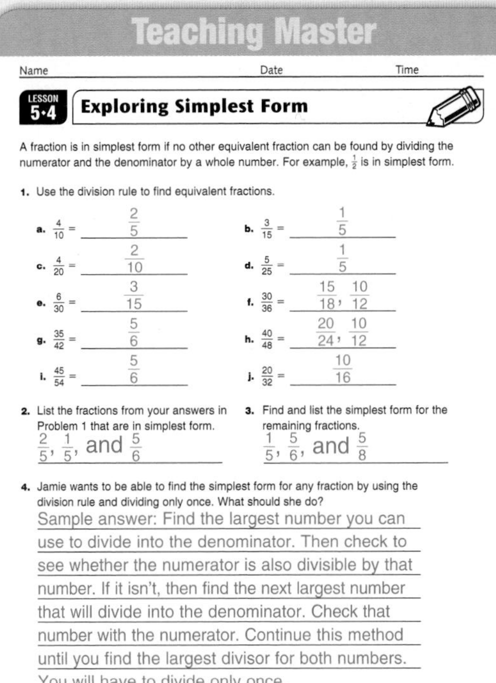

Teaching Master

Name Date Time

LESSON 5•4 **Exploring Simplest Form**

A fraction is in simplest form if no other equivalent fraction can be found by dividing the numerator and the denominator by a whole number. For example, $\frac{1}{2}$ is in simplest form.

1. Use the division rule to find equivalent fractions.
   a. $\frac{4}{10} = \frac{2}{5}$
   b. $\frac{3}{15} = \frac{1}{5}$
   c. $\frac{4}{20} = \frac{2}{10}$
   d. $\frac{5}{25} = \frac{1}{5}$
   e. $\frac{6}{30} = \frac{3}{15}$
   f. $\frac{30}{36} = \frac{15}{18}, \frac{10}{12}$
   g. $\frac{35}{42} = \frac{5}{6}$
   h. $\frac{40}{48} = \frac{20}{24}, \frac{10}{12}$
   i. $\frac{45}{54} = \frac{5}{6}$
   j. $\frac{20}{32} = \frac{10}{16}$
2. List the fractions from your answers in Problem 1 that are in simplest form. $\frac{2}{5}, \frac{1}{5}$, and $\frac{5}{6}$
3. Find and list the simplest form for the remaining fractions. $\frac{1}{5}, \frac{5}{6}$, and $\frac{5}{8}$
4. Jamie wants to be able to find the simplest form for any fraction by using the division rule and dividing only once. What should she do?
   Sample answer: Find the largest number you can use to divide into the denominator. Then check to see whether the numerator is also divisible by that number. If it isn't, then find the next largest number that will divide into the denominator. Check that number with the numerator. Continue this method until you find the largest divisor for both numbers. You will have to divide only once.

Math Masters, p. 133

SMALL-GROUP ACTIVITY

▶ *5-Minute Math*

5–15 Min

To offer students more experience with equivalent fractions, see *5-Minute Math,* page 17.

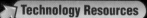

5•5 Fractions and Decimals: Part 1

Objectives To provide practice with renaming fractions as decimals; and to review rounding decimals.

Technology Resources www.everydaymathonline.com

ePresentations

eToolkit

Algorithms Practice

EM Facts Workshop Game™

Family Letters

Assessment Management

Common Core State Standards

Curriculum Focal Points

Interactive Teacher's Lesson Guide

1 Teaching the Lesson

Key Concepts and Skills

- Rename fractions and mixed numbers as decimals. [Number and Numeration Goal 5]
- Compare and order decimals. [Number and Numeration Goal 6]
- Round decimals. [Operations and Computation Goal 6]

Key Activities

Students change fractions to equivalent fractions having denominators of 10 or 100 and then rename these fractions as decimals. They practice rounding decimal numbers up, down, or to the nearest specified place. They play *Estimation Squeeze* to practice finding decimals between two decimals.

Ongoing Assessment: Recognizing Student Achievement
Use Mental Math and Reflexes. [Number and Numeration Goal 5]

Key Vocabulary

round down ◆ round up ◆ round to the nearest . . .

Materials

Math Journal 1, pp. 137–140
Student Reference Book, p. 304
Study Link 5•4
transparency of *Math Masters,* p. 424 (optional) ◆ slate ◆ calculator ◆ base-10 blocks (optional)

2 Ongoing Learning & Practice

Math Boxes 5•5
Math Journal 1, p. 141
Students practice and maintain skills through Math Box problems.

Study Link 5•5
Math Masters, p. 134
Students practice and maintain skills through Study Link activities.

3 Differentiation Options

READINESS

Rounding Numbers
Math Masters, p. 136
Students round whole numbers and decimals by completing number lines.

EXTRA PRACTICE

Renaming Fractions as Decimals
Math Masters, p. 135
Students practice finding equivalent fractions and converting them to decimals.

Advance Preparation

***Teacher's Reference Manual,* Grades 4–6** pp. 261–264

Getting Started

Mental Math and Reflexes ★

Have students write each number as a fraction or mixed number and then as a decimal.

●○○ seven-tenths $\frac{7}{10}$; 0.7
six-hundredths $\frac{6}{100}$; 0.06
three point nine $3\frac{9}{10}$; 3.9

●●○ three and nine-tenths $3\frac{9}{10}$; 3.9
forty-five hundredths $\frac{45}{100}$; 0.45
six and nine-hundredths $6\frac{9}{100}$; 6.09

●●● seven hundred eight thousandths $\frac{708}{1,000}$; 0.708
nineteen-thousandths $\frac{19}{1,000}$; 0.019
six and nineteen-thousandths $6\frac{19}{1,000}$; 6.019

Have students use calculators to enter each fraction or mixed number and then convert to a decimal.

$\frac{4}{9}$ $0.\overline{4}$ $\frac{2}{13}$ 0.1538461 $\frac{19}{6}$ $3.1\overline{6}$ $2\frac{5}{8}$ 2.625 $1\frac{1}{7}$ 1.1428571 $4\frac{16}{27}$ $4.\overline{592}$

Math Message

Solve Problems 1 and 2 on journal page 137.

Study Link 5·4 Follow-Up

Allow partners five minutes to compare their answers and correct any errors.

Ongoing Assessment: Recognizing Student Achievement

Mental Math and Reflexes ★

Use the **Mental Math and Reflexes** problems to assess students' ability to convert between equivalent number forms. Students are making adequate progress if they correctly write fractions as decimals.

[Number and Numeration Goal 5]

NOTE Decimal numbers between 0 and 1 are usually written with a leading zero (0) in the ones place: .7 and .06 are acceptable, but 0.7 and 0.06 are preferred. The 0 emphasizes the decimal point and that the number is less than 1.

1 Teaching the Lesson

▶ Math Message Follow-Up

WHOLE-CLASS ACTIVITY

(*Math Journal 1*, p. 137)

Draw the number line for Problem 1 on the board, and ask volunteers to mark and label the location of their decimals. Ask students to explain their choices. Use these explanations to emphasize that tick marks between tenths indicate hundredths and tick marks between hundredths indicate thousandths.

Draw another number line and ask: *What could be the first and last numbers if you wanted the tick marks to indicate ten-thousandths?* Answers will vary but should count by thousandths, for example, 0.234 and 0.235. Ask students to draw a number line on their slates and label the first and last numbers using decimals. Remind students to draw arrows at the ends of their number lines because they are drawing only a portion of an infinite line. Have partners exchange number lines and mark and label at least 3 decimals. Circulate and assist.

Student Page

Date Time

LESSON 5·5 Math Message

Mark and label 3 decimals on each number line below. Sample answers:

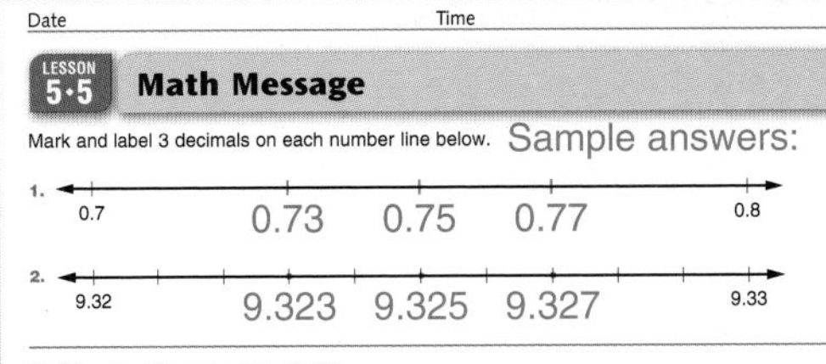

Writing Fractions and Decimals

Write the numbers that your teacher dictates in the first column. Use the second column to show how you change these numbers to equivalent decimals. Write the decimal in the third column.

Sample answers:

Fraction or Mixed Number	Calculations	Equivalent Decimals
$\frac{3}{4}$	$\frac{3 * 25}{4 * 25} = \frac{75}{100}$	0.75
$\frac{4}{5}$	$\frac{4 * 2}{5 * 2} = \frac{8}{10}$	0.8
$\frac{6}{50}$	$\frac{6 * 2}{50 * 2} = \frac{12}{100}$	0.12
$5\frac{1}{2}$	$5\frac{1 * 5}{2 * 5} = 5\frac{5}{10}$	5.5
$2\frac{9}{25}$	$2\frac{9 * 4}{25 * 4} = 2\frac{36}{100}$	2.36
$7\frac{6}{20}$	$7\frac{6 \div 2}{20 \div 2} = 7\frac{3}{10}$	7.3

Math Journal 1, p. 137

Student Page

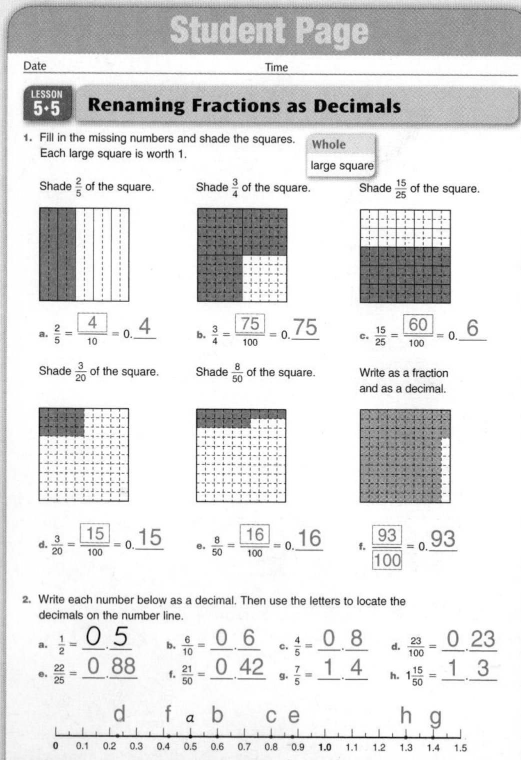

Date Time

LESSON 5·5 **Renaming Fractions as Decimals**

1. Fill in the missing numbers and shade the squares. Each large square is worth 1. Whole: large square

Shade $\frac{2}{5}$ of the square. Shade $\frac{3}{4}$ of the square. Shade $\frac{15}{25}$ of the square.

a. $\frac{2}{5} = \frac{4}{10} = 0.4$ b. $\frac{3}{4} = \frac{75}{100} = 0.75$ c. $\frac{15}{25} = \frac{60}{100} = 0.6$

Shade $\frac{3}{20}$ of the square. Shade $\frac{8}{50}$ of the square. Write as a fraction and as a decimal.

d. $\frac{3}{20} = \frac{15}{100} = 0.15$ e. $\frac{8}{50} = \frac{16}{100} = 0.16$ f. $\frac{93}{100} = 0.93$

2. Write each number below as a decimal. Then use the letters to locate the decimals on the number line.

a. $\frac{1}{2} = 0.5$ b. $\frac{6}{10} = 0.6$ c. $\frac{4}{5} = 0.8$ d. $\frac{23}{100} = 0.23$

e. $\frac{22}{25} = 0.88$ f. $\frac{21}{50} = 0.42$ g. $\frac{7}{5} = 1.4$ h. $1\frac{15}{50} = 1.3$

d f a b c e h g

0 0.1 0.2 0.3 0.4 0.5 0.6 0.7 0.8 0.9 1.0 1.1 1.2 1.3 1.4 1.5

Math Journal 1, p. 138

Student Page

Date Time

LESSON 5·5 **Rounding Decimals**

Rounding removes extra digits from a number. Sometimes decimals are shown with more digits than are useful. Data with too many decimal places can be misleading. For example, measurements with too many digits might seem more precise than they actually are. Many calculators display results to eight or more decimal places. In most situations, one or two places are enough.

Example:

The interest earned on a savings account at a bank is calculated to the nearest tenth of a cent. But the bank can't pay a fraction of a cent. Suppose one bank always *rounds* the interest down, and ignores any fraction of a cent.

The First Community Bank calculates interest on one account as $17.218 (17 dollars and 21.8 cents). The bank ignores the 0.8 (or $\frac{8}{10}$) cent. It pays $17.21 interest.

1. Here is the calculated monthly interest on Mica's First Community Bank savings account. Round each amount down to find the interest paid each month.

January	$21.403	$21.40	February	$22.403	$22.40
March	$18.259	$18.25	April	$19.024	$19.02
May	$17.427	$17.42	June	$18.916	$18.91

How much total interest did the bank pay Mica for these 6 months? (Add the rounded amounts.) $117.40

Example:

At the Olympic Games, each running event is timed to the nearest thousandth of a second. The timer *rounds* the time *up* to the *next* hundredth of a second (not the *nearest* hundredth). The rounded time becomes the official time.

11.437 seconds is rounded up to 11.44 seconds.

11.431 seconds is rounded up to 11.44 seconds.

11.430 seconds is reported as 11.43 seconds because 11.430 is equal to 11.43.

Michael Johnson with his record-breaking time

Math Journal 1, p. 139

▶ Writing Fractions and Decimals

(*Math Journal 1*, p. 137)

Extend the Mental Math and Reflexes activity with problems like the following. Ask students to write each number as a fraction or a mixed number in the table on journal page 137.

- three-fourths
- four-fifths
- six-fiftieths
- five and one-half
- two and nine twenty-fifths
- seven and six-twentieths

Ask: *How can you convert these numbers so they can be written as decimals?* Use mental math, the multiplication rule, or the division rule to change each fraction to an equivalent fraction having a denominator of 10 or 100. Then write the new fraction as a decimal. Have students complete the table by showing how they converted the fractions or mixed numbers to equivalent fractions in order to write the decimals. Ask volunteers to write their solutions on the board.

Examples:

▷ $\frac{3 * 25}{4 * 25} = \frac{75}{100} = 0.75$; Some students may know that $\frac{3}{4} = \frac{75}{100}$ and go directly from $\frac{3}{4}$ to 0.75 mentally.

▷ $7\frac{6}{20} = 7\frac{6 * 5}{20 * 5} = 7\frac{30}{100} = 7\frac{30 \div 10}{100 \div 10} = 7\frac{3}{10} = 7.3$; Some students may know that 20 is a factor of 100 and $7\frac{30}{100} = 7\frac{3}{10}$ and go directly from $7\frac{6}{20}$ to 7.3 mentally.

Adjusting the Activity

Use base-10 blocks and a transparency of *Math Masters*, page 424 to model using the multiplication rule to convert the fractions to equivalent fractions with a denominator of 10 or 100.

AUDITORY ◆ KINESTHETIC ◆ TACTILE ◆ VISUAL

▶ Renaming Fractions as Decimals

(*Math Journal 1*, p. 138)

Ask students to complete the journal page. Refer students to Problem 2, and ask them to name the decimals for the smaller marks on the number line. For example, the mark between 0.2 and 0.3 represents 0.25. 0.05, 0.15, 0.25, 0.35, ..., 1.45 Circulate and assist. When most students have finished, bring the class together to discuss the answers.

▶ Rounding Decimals

SMALL-GROUP ACTIVITY

(*Math Journal 1,* pp. 139 and 140)

Explain that rounding decimals is often used to present data in a form that makes the most sense for the situation. Decimals can be **rounded** to a particular place in one of three ways: always **down,** always **up,** or **to the nearest** selected place. To support English language learners, write *round* on the board and discuss its various meanings. Assign small groups to complete journal pages 139 and 140 in the following manner: For each problem, have students read and discuss the example, independently solve the problem, and then compare answers and correct any errors. Circulate and assist.

▶ Playing *Estimation Squeeze*

PARTNER ACTIVITY

(*Student Reference Book,* p. 304)

Playing *Estimation Squeeze* provides practice in finding decimals between two decimals. Refer to the directions on page 304 of the *Student Reference Book,* and play a game against the class to be sure that students understand the directions.

NOTE Some calculators, like the TI-15, do not have a squaring key [x^2]. The [Op1] key can be converted to a squaring key by performing these steps.

1. Press the [On/Off] and [Clear] keys simultaneously. This clears the calculator memory. The display will read *MEM CLEARED.* Press [Clear] again to clear the display.
2. Enter the key sequence: [Op1] [∧] 2 [Op1]. The [Op1] key will now function as a squaring key.

Adjusting the Activity

Allow students to choose any number they like that is not a perfect square. Partners must agree on the range before beginning the game. For example, partners may agree that the number will be between 500 and 5,000.

AUDITORY ♦ KINESTHETIC ♦ TACTILE ♦ VISUAL

2 Ongoing Learning & Practice

▶ Math Boxes 5·5

INDEPENDENT ACTIVITY

(*Math Journal 1,* p. 141)

Mixed Practice Math Boxes in this lesson are paired with Math Boxes in Lesson 5-7. The skills in Problems 5 and 6 preview Unit 6 content.

Student Page

Date Time

LESSON 5·5 **Rounding Decimals** *continued*

2. Find the official times for these runs. min: minute(s) s: second(s)

Electric Timer	Official Time	Electric Timer	Official Time
10.752 s	10.76 s	20.001 s	20.01 s
11.191 s	11.20 s	43.505 s	43.51 s
10.815 s	10.82 s	49.993 s	50.00 s
21.970 s	21.97 s	1 min 55.738 s	1 min 55.74 s
20.092 s	20.10 s	1 min 59.991 s	2 min 0 0 s

Example:
Supermarkets often show unit prices for items. This helps customers comparison shop. A unit price is found by dividing the price of an item (in cents, or dollars and cents) by the quantity of the item (often in ounces or pounds). When the quotient has more decimal places than are needed, it is *rounded to the nearest* tenth of a cent.

23.822 cents (per ounce) is rounded down to 23.8 cents.

24.769 cents is rounded up to 24.8 cents.

18.65 cents is halfway between 18.6 cents and 18.7 cents. It is rounded up to 18.7 cents.

3. Round these unit prices to the nearest tenth of a cent (per ounce).

a. 28.374¢ 28.4¢ b. 19.796¢ 19.8¢ c. 29.327¢ 29.3¢
d. 16.916¢ 16.9¢ e. 20.641¢ 20.6¢ f. 25.583¢ 25.6¢
g. 18.469¢ 18.5¢ h. 24.944¢ 24.9¢ i. 17.281¢ 17.3¢
j. 23.836¢ 23.8¢ k. 21.866¢ 21.9¢ l. 22.814¢ 22.8¢

4. Describe a situation involving money when the result of a computation might always be rounded up.
Sample answer: When someone owes a bank interest, the result might always be rounded up.

Math Journal 1, p. 140

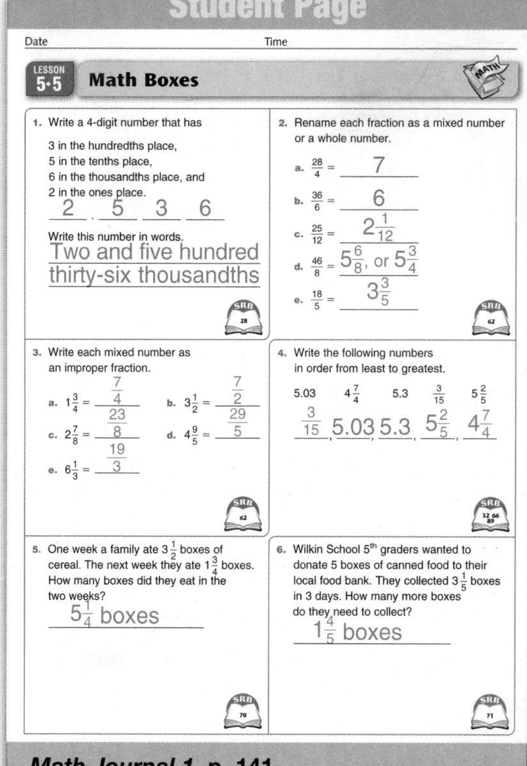

Student Page

Date Time

LESSON 5·5 **Math Boxes**

1. Write a 4-digit number that has
3 in the hundredths place,
5 in the tenths place,
6 in the thousandths place, and
2 in the ones place.
2 . 5 3 6
Write this number in words.
Two and five hundred thirty-six thousandths

2. Rename each fraction as a mixed number or a whole number.
a. $\frac{28}{4}$ = 7
b. $\frac{36}{6}$ = 6
c. $\frac{25}{12}$ = $2\frac{1}{12}$
d. $\frac{46}{8}$ = $5\frac{6}{8}$, or $5\frac{3}{4}$
e. $\frac{18}{5}$ = $3\frac{3}{5}$

3. Write each mixed number as an improper fraction.
a. $1\frac{3}{4}$ = $\frac{7}{4}$
b. $3\frac{1}{2}$ = $\frac{7}{2}$
c. $2\frac{7}{8}$ = $\frac{23}{8}$
d. $4\frac{9}{5}$ = $\frac{29}{5}$
e. $6\frac{1}{3}$ = $\frac{19}{3}$

4. Write the following numbers in order from least to greatest.
5.03 $4\frac{7}{4}$ 5.3 $\frac{3}{15}$ $5\frac{2}{5}$
$\frac{3}{15}$, 5.03, 5.3, $5\frac{2}{5}$, $4\frac{7}{4}$

5. One week a family ate $3\frac{1}{2}$ boxes of cereal. The next week they ate $1\frac{3}{4}$ boxes. How many boxes did they eat in the two weeks?
$5\frac{1}{4}$ boxes

6. Wilkin School 5th graders wanted to donate 5 boxes of canned food to their local food bank. They collected $3\frac{1}{5}$ boxes in 3 days. How many more boxes do they need to collect?
$1\frac{4}{5}$ boxes

Math Journal 1, p. 141

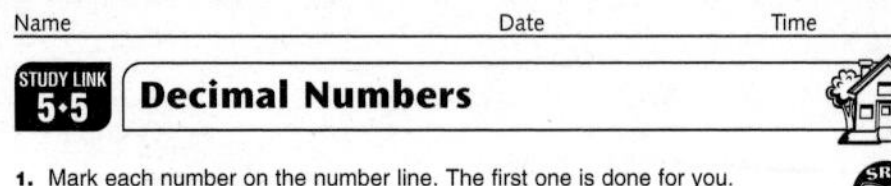

Study Link Master

Name Date Time

STUDY LINK 5·5 Decimal Numbers

1. Mark each number on the number line. The first one is done for you.
30.13 30.72 31.05 29.94 30.38

29.94 30.13 30.38 30.72 31.05

29.9 30.0 30.1 30.2 30.3 30.4 30.5 30.6 30.7 30.8 30.9 31.0 31.1

2. Round the area of each country to the nearest tenth of a square kilometer.

	Ten Smallest Countries	Area in Square Kilometers	Area Rounded to the Nearest Tenth of a Square Kilometer
1	Vatican City	0.44 km²	0.4 km²
2	Monaco	1.89 km²	1.9 km²
3	Nauru	20.72 km²	20.7 km²
4	Tuvalu	23.96 km²	24.0 km²
5	San Marino	60.87 km²	60.9 km²
6	Liechtenstein	160.58 km²	160.6 km²
7	Marshall Islands	181.30 km²	181.3 km²
8	St. Kitts and Nevis	296.37 km²	296.4 km²
9	Maldives	297.85 km²	297.9 km²
10	Malta	315.98 km²	316.0 km²

Source: *The Top 10 of Everything 2005*

Practice

Solve and write the fact family number sentences.

3. 32)768
768 ÷ 32 = 24   768 ÷ 24 = 32
32 ∗ 24 = 768   24 ∗ 32 = 768

Math Masters, p. 134

▶ Study Link 5·5

INDEPENDENT ACTIVITY

(*Math Masters*, p. 134)

Home Connection Students mark and label the location of decimal numbers on a number line. They round the areas of the world's ten smallest countries to the nearest tenth of a square kilometer.

3 Differentiation Options

READINESS

INDEPENDENT ACTIVITY

▶ Rounding Numbers

15–30 Min

(*Math Masters*, p. 136)

To explore rounding numbers using a visual model, have students use number line models to round numbers. When students have completed the page, have them explain how to round a number.

EXTRA PRACTICE

INDEPENDENT ACTIVITY

▶ Renaming Fractions as Decimals

15–30 Min

(*Math Masters*, p. 135)

Students practice finding equivalent fractions and renaming fractions and mixed numbers as decimals.

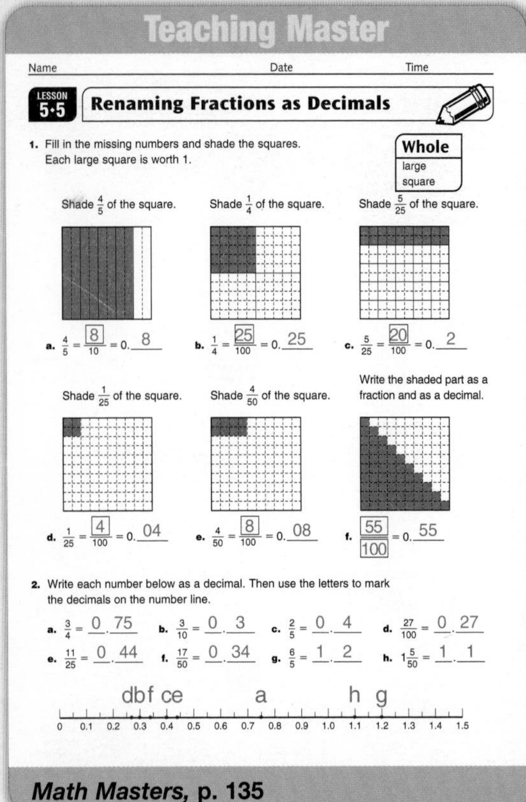

Teaching Master

Name Date Time

LESSON 5·5 Renaming Fractions as Decimals

1. Fill in the missing numbers and shade the squares. Each large square is worth 1.

Whole
large square

Shade $\frac{4}{5}$ of the square. Shade $\frac{1}{4}$ of the square. Shade $\frac{5}{25}$ of the square.

a. $\frac{4}{5} = \frac{8}{10}$ = 0.8 b. $\frac{1}{4} = \frac{25}{100}$ = 0.25 c. $\frac{5}{25} = \frac{20}{100}$ = 0.2

Shade $\frac{1}{25}$ of the square. Shade $\frac{4}{50}$ of the square. Write the shaded part as a fraction and as a decimal.

d. $\frac{1}{25} = \frac{4}{100}$ = 0.04 e. $\frac{4}{50} = \frac{8}{100}$ = 0.08 f. $\frac{55}{100}$ = 0.55

2. Write each number below as a decimal. Then use the letters to mark the decimals on the number line.

a. $\frac{3}{4}$ = 0.75 b. $\frac{3}{10}$ = 0.3 c. $\frac{2}{5}$ = 0.4 d. $\frac{27}{100}$ = 0.27
e. $\frac{11}{25}$ = 0.44 f. $\frac{17}{50}$ = 0.34 g. $\frac{6}{5}$ = 1.2 h. $1\frac{5}{50}$ = 1.1

dbf ce a h g

0 0.1 0.2 0.3 0.4 0.5 0.6 0.7 0.8 0.9 1.0 1.1 1.2 1.3 1.4 1.5

Math Masters, p. 135

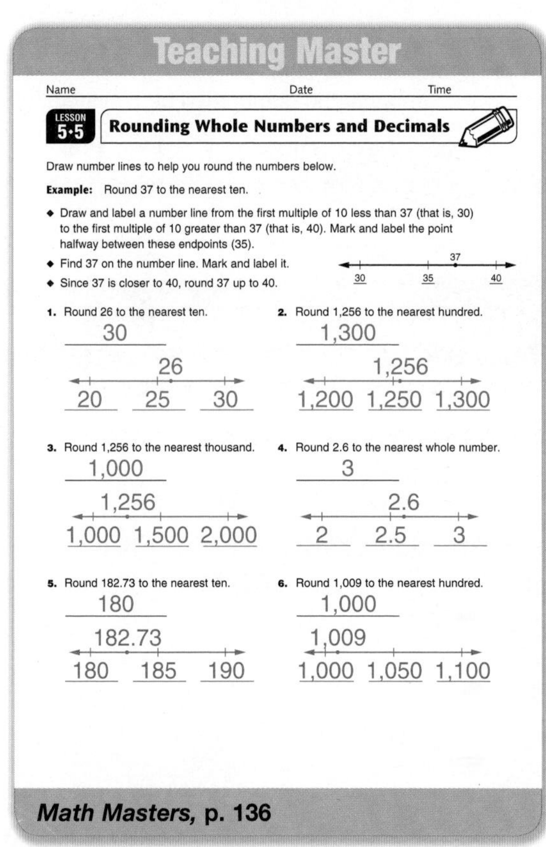

Teaching Master

Name Date Time

LESSON 5·5 Rounding Whole Numbers and Decimals

Draw number lines to help you round the numbers below.

Example: Round 37 to the nearest ten.

- Draw and label a number line from the first multiple of 10 less than 37 (that is, 30) to the first multiple of 10 greater than 37 (that is, 40). Mark and label the point halfway between these endpoints (35).
- Find 37 on the number line. Mark and label it.
- Since 37 is closer to 40, round 37 up to 40.

30 35 37 40

1. Round 26 to the nearest ten. 30
26
20 25 30

2. Round 1,256 to the nearest hundred. 1,300
1,256
1,200 1,250 1,300

3. Round 1,256 to the nearest thousand. 1,000
1,256
1,000 1,500 2,000

4. Round 2.6 to the nearest whole number. 3
2.6
2 2.5 3

5. Round 182.73 to the nearest ten. 180
182.73
180 185 190

6. Round 1,009 to the nearest hundred. 1,000
1,009
1,000 1,050 1,100

Math Masters, p. 136

5•6 Fractions and Decimals: Part 2

Objective To provide experience with several graphic models for renaming fractions as decimals.

www.everydaymathonline.com

ePresentations

eToolkit

Algorithms Practice

EM Facts Workshop Game™

Family Letters

Assessment Management

Common Core State Standards

Curriculum Focal Points

Interactive Teacher's Lesson Guide

1 Teaching the Lesson

Key Concepts and Skills

- Convert between fractions, mixed numbers, and decimals.
  [Number and Numeration Goal 5]
- Order rational numbers.
  [Number and Numeration Goal 6]
- Order fractions and decimals on a number line.
  [Number and Numeration Goal 6]

Key Activities

Students use the Probability Meter and Fraction-Stick Chart to approximate decimal equivalents for fractions. They begin filling in a table of decimal equivalents.

Materials

Math Journal 1, pp. 142, 205, and the inside back cover
Study Link 5•5
transparencies of *Math Masters,* pp. 137 and 138 ◆ slate ◆ straightedge

2 Ongoing Learning & Practice

Converting Improper Fractions with Division
Math Journal 1, p. 143
Students review and practice converting improper fractions to mixed numbers using division.

Math Boxes 5•6
Math Journal 1, p. 144
Students practice and maintain skills through Math Box problems.

Ongoing Assessment: Recognizing Student Achievement
Use Math Boxes, Problem 5.
[Number and Numeration Goal 6]

Study Link 5•6
Math Masters, p. 139
Students practice and maintain skills through Study Link activities.

3 Differentiation Options

READINESS

Playing *Number Top-It* (3-Place Decimals)
Student Reference Book, p. 327
Math Masters, p. 493
per partnership: 4 each of number cards 0–9 (from the Everything Math Deck, if available)
Students practice forming and comparing decimals.

ENRICHMENT

Writing Fraction and Decimal Equivalents for a Shaded 100-Grid
Math Masters, pp. 140 and 141
transparency of *Math Masters,* p. 141
Students write equivalent fractions and decimals for the shaded portion of a 100-grid.

EXTRA PRACTICE

5-Minute Math
5-Minute Math™, p. 93
Students compare fractions, decimals, and percentages.

Advance Preparation

For Part 1, make transparencies of *Math Masters,* pages 137 and 138.

For the optional Enrichment activity in Part 3, make one transparency of *Math Masters,* page 141 for each group of six students. Cut apart the transparency grids so that there is one per student.

***Teacher's Reference Manual,* Grades 4–6** pp. 88, 89, 172

Getting Started

Mental Math and Reflexes

Ask questions like the following. Students refer to the Probability Meter on *Math Journal 1*, page 205 and respond by writing number sentences.

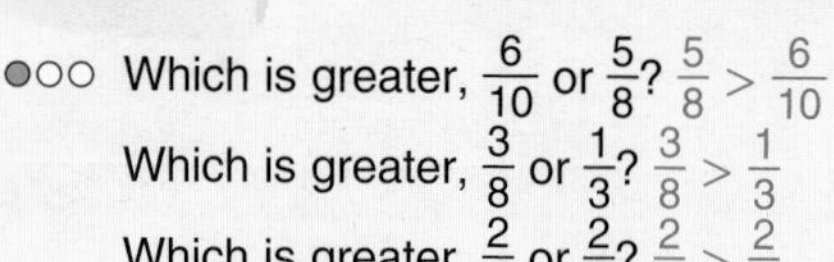

●○○ Which is greater, $\frac{6}{10}$ or $\frac{5}{8}$? $\frac{5}{8} > \frac{6}{10}$

Which is greater, $\frac{3}{8}$ or $\frac{1}{3}$? $\frac{3}{8} > \frac{1}{3}$

Which is greater, $\frac{2}{3}$ or $\frac{2}{5}$? $\frac{2}{3} > \frac{2}{5}$

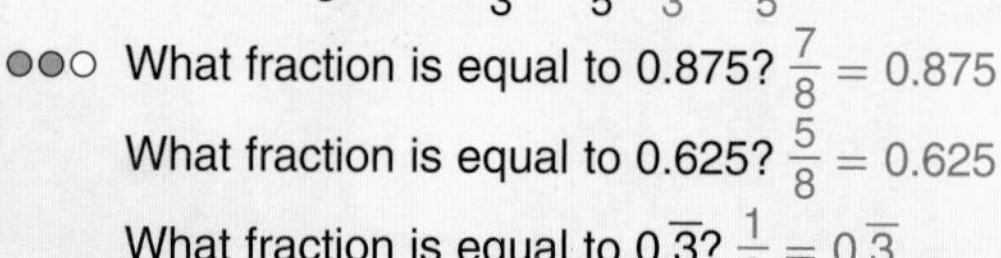

●●○ What fraction is equal to 0.875? $\frac{7}{8} = 0.875$

What fraction is equal to 0.625? $\frac{5}{8} = 0.625$

What fraction is equal to $0.\overline{3}$? $\frac{1}{3} = 0.\overline{3}$

●●● What fraction is equal to 0.05? $\frac{1}{20} = 0.05$

What fraction is equal to $0.1\overline{6}$? $\frac{1}{6} = 0.1\overline{6}$

What fraction is equal to $0.8\overline{3}$? $\frac{5}{6} = 0.8\overline{3}$

Math Message

How would you use the Probability Meter on journal page 205 to show someone what $\frac{1}{8}$ dollar is worth?

Study Link 5·5 Follow-Up

Allow partners five minutes to compare their answers and correct any errors.

Ask volunteers to share their strategies for rounding the area of Malta to the nearest tenth km^2. Highlight that rounding to the nearest tenth rounds 315.98 km^2 to the nearest whole number—316.0 km^2.

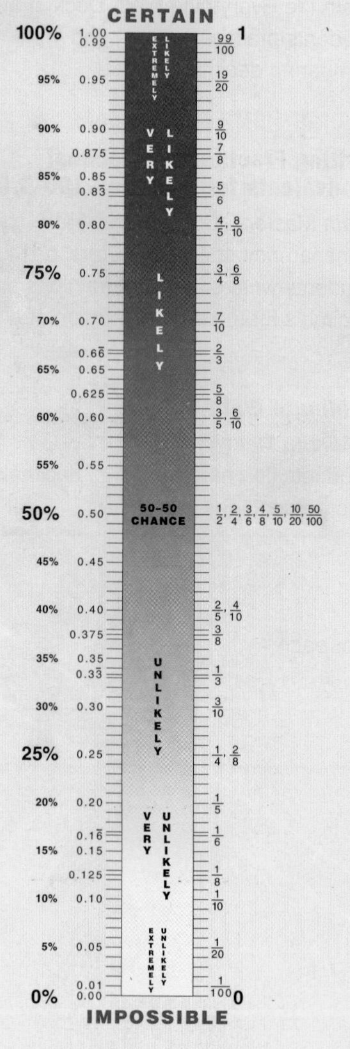

Probability Meter

1 Teaching the Lesson

▶ Math Message Follow-Up

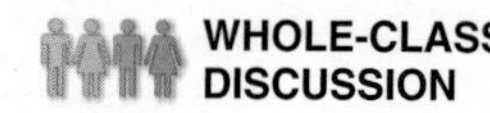

WHOLE-CLASS DISCUSSION

(*Math Journal 1*, p. 205)

Ask volunteers to show how they used the Probability Meter to find the value of $\frac{1}{8}$ dollar. Use their explanations to discuss the meter's decimal labels as dollar notation.

In dollar notation, hundredths are equivalent to pennies or cents: $\frac{1}{4}$ is 0.25, or 25 cents. The fraction $\frac{1}{8}$ is directly opposite the decimal 0.125. Point out that 0.12 is 12 cents and 0.005 is $\frac{1}{2}$ of $\frac{1}{100}$, or $\frac{1}{2}$ of 1 cent, so $\frac{1}{8}$ dollar is worth \$0.125, or $12\frac{1}{2}$ cents.

- What is $\frac{3}{8}$ dollar worth? \$0.375, or $37\frac{1}{2}$ cents
- What is $\frac{5}{8}$ dollar worth? \$0.625, or $62\frac{1}{2}$ cents
- What is $\frac{7}{8}$ dollar worth? \$0.875, or $87\frac{1}{2}$ cents

▶ Writing Fractions as Decimals

WHOLE-CLASS ACTIVITY

(*Math Journal 1*, p. 142; *Math Masters*, p. 137)

Use a transparency of *Math Masters*, page 137 to demonstrate how the Fraction-Stick Chart can be used to approximate the decimal names for fractions.

Example: What decimal is about equal to $\frac{2}{3}$?

Step 1: Use the thirds row, and locate the fraction $\frac{2}{3}$. Count the $\frac{1}{3}$ bars from left to right: $\frac{2}{3}$ is the right edge of the second bar.

Step 2: Place one edge of a ruler or straightedge at $\frac{2}{3}$; that is, along the right edge of the second $\frac{1}{3}$ piece and perpendicular to the Decimal Number Line.

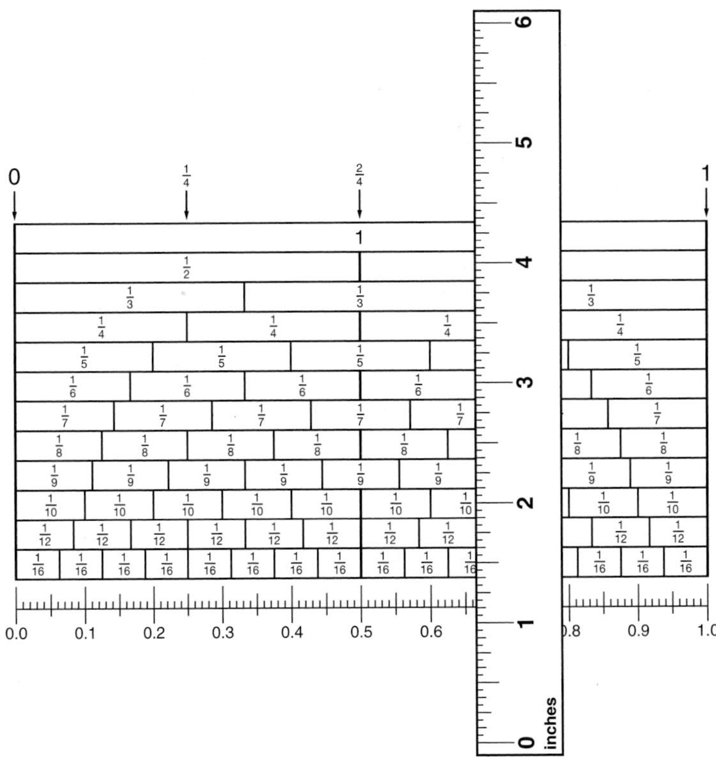

Step 3: Find where the straightedge crosses the number line. It crosses at about 0.67, so $\frac{2}{3}$ is about 0.67.

Refer students to journal page 142. Ask them to use the chart and number line on the page to mirror the steps as you demonstrate finding the decimal name for $\frac{5}{8}$.

Ask students how they would use the chart to find the decimal name for $6\frac{2}{3}$. Use their responses to emphasize that with mixed numbers it is necessary to approximate only the fraction part. The whole number part is unchanged when they write the decimal name, so $6\frac{2}{3}$ is about 6.67.

Assign students to complete the estimates for each problem on the journal page. Circulate and assist. When most students have finished, review the answers and strategies, and discuss any problems that students found particularly difficult or interesting.

NOTE The Fraction-Stick Chart is a useful visual device but is not intended to provide precise equivalencies between all fractions and decimals. In Lesson 5-7, students will use their calculators to find decimal equivalents for fractions.

Student Page

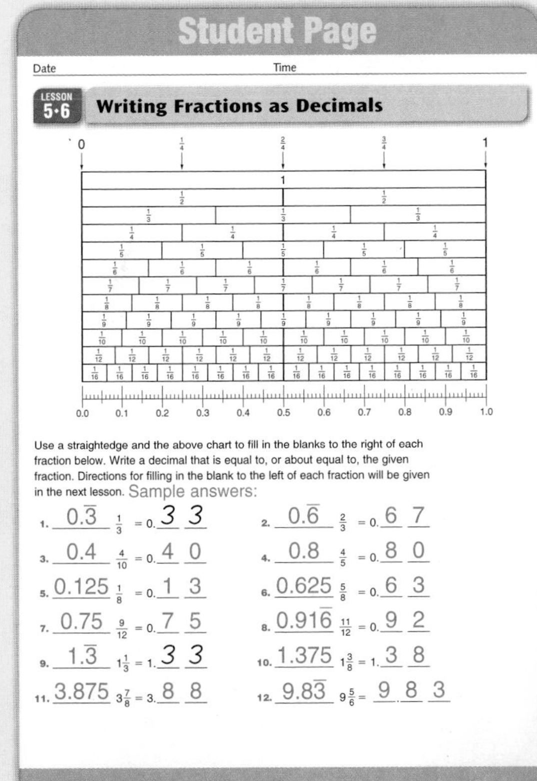

Date Time

LESSON 5·6 **Writing Fractions as Decimals**

Use a straightedge and the above chart to fill in the blanks to the right of each fraction below. Write a decimal that is equal to, or about equal to, the given fraction. Directions for filling in the blank to the left of each fraction will be given in the next lesson. Sample answers:

1. $0.\overline{3}$ $\frac{1}{3}$ = 0.33
2. $0.\overline{6}$ $\frac{2}{3}$ = 0.67
3. 0.4 $\frac{4}{10}$ = 0.40
4. 0.8 $\frac{4}{5}$ = 0.80
5. 0.125 $\frac{1}{8}$ = 0.13
6. 0.625 $\frac{5}{8}$ = 0.63
7. 0.75 $\frac{9}{12}$ = 0.75
8. $0.91\overline{6}$ $\frac{11}{12}$ = 0.92
9. $1.\overline{3}$ $1\frac{1}{3}$ = 1.33
10. 1.375 $1\frac{3}{8}$ = 1.38
11. 3.875 $3\frac{7}{8}$ = 3.88
12. $9.8\overline{3}$ $9\frac{5}{6}$ = 9.83

Math Journal 1, p. 142

Teaching Master

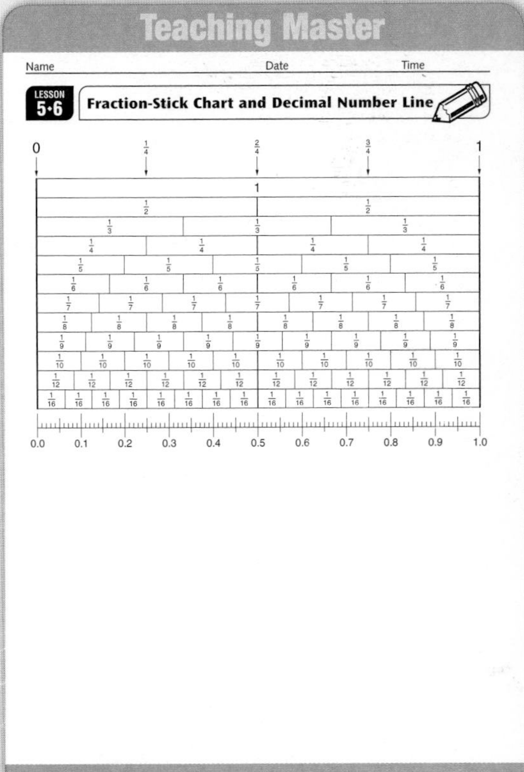

Name Date Time

LESSON 5·6 **Fraction-Stick Chart and Decimal Number Line**

Math Masters, p. 137

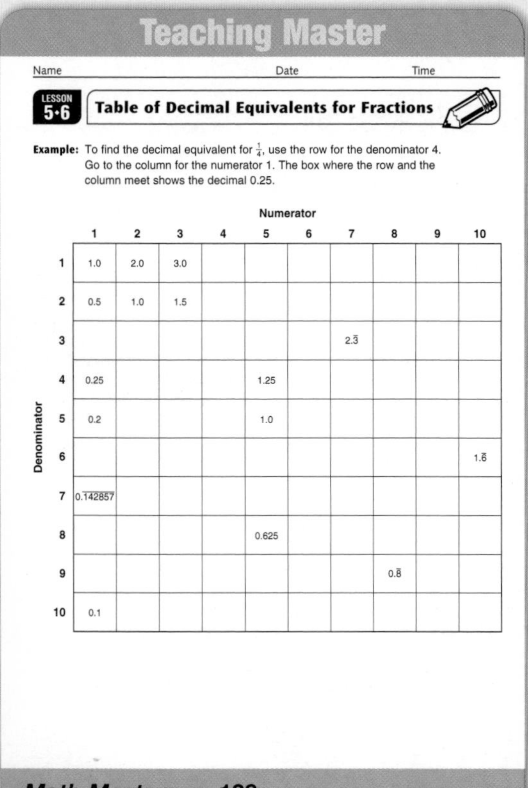
Teaching Master

Name Date Time

LESSON 5·6 **Table of Decimal Equivalents for Fractions**

Example: To find the decimal equivalent for $\frac{1}{4}$, use the row for the denominator 4. Go to the column for the numerator 1. The box where the row and the column meet shows the decimal 0.25.

Numerator

Denominator	1	2	3	4	5	6	7	8	9	10
1	1.0	2.0	3.0							
2	0.5	1.0	1.5							
3							$2.\overline{3}$			
4	0.25				1.25					
5	0.2				1.0					
6										$1.\overline{6}$
7	0.142857									
8					0.625					
9								$0.\overline{8}$		
10	0.1									

Math Masters, p. 138

▶ Filling In a Table of Decimal Equivalents for Fractions

PARTNER ACTIVITY

(*Math Journal 1,* inside back cover; *Math Masters,* p. 138)

A partially completed table of decimal equivalents for fractions appears on the inside back cover of the journal and on *Math Masters,* page 138.

Use a transparency of *Math Masters,* page 138 to show students how the table works. Each number across the top of the table identifies the numerator of a fraction. Each number down the left side of the table identifies the denominator of a fraction. The box where a row and column meet is used to show the decimal equivalent for that fraction.

Have students complete rows 1, 2, 4, 5, and 10. The fractions for the assigned rows are easy fractions. Most students will know their decimal names or will be able to calculate them mentally. Students will complete the rest of the rows in succeeding lessons.

Numerator

Denominator	1	2	3	4	5	6	7	8	9	10
1	1.0	2.0	3.0	4.0	5.0	6.0	7.0	8.0	9.0	10.0
2	0.5	1.0	1.5	2.0	2.5	3.0	3.5	4.0	4.5	5.0
4	0.25	0.5	0.75	1.0	1.25	1.5	1.75	2.0	2.25	2.5
5	0.2	0.4	0.6	0.8	1.0	1.2	1.4	1.6	1.8	2.0
10	0.1	0.2	0.3	0.4	0.5	0.6	0.7	0.8	0.9	1.0

Inside back cover of *Math Journal 1.*
Completed rows 1, 2, 4, 5, and 10.

When students have written the decimal names, ask volunteers to describe any patterns that they notice in the table. Sample answers: The rows represent whole numbers, halves, thirds, fourths, etc. The first column represents unit fractions. All boxes on the diagonal from the upper left to the lower right have a value of 1, with decimals greater than 1 in the boxes to the right of this diagonal and less than 1 in the boxes to the left. Decimals become larger as you move across rows and become smaller as you move down columns.

2 Ongoing Learning & Practice

▶ Converting Improper Fractions with Division

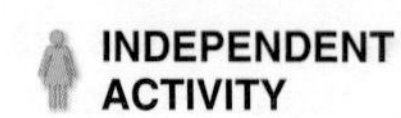
INDEPENDENT ACTIVITY

(*Math Journal 1,* p. 143)

Students review and practice converting improper fractions to mixed numbers using division.

Student Page

Date Time

LESSON 5·6 **Converting Improper Fractions to Mixed Numbers**

In the problems below, the hexagon shape has a value of 1.

- Write the improper fraction name for each diagram.
- Use division to find the mixed number.
- Show your work.

Whole: hexagon

	Improper Fraction	Mixed Number	Show your work.
Example:	$\frac{9}{2}$	$4\frac{1}{2}$	4R2 $2\overline{)9}$
1.	$\frac{14}{3}$	$4\frac{2}{3}$	
2.	$\frac{23}{6}$	$3\frac{5}{6}$	
3.	$\frac{16}{3}$	$5\frac{1}{3}$	

Use division to convert the following improper fractions to mixed numbers or whole numbers.

4. $\frac{30}{5}$ = 6
5. $\frac{29}{4}$ = $7\frac{1}{4}$
6. $\frac{17}{7}$ = $2\frac{3}{7}$

Try This

7. Jenny said that she could convert $\frac{14}{3}$ to a mixed number by repeatedly subtracting $\frac{3}{3}$ and seeing what was left over. Tell whether you agree or disagree with this method, and explain why.

Sample answer: I agree. Each time Jenny subtracts $\frac{3}{3}$, she is taking away a whole. If she writes the number of wholes she subtracts and then writes the remainder as a fraction, she will have the correct mixed number, $4\frac{2}{3}$.

Math Journal 1, p. 143

▶ Math Boxes 5·6

INDEPENDENT ACTIVITY

(*Math Journal 1,* p. 144)

Mixed Practice Math Boxes in this lesson are paired with Math Boxes in Lesson 5-8. The skill in Problem 6 previews Unit 6 content.

Ongoing Assessment: Recognizing Student Achievement

Math Boxes Problem 5 

Use **Math Boxes, Problem 5** to assess students' ability to compare fractions. Students are making adequate progress if they write the fractions correctly from least to greatest.

[Number and Numeration Goal 6]

▶ Study Link 5·6

INDEPENDENT ACTIVITY

(*Math Masters,* p. 139)

Home Connection Students practice converting between decimals, fractions, and mixed numbers.

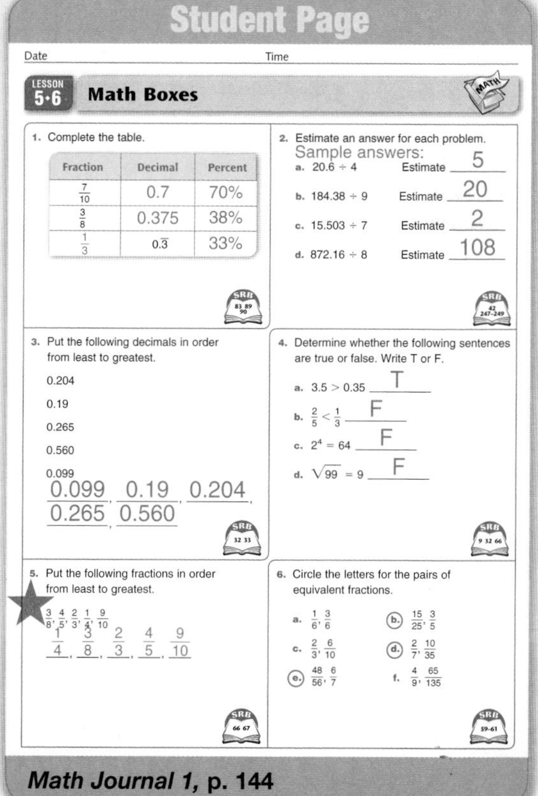

Student Page

Date Time

LESSON 5·6 **Math Boxes**

1. Complete the table.

Fraction	Decimal	Percent
$\frac{7}{10}$	0.7	70%
$\frac{3}{8}$	0.375	38%
$\frac{1}{3}$	$0.\overline{3}$	33%

SRB 83 89 90

2. Estimate an answer for each problem.
Sample answers:
a. $20.6 \div 4$ Estimate 5
b. $184.38 \div 9$ Estimate 20
c. $15.503 \div 7$ Estimate 2
d. $872.16 \div 8$ Estimate 108

SRB 42 247–249

3. Put the following decimals in order from least to greatest.
0.204
0.19
0.265
0.560
0.099
0.099, 0.19, 0.204, 0.265, 0.560

SRB 32 33

4. Determine whether the following sentences are true or false. Write T or F.
a. $3.5 > 0.35$ T
b. $\frac{2}{5} < \frac{1}{3}$ F
c. $2^4 = 64$ F
d. $\sqrt{99} = 9$ F

SRB 9 32 66

5. Put the following fractions in order from least to greatest.
$\frac{3}{8}, \frac{4}{5}, \frac{2}{3}, \frac{1}{4}, \frac{9}{10}$
$\frac{1}{4}, \frac{3}{8}, \frac{2}{3}, \frac{4}{5}, \frac{9}{10}$

SRB 66 67

6. Circle the letters for the pairs of equivalent fractions.
a. $\frac{1}{6}, \frac{3}{6}$
(b.) $\frac{15}{25}, \frac{3}{5}$
c. $\frac{2}{3}, \frac{6}{10}$
(d.) $\frac{2}{7}, \frac{10}{35}$
(e.) $\frac{48}{56}, \frac{6}{7}$
f. $\frac{4}{9}, \frac{65}{135}$

SRB 59–61

Math Journal 1, **p. 144**

Study Link Master

Name Date Time

STUDY LINK 5·6 **Decimals, Fractions, and Mixed Numbers**

1. Convert each decimal measurement to a mixed number.

SRB 63 83 89

Longest Road and Rail Tunnels in the U.S.	Decimal Length	Mixed-Number Length
Cascade Tunnel (Washington)	7.79 miles	$7\frac{79}{100}$ miles
Flathead Tunnel (Montana)	7.78 miles	$7\frac{78}{100}$, or $7\frac{39}{50}$ miles
Moffat Tunnel (Colorado)	6.21 miles	$6\frac{21}{100}$ miles
Hoosac Tunnel (Massachusetts)	4.7 miles	$4\frac{7}{10}$ miles
BART Transbay Tubes (San Francisco, CA)	3.6 miles	$3\frac{6}{10}$, or $3\frac{3}{5}$ miles

Source: *The Top 10 of Everything 2005*

2. The longest one-word name of any place in America is Chargoggagoggmanchauggagoggchaubunagungamaugg.

This name for a lake near Webster, Massachusetts, is 45 letters long. It is a Native American name that means "You fish on your side, I'll fish on mine, and no one fishes in the middle." Use this word to answer the problems below.

a. What fraction of the word is made up of the letter *g*? $\frac{15}{45}$, or $\frac{1}{3}$ $= 0.\overline{3}$

b. What fraction of the word is made up of the letter *a*? $\frac{9}{45}$, or $\frac{1}{5}$ $= 0.2$

c. What fraction of the word is made up of the letter *c*? $\frac{3}{45}$, or $\frac{1}{15}$ $= 0.0\overline{6}$

3. In the space above, write the decimal equivalents for the fractions in Problem 2.

Practice

4. $10\overline{)7,146}$ → 714 R6 5. $10\overline{)84}$ → 8 R4 6. $10\overline{)675}$ → 67 R5

Math Masters, **p. 139**

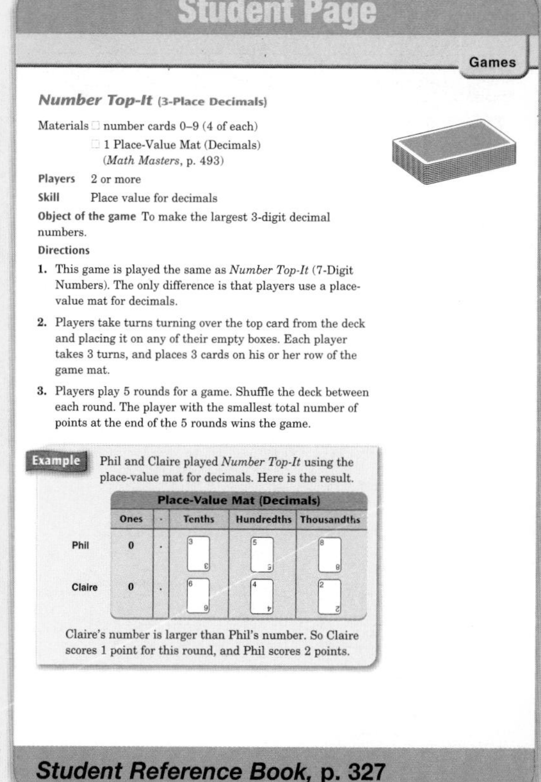

Student Page

Games

Number Top-It **(3-Place Decimals)**

Materials □ number cards 0–9 (4 of each)
□ 1 Place-Value Mat (Decimals) (*Math Masters*, p. 493)

Players 2 or more

Skill Place value for decimals

Object of the game To make the largest 3-digit decimal numbers.

Directions

1. This game is played the same as *Number Top-It* (7-Digit Numbers). The only difference is that players use a place-value mat for decimals.
2. Players take turns turning over the top card from the deck and placing it on any of their empty boxes. Each player takes 3 turns, and places 3 cards on his or her row of the game mat.
3. Players play 5 rounds for a game. Shuffle the deck between each round. The player with the smallest total number of points at the end of the 5 rounds wins the game.

Example Phil and Claire played *Number Top-It* using the place-value mat for decimals. Here is the result.

Place-Value Mat (Decimals)

	Ones	.	Tenths	Hundredths	Thousandths
Phil	0	.	3	5	8
Claire	0	.	6	4	2

Claire's number is larger than Phil's number. So Claire scores 1 point for this round, and Phil scores 2 points.

Student Reference Book, **p. 327**

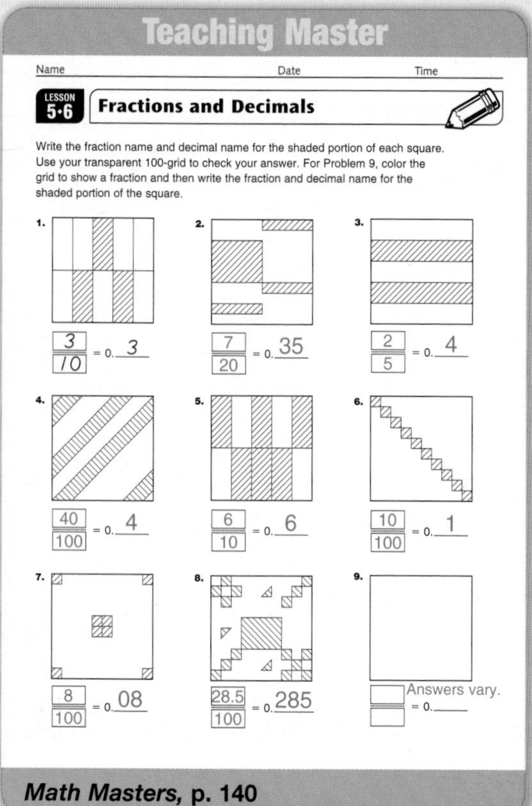

Teaching Master

Name Date Time

LESSON 5·6 **Fractions and Decimals**

Write the fraction name and decimal name for the shaded portion of each square. Use your transparent 100-grid to check your answer. For Problem 9, color the grid to show a fraction and then write the fraction and decimal name for the shaded portion of the square.

1. $\frac{3}{10}$ = 0.3
2. $\frac{7}{20}$ = 0.35
3. $\frac{2}{5}$ = 0.4
4. $\frac{40}{100}$ = 0.4
5. $\frac{6}{10}$ = 0.6
6. $\frac{10}{100}$ = 0.1
7. $\frac{8}{100}$ = 0.08
8. $\frac{28.5}{100}$ = 0.285
9. Answers vary. = 0.____

Math Masters, p. 140

Teaching Master

Name Date Time

LESSON 5·6 **100-Grids**

Math Masters, p. 141

3 Differentiation Options

READINESS

PARTNER ACTIVITY

15–30 Min

▶ Playing *Number Top-It* (3-Place Decimals)

(*Student Reference Book,* p. 327)

To provide experience with decimal place value and ordering decimals, have students play *Number Top-It* (3-Place Decimals). See *Student Reference Book,* page 327 for directions.

ENRICHMENT

PARTNER ACTIVITY

15–30 Min

▶ Writing Fraction and Decimal Equivalents for a Shaded 100-Grid

(*Math Masters,* pp. 140 and 141)

Portfolio Ideas

To apply students' understanding of fractions and decimals, have them complete *Math Masters*, page 140. Distribute the transparent 100-grids. Students write the fraction and decimal names for the shaded portions of squares and use a transparent 100-grid to check their answers. Students then shade a copy of *Math Masters,* page 141 to create their own designs and estimate the fraction and decimal names for the shaded portions. Have students copy their favorite design from Problem 9 and display their designs in the Fractions, Decimals, and Percents Museum.

EXTRA PRACTICE

SMALL-GROUP ACTIVITY

5–15 Min

▶ *5-Minute Math*

To offer students more experience with comparing fractions, decimals, and percentages, see *5-Minute Math,* page 93.

5·7 Fractions and Decimals: Part 3

Objective To use a calculator to find decimal equivalents for fractions.

Technology Resources www.everydaymathonline.com

ePresentations

eToolkit

Algorithms Practice

EM Facts Workshop Game™

Family Letters

Assessment Management

Common Core State Standards

Curriculum Focal Points

Interactive Teacher's Lesson Guide

1 Teaching the Lesson

Key Concepts and Skills

- Differentiate between repeating and terminating decimals. [Number and Numeration Goal 1]
- Use a calculator to rename fractions as decimals. [Number and Numeration Goal 5]
- Convert between fractions and decimals. [Number and Numeration Goal 5]
- Compare fractions, whole numbers, and mixed numbers. [Number and Numeration Goal 6]

Key Activities

Students rename fractions as decimals using a calculator. They play *Frac-Tac-Toe* to develop automatic recall of fraction-decimal equivalents.

Ongoing Assessment: Informing Instruction See page 327.

Ongoing Assessment: Recognizing Student Achievement Use journal page 145. [Number and Numeration Goal 5]

Key Vocabulary

repeating decimal

Materials

Math Journal 1, pp. 142 and 145
Student Reference Book, pp. 88 and 309–311
Study Link 5•6
Math Masters, pp. 472 and 474; pp. 478 and 482 (optional)
transparency of *Math Masters,* p. 472 (optional) ◆ slate ◆ per partnership: calculator, two-color counters or pennies, 4 each of number cards 0–10

2 Ongoing Learning & Practice

Finding Decimal Equivalents for Thirds, Sixths, and Ninths
Math Journal 1, inside back cover
Students fill in the decimals for thirds, sixths, and ninths in the Table of Decimal Equivalents.

Math Boxes 5•7
Math Journal 1, p. 146
Students practice and maintain skills through Math Box problems.

Study Link 5•7
Math Masters, p. 142
Students practice and maintain skills through Study Link activities.

3 Differentiation Options

READINESS

Recording Decimal Place Value
slate
Students review the relationship between decimal place values and denominators.

ENRICHMENT

Extending the Partial-Quotients Division Algorithm to Decimals
Math Journal 1, p. 145
Students convert between fractions and decimals by using the partial-quotients division algorithm.

Advance Preparation

For Part 1, make a transparency of *Math Masters,* page 472 to use when demonstrating *Frac-Tac-Toe.* Plan to collect and store the number-card boards and gameboards for use throughout the year. They should be easily accessible.

***Teacher's Reference Manual,* Grades 4–6** pp. 149–154

Getting Started

Mental Math and Reflexes

Fraction-of problems

●○○ There are 12 counters in a set. How many counters are in $\frac{3}{4}$ of the set? 9 counters

There are 18 counters in a set. How many counters are in $\frac{2}{9}$ of the set? 4 counters

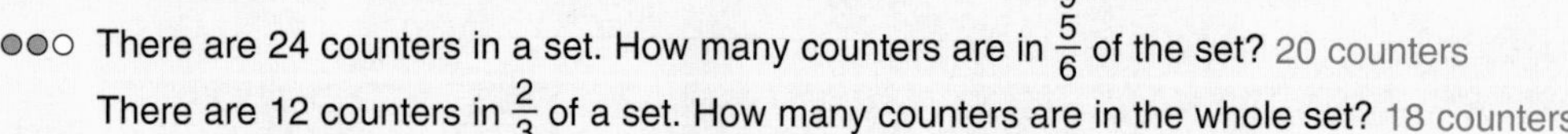

●●○ There are 24 counters in a set. How many counters are in $\frac{5}{6}$ of the set? 20 counters

There are 12 counters in $\frac{2}{3}$ of a set. How many counters are in the whole set? 18 counters

●●● There are 15 counters in $\frac{3}{5}$ of a set. How many counters are in the whole set? 25 counters

There are 32 counters in $\frac{4}{5}$ of a set. How many counters are in the whole set? 40 counters

Have students divide using a calculator. Display remainders as whole numbers.

- $\frac{125}{6}$ 20 R5
- $\frac{162}{4}$ 40 R2
- $\frac{493}{7}$ 70 R3
- $\frac{9,543}{67}$ 142 R 29

Math Message

Write the following fractions as decimals:

$\frac{7}{100}$ 0.07 $\frac{7}{16}$ 0.4375

Study Link 5·6 Follow-Up

Allow partners five minutes to compare their answers and correct any errors.

1 Teaching the Lesson

▶ Math Message Follow-Up

WHOLE-CLASS DISCUSSION

Ask volunteers to share how they found the decimal names for the fractions. Their strategies may include using a Fraction-Stick Chart, a calculator, the Probability Meter, logical reasoning, or another method.

▷ The Fraction-Stick Chart and Probability Meter yield about 0.44 as the decimal equivalent of $\frac{7}{16}$, which is a good approximation but is not exact.

▷ To use logical reasoning, a student might begin with the fact that $\frac{1}{4} = 0.25$; $\frac{1}{8}$ is half of $\frac{1}{4}$, so $\frac{1}{8} = 0.125$; $\frac{1}{16}$ is half of $\frac{1}{8}$, so $\frac{1}{16} = 0.0625$.

Because $\frac{1}{4} = \frac{4}{16}$ and $\frac{1}{8} = \frac{2}{16}$, $\frac{1}{4} + \frac{1}{8} + \frac{1}{16} = \frac{7}{16}$. So $\frac{7}{16} = 0.25 + 0.125 + 0.0625 = 0.4375$.

Neither method is completely satisfactory. The Fraction-Stick Chart approach is easy, but not exact. Logical reasoning is exact, but complicated.

▷ Using a calculator, students can toggle between fractions and decimals. The calculator method is an efficient way to find the decimal names for fractions. Ask volunteers what operation is programmed into the toggle keys to make the conversions. Multiplication and division Remind students that fractions represent division. Explain that in this lesson, students will explore the connections between fractions, decimals, and division.

Using a Calculator to Convert Fractions to Decimals

(*Math Journal 1,* p. 142; *Student Reference Book,* p. 88)

On the board or a transparency, write several easy fractions, such as $\frac{1}{2}, \frac{2}{4}, \frac{3}{6}, \frac{50}{100}, \frac{100}{200}, \frac{3}{10}, \frac{1}{4}$, and so on. For each fraction, have students say the decimal name and then use their calculators to divide the numerator by the denominator.

Ask students whether the calculator display agrees with the decimal name that they know. It does, and this process of dividing will convert all fractions to their decimal equivalents, with or without the use of a calculator.

The fraction bar separating the numerator and the denominator has the same meaning as the slash for division.

Have students turn to journal page 142. In Lesson 5–6, students used the Fraction-Stick Chart to write the decimal for each fraction in the spaces to the right of the decimal names. Tell them that they will now use their calculators to divide the numerators by the denominators and write the decimal names in the spaces to the left of the fraction names. As they work, emphasize the following ideas:

- ▷ For mixed numbers, students need to divide only the fraction part. The whole number remains the same when they write the decimal name.
- ▷ Several of the fractions involve eighths. Have students compare the decimals they noticed on the Probability Meter in Lesson 5-6 with the result when they converted these fractions using a calculator.
- ▷ Some fractions, when converted without using the calculator's fix function to limit decimal places, will fill the calculator display with one or more decimal digits that would repeat forever if the display were big enough. Such a decimal is a **repeating decimal.** It is represented by drawing a bar over the digit or digits that repeat. For example, $\frac{1}{3}$ is a repeating decimal.

$$\frac{1}{3} = 0.333333333... = 0.\overline{3}$$

Have students turn to page 88 in the *Student Reference Book* and note the examples of repeating decimals.

Converting Fractions to Decimals

(*Math Journal 1,* p. 145)

Assign partners to complete journal page 145. Students compare and convert fractions to decimals by using calculators to divide numerators by denominators. Remind them to represent repeating decimals with a bar over the repeating digit or digits. Circulate and assist.

Student Page

Date Time

More about Writing Fractions as Decimals

Sometimes when you divide without using the calculator's fix function to limit decimal places, you see that the display is filled with decimal digits. If the display were big enough, these digits would repeat forever.

Writing a bar over the digit or digits that repeat is a simple way to write these repeating decimals. Some calculators will display repeating decimals by rounding the last digit in the display. Study this table.

Fraction	Calculator Display	Decimal
$\frac{1}{3}$	0.33333333333	$0.\overline{3}$
$\frac{2}{3}$	0.66666666666 or 0.666666666667	$0.\overline{6}$
$\frac{1}{12}$	0.08333333333	$0.08\overline{3}$
$\frac{8}{9}$	0.8888888888 or 0.8888888888889	$0.\overline{8}$
$\frac{1}{22}$	0.045454545 or 0.045454545455	$0.0\overline{45}$

1. Explain how you would predict whether $\frac{2}{9}$ or $\frac{3}{9}$ is closer to 0.25 before using your calculator.
   Sample answer: I know that $\frac{3}{9}$ is equal to $\frac{1}{3}$, which is larger than $\frac{1}{4}$, or 0.25. So I would guess that $\frac{2}{9}$ is closer to 0.25 than $\frac{3}{9}$ is.

Use your calculator and convert each fraction below to a decimal by dividing the numerator by the denominator. If the result is a repeating decimal, write a bar over the digit or digits that repeat. Then circle the correct answer to each question.

2. Which is closer to 0.25? ($\frac{2}{9}$) $0.\overline{2}$ or $\frac{3}{9}$ $0.\overline{3}$
3. Which is closer to 0.8? $\frac{6}{8}$ 0.75 or ($\frac{5}{6}$) $0.8\overline{3}$
4. Which is closer to 0.6? $\frac{4}{7}$ $0.\overline{571428}$ or ($\frac{7}{12}$) $0.58\overline{3}$
5. Which is closer to 0.05? ($\frac{1}{30}$) $0.0\overline{3}$ or $\frac{1}{12}$ $0.08\overline{3}$
6. Which is closer to 0.39? ($\frac{3}{8}$) 0.375 or $\frac{7}{16}$ 0.4375

Math Journal 1, p. 145

NOTE In *Fourth Grade Everyday Mathematics*, the slash was introduced as an alternative to the traditional ÷ symbol for division. The use of the slash for division prepares students for the idea that a fraction represents a quotient. A fraction may be written as $\frac{a}{b}$ or *a/b,* and either form also means division.

Ongoing Assessment: Informing Instruction

Watch for students who are having difficulty organizing their work with mixed numbers. Ask them to circle the fraction portion of each mixed number, copy the part of the number that is not circled (the whole-number part) into the answer blank, and then perform the division on the circled fraction portion.

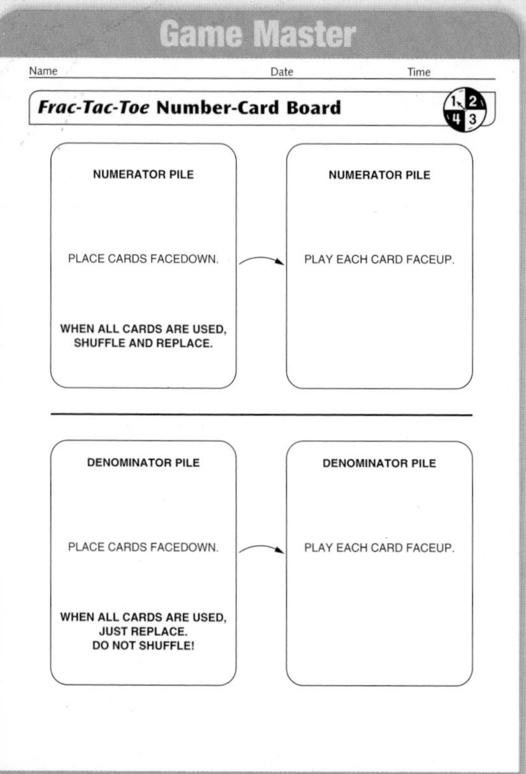
Game Master

Name Date Time

Frac-Tac-Toe **Number-Card Board**

NUMERATOR PILE

PLACE CARDS FACEDOWN.

WHEN ALL CARDS ARE USED, SHUFFLE AND REPLACE.

NUMERATOR PILE

PLAY EACH CARD FACEUP.

DENOMINATOR PILE

PLACE CARDS FACEDOWN.

WHEN ALL CARDS ARE USED, JUST REPLACE. DO NOT SHUFFLE!

DENOMINATOR PILE

PLAY EACH CARD FACEUP.

***Math Masters*, p. 472**

NOTE There are three variations of *Frac-Tac-Toe* (2-4-5-10, 2-4-8, and 3-6-9) that increase in difficulty. Each variation has four versions (Decimal, Percent, Decimal Bingo, and Percent Bingo). Playing *Frac-Tac-Toe* regularly will promote automatic recall of fraction, decimal, and percent equivalents. Allow students to use a calculator or a table of decimal equivalents when playing. Given repeated experiences with the games, they will rely less and less on these resources.

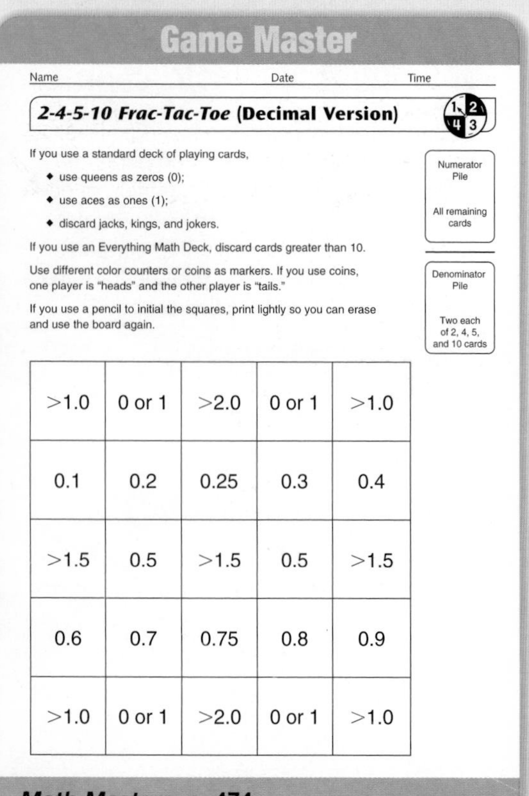
Game Master

Name Date Time

***2-4-5-10 Frac-Tac-Toe* (Decimal Version)**

If you use a standard deck of playing cards,
- use queens as zeros (0);
- use aces as ones (1);
- discard jacks, kings, and jokers.

If you use an Everything Math Deck, discard cards greater than 10.

Use different color counters or coins as markers. If you use coins, one player is "heads" and the other player is "tails."

If you use a pencil to initial the squares, print lightly so you can erase and use the board again.

Numerator Pile: All remaining cards

Denominator Pile: Two each of 2, 4, 5, and 10 cards

>1.0	0 or 1	>2.0	0 or 1	>1.0
0.1	0.2	0.25	0.3	0.4
>1.5	0.5	>1.5	0.5	>1.5
0.6	0.7	0.75	0.8	0.9
>1.0	0 or 1	>2.0	0 or 1	>1.0

***Math Masters*, p. 474**

Ongoing Assessment: Recognizing Student Achievement

Journal Page 145 Problem 1

Use **journal page 145, Problem 1** to assess students' understanding of fraction and decimal relationships and equivalencies. Students are making adequate progress if their prediction strategies refer to the relative sizes of numerators and denominators and relate these to reasonable decimal equivalents.

[Number and Numeration Goal 5]

▶ Introducing *2-4-5-10 Frac-Tac-Toe* (Decimal Version)

PARTNER ACTIVITY

(*Student Reference Book,* pp. 309–311; *Math Masters,* pp. 472 and 474)

Pass out 1 copy per partnership of both *Math Masters*, page 472, the *Frac-Tac-Toe* Number-Card Board, and page 474, the *2-4-5-10 Frac-Tac-Toe* (Decimal Version) gameboard.

Introduce *Frac-Tac-Toe* by playing a practice game of the 2-4-5-10 (Decimal Version) with the class. During this demonstration, you play the cards for everybody. If using a deck of playing cards, the aces represent *1* and the queens represent *0*.

1. Draw cards and name the fractions. Write the fractions on the board or on a transparency of the Number-Card Board.
2. Partners alternate and use the fractions you have drawn to play the game.
3. Play until there are a few winners and you are sure students know how to play. As you play, check that students are using the "0 or 1" and the "greater than" grid squares correctly.
4. There are 4 squares with the labels 0 or 1. Any one of these squares, if not already marked, may be selected if the fraction is 0 or 1. Point out that a fraction equals 0 if the numerator is 0.
5. There are 9 squares with the greater than symbol (>). Fractions equal to 1, 1.5, or 2 may cause students some difficulty at first. For example, if the fraction is $\frac{3}{2}$ (= 1.5), grid squares marked > 1.5 may not be selected, because $\frac{3}{2}$ is not greater than 1.5.

Adjusting the Activity

To extend *Frac-Tac-Toe*, have students play a more difficult variation: the *2-4-8* (Decimal Version) found on *Math Masters*, page 478 or the *3-6-9* (Decimal Version) found on *Math Masters*, page 482.

AUDITORY ◆ KINESTHETIC ◆ TACTILE ◆ VISUAL

5·8 Using a Calculator to Convert Fractions to Percents

Objectives To discuss the meaning and uses of percents; and to introduce using a calculator to convert decimals to percents.

Technology Resources www.everydaymathonline.com

ePresentations

eToolkit

Algorithms Practice

EM Facts Workshop Game™

Family Letters

Assessment Management

Common Core State Standards

Curriculum Focal Points

Interactive Teacher's Lesson Guide

1 Teaching the Lesson

Key Concepts and Skills

- Use correct notation to write terminating and repeating decimals. [Number and Numeration Goal 1]
- Define the uses and meaning of percents. [Number and Numeration Goal 2]
- Use a calculator to rename fractions as decimals. [Number and Numeration Goal 5]
- Convert between fractions, decimals, and percents. [Number and Numeration Goal 5]

Key Activities

Students review the meanings and uses of percents. They use a calculator to convert fractions to decimals and decimals to percents.

Ongoing Assessment: Informing Instruction See page 334.

Key Vocabulary

percent

Materials

Math Journal 1, pp. 147 and 148
Study Link 5·7
calculator ◆ overhead calculator (optional)

2 Ongoing Learning & Practice

Playing *2-4-5-10 Frac-Tac-Toe* (Percent Version)
Student Reference Book, pp. 309–311
per partnership: *Math Masters,* pp. 472 and 476, 4 each of number cards 0–10 (from the Everything Math Deck, if available), counters or pennies, calculator
Students convert fractions to percents.

Ongoing Assessment: Recognizing Student Achievement
Use *Math Masters,* page 476.
[Number and Numeration Goal 5]

Math Boxes 5·8
Math Journal 1, p. 149
Students practice and maintain skills through Math Box problems.

Study Link 5·8
Math Masters, p. 143
Students practice and maintain skills through Study Link activities.

3 Differentiation Options

READINESS

Playing *Fraction/Percent Concentration*
Student Reference Book, p. 315
Math Masters, pp. 467 and 468
calculator
Students convert between fractions and percents.

ENRICHMENT

Solving Percent-of Number Stories
Math Masters, p. 144
Students solve percent-of number stories.

EXTRA PRACTICE

Writing and Solving Number Stories
Math Masters, p. 425
Students write and solve number stories.

ELL SUPPORT

Building a Math Word Bank
Differentiation Handbook, p. 142
Students add the term *percent* to their Math Word Banks.

Advance Preparation

For the optional Readiness activity in Part 3, students will need one set of 24 *Fraction/Percent Concentration* Tiles. Make two-sided copies using *Math Masters,* pages 467 and 468 to form the fronts and backs of the tiles. Cut out the tiles prior to play.

Review how to use the fix key on the calculator prior to having students complete the Mental Math and Reflexes. See *Student Reference Book,* pages 268 and 269.

***Teacher's Reference Manual,* Grades 4–6** 69–71, 153, 154

Getting Started

Mental Math and Reflexes

Use the following problems to practice rounding numbers. Students write decimals from dictation then round the decimals to a specified place.
Suggestions:

●○○ Two and eighty-seven hundredths rounded to the nearest tenth 2.87 → 2.9

Seven and seven hundredths rounded to the nearest tenth 7.07 → 7.1

●●○ Fourteen and one hundred eight thousandths rounded to the nearest hundredth 14.108 → 14.11

Five and five hundred fifty-five thousandths rounded to the nearest tenth 5.555 → 5.6

●●● Sixty and three hundred fifty-seven thousandths rounded to the nearest tenth 60.357 → 60.4

Twenty-five and three thousandths rounded to the nearest tenth 25.003 → 25.0

Math Message

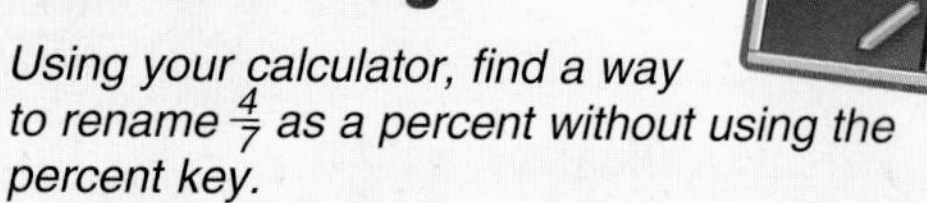

Using your calculator, find a way to rename $\frac{4}{7}$ as a percent without using the percent key.

Study Link 5•7 Follow-Up

Allow partners five minutes to compare their answers and correct any errors.

NOTE Examples of fraction-to-decimal conversions in this lesson are obtained from a calculator with an 11-digit display that rounds to the 11th place. Check the number of digits in the display and how the last digit is handled by your class calculators, and make appropriate adjustments as you work through the lesson.

1 Teaching the Lesson

▶ Math Message Follow-Up

WHOLE-CLASS DISCUSSION

Ask volunteers to share their strategies. Use their responses to emphasize that a fraction can be renamed as an equivalent **percent** by first renaming the fraction as a decimal, and then multiplying the result by 100. Use an overhead calculator, if available, to model this process.

Example: Rename $\frac{4}{7}$ as a percent.

1. Divide 4 by 7. The calculator displays 0.5714285714.
2. Multiply the result by 100. This is the approximate percent equivalent of $\frac{4}{7}$.

   $100 * 0.5714285714 = 57.14285714.$
3. The whole-number portion of the display represents whole percents. Round to the nearest whole percent: 57%.

Ask students to use their calculators to mirror each step as you rename several more fractions as percents.

▶ Reviewing the Meaning of *Percent*

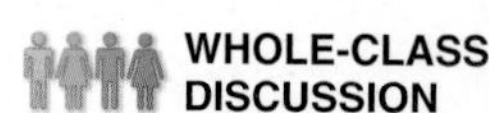

WHOLE-CLASS DISCUSSION

Language Arts Link The word *percent* comes from the Latin *per centum: per* means *for* and *centum* means *one hundred.*

Remind students that just as a fraction represents a fraction of something, a percent represents a percent of something. That something is the whole (the ONE or unit). To understand a percent, you must know what the ONE represents: 50% of $1 is not the same as 50% of $1 million.

Ask students to restate the following examples in a variety of ways to express what the percent means.

Example 1: Allison scored 80% on a test.

▷ If the test had 100 questions, Allison answered 80, or $\frac{80}{100}$, questions correctly.

▷ Allison answered 80 out of every 100 questions correctly, or for every 100 questions, Allison answered 80 correctly.

Ask students to find how many questions Allison answered correctly if there were 50 questions on the test. 40 questions If there were 10 questions? 8 questions 200 questions? 160 questions Ask volunteers to share their strategies.

Example 2: Emily spent 18% of the money she earned babysitting last summer on school clothes.

▷ For every \$100 she earned, Emily spent \$18 on school clothes; or Emily spent \$18 out of every \$100 she earned on school clothes.

▷ If 100 babysitting dollars were earned, 18 of those dollars were spent on school clothes.

▷ Emily spent $\frac{18}{100}$ of her money on school clothes.

Emphasize that "18 out of 100" does not mean that exactly \$100 was earned, but that \$18 out of every \$100 earned was spent on school clothes. Ask students how much Emily would have spent on school clothes if she earned \$200. \$36 If she earned \$400. \$72 If she earned \$50. \$9

▶ Exploring the Purpose of Percents

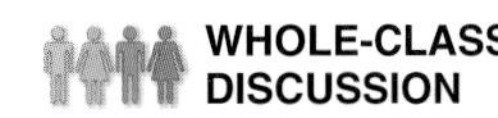

WHOLE-CLASS DISCUSSION

Explain that percents are useful for making comparisons between quantities when the whole is not the same. For example, 8 correct on a test seems better than 4 correct on a test, but it depends on how many questions were on each test—8 out of 20 questions, or 40%, is worse than 4 out of 5 questions, or 80%. Using percents is an efficient way to make comparisons when the whole or ONE differs.

Example: Tonya earned \$167 setting up new computers for her neighbors. She spent \$43 on software. Juan earned \$219 teaching piano to children. He spent \$51 on sheet music. Who spent the larger portion of their earnings?

Ask students what strategies they would use to compare the fractions $\frac{43}{167}$ to $\frac{51}{219}$. Most students will probably suggest converting the fractions to decimals. Or they might suggest changing the fractions to a simpler form, but this would be difficult because 43 and 51 are prime numbers and neither of them are multiples of their denominators.

Student Page

Date Time

LESSON 5·8 Converting to Decimals and Percents

Example: Teneil used her calculator to rename the following fraction as a decimal and as a percent.

Fraction	Decimal	Percent
$\frac{14}{23}$	14 ÷ 23 = 0.6086956522	100 × 0.6086956522 = 60.86956522%

Teneil needed to work with only a whole percent, so she rounded 60.86956522% to 61%.

1. Use your calculator to convert each fraction to a decimal. Write all of the digits shown in the display. Then write the equivalent percent rounded to the nearest whole percent. The first row has been done for you.

Fraction	Decimal	Percent
$\frac{18}{35}$	0.5142857143	51%
$\frac{12}{67}$	0.1791044776	18%
$\frac{24}{93}$	0.2580645161	26%
$\frac{13}{24}$	0.5416666667	54%
$\frac{576}{1,339}$	0.43017177	43%

2. Lionel got 80% of the questions correct on a spelling test. If the test had 20 questions, how many did Lionel get correct? 16 questions

3. Jamie spent 50% of his money on a baseball cap. The cap cost \$15. How much money did Jamie have at the beginning? \$30

4. Hunter got 75% of the questions correct on a music test. If he got 15 questions correct, how many questions were on the test? 20 questions

Math Journal 1, p. 147

Student Page

Date Time

LESSON 5·8 Converting to Decimals and Percents *cont.*

5. The chart lists 6 animals and the average number of hours per day that each spends sleeping.

   Write the fraction of a day that each animal sleeps. Then calculate the equivalent decimal and percent, rounded to the nearest whole percent. You may use your calculator. The first row has been done for you.

Animal	Average Hours of Sleep per Day	Fraction of Day Spent Sleeping	Decimal Equivalent	Percent of Day Spent Sleeping
Lion and Sloth	20	$\frac{20}{24}$	$0.8\overline{3}$	83%
Opossum	19	$\frac{19}{24}$	$0.791\overline{6}$	79%
Armadillo and Koala	18	$\frac{18}{24}$	0.75	75%
Southern Owl Monkey	17	$\frac{17}{24}$	$0.708\overline{3}$	71%

Source: *The Top 10 of Everything 2005*

6. The total number of horses in the world is about 60,800,000. China is the country with the greatest number of horses (about 8,900,000). What percent of the world's horses live in China? About 15%

7. In the United States, about 45% of the population has blood type O. About how many people out of every 100 have blood type O? About 45 people

8. About 11 out of every 100 households in the United States has a parakeet. How would you express this as a percent? 11%

9. It is thought that adults need an average of 8 hours of sleep per day.

   a. What percent of the day should adults sleep? 33%

   b. If infants average 16 hours of sleep per day, what percent of the day do they sleep? 67%

Math Journal 1, p. 148

Student Page

Games

Frac-Tac-Toe

2-4-5-10 *Frac-Tac-Toe*

Materials
- number cards 0—10 (4 of each)
- 1 *Frac-Tac-Toe* Number-Card Board (*Math Masters,* p. 472)
- 1 *2-4-5-10 Frac-Tac-Toe* (Decimals) gameboard (*Math Masters,* p. 474)
- counters (2 colors), or pennies (one player using heads; the other, tails)
- 1 calculator

Players 2

Skill Renaming fractions as decimals and percents

Object of the game To cover 3 squares in a row, in any direction (horizontal, vertical, diagonal).

Advance Preparation Separate the cards into 2 piles on the Number-Card Board a numerator pile and a denominator pile. For a *2-4-5-10* game, place 2 each of the 2, 4, 5, and 10 cards in the denominator pile. All other cards are placed on the numerator pile. Shuffle the cards in each pile. Place the piles number-side down in the left-hand spaces. When the numerator pile is completely used, reshuffle that pile, and place it number-side down in the left-hand space. When the denominator pile is completely used, turn it over and place it number-side down in the left-hand space without reshuffling it.

Directions

1. Players take turns. When it is your turn:
   - Turn over the top card from each pile to form a fraction (numerator card above denominator card).
   - Try to match the fraction shown with one of the grid squares on the gameboard. If a match is found, cover that grid square with your counter and your turn is over. If no match is found, your turn is over.
2. To change the fraction shown by the cards to a decimal, players may use either a calculator or the *Table of Decimal Equivalents for Fractions* on page 400.

***Frac-Tac-Toe* Number-Card Board**

NUMERATOR PILE — PLACE CARDS NUMBER-SIDE DOWN. WHEN ALL CARDS ARE USED, SHUFFLE AND REPLACE.

NUMERATOR PILE — PLAY EACH CARD NUMBER-SIDE UP.

DENOMINATOR PILE — PLACE CARDS NUMBER-SIDE DOWN. WHEN ALL CARDS ARE USED, JUST REPLACE. DO NOT SHUFFLE!

DENOMINATOR PILE — PLAY EACH CARD NUMBER-SIDE UP.

Gameboard for *2-4-5-10 Frac-Tac-Toe* (Decimals)

>1.0	0 or 1	>2.0	0 or 1	>1.0
0.1	0.2	0.25	0.3	0.4
>1.5	0.5	>1.5	0.5	>1.5
0.6	0.7	0.75	0.8	0.9
>1.0	0 or 1	>2.0	0 or 1	>1.0

***Student Reference Book,* p. 309**

Game Master

Name Date Time

2-4-5-10 *Frac-Tac-Toe* (Percent Version)

If you use a standard deck of playing cards,
- use queens as zeros (0);
- use aces as ones (1);
- discard jacks, kings, and jokers.

If you use an Everything Math Deck, discard cards greater than 10.

Use different color counters or coins as markers. If you use coins, one player is "heads" and the other player is "tails."

If you use a pencil to initial the squares, print lightly so you can erase and use the board again.

Numerator Pile — All remaining cards

Denominator Pile — Two each of 2, 4, 5, and 10 cards

>100%	0% or 100%	>200%	0% or 100%	>100%
10%	20%	25%	30%	40%
>100%	50%	>200%	50%	>100%
60%	70%	75%	80%	90%
>100%	0% or 100%	>200%	0% or 100%	>100%

***Math Masters,* p. 476**

Ask students to rename the fractions as decimals and compare. Then rename the decimals as percents and compare. Ask students which comparison was easier and why.

This situation illustrates why, when you are making comparisons, fractions are renamed so they have the same denominator (if that is easy to do). Or fractions are converted to percents if a common denominator is difficult to find. In effect, conversion to percents gives these fractions a common denominator of 100, making them easy to compare.

▶ Converting Fractions to Percents

PARTNER ACTIVITY

ELL

PROBLEM SOLVING

(*Math Journal 1,* pp. 147 and 148)

Explain that mathematically, a comparison with decimals is equivalent to a comparison with percents, but in everyday situations, people usually prefer percents. This is because with percents, the denominator is always 100. With decimals, the denominator can be 100, or 10, or 1,000, and so on.

In addition to multiplying by 100, decimals can be changed to percents in two other ways. To support English language learners, write examples of each way on the board.

- ▷ Round to the nearest hundredth. The decimal for Tonya, 0.2574850299 becomes 0.26, or 26%, and the decimal for Juan, 0.2328767123 becomes 0.23, or 23%.
- ▷ Truncate the decimals after the hundredths place. 0.2574850299 becomes 0.25, or 25%, and 0.2328767123 becomes 0.23, or 23%.

Tonya spent $\frac{\$43}{\$167}$, or about 26% of her earnings, and Juan spent $\frac{\$51}{\$219}$, or about 23%. Tonya spent a larger portion of her earnings than Juan did of his.

Ongoing Assessment: Informing Instruction

Watch for students who are unclear about how to interpret the calculator display when converting a decimal to a percent. Refer to a decimal place-value chart, and remind students to count decimal places by starting at the decimal point in the display.

Review the example on page 147 with the class. Assign partners to complete pages 147 and 148. Circulate and assist.

2 Ongoing Learning & Practice

▶ Playing *2-4-5-10 Frac-Tac-Toe* (Percent Version)

PARTNER ACTIVITY

(*Student Reference Book*, pp. 309–311; *Math Masters*, pp. 472 and 476)

Play the Percent Version of *2-4-5-10 Frac-Tac-Toe.* The game is like the Decimal Version played in Lesson 5-7, except that players convert fractions to percents. Distribute one copy of both *Math Masters,* pages 472 and 476 to each partnership. Partners will also need counters, a calculator, and 4 each of the number cards 0–10.

Ongoing Assessment: Recognizing Student Achievement

***Math Masters* Page 476**

Use **Math Masters, page 476** to assess students' ability to recognize percent equivalents for fractions. Have students write their fractions in their chosen squares on the *Frac-Tac-Toe* gameboard as they play. They can identify their squares by writing their initials next to the fractions or by color coding the squares. Students are making adequate progress if they correctly identify fraction/percent equivalents.

[Number and Numeration Goal 5]

▶ Math Boxes 5•8

INDEPENDENT ACTIVITY

(*Math Journal 1,* p. 149)

Mixed Practice Math Boxes in this lesson are paired with Math Boxes in Lesson 5-6. The skill in Problem 6 previews Unit 6 content.

Writing/Reasoning Have students write a response to the following: *Explain the strategies you used to compare and order the fractions in Problem 5.* Sample answer: I started by finding the least and the greatest fractions: The closest to 0 was $\frac{2}{8}$, and the closest to 1 was $\frac{8}{9}$. Of the other 3 fractions, $\frac{5}{6}$ was the largest. Lastly, I compared $\frac{3}{7}$ and $\frac{3}{5}$. They have the same numerator, so I had to compare only the denominators: Sevenths are smaller than fifths.

▶ Study Link 5•8

INDEPENDENT ACTIVITY

(*Math Masters,* p. 143)

Home Connection Students practice converting fractions to decimals and decimals to percents. They compare fractions by converting them to decimals and to percents, and they use percents to solve number stories.

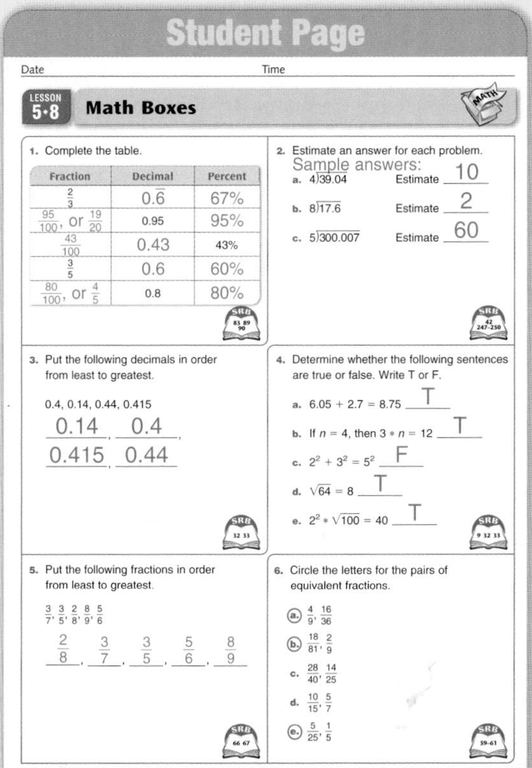

Student Page

Date Time

LESSON 5•8 **Math Boxes**

1. Complete the table.

Fraction	Decimal	Percent
$\frac{2}{3}$	0.6	67%
$\frac{95}{100}$, or $\frac{19}{20}$	0.95	95%
$\frac{43}{100}$	0.43	43%
$\frac{3}{5}$	0.6	60%
$\frac{80}{100}$, or $\frac{4}{5}$	0.8	80%

2. Estimate an answer for each problem. Sample answers:

a. $4\overline{)39.04}$ Estimate 10

b. $8\overline{)17.6}$ Estimate 2

c. $5\overline{)300.007}$ Estimate 60

3. Put the following decimals in order from least to greatest.

0.4, 0.14, 0.44, 0.415

0.14, 0.4, 0.415, 0.44

4. Determine whether the following sentences are true or false. Write T or F.

a. $6.05 + 2.7 = 8.75$ T

b. If $n = 4$, then $3 * n = 12$ T

c. $2^2 + 3^2 = 5^2$ F

d. $\sqrt{64} = 8$ T

e. $2^2 * \sqrt{100} = 40$ T

5. Put the following fractions in order from least to greatest.

$\frac{3}{7}, \frac{3}{5}, \frac{2}{8}, \frac{8}{9}, \frac{5}{6}$

$\frac{2}{8}, \frac{3}{7}, \frac{3}{5}, \frac{5}{6}, \frac{8}{9}$

6. Circle the letters for the pairs of equivalent fractions.

(a.) $\frac{4}{9}, \frac{16}{36}$

(b.) $\frac{18}{81}, \frac{2}{9}$

c. $\frac{28}{40}, \frac{14}{25}$

d. $\frac{10}{15}, \frac{5}{7}$

(e.) $\frac{5}{25}, \frac{1}{5}$

Math Journal 1, p. 149

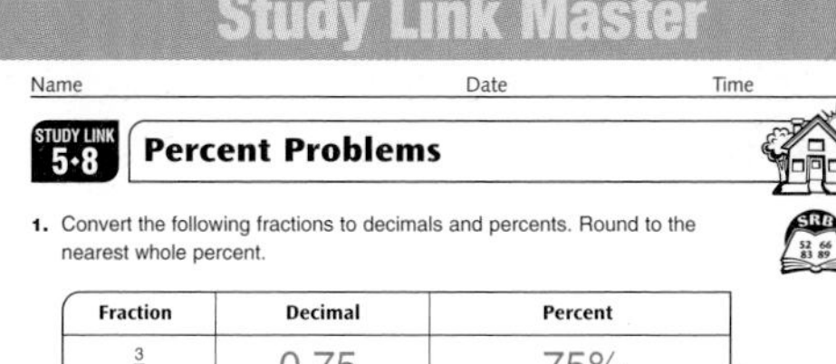

Study Link Master

Name Date Time

STUDY LINK 5•8 **Percent Problems**

1. Convert the following fractions to decimals and percents. Round to the nearest whole percent.

Fraction	Decimal	Percent
$\frac{3}{4}$	0.75	75%
$\frac{14}{16}$	0.875	88%
$\frac{15}{25}$	0.6	60%
$\frac{17}{20}$	0.85	85%
$\frac{3}{8}$	0.375	38%

2. On the back of this page, explain how you could find the percent equivalent to $\frac{17}{20}$ without using a calculator. Answers vary.

3. Write the five fractions from Problem 1 in order from least to greatest.

$\frac{3}{8}$, $\frac{15}{25}$, $\frac{3}{4}$, $\frac{17}{20}$, $\frac{14}{16}$

4. Katie spent 50% of her money on shoes for soccer. The shoes cost \$65. How much money did Katie start with? \$130

5. Tom got 70% of the questions correct on a music test. If he got 7 questions correct, how many questions were on the test? 10 questions

Practice

6. $10\overline{)975}$ → 97 R5

7. $20\overline{)975}$ → 48 R15

8. $30\overline{)975}$ → 32 R15

9. $40\overline{)975}$ → 24 R15

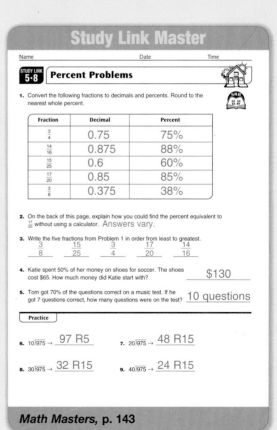

Math Masters, p. 143

Game Master

Name Date Time

Fraction/Percent Concentration Tiles (Front)

10%	20%	25%	30%
40%	50%	60%	70%
75%	80%	90%	100%
$\frac{1}{2}$	$\frac{1}{4}$	$\frac{3}{4}$	$\frac{1}{5}$
$\frac{2}{5}$	$\frac{3}{5}$	$\frac{4}{5}$	$\frac{1}{10}$
$\frac{3}{10}$	$\frac{7}{10}$	$\frac{9}{10}$	$\frac{2}{2}$

Math Masters, p. 467

Teaching Master

Name Date Time

LESSON 5·8 **Solving Percent Number Stories**

Solve.

1. Paul has 150 marbles in his collection. How many marbles are about 25% of the collection? 38 marbles

   About how many marbles are 66%? 99 marbles

2. Beatrice decided to sell some of her doll collection. She sold 20 dolls. This was 40% of her collection. How many dolls did she have left? 30 dolls

3. Each day, the bakery makes pastries: 25% are chocolate donuts, 37.5% are butter cookies, 25% are breakfast buns, and the rest are the daily special. There are 90 breakfast buns.

   How many pastries are made each day? 360 pastries

   What percent of each day's pastries are the daily special? 12.5%

   How many of the daily special pastries are made? 45 daily specials

4. After the first 85 days of school, a fifth-grade class had perfect attendance for 80% of that time. How many days did the class have perfect attendance? 68 days

5. Write a percent of story problem for your partner to solve. Remember that you must provide either the whole, or an amount and the percent of the whole that it represents.

   Answers vary.

Math Masters, p. 144

3 Differentiation Options

READINESS

PARTNER ACTIVITY | 15–30 Min

▶ Playing *Fraction/Percent Concentration*

(*Student Reference Book,* p. 315; *Math Masters,* pp. 467 and 468)

To provide experience with converting between fractions and percents, have students play *Fraction/Percent Concentration* prior to teaching Part 1. Consider having students make posters of their winning tiles to place in the Fractions, Decimals, and Percents Museum.

ENRICHMENT

PARTNER ACTIVITY | 15–30 Min | PROBLEM SOLVING

▶ Solving Percent-of Number Stories

(*Math Masters,* p. 144)

To apply students' understanding of percents, have them solve the number stories on *Math Masters,* page 144. Have partners compare and discuss their solutions and then create problems for each other to solve.

EXTRA PRACTICE

PARTNER ACTIVITY | 15–30 Min

▶ Writing and Solving Number Stories

(*Math Masters,* p. 425)

Students write number stories using a data bank of whole and mixed numbers, fractions, decimals, and percents. As students complete their stories, have them exchange with a partner. Then have them solve the number story and explain their solution. Encourage students to work together to revise any stories that do not have appropriate questions or other elements that make the story difficult to solve.

ELL SUPPORT

SMALL-GROUP ACTIVITY | 5–15 Min

▶ Building a Math Word Bank

(*Differentiation Handbook,* p. 142)

To provide language support for fractions, decimals, and percents, have students use the Word Bank Template on *Differentiation Handbook,* page 142. Ask students to write the term *percent,* draw a picture relating to the term, and write other related words. See the *Differentiation Handbook* for more information.

5•9 Bar and Circle Graphs

Objectives To review the properties and construction of bar graphs; and to discuss the properties of circle graphs.

www.everydaymathonline.com

ePresentations

eToolkit

Algorithms Practice

EM Facts Workshop Game™

Family Letters

Assessment Management

Common Core State Standards

Curriculum Focal Points

Interactive Teacher's Lesson Guide

1 Teaching the Lesson

Key Concepts and Skills

- Create a bar graph for a data set. [Data and Chance Goal 1]
- Explore how circle graphs represent data. [Data and Chance Goal 2]

Key Activities

Students use class data to construct and label a bar graph. They discuss circle graphs and describe how they might be made.

Ongoing Assessment: Recognizing Student Achievement
Use the Math Message.
[Data and Chance Goal 1]

Key Vocabulary

bar graph ◆ circle (or pie) graph

Materials

Math Journal 1, pp. 150 and 151
Study Link 5•8
slate ◆ 4 each of number cards 0–10 (from the Everything Math Deck, if available) ◆ calculator ◆ Class Data Pad ◆ posterboard (optional)

2 Ongoing Learning & Practice

Math Boxes 5•9
Math Journal 1, p. 152
Students practice and maintain skills through Math Box problems.

Study Link 5•9
Math Masters, p. 145
Students practice and maintain skills through Study Link activities.

3 Differentiation Options

READINESS

Acting Out the Construction of a Circle Graph
string ◆ chalk (optional) ◆ masking tape ◆ ruler ◆ paper circles
Students act out the construction of a circle graph.

EXTRA PRACTICE

Finding Equivalent Fractions
Math Masters, p. 146
calculator
Students practice using the multiplication and division rules to find equivalent fractions.

ELL SUPPORT

Comparing Bar and Circle Graphs
Differentiation Handbook, p. 149
Students construct a Venn Diagram to compare bar graphs and circle graphs.

Advance Preparation

For Part 1, use the Class Data Pad or posterboard to make the table from Study Link 5•8. Include the column headings, but leave the cells blank.

For the optional Readiness activity in Part 3, cut two 6-foot lengths of string and tie a small loop at one end of each one (big enough to fit around the end of a pencil). Draw a circle, 7 inches in diameter, on unlined paper. Mark the center of the circle with a large dot.

***Teacher's Reference Manual,* Grades 4–6** pp. 161–167, 234–236

Getting Started

Mental Math and Reflexes

Students write decimal and percent equivalents for easy fractions without using a calculator.

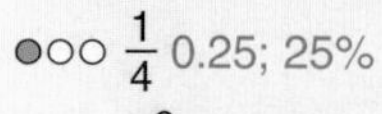

●○○ $\frac{1}{4}$ 0.25; 25%
$\frac{6}{100}$ 0.06; 6%

●●○ $\frac{14}{100}$ 0.14;14%
$\frac{3}{4}$ 0.75; 75%

●●● $\frac{3}{5}$ 0.6; 60%
$\frac{7}{20}$ 0.35; 35%

Use playing cards to randomly generate fractions: Deal 2 cards—1 for the numerator, 1 for the denominator. Students use their calculators to convert the fractions to percents. For example, $\frac{2}{10}$ = 20%, and $\frac{8}{3}$ = 267% (rounded to the nearest whole percent).

Math Message

Complete journal page 150.

Study Link 5·8 Follow-Up

Assign partners to fill in the table on the Class Data Pad or posterboard with their solutions from Problem 1 of the Study Link. Ask volunteers to share their strategies for converting $\frac{17}{20}$ to a percent with and without a calculator. Review strategies for solving Problems 4 and 5. *Suggestions:*

- For Problem 4, double the amount to find the total.
- For Problem 5, notice that each question must be worth 10%, so there are 10 questions in 100%.

Display the completed table in the Fractions, Decimals, and Percents Museum.

1 Teaching the Lesson

▶ Math Message Follow-Up

WHOLE-CLASS ACTIVITY

(*Math Journal 1,* p. 150)

Survey the class to compare the graph similarities. Make a list of the similarities on the Class Data Pad. Repeat for the graph differences.

Ongoing Assessment: Recognizing Student Achievement

Math Message

Use the **Math Message** to assess students' knowledge of bar and circle graphs. Students are making adequate progress if they are able to identify major similarities and differences.

[Data and Chance Goal 1]

▶ Reviewing the Parts of Bar Graphs

WHOLE-CLASS DISCUSSION

ELL

(*Math Journal 1,* p. 151)

Ask students to circle their favorite after-school snack on the journal page. Then poll students for their choices and record the class results on the board or a transparency as students record and total the results on their journal pages. Explain that students will construct a bar graph of this data in Problem 3.

Student Page

Date Time

LESSON 5·9 **Math Message**

Vegetable Crop

Bushels Harvested: 0, 10, 20, 30, 40, 50, 60, 70

Tomatoes, Zucchini, Cucumbers, Potatoes, Squash

Vegetable Crop

tomatoes 32%
zucchini 25%
squash 7%
potatoes 14%
cucumbers 22%

List how the 2 graphs above are the same and how they are different. Sample answers:

Similarities

Both graphs have the same title.
Both graphs have the same vegetables.
If you find the percent of the vegetables that were harvested in the bar graph, that percent is about equal to the percents listed in the circle graph.

Differences

Bar Graph	Circle Graph
The bar graph gives the amounts in bushels. The length of each bar shows the amount that was harvested.	The circle graph gives the percent of each harvest. The size of each part of the circle shows the percent of the harvest.

***Math Journal 1,* p. 150**

Remind students that a **bar graph** should have the following parts. To support English language learners, write these important ideas on the board:

A Bar Graph Must Have These Parts:

1. A title that describes what is being graphed.
2. A list of the groups or categories for which bars are drawn.
3. A number line with a scale; the scale is used to draw bars of lengths that show the amount of data in each group or category. The scale is usually labeled.

NOTE *Double-bar graphs,* also known as *side-by-side bar graphs,* display two sets of similar data on one graph. To introduce students to double-bar graphs, see www.everydaymathonline.com.

Graphing Snack-Survey Data

(*Math Journal 1,* p. 151)

Ask students to make the bar graph in Problem 3.

When most students have finished, bring the class together. Ask volunteers to share the process they used to make the bar graph.

Expect students to take a variety of approaches in graphing the snack-survey data. Some will use horizontal bars; others will use vertical bars. Some will draw thick bars; others will draw thin ones, or perhaps draw lines instead of bars. In all cases, it is important that the graphs be titled and labeled.

NOTE Bars on a bar graph can be vertical (columns) or horizontal (rows). Either version is correct.

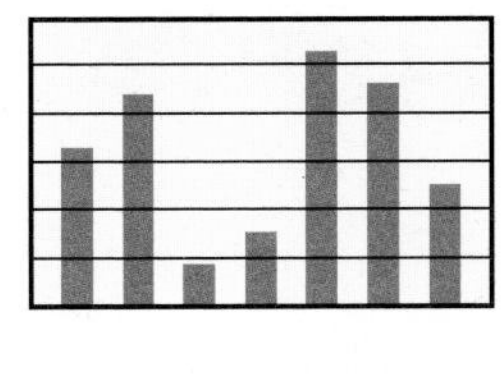

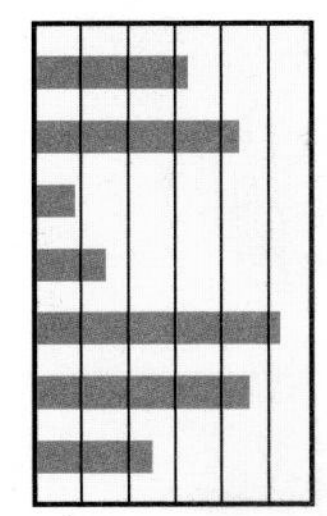

Discussing Properties of Circle Graphs

(*Math Journal 1,* p. 151)

Use Problem 4 on the journal page to begin a discussion of **circle graphs.** Ask questions and encourage responses such as the following:

- What is the graph in Problem 4 called? Explain why. It's called a circle graph, because a circle has been divided to show each kind of snack. It's also called a pie graph because the circle is sliced up like a pie—one slice for each kind of snack.

NOTE Both names—circle graph and pie graph—are accepted and used extensively in mathematics. Write circle graph and pie graph next to an example on the board to support English language learners.

- Why do you think the slices or sectors are different sizes? Popular snacks get bigger slices; less popular snacks get smaller slices.
- Do you notice any interesting slices or sectors or other features in the graph? Sample answers: 5 students out of 20 picked cookies.That's $\frac{1}{4}$ of the students—and you can see that the cookie part is $\frac{1}{4}$ of the pie. Half the students (10) picked either fruit or candy bar and those two pieces together are half the pie.
- How do you think the students made the graph? One way would have been to divide the circle into 20 slices of the same

Student Page

Date Time

LESSON 5·9 **Bar Graphs and Circle (Pie) Graphs**

1. Circle the after-school snack you like best. Mark only one answer.
cookies granola bar candy bar fruit other
Sample answers for Problems 2–4.
2. Record the class results of the survey.
cookies 8 granola bar 4 candy bar 10 fruit 2 other 1
Add all of the votes. Total: 25
The total is the number of students who voted.
3. Make and label a bar graph of the class data showing the results.

Our Snacks

Number of Students (0–14); Cookies, Granola Bar, Candy Bar, Fruit, Other

4. Another fifth-grade class with 20 students collected snack-survey data. The class made the circle graph (also called a pie graph) below.
Tell how you think they made the graph.
They divided the circle into 20 equal parts and shaded the slices according to the number of students in each category.

Our Snacks: granola bar 4, cookies 5, other 1, fruit 3, candy bar 7

Math Journal 1, p. 151

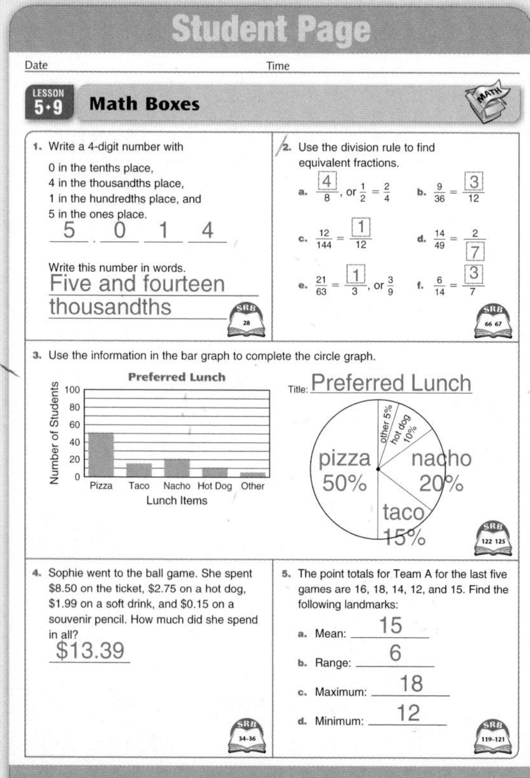
Student Page

Date Time

LESSON 5•9 **Math Boxes**

1. Write a 4-digit number with 0 in the tenths place, 4 in the thousandths place, 1 in the hundredths place, and 5 in the ones place.
   5 . 0 1 4
   Write this number in words.
   Five and fourteen thousandths
   SRB 28

2. Use the division rule to find equivalent fractions.
   a. $\frac{\boxed{4}}{8}$, or $\frac{1}{2} = \frac{2}{4}$
   b. $\frac{9}{36} = \frac{\boxed{3}}{12}$
   c. $\frac{12}{144} = \frac{\boxed{1}}{12}$
   d. $\frac{14}{49} = \frac{2}{\boxed{7}}$
   e. $\frac{21}{63} = \frac{\boxed{1}}{3}$, or $\frac{3}{9}$
   f. $\frac{6}{14} = \frac{\boxed{3}}{7}$
   SRB 66 67

3. Use the information in the bar graph to complete the circle graph.
   Preferred Lunch
   Number of Students: 0, 20, 40, 60, 80, 100
   Pizza, Taco, Nacho, Hot Dog, Other
   Lunch Items
   Title: Preferred Lunch
   pizza 50%, nacho 20%, taco 15%, hot dog 10%, other 5%
   SRB 122 125

4. Sophie went to the ball game. She spent \$8.50 on the ticket, \$2.75 on a hot dog, \$1.99 on a soft drink, and \$0.15 on a souvenir pencil. How much did she spend in all?
   \$13.39
   SRB 34-36

5. The point totals for Team A for the last five games are 16, 18, 14, 12, and 15. Find the following landmarks:
   a. Mean: 15
   b. Range: 6
   c. Maximum: 18
   d. Minimum: 12
   SRB 119-121

Math Journal 1, p. 152

size, and then call 3 of the slices fruit, 7 of the slices candy bar, and so on for the other snack choices.

Conclude the discussion by emphasizing that circle graphs should have the following parts. Write these important ideas on the board:

1. A title that describes what is being graphed
2. Sectors or slices that indicate the portion of the whole represented by a group or category
3. Labels that identify the group or category represented by each sector or slice

2 Ongoing Learning & Practice

▶ Math Boxes 5•9

(*Math Journal 1*, p. 152)

Mixed Practice Math Boxes in this lesson are paired with Math Boxes in Lesson 5-11. The skill in Problem 5 previews Unit 6 content.

Writing/Reasoning Have students write a response to the following: *You have been asked to report the results of the preferred lunch survey in Problem 3. Which graph would you use in your presentation? Explain why.* Sample answer: I would use the bar graph because it readily shows how pizza compares to each of the other lunches.

▶ Study Link 5•9

(*Math Masters*, p. 145)

Home Connection Students match graphs with data. They choose the representation that best shows the results.

Study Link Master

Name Date Time

STUDY LINK 5•9 **Graphs**

Brenda's class made a list of their favorite colors. Here are the results.

Blue 8 Red 7 Yellow 3 Green 2 Other 4

SRB 122 124 125

1. Circle each graph that correctly represents the data above. (There may be more than one.)

Marsha kept track of low temperatures. Here are the results for the end of May:

May 17	50°F	May 18	63°F	May 19	58°F	May 20	60°F
May 21	65°F	May 22	57°F	May 23	58°F	May 24	65°F
May 25	68°F	May 26	70°F	May 27	66°F	May 28	65°F
May 29	64°F	May 30	68°F	May 31	74°F		

Line Graph Bar Graph

2. Which graph do you think is more helpful for answering the question, "On how many days was the low temperature 65°F?" Bar graph
3. Which graph do you think is more helpful for showing trends in the temperature for the last two weeks of May? Line graph
4. On the back of this page, explain your choices for Problems 2 and 3.
   The bar graph shows the number of days at each temperature, so I chose it for Problem 2. The line graph shows the temperature for each day, so I chose it for Problem 3.

Math Masters, p. 145

3 Differentiation Options

READINESS

▶ Acting Out the Construction of a Circle Graph

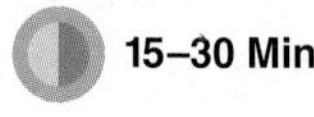

To provide experience with circle graphs, have students make human circle graphs. Clear a large area of the classroom. (If you cannot clear a large enough area in your classroom, consider doing this activity on the playground and drawing the circle with chalk;

or perhaps use a circle painted on the basketball court in the gym.) Follow the steps below:

1. Make a large circle. This is the pie.
   a. Record the numbers of boys and girls in the class.
   b. Stick a small piece of tape to the floor to mark the center of the circle.
   c. Put a pencil through the loop end of one of the 6-foot lengths of string. This string compass will be used to draw a circle with a radius of 6 feet.
   d. One student holds the free end of the string to the floor on top of the tape, at the center of the circle.
   e. A second student holds the pencil end of the string compass taut and uses it to slowly trace a circle.
   f. As the student traces the circle, follow along and lay masking tape on the floor to create a circle of tape.
2. Make a human circle graph for the boy-girl data.
   a. Students stand on the edge of the circle: all boys together and all girls together. (*See margin.*)
   b. Everyone faces the center of the circle. Students adjust their distances relative to one another until they are equally spaced around the circle.
3. Make a paper-and-pencil model for the human graph.
   a. Place the 7-inch-diameter paper circle so its center is on top of the center of the human circle.
   b. Put a pencil through the loop ends of two different 6-foot lengths of string.
   c. Place the pencil point at the center of the circle.
   d. Pull the free end of one string between a boy and girl who are standing next to each other.
   e. Repeat for the other boy and girl standing next to each other, using the second string.
   f. Hold the two pencil points at the center of the circle, and ask the boys and girls who are next to each other to hold the strings taut.
   g. Finally, ask any student who has a free hand to use a ruler to draw a line along each of the two strings from the center to the edge of the paper circle.

Have students remain standing in the circle and share the features that the human graph and the paper-and-pencil graph have in common.

Example:

▷ There are 10 boys and 15 girls. So $\frac{10}{25}$ of the class are boys. Boys take up $\frac{10}{25}$, or $\frac{2}{5}$, of the circumference of the human graph. The paper graph shows that, too. The slice of the pie representing boys is $\frac{2}{5}$ of the whole pie.

NOTE Laying a continuous strip of tape is faster than laying several smaller strips. But a continuous strip uses much more tape (about 40 feet). The student should not mark the carpet or floor with the pencil. The students' objective is to trace a path for you to tape.

Human circle graph for boy-girl data

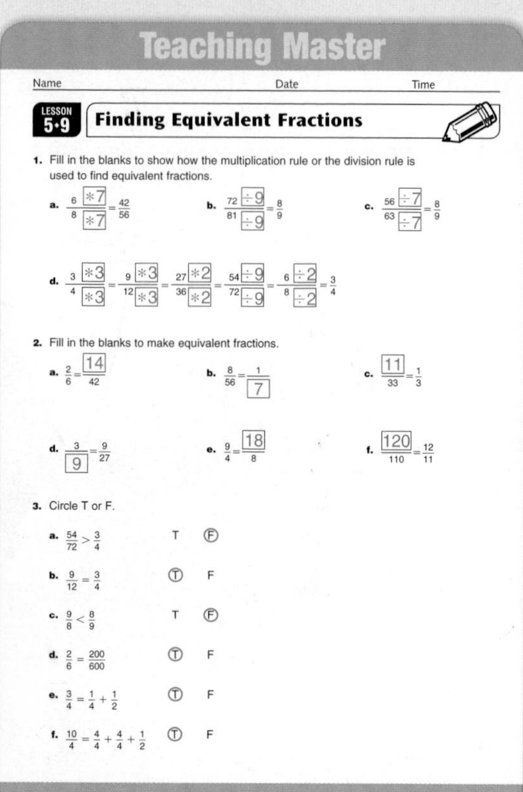

Teaching Master

Name Date Time

LESSON 5•9 **Finding Equivalent Fractions**

1. Fill in the blanks to show how the multiplication rule or the division rule is used to find equivalent fractions.

   a. $\frac{6 \boxed{*7}}{8 \boxed{*7}} = \frac{42}{56}$ b. $\frac{72 \boxed{\div 9}}{81 \boxed{\div 9}} = \frac{8}{9}$ c. $\frac{56 \boxed{\div 7}}{63 \boxed{\div 7}} = \frac{8}{9}$

   d. $\frac{3 \boxed{*3}}{4 \boxed{*3}} = \frac{9 \boxed{*3}}{12 \boxed{*3}} = \frac{27 \boxed{*2}}{36 \boxed{*2}} = \frac{54 \boxed{\div 9}}{72 \boxed{\div 9}} = \frac{6 \boxed{\div 2}}{8 \boxed{\div 2}} = \frac{3}{4}$

2. Fill in the blanks to make equivalent fractions.

   a. $\frac{2}{6} = \frac{\boxed{14}}{42}$ b. $\frac{8}{56} = \frac{1}{\boxed{7}}$ c. $\frac{\boxed{11}}{33} = \frac{1}{3}$

   d. $\frac{3}{\boxed{9}} = \frac{9}{27}$ e. $\frac{9}{4} = \frac{\boxed{18}}{8}$ f. $\frac{\boxed{120}}{110} = \frac{12}{11}$

3. Circle T or F.

   a. $\frac{54}{72} > \frac{3}{4}$ T (F)

   b. $\frac{9}{12} = \frac{3}{4}$ (T) F

   c. $\frac{9}{8} < \frac{8}{9}$ T (F)

   d. $\frac{2}{6} = \frac{200}{600}$ (T) F

   e. $\frac{3}{4} = \frac{1}{4} + \frac{1}{2}$ (T) F

   f. $\frac{10}{4} = \frac{4}{4} + \frac{4}{4} + \frac{1}{2}$ (T) F

Math Masters, p. 146

Then ask: *What fraction of any class of fifth graders would you expect to be boys (or girls)?* About $\frac{1}{2}$ *Does our class seem to be typical?* Answers vary.

EXTRA PRACTICE

PARTNER ACTIVITY

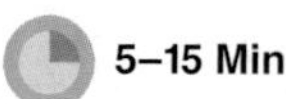

5–15 Min

▶ Finding Equivalent Fractions

(*Math Masters,* p. 146)

Students practice using the multiplication rule and the division rule to find equivalent fractions. When students have completed the *Math Masters* page, ask them to predict whether the decimal names for the pairs of fractions in Problem 2 will be the same or different.

Ask partners to use their calculators to find the decimal names for one pair of the fractions in the problem; each student converts one fraction of a pair. Then have partners compare the decimal names. Emphasize that this is another way of confirming that the fractions are equivalent. Write *the decimal name is the same for all fractions that are equivalent to each other* on the board.

ELL SUPPORT

SMALL-GROUP ACTIVITY

5–15 Min

▶ Comparing Bar and Circle Graphs

(*Differentiation Handbook,* p. 149)

To provide language for graphs, have students use the Venn Diagram from the *Differentiation Handbook* to compare bar and circle graphs.

Planning Ahead

Keep a record of the snack-survey data students collect in Part 1. You will need this data for Lesson 5-11.

5•10 The Percent Circle: Reading Circle Graphs

Objective To introduce the use of the Percent Circle to measure circle graph sectors.

www.everydaymathonline.com

ePresentations

eToolkit

Algorithms Practice

EM Facts Workshop Game™

Family Letters

Assessment Management

Common Core State Standards

Curriculum Focal Points

Interactive Teacher's Lesson Guide

1 Teaching the Lesson

Key Concepts and Skills

- Convert between fractions and percents. [Number and Numeration Goal 5]
- Estimate circle-graph sector sizes. [Measurement and Reference Frames Goal 1]
- Measure sectors of a circle graph using the Percent Circle. [Measurement and Reference Frames Goal 1]
- Interpret circle graph sectors. [Data and Chance Goal 2]

Key Activities

Students use the Percent Circle to find the percent of the area of a circle graph that is represented by each sector.

Ongoing Assessment: Informing Instruction See page 346.

Ongoing Assessment: Recognizing Student Achievement Use journal page 154. [Measurement and Reference Frames Goal 1]

Key Vocabulary

Percent Circle ◆ sector

Materials

Math Journal 1, pp. 153 and 154
Study Link 5•9
Math Masters, p. 147; pp. 426 and 427 (optional)
transparencies of *Math Masters,* pp. 147 and 426 ◆ Geometry Template

2 Ongoing Learning & Practice

Measuring Angles, Perimeter, and Area

Math Journal 1, p. 155
Geometry Template
Students practice measuring and drawing angles and finding the perimeter and area of rectangles.

Math Boxes 5•10

Math Journal 1, p. 156
Geometry Template
Students practice and maintain skills through Math Box problems.

Study Link 5•10

Math Masters, pp. 148 and 149
Students practice and maintain skills through Study Link activities.

3 Differentiation Options

READINESS

Making References for Circle Graph Sectors

paper ◆ compass
Students fold paper circles to identify sectors that are halves, fourths, and eighths.

ENRICHMENT

Conducting an Eye Test

Math Masters, p. 426
Probability Meter ◆ stick-on note ◆ calculator
Students conduct a class experiment to determine which eye is dominant and post the results on the Probability Meter.

EXTRA PRACTICE

5-Minute Math

5-Minute Math™, p. 181
Students convert between fractions and decimals.

Advance Preparation

For Part 1, if you are not using an overhead projector, cut out a copy of the Percent Circle from *Math Masters,* page 426, and make a hole in the center. Cut out the circle graph from *Math Masters,* page 147, and tape it to the board. If Geometry Templates are not available, make a copy of *Math Masters,* page 427 for every 6 students and cut apart the Percent Circles.

For the optional Enrichment activity in Part 3, draw a circle with a 2-inch diameter on a piece of paper, color it black, and tape it to the board.

***Teacher's Reference Manual,* Grades 4–6** pp. 44–46, 234–236

Getting Started

Mental Math and Reflexes

Students stand and rotate their positions according to given degrees and fractions of a circle. Suggestions:

●○○ Turn $\frac{1}{4}$-turn to the right.

Turn 90° to the right.

●●○ Turn $\frac{1}{2}$-turn clockwise.

Turn $\frac{3}{4}$-turn counterclockwise.

●●● Turn 60° to the left.

Turn 30° to the left.

Math Message

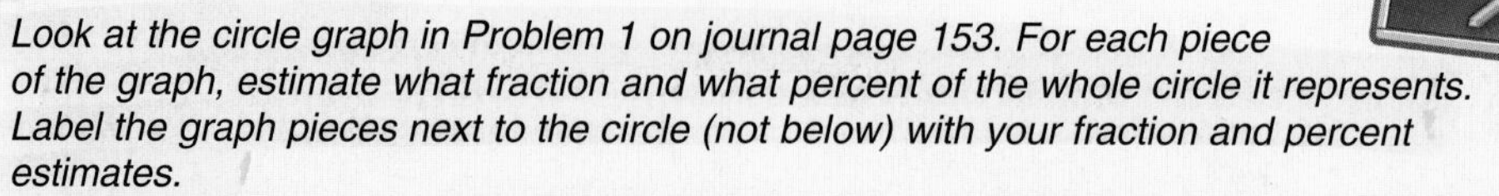

Look at the circle graph in Problem 1 on journal page 153. For each piece of the graph, estimate what fraction and what percent of the whole circle it represents. Label the graph pieces next to the circle (not below) with your fraction and percent estimates.

Study Link 5·9 Follow-Up

Allow students five minutes to compare answers and correct any errors. Ask volunteers to share their written responses to Problem 4.

For Problem 2, the bar graph is more helpful for answering the question quickly. Expect that some students might say that they think the line graph is best. Accept this answer, too, with a reasonable explanation.

For Problem 3, the best answer is the line graph because it displays a trend: The low temperatures rose over the course of the two weeks.

1 Teaching the Lesson

▶ Math Message Follow-Up

PARTNER ACTIVITY

(*Math Journal 1,* p. 153)

Ask partners to compare their estimates.

▶ Introducing the Percent Circle

WHOLE-CLASS DISCUSSION

(*Math Masters,* p. 426)

Ask students to describe the features of the **Percent Circle** on the Geometry Template. Use their responses to emphasize the following:

▷ There are 100 equally spaced marks around the circle.

▷ The 100 marks show the edges of thin pieces, shaped like slices of pie, dividing the circle into 100 pieces.

▷ The area of each piece is $\frac{1}{100}$, or 1 percent (1%) of the total area of the circle.

▷ The complete circle, the whole, includes all 100 pieces and represents 100%.

▷ The arc from 0% to 5% has additional marks at the $\frac{1}{2}$ positions.

Ask: *What percents do these marks represent?* They represent $\frac{1}{2}$%, $1\frac{1}{2}$%, $2\frac{1}{2}$%, $3\frac{1}{2}$%, and $4\frac{1}{2}$%.

Student Page

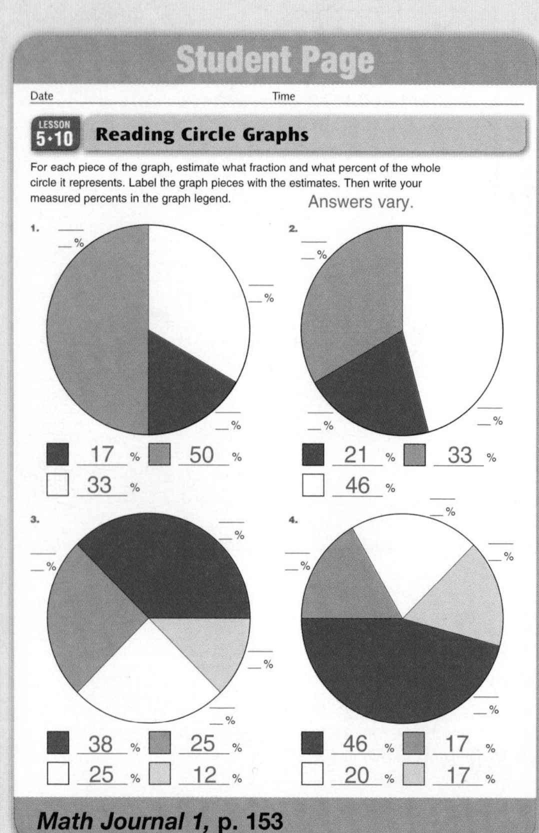

Date Time

LESSON 5·10 **Reading Circle Graphs**

For each piece of the graph, estimate what fraction and what percent of the whole circle it represents. Label the graph pieces with the estimates. Then write your measured percents in the graph legend. Answers vary.

1. 17 % 50 % 33 %

2. 21 % 33 % 46 %

3. 38 % 25 % 25 % 12 %

4. 46 % 17 % 20 % 17 %

Math Journal 1, p. 153

Demonstrating Methods for Using a Percent Circle

(*Math Journal 1,* p. 153; *Math Masters,* pp. 147 and 426)

Use Problem 1 on the journal page to demonstrate two methods for using the Percent Circle to measure the percents for each piece of a circle graph. Ask students to watch you perform the steps first and then mirror the steps along with you as you repeat them a second time. Use transparencies or copies of *Math Masters,* pages 147 and 426. (*See margin.*)

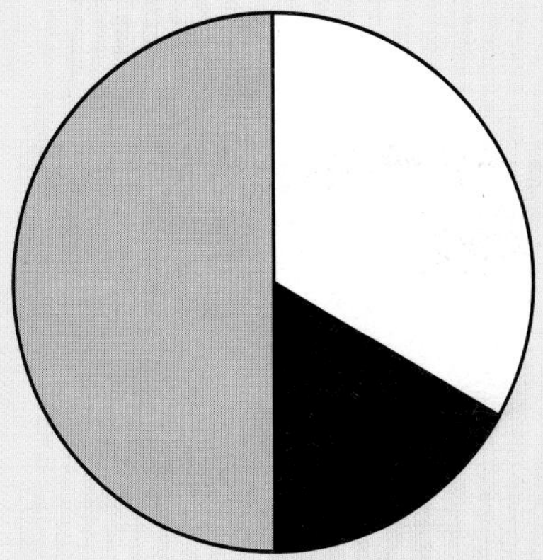

The Circle Graph from *Math Masters,* page 147

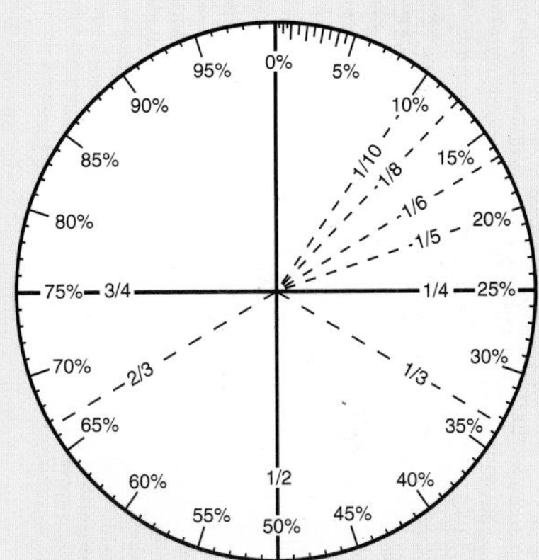

The Percent Circle from *Math Masters,* page 426

Method 1: Direct Comparison

1. Center the Percent Circle over the center of the circle graph.
2. Aim the Percent Circle 0% mark at one of the dividing lines that separates two pieces of the graph.
3. Move in a clockwise direction and read the percent at the next dividing line.
4. Move the 0% mark to the next dividing line and repeat until all pieces have been measured.

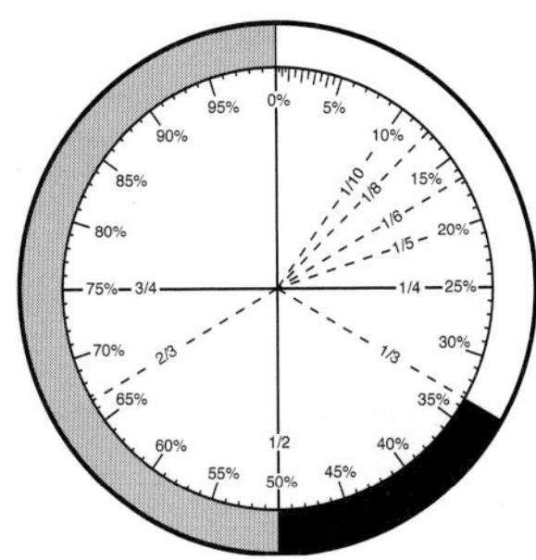

Place the 0% mark where the white piece begins. Read 33% for the white area. Read the percents for the black and gray areas in the same way.

Method 2: Difference Comparison

1. Center the Percent Circle over the center of the circle graph.
2. Aim the Percent Circle 0% mark at one of the dividing lines that separates two pieces.
3. Estimate the percent for each piece by finding the difference between the Percent Circle readings of adjacent dividing lines.

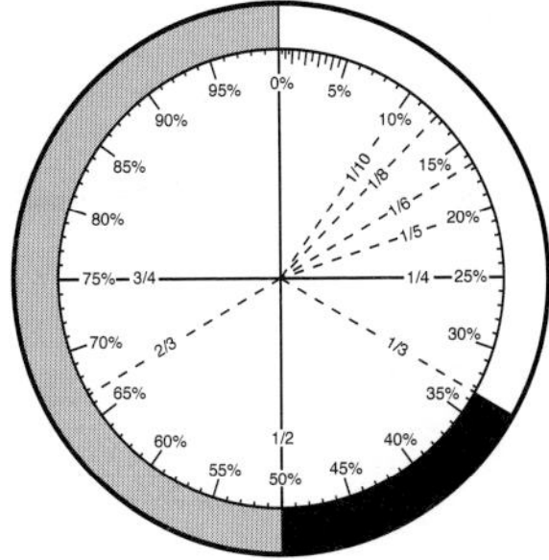

Place the 0% mark where the white piece begins. Read 33% for the white area. The black area goes from 33% to 50%. That's 50 minus 33, or 17%. The gray area goes from 50% to 100%. That's 50% for gray.

Have students write the measured percents in the graph legend. Ask students how their estimates compare with the measured

Student Page

Date ____ Time ____

LESSON 5·10 **How Much TV Do People Watch?**

A large sample of people was asked to report how much TV they watched during one week. The circle graph below shows the survey's results.

Estimate each percent. Then use your Percent Circle to measure the percent in each category. Write your measures in the blanks next to the pie pieces. Two percents are filled in for you: 18% of the people reported watching less than 7 hours, and 30% reported watching 7 to 14 hours of TV during the week.

Less than 7 hours 18 %
7 to 14 hours 30 %
50 or more hours 3 %
43 to 49 hours 3 %
36 to 42 hours 5 %
29 to 35 hours 7 %
22 to 28 hours 15 %
15 to 21 hours 19 %

Math Journal 1, p. 154

Student Page

Date ____ Time ____

LESSON 5·10 **Measuring Angles, Perimeter, and Area**

1. Estimate the angle measure. Then use a protractor to measure the angle.

All estimates are sample answers.

a. Estimate: 45° Measure: 50°

b. Estimate: 110° Measure: 125°

2. Use a protractor to draw an angle with the given measure.

a. 75°

b. 145°

3. Find the missing measurement in each figure.

a. 14 in., S; Perimeter = 42 in. S = 7 in.

b. R; Perimeter = 28 m R = 7 m

c. 17 m, H; Area = 51 m^2 H = 3 m

d. 13 cm, O; Area = 78 cm^2 O = 6 cm

4. The art room at Walker School is 27 feet long and 38 feet wide. What is the area of the room? 1,026 sq ft

5. Mia's backyard is 25 feet by 50 feet. Joy's backyard is 35 feet by 35 feet. Who has a bigger backyard? Mia How much bigger? 25 ft^2

Math Journal 1, p. 155

percentages. Expect that most students will be able to estimate the size of a circle graph sector relative to the nearest quarter of a circle (0%, 25%, 50%, 75%, or 100%).

▶ Reading Circle Graphs

(*Math Journal 1*, pp. 153 and 154)

Ask students to look at Problem 2 on journal page 153, and estimate and label the fraction and percent for each piece of the pie graph. You might want to introduce the word *sector* as the name for the pieces of a circle. A **sector** is a region bounded by two radii of a circle and the included arc. Then assign partners to use their Percent Circles to complete the problem. Ask students to complete the remaining problems on the journal page in this same fashion: Write estimates on the labels; measure and label each sector and record the measured percentages. Circulate and assist. When most students have finished, discuss any problems or discoveries.

Ongoing Assessment: Informing Instruction

Watch for students who have difficulty measuring with their Percent Circles. Make sure students align the center of the Percent Circle with the center of the graph. Align the 0% with the left edge of the sector they are measuring, and read the Percent Circle in a clockwise direction.

Assign journal page 154. Remind students to make an estimate for each sector of the pie graph before using their Percent Circles.

Ongoing Assessment: Recognizing Student Achievement

Journal page 154 

Use journal page 154 to assess students' ability to estimate and find the percent measure of circle graph sectors. Students are making adequate progress if their percents total 100% and reflect an understanding of relative size. Some students' individual measurements may be off by several percentage points since this lesson is the introduction to measuring circle graph sectors.

[Measurement and Reference Frames Goal 1]

2 Ongoing Learning & Practice

▶ Measuring Angles, Perimeter, and Area

(*Math Journal 1*, p. 155)

Students practice measuring and drawing angles. They find the perimeter and area of rectangles.

Math Boxes 5·10

INDEPENDENT ACTIVITY

(*Math Journal 1,* p. 156)

Mixed Practice Math Boxes in this lesson are paired with Math Boxes in Lesson 5-12. The skill in Problem 4 previews Unit 6 content.

Study Link 5·10

INDEPENDENT ACTIVITY

(*Math Masters,* pp. 148 and 149)

Home Connection Note that this is a two-page Study Link. On the first page, students estimate the size of circle graph pieces and match the graphs with data sets. On the second page, they count and record the number of states they and interviewed adults have visited.

3 Differentiation Options

READINESS

SMALL-GROUP ACTIVITY

5–15 Min

Making References for Circle Graph Sectors

To provide experience with fraction and percent names for circle sectors, have students create a visual reference. Ask students to fold a sheet of paper in half. Then use a point on the fold line and their compasses to draw a circle. Students then label one of the parts of the circle on either side of the fold line with the fraction $\frac{1}{2}$. Repeat this process for fourths and eighths, using the point where the fold lines intersect as the center of the circle so that radius lengths are the same.

Ask students to refold their circles so only one sector shows. Do not instruct students to show a certain sector. Ask students what percent of the circle that sector represents. Halves = 50%; quarters = 25%; eighths = $12\frac{1}{2}$%

Place two sectors next to each other and ask students to identify the percent of the circle represented by the two sectors. Then have students place different pairings of sectors next to each other for partners to identify the percent of the circle represented. Conclude by reminding students to use what they know about halves, fourths, and eighths to estimate percents.

Student Page

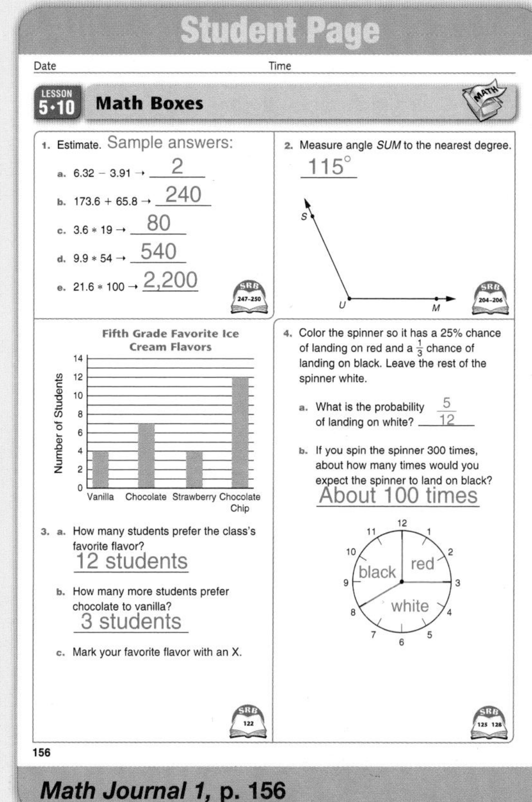

Date Time

LESSON 5·10 **Math Boxes**

1. Estimate. Sample answers:

a. 6.32 − 3.91 → 2

b. 173.6 + 65.8 → 240

c. 3.6 ∗ 19 → 80

d. 9.9 ∗ 54 → 540

e. 21.6 ∗ 100 → 2,200

SRB 247–250

2. Measure angle *SUM* to the nearest degree. 115°

SRB 204–206

Fifth Grade Favorite Ice Cream Flavors

3. a. How many students prefer the class's favorite flavor? 12 students

b. How many more students prefer chocolate to vanilla? 3 students

c. Mark your favorite flavor with an X.

SRB 122

4. Color the spinner so it has a 25% chance of landing on red and a $\frac{1}{3}$ chance of landing on black. Leave the rest of the spinner white.

a. What is the probability of landing on white? $\frac{5}{12}$

b. If you spin the spinner 300 times, about how many times would you expect the spinner to land on black? About 100 times

SRB 125 128

156

Math Journal 1, p. 156

Study Link Master

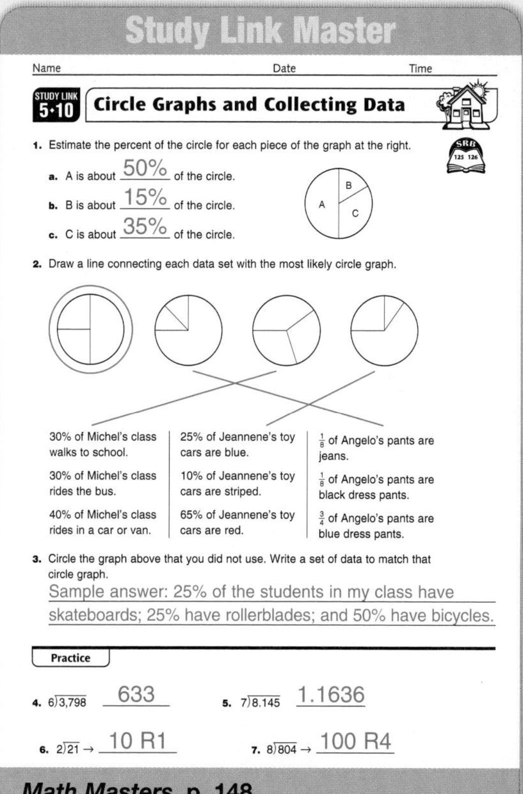

Name Date Time

STUDY LINK 5·10 **Circle Graphs and Collecting Data**

1. Estimate the percent of the circle for each piece of the graph at the right.

a. A is about 50% of the circle.

b. B is about 15% of the circle.

c. C is about 35% of the circle.

SRB 125 126

2. Draw a line connecting each data set with the most likely circle graph.

30% of Michel's class walks to school.	25% of Jeannene's toy cars are blue.	$\frac{1}{8}$ of Angelo's pants are jeans.
30% of Michel's class rides the bus.	10% of Jeannene's toy cars are striped.	$\frac{1}{8}$ of Angelo's pants are black dress pants.
40% of Michel's class rides in a car or van.	65% of Jeannene's toy cars are red.	$\frac{3}{4}$ of Angelo's pants are blue dress pants.

3. Circle the graph above that you did not use. Write a set of data to match that circle graph.
Sample answer: 25% of the students in my class have skateboards; 25% have rollerblades; and 50% have bicycles.

Practice

4. 6)3,798 633

5. 7)8.145 1.1636

6. 2)21 → 10 R1

7. 8)804 → 100 R4

Math Masters, p. 148

Study Link Master

Name Date Time

STUDY LINK 5·10 **Circle Graphs and Collecting Data** *cont.*

The Number of States We've Been In

Answers vary.

8. Talk with an adult at home and think of all the states you have visited. (Be sure to include the state you're living in.) Look at the map below to help you remember.

Use a pencil or crayon to mark each state you have visited.

Don't count any state that you have flown over in an airplane unless the plane landed, and you left the airport.

9. Count the number of states you have marked.

I have been in ________ states in my lifetime.

10. Now ask the adult to mark the map to show the states he or she has been in, using a different color or mark from yours.

Keep a tally as states are marked.

The adult I interviewed has visited ________ states.

Note: Alaska and Hawaii are not shown to scale.

Student and adult: This data is important for an upcoming lesson on data organization. Please bring this completed Study Link back to school tomorrow.

***Math Masters,* p. 149**

ENRICHMENT

WHOLE-CLASS ACTIVITY

15–30 Min

▶ Conducting an Eye Test

(*Math Masters,* p. 426)

To apply students' understanding of fractions, decimals, and percents, have students conduct an experiment.

Science Link Tape the paper with the black circle to the board. Have available a Percent Circle cut out of *Math Masters,* page 426. (*See Advance Preparation.*) Instruct students to do the following:

1. Stand 5 to 10 feet away from the black circle. Look directly at the black circle with both eyes open.
2. Hold the cut-out Percent Circle in front of your face, so that you can see the black circle through the hole in the Percent Circle with both eyes open.
3. Don't move the paper. Close your left eye. If you can still see the black circle, your right eye is dominant.
4. Don't move the paper. Open your left eye and close your right eye. If you see the black circle, your left eye is dominant.

Take a class count and tally the results on the board. For example, 17 right, 11 left. Write the fraction of students whose right eye is dominant, for *example,* $\frac{17}{28}$.

Ask students to convert this fraction to a decimal and then write it as a percent. In the example, $\frac{17}{28} = 0.6071428571$, which is about 0.61, or 61%. Write the result on a stick-on note and post it on the Probability Meter, for example, with a note saying "Right eye dominant—61%."

EXTRA PRACTICE

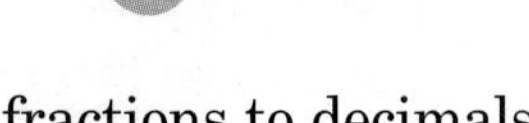

SMALL-GROUP ACTIVITY

5–15 Min

▶ *5-Minute Math*

To offer students more experience converting fractions to decimals, see *5-Minute Math,* page 181.

Planning Ahead

Collect bar graphs from newspapers or magazines. In Lesson 5-12, students will make displays for the Fractions, Decimals, and Percents Museum. You will need one graph per partnership. Also the visited-states data from Study Link 5-10 will be combined, organized, and discussed in Lesson 6-1.

5•11 The Percent Circle: Making Circle Graphs

Objective To introduce constructing circle graphs using the Percent Circle.

Technology Resources www.everydaymathonline.com

ePresentations

eToolkit

Algorithms Practice

EM Facts Workshop Game™

Family Letters

Assessment Management

Common Core State Standards

Curriculum Focal Points

Interactive Teacher's Lesson Guide

1 Teaching the Lesson

Key Concepts and Skills

- Find fraction and percent equivalents. [Number and Numeration Goal 5]
- Measure sectors of a circle graph using the Percent Circle. [Measurement and Reference Frames Goal 1]
- Construct circle graphs from table data. [Data and Chance Goal 1]
- Interpret data presented in various forms. [Data and Chance Goal 2]

Key Activities

Students use the Percent Circle to construct circle graphs. They use journal page data and the snack-survey data collected in Lesson 5•9. They practice finding fractional parts of sets by playing *Fraction Of.*

Ongoing Assessment: Informing Instruction See page 351.

Ongoing Assessment: Recognizing Student Achievement Use an Exit Slip (*Math Masters,* page 414). [Data and Chance Goal 1]

Materials

Math Journal 1, pp. 151, 157, and 158
Student Reference Book, p. 313
Study Link 5•10
Math Masters, pp. 414, 426, and 427 (optional); pp. 464–466 and 469
Geometry Template ◆ Class Data Pad (optional) ◆ chalkboard compass, for demonstration purposes ◆ counters

2 Ongoing Learning & Practice

Finding Decimal Equivalents for Sevenths and Eighths
Math Journal 1, inside back cover
Students fill in the decimals for sevenths and eighths in the Table of Decimal Equivalents.

Math Boxes 5•11
Math Journal 1, p. 159
Students practice and maintain skills through Math Box problems.

Study Link 5•11
Math Masters, p. 150
Students practice and maintain skills through Study Link activities.

3 Differentiation Options

READINESS

Measuring Circle Graphs
Math Masters, p. 428
Geometry Template
Students use a Percent Circle to measure sectors in a circle graph.

ENRICHMENT

Calculating Percents: On the Square
1 index card ◆ 1 sheet of scrap paper ◆ per group: masking tape, 12" by 12" paper square
Students collect, calculate, and compare fractions and percents in statistical data.

Advance Preparation

For Part 1, convert snack-survey data from Lesson 5•9 to percents, rounded to the nearest whole percent. List the snacks and percents in a table on the board or the Class Data Pad. Students will need Percent Circles from the Geometry Template or *Math Masters,* page 426 or 427. For the optional Readiness activity in Part 3, divide each circle on *Math Masters,* page 428 into three or four sections and label them A, B, C, and D. Write the same labels in the boxes to the left of the answer blanks before copying the master.

***Teacher's Reference Manual,* Grades 4–6** pp. 44–46, 161–167, 234–236

Getting Started

Mental Math and Reflexes

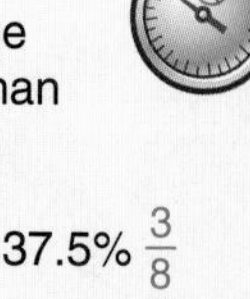

Have students rename percents as fractions. Encourage them to find fractions with denominators that are less than 100. *Suggestions:*

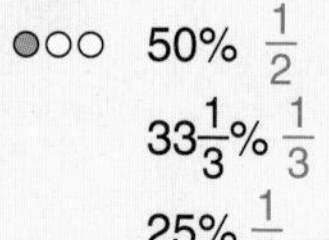

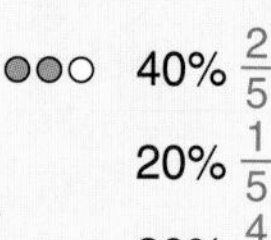

- ●○○ 50% $\frac{1}{2}$
  - $33\frac{1}{3}$% $\frac{1}{3}$
  - 25% $\frac{1}{4}$
- ●●○ 40% $\frac{2}{5}$
  - 20% $\frac{1}{5}$
  - 80% $\frac{4}{5}$
- ●●● 37.5% $\frac{3}{8}$
  - 87.5% $\frac{7}{8}$
  - 68% $\frac{17}{25}$

Math Message

Turn to Problem 2 on journal page 151. Copy the number of votes for each snack into the second column of the table on journal page 158. Leave the rest of the table blank.

Study Link 5·10 Follow-Up

Briefly review answers for Problems 1 and 2. Ask volunteers to share their data sets for Problem 3.

1 Teaching the Lesson

▶ Math Message Follow-Up

INDEPENDENT ACTIVITY

(*Math Journal 1,* pp. 151 and 158)

Survey the class to verify that students have copied the data from Lesson 5-9 correctly. Ask students to write the number of votes for each snack as a fraction of the total number of votes. Students should write this fraction in the third column of the table on journal page 158.

▶ Constructing a Circle Graph Using the Percent Circle

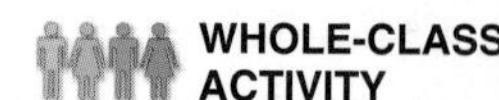

WHOLE-CLASS ACTIVITY

(*Math Journal 1,* p. 157)

As a class, read the information about mixing concrete on journal page 157. Ask volunteers how they would go about constructing a circle graph for this data. Ask students questions such as the following:

- How many pieces (sectors) must the graph have? Three—one for each dry ingredient (concrete, sand, and gravel)
- How should the pieces be labeled or colored? If the graph is labeled correctly, colors might help, but they are not necessary. Some students may suggest using symbols to mark the pieces.
- How can the Percent Circle be used to make each piece the correct size? Use the tick marks on the Percent Circle to draw sectors with measures matching the percents given on the table.

Have students demonstrate their circle-graph construction methods, using a chalkboard compass and a large paper Percent Circle on the board (or a compass and transparency of the Percent Circle on the overhead). Have students take turns sketching sections of the circle. Then have them complete the circle graph on journal page 157.

Student Page

Date Time

LESSON 5·11 **Making Circle Graphs: Concrete Recipe**

Concrete is an artificial stone. It is made by first mixing cement and sand with gravel or other broken stone. Then enough water is mixed in to cause the cement to set. After drying (or curing), the result is a hard piece of concrete.

The cement, sand, and gravel are commonly mixed using this recipe.

Recipe for Dry Mix for Concrete		
Material	Fractional Part of Mix	Percent Part of Mix
Cement	$\frac{1}{6}$	$16\frac{2}{3}$%
Sand	$\frac{1}{3}$	$33\frac{1}{3}$%
Gravel	$\frac{1}{2}$	50%

Use your Percent Circle to make a circle graph for the above recipe in the circle below. Label each sector of the graph and give it a title.

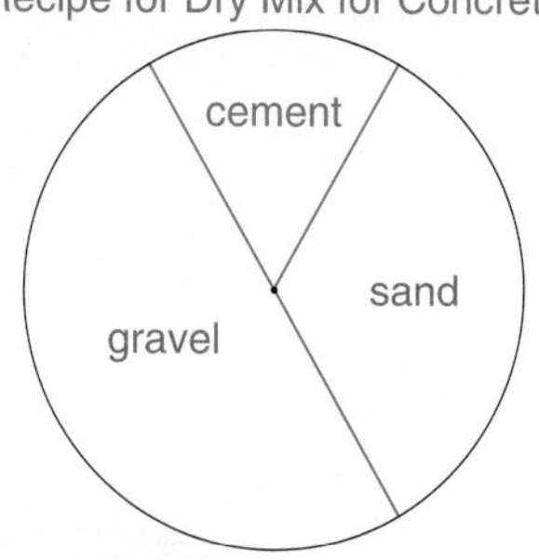

Math Journal 1, p. 157

NOTE Water is a necessary fourth ingredient in concrete. It is usually added to a dry mix of the other ingredients. About 5 to 7 gallons of water are used for a 94-pound bag of cement. When the concrete has dried (cured), the water is gone and the proportions of cement:sand:gravel are still 1:2:3.

Ongoing Assessment: Informing Instruction

Watch for students who have difficulty devising a method for constructing the circle graph. Demonstrate the following.

1. Use a board compass to draw a 12-inch diameter circle. Mark the center with a dot.
2. Place the center of the Percent Circle over the center of the circle on the board and make tick marks on the chalk circle at the 0 and $\frac{1}{6}$ ($16\frac{2}{3}$%) points.
3. Remove the Percent Circle and draw a line segment from the center of the circle through the tick marks. This $\frac{1}{6}$ section represents the proportion of cement in the mix.
4. Now place the Percent Circle 0% line along the line segment drawn at the $\frac{1}{6}$ mark. Then mark the $\frac{1}{3}$ (33%) measure. Draw a line segment from the center of the chalk circle to the tick mark to get the $\frac{1}{3}$ section. This represents the proportion of sand in the mix.
5. Measure the remaining section to verify that it is $\frac{1}{2}$ (50%) of the circle. This represents the amount of gravel in the mix.
6. Label the graph and add a title.

Constructing a Circle Graph for the Snack-Survey Data

(*Math Journal 1,* p. 158)

Display the snack-survey percents on the board or Class Data Pad. (*See Advance Preparation.*) Ask students to copy the percents into column 4 of the table. Ask: *Why do you think the table has* About 100% *in the Percent column?* The total should be 100%, but it may not be exact because of rounding.

Have students check their totals, then construct a circle graph using the snack-survey data. Suggest that they draw the smallest sector of the circle graph first and work their way up to the largest. This way, slight errors in their sections will be absorbed into the largest piece at the end. Circulate and assist.

Ongoing Assessment: Recognizing Student Achievement

Exit Slip

Use an Exit Slip (*Math Masters,* p. 414) to assess students' understanding of how to use the data-set fractions to draw circle-graph sectors. Have students write a response to the following: *How can finding the fraction of the whole for each category in the data set help you construct a circle graph?* Students are making adequate progress if they relate the fractions to estimating the size of the sector before or after drawing it and/or refer to using the fraction to align the Percent Circle.

[Data and Chance Goal 1]

Student Page

Date Time

LESSON 5·11 **Making Circle Graphs: Snack Survey**

Your class recently made a survey of favorite snacks. As your teacher tells you the percent of votes each snack received, record the data in the table at the right. Make a circle graph of the snack-survey data in the circle below. Remember to label each piece of the graph and give it a title.

Sample answers:

Snack	Votes: Number	Fraction	Percent
Cookies	8	$\frac{8}{25}$	32%
Granola Bar	4	$\frac{4}{25}$	16%
Candy Bar	10	$\frac{10}{25}$	40%
Fruit	2	$\frac{2}{25}$	8%
Other	1	$\frac{1}{25}$	4%
Total	25	$\frac{25}{25}$	About 100%

Favorite-Snack Survey Results

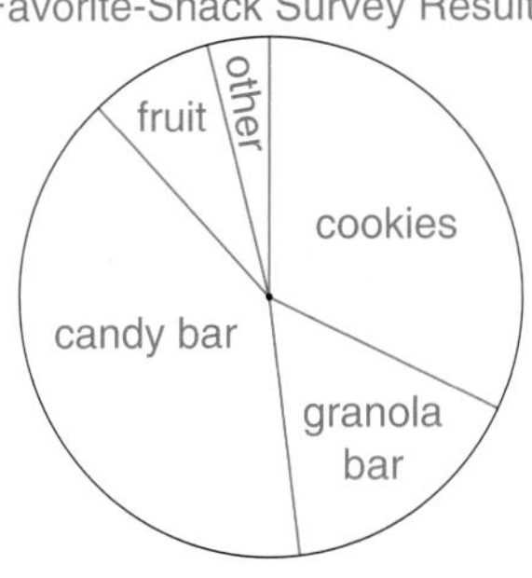

Math Journal 1, p. 158

Game Master

Name Date Time

Fraction Of Set Cards

3 counters 20 counters 15 counters	4 counters 21 counters 30 counters	5 counters 12 counters 20 counters	6 counters 28 counters 40 counters
8 counters 27 counters 20 counters	10 counters 32 counters 24 counters	12 counters 30 counters 25 counters	15 counters 36 counters 20 counters
18 counters 36 counters 10 counters	20 counters 4 counters 3 counters	21 counters 30 counters 24 counters	25 counters 6 counters 40 counters
28 counters 35 counters 30 counters	30 counters 32 counters 15 counters	36 counters 20 counters 24 counters	40 counters 18 counters 25 counters

Math Masters, p. 469

Adjusting the Activity

To make the activity a challenge to mental math skills, encourage students to use their calculators for the first 3 or 4 columns in a row and identify the pattern. Students then use the pattern and mental math to complete the row.

AUDITORY ◆ KINESTHETIC ◆ TACTILE ◆ VISUAL

▶ Playing *Fraction Of*

(*Math Masters,* pp. 464–466, and 469; *Student Reference Book,* p. 313)

Students practice finding fractional parts of sets by playing *Fraction Of.* Review the directions on *Student Reference Book,* page 313, and then play several sample turns with the class.

2 Ongoing Learning & Practice

▶ Finding Decimal Equivalents for Sevenths and Eighths

PARTNER ACTIVITY

(*Math Journal 1,* inside back cover)

Students continue to find and record decimal equivalents for fractions in the table on the inside back cover of the journal. Assign the denominators in rows 7 (sevenths) and 8 (eighths).

Numerator

Denominator	1	2	3	4	5	6	7	8	9	10
7	$0.\overline{142857}$	$0.\overline{285714}$	$0.\overline{428571}$	$0.\overline{571428}$	$0.\overline{714285}$	$0.\overline{857142}$	1.0	$1.\overline{142857}$	$1.\overline{285714}$	$1.\overline{428571}$
8	0.125	0.25	0.375	0.5	0.625	0.75	0.875	1.0	1.125	1.25

Inside back cover of *Math Journal 1.* Completed rows 7 and 8.

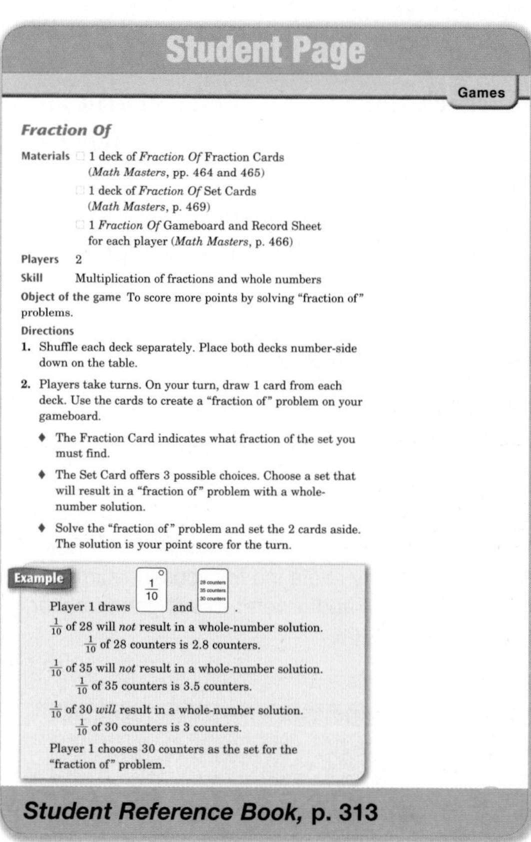

Student Page

Games

Fraction Of

Materials □ 1 deck of *Fraction Of* Fraction Cards (*Math Masters*, pp. 464 and 465)
□ 1 deck of *Fraction Of* Set Cards (*Math Masters*, p. 469)
□ 1 *Fraction Of* Gameboard and Record Sheet for each player (*Math Masters*, p. 466)

Players 2

Skill Multiplication of fractions and whole numbers

Object of the game To score more points by solving "fraction of" problems.

Directions

1. Shuffle each deck separately. Place both decks number-side down on the table.
2. Players take turns. On your turn, draw 1 card from each deck. Use the cards to create a "fraction of" problem on your gameboard.
   - The Fraction Card indicates what fraction of the set you must find.
   - The Set Card offers 3 possible choices. Choose a set that will result in a "fraction of" problem with a whole-number solution.
   - Solve the "fraction of" problem and set the 2 cards aside. The solution is your point score for the turn.

Example

Player 1 draws $\frac{1}{10}$ and [28 counters, 35 counters, 30 counters].

$\frac{1}{10}$ of 28 will *not* result in a whole-number solution.
$\frac{1}{10}$ of 28 counters is 2.8 counters.

$\frac{1}{10}$ of 35 will *not* result in a whole-number solution.
$\frac{1}{10}$ of 35 counters is 3.5 counters.

$\frac{1}{10}$ of 30 *will* result in a whole-number solution.
$\frac{1}{10}$ of 30 counters is 3 counters.

Player 1 chooses 30 counters as the set for the "fraction of" problem.

Student Reference Book, p. 313

Math Boxes 5•11

INDEPENDENT ACTIVITY

(*Math Journal 1,* p. 159)

Mixed Practice Math Boxes in this Lesson are paired with Math Boxes in Lesson 5-9. The skill in Problem 5 previews Unit 6 content.

Writing/Reasoning Have students write a response to the following: *Describe the strategy you used to solve Problem 4 and explain your reasoning.* Answers vary.

Study Link 5•11

INDEPENDENT ACTIVITY

(*Math Masters,* p. 150)

Home Connection Students use the Percent Circle to make a circle graph. They do not have to calculate the percents because all percents are given.

3 Differentiation Options

READINESS

INDEPENDENT ACTIVITY

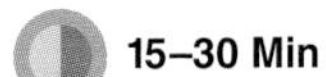

15–30 Min

Measuring Circle Graphs

(*Math Masters,* p. 428)

To explore measuring sectors of a circle graph with the Percent Circle, have students complete the *Math Masters* page. Individualize the problems to address specific student needs, such as using the fraction marks on the Percent Circle, or measuwring smaller sectors. (*See Advance Preparation.*)

ENRICHMENT

SMALL-GROUP ACTIVITY

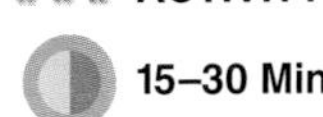

15–30 Min

Calculating Percents: On the Square

To apply students' knowledge of percents, have them conduct an experiment and report the results. Number index cards from 1 to the number of students in the class, and give one card to each student. Each student also needs a sheet of scrap paper wadded into a ball.

Place groups in separate areas of the room to set up for this activity. Students tape a 12-inch square to the floor and mark a tape line 6 feet from the square. The object is to see how many times a student can toss a paper ball so it lands inside of the taped square. Give students the following instructions:

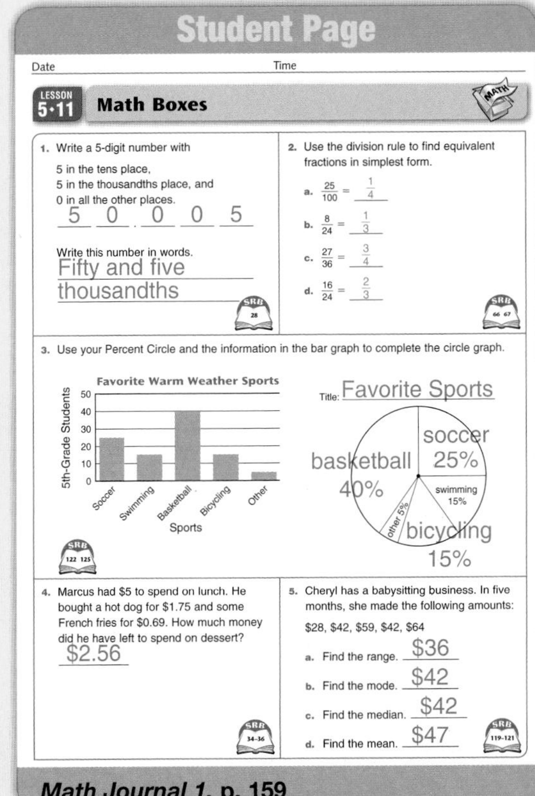

Student Page

Date Time

LESSON 5•11 **Math Boxes**

1. Write a 5-digit number with 5 in the tens place, 5 in the thousandths place, and 0 in all the other places.
5 0 . 0 0 5
Write this number in words.
Fifty and five thousandths

2. Use the division rule to find equivalent fractions in simplest form.
a. $\frac{25}{100} = \frac{1}{4}$
b. $\frac{8}{24} = \frac{1}{3}$
c. $\frac{27}{36} = \frac{3}{4}$
d. $\frac{16}{24} = \frac{2}{3}$

3. Use your Percent Circle and the information in the bar graph to complete the circle graph.

4. Marcus had \$5 to spend on lunch. He bought a hot dog for \$1.75 and some French fries for \$0.69. How much money did he have left to spend on dessert?
\$2.56

5. Cheryl has a babysitting business. In five months, she made the following amounts: \$28, \$42, \$59, \$42, \$64
a. Find the range. \$36
b. Find the mode. \$42
c. Find the median. \$42
d. Find the mean. \$47

Math Journal 1, p. 159

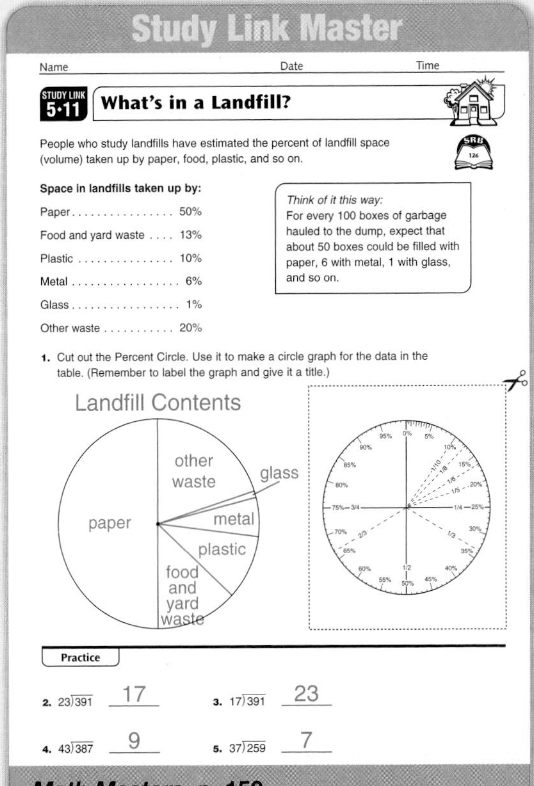

Study Link Master

Name Date Time

STUDY LINK 5•11 **What's in a Landfill?**

People who study landfills have estimated the percent of landfill space (volume) taken up by paper, food, plastic, and so on.

Space in landfills taken up by:

Paper	50%
Food and yard waste	13%
Plastic	10%
Metal	6%
Glass	1%
Other waste	20%

Think of it this way:
For every 100 boxes of garbage hauled to the dump, expect that about 50 boxes could be filled with paper, 6 with metal, 1 with glass, and so on.

1. Cut out the Percent Circle. Use it to make a circle graph for the data in the table. (Remember to label the graph and give it a title.)

Practice

2. $23\overline{)391}$ 17
3. $17\overline{)391}$ 23
4. $43\overline{)387}$ 9
5. $37\overline{)259}$ 7

Math Masters, p. 150

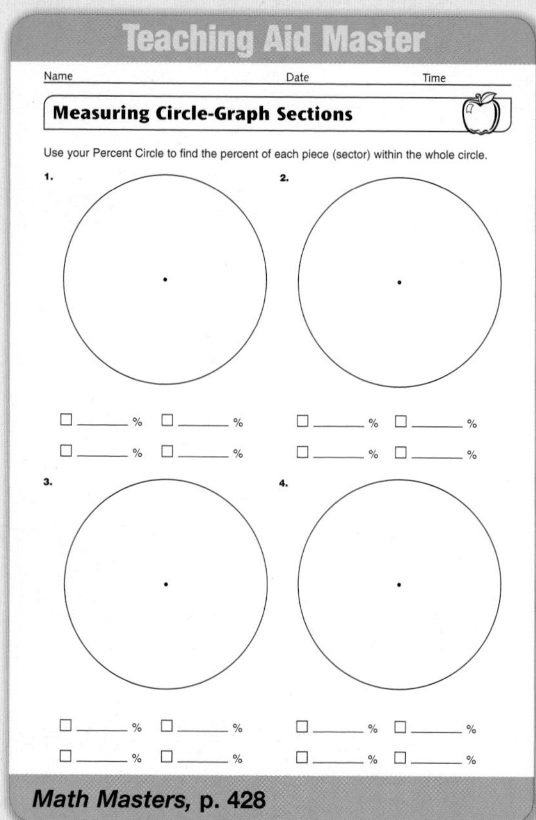
Teaching Aid Master

Name ________ Date ________ Time ________

Measuring Circle-Graph Sections

Use your Percent Circle to find the percent of each piece (sector) within the whole circle.

1.

☐ ____% ☐ ____%
☐ ____% ☐ ____%

2.

☐ ____% ☐ ____%
☐ ____% ☐ ____%

3.

☐ ____% ☐ ____%
☐ ____% ☐ ____%

4.

☐ ____% ☐ ____%
☐ ____% ☐ ____%

Math Masters, p. 428

1. Students take turns standing at the taped line. They are allowed to toss the ball as many times as the number indicated on their index cards.
2. Each student tosses the paper ball toward the taped square.
3. The group counts the number of times the ball lands inside the square.
4. At the end of a turn, the student writes how many times the ball landed inside the square as a fraction of the number of times he or she tossed the ball.
5. After every member of the group has had a turn, students convert their fractions to percents.

When students have calculated their percentages, discuss questions such as the following:

- Who had the greatest percentage in each group? Who had the greatest percentage in the class?
- Was the activity fair, or did it favor some students more than others? The activity might favor those students who had more tosses. However, some students might be more accurate with their tosses regardless of the number of tosses.
- How could students improve their percents? The more tosses they make, the greater the opportunity becomes to land in the square.

5·12 American Tour: School Days

Objective To extend the American Tour with information about mathematics instruction and related historical problems.

www.everydaymathonline.com

ePresentations

eToolkit

Algorithms Practice

EM Facts Workshop Game™

Family Letters

Assessment Management

Common Core State Standards

Curriculum Focal Points

Interactive Teacher's Lesson Guide

1 Teaching the Lesson

Key Concepts and Skills

- Convert between fractions, decimals, and percents.
  [Number and Numeration Goal 5]
- Solve problems involving ratios.
  [Operations and Computation Goal 7]
- Use graphs to ask and answer questions and draw conclusions.
  [Data and Chance Goal 2]
- Answer questions based on tables.
  [Data and Chance Goal 2]

Key Activities

Students read the essay "School" in the American Tour section of the *Student Reference Book.* They interpret information in the text and displays and solve a series of problems about the changing emphases in mathematics instruction. Students explore and practice concepts involving fractions, decimals, and percents.

Materials

Math Journal 1, pp. 160 and 161
Student Reference Book, pp. 259–262, 266, and 360–362
Study Link 5•11
slate ◆ calculator ◆ Class Data Pad

2 Ongoing Learning & Practice

Playing *Name That Number*
Student Reference Book, p. 325
per partnership: 4 each of number cards 0–9 (from the Everything Math Deck, if available), calculator
Students practice finding equivalent names for numbers.

Math Boxes 5•12
Math Journal 1, p. 162
Geometry Template
Students practice and maintain skills through Math Box problems.

Ongoing Assessment: Recognizing Student Achievement
Use Math Boxes, Problem 1.
[Operations and Computation Goal 6]

Study Link 5•12
Math Masters, p. 151
Students practice and maintain skills through Study Link activities.

3 Differentiation Options

ENRICHMENT

Reading about Mathematics Instruction in History and Solving Related Problems
Math Masters, p. 152
Students read about and solve problems taken from nineteenth-century math instruction.

EXTRA PRACTICE

Converting Bar Graphs to Circle Graphs
Geometry Template ◆ sample newspaper or magazine bar graphs ◆ calculator (optional)
Students use the information from bar graphs to construct circle graphs.

Advance Preparation

For the optional Extra Practice activity in Part 3, students will need sample bar graphs from newspapers or magazines.

Getting Started

Mental Math and Reflexes

Students write equivalent decimals and percents for given fractions. Suggestions:

●○○ $\frac{1}{2}$ 0.50; 50%
$\frac{1}{4}$ 0.25; 25%
$\frac{3}{4}$ 0.75; 75%

●●○ $\frac{7}{20}$ 0.35; 35%
$\frac{2}{5}$ 0.40; 40%
$\frac{2}{3}$ $0.\overline{6}$; $66\frac{2}{3}$%

●●● $\frac{9}{25}$ 0.36; 36%
$\frac{35}{50}$ 0.70; 70%
$\frac{1}{8}$ 0.125; 12.5%

Math Message

Write one question that can be answered by using the information on pages 360–362 in the Student Reference Book.

Study Link 5·11 Follow-Up

Review the steps for constructing a circle graph. Write them on the Class Data Pad.

1. Begin with the smallest piece.
2. Line up the centers of the Percent Circle and the graph.
3. Line up the radius that forms the left side of the first sector with 0 on the Percent Circle.
4. Read the Percent Circle in a clockwise direction.
5. Make a point at the correct percent mark. Draw a line segment to connect the center of the circle and the point.
6. Continue in a clockwise direction to draw the remaining sectors.

1 Teaching the Lesson

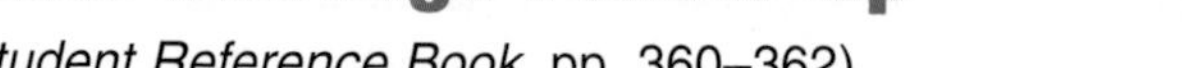

▶ Math Message Follow-Up

WHOLE-CLASS DISCUSSION

(*Student Reference Book,* pp. 360–362)

Ask students to read their questions, and then call on volunteers to give the answers. Build on students' comments to examine the line graph on page 360 of the *Student Reference Book.* Emphasize how to read the graph for the trends shown. Increasing length of school year and decreasing number of days absent

Links to the Future

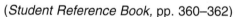

The stem-and-leaf display on page 361 of the *Student Reference Book* has the same data as the table above it. Stem-and-leaf plots are introduced in Unit 6.

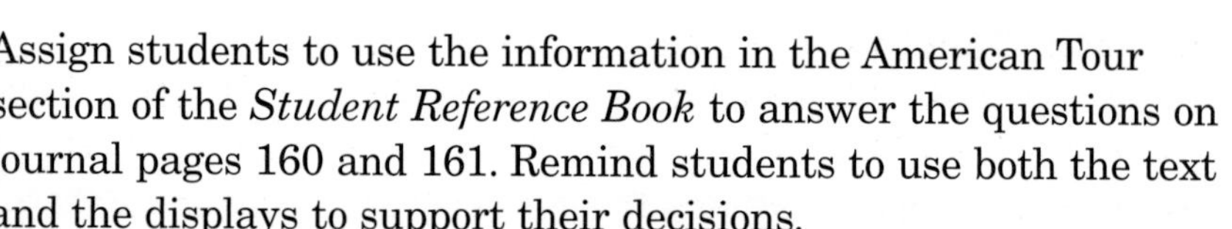

▶ Interpreting Mathematics in Text and Graphics

SMALL-GROUP ACTIVITY

PROBLEM SOLVING

(*Math Journal 1,* pp. 160 and 161; *Student Reference Book,* pp. 360–362)

Assign students to use the information in the American Tour section of the *Student Reference Book* to answer the questions on journal pages 160 and 161. Remind students to use both the text and the displays to support their decisions.

Avoid specific directions, such as "Look at the third paragraph to find the information you need." One goal of the lesson is to develop students' ability to locate and interpret mathematical information. Encourage students to discuss the questions in their groups.

Student Page

American Tour

School

Throughout the history of the United States, schooling has been important.

The Northwest Ordinance of 1787 created the rules for forming new states. It also showed the nation's belief in the importance of schooling. It stated —

> Being necessary to good government and the happiness of mankind, schools and the means of education shall forever be preserved.

Who Went to School in 1790?

In the northern states, most children between the ages of 4 and 14 went to school for part of the year. In the southern states, many, but not all, white children of these ages went to school. African Americans who were slaves did not receive formal schooling. Often they were not allowed to learn how to read. Some, however, found ways to learn secretly.

Most schools were in rural areas. Many children had to walk long distances to reach them. Schools were often in session for only two to three months in winter and then again in the summer. After age 10, many children attended school only in the winter, when farm work was light.

Who Went to School in 1900?

In 1900, parents reported to census takers that 80% of 10- to 14-year-olds had attended school at some point during the previous six months.

Almost all children who went to school in 1900 attended elementary school, which usually had eight grades. Approximately 15 million students attended public school in 1900. Only about 500,000 (roughly 3%) were in high school.

In rural schools, students were usually not separated by age. Five-and 6-year-olds were often in the same elementary classroom with 15- and 16-year-olds. The older students were not slow learners. They had to do farm work and could only attend school part time.

Three examples of early American schoolhouses

Student Reference Book, p. 360

After students have completed Problems 1 and 2 (which refer to page 360 of the American Tour), mix the groups and have them share their solution strategies. Then have the newly formed groups complete Problems 3–6 (which refer to pages 361 and 362). Again, mix the groups and share solution strategies.

▶ Exploring with a Calculator: Fractions, Decimals, and Percents

WHOLE-CLASS ACTIVITY

(*Student Reference Book,* pp. 259–262 and 266)

Use calculators with the following activities to explore and practice the Unit 5 concepts of fractions, decimals, and percents.

Fractions on a Calculator

Dictate mixed numbers and ask students to convert these to fractions and then to decimals. Students write the dictated numbers and the conversions.

Ask volunteers to share any discoveries or curiosities. Guide students to recognize that converting the mixed numbers to decimals only converts the fraction part of the mixed number to a decimal.

Percents on a Calculator

Dictate fractions and ask students to convert these to decimals and then to percents. Ask volunteers to explain how to convert using the multiplication method and the fix function. Students should follow the steps as they are given. Explain that another way to find percents on the calculator is to use the percent key.

Refer students to page 266 in the *Student Reference Book,* and then ask volunteers to explain this method.

2 Ongoing Learning & Practice

▶ Playing *Name That Number*

PARTNER ACTIVITY

(*Student Reference Book,* p. 325)

Students practice finding equivalent names for numbers by playing *Name That Number.* Encourage students to try using two of their cards to form a fraction so that the fraction is one of the numbers in an equivalent expression. For example, a student draws 1, 2, 4, and 6 for a target number of 12. The student might use two cards to form $\frac{1}{2}$, then create the expression $\frac{1}{2} * 6$. They can then use this expression to represent a 3 in the equivalent expression. $\frac{1}{2} * 6 * 4$

You may want to pose questions about the Associative Property of Addition or Multiplication, such as the following: When three numbers are added (or multiplied) together to name the target number, does it make a difference in which order you add (or multiply) them? no

Student Page

Date Time

LESSON 5·12 **School Days**

Read the article "School" on pages 360–362 in the American Tour section of the *Student Reference Book.*

1. Tell whether the statement below is true or false. Support your answer with evidence from page 360 of the American Tour.

   In 1790, it was common for 11-year-olds to go to school fewer than 90 days per year.
   True. Sample answer: Many children after age 10 attended school for only the winter session, which was 2 to 3 months long.

2. About how many days will you go to school this year? About 180 days

   Write a fraction to compare the number of days you will go to school this year to the number of days an 11-year-old might have gone to school in 1790.
   $\frac{180}{60}$, $\frac{3}{1}$, or 3

3. Tell whether the statement below is true or false. Support your answer with evidence from page 361 of the American Tour.

   In 1900, students in some states spent twice as many days in school, on average, as students in some other states.
   True. In New Mexico and Idaho, students went to school for about 60 days. In Illinois, Pennsylvania, New Jersey, and California, students went to school for about twice as many days.

4. In 1900, in which region (Northeast, South, Midwest, or West) did students go to school ...

   the greatest number of days per year? northeast

   the fewest number of days per year? south

Math Journal 1, p. 160

Student Page

Date Time

LESSON 5·12 **School Days** *continued*

Tell whether each statement below is true or false. Support your answer with evidence from the graphs on page 362 of the American Tour.

5. On average, students in 2000 were absent from school about one-third as many days as students were absent in 1900.
   True. The top graph shows about 45 days absent in 1900 and about 15 days absent in 2000; 15 is one-third of 45.

6. The average number of days students spent in school per year has not changed much since 1960.
   True. The bottom graph shows about 160 days in school for 1960, and about 165 days in school for 1980 and 2000. An increase of 5 days is not a large change.

Try This

7. Tell whether the statement below is true or false. Support your answer with evidence from the American Tour.

   From 1900 to 1980, the average number of days students spent in school per year more than doubled.
   False. The graph shows that the number increased from about 100 to about 165. Doubling would require an increase to about 200.

8. Locate your state in the table Average Number of Days in School per Student, 1900 on page 361 of the American Tour. If you are in Alaska or Hawaii, choose another state.

   Was your state above or below the median for its region? Answers vary.

9. Locate the number of days in school for your state in the stem-and-leaf plot on page 361 of the American Tour.

   Was your state above or below the median for all states? Answers vary.

Math Journal 1, p. 161

Student Page

Games

Name That Number

Materials □ 1 complete deck of number cards

Players 2 or 3

Skill Naming numbers with expressions

Object of the game To collect the most cards.

Directions

1. Shuffle the deck and deal 5 cards to each player. Place the remaining cards number-side down on the table between the players. Turn over the top card and place it beside the deck. This is the **target number** for the round.
2. Players try to match the target number by adding, subtracting, multiplying, or dividing the numbers on as many of their cards as possible. A card may only be used once.
3. Players write their solutions on a sheet of paper. When players have written their best solutions:
   - Each player sets aside the cards they used to match the target number.
   - Each player replaces the cards they set aside by drawing new cards from the top of the deck.
   - The old target number is placed on the bottom of the deck.
   - A new target number is turned over, and another round is played.
4. Play continues until there are not enough cards left to replace all of the players' cards. The player who has set aside the most cards wins the game.

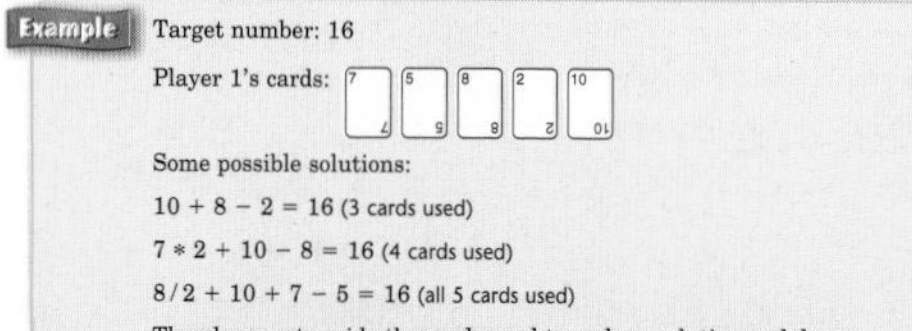

Example Target number: 16

Player 1's cards: 7 5 8 2 10

Some possible solutions:

10 + 8 − 2 = 16 (3 cards used)

7 ∗ 2 + 10 − 8 = 16 (4 cards used)

8/2 + 10 + 7 − 5 = 16 (all 5 cards used)

The player sets aside the cards used to make a solution and draws the same number of cards from the top of the deck.

***Student Reference Book,* p. 325**

Math Boxes 5·12

INDEPENDENT ACTIVITY

(*Math Journal 1*, p. 162)

Mixed Practice Math Boxes in this lesson are paired with Math Boxes in Lesson 5-10. The skill in Problem 4 previews Unit 6 content.

Writing/Reasoning Have students write a response to the following: *Explain how you would rename $\frac{2}{5}$ as a decimal and as a percent without using a calculator.* Sample answer: I know that $5 * 2 = 10$, and ten is a multiple of 100. So $\frac{2*2}{5*2} = \frac{4}{10}$ which is 0.4. $\frac{4*10}{10*10} = \frac{40}{100}$ or 40%.

Ongoing Assessment: Recognizing Student Achievement

Math Boxes Problem 1

Use **Math Boxes, Problem 1** to assess students' ability to estimate answers. Students are making adequate progress if their estimates are whole numbers and show reasonable results for the operations.

[Operations and Computation Goal 6]

Study Link 5·12

INDEPENDENT ACTIVITY

(*Math Masters,* p. 151)

Home Connection Students solve fraction-of number stories, and explain their solutions.

Student Page

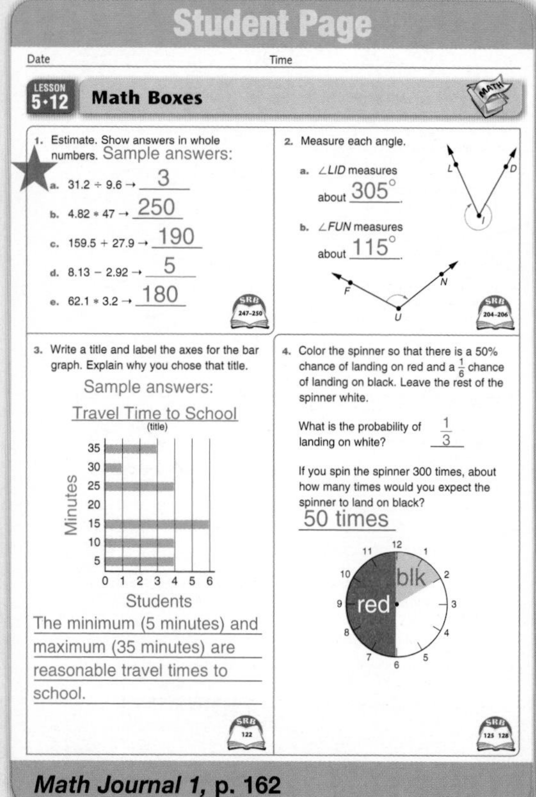

Date Time

LESSON 5·12 **Math Boxes**

1. Estimate. Show answers in whole numbers. Sample answers:
   a. 31.2 ÷ 9.6 → 3
   b. 4.82 ∗ 47 → 250
   c. 159.5 + 27.9 → 190
   d. 8.13 − 2.92 → 5
   e. 62.1 ∗ 3.2 → 180

2. Measure each angle.
   a. ∠LID measures about 305°
   b. ∠FUN measures about 115°

3. Write a title and label the axes for the bar graph. Explain why you chose that title.

   Sample answers:

   Travel Time to School (title)

   Minutes; Students

   The minimum (5 minutes) and maximum (35 minutes) are reasonable travel times to school.

4. Color the spinner so that there is a 50% chance of landing on red and a $\frac{1}{6}$ chance of landing on black. Leave the rest of the spinner white.

   What is the probability of landing on white? $\frac{1}{3}$

   If you spin the spinner 300 times, about how many times would you expect the spinner to land on black? 50 times

***Math Journal 1,* p. 162**

Study Link Master

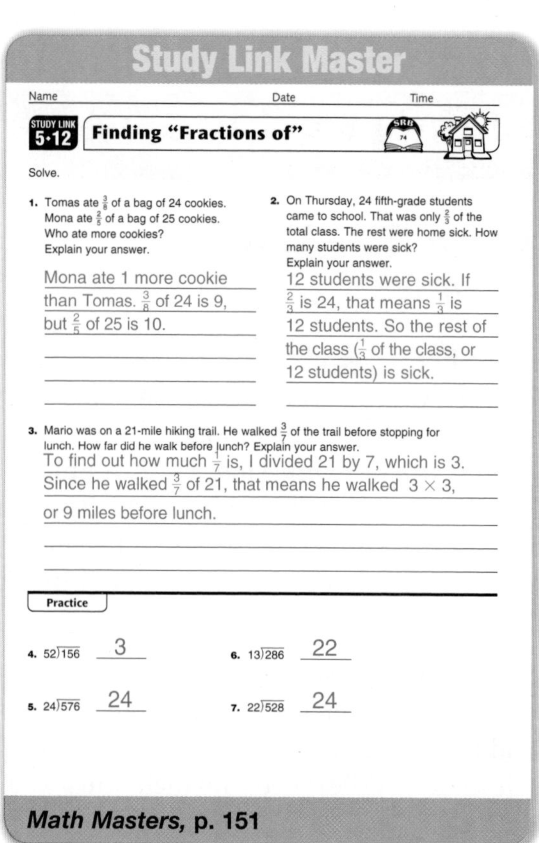

Name Date Time

STUDY LINK 5·12 **Finding "Fractions of"**

Solve.

1. Tomas ate $\frac{3}{8}$ of a bag of 24 cookies. Mona ate $\frac{2}{5}$ of a bag of 25 cookies. Who ate more cookies? Explain your answer.

   Mona ate 1 more cookie than Tomas. $\frac{3}{8}$ of 24 is 9, but $\frac{2}{5}$ of 25 is 10.

2. On Thursday, 24 fifth-grade students came to school. That was only $\frac{2}{3}$ of the total class. The rest were home sick. How many students were sick? Explain your answer.

   12 students were sick. If $\frac{2}{3}$ is 24, that means $\frac{1}{3}$ is 12 students. So the rest of the class ($\frac{1}{3}$ of the class, or 12 students) is sick.

3. Mario was on a 21-mile hiking trail. He walked $\frac{3}{7}$ of the trail before stopping for lunch. How far did he walk before lunch? Explain your answer.

   To find out how much $\frac{1}{7}$ is, I divided 21 by 7, which is 3. Since he walked $\frac{3}{7}$ of 21, that means he walked 3×3, or 9 miles before lunch.

Practice

4. 52)156 3
5. 24)576 24
6. 13)286 22
7. 22)528 24

***Math Masters,* p. 151**

3 Differentiation Options

ENRICHMENT

PARTNER ACTIVITY

15–30 Min

▶ Reading about Mathematics Instruction in History and Solving Related Problems

(*Math Masters,* p. 152)

Social Studies Link To further explore interpreting historical texts, have partners complete the problems on *Math Masters,* page 152. As students work, encourage them to discuss the questions and share their solutions. Explain that the challenge of this activity is that, in the historical periods mentioned, people would not have expected fifth graders to be able to solve these problems.

EXTRA PRACTICE

PARTNER ACTIVITY

15–30 Min

▶ Converting Bar Graphs to Circle Graphs

Portfolio Ideas

To provide additional practice with constructing circle graphs, have students construct circle graphs from sample newspaper or magazine bar graphs. If the data needs to be converted from fractions to percents, allow students to use calculators. Students should display the bar graph and the circle graph next to each other in the Fractions, Decimals, and Percents Museum.

Planning Ahead

Make sure students have completed Study Link 5-10. The class will use the information in Lesson 6-1.

Teaching Master

Name Date Time

LESSON 5•12

Mathematics Instruction in History

Throughout our nation's history, students have learned mathematics in different ways and have spent their time working on different kinds of problems. This is because people's views of what students can and should learn are constantly changing.

1. *1840s* It was discovered that children could be very good at mental arithmetic, and students began to solve mental arithmetic problems as early as age 4. A school in Connecticut reported that its arithmetic champion could mentally multiply 314,521,325 by 231,452,153 in $5\frac{1}{2}$ minutes.

   After studying arithmetic two hours per day for 7 to 9 years, 94% of eighth graders in Boston in 1845 could solve the following problem. Try to solve it.

   What is $\frac{1}{2}$ of $\frac{1}{3}$ of 9 hours and 18 minutes? 93 min, or 1 hr and 33 min (unit)

   Explain your solution: Sample answer: $\frac{1}{3}$ of 9 hours is 3, and $\frac{1}{3}$ of 18 minutes is 6. $\frac{1}{2}$ of 3 hours is $1\frac{1}{2}$ hours, or 90 minutes. $\frac{1}{2}$ of 6 minutes is 3. So the total is $90 + 3 = 93$ minutes, or 1 hour and 33 minutes.

2. *1870s* Many textbooks were step-by-step guides on how to solve various problems. Students were given problems and answers. They had to show how the rules in the textbook could be used to produce the given answers.

   Here is a problem from around 1870 (without the answer) given to students at the end of 6 to 8 years of elementary arithmetic study. Try to solve it.

   I was married at the age of 21. If I live 19 years longer, I will have been married 60 years. What is my age now? 62 years (unit)

   Explain your solution: Sample answer: I subtracted 19 from 60 and found $60 - 19 = 41$. Then I added the age at the time of marriage, $41 + 21 = 62$, or 62 years.

Math Masters, p. 152

5•13 Progress Check 5

Objective To assess students' progress on mathematical content through the end of Unit 5.

1 Looking Back: Cumulative Assessment

Input student data from Progress Check 5 into the **Assessment Management Spreadsheets**.

Materials
- Study Link 5•12
- *Assessment Handbook,* pp. 84–91, 175–179, 220, and 262–265
- slate

CONTENT ASSESSED	LESSON(S)	ASSESSMENT ITEMS				
		SELF	ORAL/SLATE	WRITTEN PART A	WRITTEN PART B	OPEN RESPONSE
Use numerical expressions to represent equivalent names for fractions, decimals, and percents. Convert between fractions and mixed numbers. [Number and Numeration Goal 5]	5•1–5•12	1–3	1, 3, 4	1–10	20	✓
Order and compare fractions. [Number and Numeration Goal 6]	5•3, 5•5–5•7	5	2	14–16	17–19	
Add fractions. [Operations and Computation Goal 4]	5•2, 5•3	4		11–13		✓
Construct circle graphs from data. [Data and Chance Goal 1]	5•11	8			23	
Use graphs to answer questions. [Data and Chance Goal 2]	5•9–5•12				24–26	
Estimate and measure sectors of a circle graph. [Measurement and Reference Frames Goal 1]	5•9–5•11	6, 7			21–23	

2 Looking Ahead: Preparing for Unit 6

Math Boxes 5•13

Study Link 5•13: Unit 6 Family Letter

Materials
- *Math Journal 1,* p. 163
- *Math Masters,* pp. 153–156

Getting Started

Math Message • Self Assessment

Complete the Self Assessment (Assessment Handbook, *p. 175*).

Study Link 5·12 Follow-Up

Allow students five minutes to compare answers and correct any errors.

1 Looking Back: Cumulative Assessment

▶ Math Message Follow-Up

INDEPENDENT ACTIVITY

(Self Assessment, *Assessment Handbook,* p. 175)

The Self Assessment offers students the opportunity to reflect upon their progress.

▶ Oral and Slate Assessments

WHOLE-CLASS ACTIVITY

Problems 3 and 4 provide summative information and can be used for grading purposes. Problems 1 and 2 provide formative information that can be useful in planning future instruction.

Oral Assessment

1. Dictate fractions such as the following. Have students give an equivalent decimal and percent for each.
   - $\frac{19}{100}$ 0.19; 19%
   - $\frac{9}{10}$ 0.9; 90%
   - $\frac{3}{4}$ 0.75; 75%
   - $\frac{2}{5}$ 0.4, or 0.40; 40%
   - $\frac{43}{50}$ 0.86; 86%
   - $\frac{11}{25}$ 0.44; 44%
2. Have students compare and order sets of fractions such as the following: $\frac{9}{14}$; $\frac{8}{13}$; $\frac{2}{32}$ $\frac{2}{32}$, $\frac{8}{13}$, $\frac{9}{14}$

Slate Assessment

3. Pose fractions such as the following. Have students write equivalent mixed numbers or whole numbers on their slates.
   - $\frac{9}{3}$ 3
   - $\frac{13}{6}$ $2\frac{1}{6}$
   - $\frac{18}{4}$ $4\frac{2}{4}$, or $4\frac{1}{2}$
   - $\frac{25}{4}$ $6\frac{1}{4}$
   - $\frac{22}{8}$ $2\frac{6}{8}$, or $2\frac{3}{4}$
   - $\frac{55}{25}$ $2\frac{5}{25}$, or $2\frac{1}{5}$
4. Pose mixed numbers such as the following. Have students write equivalent improper fractions on their slates.
   - $2\frac{3}{7}$ $\frac{17}{7}$
   - $4\frac{1}{2}$ $\frac{9}{2}$
   - $7\frac{3}{8}$ $\frac{59}{8}$
   - $10\frac{4}{5}$ $\frac{54}{5}$

Assessment Master

Name Date Time

LESSON 5·13 **Self Assessment** Progress Check 5

Think about each skill listed below. Assess your own progress by checking the most appropriate box.

Skills	I can do this on my own and explain how to do it.	I can do this on my own.	I can do this if I get help or look at an example.
1. Find equivalent fractions.			
2. Convert between fractions and mixed numbers.			
3. Convert between fractions and percents.			
4. Add fractions using fraction sticks.			
5. Order and compare fractions.			
6. Estimate the value of circle graph sectors.			
7. Measure sectors of a circle graph.			
8. Construct circle graphs from data.			

***Assessment Handbook,* p. 175**

Assessment Master

Name Date Time

LESSON 5·13 **Written Assessment** Progress Check 5

Part A

Write three equivalent fractions for each fraction below. Sample answers:

1. $\frac{3}{7}$ $\frac{6}{14}$, $\frac{9}{21}$, $\frac{30}{70}$
2. $\frac{6}{9}$ $\frac{2}{3}$, $\frac{12}{18}$, $\frac{18}{27}$
3. $\frac{9}{10}$ $\frac{18}{20}$, $\frac{27}{30}$, $\frac{90}{100}$

Fill in the oval next to each equivalent fraction or mixed number. (*Hint:* There may be more than one correct answer.)

4. $\frac{12}{5}$	5. $\frac{18}{8}$	6. $3\frac{4}{9}$	7. $5\frac{7}{3}$
○ 3	○ 2	○ $\frac{7}{9}$	○ $\frac{35}{3}$
○ $2\frac{4}{5}$	● $2\frac{1}{4}$	● $\frac{31}{9}$	○ $\frac{12}{3}$
● $1\frac{7}{5}$	○ $3\frac{1}{8}$	○ $\frac{15}{9}$	○ $\frac{15}{3}$
● $2\frac{2}{5}$	● $2\frac{2}{8}$	○ $\frac{34}{9}$	● $\frac{22}{3}$

Write the mixed number and fraction for each diagram below. In each diagram, the square is worth 1.

Whole
square

8. Mixed number $1\frac{2}{4}$, or $1\frac{1}{2}$ Fraction $\frac{6}{4}$, or $\frac{3}{2}$
9. Mixed number $2\frac{1}{4}$ Fraction $\frac{9}{4}$
10. Mixed number $1\frac{5}{4}$, or $2\frac{1}{4}$ Fraction $\frac{9}{4}$

***Assessment Handbook,* p. 176**

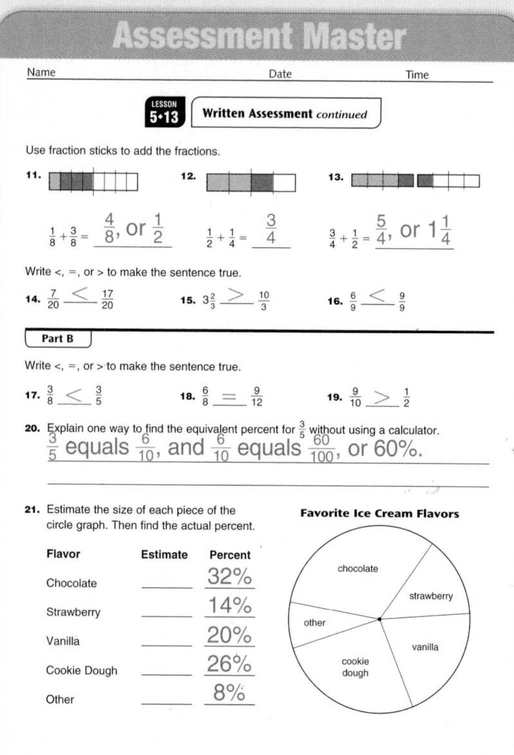
Assessment Master

Name Date Time

LESSON 5•13 Written Assessment *continued*

Use fraction sticks to add the fractions.

11. $\frac{1}{8} + \frac{3}{8} = \frac{4}{8}$, or $\frac{1}{2}$

12. $\frac{1}{2} + \frac{1}{4} = \frac{3}{4}$

13. $\frac{3}{4} + \frac{1}{2} = \frac{5}{4}$, or $1\frac{1}{4}$

Write <, =, or > to make the sentence true.

14. $\frac{7}{20} < \frac{17}{20}$

15. $3\frac{2}{3} > \frac{10}{3}$

16. $\frac{6}{9} < \frac{9}{9}$

Part B

Write <, =, or > to make the sentence true.

17. $\frac{3}{8} < \frac{3}{5}$

18. $\frac{6}{8} = \frac{9}{12}$

19. $\frac{9}{10} > \frac{1}{2}$

20. Explain one way to find the equivalent percent for $\frac{3}{5}$ without using a calculator.
$\frac{3}{5}$ equals $\frac{6}{10}$, and $\frac{6}{10}$ equals $\frac{60}{100}$, or 60%.

21. Estimate the size of each piece of the circle graph. Then find the actual percent.

Flavor	Estimate	Percent
Chocolate		32%
Strawberry		14%
Vanilla		20%
Cookie Dough		26%
Other		8%

Favorite Ice Cream Flavors

chocolate, strawberry, vanilla, cookie dough, other

Assessment Handbook, p. 177

Assessment Master

Name Date Time

LESSON 5•13 Written Assessment *continued*

22. Why is it helpful to make an estimate before finding the size of a piece of a circle graph?
Answers vary.

A survey reported favorite types of books for fifth graders. The results of the survey were as follows:

38% Adventure books 30% Mystery books 22% Humor books 10% Other

23. Make and label a circle graph for this data below. Use your Percent Circle.

Favorite Books

other, humor, adventure, mystery

24. If 100 students answered the survey, how many of them chose adventure books?
38 students

25. If 10 students answered the survey, how many of them chose other books?
1 student

26. If 50 students answered the survey, how many of them chose mystery books?
15 students

Assessment Handbook, p. 178

▶ Written Assessment

(*Assessment Handbook,* pp. 176–178)

Part A Recognizing Student Achievement

Problems 1–16 provide summative information and may be used for grading purposes.

Problem(s)	Description
1–3	Equivalent fractions
4–10	Convert between fractions and mixed numbers.
11–13	Add fractions using fraction sticks.
14–16	Order and compare fractions.

Part B Informing Instruction

Problems 17–26 provide formative information that can be useful in planning future instruction.

Problem(s)	Description
20	Convert between fractions and percents.
17–19	Order and compare fractions with unlike denominators.
21–26	Read and construct circle graphs.

Use the checklists on pages 263 and 265 of the *Assessment Handbook* to record results. Then input the data into the **Assessment Management Spreadsheets** to keep an ongoing record of students' progress toward Grade-Level Goals.

▶ Open Response

(*Assessment Handbook,* p. 179)

Finding Fractions

The open-response item requires students to apply skills and concepts from Unit 5 to solve a multistep problem. See *Assessment Handbook,* pages 87–91 for rubrics and students' work samples for this problem.

2 Looking Ahead: Preparing for Unit 6

Math Boxes 5·13

INDEPENDENT ACTIVITY

(*Math Journal 1,* p. 163)

Mixed Review This Math Boxes page previews Unit 6 content.

Study Link 5·13: Unit 6 Family Letter

INDEPENDENT ACTIVITY

(*Math Masters,* pp. 153–156)

Home Connection The Unit 6 Family Letter provides parents and guardians with information and activities related to Unit 6 topics.

Assessment Master

Name Date Time

LESSON 5·13 **Open Response** Progress Check 5

Finding Fractions

The figure below represents One.

Find and write the correct fraction in each of the figure's parts.

Check to be sure that the sum of the fractions is 1.

A B C D E F G H I

Explain how you found the fraction for the part labeled F.

List a combination of parts that is worth about $\frac{2}{3}$. Explain your answer.

Assessment Handbook, p. 179

Student Page

Date Time

LESSON 5·13 **Math Boxes**

1. Mr. Hernandez's class took a survey to find out when students prefer to do their homework. 125 fifth-grade students responded.

As soon as I get home	17%
After having an after-school snack	30%
Right after dinner	39%
Just before going to bed	14%

Use your Geometry Template to make a circle graph of the results. Give the graph a title. Label the sectors of the graph.

Preferred Homework Time (title)

17% after school; 14% before bed; 30% after snack; 39% after dinner

SRB 125 126

2. List a set of at least twelve numbers that has the following landmarks:

Minimum: 28 Maximum: 34 Median: 30 Mode: 29

Sample answer: 28, 28, 29, 29, 29, 29, 31, 32, 32, 33, 33, 34

Make a bar graph for what this set of numbers might represent.

Hiking Club Plant Sales

Plants Sold

Jan Feb Mar Apr May Jun Jul Aug Sep Oct Nov Dec

Months

SRB 119 122

3. If you roll a regular 6-sided die, what is the probability of getting ...

a. 5? $\frac{1}{6}$

b. a prime number? $\frac{3}{6}$, or $\frac{1}{2}$

c. an even number? $\frac{3}{6}$, or $\frac{1}{2}$

d. a multiple of 3? $\frac{2}{6}$, or $\frac{1}{3}$

SRB 128 129

4. Draw and label a 30° angle.

Sample answer:

O D E

SRB 204-206

Math Journal 1, p. 163

Study Link Master

Name Date Time

STUDY LINK 5·13 **Unit 6: Family Letter**

Using Data; Addition and Subtraction of Fractions

The authors of *Everyday Mathematics* believe that students should work substantially with data. Unit 6 is designed to present and teach relevant data skills and concepts, allowing your child ample opportunities to practice organizing and analyzing the data that he or she collects.

The data that your child collects at first will usually be an unorganized set of numbers. After organizing the data using a variety of methods, he or she will study the **landmarks** of the data. The following terms are called landmarks because they show important features of the data.

- The **maximum** is the largest data value observed.
- The **minimum** is the smallest data value observed.
- The **range** is the difference between the maximum and the minimum.
- The **mode** is the most popular data value—the value observed most often.
- The **median** is the middle data value observed.
- The **mean,** commonly known as the average, is a central value for a set of data.

At the end of the unit, students will demonstrate their skills by conducting a survey of their peers, gathering and organizing the data, analyzing their results, and writing a summary report.

Your child will continue the American Tour by studying Native American measurements for length and distance, based on parts of the body. Students will convert these body measures to personal measures by measuring their fingers, hands, and arms in both metric and U.S. customary units. In addition, your child will learn how to read a variety of contour-type maps, such as climate, precipitation, and growing-seasons maps.

Finally, students will explore addition and subtraction of fractions by using a clock face and fraction sticks. They will learn to find common denominators and apply this skill to add and subtract fractions with unlike denominators.

Please keep this Family Letter for reference as your child works through Unit 6.

Math Masters, p. 153

Unit 6 Organizer

Using Data; Addition and Subtraction of Fractions

Overview

In Unit 6 students investigate data displays and sample size. Students learn how to match "mystery plots" with data, and they learn how to read and use contour maps to display certain kinds of data. Also in Unit 6, students add and subtract fractions and relate finding common denominators to the idea that every fraction has many equivalent names. Unit 6 has three main areas of focus:

- To use data from surveys, investigate the effect of sample size, and use stem-and-leaf plots and other data displays,
- To read and use contour maps that show climate and growing-season data, and
- To revisit addition and subtraction of fractions.

Linking to the Common Core State Standards

The content of Unit 6 addresses the Common Core State Standards for Mathematics in *Number and Operations–Fractions.* The correlation of the Common Core State Standards to the *Everyday Mathematics* Grade 5 lessons begins on page CS1.

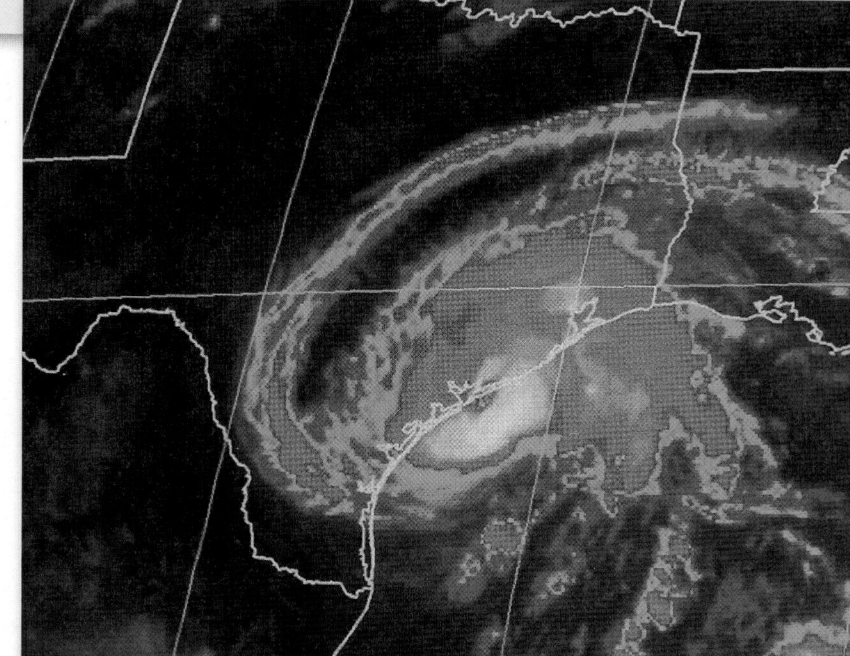

Contents

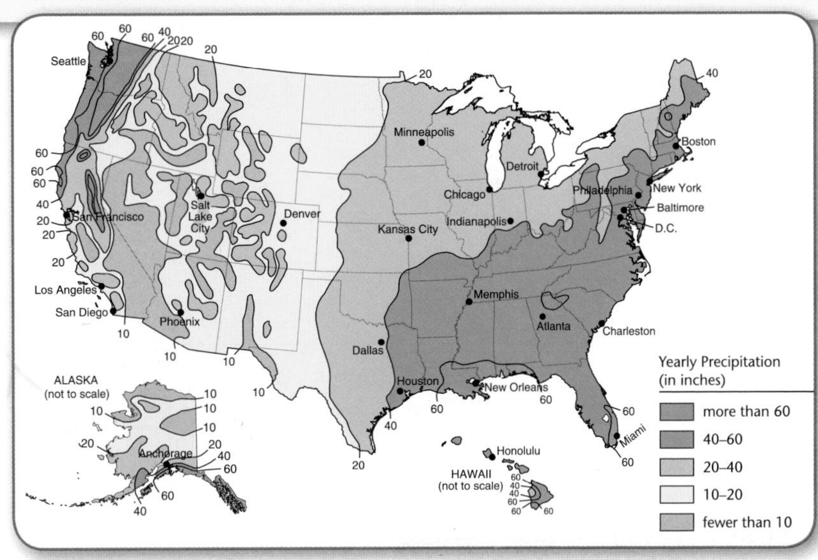

Seattle
San Francisco
Salt Lake City
Denver
Los Angeles
San Diego
Phoenix
Minneapolis
Detroit
Chicago
Indianapolis
Kansas City
Memphis
Atlanta
Charleston
Dallas
Houston
New Orleans
Miami
Boston
New York
Philadelphia
Baltimore
D.C.
ALASKA
(not to scale)
Anchorage
HAWAII
(not to scale)
Honolulu
Yearly Precipitation
(in inches)
more than 60
40–60
20–40
10–20
fewer than 10

Learning In Perspective

	Lesson Objectives	Links to the Past	Links to the Future
6•1	To review data landmarks and methods for organizing data.	In fourth grade, students organize data using tally charts, line plots, and bar graphs.	In sixth grade, students explain ways in which data can be presented to misrepresent or mislead.
6•2	To develop measurement and probability concepts.	In fourth grade, students measure to the nearest millimeter and review the relationships among metric units of length.	In sixth grade, students simulate a situation using random numbers. Students use results to estimate the chance of each possible outcome.
6•3	To introduce stem-and-leaf plots; and to provide practice measuring lengths and using a protractor.	In fourth grade, students display data with line plots, bar graphs, and tally charts.	In sixth grade, students use stem-and-leaf plots to organize and analyze data.
6•4	To provide experiences with data presented in line plots and stem-and-leaf plots.	In fourth grade, students use data tables and display data with line plots, bar graphs, line graphs, and tally charts.	In sixth grade, students use stem-and-leaf plots to organize and analyze data.
6•5	To investigate the relationship between sample size and the reliability of derived results.	In fourth grade, students examine data and explore the validity of data.	In sixth grade, students determine whether a sample is random or biased.
6•6	To provide experiences with displaying and analyzing data.	In fourth grade, students display sets of data and compare numerical data.	In Unit 10, students create and interpret different kinds of graphs.
6•7	To introduce contour maps as data displays.	In fourth grade, students use a map scale.	In sixth grade, students maintain and apply skills related to data displays.
6•8	To review estimating with fractions using benchmarks.	In fourth grade, students use benchmarks to make comparisons.	In Unit 8, students review adding and subtracting fractions with like and unlike denominators.
6•9	To provide additional references for fraction concepts.	In fourth grade, students order sets of fractions.	In sixth grade, students use proportions to model and solve rate problems.
6•10	To reinforce the use of common denominators to compare, add, and subtract fractions.	In fourth grade, students practice finding common denominators.	In Unit 8, students review adding and subtracting fractions with like and unlike denominators.

	Key Concepts and Skills	Grade 5 Goals*
6•1	Organize data using a picture, graph, line plot, table, or list.	Data and Chance Goal 1
	Identify data landmarks for data sets.	Data and Chance Goal 2
	Compare and answer questions about data sets and their organization.	Data and Chance Goal 2
6•2	Organize and display data using a table.	Data and Chance Goal 1
	Use collected data to make predictions about future outcomes of a simple game.	Data and Chance Goal 3
	Measure to the nearest millimeter, centimeter, and inch.	Measurement and Reference Frames Goal 1
6•3	Collect and organize class data.	Data and Chance Goal 1
	Identify data landmarks.	Data and Chance Goal 2
	Measure finger and hand spans to the nearest millimeter.	Measurement and Reference Frames Goal 1
	Measure angles with half-circle protractors.	Measurement and Reference Frames Goal 1
6•4	Interpret line plots and stem-and-leaf plots.	Data and Chance Goal 2
	Use landmarks to identify data sets.	Data and Chance Goal 2
	Use landmarks to draw conclusions about data sets.	Data and Chance Goal 2
6•5	Solve problems involving percent.	Number and Numeration Goal 2
	Convert fractions to percents.	Number and Numeration Goal 5
	Construct circle graphs of class data.	Data and Chance Goal 1
	Make predictions based on sampling.	Data and Chance Goal 2
6•6	Convert fractions to percents.	Number and Numeration Goal 5
	Construct bar and circle graphs and a stem-and-leaf plot.	Data and Chance Goal 1
	Identify data landmarks.	Data and Chance Goal 2
6•7	Investigate the use of contour maps to organize collected data.	Data and Chance Goal 1
	Use the data displayed in contour maps to answer questions and draw conclusions.	Data and Chance Goal 2
6•8	Identify benchmarks on a number line.	Number and Numeration Goal 6
	Add fractions and mixed numbers with like and unlike denominators.	Operations and Computation Goal 4
	Use benchmarks to estimate sums and differences.	Operations and Computation Goal 6
6•9	Find common denominators.	Number and Numeration Goal 5
	Use clock models and pencil-and-paper algorithms to add and subtract fractions.	Operations and Computation Goal 4
	Use benchmarks to estimate sums and differences.	Operations and Computation Goal 6
6•10	Use the products of denominators to find equivalent fractions.	Number and Numeration Goal 5
	Rename pairs of fractions using a common denominator.	Number and Numeration Goal 5
	Use common denominators to add and subtract fraction pairs.	Operations and Computation Goal 4

*See the Appendix for a complete list of Grade 5 Goals.

A Balanced Curriculum

Ongoing Practice

Everyday Mathematics provides numerous opportunities for ongoing practice. These activities are embedded throughout the lessons:

Mental Math and Reflexes activities promote speed and accuracy in mental computation.

Math Boxes offer mixed practice and are paired across lessons as shown in the brackets below. This makes them useful as assessment tools. The last one or two boxes on each page preview the next unit's content.

Mixed practice	[6•1, 6•3], [6•2, 6•4], [6•5, 6•7], [6•6, 6•9], [6•8, 6•10]
Mixed practice with multiple choice	6•5, 6•7
Mixed practice with writing/reasoning opportunity	6•1, 6•4, 6•5, 6•7, 6•9, 6•10

Study Links are daily homework assignments that review the content of the lesson and often contain ongoing facts practice or computation practice.

5-Minute Math problems are offered for additional practice in Lessons 6•1 and 6•8.

EM Facts Workshop Game provides online practice of basic facts and computation.

EXTRA PRACTICE **Extra Practice** activities are included in Lessons 6•1, 6•3, 6•4, 6•6, 6•7, 6•8, 6•9, and 6•10.

Practice through Games

Games are an essential component of practice in the *Everyday Mathematics* program. Games offer skills practice and promote strategic thinking. See the *Differentiation Handbook* for ways to adapt games to meet students' needs.

Lesson	Game	Skill Practiced
6•2, 6•3, 6•4, 6•5	*Finish First*	**Collecting data** [DC Goal 1]
6•6	*Frac-Tac-Toe*	**Renaming fractions as decimals or percents** [NN Goal 5]
6•8	*Fraction Top-It* (Advanced Version)	**Estimate sums of fractions and compare them** [OC Goal 6]
6•9	*Fraction Capture*	**Naming equivalent fractions** [NN Goal 5 and OC Goal 4]

[NN] Number and Numeration
[MRF] Measurement and Reference Frames
[OC] Operations and Computation
[GEO] Geometry
[DC] Data and Chance
[PFA] Patterns, Functions, and Algebra

Problem Solving 

Experts at problem solving and mathematical modeling generally do these things:

- Identify the problem.
- Decide what information is needed to solve the problem.
- Play with and study the data to find patterns and meaning.
- Identify and use mathematical procedures to solve the problem.
- Decide whether the solution makes sense and whether it can be applied to other problems.

The table below lists some of the opportunities in this unit for students to practice these strategies.

Lesson	Activity
6•1, 6•3	Organize and describe data and create stem-and-leaf plots.
6•2–6•6	Determine whether a game is a fair game.
6•4	Interpret data in line plots and stem-and-leaf plots.
6•5	Determine trustworthy samples and make predictions about data.
6•7	Use contour maps for precipitation and growing seasons to compare the climate of various U.S. locations.
6•9	Use clocks to add and subtract fractions.

Lessons that teach *through* problem solving, not just *about* problem solving

See Chapter 18: Problem Solving in the *Teacher's Reference Manual* for more information.

The Language of Mathematics

Everyday Mathematics provides lesson-specific suggestions to help all students acquire, process, and express mathematical ideas. Throughout Unit 6, there are lesson-specific language development notes that address the needs of English language learners, indicated by ELL.

ELL SUPPORT Activities to support English language learners are in Part 3 of Lessons 6•1, 6•3, 6•6, and 6•7.

The *English Learners Handbook* and the *Differentiation Handbook* have suggestions for promoting language development and acquisition of mathematics vocabulary. See Unit 6 in each handbook.

Unit 6 Vocabulary

angle of separation
climate
common denominator
contour line
contour map
cubit
fair game
fathom
frequency table
great span
landmark
leaf
line plot
map legend (map key)
maximum
median
minimum
mode
normal span
population
precipitation
quick common denominator
sample
simplest form
span
stem
stem-and-leaf plot
survey
unlike denominators

Literacy Connection

Do You Wanna Bet? Your Chance to Find Out About Probability, by Jean Cushman, Houghton Mifflin, 2007

Jim and the Beanstalk, by Raymond Briggs, Putnam Juvenile, 1997

Esio Trot, by Roald Dahl, Puffin, 2009

Fraction Action, by Loreen Leedy, Holiday House, 1996

For more literacy connections, see the *Home Connection Handbook,* Grades 4–6.

Cross-Curricular Links 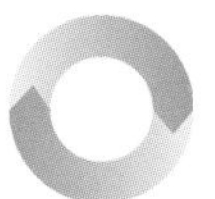

Language Arts – Lesson 6•3

Science – Lesson 6•7

Social Studies – Lessons 6•2, 6•6

Balanced Assessment

Daily Assessments

- **Recognizing Student Achievement** – A daily assessment that is included in every lesson to evaluate students' progress toward the Grade 5 Grade-Level Goals.
- **Informing Instruction** – Notes that appear throughout the unit to help anticipate students' common errors and suggest appropriate problem-solving strategies.

Lesson	Recognizing Student Achievement	Informing Instruction
6•1	Display data on a line plot and discuss the data's organization. [DC Goals 1 and 2]	
6•2	Use linear measuring tools to measure to the nearest centimeter and $\frac{1}{4}$ inch. [MRF Goal 1]	
6•3	Understand the structure of stem-and-leaf plots. [DC Goal 1]	Keep numbers organized when copying from the Class Data Pad.
6•4	Interpret data displayed in line plots. [DC Goal 2]	Find the median by crossing out numbers in pairs. Read the leaves as separate numbers in the stem-and-leaf plots.
6•5	Understand the concept of percent. [NN Goal 2]	
6•6	Name fraction-decimal equivalents. [NN Goal 5]	Check for necessary elements on graphs.
6•7	Rename fractions as decimals and percents. [NN Goal 5]	
6•8	Use benchmarks to estimate sums and differences. [OC Goal 6]	Use benchmarks and equivalent fractions.
6•9	Use a visual model to add and subtract fractions with unlike denominators. [OC Goal 4]	
6•10	Find common denominators. [NN Goal 5]	

[NN] Number and Numeration
[MRF] Measurement and Reference Frames
[OC] Operations and Computation
[GEO] Geometry
[DC] Data and Chance
[PFA] Patterns, Functions, and Algebra

Portfolio Opportunities

The following lessons provide opportunities to gather samples of students' mathematical writings, drawings, and creations to add balance to the assessment process: Lessons 6•1, 6•3, 6•4, 6•5, 6•6, 6•7, 6•9, 6•10, and 6•11.

See pages 16 and 17 in the *Assessment Handbook* for more information about portfolios and how to use them.

Unit Assessment

Progress Check 6 – A cumulative assessment of concepts and skills taught in Unit 6 and in previous units, providing information for evaluating students' progress and planning for future instruction. These assessments include oral/slate, written, and open-response activities, as shown below in the sample Progress Check lesson opener.

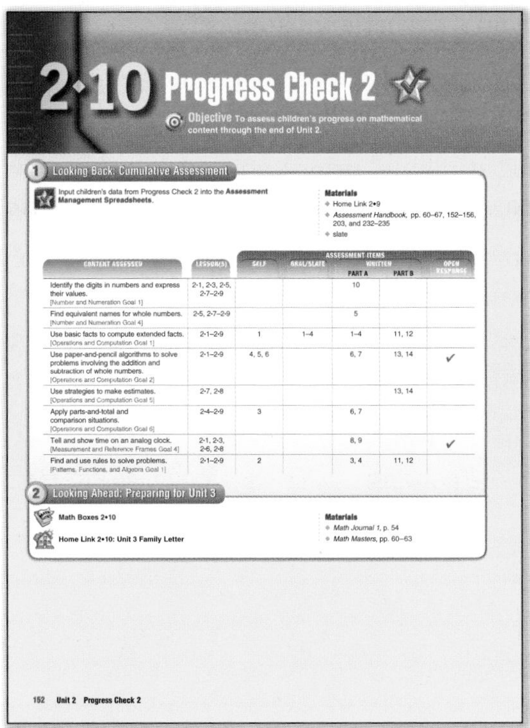

2•10 Progress Check 2

Objective To assess children's progress on mathematical content through the end of Unit 2.

1 Looking Back: Cumulative Assessment

Input children's data from Progress Check 2 into the **Assessment Management Spreadsheets.**

Materials
- Home Link 2•9
- *Assessment Handbook,* pp. 60–67, 152–156, 203, and 232–235
- slate

Content Assessed	Lesson(s)	Assessment Items: Self	Oral/Slate	Written: Part A	Written: Part B	Open Response
Identify the digits in numbers and express their values. [Number and Numeration Goal 1]	2•1, 2•3, 2•5, 2•7–2•9			10		
Find equivalent names for whole numbers. [Number and Numeration Goal 4]	2•5, 2•7–2•9			5		
Use basic facts to compute extended facts. [Operations and Computation Goal 1]	2•1–2•9	1	1–4	1–4	11, 12	
Use paper-and-pencil algorithms to solve problems involving the addition and subtraction of whole numbers. [Operations and Computation Goal 2]	2•1–2•9	4, 5, 6		6, 7	13, 14	✓
Use strategies to make estimates. [Operations and Computation Goal 5]	2•7, 2•8				13, 14	
Apply parts-and-total and comparison situations. [Operations and Computation Goal 6]	2•4–2•9	3		6, 7		
Tell and show time on an analog clock. [Measurement and Reference Frames Goal 4]	2•1, 2•3, 2•6, 2•8			8, 9		✓
Find and use rules to solve problems. [Patterns, Functions, and Algebra Goal 1]	2•1–2•9	2		3, 4	11, 12	

2 Looking Ahead: Preparing for Unit 3

Math Boxes 2•10

Home Link 2•10: Unit 3 Family Letter

Materials
- *Math Journal 1,* p. 54
- *Math Masters,* pp. 60–63

152 Unit 2 Progress Check 2

Core Assessment Resources

Assessment Handbook

- **Unit 6 Assessment Overview,** pages 92–101
- **Unit 6 Assessment Masters,** pages 180–184
- **Unit 6 Individual Profiles of Progress,** pages 266, 267, and 302
- **Unit 6 Class Checklists,** pages 268, 269, and 303
- **Mid-Year Assessment,** pages 228–233
- **Quarterly Checklist: Quarter 2,** pages 296 and 297
- **Math Logs,** pages 306–308
- **Exit Slip,** page 311
- **Other Student Assessment Forms,** pages 304, 305, 309, and 310

Assessment Management Spreadsheets

The Assessment Management Spreadsheets consist of the Digital Class Checklists and Individual Profile of Progress Checklists. Use them to monitor, record, and report student progress.

Addressing All Needs

Differentiated Instruction

Adjusting the Activity – suggests adaptations that target advanced learners, English language learners, or learners who need additional instructional support.

ELL SUPPORT / **ELL** – provides lesson-specific suggestions to help English language learners understand and process the mathematical content.

READINESS – accesses students' prior knowledge or previews content that prepares students to engage in the lesson's Part 1 activities.

EXTRA PRACTICE – provides additional opportunities to apply the mathematical content of the lesson.

ENRICHMENT – enables students to apply or further explore the mathematical content of the lesson.

Lesson	Adjusting the Activity	ELL Support/ ELL	Readiness	Extra Practice	Enrichment
6•1	•	•	•	•	•
6•2	•	•	•		•
6•3	•	•	•	•	
6•4			•	•	•
6•5	•	•	•		•
6•6	•	•	•	•	
6•7		•		•	•
6•8	•		•	•	•
6•9	•	•		•	•
6•10		•		•	•

Additional Resources

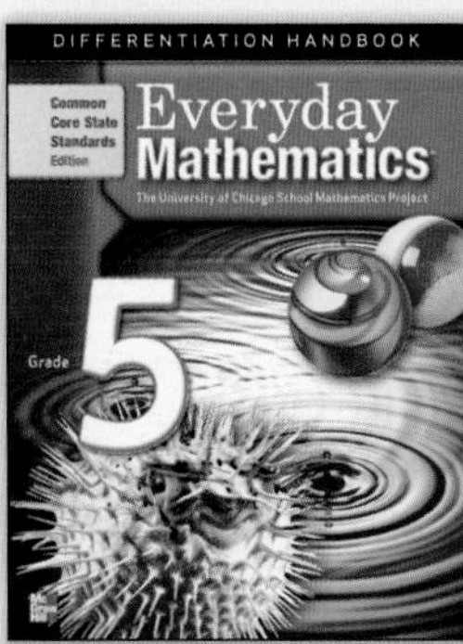

Differentiation Handbook
Provides ideas and strategies for differentiating instruction.
Pages 85–91

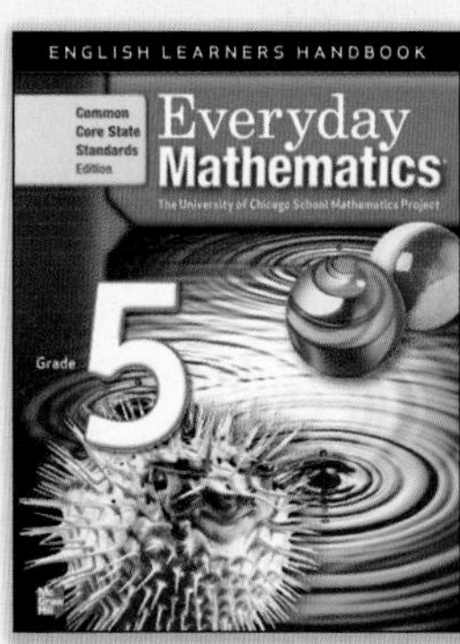

English Learners Handbook
Contains lesson-specific comprehension strategies.
Pages 49–58

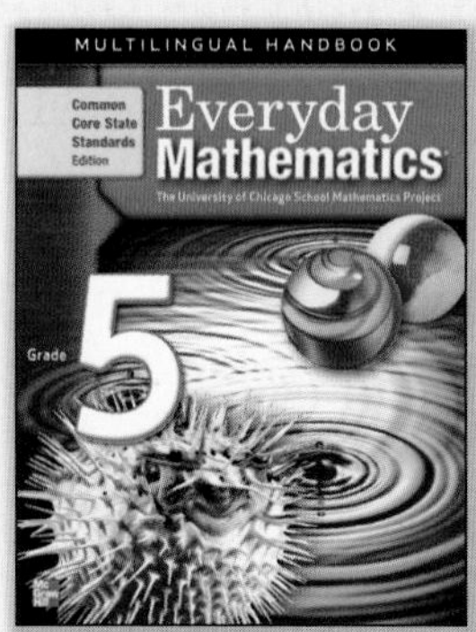

Multilingual Handbook
Previews concepts and vocabulary. It is written in six languages.
Pages 97–116

Planning Tips

Multiage Classroom

Companion Lessons from Grades 4 and 6 can help you meet instructional needs of a multiage classroom. The full Scope and Sequence can be found in the Appendix.

Grade 4	2•5	4•9	2•5, 4•9					7•9	9•1	7•6	
Grade 5	6•1	6•2	6•3	6•4	6•5	6•6	6•7	6•8	6•9	6•10	6•11
Grade 6			1•3	1•2				4•3–4•5	4•3–4•5		

Pacing for Success

Pacing depends on a number of factors, such as students' individual needs and how long your school has been using *Everyday Mathematics.* At the beginning of Unit 6, you may want to use tools available at www.everydaymathonline.com to help you set your pace.

Home Support

Unit 6 Family Letter (English/Spanish) provides families with an overview, Do-Anytime Activities, Building Skills through Games, a list of vocabulary, and answers to the daily homework (Study Links). Family Letters in English, Spanish, and seven other languages are also available online.

Study Links are the daily homework assignments. They consist of active projects and ongoing review problems.

Home Support Resources

Home Connection Handbook
Offers ideas and reproducible masters for communicating with families. See Table of Contents for unit information.

Student Reference Book
Provides a resource for students and parents.

Pages 62, 63, 65, 78C, 78D, 116, 119–122, 126, 182, 302, 309, 310, 378–380, 401

Technology Resources

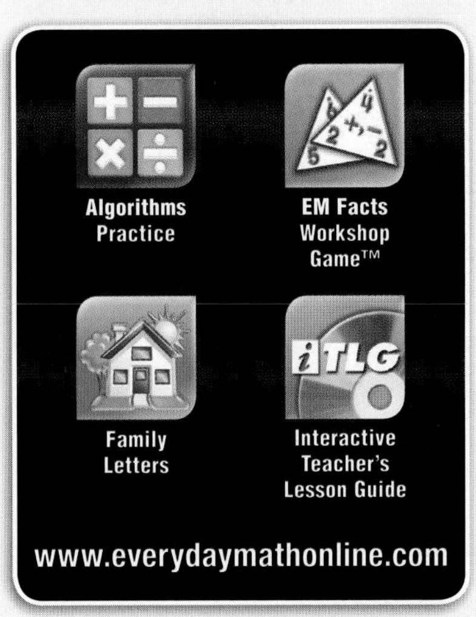

Materials

Technology Resources www.everydaymathonline.com

ePresentations

eToolkit

Algorithms Practice

EM Facts Workshop Game™

Family Letters

Assessment Management

Common Core State Standards

Curriculum Focal Points

Interactive Teacher's Lesson Guide

Lesson	Masters	Manipulative Kit	Other Items
6•1	Study Link Master, p. 157 *Differentiation Handbook,* p. 143 Teaching Masters, pp. 186A and 186B		Class Data Pad; chart paper; stick-on notes; index cards or paper; colored pencils; calculator
6•2	Study Link Master, p. 158 Teaching Masters, pp. 159 and 160	tape measure with centimeters and inches; per partnership: 4 each of number cards 4–8; slate	Probability Meter Poster; ruler with centimeters and inches; stick-on notes; chart paper; calculator
6•3	Teaching Aid Master, p. 414 Study Link Master, p. 161 Teaching Master, p. 162 *Differentiation Handbook,* p. 142	per partnership: 4 each of number cards 4–8; slate	Class Data Pad; demonstration protractor: protractor; ruler; colored chalk*
6•4	Teaching Masters, pp. 163, 165, and 166 Study Link Master, p. 164 Teaching Aid Master, p. 429	slate; per partnership: 4 each of number cards 4–8	calculator
6•5	Teaching Aid Master, p. 430 Study Link Master, p. 167 Teaching Masters, pp. 168 and 169	slate; per partnership: 4 each of number cards 4–8; per partnership: coin or six-sided die	Class Data Pad; small pieces of colored candy; crayons or markers; calculator; Geometry Template
6•6	Study Link Master, p. 170 Game Masters, pp. 472 and 474 Teaching Masters, pp. 171 and 172 Teaching Aid Master, p. 436* *Differentiation Handbook,* p. 142	slate	calculator
6•7	Study Link Master, p. 173	slate	physical and political maps of the United States*; stick-on notes*; contour maps
6•8	Study Link Master, p. 174 Teaching Masters, pp. 175 and 176 Game Master, p. 493		Fraction Cards (*Math Journal 2,* Activity Sheets 5–7)
6•9	Teaching Masters, pp. 177, 179, and 180 Study Link Master, p. 178 Game Master, p. 460	per partnership: 2 six-sided dice	
6•10	Teaching Aid Master, p. 414 Study Link Master, p. 181 Teaching Master, p. 182	slate	multiplication table*
6•11	Study Link Masters, pp. 183–186 Assessment Masters, pp. 180–184 and 228–233*	slate	

*Denotes optional materials

Mathematical Background

The discussion below highlights the major content areas presented in Unit 6 and helps establish instructional priorities.

Landmarks in Data Sets (Lesson 6•1)

The data landmarks reviewed in this lesson have been a focus of informal work since *Kindergarten Everyday Mathematics.* Using data landmarks to make sense of data can serve five-year-olds as well as adults. The contexts may become more complicated; the data sets may grow larger and more difficult to collect; and more complex algorithms, procedures, and statistical tools may be needed, but the basic ideas remain the same.

For more information about landmarks in data sets, see Section 12.2 of the *Teacher's Reference Manual.*

"Natural" Measures versus Standardized Measures

(Lessons 6•2 and 6•3)

Almost every human society has invented systems for counting and measuring. Measurement systems typically began with units of length based on body parts (the foot, the span, and so on) and with commonly used food or water containers for capacity. As people gathered into larger groups and commerce developed, they began to establish common standards for units of measure.

Lessons 6-2 and 6-3 remind students how measurement systems developed in human history, and how natural measures became standardized measures. The lessons review data gathering, use of landmarks, and angle-measure skills.

More information about natural and standardized measures can be found in Sections 14.1 and 14.2 of the *Teacher's Reference Manual.*

"Mystery Plots"—Establishing a New Routine (Lesson 6•4)

Students act as consumers and critics of data and data displays, rather than as producers. They need to develop judgment, common sense, and a healthy skepticism in order to adjust to the data-filled world. The mystery-plots routine will recur in later lessons. You may want to use it with data or graphs that you or your students find in newspapers and other sources.

For additional ways of displaying data, refer to Section 12.2.3 of the *Teacher's Reference Manual.*

Survey Design, Implementation, and Data Analysis (Lessons 6•5 and 6•5)

Much of the information used to make decisions today comes from surveys. Consumers are surveyed by manufacturers, television stations, politicians, newspapers, and magazines, among others. Sometimes the information needed comes from a small enough group so that everyone involved can be questioned. More often it is impossible to talk to everyone, and a representative sample of people is surveyed. The initial design of these surveys is crucial; a flawed design will yield either no results or questionable results. The size of the sample and the extent to which the sample represents the larger population are important. Students should keep in mind that:

Favorite TV Shows

News	||
Cartoons	~~||||~~ ||
Sit-Coms	||||
Documentaries	|
Sports	~~||||~~ ~~||||~~
Movies	~~||||~~ |||

- It is hazardous to draw conclusions from small samples of large populations.
- It is possible, with planning and precautions, to combine many small samples with unreliable and volatile results into large samples yielding reliable conclusions.

You and your students should feel free to survey on a topic that interests you. The particular topics don't matter; what's important is the process of formulating questions and gathering data to illuminate those questions.

See Section 12.2.4 of the *Teacher's Reference Manual* for additional information about data analysis.

Contour Maps: Showing a Third Dimension on a 2-Dimensional Map (Lesson 6•7)

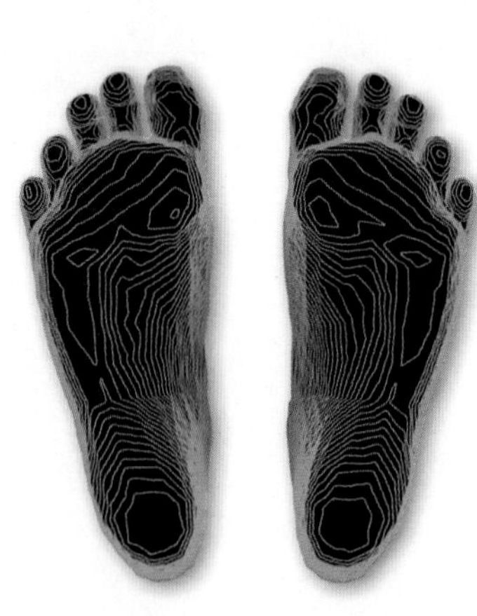

In this unit, students will use climate maps in the American Tour, and interpret contour lines on the maps.

Temperature and altitude maps are common examples in the use of contour maps in newspapers and on television. The important point of this lesson is that contour lines can convey many kinds of information. Students are cast in the roles of consumers and interpreters of data displays.

In this lesson, the maps are mathematical models of vast amounts of data collected over many years.

For additional information about contour maps, see Section 15.4.3 of the *Teacher's Reference Manual.*

Benchmarks for Adding and Subtracting Fractions (Lesson 6•8)

Students use benchmarks to estimate solutions to number stories involving addition and subtraction of fractions with like and unlike denominators that refer to the same whole. Common benchmarks used are

0, $\frac{1}{2}$, and 1. Students use benchmarks, number lines, and number sense of fractions to estimate mentally and assess reasonableness of answers.

Common Denominator Uses

(Lessons 6◆9 and 6◆10)

In principle, any two fractions can be rewritten as fractions with the same denominator, which can be found among the endless supply of equivalent names for each fraction. With common denominators, it is easy to add or subtract any two (or more) fractions.

In adding, subtracting, or comparing fractions, any common denominator works as well as any other, and finding a "quick common denominator" (QCD) as the product of two denominators (Lesson 6-10) is very useful. Hence, finding QCDs is suggested as the preferred method whenever the fractions are complex enough that the least common denominator (LCD) or other common denominators are not obvious. The algebra rule for adding fractions thus becomes $\frac{a}{b} + \frac{c}{d} = \frac{(a * d) + (c * b)}{b * d}$.

For additional information about common denominators, refer to Section 11.3.1 of the *Teacher's Reference Manual.*

$\frac{1}{4}$ = 25%

$\frac{2}{8}$ = 25%

Misconceptions Regarding Simplest Form, Mixed Numbers, and Fractions Greater Than One

It is important to know how to exploit the fact that there are many equivalent names for any fraction. It is useful to know that among the names, there is a fraction in "simplest form"—that is, its numerator and denominator have no common factors except 1—and that the simplest form is a convenient label for the entire collection of equivalent fractions.

It is also useful to know that if the numerator is larger than the denominator, there are equivalent names that are "mixed numbers," some with the numerator still larger than the denominator, some with the fraction part in simplest form, and some with the fraction part not in simplest form.

It is not useful to insist that "simplest form" is preferred to all other equivalent names. In fact, flexibility in arithmetic is gained by freely using whatever form is most convenient or illuminating for the purpose at hand. Truly numerate people artfully use one form of a number rather than another to express what they want or need to say. Also, "reducing" ratios or rates to "simpler" forms may result in important information being lost. For example, saying that the fraction of people voting for a candidate was $\frac{7{,}500}{10{,}000}$ conveys more information than giving the portion as $\frac{3}{4}$, or 75%.

For more information about simplifying mixed numbers and fractions, see Section 11.3 of the *Teacher's Reference Manual.*

6•1 Organizing Data

Objective To review data landmarks and methods for organizing data.

www.everydaymathonline.com

ePresentations

eToolkit

Algorithms Practice

EM Facts Workshop Game™

Family Letters

Assessment Management

Common Core State Standards

Curriculum Focal Points

Interactive Teacher's Lesson Guide

1 Teaching the Lesson

Key Concepts and Skills

- Organize data using a picture, graph, line plot, table, or list. [Data and Chance Goal 1]
- Identify data landmarks for data sets. [Data and Chance Goal 2]
- Compare and answer questions about data sets and their organization. [Data and Chance Goal 2]

Key Activities

Students organize and describe previously collected data and review the minimum, maximum, mode, median, and mean as data set descriptions.

Ongoing Assessment: Recognizing Student Achievement Use journal page 165. [Data and Chance Goals 1 and 2]

Key Vocabulary

minimum ◆ maximum ◆ mode ◆ median ◆ landmark ◆ line plot

Materials

Math Journal 1, pp. 164 and 165
Math Masters, p. 149
Class Data Pad ◆ stick-on notes ◆ calculator

2 Ongoing Learning & Practice

Rounding Numbers
Math Journal 1, p. 166
calculator
Students round numbers using paper-and-pencil methods and then explain how to round numbers using a calculator.

Math Boxes 6•1
Math Journal 1, p. 167
Students practice and maintain skills through Math Box problems.

Study Link 6•1
Math Masters, p. 157
Students practice and maintain skills through Study Link activities.

3 Differentiation Options

READINESS
Reviewing Data Landmarks
Math Journal 1, p. 158
Student Reference Book, pp. 119–121
Students review definitions and strategies for finding data landmarks.

ELL SUPPORT
Creating a Data Landmark Poster
Math Journal 1, p. 158
Differentiation Handbook, p. 143
per group: chart paper, stick-on notes, index cards or paper, colored pencils
Students make a poster to review and display the vocabulary for data landmarks.

EXTRA PRACTICE
5-Minute Math
5-Minute Math™, pp. 34, 116, 198
Students practice finding the median in a set of data.

ENRICHMENT
Plotting Arm Circumference
Math Masters, pp. 186A and 186B
Students use fraction data to make a line plot.

Advance Preparation

For Part 1, draw two number lines on the board and one on the Class Data Pad, labeling the points 0, 5, and 10. Leave enough room for small stick-on notes. Use the number lines on the board to plot the number of states students and adults have visited. The adult line may need to be longer than the student line. Use the line on the Class Data Pad with the Math Message. For Part 2, familiarize yourself with the rounding feature of your classroom calculators.

***Teacher's Reference Manual,* Grades 4–6** pp. 160–169

Getting Started

Mental Math and Reflexes

Dictate the following problems. Have students use thumbs up to indicate whether their magnitude estimate is in the tens, hundreds, or thousands. They use thumbs down for the place values that do not apply. Suggestions:

●○○ 650 ÷ 6 hundreds
35 ∗ 100 thousands
10^3 thousands

●●○ 3.5 ∗ 10 tens
7,780 ÷ 100 tens
640 ∗ 20 thousands

●●● 9.24 ∗ 1,000 thousands
24,925 ÷ 1,000 tens
35 ∗ 9.9 hundreds

Math Message

Predict how many states the average student has visited. Write your prediction on a stick-on note. Be prepared to explain the information you used to make your prediction.

1 Teaching the Lesson

Interactive whiteboard-ready ePresentations are available at www.everydaymathonline.com to help you teach the lesson.

▶ Math Message Follow-Up

WHOLE-CLASS DISCUSSION

Have students position their stick-on notes on the Class Data Pad number line and explain the reason why they picked that number of states. Sample answer: I chose 2 states because the people I know go on vacation to the same place each year. Ask volunteers to find the **minimum, maximum, mode,** mean, and **median** for the displayed data. Add these **landmark** labels and values to the Class Data Pad.

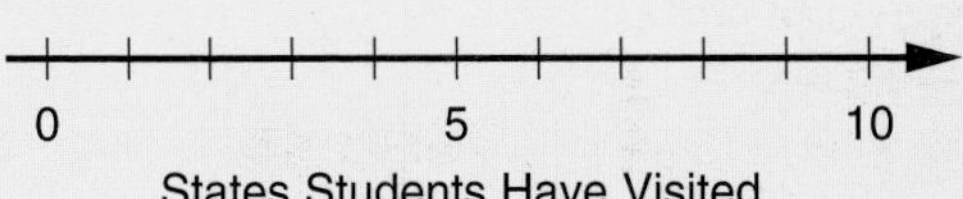

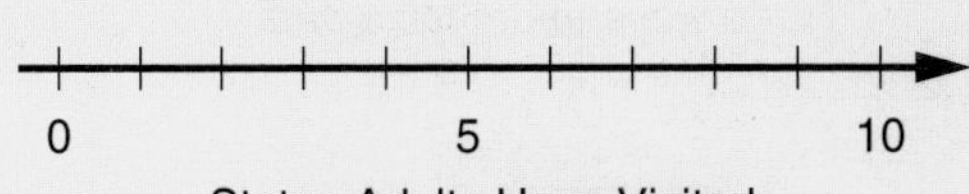

Two number lines: one for the board, one for the Class Data Pad

▶ Organizing the Class Data: States Students Have Visited

SMALL-GROUP ACTIVITY

PROBLEM SOLVING

(*Math Journal 1,* p. 164; *Math Masters,* p. 149)

Refer students to Study Link 5-10, and ask them to report the number of states they have each visited. List these on the board or a transparency in the order they are presented. Students should also record these data on journal page 164.

Ask students how they might organize the class data so that the information being presented is easy to understand. A picture, graph, table, or list is usually easier to interpret than an unorganized set of data.

Working in small groups, students decide on a method to organize the class data. Each student then completes Problems 2 and 3 on journal page 164, using their group's method. When most students have completed Problems 2 and 3, bring the class together to discuss the results.

Student Page

Date Time

LESSON 6·1 States Students Have Visited

1. You and your classmates counted the number of states each of you has visited. As the counts are reported and your teacher records them, write them in the space below. When you finish, circle your own count in the list. Sample answer:
1 3 7 3 7 14 14 16 3 4 7 9 22
4 5 7 9 13 3 1 2 14 20 22 16 (18)

2. Decide with your group how to organize the data you just listed. (For example, you might make a line plot or a tally table.) Then organize the data and show the results below.
1, 1, 2, 3, 3, 3, 3, 4, 4, 5, 7, 7, 7,
7, 9, 9, 13, 14, 14, 14, 16, 16, 18, 20, 22, 22

0 1 2 3 4 5 6 7 8 9 10 11 12 13 14 15 16 17 18 19 20 21 22

3. Write two things that you think are important about the data. Sample answer:
   a. The number of states visited ranges from 1 to 22.
   b. Most students have visited more than 2 states.

4. Compare your own count of states with those of your classmates.
Sample answer: I have visited more states than most of my classmates.

Math Journal 1, p. 164

NOTE Students' plots, tables, and other ways of organizing the data should be easy to make and easy to read. The graphs do not have to be precisely drawn and labeled in order to be useful for this exercise.

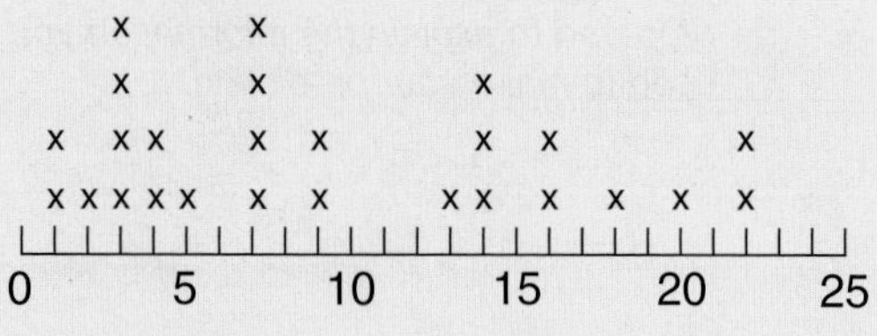

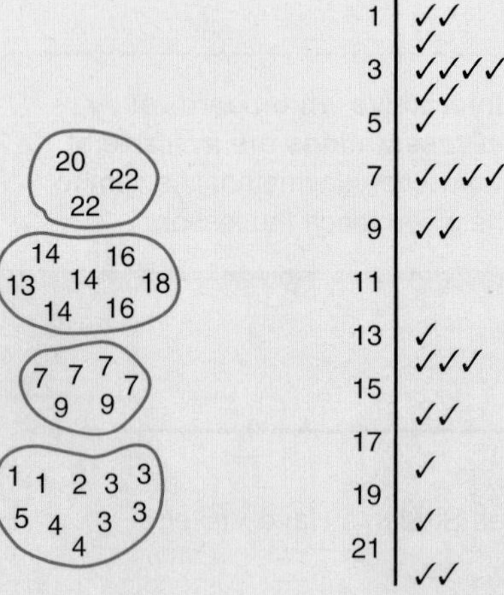

Three ways to organize data

▶ Describing the Data

(*Math Journal 1,* p. 164)

Ask students to share their methods for organizing the data. Make sure several ways are presented, including a **line plot.** Three methods you might expect from students are shown in the margin.

Groups may have also arranged the data in numerical order, from smallest to largest or vice versa. Emphasize that ordering data helps the reader recognize the data landmarks, such as the minimum, maximum, mode, and median. To support English language learners, ask students to describe the similarities and differences between the median and the mode.

Ask students to print their personal counts for states visited on stick-on notes and attach them above the appropriate marks on the number line labeled States Students Have Visited. If the stick-on notes are carefully stacked, the result models a bar graph.

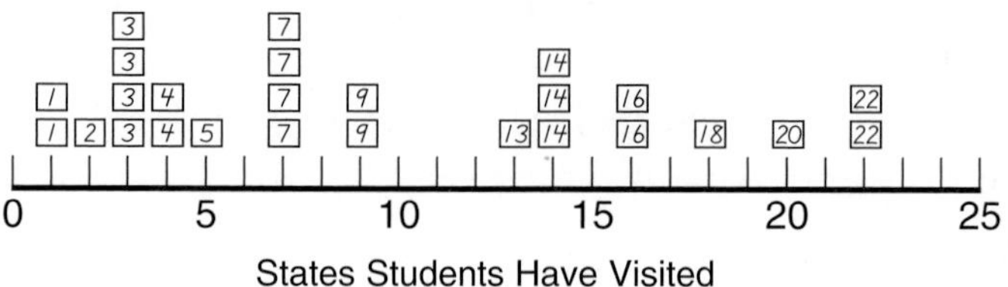

Ask students to compare their personal counts with the whole-class results. Encourage students to use descriptions of the shape of the stick-on note graph in their comparisons. Informal terms such as *bunches, bumps,* and *far away from most* are fine.

Have students compare the whole-class results with their predictions of the number of states visited by an average student. To support English language learners, discuss the meaning of the word *average* in this context. Ask questions like the following:

- Do the whole-class results support the predictions?
- What relationships can you describe between the predictions and the results?
- Are the shapes of the two graphs similar? Explain.
- What do the shapes of the two graphs suggest about the data landmarks? Do you see any connections between the shape of the graphs and the landmarks?

Then have students complete Problem 4 on the journal page.

Student Page

Date Time

LESSON 6·1 **States Adults Have Visited**

1. You and your classmates each recorded the number of states an adult has visited. As the numbers are reported and your teacher records them, write them in the space below.

Sample answer:

1 6 14 3 7 28 30 40 22 5 8 14 18
8 10 14 18 26 30 40 2 4 6 18 40 30

2. Draw a line plot to organize the data you just listed.

0 2 4 6 8 10 12 14 16 18 20 22 24 26 28 30 32 34 36 38 40

3. How does the line plot help a viewer see what is important about the data?

It is easier to see the landmarks.

4. Record landmarks for the data about adults and students in the table below.

Sample answer:

Landmark	Adults	Students
Minimum	1	1
Maximum	40	22
Mode(s)	14, 18, 30, and 40	3 and 7
Median	14	7

Math Journal 1, p. 165

Getting Started

Mental Math and Reflexes

Dictate the following problems. Have students use thumbs up to indicate whether their magnitude estimate is in the tens, hundreds, or thousands. They use thumbs down for the place values that do not apply. Suggestions:

●○○	●●○	●●●
650 ÷ 6 hundreds	3.5 ∗ 10 tens	9.24 ∗ 1,000 thousands
35 ∗ 100 thousands	7,780 ÷ 100 tens	24,925 ÷ 1,000 tens
10^3 thousands	640 ∗ 20 thousands	35 ∗ 9.9 hundreds

Math Message

Predict how many states the average student has visited. Write your prediction on a stick-on note. Be prepared to explain the information you used to make your prediction.

1 Teaching the Lesson

Interactive whiteboard-ready ePresentations are available at www.everydaymathonline.com to help you teach the lesson.

▶ Math Message Follow-Up

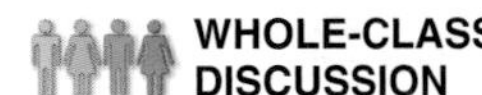

WHOLE-CLASS DISCUSSION

Have students position their stick-on notes on the Class Data Pad number line and explain the reason why they picked that number of states. Sample answer: I chose 2 states because the people I know go on vacation to the same place each year. Ask volunteers to find the **minimum, maximum, mode,** mean, and **median** for the displayed data. Add these **landmark** labels and values to the Class Data Pad.

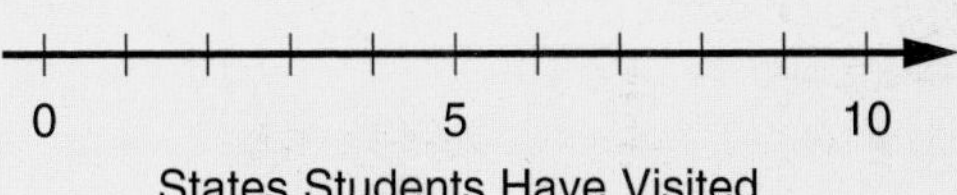

States Students Have Visited

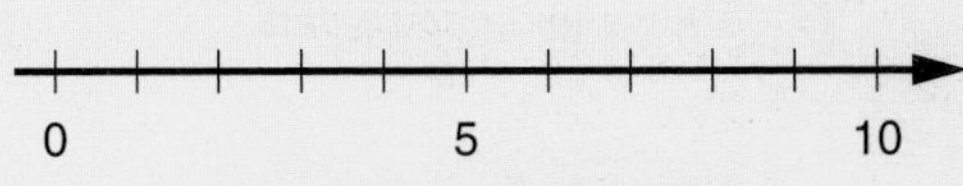

States Adults Have Visited

Two number lines: one for the board, one for the Class Data Pad

▶ Organizing the Class Data: States Students Have Visited

SMALL-GROUP ACTIVITY

PROBLEM SOLVING

(*Math Journal 1,* p. 164; *Math Masters,* p. 149)

Refer students to Study Link 5-10, and ask them to report the number of states they have each visited. List these on the board or a transparency in the order they are presented. Students should also record these data on journal page 164.

Ask students how they might organize the class data so that the information being presented is easy to understand. A picture, graph, table, or list is usually easier to interpret than an unorganized set of data.

Working in small groups, students decide on a method to organize the class data. Each student then completes Problems 2 and 3 on journal page 164, using their group's method. When most students have completed Problems 2 and 3, bring the class together to discuss the results.

Student Page

Date Time

LESSON 6·1 **States Students Have Visited**

1. You and your classmates counted the number of states each of you has visited. As the counts are reported and your teacher records them, write them in the space below. When you finish, circle your own count in the list.

Sample answer:

1 3 7 3 7 14 14 16 3 4 7 9 22
4 5 7 9 13 3 1 2 14 20 22 16 (18)

2. Decide with your group how to organize the data you just listed. (For example, you might make a line plot or a tally table.) Then organize the data and show the results below.

1, 1, 2, 3, 3, 3, 3, 4, 4, 5, 7, 7, 7,
7, 9, 9, 13, 14, 14, 14, 16, 16, 18, 20, 22, 22

0 1 2 3 4 5 6 7 8 9 10 11 12 13 14 15 16 17 18 19 20 21 22

3. Write two things that you think are important about the data. Sample answer:

a. The number of states visited ranges from 1 to 22.

b. Most students have visited more than 2 states.

4. Compare your own count of states with those of your classmates.

Sample answer: I have visited more states than most of my classmates.

Math Journal 1, p. 164

NOTE Students' plots, tables, and other ways of organizing the data should be easy to make and easy to read. The graphs do not have to be precisely drawn and labeled in order to be useful for this exercise.

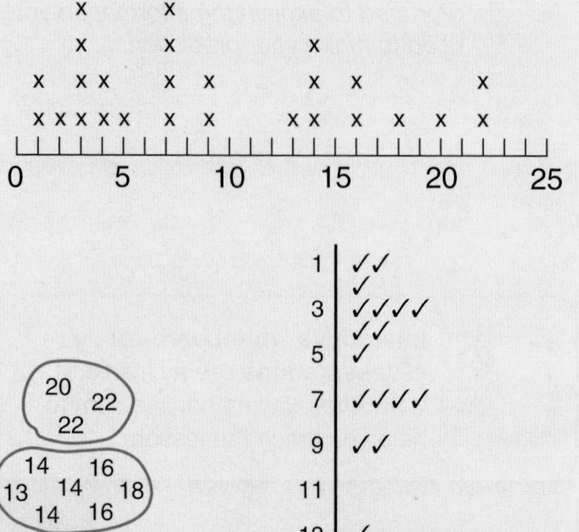

Three ways to organize data

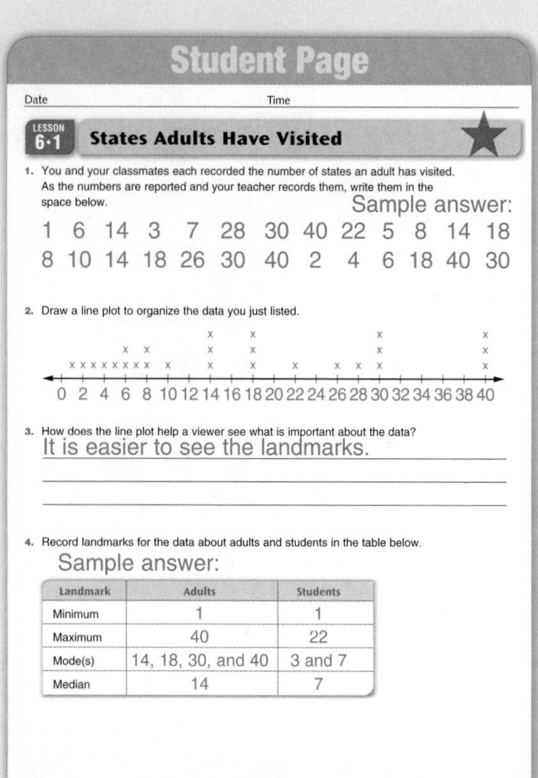

Student Page

Date Time

LESSON 6·1 **States Adults Have Visited**

1. You and your classmates each recorded the number of states an adult has visited. As the numbers are reported and your teacher records them, write them in the space below.

Sample answer:
1 6 14 3 7 28 30 40 22 5 8 14 18
8 10 14 18 26 30 40 2 4 6 18 40 30

2. Draw a line plot to organize the data you just listed.

0 2 4 6 8 10 12 14 16 18 20 22 24 26 28 30 32 34 36 38 40

3. How does the line plot help a viewer see what is important about the data?

It is easier to see the landmarks.

4. Record landmarks for the data about adults and students in the table below.

Sample answer:

Landmark	Adults	Students
Minimum	1	1
Maximum	40	22
Mode(s)	14, 18, 30, and 40	3 and 7
Median	14	7

Math Journal 1, **p. 165**

▶ Describing the Data

(*Math Journal 1,* p. 164)

Ask students to share their methods for organizing the data. Make sure several ways are presented, including a **line plot.** Three methods you might expect from students are shown in the margin.

Groups may have also arranged the data in numerical order, from smallest to largest or vice versa. Emphasize that ordering data helps the reader recognize the data landmarks, such as the minimum, maximum, mode, and median. To support English language learners, ask students to describe the similarities and differences between the median and the mode.

Ask students to print their personal counts for states visited on stick-on notes and attach them above the appropriate marks on the number line labeled States Students Have Visited. If the stick-on notes are carefully stacked, the result models a bar graph.

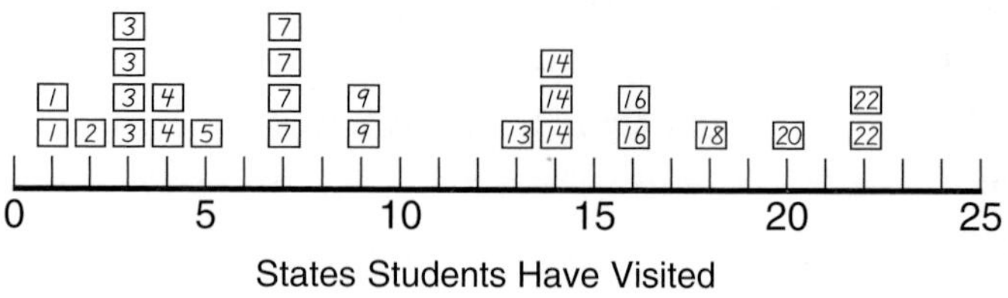

Ask students to compare their personal counts with the whole-class results. Encourage students to use descriptions of the shape of the stick-on note graph in their comparisons. Informal terms such as *bunches, bumps,* and *far away from most* are fine.

Have students compare the whole-class results with their predictions of the number of states visited by an average student. To support English language learners, discuss the meaning of the word *average* in this context. Ask questions like the following:

- Do the whole-class results support the predictions?
- What relationships can you describe between the predictions and the results?
- Are the shapes of the two graphs similar? Explain.
- What do the shapes of the two graphs suggest about the data landmarks? Do you see any connections between the shape of the graphs and the landmarks?

Then have students complete Problem 4 on the journal page.

▶ Organizing the Class Data: States Adults Have Visited

PARTNER ACTIVITY

(*Math Journal 1,* pp. 164 and 165; *Math Masters,* p. 149)

Refer students to Study Link 5-10 and ask them to report the number of states visited by the adults they interviewed. As before, list these on the board or a transparency in the order they are presented. Students should also record these data on journal page 165.

Have partners complete the journal page. Circulate and assist.

Adjusting the Activity

Ask several volunteers to find the mean (average) number of states students have visited and circle this point on the displayed line plot. They should use calculators to add the counts recorded in Problem 1 on journal page 164 and then divide by the number of counts. Ask other volunteers to find the mean number of states adults have visited, using the counts recorded in Problem 1 on journal page 165, and circle this point on the displayed line plot.

AUDITORY ◆ KINESTHETIC ◆ TACTILE ◆ VISUAL

When most students have finished, have them print their counts for states visited by an adult onto stick-on notes and attach them above the appropriate marks on the number line. For each data set, record the data landmarks and corresponding values on the board. Compare landmarks for the two line plots. Expect that adults will have a larger median. Ask students why this may be the case. Adults have lived longer and have traveled more, so there are more values at the higher end of the scale.

Ongoing Assessment: Recognizing Student Achievement

Journal Page 165

Use **journal page 165,** to assess students' abilities to display data on a line plot, discuss the data's organization, and identify minimum, maximum, mode(s), and median for data sets. Students are making adequate progress if they have correctly constructed the line plot and identified the landmarks. Some students may also describe the shape of the line plot in terms of the landmarks.

[Data and Chance Goals 1 and 2]

2 Ongoing Learning & Practice

▶ Rounding Numbers

INDEPENDENT ACTIVITY

(*Math Journal 1,* p. 166)

Students practice rounding numbers using paper-and-pencil methods. Then they explain how to round numbers using a calculator. Any calculator with the fix feature can be used with this activity.

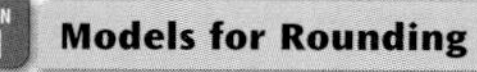

Date Time

LESSON 6•1 **Models for Rounding Numbers**

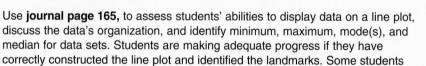

Rounding numbers makes mental calculations and estimates easier. The first step to rounding to a given place is to locate the number between two consecutive numbers. For example, what whole number comes right before 12.6? (12) What whole number comes right after 12.6? (13)

1. Complete the table below.

	Rounding to the nearest whole number:	Rounding to the nearest ten:
12.6	Is between 12 and 13	Is between 10 and 20
26.3	Is between 26 and 27	Is between 20 and 30

	Rounding to the nearest ten:	Rounding to the nearest hundred:
119.9	Is between 110 and 120	Is between 100 and 200
3,502	Is between 3,500 and 3,510	Is between 3,500 and 3,600

Next determine if the number you are rounding is closer to the lower number or to the higher number. The models below represent different ways of thinking about making this choice. On the number line, 12.6 is close to 13, so 12.6 rounded to the nearest whole number is 13. If the number line were curved, 12.6 would "roll" toward 10.

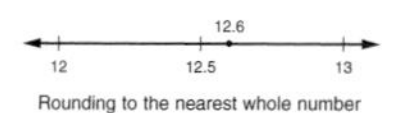

Rounding to the nearest whole number

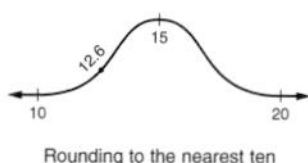

Rounding to the nearest ten

Numbers that are halfway between the lower number and the higher number are rounded up to the higher number. Round . . .

2. 16.4 to the nearest whole number. 16
3. 482 to the nearest hundred. 500
4. 7.36 to the nearest tenth. 7.4
5. 9,282 to the nearest hundred. 9,300
6. 423,897 to the nearest hundred-thousand. 400,000
7. 30.08 to the nearest tenth. 30.1
8. Explain how you would use your calculator to round 5.3458 to the nearest hundredth.
Sample answer: I would set the (Fix) key to 2 decimal places, enter the number 5.3458, and press either (Enter) or (=).

Math Journal 1, p. 166

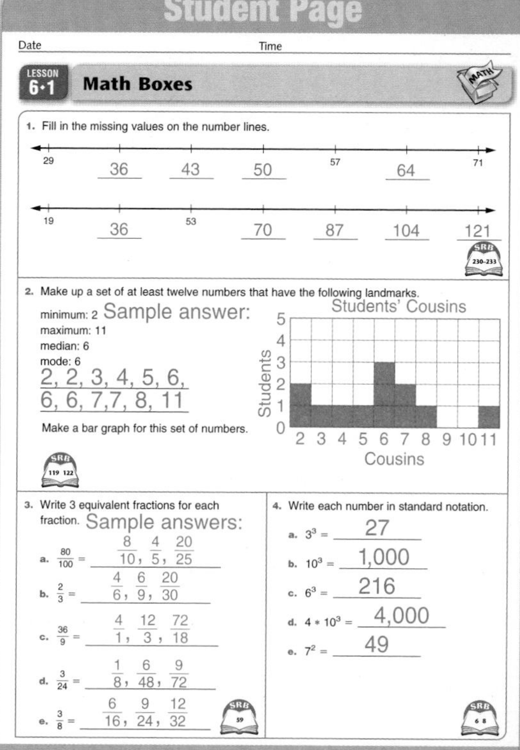
Student Page

Date Time

LESSON 6•1 **Math Boxes**

1. Fill in the missing values on the number lines.

29, 36, 43, 50, 57, 64, 71

19, 36, 53, 70, 87, 104, 121

2. Make up a set of at least twelve numbers that have the following landmarks.
minimum: 2
maximum: 11
median: 6
mode: 6
Sample answer:
2, 2, 3, 4, 5, 6, 6, 6, 7, 7, 8, 11
Make a bar graph for this set of numbers.

3. Write 3 equivalent fractions for each fraction. Sample answers:
a. $\frac{80}{100}$ = $\frac{8}{10}$, $\frac{4}{5}$, $\frac{20}{25}$
b. $\frac{2}{3}$ = $\frac{4}{6}$, $\frac{6}{9}$, $\frac{20}{30}$
c. $\frac{36}{9}$ = $\frac{4}{1}$, $\frac{12}{3}$, $\frac{72}{18}$
d. $\frac{3}{24}$ = $\frac{1}{8}$, $\frac{6}{48}$, $\frac{9}{72}$
e. $\frac{3}{8}$ = $\frac{6}{16}$, $\frac{9}{24}$, $\frac{12}{32}$

4. Write each number in standard notation.
a. 3^3 = 27
b. 10^3 = 1,000
c. 6^3 = 216
d. $4 * 10^3$ = 4,000
e. 7^2 = 49

Math Journal 1, p. 167

Student Link Master

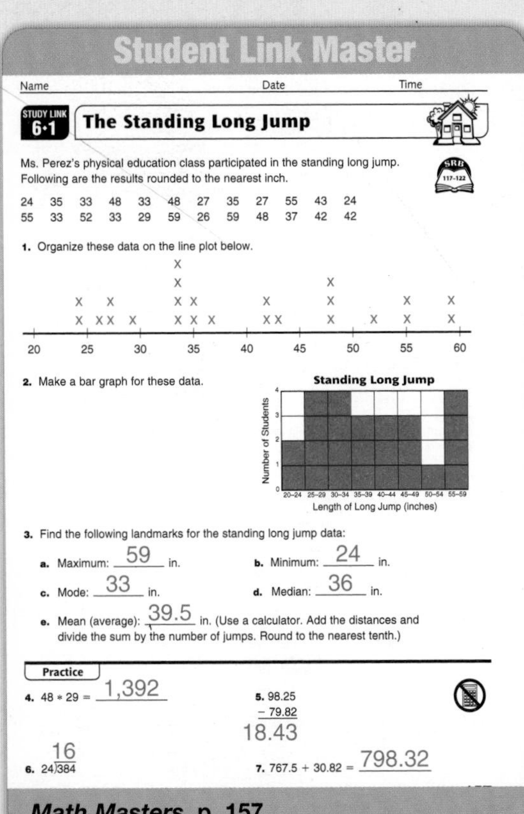
Name Date Time

STUDY LINK 6·1 **The Standing Long Jump**

Ms. Perez's physical education class participated in the standing long jump. Following are the results rounded to the nearest inch.

24 35 33 48 33 48 27 35 27 55 43 24
55 33 52 33 29 59 26 59 48 37 42 42

1. Organize these data on the line plot below.

2. Make a bar graph for these data.

Standing Long Jump

3. Find the following landmarks for the standing long jump data:

a. Maximum: 59 in.
b. Minimum: 24 in.
c. Mode: 33 in.
d. Median: 36 in.
e. Mean (average): 39.5 in. (Use a calculator. Add the distances and divide the sum by the number of jumps. Round to the nearest tenth.)

Practice

4. 48 ∗ 29 = 1,392
5. 98.25 − 79.82 = 18.43
6. 24)384 = 16
7. 767.5 + 30.82 = 798.32

Math Masters, p. 157

▶ Math Boxes 6·1

(*Math Journal 1,* p. 167)

Mixed Practice Math Boxes in this lesson are paired with Math Boxes in Lesson 6-3. The skill in Problem 4 previews Unit 7 content.

Writing/Reasoning Have students respond to the following: *If you extended the top number line in Problem 1, would 100 be one of the missing numbers? Explain.* No, each number increases by 7. If I add 7 to 71 four more times, the answer is 99, which is 1 less than 100.

▶ Study Link 6·1

INDEPENDENT ACTIVITY

(*Math Masters,* p. 157)

Home Connection Students construct a line plot and a bar graph from a set of given data. Then students identify the landmarks.

3 Differentiation Options

READINESS

▶ Reviewing Data Landmarks

15–30 Min

(*Math Journal 1,* p. 158; *Student Reference Book,* pp. 119–121)

To provide experience with the definitions of and methods for finding data landmarks, have students analyze the snack-survey data on journal page 158. Use pages 119–121 in the *Student Reference Book.*

Explain the following prominent features of a data set:

- ▷ minimum—smallest value
- ▷ maximum—largest value
- ▷ range—difference between the minimum and the maximum
- ▷ mode—most frequent value or values
- ▷ median—middle value
- ▷ mean (average)—quotient of the sum of the data set divided by the number of values in the set

Discuss the examples in the *Student Reference Book,* and have students find each landmark using the snack-survey data.

Student Page

Date Time

LESSON 5·11 **Making Circle Graphs: Snack Survey**

Your class recently made a survey of favorite snacks. As your teacher tells you the percent of votes each snack received, record the data in the table at the right. Make a circle graph of the snack-survey data in the circle below. Remember to label each piece of the graph and give it a title.

Sample answers:

Snack	Votes: Number	Fraction	Percent
Cookies	8	$\frac{8}{25}$	32%
Granola Bar	4	$\frac{4}{25}$	16%
Candy Bar	10	$\frac{10}{25}$	40%
Fruit	2	$\frac{2}{25}$	8%
Other	1	$\frac{1}{25}$	4%
Total	25	$\frac{25}{25}$	About 100%

Favorite-Snack Survey Results

Math Journal 1, p. 158

ELL SUPPORT

SMALL-GROUP ACTIVITY

▶ Creating a Data Landmark Poster

15–30 Min

(*Math Journal 1,* p. 158; *Differentiation Handbook,* p. 143)

To provide a visual reference for data landmark words, have students create a line plot poster using the snack-survey data from journal page 158. As a group, make a line plot of the snack-survey data using chart paper and stick-on notes. Assign students the data landmark words to write on an index card or strips of paper, using a different-colored pencil for each word.

To complete the poster, ask students to discuss, find, and label the landmarks on the line plot with the cards or strips of paper. Consider having students use the Word Bank Template found on *Differentiation Handbook,* page 143. Ask students to write the terms *minimum, maximum, range, mode, median, mean,* and *outlier;* to draw a picture relating to each term; and to write other related words. See the *Differentiation Handbook* for more information.

EXTRA PRACTICE

SMALL-GROUP ACTIVITY

▶ 5-Minute Math

5–15 Min

To offer students more experience with finding the median in a set of data, see *5-Minute Math,* pages 34, 116 and 198.

ENRICHMENT

INDEPENDENT ACTIVITY

▶ Plotting Arm Circumference

15–30 Min

(*Math Masters,* pp. 186A and 186B)

To apply students' understanding of line plots, have them create a line plot with measurements in fractions of a unit. When students have completed the line plot on *Math Masters,* page 186A, ask them to solve the problems on *Math Masters,* page 186B using the data in the line plot.

Teaching Master

Name Date Time

LESSON 6•1 **Arm Circumference Data**

Sometimes measurements need to be very precise. When a blood pressure reading is taken, it is important that the proper cuff size is used. Blood pressure cuffs come in different sizes and are adjustable. Using a blood pressure cuff that is too small or too large can lead to inaccurate results. Before doing a blood pressure screening of the members of the fifth-grade running club, the school nurse measured the circumference of each student's upper arm to the nearest $\frac{1}{8}$ inch. Measurements are shown in the table below.

Student	Upper Arm Circumference (to the nearest $\frac{1}{8}$ in.)	Student	Upper Arm Circumference (to the nearest $\frac{1}{8}$ in.)
Jason	$5\frac{1}{4}$	Robin	$6\frac{3}{8}$
Mike	$6\frac{1}{8}$	Javon	6
Kylie	$6\frac{1}{2}$	Beatrice	$5\frac{1}{4}$
Peter	$6\frac{1}{8}$	Charlie	$6\frac{1}{8}$
Diego	5	Shawn	$6\frac{3}{8}$
Juan Carlos	6	India	6
Lisa	$5\frac{1}{2}$	Katy	$6\frac{3}{8}$
Pamela	7		

Make a line plot in the grid below to display the arm circumference measurements. Begin by completing the labeling of the *x*-axis. Use these data and the completed line plot to answer the questions on the next page.

Upper Arm Circumference

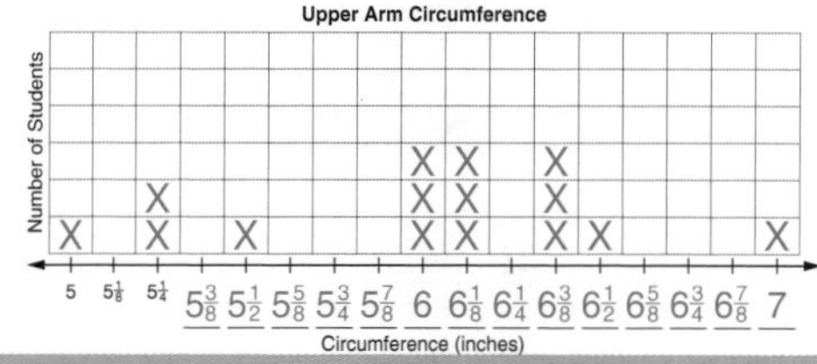

Math Masters, p. 186A

Teaching Master

Name Date Time

LESSON 6•1 **Arm Circumference Data** *continued*

Use the line plot on *Math Masters,* page 186A to answer the questions.

1. What is the minimum arm circumference of the students in the fifth-grade running club? 5 in.
2. How much smaller is Kylie's upper arm circumference than the club's maximum? $\frac{1}{2}$ in.
3. What is the range in arm circumference of the members of the fifth-grade running club? 2 in.
4. a. What is the median of the data set? $6\frac{1}{8}$ in.
   b. How much greater is the median arm circumference than the minimum arm circumference? $1\frac{1}{8}$ in.
5. What is the mode (or modes) for the data set? 6 in., $6\frac{1}{8}$ in., and $6\frac{3}{8}$ in.
6. What is the mean arm circumference measurement? 6 in.
7. On the day of the blood pressure screening, the nurse brought a cuff that is made for people with arm circumferences between $5\frac{1}{8}$ in. and $6\frac{3}{4}$ in. What fraction of the fifth-grade running club was able to use that cuff? $\frac{13}{15}$ of the club
8. Suppose a new member, Denise, joins the club. The circumference of her upper arm is $6\frac{1}{2}$ in. Tell whether each of these club's landmarks will increase, decrease, or stay the same. Determine your answers without doing any calculations.
   a. Mean: increase
   b. Median: Stay the same
   c. Mode: Stay the same

Math Masters, p. 186B

6•2 Natural Measures of Length

Objectives To develop measurement and probability concepts.

Technology Resources www.everydaymathonline.com

ePresentations

eToolkit

Algorithms Practice

EM Facts Workshop Game™

Family Letters

Assessment Management

Common Core State Standards

Curriculum Focal Points

Interactive Teacher's Lesson Guide

1 Teaching the Lesson

Key Concepts and Skills

- Organize and display data using a table. [Data and Chance Goal 1]
- Use collected data to make predictions about future outcomes of a simple game. [Data and Chance Goal 3]
- Measure to the nearest millimeter, centimeter, and inch. [Measurement and Reference Frames Goal 1]

Key Activities

Students measure their fingers, hands, and arms to find their personal measures. They begin an extended investigation to determine whether the card game *Finish First* is a fair game.

Ongoing Assessment: Recognizing Student Achievement
Use journal page 169.
[Measurement and Reference Frames Goal 1]

Key Vocabulary

fathom ◆ cubit ◆ fair game

Materials

Math Journal 1, pp. 168–171
Student Reference Book, p. 182
Study Link 6•1
4 each of number cards 4–8 (from the Everything Math Deck, if available) ◆ Probability Meter Poster ◆ ruler with centimeters and inches ◆ tape measure with centimeters and inches ◆ stick-on notes ◆ chart paper ◆ slate ◆ calculator

2 Ongoing Learning & Practice

Math Boxes 6•2
Math Journal 1, p. 172
Students practice and maintain skills through Math Box problems.

Study Link 6•2
Math Masters, p. 158
Students practice and maintain skills through Study Link activities.

3 Differentiation Options

READINESS

Measuring in Centimeters and Millimeters
Math Masters, p. 159
centimeter ruler
Students measure and draw line segments using centimeters and millimeters to look for a pattern.

ENRICHMENT

Investigating Natural Measure Relationships
Math Journal 1, p. 168
Math Masters, p. 160
Students analyze and compare data for finger joint lengths and palm widths.

Advance Preparation

For Part 1, prepare a tally sheet, a cumulative totals table, and the axes for a bar graph to record class results for the *Finish First* activity. (See the tables and graph in the *Teacher's Lesson Guide,* page 387.)

***Teacher's Reference Manual,* Grades 4–6** pp. 44–46, 214–217

Getting Started

Mental Math and Reflexes

Slate Practice: Have students write numbers in standard notation and in expanded notation.

●○○ Eighty-five hundredths 0.85 *and* $8 * (\frac{1}{10}) + 5 * (\frac{1}{100})$
Sixteen and five tenths 16.5 *and* $1 * 10 + 6 * 1 + 5 * (\frac{1}{10})$

●●○ Two and seven hundredths 2.07 *and* $2 * 1 + 7 * (\frac{1}{100})$
Ten and sixty-nine hundredths 10.69 *and* $1 * 10 + 6 * (\frac{1}{10}) + 9 * (\frac{1}{100})$

●●● Eight hundred four and nine hundredths 804.09 *and* $8 * 100 + 4 * 1 + 9 * (\frac{1}{100})$
Twenty-two thousandths 0.022 *and* $2 * (\frac{1}{100}) + 2 * (\frac{1}{1,000})$

Math Message

Find two interesting facts on page 182 of the Student Reference Book.

Study Link 6·1 Follow-Up

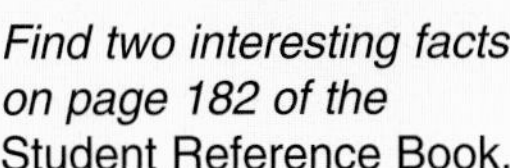

Students compare their answers and resolve any differences.

1 Teaching the Lesson

▶ Math Message Follow-Up

WHOLE-CLASS DISCUSSION

(*Student Reference Book,* p. 182)

Social Studies Link Ask students to share their interesting facts with partners and then in small groups. Ask each group to write its facts on chart paper to present to the class. Point out that none of these measures was originally an exact unit of length because the lengths and shapes of body parts differ from person to person.

NOTE The cubit is probably the most ancient unit of length. The Latin word *cubitum* means *elbow.*

▶ Finding Personal Measures

PARTNER ACTIVITY

(*Math Journal 1,* pp. 168 and 169)

Ask partners to work together to complete journal pages 168 and 169. Note that there are two methods for finding finger and hand measures:

▷ Use the illustration on the journal page as a guide. Arrange your fingers or hand on a sheet of paper as shown. Mark the ends of the desired length with a pencil. Then measure between the marks.

▷ Measure your partner's fingers or hand directly.

Let students use the method they like best.

Students will measure in metric and U.S. customary units. Circulate and assist to verify that students are measuring the small finger and hand measures to the nearest millimeter and to the nearest $\frac{1}{16}$ in. For the natural yard, **fathom**, and **cubit**, measuring to the nearest centimeter and nearest $\frac{1}{4}$ in. is sufficient.

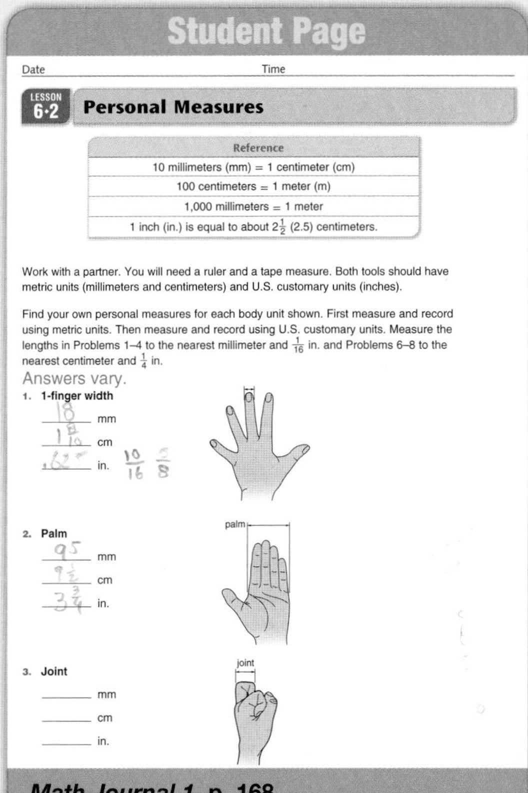

Student Page

Date ______ Time ______

LESSON 6·2 **Personal Measures**

Reference
10 millimeters (mm) = 1 centimeter (cm)
100 centimeters = 1 meter (m)
1,000 millimeters = 1 meter
1 inch (in.) is equal to about $2\frac{1}{2}$ (2.5) centimeters.

Work with a partner. You will need a ruler and a tape measure. Both tools should have metric units (millimeters and centimeters) and U.S. customary units (inches).

Find your own personal measures for each body unit shown. First measure and record using metric units. Then measure and record using U.S. customary units. Measure the lengths in Problems 1–4 to the nearest millimeter and $\frac{1}{16}$ in. and Problems 6–8 to the nearest centimeter and $\frac{1}{4}$ in.

Answers vary.

1. **1-finger width**
   ______ mm
   ______ cm
   ______ in.

2. **Palm**
   ______ mm
   ______ cm
   ______ in.

3. **Joint**
   ______ mm
   ______ cm
   ______ in.

Math Journal 1, p. 168

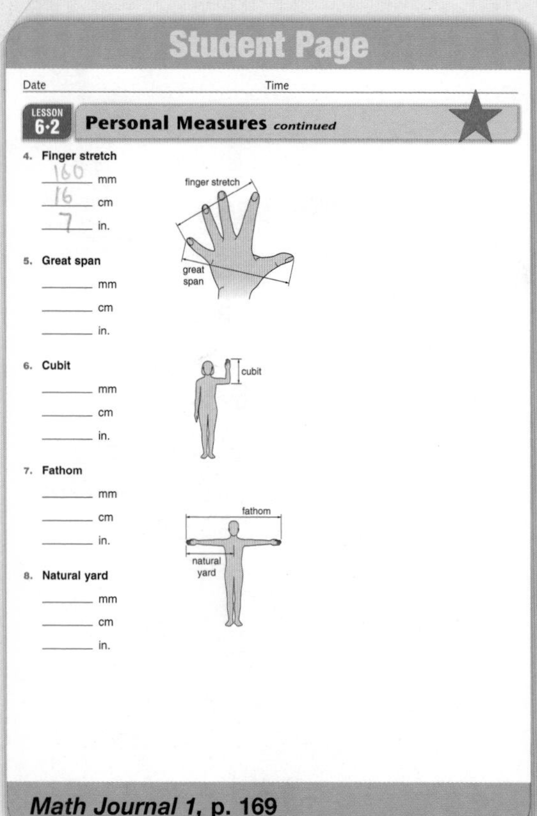
Student Page

Date Time

LESSON 6·2 **Personal Measures** *continued*

4. Finger stretch
160 mm
16 cm
7 in.

5. Great span
_____ mm
_____ cm
_____ in.

6. Cubit
_____ mm
_____ cm
_____ in.

7. Fathom
_____ mm
_____ cm
_____ in.

8. Natural yard
_____ mm
_____ cm
_____ in.

Math Journal 1, p. 169

Adjusting the Activity

Discuss why it is necessary to measure to the nearest millimeter or $\frac{1}{16}$ in. for smaller measurements, but only to the nearest centimeter or $\frac{1}{4}$ in. for the larger measurements. A small error is much more significant on the smaller measurements.

AUDITORY ◆ KINESTHETIC ◆ TACTILE ◆ VISUAL

Bring the class together to discuss the results. Ask questions like the following:

- How close were your personal measures for a natural yard to the standard yard of 3 ft? (The average natural yard for a 10-year-old is about 28 in.)
- The cubit is usually thought of as 18 inches. Given the class's personal measures for the cubit, is this reasonable? (The average cubit for a 10-year-old is about 15 in.)
- Would these measures for adults be about the same as measures for fifth graders? Probably not. (The average measures for adults are about 25% greater.)
- Why do we need standard measures? When are natural measures useful? Standard measures let us communicate measurements reliably with others. Natural measures are useful references for estimating.

Ongoing Assessment: Recognizing Student Achievement

Journal Page 169 

Use **journal page 169,** to assess students' ability to use linear measuring tools. Students are making adequate progress if they correctly measure to the nearest centimeter and $\frac{1}{4}$ in. Some students will be able to accurately measure to the nearest millimeter and $\frac{1}{16}$ in.

[Measurement and Reference Frames Goal 1]

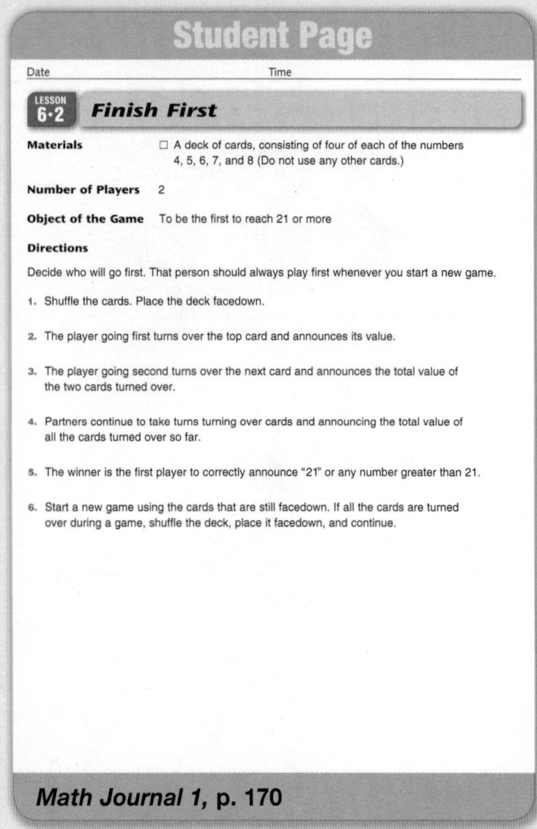
Student Page

Date Time

LESSON 6·2 ***Finish First***

Materials ☐ A deck of cards, consisting of four of each of the numbers 4, 5, 6, 7, and 8 (Do not use any other cards.)

Number of Players 2

Object of the Game To be the first to reach 21 or more

Directions

Decide who will go first. That person should always play first whenever you start a new game.

1. Shuffle the cards. Place the deck facedown.
2. The player going first turns over the top card and announces its value.
3. The player going second turns over the next card and announces the total value of the two cards turned over.
4. Partners continue to take turns turning over cards and announcing the total value of all the cards turned over so far.
5. The winner is the first player to correctly announce "21" or any number greater than 21.
6. Start a new game using the cards that are still facedown. If all the cards are turned over during a game, shuffle the deck, place it facedown, and continue.

Math Journal 1, p. 170

▶ Explaining the Challenge Questions for *Finish First*

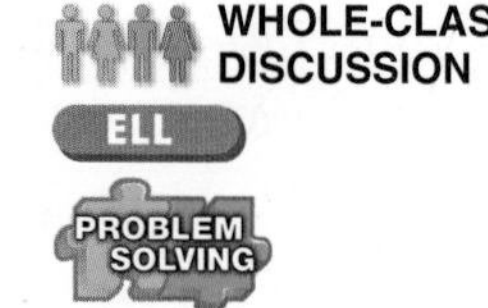

(*Math Journal 1,* pp. 170 and 171)

Go over the rules with the class for the *Finish First* game on journal page 170. Have partners play a few practice games as you circulate to make sure that students understand the rules.

Present the Estimation Challenge on journal page 171. Students will estimate the chances of winning for both players and compare their estimates with the actual results in order to determine whether *Finish First* is a **fair game.** To support English language learners, discuss the meaning of *fair game.* Partners will play at least 50 times over the next week, making an estimate each day they play and recording the results. Each partner will keep a separate tally of results in the table on journal page 171.

Have partners play 2 or 3 times now and tally their results on journal page 171. Then display the classroom tally sheet (Table A), the table for recording cumulative totals (Table B), and the graph that you have prepared. Explain the routine students will use to record and update each day's results.

1. Whenever partners have finished a series of games during a day, one of the partners should enter the tallies for their results on the classroom tally sheet (Table A).

Date	First Player Wins	Second Player Wins
2/6/07	HHT HHT HHT I	HHT HHT HHT HHT HHT HHT II
2/7/07	HHT HHT III	HHT HHT HHT HHT HHT HHT HHT HHT

Table A

2. Appoint a Statistician and Checker for the day. They work together to count the tallies in Table A for that day and use these tallies to update the totals in Table B. Note that these totals are cumulative.

Totals to Date		
	2/6/07	2/7/07
First Player Wins	16	29
Second Player Wins	32	72
Games Played	48	101

Table B

3. The Statistician and Checker also update the bar graph. They use the most recent cumulative totals from Table B to calculate the percent of all games won by the player going first. They then draw a new bar on the graph to show this percent. (*See below.*)

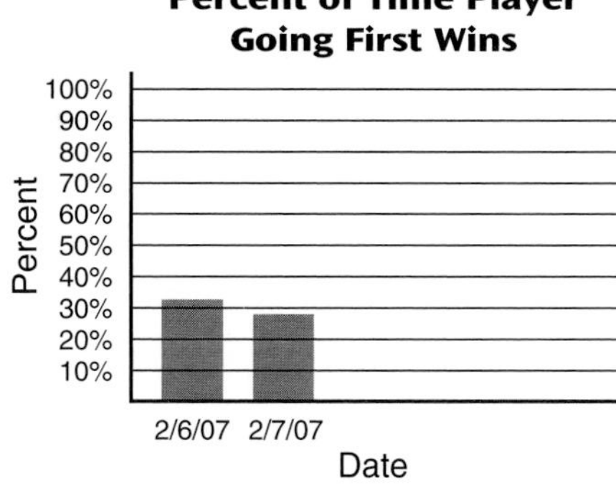

Games played to date: 101

Post a stick-on note on the Probability Meter each day to show the percent of all games won by the player going first.

NOTE Students will soon realize that the game is not fair because the second player has an advantage. To estimate the chance that the first player will win, students need to play many games. If you have 25 students and each plays 50 games, your class estimate will very likely be within 2% of the actual chance, and almost certainly within 4% of the actual chance. The cumulative results of this game will be used in Lesson 6-6.

Student Page

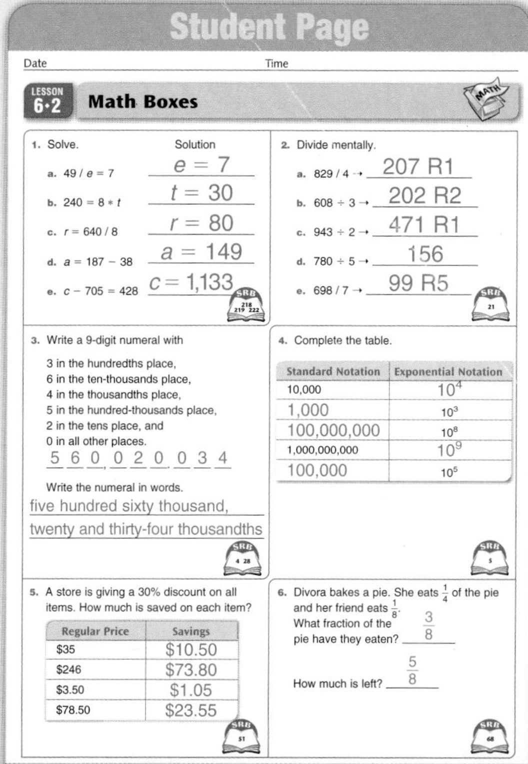

Date Time

LESSON 6•2 **Math Boxes**

1. Solve.

	Solution
a. 49 / e = 7	e = 7
b. 240 = 8 ∗ t	t = 30
c. r = 640 / 8	r = 80
d. a = 187 − 38	a = 149
e. c − 705 = 428	c = 1,133

2. Divide mentally.

a. 829 / 4 → 207 R1
b. 608 ÷ 3 → 202 R2
c. 943 ÷ 2 → 471 R1
d. 780 ÷ 5 → 156
e. 698 / 7 → 99 R5

3. Write a 9-digit numeral with
3 in the hundredths place,
6 in the ten-thousands place,
4 in the thousandths place,
5 in the hundred-thousands place,
2 in the tens place, and
0 in all other places.
5 6 0 0 2 0 . 0 3 4

Write the numeral in words.
five hundred sixty thousand, twenty and thirty-four thousandths

4. Complete the table.

Standard Notation	Exponential Notation
10,000	10^4
1,000	10^3
100,000,000	10^8
1,000,000,000	10^9
100,000	10^5

5. A store is giving a 30% discount on all items. How much is saved on each item?

Regular Price	Savings
$35	$10.50
$246	$73.80
$3.50	$1.05
$78.50	$23.55

6. Divora bakes a pie. She eats $\frac{1}{4}$ of the pie and her friend eats $\frac{1}{8}$. What fraction of the pie have they eaten? $\frac{3}{8}$

How much is left? $\frac{5}{8}$

Math Journal 1, p. 172

Study Link Master

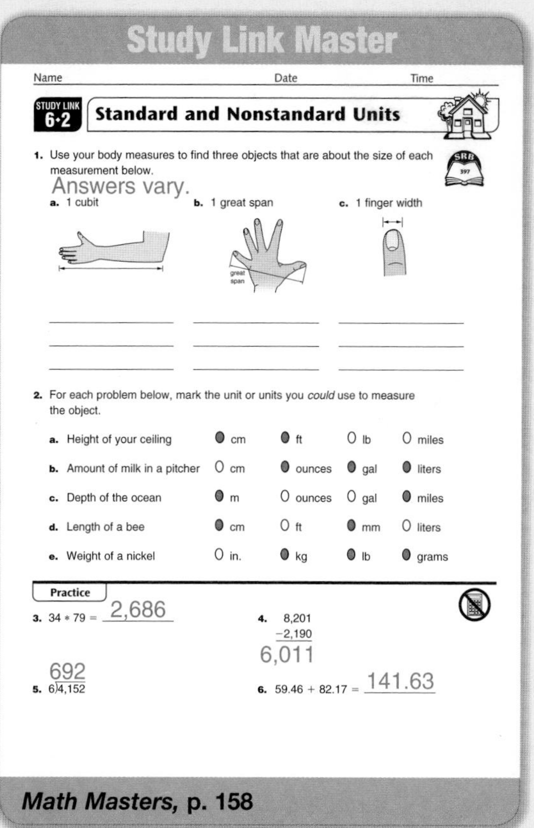

Name Date Time

STUDY LINK 6•2 **Standard and Nonstandard Units**

1. Use your body measures to find three objects that are about the size of each measurement below.
Answers vary.
a. 1 cubit b. 1 great span c. 1 finger width

2. For each problem below, mark the unit or units you *could* use to measure the object.

a. Height of your ceiling	● cm	● ft	O lb	O miles
b. Amount of milk in a pitcher	O cm	● ounces	● gal	● liters
c. Depth of the ocean	● m	O ounces	O gal	● miles
d. Length of a bee	● cm	O ft	● mm	O liters
e. Weight of a nickel	O in.	● kg	● lb	● grams

Practice

3. 34 ∗ 79 = 2,686
4. 8,201 − 2,190 = 6,011
5. 6)4,152 = 692
6. 59.46 + 82.17 = 141.63

Math Masters, p. 158

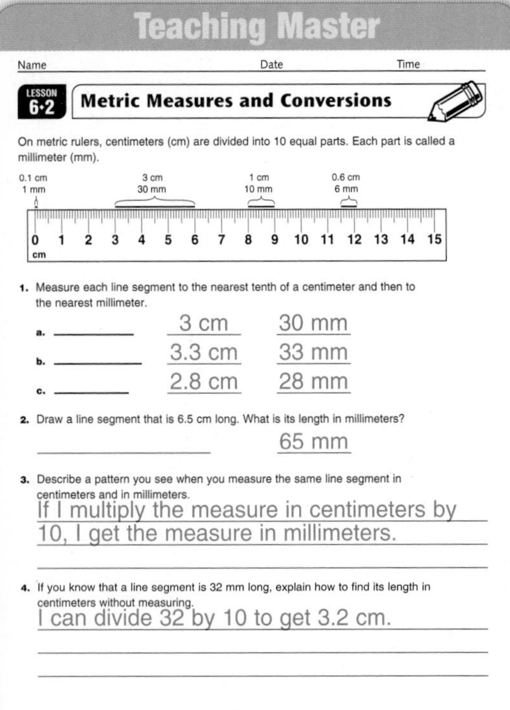
Teaching Master

Name Date Time

LESSON 6•2 **Metric Measures and Conversions**

On metric rulers, centimeters (cm) are divided into 10 equal parts. Each part is called a millimeter (mm).

0.1 cm 1 mm; 3 cm 30 mm; 1 cm 10 mm; 0.6 cm 6 mm

0 1 2 3 4 5 6 7 8 9 10 11 12 13 14 15 cm

1. Measure each line segment to the nearest tenth of a centimeter and then to the nearest millimeter.
   a. 3 cm 30 mm
   b. 3.3 cm 33 mm
   c. 2.8 cm 28 mm
2. Draw a line segment that is 6.5 cm long. What is its length in millimeters? 65 mm
3. Describe a pattern you see when you measure the same line segment in centimeters and in millimeters. If I multiply the measure in centimeters by 10, I get the measure in millimeters.
4. If you know that a line segment is 32 mm long, explain how to find its length in centimeters without measuring. I can divide 32 by 10 to get 3.2 cm.

Math Masters, p. 159

2 Ongoing Learning & Practice

Math Boxes 6•2

INDEPENDENT ACTIVITY

(*Math Journal 1,* p. 172)

Mixed Practice Math Boxes in this lesson are paired with Math Boxes in Lesson 6-4. The skill in Problem 4 previews Unit 7 content.

Study Link 6•2

INDEPENDENT ACTIVITY

(*Math Masters,* p. 158)

Home Connection Students find objects the size of given nonstandard units of measure and give the standard units of measure they would use to measure the objects.

3 Differentiation Options

READINESS

SMALL-GROUP ACTIVITY

15–30 Min

Measuring in Centimeters and Millimeters

(*Math Masters,* p. 159)

To explore the relationship between centimeters and millimeters, have students measure and draw line segments using both units. When students have completed *Math Masters,* page 159, have them share their descriptions of the pattern when measuring the same length in centimeters and millimeters. Consider having them solve related problems using this pattern. *Suggestions:*

- How many millimeters in 5 cm? 50 mm
- How many centimeters in 48 mm? 4.8 cm
- How many millimeters in 7 cm? 70 mm

ENRICHMENT

SMALL-GROUP ACTIVITY

15–30 Min

Investigating Natural Measure Relationships

(*Math Journal 1,* p. 168; *Math Masters,* p. 160)

To apply students' understanding of data landmarks to the interpretation of data, have them predict relationships between palm width and joint length measures. They investigate their predictions by collecting, organizing, and comparing palm width and joint length measures for the class and the associated landmarks.

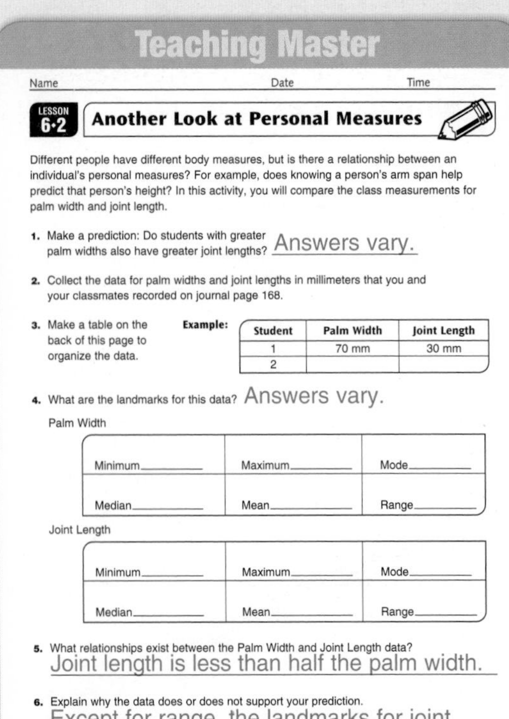
Teaching Master

Name Date Time

LESSON 6•2 **Another Look at Personal Measures**

Different people have different body measures, but is there a relationship between an individual's personal measures? For example, does knowing a person's arm span help predict that person's height? In this activity, you will compare the class measurements for palm width and joint length.

1. Make a prediction: Do students with greater palm widths also have greater joint lengths? Answers vary.
2. Collect the data for palm widths and joint lengths in millimeters that you and your classmates recorded on journal page 168.
3. Make a table on the back of this page to organize the data. **Example:**

Student	Palm Width	Joint Length
1	70 mm	30 mm
2		

4. What are the landmarks for this data? Answers vary.

Palm Width

Minimum___	Maximum___	Mode___
Median___	Mean___	Range___

Joint Length

Minimum___	Maximum___	Mode___
Median___	Mean___	Range___

5. What relationships exist between the Palm Width and Joint Length data? Joint length is less than half the palm width.
6. Explain why the data does or does not support your prediction. Except for range, the landmarks for joint length are less than half those for palm width. The range for both is about the same.

Math Masters, p. 160

6•3 Stem-and-Leaf Plots for Hand and Finger Measures

Objectives To introduce stem-and-leaf plots; and to provide practice measuring lengths and using a protractor.

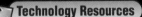

Technology Resources www.everydaymathonline.com

ePresentations

eToolkit

Algorithms Practice

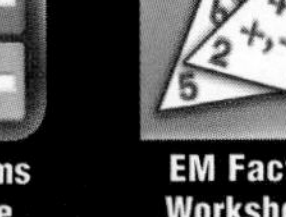
EM Facts Workshop Game™

Family Letters

Assessment Management

Common Core State Standards

Curriculum Focal Points

Interactive Teacher's Lesson Guide

1 Teaching the Lesson

Key Concepts and Skills

- Collect and organize class data.
  [Data and Chance Goal 1]
- Identify data landmarks.
  [Data and Chance Goal 2]
- Measure finger and hand spans to the nearest millimeter.
  [Measurement and Reference Frames Goal 1]
- Measure angles with half-circle protractors.
  [Measurement and Reference Frames Goal 1]

Key Activities

Students measure their hand spans and angles of finger separation. They make stem-and-leaf plots to display the class data.

Ongoing Assessment: Informing Instruction See page 392.

Ongoing Assessment: Recognizing Student Achievement Use an Exit Slip (*Math Masters,* page 414).
[Data and Chance Goal 1]

Key Vocabulary

span ◆ normal span ◆ great span ◆ stem-and-leaf plot ◆ stem ◆ leaf ◆ angle of separation

Materials

Math Journal 1, pp. 173 and 174
Study Link 6•2
Math Masters, p. 414
Class Data Pad ◆ demonstration protractor ◆ protractor ◆ ruler ◆ slate ◆ colored chalk (optional)

2 Ongoing Learning & Practice

Playing *Finish First*

Math Journal 1, pp. 170 and 171
per partnership: 4 each of number cards 4–8 (from the Everything Math Deck, if available)
Students continue to collect data by playing *Finish First.*

Math Boxes 6•3

Math Journal 1, p. 175
Students practice and maintain skills through Math Box problems.

Study Link 6•3

Math Masters, p. 161
Students practice and maintain skills through Study Link activities.

3 Differentiation Options

READINESS

Measuring Angles with a Half-Circle Protractor

Math Masters, p. 162
half-circle protractor
Students review measuring angles with a protractor.

EXTRA PRACTICE

Organizing Data into a Stem-and-Leaf Plot

Math Journal 1, pp. 164 and 165
Students use a stem-and-leaf plot to display data about states visited.

ELL SUPPORT

Building a Math Word Bank

Differentiation Handbook, p. 142
Students add the term *stem-and-leaf plot* to their Math Word Banks.

Advance Preparation

For Part 1, copy the stem-and-leaf plot from journal page 173 onto the board.

***Teacher's Reference Manual,* Grades 4–6** pp. 214–217

Getting Started

Mental Math and Reflexes

Give these fractions orally. Students write the decimal and percent equivalents. Proceed fairly rapidly.

●○○ $\frac{1}{4}$ 0.25; 25%
$\frac{9}{10}$ 0.9; 90%

●●○ $\frac{4}{8}$ 0.5; 50%
$\frac{23}{100}$ 0.23; 23%

●●● $\frac{1}{3}$ $0.\overline{3}$; $33\frac{1}{3}$%
$\frac{1}{8}$ 0.125; $12\frac{1}{2}$%

Math Message

Write a sentence using the word span. *If you don't know this word, find its meaning in a dictionary to help you.*

Study Link 6•2 Follow-Up

Survey students for the objects they found for each measurement. Briefly review the answers to Problem 2.

1 Teaching the Lesson

▶ Math Message Follow-Up

NOTE In the United States and in Great Britain, a standard span is sometimes defined as 9 inches (22.86 centimeters).

Language Arts Link The word ***span*** is used in several related ways. For a bridge, span is the distance from one end to the other or the distance between major supports. The span of an airplane's or bird's wings is the distance from wingtip to wingtip. A span of time is the length of time between one event and another; a life span is the length of time an organism is alive. There are hand measures that are also called spans:

▷ A **normal span** is the distance from the tip of the thumb to the tip of the first (index) finger, stretched as far apart as possible. (*See margin.*)

▷ A **great span** is the distance from the tip of the thumb to the tip of the fourth (little) finger, stretched as far apart as possible. (*See margin.*)

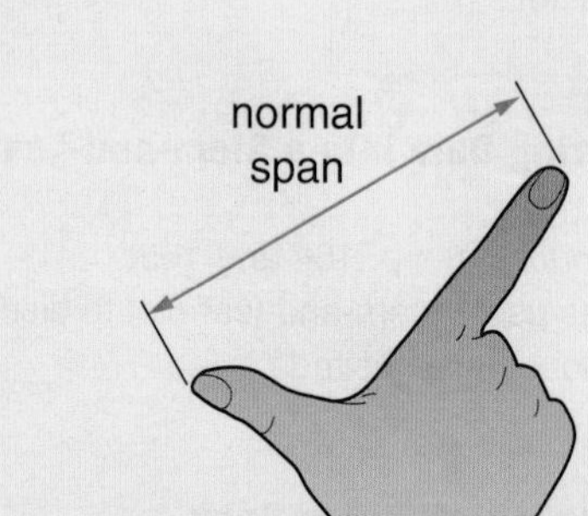

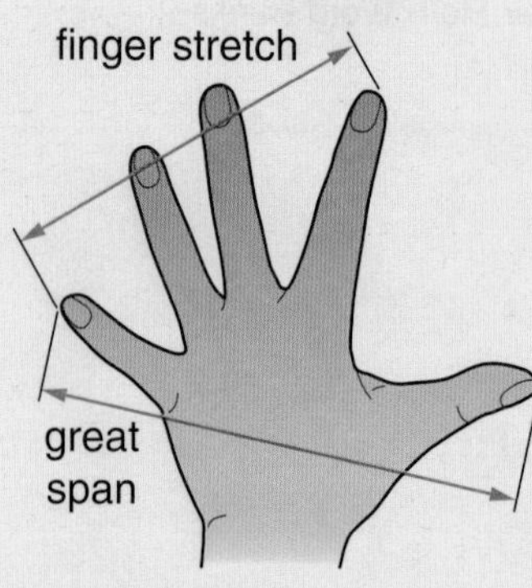

To support English language learners, write the phrases *normal span* and *great span* on the board with a drawing to represent their meaning.

Normal and great spans do not have a definite length because different people have different-sized hands.

▶ Measuring the Great Span

(*Math Journal 1,* p. 173)

Ask students why it might be interesting or important to know their hand spans and how far apart they can separate their fingers. Sample answers: Span and finger separation angles determine how big a person's "grab" is. Span and flexibility are important in playing musical instruments, for handling sports equipment, and for operating various machinery and switches. Have partners work together to measure each other's great span and record their personal measures on journal page 173 and on the Class Data Pad.

NOTE If any students are unable to perform this activity, provide an alternative data set.

▶ Organizing the Data in a Stem-and-Leaf Plot

(*Math Journal 1,* p. 173)

When all students have completed their measurements, label the list on the Class Data Pad with the table name, and explain that the class will use this data to make **stem-and-leaf plots.** To support English language learners, write *stem-and-leaf plot* on the board. Use a volunteer's great span (for example, 186 millimeters) to demonstrate plotting a number as a stem and a leaf:

1. Ask students to name the two digits that are in the hundreds and tens places of the number you just wrote (in the example, 18). These digits are a **stem** in the plot. Refer students to the incomplete table on the board, and ask them to find the stem in the left column of the table.

2. The digit in the ones place of the number (in the example, 6) is the **leaf.** The leaf is recorded in the right column in the same row as its stem.

Adjusting the Activity

ELL

Record the example values using two colors of chalk, one for the stem (hundreds and tens) and one for the leaves (ones). Use these same colors when recording the data in the stem-and-leaf plot.

AUDITORY ◆ KINESTHETIC ◆ TACTILE ◆ VISUAL

Repeat this process with two or three more great span measures. Emphasize that each one-digit leaf in the Leaves column is written to the right of the corresponding two-digit stem in the Stems column. Ask volunteers to read the numbers in the plot. (The plot in the margin shows spans of 149, 186, and 180 mm.)

Ask: *Why do you think this is called a stem-and-leaf plot?* Sample answers: It's like a plant or a tree. One stem can have many leaves. The stems are on the left. You put 1-digit leaves on the right, making sure you put them next to the correct stems.

Tell students that when making a stem-and-leaf plot, the leaves should be arranged in numerical order. Adjust the sample on the board, if needed. Ask: *Why is it useful to order the data in this way?* Sample answer: Arranging the data in order makes it easier to find the exact landmarks: minimum, maximum, mode(s), and median.

Ask several volunteers to record their great span measures in the plot on the board, reordering leaves as necessary. Have students use the spans on the Class Data Pad and the example plot to complete the stem-and-leaf plot on journal page 173. Then record the indicated landmarks.

Great-Span Measurements for the Class (Millimeters)

Stems (100s and 10s)	Leaves (1s)
13	
14	9
15	
16	
17	
18	6 0
19	
20	
21	
22	
23	
24	

Student Page

Date Time

LESSON 6·3 **Hand Measures: The Great Span**

For measurements on this page and the next page:

If you are right-handed, measure your left hand.
If you are left-handed, measure your right hand.

Your **great span** is the distance from the tip of your thumb to the tip of your little finger. Place the tip of your thumb at the top of the ruler in the margin (at 0). Extend your fingers. Stretch your little finger as far along the ruler as you can. Read your great span measurement to the nearest millimeter, and record it below. Answers vary.

great span

My great span is about ______ mm.

Your teacher will show you how to use the table below. Use it to record the great-span data for your class. The result is called a **stem-and-leaf plot.**

Great-Span Measurements for the Class (Millimeters)

Stems (100s and 10s)	Leaves (1s)
13	______
14	______
15	______
16	______
17	______
18	______
19	______
20	______
21	______
22	______
23	______
24	______

Landmarks for the Class Great-Span Data

minimum: ______ mm
maximum: ______ mm
mode(s): ______ mm
median: ______ mm

cm 1 2 3 4 5 6 7 8 9 10 11 12 13 14 15 16 17 18 19 20 21 22 23 24

Math Journal 1, p. 173

Student Page

Date Time

LESSON 6·3 **Finger Measures: Finger Flexibility**

The picture shows how to measure the **angle of separation** between your thumb and first (index) finger. This is a measure of finger flexibility.

Answers vary.

1. Spread your thumb and first finger as far apart as you can. Do this in the air. Don't use your other hand to help. Lower your hand onto a sheet of paper. Trace around your thumb and first finger. With a straightedge, draw two line segments to make a V shape, or angle, that fits the finger opening. Use a protractor to measure the angle between your thumb and first finger. Record the measure of the angle.

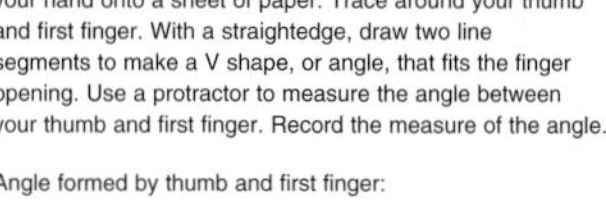

Measure this angle.

Angle formed by thumb and first finger:

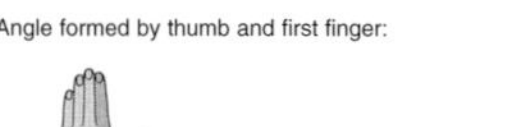

_______ °

2. In the air, spread your first and second fingers as far apart as possible. On a sheet of paper, trace these fingers, and draw the angle of separation between them. Measure the angle and record its measure.

Angle formed by first and second fingers:

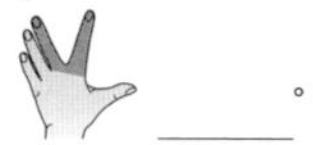

_______ °

3. Record the class landmarks for both finger-separation angles in the table at the right.

Landmark	Thumb and First	First and Second
Minimum		
Maximum		
Mode(s)		
Median		

Math Journal 1, p. 174

Thumb and First Finger Separation (Degrees)

Stems (100s and 10s)	**Leaves** (1s)
7	
8	
9	
10	
11	
12	
13	
14	
15	

First and Second Finger Separation (Degrees)

Stems (10s)	**Leaves** (1s)
1	
2	
3	
4	
5	
6	
7	

Ongoing Assessment: Informing Instruction

Watch for students who have difficulty keeping the numbers organized as they copy from the Class Data Pad. Have them make a personal list and mark off each number as it is used in their plots.

When most students have finished, ask questions such as the following:

- Where is your span in this plot?
- Is your span near the minimum?
- Which is closer to your span, the maximum span or the mode?
- How does your span compare with the median span?
- How do you think the data on spans for our class would compare with the data on spans for a second grade class? For a professional basketball team?

▶ Measuring Finger-Separation Angles

WHOLE-CLASS ACTIVITY

(*Math Journal 1,* p. 174)

Demonstrate the following procedure for measuring the angle of separation for the thumb and first finger:

1. Spread your thumb and first finger as far apart as possible and trace them on the board.
2. Discuss how to "fit" an angle to the drawing. Where should the vertex be? The inside base of the thumb Should the sides of the angle be entirely within the tracing? As much as possible
3. Draw an angle that fits the drawing and measure it with the board protractor. Explain that this angle formed by the spread of the thumb and first finger is called the **angle of separation,** and write the phrase on the board.

Have students measure the angle of separation between their thumb and first finger and between their first and second fingers. They record these angle measures on journal page 174.

On the board or transparencies, make separate stem-and-leaf plots for the two different finger-separation angle measurements. After recording all the class data, rewrite each row of leaves in numerical order.

Adjusting the Activity

Record the class data for the two different finger-separation angle measurements, and ask students to make the two stem-and-leaf plots. Encourage them to think about what should be the first stem and how many stems should be listed.

AUDITORY ◆ KINESTHETIC ◆ TACTILE ◆ VISUAL

Have students find the landmarks for each plot and record them on journal page 174.

Ongoing Assessment: Recognizing Student Achievement

Exit Slip

Use an **Exit Slip** (*Math Masters,* page 414) to assess students' understanding of the structure of stem-and-leaf plots. Ask students to complete the following statement: Stem-and-leaf plots are a good way to display data because... Students are making adequate progress if their responses demonstrate an understanding of how the plots are structured. Some students may also include references to how the structure supports finding landmarks and interpreting the data.

[Data and Chance Goal 1]

2 Ongoing Learning & Practice

▶ Playing *Finish First*

PARTNER ACTIVITY

(*Math Journal 1,* pp. 170 and 171)

Partners continue to collect data by playing *Finish First.* They record their results on journal page 171 and on the classroom tally sheet.

Reminder: The data from the game will be used in Lesson 6-6. For detailed instructions, see Lesson 6-2.

▶ Math Boxes 6·3

INDEPENDENT ACTIVITY

(*Math Journal 1,* 175)

Mixed Practice Math Boxes in this lesson are paired with Math Boxes in Lesson 6-1. The skill in Problem 4 previews Unit 7 content.

▶ Study Link 6·3

INDEPENDENT ACTIVITY

(*Math Masters,* p. 161)

Home Connection Students answer questions based on a stem-and-leaf plot. They identify data landmarks and explain how to find the median.

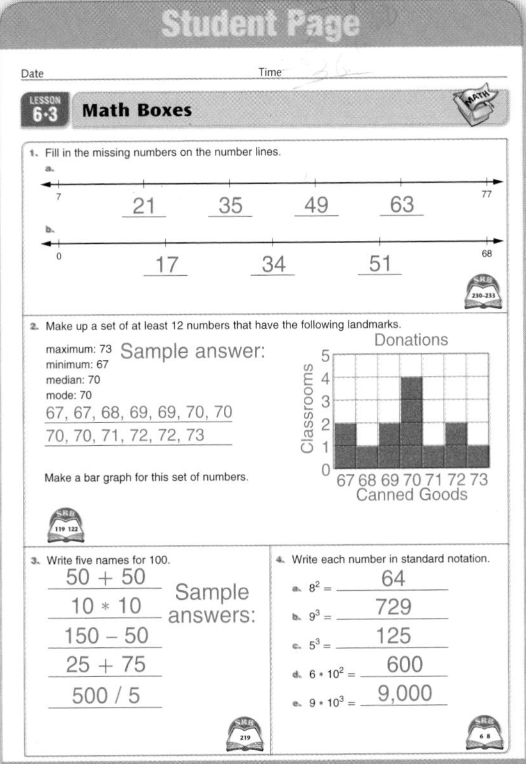

Student Page

Date Time

LESSON 6·3 **Math Boxes**

1. Fill in the missing numbers on the number lines.

a. 7, 21, 35, 49, 63, 77

b. 0, 17, 34, 51, 68

2. Make up a set of at least 12 numbers that have the following landmarks.

maximum: 73
minimum: 67
median: 70
mode: 70

Sample answer:
67, 67, 68, 69, 69, 70, 70
70, 70, 71, 72, 72, 73

Make a bar graph for this set of numbers.

3. Write five names for 100.

Sample answers:
50 + 50
10 * 10
150 − 50
25 + 75
500 / 5

4. Write each number in standard notation.

a. 8^2 = 64
b. 9^3 = 729
c. 5^3 = 125
d. $6 * 10^2$ = 600
e. $9 * 10^3$ = 9,000

Math Journal 1, **p. 175**

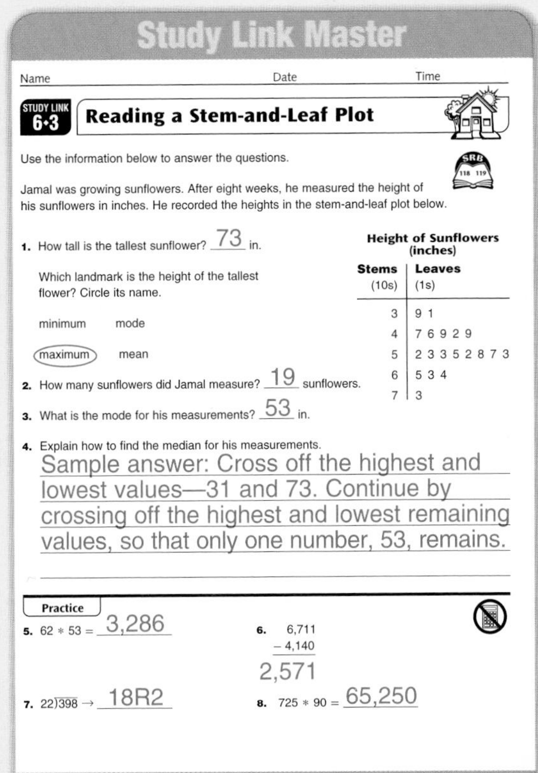

Study Link Master

Name Date Time

STUDY LINK 6·3 **Reading a Stem-and-Leaf Plot**

Use the information below to answer the questions.

Jamal was growing sunflowers. After eight weeks, he measured the height of his sunflowers in inches. He recorded the heights in the stem-and-leaf plot below.

Height of Sunflowers (inches)

Stems (10s)	Leaves (1s)
3	9 1
4	7 6 9 2 9
5	2 3 3 5 2 8 7 3
6	5 3 4
7	3

1. How tall is the tallest sunflower? 73 in.

Which landmark is the height of the tallest flower? Circle its name.

minimum mode
(maximum) mean

2. How many sunflowers did Jamal measure? 19 sunflowers.

3. What is the mode for his measurements? 53 in.

4. Explain how to find the median for his measurements.

Sample answer: Cross off the highest and lowest values—31 and 73. Continue by crossing off the highest and lowest remaining values, so that only one number, 53, remains.

Practice

5. 62 * 53 = 3,286

6. 6,711 − 4,140 = 2,571

7. 22)398 → 18R2

8. 725 * 90 = 65,250

Math Masters, **p. 161**

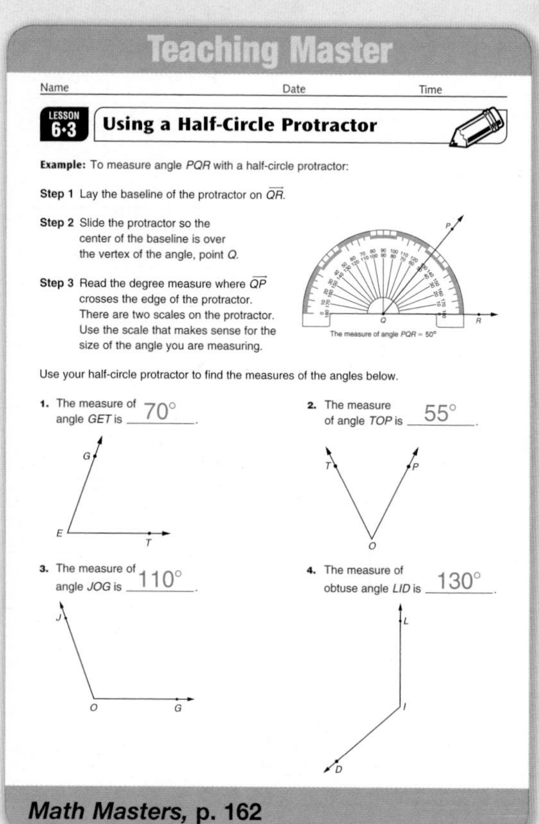
Teaching Master

Name Date Time

LESSON 6·3 **Using a Half-Circle Protractor**

Example: To measure angle *PQR* with a half-circle protractor:

Step 1 Lay the baseline of the protractor on $\overline{QR}$.

Step 2 Slide the protractor so the center of the baseline is over the vertex of the angle, point *Q*.

Step 3 Read the degree measure where $\overline{QP}$ crosses the edge of the protractor. There are two scales on the protractor. Use the scale that makes sense for the size of the angle you are measuring.

The measure of angle *PQR* = 50°

Use your half-circle protractor to find the measures of the angles below.

1. The measure of angle *GET* is 70°.
2. The measure of angle *TOP* is 55°.
3. The measure of angle *JOG* is 110°.
4. The measure of obtuse angle *LID* is 130°.

Math Masters, p. 162

3 Differentiation Options

READINESS

SMALL-GROUP ACTIVITY

15–30 Min

▶ Measuring Angles with a Half-Circle Protractor

(*Math Masters,* p. 162)

To provide experience using a half-circle protractor to measure angles, have students measure the angles on the *Math Masters* page. Remind students to use references (right angles, circles, clock angles, and so on) to estimate the angle measures before using the protractor. Ask students to share the methods or strategies they used to check their measurements.

EXTRA PRACTICE

PARTNER ACTIVITY

15–30 Min

▶ Organizing Data into a Stem-and-Leaf Plot

(*Math Journal 1,* pp. 164 and 165)

Have students use the data collected in Lesson 6-1 to construct a stem-and-leaf plot of the number of states students have visited. Consider having students make posters that show their plots, data landmarks, and summary statements of their interpretation of this data.

ELL SUPPORT

SMALL-GROUP ACTIVITY

15–30 Min

▶ Building a Math Word Bank

(*Differentiation Handbook,* p. 142)

To provide language support for graphing, have students use the Word Bank Template found on *Differentiation Handbook,* page 142. Ask students to write the term *stem-and-leaf plot,* draw pictures relating to the term, and write other related words. See the *Differentiation Handbook* for more information.

6•4 Mystery Plots

Objective To provide experiences with data presented in line plots and stem-and-leaf plots.

www.everydaymathonline.com

ePresentations

eToolkit

Algorithms Practice

EM Facts Workshop Game™

Family Letters

Assessment Management

Common Core State Standards

Curriculum Focal Points

Interactive Teacher's Lesson Guide

1 Teaching the Lesson

Key Concepts and Skills

- Interpret line plots and stem-and-leaf plots. [Data and Chance Goal 2]
- Use landmarks to identify data sets. [Data and Chance Goal 2]
- Use landmarks to draw conclusions about data sets. [Data and Chance Goal 2]

Key Activities

Students interpret and then match the data in line and stem-and-leaf plots to given data descriptions.

Ongoing Assessment: Informing Instruction See page 396.

Ongoing Assessment: Recognizing Student Achievement Use journal page 176. [Data and Chance Goal 2]

Ongoing Assessment: Informing Instruction See page 397.

Materials

Math Journal 1, pp. 176–178
Study Link 6•3
Math Masters, p. 163
slate ◆ calculator

2 Ongoing Learning & Practice

Playing *Finish First*

Math Journal 1, pp. 170 and 171
per partnership: 4 each of number cards 4–8 (from the Everything Math Deck, if available)
Students continue to collect data by playing *Finish First.*

Math Boxes 6•4

Math Journal 1, p. 179
Students practice and maintain skills through Math Box problems.

Study Link 6•4

Math Masters, p. 164
Students practice and maintain skills through Study Link activities.

3 Differentiation Options

READINESS

Finding the Median

Math Masters, p. 429
scissors
Students explore finding the median using a concrete model.

ENRICHMENT

Analyzing Spelling Test Scores

Math Masters, p. 166
Students find the median and the mean to analyze their relationship to the data set.

EXTRA PRACTICE

Matching Mystery Plots

Math Masters, p. 165
Students practice matching line plots with data descriptions.

Advance Preparation

For the Math Message, make several copies of *Math Masters,* page 163 and cut them in half. For the optional Readiness activity in Part 3, cut *Math Masters,* page 429 (1-inch grid paper) into 1 inch by 9 inch strips.

***Teacher's Reference Manual,* Grades 4–6** p. 169

Getting Started

Mental Math and Reflexes

Use the following problems to practice rounding numbers. Students write decimals from dictation then round the decimals to a specified place. *Suggestions:*

●○○ Thirty-two and six hundredths to the nearest whole number 32.06; 32
Four and thirty-eight hundredths to the nearest tenth 4.38; 4.4

●●○ Seven and eighteen hundredths to the nearest whole number 7.18; 7
Seven and eighteen hundredths to the nearest tenth 7.18; 7.2

●●● Eighty-six and fifty-five hundredths to the nearest ten 86.55; 90
Nine thousandths to the nearest hundredth 0.009; 0.01

Math Message

Take a Math Message half-sheet of paper. Use the stem-and-leaf plot to find the landmarks.

Study Link 6·3 Follow-Up

Ask partners to compare their answers and resolve any differences.

Unit: Inches

Stems (10s)	Leaves (1s)
4	4 7
5	0 0 6 8
6	1 3 5

Stem-and-leaf plot for the Math Message, with leaves in numerical order

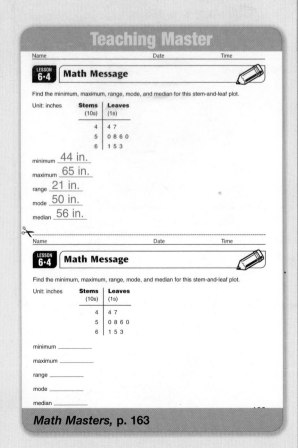

Teaching Master

Name Date Time

LESSON 6·4 **Math Message**

Find the minimum, maximum, range, mode, and median for this stem-and-leaf plot.

Unit: inches

Stems (10s)	Leaves (1s)
4	4 7
5	0 8 6 0
6	1 5 3

minimum 44 in.
maximum 65 in.
range 21 in.
mode 50 in.
median 56 in.

Name Date Time

LESSON 6·4 **Math Message**

Find the minimum, maximum, range, mode, and median for this stem-and-leaf plot.

Unit: inches

Stems (10s)	Leaves (1s)
4	4 7
5	0 8 6 0
6	1 5 3

minimum ______
maximum ______
range ______
mode ______
median ______

Math Masters, p. 163

1 Teaching the Lesson

▶ Math Message Follow-Up

(*Math Masters,* p. 163)

Ask volunteers to name the nine data items shown in the stem-and-leaf plot. List the numbers in order on the board. 44, 47, 50, 50, 56, 58, 61, 63, and 65 Ask students to identify the minimum 44 in., maximum 65 in., range 21 in., median 56 in., and mode 50 in. Circle and label these numbers in the data list.

Draw a second version of the stem-and-leaf plot by rewriting each row of leaves in numerical order. (*See margin.*) Ask students which version of the stem-and-leaf plot makes it easier to find the landmarks and why. The second version because data is ordered.

Ongoing Assessment: Informing Instruction

Watch for students who have difficulty finding the median. Have them write the ordered data list from the board and cross off number pairs, one at each end, until they reach the middle number. This is the median. Then have them copy the second version of the stem-and-leaf plot and cross off pairs of leaves in the same way, by crossing off one leaf from the top and one leaf from the bottom, to identify the median.

▶ Identifying Mystery Line Plots

(*Math Journal 1,* pp. 176 and 177)

Assign partners to complete journal pages 176 and 177 by matching the four sets of described data with the appropriate line plot. Emphasize that students are looking for the matches that make the most sense. Tell them that no plot is used more than once, and one of the plots is not used at all. Circulate and assist.

After ten to fifteen minutes, gather the class and discuss the answers:

- ▷ Data Set 1, hours of TV watched, is represented by Plot #2.
- ▷ Data Set 2, ages of younger siblings, is represented by Plot #5.

None of the other plots could describe Data Sets 1 or 2 because the numbers in those other plots are too large.

If Plot #5 represented TV hours, then more than half of the students watched TV for 5 or more hours the previous night. That's possible, but unlikely. However, Plot #5 could represent hours on a nonschool day or when there is a significant national or international event, such as the Olympics.

If Plot #2 represented sibling ages, then no fifth grader would have a sibling aged 7 through 10. That's possible, but unlikely.

- ▷ Data Set 3, heights, is represented by Plot #1.
- ▷ Data Set 4, ages of grandmothers, is represented by Plot #3.

Plot #3 cannot represent heights because the largest numbers are too large. (Some students would be nearly 7 feet tall!) It does, however, show a reasonable range for grandmothers' ages.

Plot #4 does not represent any of the data described on journal page 176. Ask students to describe any data that could be represented by Plot #4. Sample answers: Ages of the students' mothers; average time in minutes spent on homework each night

Ongoing Assessment: Recognizing Student Achievement

Journal page 176 Problems 5 and 6 ★

Use **journal page 176, Problems 5 and 6** to assess students' facility with interpreting data displayed in line plots. Students are making adequate progress if their writing demonstrates an understanding of the data's meanings in relation to data descriptions. Some students may refer to data landmarks in their explanations.

[Data and Chance Goal 2]

▶ Identifying Mystery Stem-and-Leaf Plots

PARTNER ACTIVITY

(*Math Journal 1,* p. 178)

In this activity, similar to the previous one, students match data with stem-and-leaf plots instead of line plots. Students identify a data set that reasonably represents arm reach and then a data set for standing jump distances.

Ongoing Assessment: Informing Instruction

Watch for students who have difficulty reading the leaves as separate numbers in the stem-and-leaf plots. Have them list the numbers from the plot, use the list to help them answer the questions, and verify their selection of the median.

Student Page

Date Time

LESSON 6•4 **Mystery Plots**

There are five line plots on page 177. Each plot shows a different set of data about a fifth-grade class.

Match each of the following four data set descriptions with one of the five plots. Then fill in the unit for each matched graph on page 177.

1. The number of hours of TV each fifth grader watched last night Plot #2
2. The ages of the younger brothers and sisters of the fifth graders Plot #5
3. The heights, in inches, of some fifth graders Plot #1
4. The ages of some fifth graders' grandmothers Plot #3
5. Explain how you selected the line plot for Data Set 4. ★ Sample answer: Plot #1 and Plot #3 show reasonable numbers for grandmothers' ages. But Plot #3 shows numbers in the 70s and 80s and is more reasonable for showing grandmothers' ages.
6. Tell why you think the other line plots are not correct for Data Set 4. ★ Sample answer: Some or all of the numbers in Plots #2, #4, and #5 are too small to represent ages of fifth graders' grandmothers. If Plot #3 represents fifth graders' heights, then 6 of them would be taller than 6 ft. So Plot #1 represents heights, which means Plot #3 must represent grandmothers' ages.

Math Journal 1, p. 176

Student Page

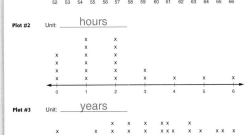

Date Time

LESSON 6•4 **Mystery Plots** *continued*

Plot #1 Unit: inches

52 53 54 55 56 57 58 59 60 61 62 63 64 65 66

Plot #2 Unit: hours

0 1 2 3 4 5 6

Plot #3 Unit: years

50 52 54 56 58 60 62 64 66 68 70 72 74 76 78 80 82

Plot #4 Unit: NA

26 28 30 32 34 36 38 40 42 44 46 48 50 52 54

Plot #5 Unit: years

0 1 2 3 4 5 6 7 8 9 10

Math Journal 1, p. 177

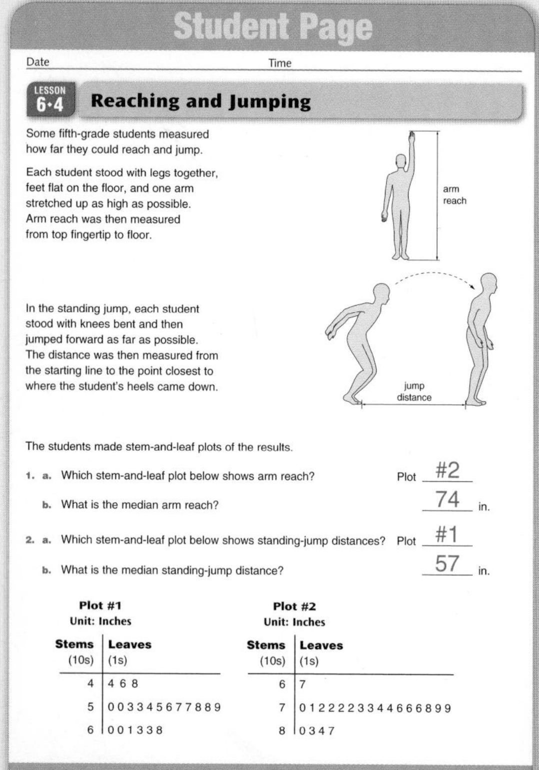
Student Page

Date Time

LESSON 6•4 **Reaching and Jumping**

Some fifth-grade students measured how far they could reach and jump.

Each student stood with legs together, feet flat on the floor, and one arm stretched up as high as possible. Arm reach was then measured from top fingertip to floor.

In the standing jump, each student stood with knees bent and then jumped forward as far as possible. The distance was then measured from the starting line to the point closest to where the student's heels came down.

The students made stem-and-leaf plots of the results.

1. a. Which stem-and-leaf plot below shows arm reach? Plot #2
   b. What is the median arm reach? 74 in.
2. a. Which stem-and-leaf plot below shows standing-jump distances? Plot #1
   b. What is the median standing-jump distance? 57 in.

Plot #1
Unit: Inches

Stems (10s)	Leaves (1s)
4	4 6 8
5	0 0 3 3 4 5 6 7 7 8 8 9
6	0 0 1 3 3 8

Plot #2
Unit: Inches

Stems (10s)	Leaves (1s)
6	7
7	0 1 2 2 2 2 3 3 4 4 6 6 6 8 9 9
8	0 3 4 7

Math Journal 1, p. 178

Most students will correctly identify Plot #1 as standing-jump distance and Plot #2 as arm reach. Expect a variety of explanations.

Examples:

▷ The smallest number in Plot #2 is in the 60s. That's more than 5 feet, and many kids can't jump that far. So Plot #2 must be arm reach.

▷ The smallest numbers in Plot #1 are in the 40s. Four feet is 48 in., so the smallest numbers are about 4 ft. Those numbers are too small to be arm reaches.

▷ I just held my arm up, and I found that I can reach about 15 in. above the top of my head. If you take 15 away from each number in Plot #2, you get numbers that are possible fifth graders' heights in inches. So Plot #2 is arm reach.

2 Ongoing Learning & Practice

▶ Playing *Finish First*

(*Math Journal 1*, pp. 170 and 171)

Partners continue to collect data by playing *Finish First*. They record their results on journal page 171 and on the classroom tally sheet. For detailed instructions, see Lesson 6-2.

NOTE Remind students that the game data will be used in Lesson 6-6, so they must play their designated number of games by that time.

▶ Math Boxes 6•4

INDEPENDENT ACTIVITY

(*Math Journal 1*, p. 179)

Mixed Practice Math Boxes in this lesson are paired with Math Boxes in Lesson 6-2. The skill in Problem 4 previews Unit 7 content.

Writing/Reasoning Have students respond to the following: *Explain your method for finding the savings in Problem 5.* Sample answer: I know that 20% is $\frac{1}{5}$, so I divided each regular price by 5 to find the savings amount.

▶ Study Link 6•4

INDEPENDENT ACTIVITY

(*Math Masters*, p. 164)

Home Connection Students match descriptions of data sets with line plots.

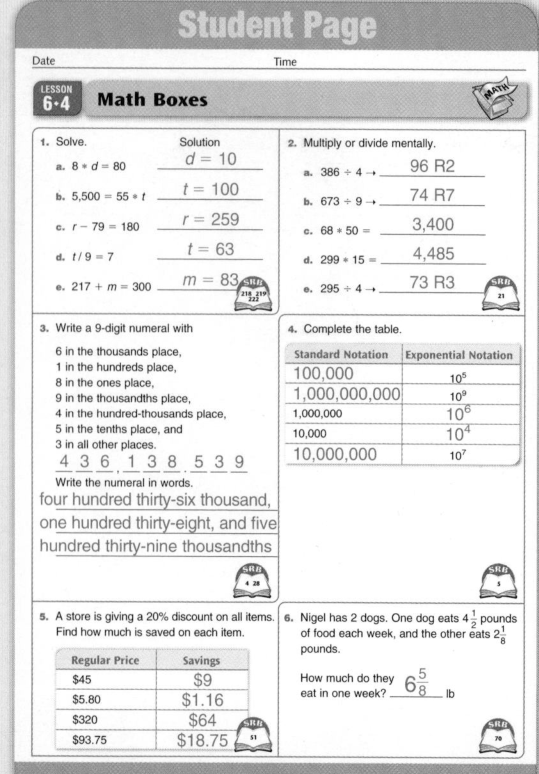
Student Page

Date Time

LESSON 6•4 **Math Boxes**

1. Solve.
   a. $8 * d = 80$ Solution: $d = 10$
   b. $5{,}500 = 55 * t$ $t = 100$
   c. $r - 79 = 180$ $r = 259$
   d. $t / 9 = 7$ $t = 63$
   e. $217 + m = 300$ $m = 83$

2. Multiply or divide mentally.
   a. 386 ÷ 4 → 96 R2
   b. 673 ÷ 9 → 74 R7
   c. 68 ∗ 50 = 3,400
   d. 299 ∗ 15 = 4,485
   e. 295 ÷ 4 → 73 R3

3. Write a 9-digit numeral with
   6 in the thousands place,
   1 in the hundreds place,
   8 in the ones place,
   9 in the thousandths place,
   4 in the hundred-thousands place,
   5 in the tenths place, and
   3 in all other places.
   4 3 6, 1 3 8 . 5 3 9
   Write the numeral in words.
   four hundred thirty-six thousand, one hundred thirty-eight, and five hundred thirty-nine thousandths

4. Complete the table.

Standard Notation	Exponential Notation
100,000	10^5
1,000,000,000	10^9
1,000,000	10^6
10,000	10^4
10,000,000	10^7

5. A store is giving a 20% discount on all items. Find how much is saved on each item.

Regular Price	Savings
\$45	\$9
\$5.80	\$1.16
\$320	\$64
\$93.75	\$18.75

6. Nigel has 2 dogs. One dog eats $4\frac{1}{2}$ pounds of food each week, and the other eats $2\frac{1}{8}$ pounds.
   How much do they eat in one week? $6\frac{5}{8}$ lb

Math Journal 1, p. 179

3 Differentiation Options

READINESS

SMALL-GROUP ACTIVITY

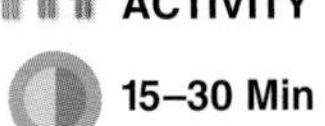
15–30 Min

▶ Finding the Median

(*Math Masters,* p. 429)

To explore finding the median using a concrete model, have students prepare and fold grid paper. Record the data set below on the board or a transparency. Give students 1 in. by 9 in. strips of 1-inch grid paper. They will use these strips to find the median of the data set.

Spelling Scores: 100, 83, 94, 93, 85, 70, 96, 94

Have students complete the following steps:

1. Write the numbers in the data set in order from smallest to largest on scrap paper.
2. Record the ordered numbers on the grid paper. Write one number in each cell, left-to-right. Cut off any cells that do not contain a value.
3. Fold the grid-paper strip in half.
4. Find the median. Explain that if a data set has an odd number of values, the number in the cell with the folded line is the median. If a data set has an even number of values, there will be two numbers separated by the folded line. The number halfway between these two numbers is the median.

When they have finished, ask students to describe how this strategy uses the definition of median. The median is the middle value in a data set. By folding the grid-paper strip in half, the fold is in the middle and identifies the middle of the data set.

ENRICHMENT

SMALL-GROUP ACTIVITY

15–30 Min

▶ Analyzing Spelling Test Scores

(*Math Masters,* p. 166)

To apply students' understanding of the relationship between the median and the mean, have students analyze data to describe which is greater without actually finding the landmarks. When students have finished the *Math Masters* page, discuss their solutions.

EXTRA PRACTICE

INDEPENDENT ACTIVITY

15–30 Min

▶ Matching Mystery Plots

(*Math Masters,* p. 165)

Students match line plots to data descriptions. When they are finished, ask students to share their reasoning.

Study Link Master

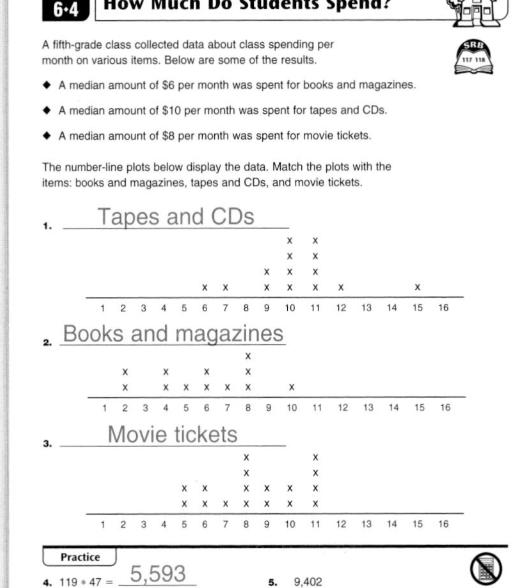
Name Date Time

STUDY LINK 6•4 **How Much Do Students Spend?**

A fifth-grade class collected data about class spending per month on various items. Below are some of the results.

- A median amount of $6 per month was spent for books and magazines.
- A median amount of $10 per month was spent for tapes and CDs.
- A median amount of $8 per month was spent for movie tickets.

The number-line plots below display the data. Match the plots with the items: books and magazines, tapes and CDs, and movie tickets.

1. Tapes and CDs
2. Books and magazines
3. Movie tickets

Practice

4. 119 ∗ 47 = 5,593
5. 9,402 + 7,137 = 16,539
6. 9)5,241 → 582R3
7. 9,487 ∗ 8 = 75,896

Math Masters, p. 164

More Mystery Plots	
Plot A	Unit: minutes
Plot B	Unit: books
Plot C	Unit: days
Plot D	Unit: years

***Math Masters,* p. 165**

Teaching Master

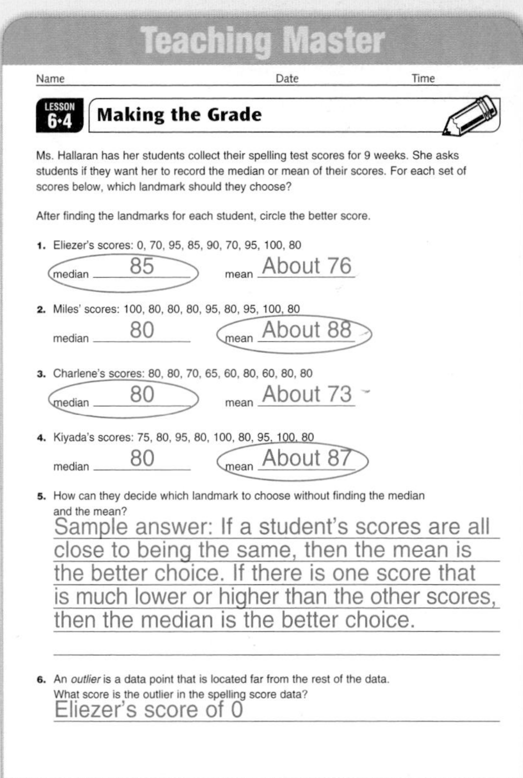
Name Date Time

LESSON 6•4 **Making the Grade**

Ms. Hallaran has her students collect their spelling test scores for 9 weeks. She asks students if they want her to record the median or mean of their scores. For each set of scores below, which landmark should they choose?

After finding the landmarks for each student, circle the better score.

1. Eliezer's scores: 0, 70, 95, 85, 90, 70, 95, 100, 80
median 85 mean About 76
2. Miles' scores: 100, 80, 80, 80, 95, 80, 95, 100, 80
median 80 mean About 88
3. Charlene's scores: 80, 80, 70, 65, 60, 80, 60, 80, 80
median 80 mean About 73
4. Kiyada's scores: 75, 80, 95, 80, 100, 80, 95, 100, 80
median 80 mean About 87
5. How can they decide which landmark to choose without finding the median and the mean?
Sample answer: If a student's scores are all close to being the same, then the mean is the better choice. If there is one score that is much lower or higher than the other scores, then the median is the better choice.
6. An *outlier* is a data point that is located far from the rest of the data. What score is the outlier in the spelling score data?
Eliezer's score of 0

Math Masters, p. 166

6•5 Sample Size and Sound Conclusions

Objective To investigate the relationship between sample size and the reliability of derived results.

www.everydaymathonline.com

ePresentations

eToolkit

Algorithms Practice

EM Facts Workshop Game™

Family Letters

Assessment Management

Common Core State Standards

Curriculum Focal Points

Interactive Teacher's Lesson Guide

1 Teaching the Lesson

Key Concepts and Skills

- Solve problems involving percent. [Number and Numeration Goal 2]
- Convert fractions to percents. [Number and Numeration Goal 5]
- Construct circle graphs of class data. [Data and Chance Goal 1]
- Make predictions based on sampling. [Data and Chance Goal 2]

Key Activities

Students take different size samples from a population and create circle graphs for these samples. They determine the more trustworthy of the samples and make predictions.

Ongoing Assessment: Recognizing Student Achievement Use the Math Message. [Number and Numeration Goal 2]

Key Vocabulary

sample ◆ population

Materials

Math Journal 1, p. 180
Study Link 6•4
Math Masters, p. 430
Geometry Template ◆ Class Data Pad ◆ small pieces of colored candy ◆ crayons or markers ◆ calculator ◆ slate ◆ half-sheet of paper

2 Ongoing Learning & Practice

Playing *Finish First*
Math Journal 1, pp. 170 and 171
per partnership: 4 each of number cards 4–8 (from the Everything Math Deck, if available)
Students continue to collect data by playing *Finish First.*

Math Boxes 6•5
Math Journal 1, p. 181
Students practice and maintain skills through Math Box problems.

Study Link 6•5
Math Masters, p. 167
Students practice and maintain skills through Study Link activities.

3 Differentiation Options

READINESS

Identifying the Whole
Math Masters, p. 168
calculator
Students convert fractions to percents by finding the parts and totals contained in number stories, writing the fractions, and then converting them to percents.

ENRICHMENT

Investigating Sample Size
Math Masters, p. 169
per partnership: coin or six-sided die
Students predict the outcome of an experiment, test the predictions, and summarize the results.

Advance Preparation

For Part 1, you will need candy of different colors, at least 5 pieces per student. Place the candy in a bowl near the Math Message. Draw a large circle on a sheet of paper and mark the center. Make copies of *Math Masters,* page 430 and cut the circles apart. Make enough for 1 per partnership.

***Teacher's Reference Manual,* Grades 4–6** pp. 44–46, 69–71, 235–236

Getting Started

Mental Math and Reflexes

Fraction-of problems:

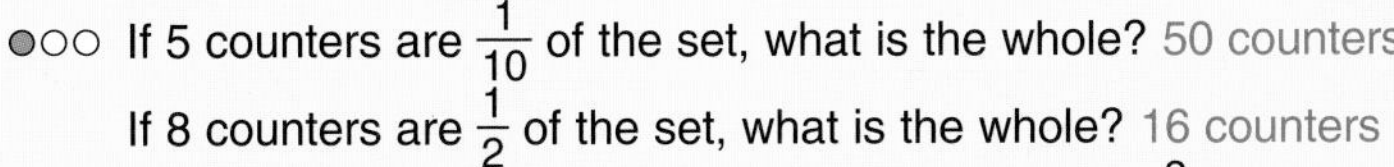

●○○ If 5 counters are $\frac{1}{10}$ of the set, what is the whole? 50 counters

If 8 counters are $\frac{1}{2}$ of the set, what is the whole? 16 counters

●●○ A set has 40 counters. How many counters are in $\frac{3}{8}$ of the set? 15 counters

If 20 counters are $\frac{2}{10}$ of the set, what is the whole? 100 counters

●●● A set has 25 counters. How many counters are in $\frac{4}{5}$ of the set? $\frac{4}{5}$ is what percent of the set? 20 counters; 80%

If 12 counters are $\frac{2}{3}$ of a set, what is the whole? 18 counters

Math Message 

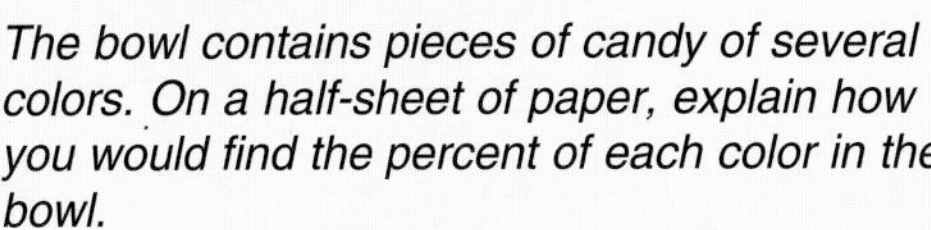

The bowl contains pieces of candy of several colors. On a half-sheet of paper, explain how you would find the percent of each color in the bowl.

Study Link 6·4 Follow-Up

Partners compare answers and resolve any differences. Ask a volunteer to share a strategy for matching the plots and data sets.

Ongoing Assessment: Recognizing Student Achievement

Math Message 

Use the **Math Message** to assess students' understanding of the concept of percent. Students are making adequate progress if their written responses name the whole as 100% and refer to pieces of a given color as a fraction or percent of the whole.

[Number and Numeration Goal 2]

1 Teaching the Lesson

▶ Math Message Follow-Up

WHOLE-CLASS DISCUSSION

ELL

Students share how they would find the percent of each color in the bowl. Most will probably suggest counting the total number of candies in the bowl as well as the number of each color in order to find the fraction and then the percent of each color.

If looking at a **sample** is not mentioned, ask:

- How could we find the percent of each color in the bowl without counting every piece?
- Would it help to look at a sample of candies from the bowl and count the number of each color in the sample?
- How many candies should we include in the sample?

Tell students that they are going to do a candy-counting experiment. The results will give them information they can use to predict the percent of each color in the bowl. Explain that the total number of candies in the bowl is called the **population.** To support English language learners, write *sample* and *population* on the board and explain their meanings in this mathematical context.

Student Page

Date ______ Time ______

LESSON 6•5 **Sampling Candy Colors**

1. You and your partner each take 5 pieces of candy from the bowl. Combine your candies, and record your results in the table under Our Sample of 10 Candies.

Sample answer:

Candy Color	Our Sample of 10 Candies		Combined Class Sample	
	Count	Percent	Count	Percent
red	1	10%	13	13%
yellow	5	50%	28	28%
green	2	20%	22	22%
orange	2	20%	12	12%
brown			25	25%

2. Your class will work together to make a sample of 100 candies. Record the counts and percents of the class sample under Combined Class Sample in the table.

3. Finally, your class will count the total number of candies in the bowl and the number of each color.

   a. How well did your sample of 10 candies predict the number of each color in the bowl? Answers vary.

   b. How well did the combined class sample predict the number of each color in the bowl? Answers vary.

   c. Do you think that a larger sample is more trustworthy than a smaller sample? Yes

   Explain your answer. Sample answer: Smaller samples vary more. A larger sample can be trusted to give a better picture of the real situation than a smaller one.

Math Journal 1, p. 180

NOTE Counting a whole population is rarely possible, which is why one is concerned with practical sampling and sampling sizes. Even if it is possible to count a whole population, it is often tedious and time-consuming.

▶ Taking a Small Sample of Candy Colors

(*Math Journal 1,* p. 180; *Math Masters,* p. 430)

Have each student take 5 pieces of candy from the bowl without looking (10 candies per partnership). Ask partners to count and record the number and percent of each candy color in their small sample on journal page 180. Tell them to put the candy back in the bowl when they have finished recording their results.

With samples of 10, percents are easy to calculate because the fractions easily convert to percents. For example, 4 yellows out of 10 candies is $\frac{4}{10} = \frac{40}{100} = 40\%$ of the sample. Point out that sample sizes are often chosen to make calculations easy.

Have each partnership make a circle graph to show their sample result for 10 candies. They can color the sections of the graph with the candy colors. Students may use the Percent Circle on their Geometry Templates and circles you provide from copies of *Math Masters,* page 430.

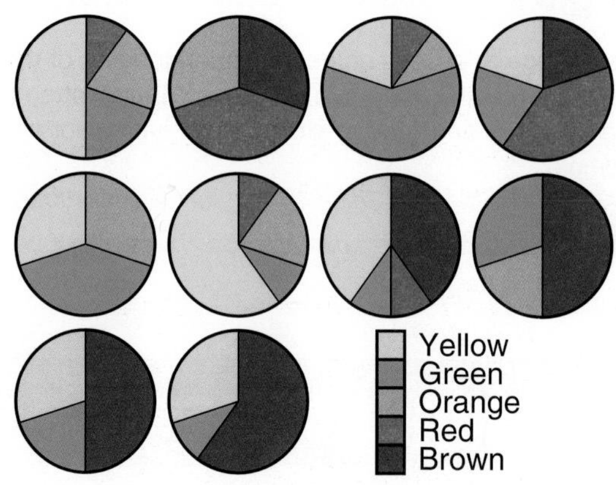

Each circle graph shows the result for one sample of 10 candies.

▶ Graphing and Predicting on the Basis of a Sample

PROBLEM SOLVING

(*Math Journal 1,* p. 180)

Ask 10 partnerships to display their circle graphs, report their results, and record them on the board. Discuss the variations in these results. Individual small samples of 10 may have many of one color, few of another color, and none of some colors.

Combine the data from the small partner samples to make a large sample. Tally the results by color on the board. Ask students to record the tallies on journal page 180.

By choosing 10 pairs of students, the combined sample total is 100—making percent calculations simple.

Make a circle graph of the combined sample. Use the large circle that you drew previously. (*See Advance Preparation.*) Ask volunteers to use a Percent Circle to mark the sections showing percents of colors in the combined sample.

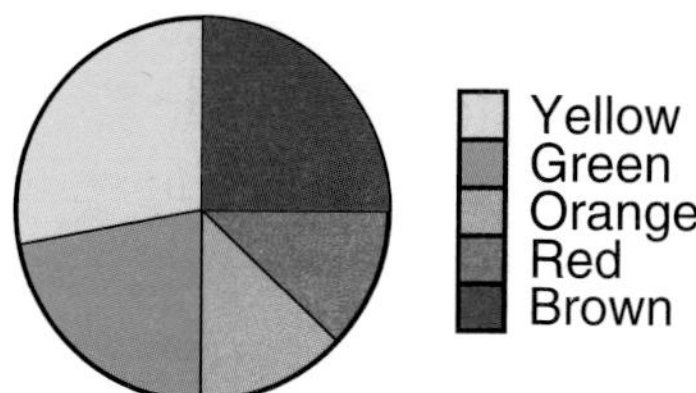

Circle graph of the combined samples of 100 candies

Discuss which is more trustworthy—a sample of 10 candies or the combined sample of 100. Prompt students with questions like the following:

- How do the small-sample results compare with one another? Sample answer: The results for our small samples jump all over. One of them shows 50% yellow, and one shows 10% yellow.
- How do the results of the larger combined sample compare with the small ones? Sample answer: The combined sample of 100 is better. Every color is represented. The sample for 100 gives a better picture than the sample for just 10.

Guide students to predict and agree on what percent of each color is in the bowl, and record these predictions on the Class Data Pad. Then have them count the total number of pieces of candy in the bowl and the number of each color. Record the results on the board.

Ask students to find the percent of each color:

1. Name each color as a fraction of the total number of candy pieces.
2. Use a calculator to divide the number of each color (the numerator) by the total number of candies in the bowl (the denominator).
3. Multiply the result by 100.

Expect the percent for each color in the bowl to be reasonably close to the percent on the circle graph for the large sample of 100.

2 Ongoing Learning & Practice

Playing *Finish First*

PARTNER ACTIVITY

(*Math Journal 1,* pp. 170 and 171)

Partners continue to collect the needed data for the specified number of games of *Finish First.* They record their results on journal page 171 and on the classroom tally sheet. For detailed instructions, see Lesson 6-2.

Reminder: The game data will be used in the next lesson.

Student Page

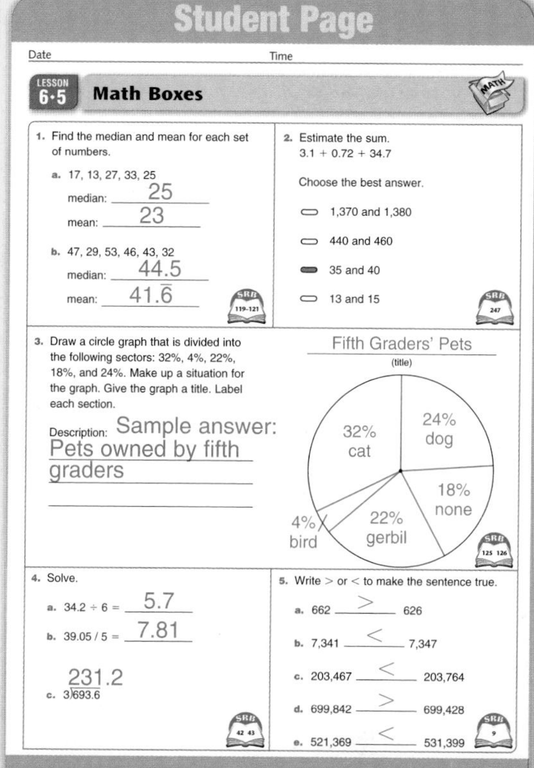

Date Time

LESSON 6·5 **Math Boxes**

1. Find the median and mean for each set of numbers.
   a. 17, 13, 27, 33, 25
   median: 25
   mean: 23
   b. 47, 29, 53, 46, 43, 32
   median: 44.5
   mean: $41.\overline{6}$

SRB 119-121

2. Estimate the sum.
   3.1 + 0.72 + 34.7
   Choose the best answer.
   - 1,370 and 1,380
   - 440 and 460
   - 35 and 40 (filled in)
   - 13 and 15

SRB 247

3. Draw a circle graph that is divided into the following sectors: 32%, 4%, 22%, 18%, and 24%. Make up a situation for the graph. Give the graph a title. Label each section.
   Description: Sample answer: Pets owned by fifth graders

Fifth Graders' Pets (title)

SRB 125 126

4. Solve.
   a. 34.2 ÷ 6 = 5.7
   b. 39.05 / 5 = 7.81
   c. 3)693.6 231.2

SRB 42 43

5. Write > or < to make the sentence true.
   a. 662 > 626
   b. 7,341 < 7,347
   c. 203,467 < 203,764
   d. 699,842 > 699,428
   e. 521,369 < 531,399

SRB 9

Math Journal 1, p. 181

Adjusting the Activity

Have students calculate the combined class sample using all partnerships in the class. If there are 17 partnerships, the whole is 170 pieces of candy. Compare these results with the results for 100 pieces of candy.

AUDITORY ♦ KINESTHETIC ♦ TACTILE ♦ VISUAL

Study Link Master

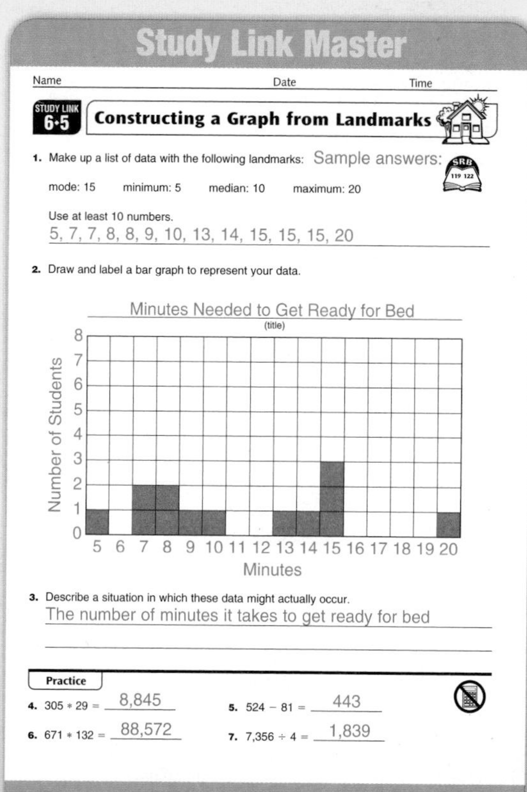

Name Date Time

STUDY LINK 6·5 **Constructing a Graph from Landmarks**

1. Make up a list of data with the following landmarks: Sample answers:
   mode: 15 minimum: 5 median: 10 maximum: 20
   Use at least 10 numbers.
   5, 7, 7, 8, 8, 9, 10, 13, 14, 15, 15, 15, 20

SRB 119 122

2. Draw and label a bar graph to represent your data.

Minutes Needed to Get Ready for Bed (title)

3. Describe a situation in which these data might actually occur.
   The number of minutes it takes to get ready for bed

Practice

4. 305 ∗ 29 = 8,845
5. 524 − 81 = 443
6. 671 ∗ 132 = 88,572
7. 7,356 ÷ 4 = 1,839

Math Masters, p. 167

Teaching Master

Name ______ Date ______ Time ______

LESSON 6•5 **Identify the Whole**

In the following number stories, find the whole using parts-and-total diagram. Write the fraction for the given part, and rename the fraction as a percent.

Example: Two girls each have 5 hats. Three of their hats are purple. What percent of the hats are purple?

Solution: $2 * 5 = 10$ hats; 3 out of $10 = \frac{3}{10}$; Rename $\frac{3}{10}$ as a fraction with 100 as the denominator, $\frac{10 * 3}{10 * 10} = \frac{30}{100}$; $\frac{30}{100} = 0.30$, or 30%.

Reminder: To use a calculator to convert a fraction to a percent, divide the numerator by the denominator. Use your fix key to round to the nearest hundredth, or multiply the decimal by 100 to display the percent.

1. Lamont, Jose, and Kenji are recycling soda cans. Lamont collects 13 cans. Jose collects 20 cans, and Kenji collects 17 cans. What percent of the cans does Jose collect?

Unit: cans Whole: $13 + 20 + 17 = 50$

Fraction: $\frac{20}{50}$ Percent: 40%

Total ?		
Part 13	Part 20	Part 17

2. Jacqui and Edna decide to share their hot lunches. They put together their fried potatoes and their onion rings. There are 33 pieces of fried potatoes and 17 onion rings. What percent of the lunches are the onion rings?

Unit: pieces Whole: 50

Fraction: $\frac{17}{50}$ Percent: 34%

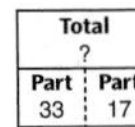

Total ?	
Part 33	Part 17

3. The boy's club is having a popcorn sale. Each of the 10 members of the club is given 5 boxes of popcorn, but Edward sells only 3. What percent of the 5 boxes remain for Edward to sell?

Unit: boxes Whole: 5

Fraction: $\frac{2}{5}$ Percent: 40%

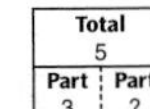

Total 5	
Part 3	Part ?

Math Masters, p. 168

Teaching Master

Name ______ Date ______ Time ______

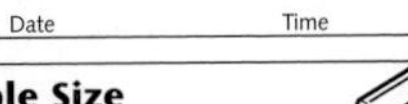

LESSON 6•5 **Investigating Sample Size**

1. Choose a specific outcome or event for one of the following actions.

   - Flipping a coin

   Example: The coin will land heads up. $\frac{1}{2}$

   - Rolling a die

   Example: The die will land with a 4 on the top. $\frac{1}{6}$

2. Predict the results of 10 trials and 100 trials. Report your predictions as the fraction of the total you think will result in a favorable outcome, or favorable event. For example, the coin will land heads up about $\frac{1}{2}$ of the time, or the die will land with a 4 on the top about $\frac{1}{6}$ of the time.

Event	10 trials		100 trials		1,000 trials
Sample answers:	Prediction	Result	Prediction	Result	Prediction
Coin will land heads up	$\frac{6}{10}$	$\frac{5}{10}$	$\frac{60}{100}$	$\frac{51}{100}$	$\frac{500}{1,000}$

3. Perform 10 trials. Record the results first with tally marks on a separate piece of paper and then in the table as a fraction.

4. Repeat for 100 trials. Record the results first with tally marks on a separate piece of paper and then in the table as a fraction.

5. How do your predictions compare with the actual results?
   Sample answer: They are very close.

6. Predict the results for 1,000 trials, and explain your prediction.
   Sample answer: Because the results have been very close to $\frac{1}{2}$, I predict the coin will land heads up about $\frac{1}{2}$ of the time.

7. On the back of this page, name two ways you and your partner could get data on the actual results for 1,000 trials.

Math Masters, p. 169

▶ Math Boxes 6•5

INDEPENDENT ACTIVITY

(*Math Journal 1,* p. 181)

Mixed Practice Math Boxes in this lesson are paired with Math Boxes in Lesson 6-7. The skill in Problem 5 previews Unit 7 content.

Writing/Reasoning Have students write a response to the following: *Explain how you solved Problem 4a, including the strategies and reasoning that you used.* Answers vary.

▶ Study Link 6•5

INDEPENDENT ACTIVITY

(*Math Masters,* p. 167)

Home Connection Students make up a list of data to fit a given set of landmarks. Students then construct a bar graph.

3 Differentiation Options

READINESS

▶ Identifying the Whole

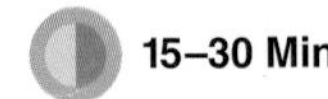

(*Math Masters,* p. 168)

To explore converting fractions to percents, have students find the parts and totals contained in number stories, write the fractions, and convert them to percents. Students can use calculators but should not use the percent key at this time.

ENRICHMENT

▶ Investigating Sample Size

15–30 Min

(*Math Masters,* p. 169)

To apply students' understanding of the relationship between sample size and the reliability of predictions, have students conduct the experiment on *Math Masters,* page 169. Students choose an event with random outcomes—flipping a coin or rolling a six-sided die. They predict and compare the results of 10 and 100 trials. Then they predict the results for 1,000 trials, explain their prediction, and design an approach to collect the actual results.

Discuss students' predictions and their prediction methods. Consider implementing one of their designs for collecting the actual results for 1,000 trials. Have partners report their findings to the class.

6•6 Analysis of Sample Data

Objective To provide experiences with displaying and analyzing data.

www.everydaymathonline.com

ePresentations

eToolkit

Algorithms Practice

EM Facts Workshop Game™

Family Letters

Assessment Management

Common Core State Standards

Curriculum Focal Points

Interactive Teacher's Lesson Guide

1 Teaching the Lesson

Key Concepts and Skills

- Convert fractions to percents.
  [Number and Numeration Goal 5]
- Construct bar and circle graphs and stem-and-leaf plots.
  [Data and Chance Goal 1]
- Identify data landmarks.
  [Data and Chance Goal 2]

Key Activities

Students analyze the class results for *Finish First* and draw conclusions about the fairness of the game. They display and analyze data from samples of a student survey.

Ongoing Assessment: Informing Instruction See page 408.

Key Vocabulary

sample ◆ survey ◆ population ◆ frequency table

Materials

Math Journal 1, pp. 182–185
Student Reference Book, p. 116; pp. 122 and 126 (optional)
Study Link 6•5
Math Masters, p. 436 (optional)
calculator ◆ slate

2 Ongoing Learning & Practice

Playing *Frac-Tac-Toe*
Student Reference Book, pp. 309 and 310
Math Masters, pp. 472 and 474
Students practice fraction-decimal conversions.

Ongoing Assessment: Recognizing Student Achievement
Use *Math Masters,* page 474.
[Number and Numeration Goal 5]

Math Boxes 6•6
Math Journal 1, p. 186
Students practice and maintain skills through Math Box problems.

Study Link 6•6
Math Masters, p. 170
Students practice and maintain skills through Study Link activities.

3 Differentiation Options

READINESS

Exploring Stem-and-Leaf Plot Data
Math Masters, p. 171
Students practice reading the values in stem-and-leaf plots.

EXTRA PRACTICE

Making Stem-and-Leaf Plots
Math Masters, p. 172
Students construct a stem-and-leaf plot for a data set and find the data landmarks.

ELL SUPPORT

Building a Math Word Bank
Differentiation Handbook, p. 142
Students add the terms *population* and *sample* to their Math Word Banks.

Advance Preparation

For Part 1, be sure the daily tally sheet and graph of *Finish First* results are up to date. As an alternative to the *Student Reference Book* data sets suggested for this lesson, allow students to devise their own question and survey two different groups. If you select this option, allow at least one more day for this lesson.

Getting Started

Mental Math and Reflexes

Write each mixed number as a fraction and each fraction as a whole or mixed number.

Slate Practice:

●○○ $\frac{8}{2}$ 4

$3\frac{8}{10}$ $\frac{38}{10}$, or $\frac{19}{5}$

●●○ $\frac{14}{5}$ $2\frac{4}{5}$

$\frac{27}{4}$ $6\frac{3}{4}$

●●● $7\frac{2}{3}$ $\frac{23}{3}$

$5\frac{7}{4}$ $\frac{27}{4}$

Math Message

Complete journal page 182.
Be prepared to discuss your answers.

Study Link 6•5 Follow-Up

Partners compare answers and resolve differences. Ask students to explain how they decided on their answers for Problem 3.

1 Teaching the Lesson

▶ Math Message Follow-Up

(*Math Journal 1,* p. 182)

For Problems 4 and 5, ask volunteers to share estimates and how they made them. Sample answers: I calculated the fraction of all games that the first player won and the fraction that the second player won. I looked at the last bar on the graph to find the percent of games the first player won. I subtracted this percent from 100% to find the percent of games the second player won.

The issue raised in Problem 6 was addressed in the candy-sampling activity in the previous lesson. The larger a **sample** is, the more confident we can be of conclusions drawn from the results.

For Problem 7, have students share and explain whether they think the game is fair. By now it should be clear to them that the player going second has an advantage. You might want to share the following explanation. The median number for any one draw is 6. So when the first player draws the third card, the total is most likely to be about 18. Therefore, when the second player draws the fourth card, the total is likely to be around 24.

Discuss how the rules could be changed to make it a fairer game. Changing the goal from 21 to a different number or using a different set of number cards might even the chances. Have students suggest alternatives and try them. For example, different partners could play with a goal of 22, 23, or 24, and so on, and make graphs to display their results.

Student Page

Date ____ Time ____

LESSON 6•6 **Is *Finish First* a Fair Game?**

Math Message Answers vary for Problems 1–6.

1. What is the total number of *Finish First* games your class has played? ______ games
2. How many games did the player going first win? ______ games
3. How many games did the player going second win? ______ games
4. What is your best estimate for the chance the player going first will win? ______
5. What is your best estimate for the chance the player going second will win? ______
6. Did your estimates change as more games were played? ______
7. Is *Finish First* a fair game? No Sample answers:
   Why or why not? It is not a fair game because the player going second has a much better chance of winning than the player going first.

   If *Finish First* isn't a fair game, how could you make it more fair?
   You could change the target number from 21 to a different number, or you could use a different set of number cards. Then play the game many times to see if it is more fair.

Math Journal 1, p. 182

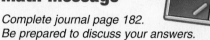

▶ Discussing the Definition and Purpose of a Survey

WHOLE-CLASS DISCUSSION

(*Student Reference Book,* p. 116)

Social Studies Link Explain the definition and the purpose of a sociological **survey:** a study based on data collected from human respondents. Surveys are used to find out about people's characteristics, behaviors, opinions, interests, and so on.

Remind students that the decennial census is an example of a survey that includes all the people in the United States. (*See Lesson 3-1.*)

Most surveys, however, study smaller populations that are of special interest. A **population** is the set of people, things, or data being studied. For example, a survey of physicians gathers information about a specific population—people who have medical degrees.

In many surveys, the population is so large that it is not practical to interview everybody. For this reason, a representative part of the population is interviewed and used to represent the whole population. This part is called a sample. To support English language learners, remind students of the candy-sampling activity in the previous lesson. The bowl of candy was the population, and the pieces of candy used by partners were samples of that population.

Refer students to the data sets listed on page 116 of the *Student Reference Book.* Ask volunteers to read the brief descriptions. Each set of data was obtained by conducting an interview with a sample of students from Lee Middle School. Ask volunteers to name the population of interest for this survey. All students who attend Lee school

▶ Displaying and Analyzing the Survey Data

PARTNER ACTIVITY

(*Math Journal 1,* pp. 183–185;
Student Reference Book, p. 116)

Explain that a **frequency table** is a chart on which data is tallied to find the frequency of given events or values. To support English language learners, write *frequency table* on the board, and discuss the meaning of frequency. On journal page 183, partners will use frequency tables to tally answers for the Entertainment and the Favorite-Sports survey data. To simplify this process, have one partner read the data items and the other partner tally. Students then count the tally marks to find a total and fraction for each category. They use calculators to find the percent, rounding each to the nearest percent.

Student Page

Data and Probability

Student Survey Data

Information was collected from samples of students at Lee Middle School. Three questions were asked.

1. Entertainment Data
Students were asked to select their favorite form of entertainment. They were given four possible choices:

TV: Watch TV/DVDs **Games:** Play video/computer games
Music: Listen to radio/CDs **Read:** Read books, magazines

Twenty-four students responded (answered the survey). Here are their data.

TV	TV	Read	TV	Games	TV	Music	Games
Games	TV	Read	Music	TV	TV	Music	TV
Games	Games	Music	TV	TV	Games	TV	Read

2. Favorite Sports Data
Students were asked to select their TWO favorite sports from this list:

Baseball **Basketball** **Bicycle riding**
Bowling **Soccer** **Swimming**

Twenty students responded. The data below include 40 answers because each student named two sports.

Basketball	Bicycle	Swimming	Soccer	Basketball
Swimming	Baseball	Swimming	Bicycle	Swimming
Bicycle	Swimming	Soccer	Bicycle	Soccer
Bowling	Soccer	Bicycle	Swimming	Bicycle
Bicycle	Swimming	Baseball	Bowling	Bicycle
Baseball	Bowling	Basketball	Basketball	Swimming
Basketball	Swimming	Soccer	Soccer	Baseball
Bicycle	Soccer	Bicycle	Swimming	Bicycle

3. Shower/Bath Time Data
A sample of 40 students was asked to estimate the number of minutes they usually spend taking a shower or bath. Here are the data.

3	20	10	5	8	4	10	7	5	5
25	5	3	25	20	17	5	30	14	35
9	20	15	7	5	10	16	40	10	15
10	5	15	10	15	5	12	22	3	9

Student Reference Book, p. 116

Student Page

Date Time

LESSON 6•6 **Frequency Tables**

A **frequency table** is a chart on which data is tallied to find the frequency of given events or values.

Use the frequency tables below to tally the Entertainment data and Favorite-Sports data on page 116 in your *Student Reference Book.* Then complete the tables. If you conducted your own survey, use the frequency tables to tally the data you collected. Then complete the tables.

1. What is the survey question? What is your favorite form of entertainment?

Category	Tallies	Number	Fraction	Percent
TV	HHT HHT /	11	$\frac{11}{24}$	46%
read	///	3	$\frac{3}{24}$, or $\frac{1}{8}$	$12\frac{1}{2}$%
games	HHT /	6	$\frac{6}{24}$, or $\frac{1}{4}$	25%
music	////	4	$\frac{4}{24}$, or $\frac{1}{6}$	$16\frac{2}{3}$%

Total number of tallies 24

2. What is the survey question? What are your two favorite sports?

Category	Tallies	Number	Fraction	Percent
baseball	////	4	$\frac{4}{40}$, or $\frac{1}{10}$	10%
basketball	HHT	5	$\frac{5}{40}$, or $\frac{1}{8}$	$12\frac{1}{2}$%
bicycling	HHT HHT /	11	$\frac{11}{40}$	$27\frac{1}{2}$%
bowling	///	3	$\frac{3}{40}$	$7\frac{1}{2}$%
soccer	HHT //	7	$\frac{7}{40}$	$17\frac{1}{2}$%
swimming	HHT HHT	10	$\frac{10}{40}$, or $\frac{1}{4}$	25%

Total number of tallies 40

Math Journal 1, p. 183

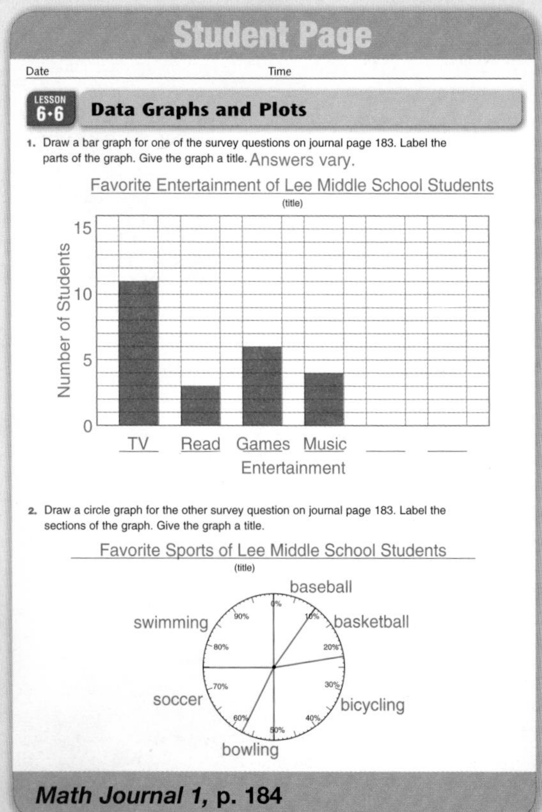

Student Page

Date Time

LESSON 6·6 **Data Graphs and Plots**

1. Draw a bar graph for one of the survey questions on journal page 183. Label the parts of the graph. Give the graph a title. Answers vary.

Favorite Entertainment of Lee Middle School Students
(title)

2. Draw a circle graph for the other survey question on journal page 183. Label the sections of the graph. Give the graph a title.

Favorite Sports of Lee Middle School Students
(title)

Math Journal 1, p. 184

After completing the frequency tables, partners will then graph the Entertainment and Favorite-Sports data on journal page 184. One graph must be a bar graph and the other a circle graph, but students may graph the data sets in either order. For example, one partner may draw a bar graph for the sports data and a circle graph for the entertainment data while the other partner draws a bar graph for the entertainment data and a circle graph for the sports data.

Ongoing Assessment: Informing Instruction

Watch for students who have missing elements on their graphs, such as titles or scales, or who have incorrectly drawn circle graph sectors. Ask them to review making bar and circle graphs, using pages 122 and 126 in the *Student Reference Book,* and check that their graphs have all the necessary elements.

Journal page 185 provides a space for students to make a stem-and-leaf plot and to find and record landmarks for the Shower/Bath survey data.

Adjusting the Activity

Remind students that it is easier to identify landmarks when each row of leaves is written in numerical order. An efficient approach is for one partner to read the data items in order as the other partner records the data in the stem-and-leaf plot. Each row of leaves will be in numerical order when initially written.

AUDITORY ◆ KINESTHETIC ◆ TACTILE ◆ VISUAL

NOTE If students have carried out their own survey projects, have them use the frequency tables on journal page 183 to record the two data sets for the same survey question. Then have them use the centimeter grid paper on *Math Masters,* page 436 to display the data as a double-bar graph. Remind students to include a title and appropriate labels.

Student Page

Date Time

LESSON 6·6 **Data Graphs and Plots** *continued*

3. Make a stem-and-leaf plot for the Shower/Bath Time data on page 116 in your *Student Reference Book.* If you conducted your own survey, make a stem-and-leaf plot for the data you collected.

Shower/Bath Time for Lee Middle School Students (title) Minutes (unit)

Stems (10s)	Leaves (1s)
	3 3 3 4 5 5 5 5 5 5 5 5 7 7 8 9 9
1	0 0 0 0 0 0 2 4 5 5 5 5 6 7
2	0 0 0 2 5 5
3	0 5
4	0

4. Find the landmarks for this set of data.

minimum: 3

maximum: 40

range: 37

median: 10

mode: 5

5. Calculate the mean (average).

mean: 12.7

Math Journal 1, p. 185

Discuss students' findings. Below are some suggested topics:

- What are the landmarks for the Favorite-Sports and the Entertainment data? Each set of data has a mode, but neither of these sets of data has a minimum, maximum, range, median, or mean (average). The sports and entertainment questions are answered by naming a category. The categories are not numbers; they cannot be arranged in order from smallest to largest. There is no middle value; they cannot be added to find a mean.
- Which category is the mode for the Favorite-Sports data? bicycling Do you think the survey results would have been very different if students had been asked to name only one favorite sport instead of two? Possibly. Suppose bicycling was everyone's second choice, but no one's first choice. If students named only their one favorite sport, bicycling would never have been mentioned.

- What is the median shower/bath time? 10 min What is the mode? 5 min Why do you think there are so many times that are multiples of 5 minutes—5, 10, 15, 20, and 25 minutes? It is hard to remember exact times. Many people likely estimate to the nearest 5 minutes.

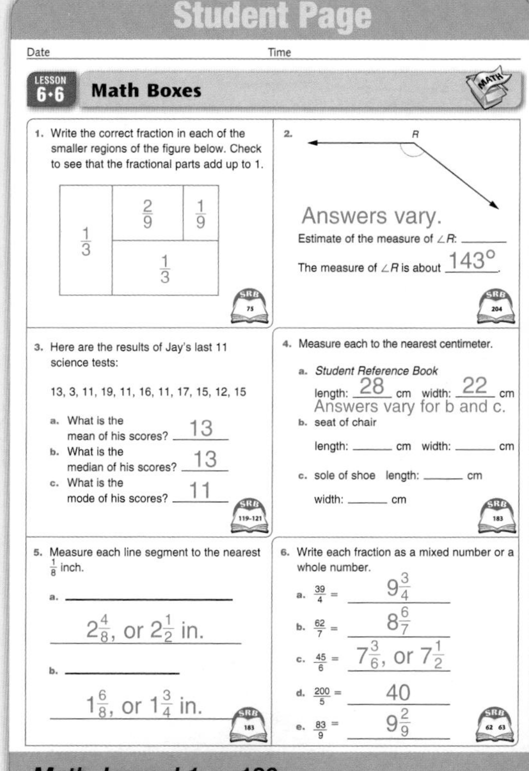

Student Page

Date Time

LESSON 6•6 **Math Boxes**

1. Write the correct fraction in each of the smaller regions of the figure below. Check to see that the fractional parts add up to 1.
$\frac{1}{3}$, $\frac{2}{9}$, $\frac{1}{9}$, $\frac{1}{3}$

2. Answers vary.
Estimate of the measure of ∠R: ______
The measure of ∠R is about 143°.

3. Here are the results of Jay's last 11 science tests:
13, 3, 11, 19, 11, 16, 11, 17, 15, 12, 15
a. What is the mean of his scores? 13
b. What is the median of his scores? 13
c. What is the mode of his scores? 11

4. Measure each to the nearest centimeter.
a. *Student Reference Book* length: 28 cm width: 22 cm
Answers vary for b and c.
b. seat of chair length: ______ cm width: ______ cm
c. sole of shoe length: ______ cm width: ______ cm

5. Measure each line segment to the nearest $\frac{1}{8}$ inch.
a. $2\frac{4}{8}$, or $2\frac{1}{2}$ in.
b. $1\frac{6}{8}$, or $1\frac{3}{4}$ in.

6. Write each fraction as a mixed number or a whole number.
a. $\frac{39}{4} = 9\frac{3}{4}$
b. $\frac{62}{7} = 8\frac{6}{7}$
c. $\frac{45}{6} = 7\frac{3}{6}$, or $7\frac{1}{2}$
d. $\frac{200}{5} = 40$
e. $\frac{83}{9} = 9\frac{2}{9}$

Math Journal 1, p. 186

2 Ongoing Learning & Practice

▶ Playing *Frac-Tac-Toe*

PARTNER ACTIVITY

(*Student Reference Book*, pp. 309 and 310; *Math Masters*, pp. 472 and 474)

Students practice automatic recall of fraction-decimal equivalents by playing *Frac-Tac-Toe (2-4-5-10)*. If you are using decks of ordinary playing cards for *Frac-Tac-Toe,* the aces represent 1 and queens represent 0.

Ongoing Assessment: Recognizing Student Achievement

***Math Masters* Page 474**

Use the ***Frac-Tac-Toe*** **gameboard (Math Masters, page 474)** to assess students' facility with naming fraction-decimal equivalents. Have students record their fractions on the gameboard instead of using removable counters. Students are making adequate progress if they have correctly identified equivalencies.

[Number and Numeration Goal 5]

▶ Math Boxes 6•6

INDEPENDENT ACTIVITY

(*Math Journal 1*, p. 186)

Mixed Practice Math Boxes in this lesson are paired with Math Boxes in Lesson 6-9. The skill in Problem 6 previews Unit 7 content.

▶ Study Link 6•6

INDEPENDENT ACTIVITY

(*Math Masters*, p. 170)

Home Connection Students analyze a line plot and a stem-and-leaf plot in order to describe a situation that would match each. They also identify the landmarks for each plot.

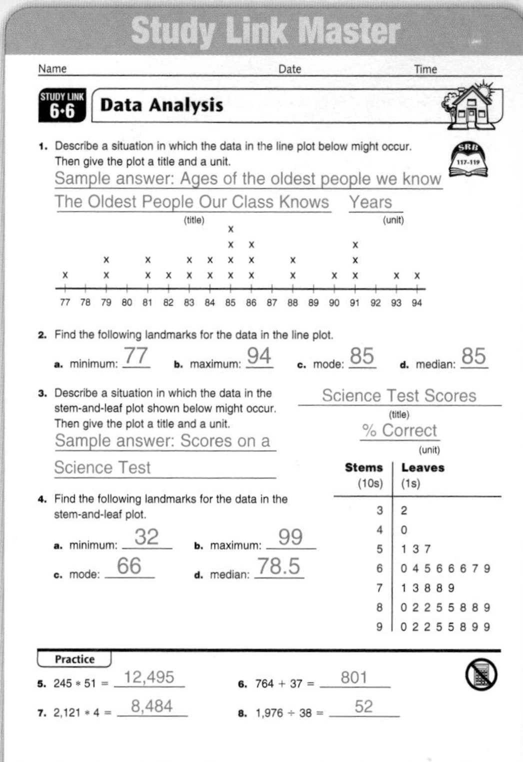

Study Link Master

Name Date Time

STUDY LINK 6•6 **Data Analysis**

1. Describe a situation in which the data in the line plot below might occur. Then give the plot a title and a unit.
Sample answer: Ages of the oldest people we know
The Oldest People Our Class Knows (title) Years (unit)

77	78	79	80	81	82	83	84	85	86	87	88	89	90	91	92	93	94
x		xx		xx	x	xx	xx	xxxx	xxx		xx		x	xxx		x	x

2. Find the following landmarks for the data in the line plot.
a. minimum: 77 b. maximum: 94 c. mode: 85 d. median: 85

3. Describe a situation in which the data in the stem-and-leaf plot shown below might occur. Then give the plot a title and a unit.
Sample answer: Scores on a Science Test
Science Test Scores (title)
% Correct (unit)

Stems (10s)	Leaves (1s)
3	2
4	0
5	1 3 7
6	0 4 5 6 6 6 7 9
7	1 3 8 8 9
8	0 2 2 5 5 8 8 9
9	0 2 2 5 5 8 9 9

4. Find the following landmarks for the data in the stem-and-leaf plot.
a. minimum: 32 b. maximum: 99
c. mode: 66 d. median: 78.5

Practice

5. 245 ∗ 51 = 12,495
6. 764 + 37 = 801
7. 2,121 ∗ 4 = 8,484
8. 1,976 ÷ 38 = 52

Math Masters, p. 170

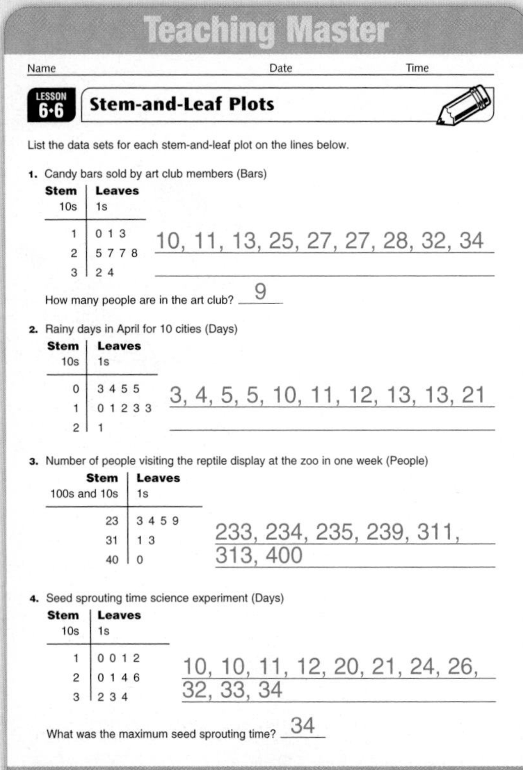

Teaching Master

Name Date Time

LESSON 6·6 **Stem-and-Leaf Plots**

List the data sets for each stem-and-leaf plot on the lines below.

1. Candy bars sold by art club members (Bars)

Stem 10s	Leaves 1s
1	0 1 3
2	5 7 7 8
3	2 4

10, 11, 13, 25, 27, 27, 28, 32, 34

How many people are in the art club? 9

2. Rainy days in April for 10 cities (Days)

Stem 10s	Leaves 1s
0	3 4 5 5
1	0 1 2 3 3
2	1

3, 4, 5, 5, 10, 11, 12, 13, 13, 21

3. Number of people visiting the reptile display at the zoo in one week (People)

Stem 100s and 10s	Leaves 1s
23	3 4 5 9
31	1 3
40	0

233, 234, 235, 239, 311, 313, 400

4. Seed sprouting time science experiment (Days)

Stem 10s	Leaves 1s
1	0 0 1 2
2	0 1 4 6
3	2 3 4

10, 10, 11, 12, 20, 21, 24, 26, 32, 33, 34

What was the maximum seed sprouting time? 34

Math Masters, **p. 171**

Teaching Master

Name Date Time

LESSON 6·6 **Making Stem-and-Leaf Plots**

1. Make a stem-and-leaf plot for the following data:

74, 86, 68, 90, 98, 60, 94, 74, 84, 72, 90, 96, 88, 92, 88, 70, 80, 90, 98, 88, 68, 76, 88, 62, 90, 82, 90, 72, 74, 98

Time Spent Doing Homework after School (title) Minutes (unit)

Stem 10s	Leaves 1s
6	0 2 8 8
7	0 2 2 4 4 4 6
8	0 2 4 6 8 8 8 8
9	0 0 0 0 0 2 4 6 8 8 8

2. Find the following landmarks for this set of data.

a. minimum: 60

b. maximum: 98

c. mode: 90

d. median: 87

3. Describe a situation in which the data in the stem-and-leaf plot might occur. Then give the plot a title and a unit.

Sample answer: Students could keep track of how much time they spend doing their homework after school each night.

Math Masters, **p. 172**

3 Differentiation Options

READINESS

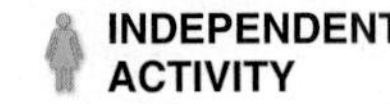

INDEPENDENT ACTIVITY

15–30 Min

▶ Exploring Stem-and-Leaf Plot Data

(*Math Masters,* p. 171)

To provide experience identifying individual values in stem-and-leaf plot data, students list the data sets from four stem-and-leaf plots. Discuss students' answers for the questions included in Problems 1 and 4.

EXTRA PRACTICE

INDEPENDENT ACTIVITY

15–30 Min

▶ Making Stem-and-Leaf Plots

(*Math Masters,* p. 172)

Students make a stem-and-leaf plot for provided data and find the data landmarks. They provide the title for the stem-and-leaf plot and a description for a situation in which the data might occur.

ELL SUPPORT

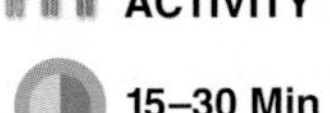

SMALL-GROUP ACTIVITY

15–30 Min

▶ Building a Math Word Bank

(*Differentiation Handbook,* p. 142)

To provide language support for sampling data, have students use the Word Bank Template found on *Differentiation Handbook,* page 142. Ask students to write the terms *sample* and *population,* to draw a picture to represent each term, and to write other related words. See the *Differentiation Handbook* for more information.

6•7 American Tour: Climate

Objective To introduce contour maps as data displays.

Technology Resources www.everydaymathonline.com

ePresentations

eToolkit

Algorithms Practice

EM Facts Workshop Game™

Family Letters

Assessment Management

Common Core State Standards

Curriculum Focal Points

Interactive Teacher's Lesson Guide

1 Teaching the Lesson

Key Concepts and Skills

- Investigate the use of contour maps to organize collected data. [Data and Chance Goal 1]
- Use the data displayed in contour maps to answer questions and draw conclusions. [Data and Chance Goal 2]

Key Activities

Students use contour maps of precipitation and growing seasons to compare the climates for various locations in the United States.

Ongoing Assessment: Recognizing Student Achievement Use Mental Math and Reflexes. [Number and Numeration Goal 5]

Key Vocabulary

contour map ◆ climate ◆ precipitation ◆ map legend (map key) ◆ contour line

Materials

Math Journal 1, pp. 187 and 188
Student Reference Book, pp. 378–380
Study Link 6•6
slate ◆ physical and political map(s) of the United States for the classroom (optional) ◆ stick-on notes (optional)

2 Ongoing Learning & Practice

Solving Number Stories
Math Journal 1, p. 189
Students solve a set of number stories involving multiplication and division.

Math Boxes 6•7
Math Journal 1, p. 190
Students practice and maintain skills through Math Box problems.

Study Link 6•7
Math Masters, p. 173
Students practice and maintain skills through Study Link activities.

3 Differentiation Options

ENRICHMENT
Writing Contour Map Questions
Student Reference Book, pp. 377, 380, and 381
Students interpret contour maps to write and answer map-related questions.

EXTRA PRACTICE
Examining Contour Maps
per partnership: contour map(s)
Students examine contour maps and list some of their features.

ELL SUPPORT
Making a Graphic Organizer for *Climate*
Differentiation Handbook, p. 34
Students make a graphic organizer for the term *climate.*

Advance Preparation

For the optional Extra Practice activity in Part 3, collect examples of maps with contour lines for temperature, moisture, elevation, or other features. Consider having a collection of print materials available that have different types of maps to use with this activity.

***Teacher's Reference Manual,* Grades 4–6** p. 253

Getting Started

Mental Math and Reflexes

Have students rename the fractions as decimals and percents.
Suggestions:

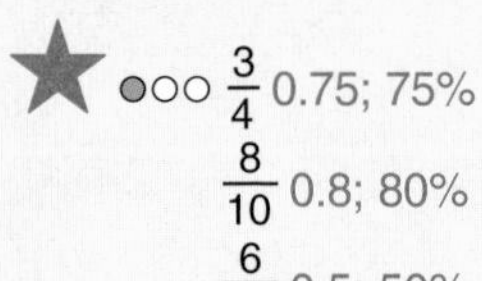

★ ●○○ $\frac{3}{4}$ 0.75; 75%
$\frac{8}{10}$ 0.8; 80%
$\frac{6}{12}$ 0.5; 50%

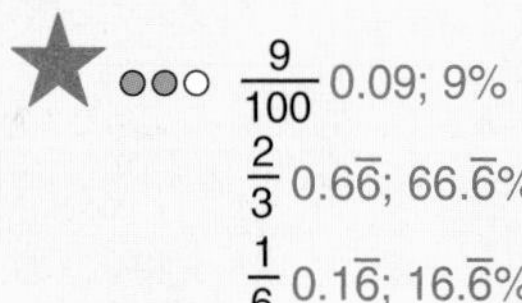

★ ●●○ $\frac{9}{100}$ 0.09; 9%
$\frac{2}{3}$ $0.6\overline{6}$; $66.\overline{6}$%
$\frac{1}{6}$ $0.1\overline{6}$; $16.\overline{6}$%

●●● $\frac{6}{25}$ 0.24; 24%
$\frac{6}{15}$ 0.4; 40%
$\frac{8}{20}$ 0.40; 40%

Have students explain how they found decimals and percents for $\frac{6}{25}$ and $\frac{8}{20}$. Sample answer: To find the decimal, find $6 \div 25 = 0.24$ and $8 \div 20 = 0.4$. To find the percent, write the decimals as fractions, $\frac{24}{100}$ and $\frac{40}{100}$, which are 24% and 40%.

Math Message

Study the map titled Average Yearly Precipitation in the United States on page 380 of the Student Reference Book. *About how much precipitation (moisture such as rain and snow) does Chicago, Illinois, receive per year? About how much precipitation does Dallas, Texas, receive per year?*

Study Link 6·6 Follow-Up

Partners compare data landmarks and resolve differences. Have them share the situations created for the data.

Ongoing Assessment: Recognizing Student Achievement

Mental Math and Reflexes

Use the **Mental Math and Reflexes, Problems** ●○○ **and** ●●○ to assess students' abilities to rename fractions as decimals and percents. Students are making adequate progress if they correctly rename the fractions.

[Number and Numeration Goal 5]

1 Teaching the Lesson

▶ Math Message Follow-Up

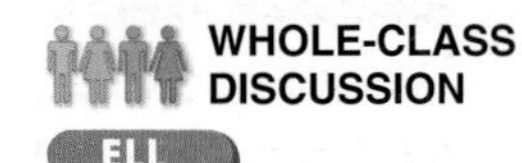

(*Student Reference Book,* p. 380)

Science Link Refer students to the precipitation map on page 380 of the American Tour section of the *Student Reference Book.* This is an example of a **contour map.** To support English language learners, draw contour lines on the board and write the word *contour.* Contour maps use curved lines to show the boundaries of areas that share the same feature, such as temperature, rainfall, elevation, and so on. The word *contour* comes from *contornare,* which is Latin for *to draw in outline.* (*See margin.*) Discuss the main vocabulary for this map:

▷ **Climate:** The word *climate* refers to the usual weather conditions for a place. Temperature, precipitation, and wind are all features of climate. Maps in the American Tour give information about temperature, precipitation, and growing seasons for the United States.

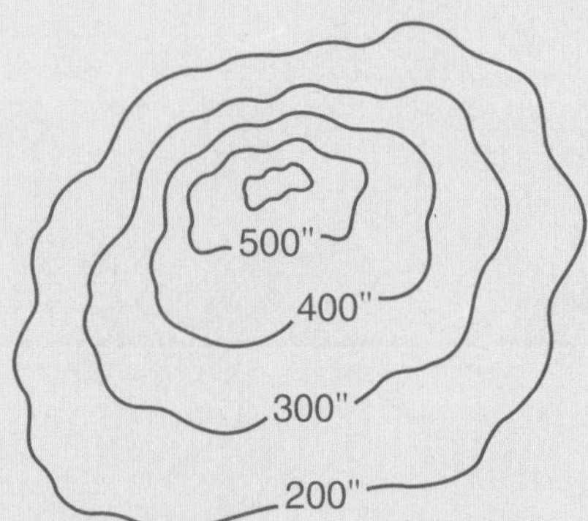

This contour map uses contour lines to show elevation.

NOTE The contour maps used in this lesson are based on vast amounts of data collected over many years. The maps are data displays that include much more information than could conveniently be shown in a set of data tables.

▷ **Precipitation:** Emphasize that precipitation includes all moisture that falls as sleet, rain, or snow.

▷ **Map legend (map key):** The legend for this map indicates that the map shows precipitation (in inches). This is the total number of inches of moisture that falls in one year on average. The average annual precipitation is an average of the yearly totals collected over many years.

NOTE When snow falls, meteorologists melt a sample to determine the equivalent amount of rain. A light, fluffy snow that is 20 inches deep might contain the same amount of moisture as 1 inch of rain. A heavy, wet snow that is 6 inches deep might also be equivalent to 1 inch of rain.

Ask students to share their answers to the Math Message questions. The average yearly precipitation in Chicago is about 20 to 40 inches. In Dallas, it is nearly 40 inches. Dallas is in the light green region but close to the dark green region. The color key shows that the separation between the light green and dark green regions occurs at 40 inches.

Ask questions about other information represented on the map:

- Which parts of the United States receive the most moisture? Parts of the Northwest, the Gulf coast near New Orleans, the Miami area, an area north of Atlanta, part of Hawaii, part of New Hampshire, and the south coast of Alaska all receive more than 60 inches per year.
- Which parts of the United States receive the least moisture? Parts of northern Alaska and several desert regions in the West receive less than 10 inches per year.

The curved lines on the map that separate colors are called **contour lines.** Numbers are printed at the ends of some contour lines and placed directly on other contour lines. The numbers on this map indicate inches of precipitation. When a contour line passes through or near a city, such as Dallas or Phoenix, the city's precipitation can be estimated fairly precisely by reading the number for the countour line.

Ask questions similar to these:

- Is Phoenix, Arizona, near a contour line? Which one? What does that mean? Phoenix is near a 10-inch contour line and a 20-inch contour line; it receives about 10 to 20 in. of precipitation per year.
- Which contour line runs through Illinois? What does that mean? The 40-inch contour line cuts through Illinois. Most of the state is light green (20 to 40 inches per year). The southern part of Illinois is dark green (40 to 60 inches per year). Regions along that contour line get about 40 inches of precipitation per year.

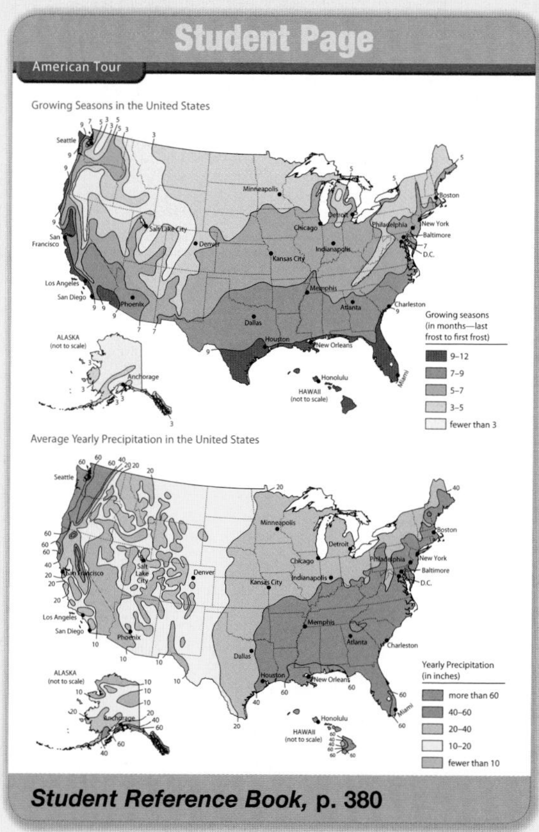

Student Reference Book, p. 380

NOTE The National Weather Service collects data on climate. It maintains about 12,000 weather stations in all parts of the United States. Some stations record weather data once per day and others take hourly readings. New York City has kept weather records since 1868. New Haven, Connecticut, has kept weather records since 1781.

NOTE The term *contour map* usually strictly refers to elevation maps. *Everyday Mathematics* calls any graph with contour lines a contour map.

Student Page

Date Time

LESSON 6•7 **Climate Maps**

To answer the questions below, use the Average Yearly Precipitation in the United States and Growing Seasons in the United States maps on page 380 of the American Tour section of your *Student Reference Book.*

The precipitation map shows the average amount of moisture that falls as sleet, hail, rain, or snow in one year. Snow is translated into an equivalent amount of rain.

The growing seasons map shows the average number of months between the last frost in spring and the first frost in fall. During this time, the temperature remains above freezing (32°F or 0°C), and crops can be grown.

1. Denver, Colorado, receives about 10 to 20 in. of precipitation as rain and snow per year.
   Denver's growing season is about 3 to 5 months long.
2. Los Angeles, California, receives about 20 in. of precipitation per year.
   The growing season in Los Angeles is 9 to 12 months long.
3. a. According to these maps, how are Los Angeles and New Orleans similar?
   Sample answer: Both have long growing seasons of 9 to 12 months.

   b. Who is more likely to be worried about a lack of rain: a farmer near Los Angeles or a farmer near New Orleans? Why?
   Sample answer: A farmer near Los Angeles because Los Angeles receives only about 20 inches per year, and New Orleans receives more than 60 inches of rain each year.

Math Journal 1, p. 187

▶ Introducing the Growing Seasons Map

WHOLE-CLASS DISCUSSION

(*Student Reference Book,* p. 380)

Ask students to look at the Growing Seasons on the U.S. map on page 380 of the American Tour section of the *Student Reference Book.* This map shows the average number of months between the last frost in spring and the first frost in fall. During this time, the temperature remains above freezing (32° F or 0° C) and crops can be grown.

Have students discuss and use the map legend. Ask questions such as the following:

- What is the average length of the growing season near Houston, Texas? About 9 months because Houston is near the contour line marked 9.
- What is the average length of the growing season around Chicago, Illinois? Chicago is between the contour lines marked 5 and 7 but is closer to the line marked 5. So the growing season is probably 5 to 6 months.
- What is the average length of the growing season near Dallas, Texas? Dallas is about halfway between the 7-month and 9-month contour lines, so it probably has about an 8-month growing season.

▶ Using Climate Maps to Answer Questions

INDEPENDENT ACTIVITY

(*Math Journal 1,* pp. 187 and 188; *Student Reference Book,* pp. 377, 380, and 381)

Have students complete journal pages 187 and 188. Problems 6–8 on journal page 188 refer to specific states and mountain ranges. Students can locate these states and landforms by using the maps on pages 377, 380, and 381 in the American Tour section of the *Student Reference Book*. Consider using stick-on notes to mark the locations on a classroom map.

When most students have finished, discuss their answers and the strategies they used as they read the maps.

NOTE You might want to explore the following Internet sites:

- University of Michigan Weather: http://cirrus.sprl.umich.edu/wxnet/
- National Weather Service Home Page: http://www.nws.noaa.gov

Student Page

Date Time

LESSON 6•7 **Climate Maps** *continued*

4. In general, does it rain more in the eastern states or in the western states?
   eastern
5. In general, is the growing season longer in the northern states or in the southern states?
   southern
6. Cotton needs a growing season of at least 6 months. In the list below, circle the states most likely to grow cotton.
   (Texas) Nebraska (Mississippi) Ohio
7. North Dakota and Kansas are the largest wheat-producing states.
   What is the length of the growing season in North Dakota? 3 to 5 months
   What is the length of the growing season in Kansas? 5 to 7 months
   About how much precipitation does North Dakota receive per year? 10 to 20 in.
   About how much precipitation does eastern Kansas receive per year? 20 to 40 in.
8. a. Locate the Rocky Mountains on your landform map (American Tour, page 381).
   What is the growing season for this mountain area?
   In general, less than 3 months

   b. What is the growing season for the Appalachian Mountains area?
   In general, 3 to 5 months

Math Journal 1, p. 188

2 Ongoing Learning & Practice

▶ Solving Number Stories

INDEPENDENT ACTIVITY

(*Math Journal 1,* p. 189)

Students solve a set of number stories involving multiplication and division. Some of the problems have extraneous information or involve more than one step.

▶ Math Boxes 6•7

INDEPENDENT ACTIVITY

(*Math Journal 1,* p. 190)

Mixed Practice Math Boxes in this lesson are paired with Math Boxes in Lesson 6-5. The skill in Problem 5 previews Unit 7 content.

Writing/Reasoning Have students write a response to the following: *Explain how you solved Problem 4a, including the strategies and reasoning that you used.* Answers vary.

▶ Study Link 6•7

INDEPENDENT ACTIVITY

(*Math Masters,* p. 173)

Home Connection Students use a contour map of climate in the United States to answer questions.

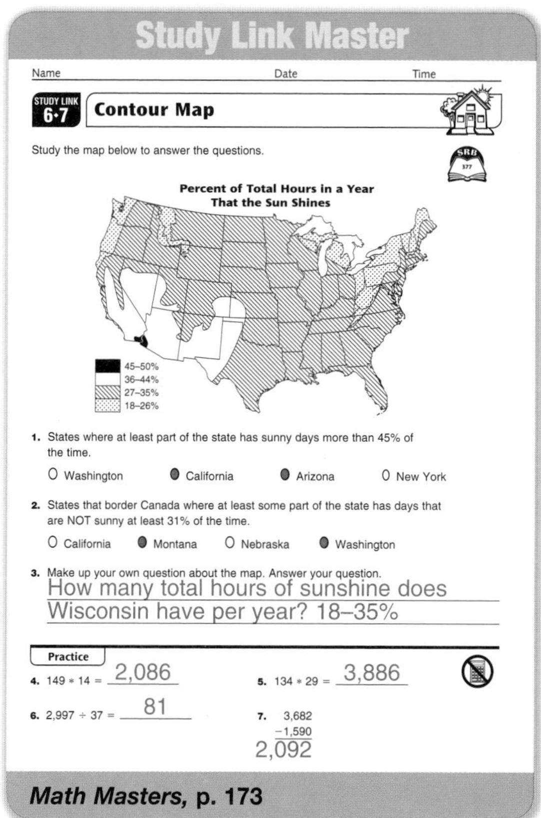

Study Link Master

Name Date Time

STUDY LINK 6•7 **Contour Map**

Study the map below to answer the questions.

1. States where at least part of the state has sunny days more than 45% of the time.
   ○ Washington ● California ● Arizona ○ New York
2. States that border Canada where at least some part of the state has days that are NOT sunny at least 31% of the time.
   ○ California ● Montana ○ Nebraska ● Washington
3. Make up your own question about the map. Answer your question.
   How many total hours of sunshine does Wisconsin have per year? 18–35%

Practice

4. 149 * 14 = 2,086
5. 134 * 29 = 3,886
6. 2,997 ÷ 37 = 81
7. 3,682 − 1,590 = 2,092

Math Masters, p. 173

Student Page

Date Time

LESSON 6•7 **Number Stories**

1. Brenda bought 4 cheeseburgers for her family for lunch. The total cost was $5.56. How much did 2 cheeseburgers cost? $2.78
2. Thomas's family went on a long trip over summer vacation. They drove for 5 days. The distances for the 5 days were as follows: 347 miles, 504 miles, 393 miles, 422 miles, and 418 miles.
   a. To the nearest mile, what was the average distance traveled per day? 417 mi/day
   b. Tell what you did with the remainder. Explain why. Sample answer: I wrote the remainder as a fraction, so the answer was $416\frac{4}{5}$. Then I rounded to the nearest mile, 417.
3. Justin's school has 15 classrooms. On average, there are 28 students per room. One fifth of the classrooms are for fifth graders. About how many students are in the school?
   Exact answer: 15 * 28 = 420 students;
   Estimate: 15 * 30 = 450 students
4. Jamokas reads 45 pages of a book every night. How many pages did she read in the month of March (31 days)? 31 * 45 = 1,395 pages
5. Lucienne and her class made 684 notecards for a school benefit.
   a. How many boxes of eight can they fill? 85 boxes
   b. Tell what you did with the remainder. Explain why.
      Sample answer: 684 ÷ 8 → 85 R4. The remainder was dropped because it represents 4 notecards, and 4 notecards do not fill a box.

Math Journal 1, p. 189

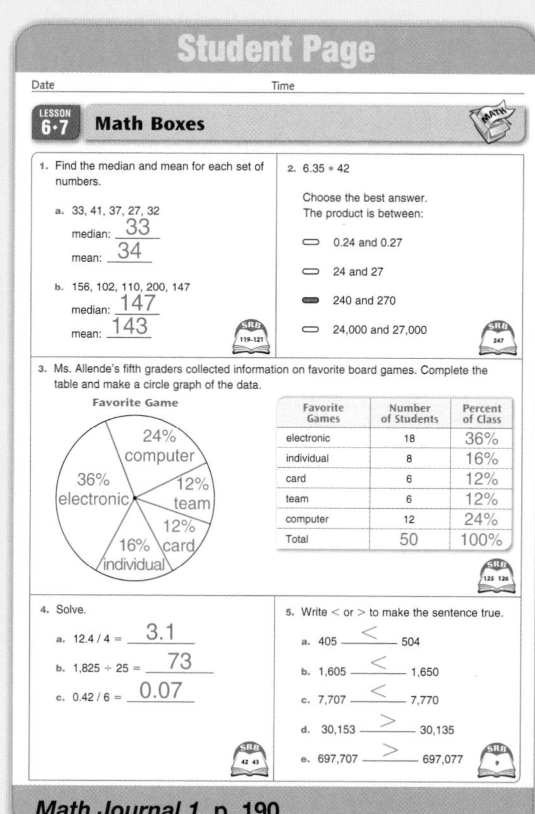

Student Page

Date Time

LESSON 6•7 **Math Boxes**

1. Find the median and mean for each set of numbers.
   a. 33, 41, 37, 27, 32
      median: 33
      mean: 34
   b. 156, 102, 110, 200, 147
      median: 147
      mean: 143
   SRB 119-121
2. 6.35 * 42
   Choose the best answer. The product is between:
   ○ 0.24 and 0.27
   ○ 24 and 27
   ● 240 and 270
   ○ 24,000 and 27,000
   SRB 247
3. Ms. Allende's fifth graders collected information on favorite board games. Complete the table and make a circle graph of the data.

Favorite Games	Number of Students	Percent of Class
electronic	18	36%
individual	8	16%
card	6	12%
team	6	12%
computer	12	24%
Total	50	100%

SRB 125 126

4. Solve.
   a. 12.4 / 4 = 3.1
   b. 1,825 ÷ 25 = 73
   c. 0.42 / 6 = 0.07
   SRB 42 43
5. Write < or > to make the sentence true.
   a. 405 < 504
   b. 1,605 < 1,650
   c. 7,707 < 7,770
   d. 30,153 > 30,135
   e. 697,707 > 697,077
   SRB 9

Math Journal 1, p. 190

3 Differentiation Options

ENRICHMENT

PARTNER ACTIVITY

15–30 Min

Writing Contour Map Questions

(*Student Reference Book*, pp. 378–380)

To further explore contour maps, have students write questions that can be answered by looking at the contour maps on *Student Reference Book,* pages 378–380. Students write at least three questions, using a different map for each question. Then they exchange questions with a partner and discuss the answers. Consider displaying posters of the questions and answers in your classroom's American Tour area.

EXTRA PRACTICE

PARTNER ACTIVITY

15–30 Min

Examining Contour Maps

Portfolio Ideas

Have students examine maps with contour lines for temperature, moisture, elevation, or other features. After examining the map, students list three things that can be learned from it. Display the maps and students' lists. Consider having students present their ideas to the class.

ELL SUPPORT

SMALL-GROUP ACTIVITY

15–30 Min

Making a Graphic Organizer for *Climate*

(*Differentiation Handbook*, p. 34)

To provide language support for *climate*, draw a graphic organizer on the board connecting words related to climate that are used in this lesson. See *Differentiation Handbook,* page 34 for more information.

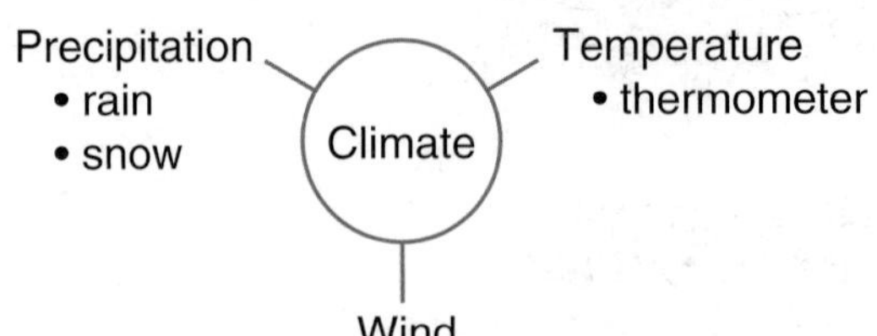

6•8 Using Benchmarks with Fraction Addition and Subtraction

Objective To review estimating with fractions using benchmarks.

www.everydaymathonline.com

ePresentations

eToolkit

Algorithms Practice

EM Facts Workshop Game™

Family Letters

Assessment Management

Common Core State Standards

Curriculum Focal Points

Interactive Teacher's Lesson Guide

1 Teaching the Lesson

Key Concepts and Skills

- Identify benchmarks on a number line.
  [Number and Numeration Goal 6]
- Add and subtract fractions and mixed numbers with like and unlike denominators.
  [Operations and Computation Goal 4]
- Use benchmarks to estimate sums and differences.
  [Operations and Computation Goal 6]

Key Activities

Students estimate solutions to number stories involving addition and subtraction of fractions with like and unlike denominators that refer to the same whole. Students use benchmarks, number lines, and number sense of fractions to estimate mentally and assess reasonableness of answers.

Ongoing Assessment: Informing Instruction See page 418.

Ongoing Assessment: Recognizing Student Achievement
Use journal pages 191 and 192.
[Operations and Computation Goal 6]

Materials

Math Journal 1, pp. 191 and 192
Math Journal 2, Activity Sheets 5–7

2 Ongoing Learning & Practice

Reviewing Fractions and Division

Math Journal 1, pp. 192A and 192B
Student Reference Book, pp. 62, 63, 78C, and 78D
Students review the relationship between, and solve problems involving, fractions and division.

Math Boxes 6•8

Math Journal 1, p. 193
Students practice and maintain skills through Math Box problems.

Study Link 6•8

Math Masters, p. 174
Students practice and maintain skills through Study Link activities.

3 Differentiation Options

READINESS

Comparing Fractions with $\frac{1}{2}$

Math Masters, p. 175
Math Journal 2, Activity Sheets 5–7
Students sort Fraction Cards using benchmarks and number sense.

EXTRA PRACTICE

Writing Fraction Number Stories

Math Masters, p. 176
Students create and solve fraction number stories and estimate solutions to problems with sums and differences of fractions.

ENRICHMENT

Playing *Fraction Top-It* (Advanced Version)

Math Journal 2, Activity Sheets 5–7
Student Reference Book, p. 316
Math Masters, p. 493
Students use benchmarks to play an advanced version of *Fraction Top-It.*

Advance Preparation

Students will need the Fraction Cards from Activity Sheets 5–7 that were first used in Lesson 5-1.

Getting Started

Mental Math and Reflexes

Pose fraction addition and subtraction problems. Have students estimate whether the sum or difference is closest to 0, $\frac{1}{2}$, or 1. Students should be prepared to explain their thinking.

●○○ $\frac{1}{12} + \frac{4}{4}$ 1
$\frac{2}{12} + \frac{3}{12}$ $\frac{1}{2}$
$\frac{2}{4} + \frac{3}{8}$ 1

●●○ $\frac{3}{4} - \frac{1}{5}$ $\frac{1}{2}$
$\frac{11}{12} - \frac{7}{8}$ 0
$\frac{3}{2} - \frac{2}{4}$ 1

●●● $\frac{2}{3} + \frac{4}{9}$ 1
$\frac{14}{7} - \frac{9}{8}$ 1
$1\frac{4}{7} - \frac{7}{6}$ $\frac{1}{2}$

Math Message

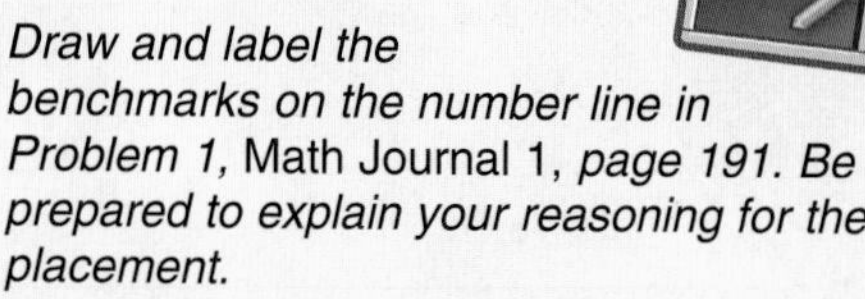

Draw and label the benchmarks on the number line in Problem 1, Math Journal 1, *page 191. Be prepared to explain your reasoning for the placement.*

Study Link 6•7 Follow-Up

Have partners compare answers and resolve differences.

> **NOTE** The Fraction Cards on Activity Sheets 5–7 were cut out in Lesson 5-1.

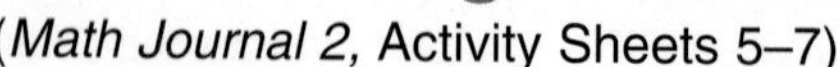

1 Teaching the Lesson

▶ Math Message Follow-Up

WHOLE-CLASS ACTIVITY

(*Math Journal 2,* Activity Sheets 5–7)

Ask students to share how they decided to label the benchmarks on the number line. Distribute the Fraction Cards from Activity Sheets 5–7. Ask each partnership to find Fraction Cards that are equal to 0, $\frac{1}{2}$, and 1 to use as a frame of reference. Ask: *How can benchmark fractions be useful when operating with fractions?* Sample answer: A benchmark is useful for comparing fractions. For example, $\frac{12}{25}$ is almost half because the numerator (12) is almost half of the whole (25); so using $\frac{1}{2}$ as the benchmark, you know that $\frac{12}{25}$ is almost $\frac{1}{2}$.

Draw and label a number line using the benchmarks 0, $\frac{1}{2}$, 1, $1\frac{1}{2}$, and 2.

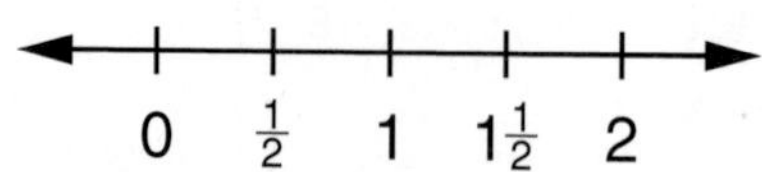

Ask students where they would place an X to represent the approximate sum for the problem $\frac{4}{12}$ and $\frac{3}{12}$.

- What is the sum? $\frac{7}{12}$ *Students should recognize that this is about $\frac{1}{2}$.*
- Should the X be closer to 0 or closer to 1? 1 Why? Sample answers: $\frac{7}{12}$ is $\frac{7}{12}$ from 0 and $\frac{5}{12}$ from 1. $\frac{7}{12}$ is greater than $\frac{1}{2}$, so it is closer to 1.
- Should the X be closer to 0 or $\frac{1}{2}$? $\frac{1}{2}$ Why? Sample answers: $\frac{7}{12}$ is closer to $\frac{1}{2}$ than to 0, because it is only $\frac{1}{12}$ away from $\frac{1}{2}$ and $\frac{7}{12}$ away from 0. $\frac{7}{12}$ is greater than $\frac{1}{2}$, so it is closer to $\frac{1}{2}$ than to 0.
- Where should the X be placed? A little more than halfway between 0 and 1 *Ask a volunteer to place the X to show where $\frac{7}{12}$ would be on the number line.*

Adjusting the Activity

Have students label the benchmarks on the number line with equivalent fractions of twelfths. For example, under 0, record $\frac{0}{12}$; under $\frac{1}{2}$, record $\frac{6}{12}$; and so on. Students can see the equivalent fractions with the benchmarks.

AUDITORY ◆ KINESTHETIC ◆ TACTILE ◆ VISUAL

Ask students to take out the $\frac{4}{12}$ and $\frac{3}{12}$ cards from the Fraction Cards. Ask: *How could I use shading on the two cards to show whether or not the sum of $\frac{4}{12}$ and $\frac{3}{12}$ is closest to 0, $\frac{1}{2}$, or 1?* Sample answer: You can lay the blue shaded parts of the two cards together and see that the sum is about $\frac{1}{2}$.

If necessary, show students how to match the shaded parts of the Fraction Cards.

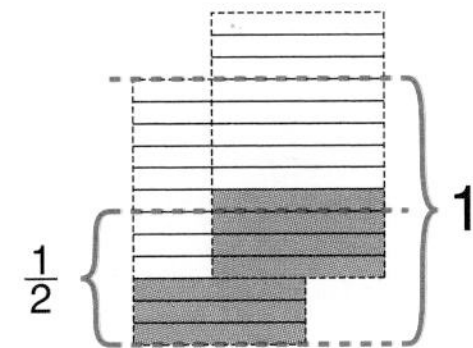

Ask: *How much greater than $\frac{1}{2}$ is the actual sum?* $\frac{1}{12}$

Ask: *Where would you place an X to represent the sum of $\frac{4}{5}$ and $\frac{1}{4}$?*

Ask a volunteer to place the X to show where the sum would be. Expect that students will know that the sum of the two fractions is about 1, but do not expect students to find the exact sum of the two fractions. Ask students how they know that the sum is about 1. Sample answers: One fraction is greater than $\frac{1}{2}$ and one fraction is less than $\frac{1}{2}$; when they are added together, they must be greater than $\frac{1}{2}$. $\frac{4}{5}$ is only $\frac{1}{5}$ away from 1, so adding $\frac{1}{4}$ would give a sum greater than 1.

Ask students to take out the $\frac{4}{5}$ and $\frac{1}{4}$ cards from the Fraction Cards and to use the cards to show that the sum of the two cards is close to 1.

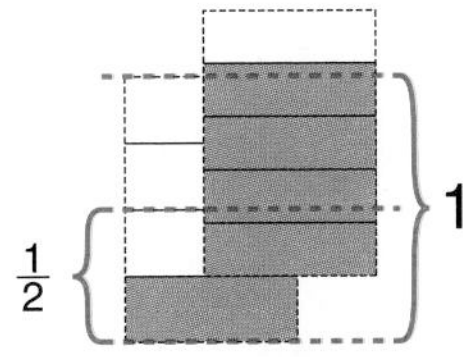

Pose additional problems as necessary. Encourage students to use their slates to draw number lines or use Fraction Cards to estimate solutions using benchmark fractions.

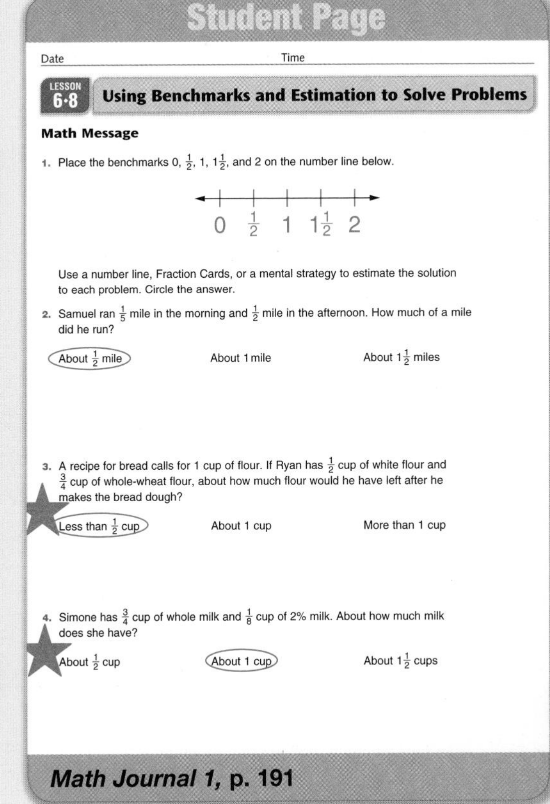

Student Page

Date Time

LESSON 6·8 **Using Benchmarks and Estimation to Solve Problems**

Math Message

1. Place the benchmarks 0, $\frac{1}{2}$, 1, $1\frac{1}{2}$, and 2 on the number line below.

0 $\frac{1}{2}$ 1 $1\frac{1}{2}$ 2

Use a number line, Fraction Cards, or a mental strategy to estimate the solution to each problem. Circle the answer.

2. Samuel ran $\frac{1}{5}$ mile in the morning and $\frac{1}{2}$ mile in the afternoon. How much of a mile did he run?

(About $\frac{1}{2}$ mile) About 1 mile About $1\frac{1}{2}$ miles

3. A recipe for bread calls for 1 cup of flour. If Ryan has $\frac{1}{2}$ cup of white flour and $\frac{3}{4}$ cup of whole-wheat flour, about how much flour would he have left after he makes the bread dough?

(Less than $\frac{1}{2}$ cup) About 1 cup More than 1 cup

4. Simone has $\frac{3}{4}$ cup of whole milk and $\frac{1}{8}$ cup of 2% milk. About how much milk does she have?

About $\frac{1}{2}$ cup (About 1 cup) About $1\frac{1}{2}$ cups

Math Journal 1, p. 191

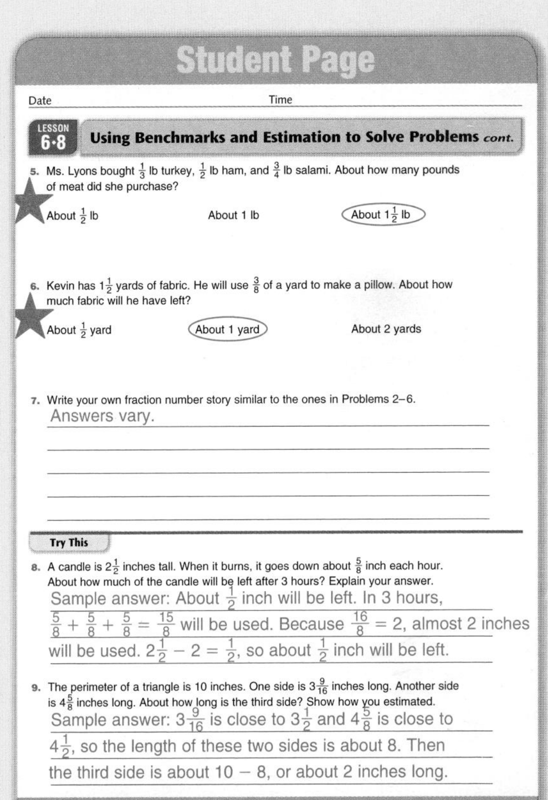

Student Page

Date Time

LESSON 6·8 **Using Benchmarks and Estimation to Solve Problems** *cont.*

5. Ms. Lyons bought $\frac{1}{3}$ lb turkey, $\frac{1}{2}$ lb ham, and $\frac{3}{4}$ lb salami. About how many pounds of meat did she purchase?

About $\frac{1}{2}$ lb About 1 lb (About $1\frac{1}{2}$ lb)

6. Kevin has $1\frac{1}{2}$ yards of fabric. He will use $\frac{3}{8}$ of a yard to make a pillow. About how much fabric will he have left?

About $\frac{1}{2}$ yard (About 1 yard) About 2 yards

7. Write your own fraction number story similar to the ones in Problems 2–6.

Answers vary.

Try This

8. A candle is $2\frac{1}{2}$ inches tall. When it burns, it goes down about $\frac{5}{8}$ inch each hour. About how much of the candle will be left after 3 hours? Explain your answer.

Sample answer: About $\frac{1}{2}$ inch will be left. In 3 hours, $\frac{5}{8} + \frac{5}{8} + \frac{5}{8} = \frac{15}{8}$ will be used. Because $\frac{16}{8} = 2$, almost 2 inches will be used. $2\frac{1}{2} - 2 = \frac{1}{2}$, so about $\frac{1}{2}$ inch will be left.

9. The perimeter of a triangle is 10 inches. One side is $3\frac{9}{16}$ inches long. Another side is $4\frac{5}{8}$ inches long. About how long is the third side? Show how you estimated.

Sample answer: $3\frac{9}{16}$ is close to $3\frac{1}{2}$ and $4\frac{5}{8}$ is close to $4\frac{1}{2}$, so the length of these two sides is about 8. Then the third side is about 10 − 8, or about 2 inches long.

Math Journal 1, p. 192

Student Page

Date ______ Time ______

LESSON 6·8 Fractions as Division

Refer to pages 62 and 63 of your *Student Reference Book* to review renaming fractions as mixed numbers or whole numbers.

Write or complete the fractions or mixed numbers for each problem.

1. $\frac{8}{3} = 2\frac{2}{3}$
2. $\frac{\boxed{27}}{9} = 3$
3. $\frac{41}{\boxed{7}} = 5\frac{6}{7}$
4. $\frac{21}{6} = 3\frac{3}{6}$, or $3\frac{1}{2}$
5. $\frac{34}{5} = 6\frac{4}{5}$
6. $\frac{\boxed{39}}{4} = 9\frac{3}{4}$

Write each of the following division problems as a mixed number.

7. 35 / 3 = $11\frac{2}{3}$
8. 29 / 4 = $7\frac{1}{4}$
9. 52 / 10 = $5\frac{2}{10}$, or $5\frac{1}{5}$

Find the missing number for each number sentence below.

10. 53 / 5 = $10\frac{3}{5}$
11. 17 / 4 = $4\frac{1}{4}$
12. 38 / 7 = $5\frac{3}{7}$

Solve.

13. Carlos was having a party. He had 5 large granola bars to share equally among the 8 boys at the party. How much of a granola bar will each boy get?
$\frac{5}{8}$ of a granola bar
Number Model: $5 \div 8 = \frac{5}{8}$

14. Debbie, Rachel, and Meg wanted to share 2 foot-long sandwiches equally. How much of a sandwich will each girl get?
$\frac{2}{3}$ sandwich
Number Model: $2 \div 3 = \frac{2}{3}$

15. There are 36 balloons in a package. $\frac{1}{4}$ of them are blue. How many blue balloons are in the package?
9 balloons
Number Model: $36 \div 4 = 9$

Math Journal 1, p. 192A

NOTE Work quickly through these problems to encourage the use of estimation rather than finding common denominators and computing exact answers.

Student Page

Date ______ Time ______

LESSON 6·8 Fractions as Division *continued*

Write the letter for the expression that makes sense for the given situation.

16. $\frac{5}{3}$ is the same as what mixed number? b
17. 5 friends share 3 pizzas. How much pizza does each friend get? a
18. $\frac{22}{8}$ is the same as what mixed number? d
19. \$8 is equally shared among 22 people. How much money does each person get? c

a. $3 \div 5$
b. $5 \div 3$
c. $8 \div 22$
d. $22 \div 8$

20. Noreen said that Picture A shows $\frac{3}{4}$. Milton says that Picture B shows $\frac{3}{4}$. With whom do you agree? Explain. Use the value of the WHOLE in your explanation.
Sample answer: They are both right. Noreen sees $\frac{1}{4}$ shaded three times which is the same as $\frac{3}{4}$. The WHOLE is one square. Milton sees $\frac{9}{12}$ of the 3 squares shaded, and that is the same as $\frac{3}{4}$. The WHOLE is the group of 3 squares.

Picture A

Picture B

21. Write a number story for this number sentence: $8 \div 3 = ?$ Draw a picture to show how you can solve your number story.
Answers vary.

Try This

Solve and show your work.

22. Mrs. Wilson's class decided to bake cookies for their spring celebration. They baked 3 cookie sheets filled with small cookies. There were 24 students in the class. Each student got $\frac{1}{24}$ of the cookies to eat or take home. What fraction of the cookies on 1 cookie sheet did each student get?
$\frac{3}{24}$, or $\frac{1}{8}$ of the cookies on 1 cookie sheet

Math Journal 1, p. 192B

▶ Using Benchmarks to Estimate Sums and Differences of Fractions

WHOLE-CLASS ACTIVITY

Have students use the Fraction Cards, number lines, or a mental strategy to estimate sums and differences for fraction number stories. Remind students to use 0, $\frac{1}{2}$, and 1 as the benchmarks as they solve the problems. Pose the following problems:

- Juan and Liz ordered two small pizzas, one cheese and one veggie. Juan ate $\frac{5}{6}$ of the cheese pizza, and Liz ate $\frac{1}{8}$ of the veggie pizza. Estimate the amount of pizza they ate together. About 1 pizza
- Jake watched $1\frac{1}{3}$ hours of TV on Saturday and $1\frac{3}{4}$ hours of TV on Sunday. About how much TV did he watch over the weekend? About 3 hours
- Mark bought $2\frac{1}{2}$ yards of fabric to make a blanket. He used $1\frac{7}{8}$ yards. About how much fabric does he have left? About $\frac{1}{2}$ yard
- McKenna has a piece of yarn that is $3\frac{1}{8}$ yards long. She needs about $\frac{7}{8}$ of a yard to make a necklace. About how many necklaces can she make? About 3

▶ Using Benchmarks and Number Sense to Mentally Estimate Solutions

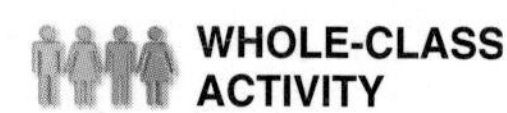

Pose the following problems orally. Have students justify their solutions as they share their responses and reasoning.

- Is $\frac{1}{12} + \frac{1}{35}$ closer to 0 or to $\frac{1}{2}$? Sample answer: Both $\frac{1}{12}$ and $\frac{1}{35}$ are very close to 0, so their sum is closer to 0 than $\frac{1}{2}$.
- Is $\frac{12}{13} + \frac{7}{8}$ closer to 1 or to 2? Sample answer: Closer to 2 because $\frac{12}{13}$ is close to 1 and $\frac{7}{8}$ is close to 1
- Is $\frac{1}{9} + \frac{1}{12}$ closer to 0 or to 1? Sample answer: Closer to 0 because $\frac{1}{9}$ and $\frac{1}{12}$ are close to 0
- Is $\frac{1}{2} - \frac{7}{17}$ closer to $\frac{1}{2}$ or to 0? Sample answer: Closer to 0 because $\frac{7}{17}$ is almost $\frac{1}{2}$
- Is $\frac{18}{19} + \frac{23}{12}$ closer to 2 or to 3? Sample answer: Closer to 3 because $\frac{23}{12}$ is close to 2 and $\frac{18}{19}$ is close to 1

▶ Using Benchmarks and Number Sense to Solve Fraction Problems

(*Math Journal 1*, pp. 191 and 192)

Students work with a partner. Have students use benchmarks to estimate the sums or differences for fraction number stories on journal pages 191 and 192. Bring the class together to share solution strategies.

Ongoing Assessment: Informing Instruction

Watch for students who do not understand how to use benchmarks. Guide them to find equivalent fractions. Consider having them write equivalent fractions next to the benchmarks for each problem.

Ongoing Assessment: Recognizing Student Achievement

Journal Page 191 Problems 3–6

Use **journal page 191, Problems 3–6** to assess students' ability to estimate solutions to addition and subtraction problems with fractions. Students are making adequate progress if they can correctly indicate that the solution is less than, greater than, or equal to 1. Some students may be able to explain their reasoning using benchmarks.

[Operations and Computation Goal 6]

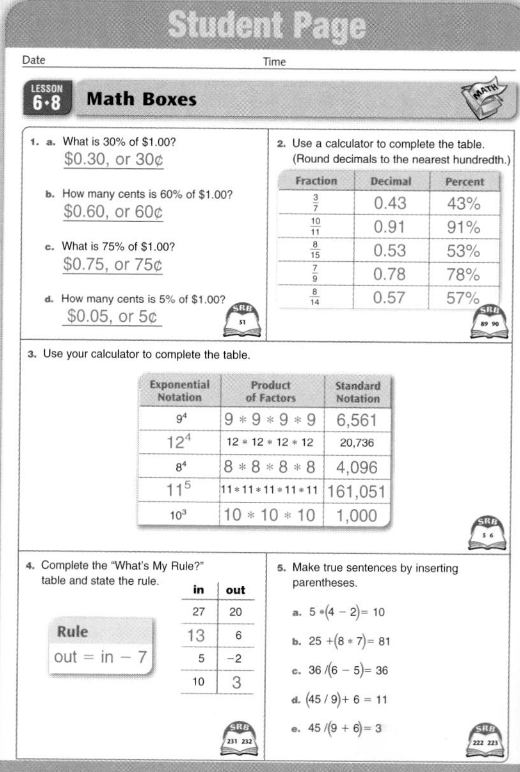

Student Page

Date Time

LESSON 6·8 **Math Boxes**

1. a. What is 30% of \$1.00? \$0.30, or 30¢
b. How many cents is 60% of \$1.00? \$0.60, or 60¢
c. What is 75% of \$1.00? \$0.75, or 75¢
d. How many cents is 5% of \$1.00? \$0.05, or 5¢

2. Use a calculator to complete the table. (Round decimals to the nearest hundredth.)

Fraction	Decimal	Percent
$\frac{3}{7}$	0.43	43%
$\frac{10}{11}$	0.91	91%
$\frac{8}{15}$	0.53	53%
$\frac{7}{9}$	0.78	78%
$\frac{8}{14}$	0.57	57%

3. Use your calculator to complete the table.

Exponential Notation	Product of Factors	Standard Notation
9^4	9 ∗ 9 ∗ 9 ∗ 9	6,561
12^4	12 ∗ 12 ∗ 12 ∗ 12	20,736
8^4	8 ∗ 8 ∗ 8 ∗ 8	4,096
11^5	11 ∗ 11 ∗ 11 ∗ 11 ∗ 11	161,051
10^3	10 ∗ 10 ∗ 10	1,000

4. Complete the "What's My Rule?" table and state the rule.

Rule: out = in − 7

in	out
27	20
13	6
5	−2
10	3

5. Make true sentences by inserting parentheses.
a. 5 ∗ (4 − 2) = 10
b. 25 + (8 ∗ 7) = 81
c. 36 / (6 − 5) = 36
d. (45 / 9) + 6 = 11
e. 45 / (9 + 6) = 3

Math Journal 1, **p. 193**

2 Ongoing Learning & Practice

▶ Reviewing Fractions and Division

PARTNER ACTIVITY

(*Math Journal 1,* pp. 192A and 192B; *Student Reference Book,* pp. 62, 63, 78C, and 78D)

Students review the relationship between fractions and division. Refer students to pages 62, 63, 78C, and 78D of the *Student Reference Book* to review improper fractions, mixed numbers, and connections between fractions and division. Have students complete journal pages 192A and 192B to practice solving problems that involve division and fractions.

▶ Math Boxes 6·8

INDEPENDENT ACTIVITY

(*Math Journal 1,* p. 193)

Mixed Practice Math Boxes in this lesson are paired with Math Boxes in Lesson 6-10. The skills in Problem 5 previews Unit 7 content.

▶ Study Link 6·8

INDEPENDENT ACTIVITY

(*Math Masters,* p. 174)

Students practice estimating sums when adding fractions.

Study Link Master

Name Date Time

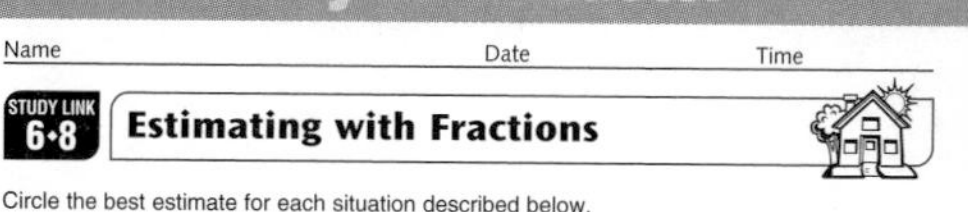

STUDY LINK 6·8 **Estimating with Fractions**

Circle the best estimate for each situation described below.

1. The sum of $\frac{3}{4}$ and $\frac{18}{19}$ is closest to
0 1 (2)

2. The sum of $\frac{1}{11}$ and $\frac{1}{15}$ is closest to
(0) 1 2

3. The sum of $\frac{9}{10}$ and $\frac{1}{32}$ is
(less than 1) greater than 1

4. Use the circle below to draw a spinner as follows:
- Shade a red sector that is more than $\frac{1}{8}$ of the circle, but less than $\frac{1}{4}$ of the circle.
- Shade a blue sector that is more than $\frac{1}{4}$ of the circle, but less than $\frac{1}{2}$ the circle.

Sample answer:

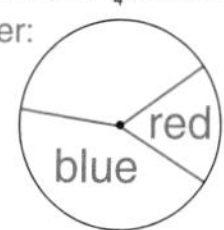

The total amount of the circle that is shaded is
(less than $\frac{3}{4}$) equal to $\frac{3}{4}$ greater than $\frac{3}{4}$

5. The number line below shows an estimate for the sum of $\frac{6}{13}$ and $\frac{1}{8}$. Explain why the sum is greater than $\frac{1}{2}$.

0 $\frac{1}{2}$ 1

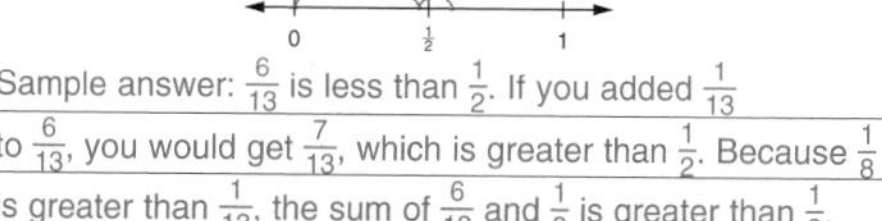

Sample answer: $\frac{6}{13}$ is less than $\frac{1}{2}$. If you added $\frac{1}{13}$ to $\frac{6}{13}$, you would get $\frac{7}{13}$, which is greater than $\frac{1}{2}$. Because $\frac{1}{8}$ is greater than $\frac{1}{13}$, the sum of $\frac{6}{13}$ and $\frac{1}{8}$ is greater than $\frac{1}{2}$.

Math Masters, **p. 174**

Teaching Master

Name Date Time

LESSON 6•8 **Comparing Fractions with $\frac{1}{2}$**

Use the Fraction Cards from *Math Journal 2,* Activity Sheets 5–7.
Sort the cards into three piles.

- Fractions less than $\frac{1}{2}$
- Fractions equal to $\frac{1}{2}$
- Fractions greater than $\frac{1}{2}$

Place the cards next to one another to check your work. When you are finished, write the fractions in each pile in the correct box below.

Less than $\frac{1}{2}$	Equal to $\frac{1}{2}$	Greater than $\frac{1}{2}$
$\frac{1}{3}, \frac{1}{4}, \frac{0}{5}, \frac{1}{5}, \frac{2}{5}, \frac{2}{6}, \frac{1}{8}, \frac{2}{8}, \frac{3}{8}, \frac{3}{9}, \frac{0}{10}, \frac{2}{10}, \frac{4}{10}, \frac{3}{12}, \frac{4}{12}, \frac{0}{16}, \frac{2}{16}, \frac{6}{16}$	$\frac{1}{2}, \frac{2}{4}, \frac{3}{6}, \frac{4}{8}, \frac{5}{10}, \frac{6}{12}, \frac{8}{16}$	$\frac{2}{2}, \frac{2}{3}, \frac{3}{3}, \frac{3}{4}, \frac{4}{4}, \frac{3}{5}, \frac{4}{5}, \frac{5}{5}, \frac{4}{6}, \frac{6}{6}, \frac{5}{8}, \frac{6}{8}, \frac{7}{8}, \frac{8}{8}, \frac{6}{9}, \frac{6}{10}, \frac{8}{10}, \frac{10}{10}, \frac{8}{12}, \frac{9}{12}, \frac{10}{16}, \frac{14}{16}, \frac{16}{16}$

Math Masters, p. 175

Teaching Master

Name Date Time

LESSON 6•8 **Math Log**

Math Masters, p. 176

3 Differentiation Options

READINESS

PARTNER ACTIVITY

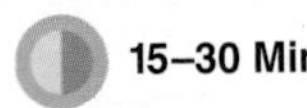
15–30 Min

▶ Comparing Fractions with $\frac{1}{2}$

(*Math Masters,* p. 175; *Math Journal 2,* Activity Sheets 5–7)

Partners work together to sort the Fraction Cards into three groups: fractions that are equal to $\frac{1}{2}$, less than $\frac{1}{2}$, or greater than $\frac{1}{2}$. First have students locate the $\frac{1}{2}$ card and place it face up. Remind students that the blue shading on the card is a model or picture for the area of $\frac{1}{2}$. Tell students they will use the $\frac{1}{2}$ card as a benchmark to determine if each Fraction Card is less than $\frac{1}{2}$, greater than $\frac{1}{2}$, or equal to $\frac{1}{2}$.

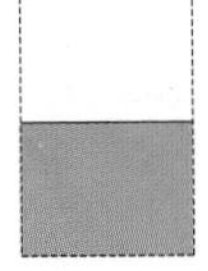

EXTRA PRACTICE

PARTNER ACTIVITY

5–15 Min

▶ Writing Fraction Number Stories

(*Math Masters,* p. 176)

Students use *Math Masters,* page 176 to write a number story using fraction addition or subtraction. Ask students to exchange and solve each other's problems using benchmarks to estimate the solution. Students should draw a picture or model for how they solved the problem.

ENRICHMENT

PARTNER ACTIVITY

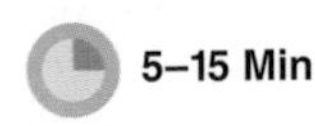
5–15 Min

▶ Playing *Fraction Top-It* (Advanced Version)

(*Math Journal 2,* Activity Sheets 5–7; *Student Reference Book,* p. 316; *Math Masters,* p. 493)

To further explore using benchmarks, have students play an advanced version of *Fraction Top-It*. In playing this version, students apply their knowledge of benchmarks to estimate sums and compare them. Each player draws two Fraction Cards from the deck and records them on *Math Masters,* page 493. Players then decide which symbol, <, >, or =, should be used to compare the two expressions.

Example:

Round	Player 1	<, >, or =	Player 2
1	$\frac{1}{2} + \frac{5}{6}$	$>$	$\frac{3}{4} + \frac{0}{5}$

6•9 Clock Fractions and Common Denominators

 **Objective** To provide additional references for fraction concepts.

Technology Resources www.everydaymathonline.com

ePresentations

eToolkit

Algorithms Practice

EM Facts Workshop Game™

Family Letters

Assessment Management

Common Core State Standards

Curriculum Focal Points

Interactive Teacher's Lesson Guide

1 Teaching the Lesson

Key Concepts and Skills

- Find common denominators.
  [Number and Numeration Goal 5]
- Use clock models and pencil-and-paper algorithms to add and subtract fractions.
  [Operations and Computation Goal 4]
- Use benchmarks to estimate sums and differences.
  [Operations and Computation Goal 6]

Key Activities

Students use a clock face to find equivalent fractions and to model addition and subtraction of fractions. They use the multiplication rule, a multiplication table, and reference lists to find common denominators.

Ongoing Assessment: Recognizing Student Achievement
Use journal page 194.
[Operations and Computation Goal 4]

Key Vocabulary

common denominator ◆ unlike denominators

Materials

Math Journal 1, pp. 194–197
Student Reference Book, p. 401
Study Link 6•8
Math Masters, p. 177
Multiplication Table Poster ◆ demonstration clock

2 Ongoing Learning & Practice

Playing *Fraction Capture*
Math Journal 1, p. 198
Math Masters, p. 460
per partnership: 2 six-sided dice
Students practice comparing fractions and finding equivalent fractions.

Math Boxes 6•9
Math Journal 1, p. 199
Students practice and maintain skills through Math Box problems.

Study Link 6•9
Math Masters, p. 178
Students practice and maintain skills through Study Link activities.

3 Differentiation Options

ENRICHMENT
Modeling Fractions with a Military Clock
Math Masters, p. 179
Students apply the clock model to a different unit by using military time.

EXTRA PRACTICE
Writing Elapsed Time Number Stories
Math Masters, p. 180
Students write a number story using fractions to represent elapsed time.

Advance Preparation

For Part 1, display the Multiplication Table Poster on the board or elsewhere for student use. When you use the *Everyday Mathematics* posters with English language learners, display either the English version only or both English and Spanish versions simultaneously; do not display the Spanish version only.

 ***Teacher's Reference Manual,* Grades 4–6** pp. 141, 142, 242, 243

Getting Started

Mental Math and Reflexes

Fraction addition and subtraction: Write the problems on the board, and have students estimate using benchmarks and then solve. Students use the estimate to assess the reasonableness of the answers.

●○○ $\frac{7}{8} + 2\frac{1}{4} = ?$ $3\frac{1}{8}$
$3\frac{5}{8} - 1\frac{3}{4} = ?$ $1\frac{7}{8}$

●●○ $2\frac{1}{4} + 2\frac{1}{2} + 1\frac{1}{4} = ?$ 6
$1\frac{5}{8} + 1\frac{1}{16} + 3\frac{3}{4} = ?$ $6\frac{7}{16}$

●●● $6\frac{1}{2} - 4 + 2\frac{1}{4} = ?$ $4\frac{3}{4}$
$4\frac{3}{8} + 2 - 1\frac{3}{4} + 1\frac{1}{2} = ?$ $6\frac{1}{8}$

Math Message

Complete Part 1 on journal page 194.

Study Link 6·8 Follow-Up

Have partners compare answers and resolve differences.

NOTE Working with elapsed time can provide students with more practice using a clock face to add and subtract fractions. Remind students that *elapsed time* is the time that passes between a given starting and ending time. Give them various problems that involve finding elapsed time and then adding or subtracting the amounts. Ask students to give the elapsed time in minutes and then in fractions of an hour. They can then use the clock face to add or subtract.

1 Teaching the Lesson

▶ Math Message Follow-Up

(*Math Journal 1,* p. 194)

Review the answers to Part 1 with the class. You might want to pose a few additional easy problems that have mixed numbers or fractions greater than 1. *Suggestions:*

- How many minutes are in $2\frac{1}{2}$ hours? 150 min
- In $\frac{5}{2}$ hours? 150 min
- In $\frac{5}{4}$ hours? 75 min
- $\frac{3}{2}$ hours is equivalent to how many minutes? 90 min

▶ Using a Clock to Add and Subtract Fractions

(*Math Journal 1,* p. 194)

Make sure students understand that they may use the clock model to help them answer the problems on the journal page. At times, students might want to "think minutes," as in the example for Part 3. At other times, students might want to look at the clock face divided into twelfths. Using a demonstration clock, work several of the problems in Part 2 with the class before students work in partnerships. Assign the remainder of the journal page.

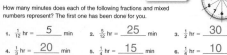

Ongoing Assessment: Recognizing Student Achievement

Journal Page 194 Problems 16–24

Use **journal page 194, Problems 16–24** to assess students' ability to use a visual model to add and subtract fractions with unlike denominators. Students are making adequate progress if they correctly solve Problems 16–24.

[Operations and Computation Goal 4]

Student Page

Date Time

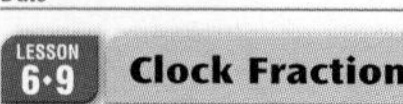

LESSON 6·9 Clock Fractions

Part 1: Math Message

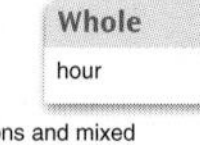

The numbers on a clock face divide one hour into twelfths. Each $\frac{1}{12}$ of an hour is 5 minutes.

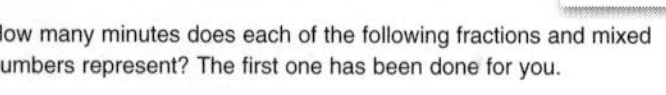

How many minutes does each of the following fractions and mixed numbers represent? The first one has been done for you.

1. $\frac{1}{12}$ hr = 5 min
2. $\frac{5}{12}$ hr = 25 min
3. $\frac{1}{2}$ hr = 30 min
4. $\frac{1}{3}$ hr = 20 min
5. $\frac{1}{4}$ hr = 15 min
6. $\frac{1}{6}$ hr = 10 min

Part 2

Using the clock face, fill in the missing numbers. The first one has been done for you.

7. $\frac{1}{4}$ hr = $\frac{3}{12}$ hr
8. $\frac{8}{12}$ hr = $\frac{2}{3}$ hr
9. $\frac{1}{3}$ hr = $\frac{2}{6}$ hr
10. $\frac{10}{12}$ hr = $\frac{5}{6}$ hr
11. $\frac{3}{4}$ hr = $\frac{9}{12}$ hr
12. $\frac{2}{12}$ hr = $\frac{1}{6}$ hr
13. $1\frac{1}{2}$ hr = $\frac{6}{4}$ hr
14. $\frac{5}{3}$ hr = $\frac{20}{12}$ hr
15. $\frac{4}{12}$ hr = $\frac{1}{3}$ hr

Part 3

Use clock fractions, if helpful, to solve these problems. Write each answer as a fraction.

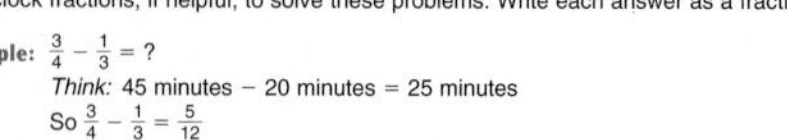

Example: $\frac{3}{4} - \frac{1}{3} = ?$
Think: 45 minutes − 20 minutes = 25 minutes
So $\frac{3}{4} - \frac{1}{3} = \frac{5}{12}$

16. $\frac{5}{12} + \frac{3}{12} =$ $\frac{8}{12}$, or $\frac{2}{3}$
17. $\frac{3}{4} + \frac{2}{4} =$ $\frac{5}{4}$, or $1\frac{1}{4}$
18. $\frac{11}{12} - \frac{3}{12} =$ $\frac{8}{12}$, or $\frac{2}{3}$
19. $1 - \frac{2}{3} =$ $\frac{1}{3}$
20. $\frac{5}{4} - \frac{2}{4} =$ $\frac{3}{4}$
21. $\frac{2}{3} + \frac{1}{6} =$ $\frac{5}{6}$
22. $\frac{1}{4} + \frac{1}{3} =$ $\frac{7}{12}$
23. $\frac{1}{3} - \frac{1}{4} =$ $\frac{1}{12}$
24. $\frac{5}{6} - \frac{3}{4} =$ $\frac{1}{12}$

Math Journal 1, p. 194

▶ Discussing Strategies for Adding and Subtracting Fractions

WHOLE-CLASS DISCUSSION

(*Math Journal 1,* p. 194)

Discuss students' solutions to Part 3. Expect that some students converted most fractions to minutes, did the operation, and then converted the answer in minutes back to a fraction. Others may have converted all fractions to twelfths and found the answer without any reference to the clock or time.

Adjusting the Activity

Pose fraction problems with denominators of 30 and 60.

Suggestions follow:

- $\frac{3}{4} + \frac{5}{60}$ $\frac{50}{60}$, or $\frac{5}{6}$
- $\frac{18}{30} + \frac{1}{3}$ $\frac{28}{30}$, or $\frac{14}{15}$
- $\frac{5}{12} + \frac{25}{60}$ $\frac{50}{60}$, or $\frac{5}{6}$

AUDITORY ◆ KINESTHETIC ◆ TACTILE ◆ VISUAL

NOTE A clock face is a convenient model for fraction operations involving halves, thirds, fourths, fifths, sixths, twelfths, and even thirtieths and sixtieths. The link between fractions and their equivalents in minutes allows students to add and subtract fractions with unlike denominators without rewriting the fractions with a common denominator.

▶ Using a Multiplication Table to Explore Equivalent Fractions

WHOLE-CLASS ACTIVITY

(*Math Journal 1,* p. 195; *Math Masters,* p. 177)

Any two rows of a multiplication table can be used to form equivalent fractions. Display the Multiplication Table Poster on the board. Ask partners to cut the strips from *Math Masters,* page 177 and place them in the middle of their workspace.

- ▷ Each student takes one strip. Ask students to make true statements about the numbers on their strip. The numbers are multiples of the first number on the strip; the numbers have a common factor. Tell them that a strip can be named by its smallest number, for example, the "4 strip."
- ▷ One partner is "numerators" and the other is "denominators." Partners then match their strips, laying the numerator strip above the denominator strip. Tell students that the columns form fractions.
- ▷ For Problem 1, on journal page 195, ask students to write down the strip names and then list all of the fractions formed by the matches.
- ▷ Partners then take two different strips and repeat this process for Problems 2 and 3. Each strip should be used only once.

Circulate and assist.

Ask students what they notice about their lists of fractions. The numerators and denominators are multiples of the numbers in the first column; the fractions are equivalent.

Student Page

Date Time

LESSON 6•9 **Number Strip Fractions**

Name the strips that you used for the numerator and denominator. Then list the fractions formed by the two strips. Sample answers:

Problem 1

	Strip Name	Fractions List									
Numerator:	7	7	14	21	28	35	42	49	56	63	70
Denominator:	9	9,	18,	27,	36,	45,	54,	63,	72,	81,	90

Problem 2

	Strip Name	Fractions List									
Numerator:	10	10	20	30	40	50	60	70	80	90	100
Denominator:	4	4,	8,	12,	16,	20,	24,	28,	32,	36,	40

Problem 3

	Strip Name	Fractions List									
Numerator:	3	3	6	9	12	15	18	21	24	27	30
Denominator:	1	1,	2,	3,	4,	5,	6,	7,	8,	9,	10

Problem 4

Explain how you can use a multiplication table to find equivalent fractions for $\frac{9}{27}$.

I can look for a column that has both 9 and 27. Then I can find the rows for those numbers. The 1 row has 9 for the numerator, and the 3 row has 27 for the denominator. I can then list the other fractions made by the numbers in the 1 row that correspond to the numbers in the 3 row.

Math Journal 1, p. 195

Student Page

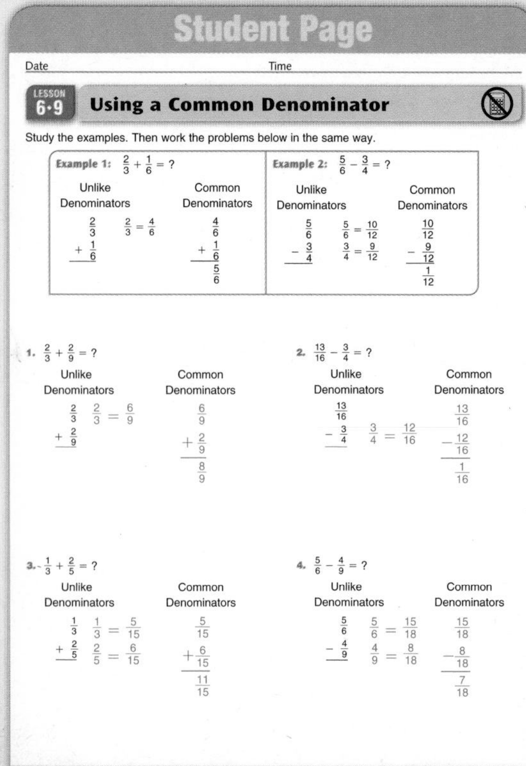
Date Time

LESSON 6·9 **Using a Common Denominator**

Study the examples. Then work the problems below in the same way.

Example 1: $\frac{2}{3} + \frac{1}{6} = ?$

Unlike Denominators: $\frac{2}{3}$, $+\frac{1}{6}$; $\frac{2}{3} = \frac{4}{6}$

Common Denominators: $\frac{4}{6} + \frac{1}{6} = \frac{5}{6}$

Example 2: $\frac{5}{6} - \frac{3}{4} = ?$

Unlike Denominators: $\frac{5}{6}$, $-\frac{3}{4}$; $\frac{5}{6} = \frac{10}{12}$; $\frac{3}{4} = \frac{9}{12}$

Common Denominators: $\frac{10}{12} - \frac{9}{12} = \frac{1}{12}$

1. $\frac{2}{3} + \frac{2}{9} = ?$

Unlike Denominators: $\frac{2}{3}$, $+\frac{2}{9}$; $\frac{2}{3} = \frac{6}{9}$

Common Denominators: $\frac{6}{9} + \frac{2}{9} = \frac{8}{9}$

2. $\frac{13}{16} - \frac{3}{4} = ?$

Unlike Denominators: $\frac{13}{16}$, $-\frac{3}{4}$; $\frac{3}{4} = \frac{12}{16}$

Common Denominators: $\frac{13}{16} - \frac{12}{16} = \frac{1}{16}$

3. $\frac{1}{3} + \frac{2}{5} = ?$

Unlike Denominators: $\frac{1}{3}$, $+\frac{2}{5}$; $\frac{1}{3} = \frac{5}{15}$; $\frac{2}{5} = \frac{6}{15}$

Common Denominators: $\frac{5}{15} + \frac{6}{15} = \frac{11}{15}$

4. $\frac{5}{6} - \frac{4}{9} = ?$

Unlike Denominators: $\frac{5}{6}$, $-\frac{4}{9}$; $\frac{5}{6} = \frac{15}{18}$; $\frac{4}{9} = \frac{8}{18}$

Common Denominators: $\frac{15}{18} - \frac{8}{18} = \frac{7}{18}$

Math Journal 1, p. 196

Adjusting the Activity

Refer students to the Equivalent Fractions, Decimals, and Percents table on *Student Reference Book,* page 401. Ask students to describe the similarities and differences between the structure of this table and their work with multiplication table number strips. 1 row of the table is similar to two number strips; the table shows the equivalent decimals and percents for the fractions.

AUDITORY ◆ KINESTHETIC ◆ TACTILE ◆ VISUAL

Ask volunteers to match two of their remaining strips and write the fraction from the first column on the board. Use these fractions to demonstrate the multiplication rule.

Example:

$$\frac{4}{9} = \frac{4 * 2}{9 * 2} = \frac{8}{18}$$

Ask students to use the appropriate strips to give another equivalent fraction for $\frac{4}{9}$. Then ask a volunteer to write the number model for this change using the multiplication rule. Sample response: $\frac{32}{72} = \frac{4 * 8}{9 * 8}$

Refer students to the Multiplication Table Poster. Explain that for any two rows, the equivalent fractions are the result of multiplying the fraction in the first column by another name for 1, such as $\frac{2}{2}$ or $\frac{8}{8}$, depending on the column. So the second column is the result of multiplying by $\frac{2}{2}$, the third column is the result of multiplying by $\frac{3}{3}$, and so on.

▶ Using a Common Denominator

(*Math Journal 1,* pp. 196 and 197; *Student Reference Book,* p. 401)

Algebraic Thinking Introduce the next activity by discussing the following points:

- It is easy to add or subtract fractions if they have the same denominator, usually called a **common denominator.** To support English language learners, discuss the meaning of *common* in this mathematical context.
- One way to add or subtract fractions with different denominators, usually called **unlike denominators,** is to rewrite the fractions with a common denominator.
- One way to find common denominators is to use the multiplication rule (or the division rule) for finding equivalent fractions. Ask volunteers to express the rules with variables. $\frac{a}{b} = \frac{a * n}{b * n}$; $\frac{a}{b} = \frac{a \div n}{b \div n}$

Have students look at Example 1 and Example 2 at the top of *Math Journal 1,* page 196. Ask: *How could you use benchmarks to estimate the solution to each problem?* Sample answer: For Problem 1, I know that $\frac{2}{3}$ is greater than $\frac{1}{2}$ and $\frac{1}{6}$ is less than $\frac{1}{2}$, so the answer will be close to 1. For Problem 2, I know that $\frac{5}{6}$ and $\frac{3}{4}$ are both close to 1, so my answer will be close to zero.

NOTE Some students may realize that $\frac{1}{6}$ is less than $\frac{1}{3}$ and conclude that the answer will be less than 1.

Then work through the examples to illustrate the use of the multiplication rule to find common denominators. Pose one or two similar problems as needed.

In addition to using the multiplication rule to find equivalent fractions, students can also refer to the Table of Equivalent Fractions, Decimals, and Percents on page 401 of the *Student Reference Book*.

Assign journal pages 196 and 197. Remind students of the importance of using benchmarks to estimate the solution and then assess the reasonableness of their answers. Students may choose to solve Problems 7 and 8 by finding a common denominator.

NOTE In Problems 1, 2, 5, 6, 7, and 8, on journal pages 196 and 197, the common denominator is the same as one of the original denominators. In Problems 3 and 4, the common denominator is different from both of the original denominators.

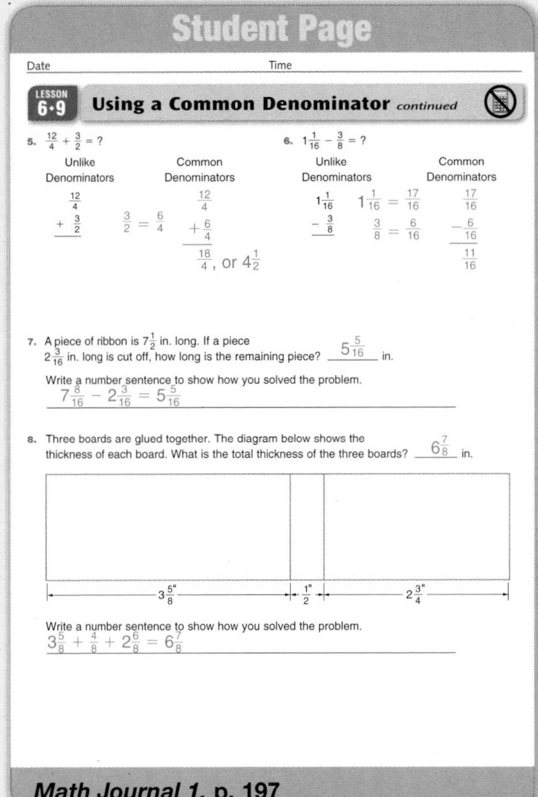
Student Page

Date ______ Time ______

LESSON 6•9 **Using a Common Denominator** *continued*

5. $\frac{12}{4} + \frac{3}{2} = ?$

Unlike Denominators: $\frac{12}{4} + \frac{3}{2}$

$\frac{3}{2} = \frac{6}{4}$

Common Denominators: $\frac{12}{4} + \frac{6}{4} = \frac{18}{4}$, or $4\frac{1}{2}$

6. $1\frac{1}{16} - \frac{3}{8} = ?$

Unlike Denominators: $1\frac{1}{16} - \frac{3}{8}$

$1\frac{1}{16} = \frac{17}{16}$

$\frac{3}{8} = \frac{6}{16}$

Common Denominators: $\frac{17}{16} - \frac{6}{16} = \frac{11}{16}$

7. A piece of ribbon is $7\frac{1}{2}$ in. long. If a piece $2\frac{3}{16}$ in. long is cut off, how long is the remaining piece? $5\frac{5}{16}$ in.

Write a number sentence to show how you solved the problem.

$7\frac{8}{16} - 2\frac{3}{16} = 5\frac{5}{16}$

8. Three boards are glued together. The diagram below shows the thickness of each board. What is the total thickness of the three boards? $6\frac{7}{8}$ in.

Write a number sentence to show how you solved the problem.

$3\frac{5}{8} + \frac{4}{8} + 2\frac{6}{8} = 6\frac{7}{8}$

Math Journal 1, p. 197

2 Ongoing Learning & Practice

Playing *Fraction Capture*

PARTNER ACTIVITY

(*Math Journal 1*, p. 198; *Math Masters*, p. 460)

Players roll dice, form fractions, and claim corresponding sections of squares. The rules are on *Math Journal 1*, page 198, and the gameboard is on *Math Masters*, page 460. Remind students of the importance of using the benchmark fraction of $\frac{1}{2}$ when playing this game.

Math Boxes 6•9

INDEPENDENT ACTIVITY

(*Math Journal 1*, p. 199)

Mixed Practice Math Boxes in this lesson are paired with Math Boxes in Lesson 6-6. The skill in Problem 6 previews Unit 7 content.

Writing/Reasoning Have students write a response to the following: *Explain your answer to the question in Problem 3 and how you chose the values for the data set.* Because the average cannot be greater than the maximum in the data set, 53 inches cannot be Esther's average since 50 is the maximum number. I chose 5 numbers for the data set that could be added together and divided by 5 so that the average would equal 53.

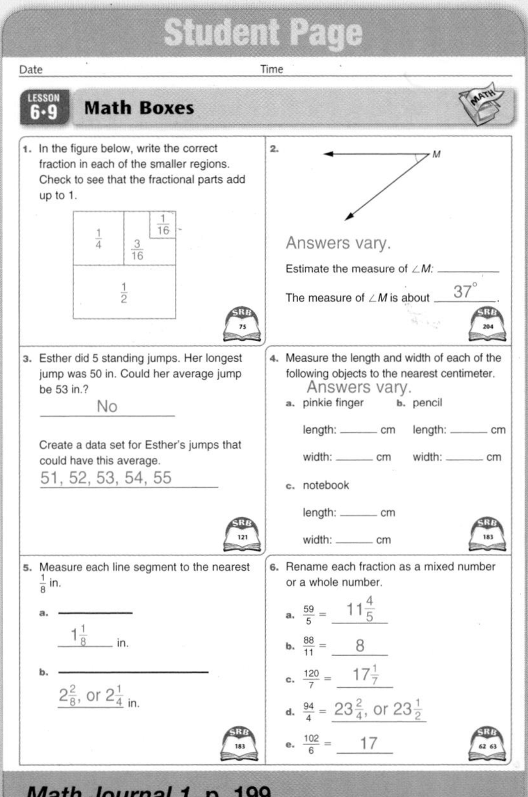
Student Page

Date ______ Time ______

LESSON 6•9 **Math Boxes**

1. In the figure below, write the correct fraction in each of the smaller regions. Check to see that the fractional parts add up to 1.

SRB 75

2.

Answers vary.

Estimate the measure of ∠*M*: ______

The measure of ∠*M* is about 37°.

SRB 204

3. Esther did 5 standing jumps. Her longest jump was 50 in. Could her average jump be 53 in.? No

Create a data set for Esther's jumps that could have this average.

51, 52, 53, 54, 55

SRB 121

4. Measure the length and width of each of the following objects to the nearest centimeter. Answers vary.

a. pinkie finger
length: ______ cm
width: ______ cm

b. pencil
length: ______ cm
width: ______ cm

c. notebook
length: ______ cm
width: ______ cm

SRB 183

5. Measure each line segment to the nearest $\frac{1}{8}$ in.

a. $1\frac{1}{8}$ in.

b. $2\frac{2}{8}$, or $2\frac{1}{4}$ in.

SRB 183

6. Rename each fraction as a mixed number or a whole number.

a. $\frac{59}{5} = 11\frac{4}{5}$

b. $\frac{88}{11} = 8$

c. $\frac{120}{7} = 17\frac{1}{7}$

d. $\frac{94}{4} = 23\frac{2}{4}$, or $23\frac{1}{2}$

e. $\frac{102}{6} = 17$

SRB 62 63

Math Journal 1, p. 199

Study Link 6•9

INDEPENDENT ACTIVITY

(*Math Masters*, p. 178)

Home Connection Students solve problems similar to those on journal pages 196 and 197. This page reinforces the idea that a common denominator can be determined by finding fractions equivalent to the given fractions.

Study Link Master

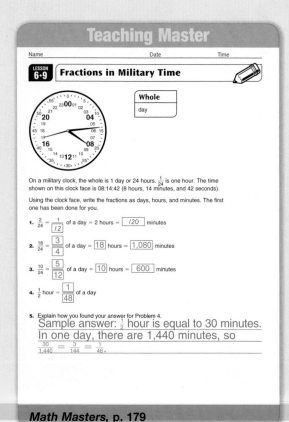

Name Date Time

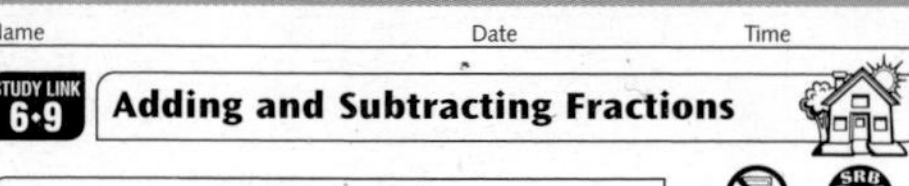

STUDY LINK 6•9 **Adding and Subtracting Fractions**

Multiplication Rule

To find a fraction equivalent to a given fraction, multiply the numerator and the denominator of the fraction by the same number. $\frac{a}{b} = \frac{a * n}{b * n}$

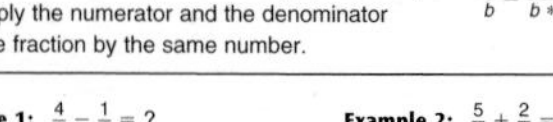

Example 1: $\frac{4}{9} - \frac{1}{3} = ?$

$\frac{1}{3} = \frac{2}{6} = \frac{3}{9} = \frac{4}{12} = \frac{5}{15} = \frac{6}{18} = \ldots$

9 is a common denominator.

$\frac{4}{9} - \frac{1}{3} = \frac{4}{9} - \frac{3}{9} = \frac{1}{9}$

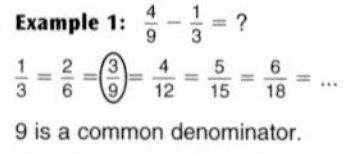

Example 2: $\frac{5}{8} + \frac{2}{5} = ?$

$\frac{5}{8} = \frac{10}{16} = \frac{15}{24} = \frac{20}{32} = \frac{25}{40} = \frac{30}{48} = \ldots$

$\frac{2}{5} = \frac{4}{10} = \frac{6}{15} = \frac{8}{20} = \frac{10}{25} = \frac{12}{30} = \frac{14}{35} = \frac{16}{40} = \frac{18}{45} = \ldots$

Both fractions can be rewritten with the common denominator 40.

$\frac{5}{8} + \frac{2}{5} = \frac{25}{40} + \frac{16}{40} = \frac{41}{40}$, or $1\frac{1}{40}$

Find a common denominator. Then add or subtract.

1. $\frac{2}{3} + \frac{4}{5} =$ $1\frac{7}{15}$
   $\frac{2}{3} = \frac{10}{15}$
   $\frac{4}{5} = \frac{12}{15}$
   $\frac{10}{15} + \frac{12}{15} = \frac{22}{15}$, or $1\frac{7}{15}$
2. $\frac{8}{9} - \frac{5}{6} =$ $\frac{1}{18}$
   $\frac{8}{9} = \frac{16}{18}$
   $\frac{5}{6} = \frac{15}{18}$
   $\frac{16}{18} - \frac{15}{18} = \frac{1}{18}$
3. $\frac{3}{4} + 1\frac{1}{2} =$ $2\frac{1}{4}$
   $1\frac{1}{2} = \frac{3}{2} = \frac{6}{4}$
   $\frac{3}{4} + \frac{6}{4} = \frac{9}{4}$, or $2\frac{1}{4}$
4. Lisa was 4 feet $10\frac{1}{2}$ inches tall at the end of fifth grade. During the year, she had grown $2\frac{3}{4}$ inches. How tall was Lisa at the start of fifth grade?
   4 feet $7\frac{3}{4}$ in.
5. Bill was baking two different kinds of bread. One recipe called for $3\frac{1}{2}$ cups of flour. The other called for $2\frac{1}{3}$ cups of flour. How much flour did Bill need in all?
   $5\frac{5}{6}$ cups

Math Masters, p. 178

3 Differentiation Options

ENRICHMENT

PARTNER ACTIVITY

15–30 Min

▶ Modeling Fractions with a Military Clock

(*Math Masters,* p. 179)

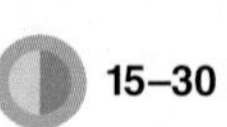

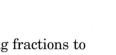

To apply students' understanding of the fractional units on a 12-hour clock face, have students use a 24-hour military clock face model to add, subtract, and find equivalent fractions. When they have finished the page, have students describe similarities and differences between using the 12-hour clock and the 24-hour clock.

EXTRA PRACTICE

INDEPENDENT ACTIVITY

15–30 Min

▶ Writing Elapsed Time Number Stories

(*Math Masters,* p. 180)

Students write a number story using fractions to represent elapsed time. Ask students to exchange and solve each other's problems and then share their solution strategies.

Teaching Master

Name Date Time

LESSON 6•9 **Fractions in Military Time**

Whole
day

On a military clock, the whole is 1 day or 24 hours. $\frac{1}{24}$ is one hour. The time shown on this clock face is 08:14:42 (8 hours, 14 minutes, and 42 seconds).

Using the clock face, write the fractions as days, hours, and minutes. The first one has been done for you.

1. $\frac{2}{24} = \frac{1}{12}$ of a day = 2 hours = 120 minutes
2. $\frac{18}{24} = \frac{3}{4}$ of a day = 18 hours = 1,080 minutes
3. $\frac{10}{24} = \frac{5}{12}$ of a day = 10 hours = 600 minutes
4. $\frac{1}{2}$ hour = $\frac{1}{48}$ of a day
5. Explain how you found your answer for Problem 4.
   Sample answer: $\frac{1}{2}$ hour is equal to 30 minutes. In one day, there are 1,440 minutes, so $\frac{30}{1,440} = \frac{3}{144} = \frac{1}{48}$.

Math Masters, p. 179

Teaching Master

Name Date Time

LESSON 6•9 **Writing Elapsed-Time Number Stories**

The numbers on a clock face divide one hour into twelfths. Each $\frac{1}{12}$ of an hour is 5 minutes.

Whole
hour

Use fractions to represent amounts of elapsed time and write a number story for a partner to solve.

Example:

Maria started her piano practice at 3:15. She practiced for $\frac{8}{12}$ of an hour. At what time did she finish practicing?

Think: $\frac{1}{12}$ hour = 5 minutes; $\frac{8}{12}$ hour is 8 ∗ 5, or 40 minutes; 40 minutes more than 3:15 is 3:55.

Maria finished practicing at 3:55.

Your Elapsed-Time Number Story:
Answers vary.

Your Partner's Solution:
Answers vary.

Explain your answer.
Answers vary.

Math Masters, p. 180

6•10 Quick Common Denominators

Objective To reinforce the use of common denominators to compare, add, and subtract fractions.

www.everydaymathonline.com

ePresentations

eToolkit

Algorithms Practice

EM Facts Workshop Game™

Family Letters

Assessment Management

Common Core State Standards

Curriculum Focal Points

Interactive Teacher's Lesson Guide

1 Teaching the Lesson

Key Concepts and Skills

- Use the products of denominators to find equivalent fractions.
  [Number and Numeration Goal 5]
- Rename pairs of fractions using a common denominator.
  [Number and Numeration Goal 5]
- Use common denominators to add and subtract fraction pairs.
  [Operations and Computation Goal 4]

Key Activities

Students use the fraction sticks from Lesson 5•4 to develop a quick way to find common denominators. They use common denominators to add, subtract, and compare fractions.

Ongoing Assessment: Recognizing Student Achievement
Use an Exit Slip (*Math Masters,* page 414).
[Number and Numeration Goal 5]

Key Vocabulary

quick common denominator ◆ simplest form

Materials

Math Journal 1, pp. 200 and 201
Student Reference Book, p. 401 (optional)
Study Link 6•9
Math Masters, p. 414
slate ◆ multiplication table (optional)

2 Ongoing Learning & Practice

Fraction Problems
Math Journal 1, p. 202
Students practice fraction concepts by solving number stories.

Math Boxes 6•10
Math Journal 1, p. 203
Students practice and maintain skills through Math Box problems.

Study Link 6•10
Math Masters, p. 181
Students practice and maintain skills through Study Link activities.

3 Differentiation Options

ENRICHMENT
Finding the Least Common Multiple
Student Reference Book, pp. 65 and 401
Students use the least common multiple method to find common denominators.

EXTRA PRACTICE
Finding Common Denominators
Math Masters, p. 182
Students practice finding common denominators to add and subtract fractions.

Advance Preparation

***Teacher's Reference Manual,* Grades 4–6** pp. 141, 142

Getting Started

Mental Math and Reflexes

Ask students to write 3 equivalent fractions for each problem. Sample answers:

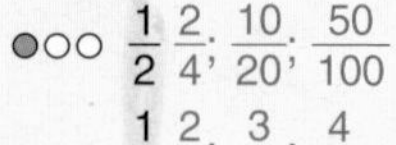

●○○ $\frac{1}{2}$ $\frac{2}{4}$, $\frac{10}{20}$, $\frac{50}{100}$
$\frac{1}{4}$ $\frac{2}{8}$, $\frac{3}{12}$, $\frac{4}{16}$

●●○ $\frac{3}{7}$ $\frac{12}{28}$, $\frac{21}{49}$, $\frac{45}{105}$
$\frac{7}{8}$ $\frac{14}{16}$, $\frac{21}{24}$, $\frac{28}{32}$

●●● $\frac{42}{70}$ $\frac{6}{10}$, $\frac{24}{40}$, $\frac{36}{60}$
$\frac{88}{99}$ $\frac{8}{9}$, $\frac{56}{63}$, $\frac{104}{117}$

Math Message

Do Problems 1 and 2 on journal page 200. Then complete the statement in Problem 3.

Study Link 6+9 Follow-Up

Have partners compare their answers and resolve differences. Ask volunteers to give their number models for Problems 4 and 5.

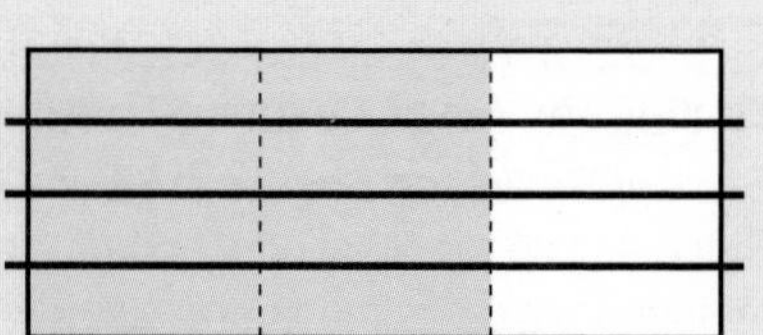

A thirds stick showing twelfths

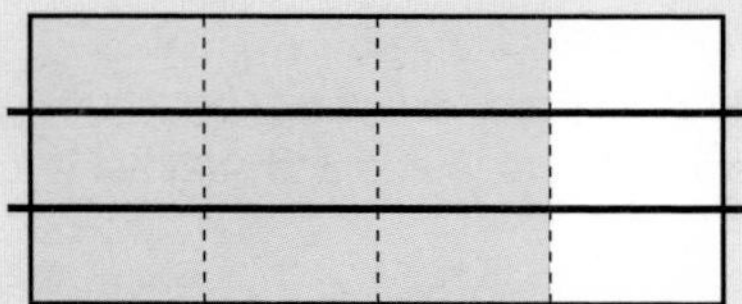

A fourths stick showing twelfths

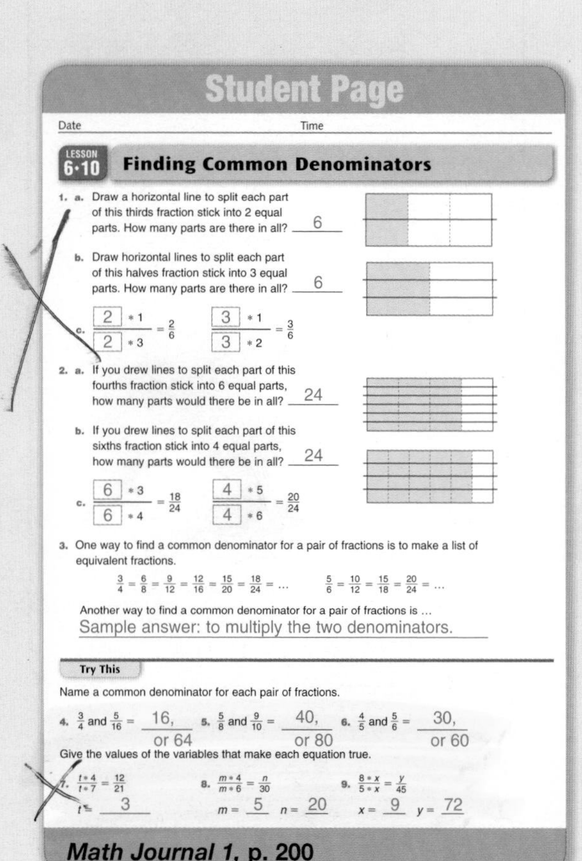

Student Page

Date Time

LESSON 6•10 **Finding Common Denominators**

1. a. Draw a horizontal line to split each part of this thirds fraction stick into 2 equal parts. How many parts are there in all? 6

   b. Draw horizontal lines to split each part of this halves fraction stick into 3 equal parts. How many parts are there in all? 6

   c. $\frac{2 * 1}{2 * 3} = \frac{2}{6}$ $\frac{3 * 1}{3 * 2} = \frac{3}{6}$

2. a. If you drew lines to split each part of this fourths fraction stick into 6 equal parts, how many parts would there be in all? 24

   b. If you drew lines to split each part of this sixths fraction stick into 4 equal parts, how many parts would there be in all? 24

   c. $\frac{6 * 3}{6 * 4} = \frac{18}{24}$ $\frac{4 * 5}{4 * 6} = \frac{20}{24}$

3. One way to find a common denominator for a pair of fractions is to make a list of equivalent fractions.

   $\frac{3}{4} = \frac{6}{8} = \frac{9}{12} = \frac{12}{16} = \frac{15}{20} = \frac{18}{24} = \dots$ $\frac{5}{6} = \frac{10}{12} = \frac{15}{18} = \frac{20}{24} = \dots$

   Another way to find a common denominator for a pair of fractions is ...
   Sample answer: to multiply the two denominators.

Try This

Name a common denominator for each pair of fractions.

4. $\frac{3}{4}$ and $\frac{5}{16}$ = 16, or 64
5. $\frac{5}{8}$ and $\frac{9}{10}$ = 40, or 80
6. $\frac{4}{5}$ and $\frac{5}{6}$ = 30, or 60

Give the values of the variables that make each equation true.

7. $\frac{t * 4}{t * 7} = \frac{12}{21}$ t = 3
8. $\frac{m * 4}{m * 6} = \frac{n}{30}$ m = 5 n = 20
9. $\frac{8 * x}{5 * x} = \frac{y}{45}$ x = 9 y = 72

Math Journal 1, p. 200

1 Teaching the Lesson

▶ Math Message Follow-Up

WHOLE-CLASS DISCUSSION

ELL

(*Math Journal 1*, p. 200)

Ask volunteers to name the strategy or resource for finding equivalent fractions. Sample answers: the multiplication rule; the division rule; a multiplication table; the Table of Equivalent Fractions, Decimals, and Percents on page 401 in the *Student Reference Book* Point out that this lesson is about a quick way to find a common denominator.

Briefly discuss answers for Problems 1 and 2. Then point out that these problems suggest a way to find a common denominator for pairs of fractions with unlike denominators.

Ask volunteers to use their answers to Problem 3 to suggest ways to find a common denominator for $\frac{2}{3}$ and $\frac{3}{4}$. Draw two fraction sticks—a thirds stick with $\frac{2}{3}$ shaded and a fourths stick with $\frac{3}{4}$ shaded on the board. Ask volunteers to demonstrate how to use these sticks to generate a common denominator. Split each part of the thirds stick into 4 equal parts and each part of the fourths stick into 3 equal parts. Ask students how many parts are now in each whole stick. 12 The fraction sticks show that $\frac{8}{12}$ is another name for $\frac{2}{3}$, and that $\frac{9}{12}$ is another name for $\frac{3}{4}$. (*See margin.*)

Point out that these fraction sticks model finding a common denominator for two fractions by multiplying the two denominators.

In *Everyday Mathematics,* the product of denominators is known as the **quick common denominator.** To support English language learners, write *quick common denominator*, and list some examples on the board. Then discuss the meaning of the term.

NOTE Fraction sticks were used in Lesson 5-4 to find equivalent fractions. Most students will remember this approach. When dividing a fraction stick into smaller parts, it is helpful to use horizontal lines so the original fraction divisions can still be seen.

▶ Using Multiples and Factors to Find Common Denominators

WHOLE-CLASS DISCUSSION

(*Math Journal 1,* p. 200)

Assign Problems 4–9. When most students have finished, briefly go over the answers. Encourage students to share their methods for finding a common denominator.

Ask students to examine the denominators in Problem 4. The quick common denominator is 64, but is there a smaller common denominator? Yes, 16 is a common denominator for this problem. Remind students to analyze the denominators before deciding what method to use to find a common denominator.

If one denominator is a factor of the other, the multiplication rule can be used, and only one of the denominators needs to be renamed. In Problem 4, 4 is a factor of 16, so $\frac{3}{4}$ can be renamed as $\frac{12}{16}$.

In Problem 5, the quick common denominator is 80. Ask students how they could use multiples to find a smaller common denominator. The multiplies of 8 are 8, 16, 24, 32, 40, and the multiples of 10 are 10, 20, 30, 40; 8 and 10 can be renamed as fractions with 40 as the denominator.

In Problem 6, the quick common denominator is 30. Ask students to analyze the denominators.

- Is one a factor of the other? No
- Do they have a multiple in common? Yes; 5 and 6 have 30 as a multiple. Both are factors of 30.
- Is there a smaller common denominator than 30? No

Do not require answers to have the lowest common denominator at this time. Any common denominator can be used. The focus here is to develop conceptual understanding of the operations.

▶ Using Common Denominators

PARTNER ACTIVITY

(*Math Journal 1,* p. 201)

Have students complete journal page 201. The example reminds students that they can use the product of denominators to find a common denominator. They can also use a multiplication table, refer to page 401 in the *Student Reference Book* or journal page 206. They can check their answers using a fraction-stick chart. (*See margin.*) Circulate and assist.

Ask volunteers to explain their solutions for Problems 6 and 7, which should include their strategy for obtaining the common denominator.

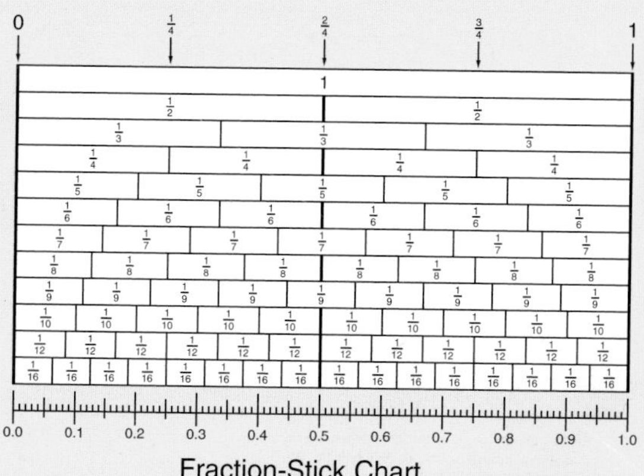

Fraction-Stick Chart

$\frac{1}{2}$	$\frac{2}{4}$	$\frac{3}{6}$	$\frac{4}{8}$	$\frac{5}{10}$	$\frac{6}{12}$	$\frac{7}{14}$	$\frac{8}{16}$	$\frac{9}{18}$	$\frac{10}{20}$	0.5	50%
$\frac{1}{3}$	$\frac{2}{6}$	$\frac{3}{9}$	$\frac{4}{12}$	$\frac{5}{15}$	$\frac{6}{18}$	$\frac{7}{21}$	$\frac{8}{24}$	$\frac{9}{27}$	$\frac{10}{30}$	$.0\overline{3}$	$33\frac{1}{3}$%
$\frac{2}{3}$	$\frac{4}{6}$	$\frac{6}{9}$	$\frac{8}{12}$	$\frac{10}{15}$	$\frac{12}{18}$	$\frac{14}{21}$	$\frac{16}{24}$	$\frac{18}{27}$	$\frac{20}{30}$	$0.\overline{6}$	$66\frac{2}{3}$%
$\frac{1}{4}$	$\frac{2}{8}$	$\frac{3}{12}$	$\frac{4}{16}$	$\frac{5}{20}$	$\frac{6}{24}$	$\frac{7}{28}$	$\frac{8}{32}$	$\frac{9}{36}$	$\frac{10}{40}$	0.25	25%
$\frac{3}{4}$	$\frac{6}{8}$	$\frac{9}{12}$	$\frac{12}{16}$	$\frac{15}{20}$	$\frac{18}{24}$	$\frac{21}{28}$	$\frac{24}{32}$	$\frac{27}{36}$	$\frac{30}{40}$	0.75	75%

Table of Equivalent Fractions, Decimals, and Percents

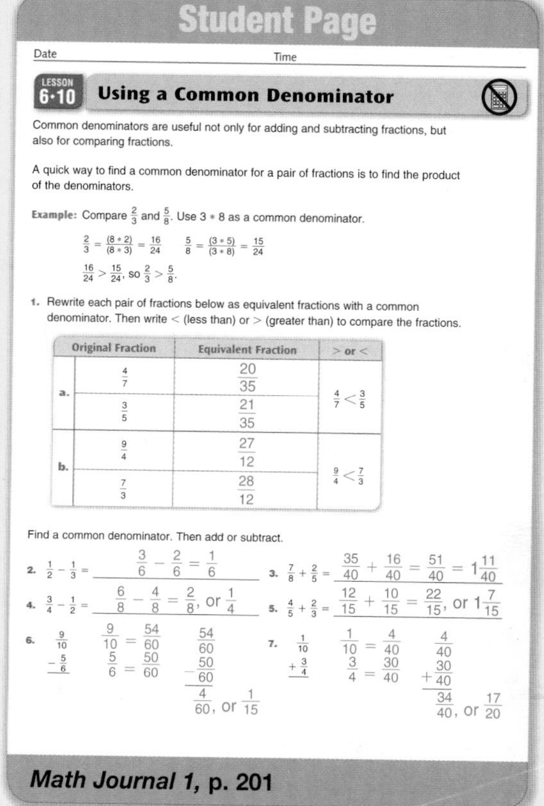

Student Page

Date Time

LESSON 6•10 **Using a Common Denominator**

Common denominators are useful not only for adding and subtracting fractions, but also for comparing fractions.

A quick way to find a common denominator for a pair of fractions is to find the product of the denominators.

Example: Compare $\frac{2}{3}$ and $\frac{5}{8}$. Use 3 ∗ 8 as a common denominator.

$\frac{2}{3} = \frac{(8 * 2)}{(8 * 3)} = \frac{16}{24}$ $\frac{5}{8} = \frac{(3 * 5)}{(3 * 8)} = \frac{15}{24}$

$\frac{16}{24} > \frac{15}{24}$, so $\frac{2}{3} > \frac{5}{8}$.

1. Rewrite each pair of fractions below as equivalent fractions with a common denominator. Then write < (less than) or > (greater than) to compare the fractions.

	Original Fraction	Equivalent Fraction	> or <
a.	$\frac{4}{7}$	$\frac{20}{35}$	$\frac{4}{7} < \frac{3}{5}$
	$\frac{3}{5}$	$\frac{21}{35}$	
b.	$\frac{9}{4}$	$\frac{27}{12}$	$\frac{9}{4} < \frac{7}{3}$
	$\frac{7}{3}$	$\frac{28}{12}$	

Find a common denominator. Then add or subtract.

2. $\frac{1}{2} - \frac{1}{3} = \frac{3}{6} - \frac{2}{6} = \frac{1}{6}$
3. $\frac{7}{8} + \frac{2}{5} = \frac{35}{40} + \frac{16}{40} = \frac{51}{40} = 1\frac{11}{40}$
4. $\frac{3}{4} - \frac{1}{2} = \frac{6}{8} - \frac{4}{8} = \frac{2}{8}$, or $\frac{1}{4}$
5. $\frac{4}{5} + \frac{2}{3} = \frac{12}{15} + \frac{10}{15} = \frac{22}{15}$, or $1\frac{7}{15}$
6. $\frac{9}{10} - \frac{5}{6}$; $\frac{9}{10} = \frac{54}{60}$, $\frac{5}{6} = \frac{50}{60}$; $\frac{54}{60} - \frac{50}{60} = \frac{4}{60}$, or $\frac{1}{15}$
7. $\frac{1}{10} + \frac{3}{4}$; $\frac{1}{10} = \frac{4}{40}$, $\frac{3}{4} = \frac{30}{40}$; $\frac{4}{40} + \frac{30}{40} = \frac{34}{40}$, or $\frac{17}{20}$

Math Journal 1, p. 201

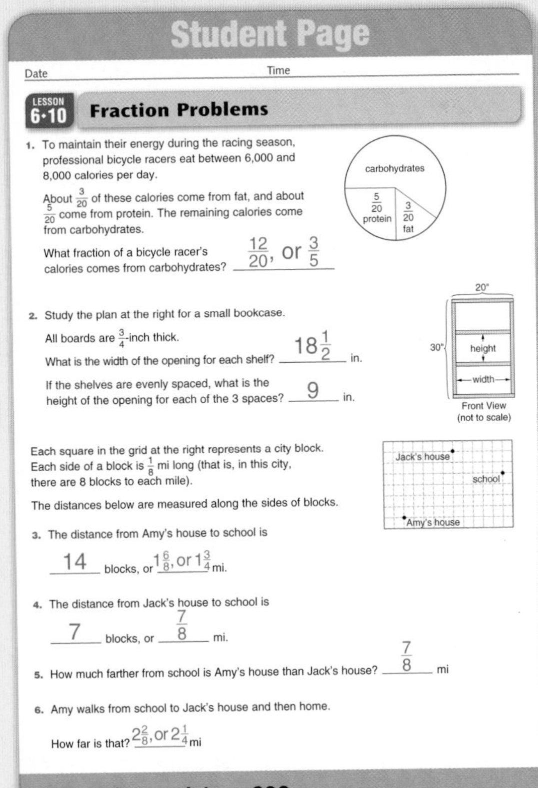

Student Page

Date ______ Time ______

LESSON 6·10 **Fraction Problems**

1. To maintain their energy during the racing season, professional bicycle racers eat between 6,000 and 8,000 calories per day.

   About $\frac{3}{20}$ of these calories come from fat, and about $\frac{5}{20}$ come from protein. The remaining calories come from carbohydrates.

   What fraction of a bicycle racer's calories comes from carbohydrates? $\frac{12}{20}$, or $\frac{3}{5}$

2. Study the plan at the right for a small bookcase.

   All boards are $\frac{3}{4}$-inch thick.

   What is the width of the opening for each shelf? $18\frac{1}{2}$ in.

   If the shelves are evenly spaced, what is the height of the opening for each of the 3 spaces? 9 in.

Each square in the grid at the right represents a city block. Each side of a block is $\frac{1}{8}$ mi long (that is, in this city, there are 8 blocks to each mile).

The distances below are measured along the sides of blocks.

3. The distance from Amy's house to school is 14 blocks, or $1\frac{6}{8}$, or $1\frac{3}{4}$ mi.

4. The distance from Jack's house to school is 7 blocks, or $\frac{7}{8}$ mi.

5. How much farther from school is Amy's house than Jack's house? $\frac{7}{8}$ mi

6. Amy walks from school to Jack's house and then home.

   How far is that? $2\frac{2}{8}$, or $2\frac{1}{4}$ mi

Math Journal 1, p. 202

Explain that a fraction is in **simplest form** if the numerator and denominator do not have any common factors except 1. In Problem 7, if 40 is used as the common denominator, the sum is $\frac{34}{40}$. The division rule for finding equivalent fractions can be applied to $\frac{34}{40}$, using 2, a common factor of 34 and 40:

$\frac{34 \div 2}{40 \div 2} = \frac{17}{20}$.

Since 17 and 20 have no common factors except 1, the division rule can't be applied to $\frac{17}{20}$. Therefore, the simplest form of $\frac{34}{40}$ is the equivalent fraction $\frac{17}{20}$.

NOTE Encourage but do not require students to write their answers in simplest form at this time.

Ongoing Assessment: Recognizing Student Achievement — **Exit Slip**

Use an **Exit Slip** (*Math Masters*, page 414) to assess students' understanding of finding common denominators. Ask students to explain how to find common denominators for two fractions such as $\frac{2}{3}$ and $\frac{4}{9}$. Students are making adequate progress if their responses refer to renaming the denominators. Some students may refer to the multiplication or division rule.

[Number and Numeration Goal 5]

2 Ongoing Learning & Practice

▶ Fraction Problems

INDEPENDENT ACTIVITY

(*Math Journal 1*, p. 202)

Students solve fraction number stories. When most students have completed the journal page, ask volunteers to write the number models on the board and explain their answers.

▶ Math Boxes 6·10

INDEPENDENT ACTIVITY

(*Math Journal 1*, p. 203)

Student Page

Date ______ Time ______

LESSON 6·10 **Math Boxes**

1. a. What is 50% of \$10.00? \$5.00

   b. What percent of \$10.00 is \$7.50? 75%

   c. What is 35% of \$10.00? \$3.50

   d. What percent of \$10.00 is \$3.20? 32%

2. Use a calculator to complete the table. (Round decimals to the nearest hundredth.)

Fraction	Decimal	Percent
$\frac{11}{12}$	0.92	92%
$\frac{5}{7}$	0.71	71%
$\frac{14}{15}$	0.93	93%
$\frac{5}{6}$	0.83	83%
$\frac{2}{9}$	0.22	22%

3. Use your calculator to complete the table.

Exponential Notation	Product of Factors	Standard Notation
4^4	4 ∗ 4 ∗ 4 ∗ 4	256
5^3	5 ∗ 5 ∗ 5	125
6^4	6 ∗ 6 ∗ 6 ∗ 6	1,296
7^5	7 ∗ 7 ∗ 7 ∗ 7 ∗ 7	16,807
9^3	9 ∗ 9 ∗ 9	729

4. Complete the "What's My Rule?" table and state the rule.

   Rule: out = in + 9

in	out
8	17
11	20
5	14
−5	4

5. Make these sentences true by inserting parentheses.

   a. (19 + 41) ∗ 3 = 180

   b. 5 = (16 / 2) + 2 − 5

   c. −1 = 16 / (2 + 2) − 5

   d. 24 ÷ (8 + 4) ∗ 3 = 6

   e. (24 ÷ 8) + (4 ∗ 3) = 15

Math Journal 1, p. 203

Mixed Practice Math Boxes in this lesson are paired with Math Boxes in Lesson 6-8. The skill in Problem 5 previews Unit 7 content.

Writing/Reasoning Have students write a response to the following: *Using 9^3 from Problem 3 as an example, explain the words* base *and* exponent. The base, or 9, is the number being multiplied. The exponent, or 3, is the number of times the base appears in a multiplication expression.

Study Link 6·10

INDEPENDENT ACTIVITY

(*Math Masters,* p. 181)

Home Connection Students practice adding and subtracting fractions with unlike denominators.

3 Differentiation Options

ENRICHMENT

PARTNER ACTIVITY

15–30 Min

Finding the Least Common Multiple

(*Student Reference Book,* pp. 65 and 401)

To apply students' understanding of using multiples to find common denominators, have students complete the following activity:

1. Partners read and study the least common multiple method presented on *Student Reference Book*, page 65.
2. Each partner selects two fractions from the Table of Equivalent Fractions, Decimals, and Percents on *Student Reference Book,* page 401 and writes them down.
3. Partners exchange papers and use the least common multiple method to find a common denominator for the fraction pair.

After students have had the opportunity to find common denominators for several fraction pairs, discuss the advantages and disadvantages of using the least common multiple to find common denominators.

EXTRA PRACTICE

INDEPENDENT ACTIVITY

15–30 Min

Finding Common Denominators

(*Math Masters,* p. 182)

Students find common denominators for pairs of fractions before adding them on *Math Masters,* page 182. Remind students to compare the denominators before they choose a method for finding the common denominator. For example, if one denominator is a factor of the other, students might want to use the larger number for the common denominator instead of finding the quick common denominator.

When most students have completed the page, explain that one strategy for working with fractions is to rewrite the fractions in simplest form before finding a common denominator. For example, $\frac{7}{14} = \frac{1}{2}$ and $\frac{6}{8} = \frac{3}{4}$, and then rename $\frac{1}{2}$ as $\frac{2}{4}$.

To extend the activity, have students change their sums to simplest form and mixed numbers.

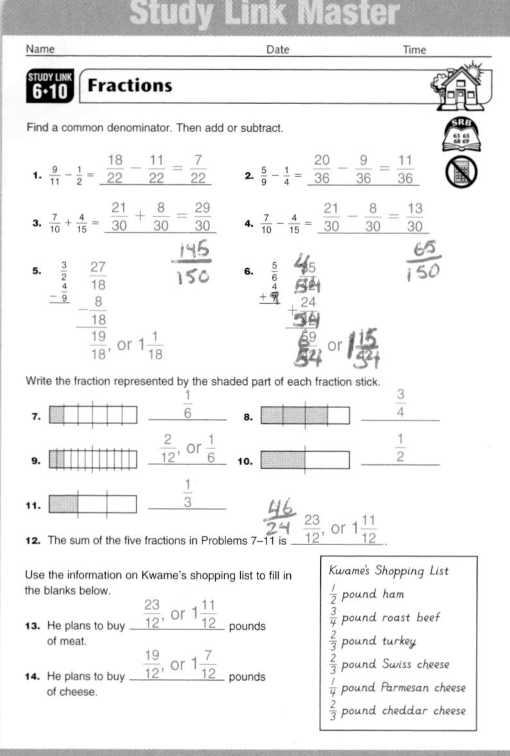

Study Link Master

Name Date Time

STUDY LINK 6·10 **Fractions**

Find a common denominator. Then add or subtract.

1. $\frac{9}{11} - \frac{1}{2} = \frac{18}{22} - \frac{11}{22} = \frac{7}{22}$
2. $\frac{5}{9} - \frac{1}{4} = \frac{20}{36} - \frac{9}{36} = \frac{11}{36}$
3. $\frac{7}{10} + \frac{4}{15} = \frac{21}{30} + \frac{8}{30} = \frac{29}{30}$
4. $\frac{7}{10} - \frac{4}{15} = \frac{21}{30} - \frac{8}{30} = \frac{13}{30}$
5. $\frac{3}{2} - \frac{4}{9}$ = $\frac{27}{18} - \frac{8}{18} = \frac{19}{18}$, or $1\frac{1}{18}$
6. $\frac{5}{6} + \frac{4}{9}$

Write the fraction represented by the shaded part of each fraction stick.

7. $\frac{1}{6}$
8. $\frac{3}{4}$
9. $\frac{2}{12}$, or $\frac{1}{6}$
10. $\frac{1}{2}$
11. $\frac{1}{3}$
12. The sum of the five fractions in Problems 7–11 is $\frac{23}{12}$, or $1\frac{11}{12}$.

Use the information on Kwame's shopping list to fill in the blanks below.

13. He plans to buy $\frac{23}{12}$, or $1\frac{11}{12}$ pounds of meat.
14. He plans to buy $\frac{19}{12}$, or $1\frac{7}{12}$ pounds of cheese.

Kwame's Shopping List
$\frac{1}{2}$ pound ham
$\frac{3}{4}$ pound roast beef
$\frac{2}{3}$ pound turkey
$\frac{2}{3}$ pound Swiss cheese
$\frac{1}{4}$ pound Parmesan cheese
$\frac{2}{3}$ pound cheddar cheese

Math Masters, p. 181

Teaching Master

Name Date Time

LESSON 6·10 **Common Denominators**

1. For each pair of fractions below:
   - Find a common denominator.
   - Rewrite the fractions with this common denominator.
   - Add the fractions.

Original Fractions	Fractions with a Common Denominator	Sum
$\frac{1}{2}$ and $\frac{3}{4}$	$\frac{2}{4}$ and $\frac{3}{4}$	$\frac{2}{4} + \frac{3}{4} = \frac{5}{4}$, or $1\frac{1}{4}$
$\frac{2}{9}$ and $\frac{7}{3}$	$\frac{2}{9}$ and $\frac{21}{9}$	$\frac{2}{9} + \frac{21}{9} = \frac{23}{9}$, or $2\frac{5}{9}$
$\frac{3}{8}$ and $\frac{5}{16}$	$\frac{6}{16}$ and $\frac{5}{16}$	$\frac{6}{16} + \frac{5}{16} = \frac{11}{16}$
$\frac{3}{5}$ and $\frac{9}{20}$	$\frac{12}{20}$ and $\frac{9}{20}$	$\frac{12}{20} + \frac{9}{20} = \frac{21}{20}$, or $1\frac{1}{20}$
$\frac{7}{14}$ and $\frac{6}{8}$	$\frac{2}{4}$ and $\frac{3}{4}$	$\frac{2}{4} + \frac{3}{4} = \frac{5}{4}$, or $1\frac{1}{4}$
$\frac{8}{10}$ and $\frac{15}{25}$	$\frac{4}{5}$ and $\frac{3}{5}$	$\frac{4}{5} + \frac{3}{5} = \frac{7}{5}$, or $1\frac{2}{5}$
$\frac{6}{9}$ and $\frac{8}{12}$	$\frac{2}{3}$ and $\frac{2}{3}$	$\frac{2}{3} + \frac{2}{3} = \frac{4}{3}$, or $1\frac{1}{3}$
$\frac{2}{3}$ and $\frac{3}{4}$	$\frac{8}{12}$ and $\frac{9}{12}$	$\frac{8}{12} + \frac{9}{12} = \frac{17}{12}$, or $1\frac{5}{12}$
$\frac{1}{5}$ and $\frac{3}{8}$	$\frac{8}{40}$ and $\frac{15}{40}$	$\frac{8}{40} + \frac{15}{40} = \frac{23}{40}$
$\frac{3}{10}$ and $\frac{6}{7}$	$\frac{21}{70}$ and $\frac{60}{70}$	$\frac{21}{70} + \frac{60}{70} = \frac{81}{70}$, or $1\frac{11}{70}$

2. Explain how you found a common denominator for one of the fraction pairs above.
Sample answer: For $\frac{7}{14}$ and $\frac{6}{8}$, $\frac{7}{14} = \frac{1}{2}$ and $\frac{6}{8} = \frac{3}{4}$. Since $\frac{1}{2} = \frac{2}{4}$, then $\frac{7}{14} = \frac{2}{4}$. So 4 is a common denominator.

Math Masters, p. 182

6•11 Progress Check 6

Objective To assess students' progress on mathematical content through the end of Unit 6.

1 Looking Back: Cumulative Assessment

The **Mid-Year Assessment** in the *Assessment Handbook* is a written assessment that you may use to determine how students are progressing toward a range of Grade-Level Goals.

Input student data from Progress Check 6 and the Mid-Year Assessment into the **Assessment Management Spreadsheets**.

Materials

- Study Link 6•10
- *Assessment Handbook,* pp. 92–99, 180–184, 221, and 266–269
- Mid-Year Assessment (*Assessment Handbook,* pp. 228–233, 242, and 243)
- slate

CONTENT ASSESSED	LESSON(S)	ASSESSMENT ITEMS				
		SELF	ORAL/SLATE	WRITTEN PART A	WRITTEN PART B	OPEN RESPONSE
Identify place value in numbers to billions. [Number and Numeration Goal 1]			2			
Solve problems involving percent. [Number and Numeration Goal 2]	6•5				20b–20d	
Convert among fractions, decimals, and percents. [Number and Numeration Goal 5]	6•5, 6•6	7	3, 4		22	
Find common denominators. [Number and Numeration Goal 5]	6•9, 6•10	4		14, 15	21	
Use paper-and-pencil algorithms to solve problems involving whole numbers. [Operations and Computation Goals 1 and 3]						✓
Add and subtract fractions with like denominators. [Operations and Computation Goal 4]	6•8–6•10	5		6, 8	19c	
Add and subtract fractions with unlike denominators. [Operations and Computation Goal 4]	6•8–6•10	6		7, 9–13	19b	
Use benchmarks to estimate sums and differences. [Operations and Computation Goal 6]	6•8–6•10		1			
Construct stem-and-leaf plots. [Data and Chance Goal 1]	6•3, 6•4, 6•6	1, 2			18	
Identify and use data landmarks; interpret data. [Data and Chance Goal 2]	6•1–6•3, 6•5–6•7			1–5a, 16	17, 20a	✓
Understand how sample size affects results. [Data and Chance Goal 2]	6•5, 6•6	3		5b, 5c	20e	
Measure to the nearest $\frac{1}{8}$ of an inch. [Measurement and Reference Frames Goal 1]	6•2, 6•3				19a	

2 Looking Ahead: Preparing for Unit 7

Math Boxes 6•11

Study Link 6•11: Unit 7 Family Letter

Materials

- *Math Journal 1,* p. 204
- *Math Masters,* pp. 183–186

Getting Started

Math Message • Self Assessment

Complete the Self Assessment (Assessment Handbook, p. 180).

Study Link 6•10 Follow-Up

Briefly review students' answers.

1 Looking Back: Cumulative Assessment

Math Message Follow-Up

(Self Assessment, *Assessment Handbook*, p. 180)

The Self Assessment offers students the opportunity to reflect upon their progress.

Oral and Slate Assessments

Problems 1 and 2 provide summative information and can be used for grading purposes. Problems 3 and 4 provide formative information that can be useful in planning future instruction.

Oral Assessment

1. Decide if the sum or difference for each fraction expression is closest to 0, $\frac{1}{2}$, or 1.
   - $\frac{3}{8} + \frac{2}{8}$ $\frac{1}{2}$
   - $\frac{3}{19} + \frac{8}{9}$ 1
   - $\frac{1}{5} + \frac{1}{4}$ $\frac{1}{2}$
   - $\frac{1}{12} + \frac{1}{9}$ 0
   - $\frac{8}{8} - \frac{1}{9}$ 1
   - $\frac{3}{4} - \frac{1}{5}$ $\frac{1}{2}$
2. Round the following numbers to the indicated place value:
   - 489 to the nearest ten 490
   - 608 to the nearest ten 610
   - 23,605 to the nearest hundred 23,600
   - 18.27 to the nearest tenth 18.3
   - 200.73 to the nearest whole number 201

Slate Assessment

3. Write the decimal and percent for each fraction:
   - $\frac{2}{3}$ $0.\overline{6}$; $66\frac{2}{3}\%$
   - $\frac{3}{10}$ 0.3; 30%
   - $\frac{7}{25}$ 0.28; 28%
4. Rename as improper fractions:
   - $2\frac{3}{7}$ $\frac{17}{7}$
   - $3\frac{8}{6}$ $\frac{26}{6}$, or $\frac{13}{3}$
   - $4\frac{1}{2}$ $\frac{9}{2}$

Assessment Master

Name Date Time

LESSON 6•11 **Self Assessment** Progress Check 6

Think about each skill listed below. Assess your own progress by checking the most appropriate box.

Skills	I can do this on my own and explain how to do it.	I can do this on my own.	I can do this if I get help or look at an example.
1. Read stem-and-leaf plots.			
2. Make stem-and-leaf plots.			
3. Explain how sample size affects results.			
4. Find common denominators.			
5. Add and subtract fractions with like denominators.			
6. Add and subtract fractions with unlike denominators.			
7. Convert between fractions, decimals, and percents.			

Assessment Handbook, p. 180

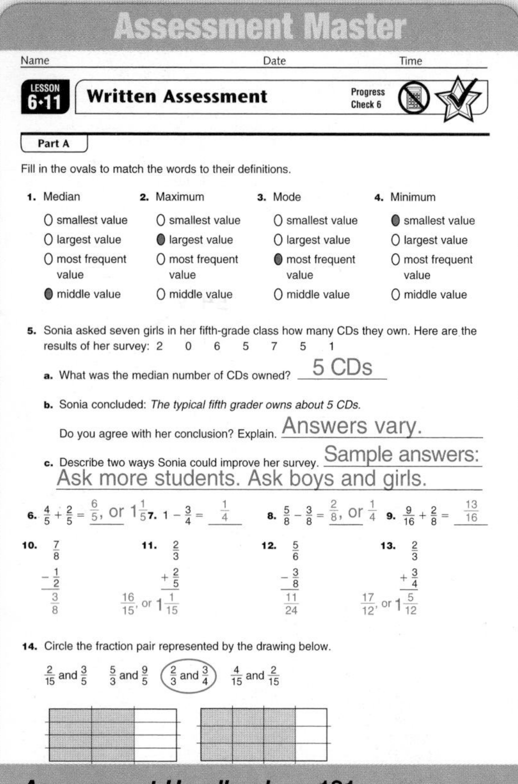

Assessment Master

Name Date Time

LESSON 6•11 **Written Assessment** Progress Check 6

Part A

Fill in the ovals to match the words to their definitions.

1. Median	2. Maximum	3. Mode	4. Minimum
○ smallest value	○ smallest value	○ smallest value	● smallest value
○ largest value	● largest value	○ largest value	○ largest value
○ most frequent value	○ most frequent value	● most frequent value	○ most frequent value
● middle value	○ middle value	○ middle value	○ middle value

5. Sonia asked seven girls in her fifth-grade class how many CDs they own. Here are the results of her survey: 2 0 6 5 7 5 1

a. What was the median number of CDs owned? 5 CDs

b. Sonia concluded: *The typical fifth grader owns about 5 CDs.*

Do you agree with her conclusion? Explain. Answers vary.

c. Describe two ways Sonia could improve her survey. Sample answers: Ask more students. Ask boys and girls.

6. $\frac{4}{5} + \frac{2}{5} = \frac{6}{5}$, or $1\frac{1}{5}$
7. $1 - \frac{3}{4} = \frac{1}{4}$
8. $\frac{5}{8} - \frac{3}{8} = \frac{2}{8}$, or $\frac{1}{4}$
9. $\frac{9}{16} + \frac{2}{8} = \frac{13}{16}$

10. $\frac{7}{8} - \frac{1}{2} = \frac{3}{8}$
11. $\frac{2}{3} + \frac{2}{5} = \frac{16}{15}$, or $1\frac{1}{15}$
12. $\frac{5}{6} - \frac{3}{8} = \frac{11}{24}$
13. $\frac{2}{3} + \frac{3}{4} = \frac{17}{12}$, or $1\frac{5}{12}$

14. Circle the fraction pair represented by the drawing below.

$\frac{2}{15}$ and $\frac{3}{5}$ $\frac{5}{3}$ and $\frac{9}{5}$ ($\frac{2}{3}$ and $\frac{3}{4}$) $\frac{4}{15}$ and $\frac{2}{15}$

Assessment Handbook, p. 181

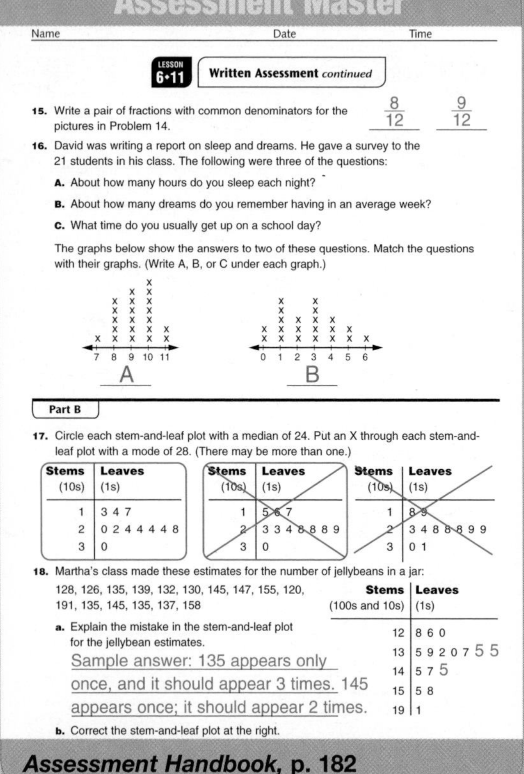

Assessment Master

Name Date Time

LESSON 6•11 **Written Assessment** *continued*

15. Write a pair of fractions with common denominators for the pictures in Problem 14. $\frac{8}{12}$ $\frac{9}{12}$

16. David was writing a report on sleep and dreams. He gave a survey to the 21 students in his class. The following were three of the questions:

A. About how many hours do you sleep each night?
B. About how many dreams do you remember having in an average week?
C. What time do you usually get up on a school day?

The graphs below show the answers to two of these questions. Match the questions with their graphs. (Write A, B, or C under each graph.)

A B

Part B

17. Circle each stem-and-leaf plot with a median of 24. Put an X through each stem-and-leaf plot with a mode of 28. (There may be more than one.)

Stems (10s)	Leaves (1s)
1	3 4 7
2	0 2 4 4 4 4 8
3	0

Stems (10s)	Leaves (1s)
1	5 6 7
2	3 3 4 8 8 8 9
3	0

Stems (10s)	Leaves (1s)
1	8 9
2	3 4 8 8 8 9 9
3	0 1

18. Martha's class made these estimates for the number of jellybeans in a jar:
128, 126, 135, 139, 132, 130, 145, 147, 155, 120, 191, 135, 145, 135, 137, 158

Stems (100s and 10s)	Leaves (1s)
12	8 6 0
13	5 9 2 0 7 5 5
14	5 7 5
15	5 8
19	1

a. Explain the mistake in the stem-and-leaf plot for the jellybean estimates. Sample answer: 135 appears only once, and it should appear 3 times. 145 appears once; it should appear 2 times.

b. Correct the stem-and-leaf plot at the right.

Assessment Handbook, p. 182

▶ Written Assessment

INDEPENDENT ACTIVITY

(*Assessment Handbook,* pp. 181–183)

Part A Recognizing Student Achievement

Problems 1–16 provide summative information and may be used for grading purposes.

Problem(s)	**Description**
1–5a, 16	Find and use data landmarks.
6, 8	Add and subtract fractions with like denominators.
7, 9–13	Add and subtract fractions with unlike denominators.
14, 15	Find a common denominator.
5b, 5c	Understand how sample size affects results.

Part B Informing Instruction

Problems 17–22 provide formative information that can be useful in planning future instruction.

Problem(s)	**Description**
17	Read and interpret stem-and-leaf plots.
18	Construct stem-and-leaf plots.
19a-b	Add and subtract fractions with unlike denominators.
19c	Add and subtract fractions with common denominators.
21	Find a common denominator.
20a–20d, 22	Convert between fractions, decimals, and percents.
20e	Understand how sample size affects results.

Use the checklists on pages 267 and 269 of the *Assessment Handbook* to record results. Then input the data into the **Assessment Management Spreadsheets** to keep an ongoing record of students' progress toward Grade-Level Goals.

▶ Open Response

INDEPENDENT ACTIVITY

(*Assessment Handbook,* p. 184)

Mean Age

Portfolio Ideas

The open-response item requires students to apply skills and concepts from Unit 6 to solve a multistep problem. See *Assessment Handbook,* pages 95–99 for rubrics and students' work samples for this problem.

▶ Mid-Year Assessment

INDEPENDENT ACTIVITY

(*Assessment Handbook*, pp. 228–233)

The Mid-Year Assessment (*Assessment Handbook,* pages 228–233) provides an additional assessment opportunity that you may use as part of your balanced assessment plan. This assessment covers some of the important concepts and skills presented in *Fifth Grade Everyday Mathematics.* They should be used to complement the ongoing and periodic assessments that appear within lessons and at the end of the units. Please see the *Assessment Handbook,* pages 100 and 101 for further information.

2 Looking Ahead: Preparing for Unit 7

▶ Math Boxes 6•11

(*Math Journal 1,* p. 204)

Mixed Practice This Math Boxes page previews Unit 7 content.

▶ Study Link 6•11: Unit 7 Family Letter

(*Math Masters,* pp. 183–186)

Home Connection The Unit 7 Family Letter provides parents and guardians with information and activities related to Unit 7 topics.

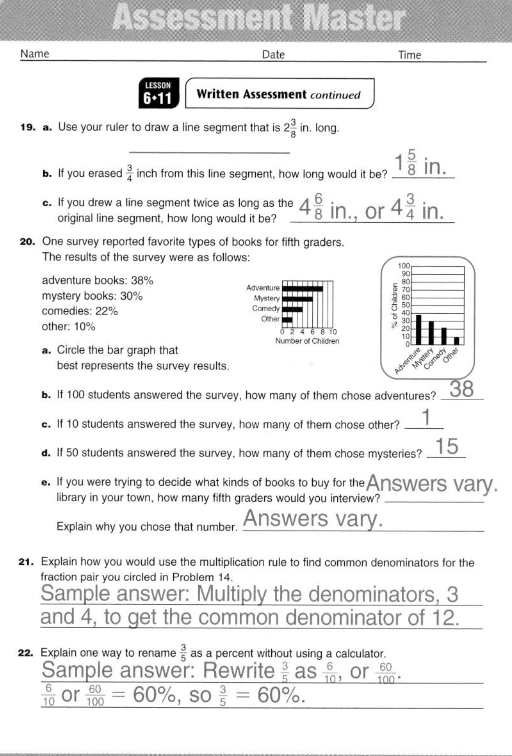

Assessment Master

Name Date Time

LESSON 6•11 Written Assessment *continued*

19. a. Use your ruler to draw a line segment that is $2\frac{3}{8}$ in. long.

b. If you erased $\frac{3}{4}$ inch from this line segment, how long would it be? $1\frac{5}{8}$ in.

c. If you drew a line segment twice as long as the original line segment, how long would it be? $4\frac{6}{8}$ in., or $4\frac{3}{4}$ in.

20. One survey reported favorite types of books for fifth graders. The results of the survey were as follows:

adventure books: 38%
mystery books: 30%
comedies: 22%
other: 10%

a. Circle the bar graph that best represents the survey results.

b. If 100 students answered the survey, how many of them chose adventures? 38

c. If 10 students answered the survey, how many of them chose other? 1

d. If 50 students answered the survey, how many of them chose mysteries? 15

e. If you were trying to decide what kinds of books to buy for the library in your town, how many fifth graders would you interview? Answers vary.

Explain why you chose that number. Answers vary.

21. Explain how you would use the multiplication rule to find common denominators for the fraction pair you circled in Problem 14.
Sample answer: Multiply the denominators, 3 and 4, to get the common denominator of 12.

22. Explain one way to rename $\frac{3}{5}$ as a percent without using a calculator.
Sample answer: Rewrite $\frac{3}{5}$ as $\frac{6}{10}$, or $\frac{60}{100}$. $\frac{6}{10}$ or $\frac{60}{100} = 60\%$, so $\frac{3}{5} = 60\%$.

Assessment Handbook, p. 183

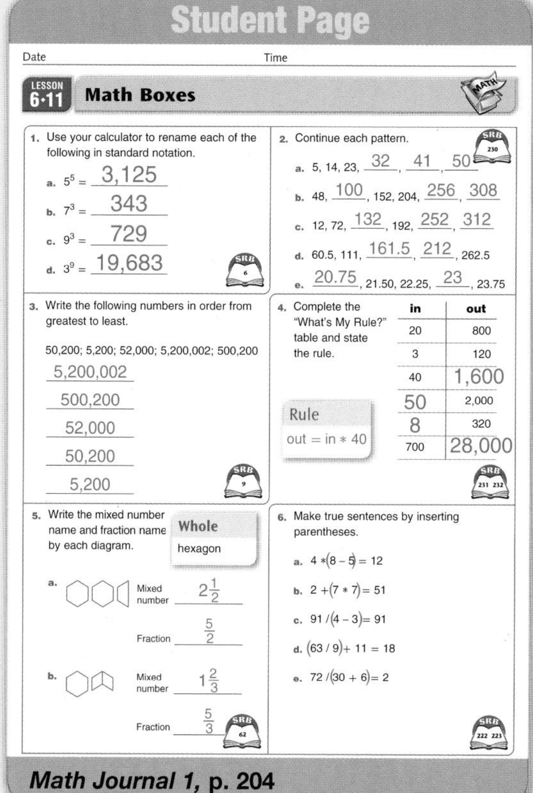

Student Page

Date Time

LESSON 6•11 **Math Boxes**

1. Use your calculator to rename each of the following in standard notation.
a. 5^5 = 3,125
b. 7^3 = 343
c. 9^3 = 729
d. 3^9 = 19,683

SRB 6

2. Continue each pattern.
a. 5, 14, 23, 32, 41, 50
b. 48, 100, 152, 204, 256, 308
c. 12, 72, 132, 192, 252, 312
d. 60.5, 111, 161.5, 212, 262.5
e. 20.75, 21.50, 22.25, 23, 23.75

SRB 230

3. Write the following numbers in order from greatest to least.
50,200; 5,200; 52,000; 5,200,002; 500,200
5,200,002
500,200
52,000
50,200
5,200

SRB 9

4. Complete the "What's My Rule?" table and state the rule.

in	out
20	800
3	120
40	1,600
50	2,000
8	320
700	28,000

Rule
out = in * 40

SRB 231 232

5. Write the mixed number name and fraction name by each diagram.

Whole
hexagon

a. Mixed number $2\frac{1}{2}$
Fraction $\frac{5}{2}$

b. Mixed number $1\frac{2}{3}$
Fraction $\frac{5}{3}$

SRB 62

6. Make true sentences by inserting parentheses.
a. 4 * (8 − 5) = 12
b. 2 + (7 * 7) = 51
c. 91 / (4 − 3) = 91
d. (63 / 9) + 11 = 18
e. 72 / (30 + 6) = 2

SRB 222 223

Math Journal 1, p. 204

Appendices

Contents

Project 1

The Sieve of Eratosthenes

Objective To provide experiences with identifying prime numbers and patterns in prime numbers.

Technology Resources www.everydaymathonline.com

eToolkit

Algorithms Practice

EM Facts Workshop Game™

Family Letters

Assessment Management

Common Core State Standards

Curriculum Focal Points

Interactive Teacher's Lesson Guide

1 Doing the Project

Recommended Use During or after Unit 1

Key Concepts and Skills

- Use the Sieve of Eratosthenes to identify prime numbers. [Number and Numeration Goal 3]
- Describe prime number patterns. [Patterns, Functions, and Algebra Goal 1]

Key Activities

Students use the Sieve of Eratosthenes, an ancient graphic device, to identify prime numbers and explore prime number patterns.

Key Vocabulary

prime number ◆ composite number ◆ multiples ◆ factors ◆ Sieve of Eratosthenes ◆ twin primes

Materials

- *Math Masters,* pp. 374–378
- transparency of *Math Masters*, p. 376
- Class Data Pad
- different-colored crayons, markers, or pencils

2 Extending the Project

Students find more information on prime numbers.

Materials

- encyclopedia
- computer with Internet access

Advance Preparation

Make a transparency of *Math Masters,* page 376 to demonstrate how to use the Sieve of Eratosthenes.

1 Doing the Project

▶ Introducing the Sieve of Eratosthenes

WHOLE-CLASS DISCUSSION

(*Math Masters,* pp. 374–376)

Have students read and discuss the essay on *Math Masters,* page 374. Be sure to review the definitions of **prime number** and **composite number.** Have the class practice finding **multiples** of numbers. It is important for students to understand that every multiple of a number n has n as one of its **factors.** For example, 8 is a multiple of 2; therefore, 2 is a factor of 8.

Use a transparency of *Math Masters,* page 376 to demonstrate how to use the **Sieve of Eratosthenes** (ĕr´ə-tŏs´thə-nēz´). Do the first three steps on *Math Masters,* page 375 with the class.

Project Master

Name Date Time

PROJECT 1 The Search for Prime Numbers

You probably know the following definitions of prime and composite numbers:

A **prime number** is a whole number that has exactly two **factors.** The factors are 1 and the number itself. For example, 7 is a prime number because its only factors are 1 and 7. A prime number is divisible by only 1 and itself.

A **composite number** is a whole number that has more than two factors. For example, 10 is a composite number because it has four factors: 1, 2, 5, and 10. A composite number is divisible by at least three whole numbers.

The number 1 is neither prime nor composite.

For centuries, mathematicians have been interested in prime and composite numbers because they are the building blocks of whole numbers. They have found that every composite number can be written as the product of prime numbers. For example, 18 can be written as 2 ∗ 3 ∗ 3.

Around 300 B.C., the Greek mathematician Euclid (yOO´klid) proved that there is no largest prime number. No matter how large a prime number you find, there will always be larger prime numbers. Since then, people have been searching for more prime numbers. In 1893, a mathematician was able to show that there are more than 50 million prime numbers between the numbers 1 and 1 billion.

The Greek mathematician Eratosthenes (ĕr´ə-tŏs´ thə-nēz´), who lived around 200 B.C., devised a simple method for finding prime numbers. His strategy was based on the fact that every **multiple of a number** is divisible by that number. For example, the numbers 2, 4, 6, 8, and 10 are multiples of 2, and each of these numbers is divisible by 2. Here is another way to say it: A whole number is a factor of every one of its multiples. For example, 2 is a factor of 2, 4, 6, 8, and 10. The number 2 has only one other factor, the number 1, so 2 is a prime number. All other multiples of 2 are composite numbers.

Eratosthenes' method is called the **Sieve of Eratosthenes.** The directions for using the sieve to find prime numbers are given on *Math Masters,* page 375.

Since the time of Eratosthenes, mathematicians have invented more powerful methods for finding prime numbers. Some methods use formulas. Today, people use computers. The largest prime number known when this book went to press had 9,152,052 digits. If that number were printed in a book with pages the same size as this page, in the same size type, the book would be about 1,400 pages long.

***Math Masters,* p. 374**

▶ Using the Sieve of Eratosthenes to Identify the Prime Numbers from 1 to 100

PARTNER ACTIVITY

(*Math Masters,* pp. 375–377)

Have students continue to circle numbers that have not already been crossed out and then cross out their multiples until all the numbers from 1 to 100 have either been circled or crossed out. Then have students list all prime numbers from 1 to 100 on *Math Masters,* page 375 and answer the questions on *Math Masters,* page 377.

Discuss students' answers. Have volunteers list the pairs of **twin primes** from 1 to 100 on the Class Data Pad. Encourage students to search for patterns, even if these are not obvious at first.

▶ Using the Sieve of Eratosthenes to Identify the Prime Numbers from 101 to 200

INDEPENDENT ACTIVITY

(*Math Masters,* p. 378)

Encourage students to identify prime numbers greater than 100 by crossing out multiples of the prime numbers from 1 to 200. Students use the extended grid on *Math Masters,* page 378.

Project Master

Name Date Time

PROJECT 1 The Sieve of Eratosthenes

Follow the directions below for *Math Masters,* page 376. When you have finished, you will have crossed out every number from 1 to 100 that is not a prime number.

1. Because 1 is not a prime number, cross it out.
2. Circle 2 with a colored marker or crayon. Then count by 2, crossing out all multiples of 2; that is, 4, 6, 8, 10, and so on.
3. Circle 3 with a different colored marker or crayon. Cross out every third number after 3—6, 9, 12, and so on. If a number is already crossed out, make a mark in a corner of the box. The numbers you have crossed out or marked are multiples of 3.
4. Skip 4, because it is already crossed out, and go on to 5. Use a new color to circle 5, and cross out multiples of 5.
5. Continue in the same pattern. Start each time by circling the next number that is not crossed out. Cross out all multiples of that number. If a number is already crossed out, make a mark in a corner of the box. Use a different color for each new set of multiples.
6. Stop when there are no more numbers to be circled or crossed out. The circled numbers are the prime numbers from 1 to 100.
7. List all the prime numbers from 1 to 100.
   2, 3, 5, 7, 11, 13, 17, 19, 23, 29, 31, 37, 41, 43, 47, 53, 59, 61, 67, 71, 73, 79, 83, 89, 97

***Math Masters,* p. 375**

2 Extending the Project

▶ Learning about Prime Numbers

Invite students to find out more about prime numbers in encyclopedias and math books and to visit Internet sites regarding prime numbers. For example, the sites listed below have information on the search for larger prime numbers and links to other prime-number sites. The largest known prime number, as of this printing, was found in 2008. It contains 12,978,189 digits.

http://primes.utm.edu/
http://www.mersenne.org/prime.htm

Project Master

Name Date Time

PROJECT 1 **The Sieve of Eratosthenes** *continued*

1	2	3	4	5	6	7	8	9	10
11	12	13	14	15	16	17	18	19	20
21	22	23	24	25	26	27	28	29	30
31	32	33	34	35	36	37	38	39	40
41	42	43	44	45	46	47	48	49	50
51	52	53	54	55	56	57	58	59	60
61	62	63	64	65	66	67	68	69	70
71	72	73	74	75	76	77	78	79	80
81	82	83	84	85	86	87	88	89	90
91	92	93	94	95	96	97	98	99	100

Math Masters, p. 376

Project Master

Name Date Time

PROJECT 1 **The Sieve of Eratosthenes** *continued*

1. What are the crossed-out numbers greater than 1 called?
   Composite numbers
2. Notice that 6 is a multiple of both 2 and 3. Find two other numbers that are multiples of both 2 and 3.
   42, 96, or any multiple of 6
3. Find a number that is a multiple of 2, 3, and 5. (*Hint:* Look at the colors.)
   30, 60, or 90
4. Find a number that is a multiple of 2, 3, 4, and 5. 60
5. Choose any crossed-out number between 50 and 60. List its factors.
   Sample answer: Factors of 54 are 1, 2, 3, 6, 9, 18, 27, 54.
6. List the crossed-out numbers that have no marks in the corners of their boxes.
   1, 4, 8, 9, 16, 25, 27, 32, 49, 64, 81
7. Find a pair of consecutive prime numbers. 2, 3
   Are there any others? No If yes, list them.
8. The numbers 3 and 5 are called **twin primes** because they are separated by just one composite number. List all the other twin primes from 1 to 100.
   5 and 7, 11 and 13, 17 and 19, 29 and 31, 41 and 43, 59 and 61, 71 and 73
9. Why do you think this grid is called a sieve? Sample answer: The grid is used like a sieve, or strainer, to separate prime and composite numbers.

Math Masters, p. 377

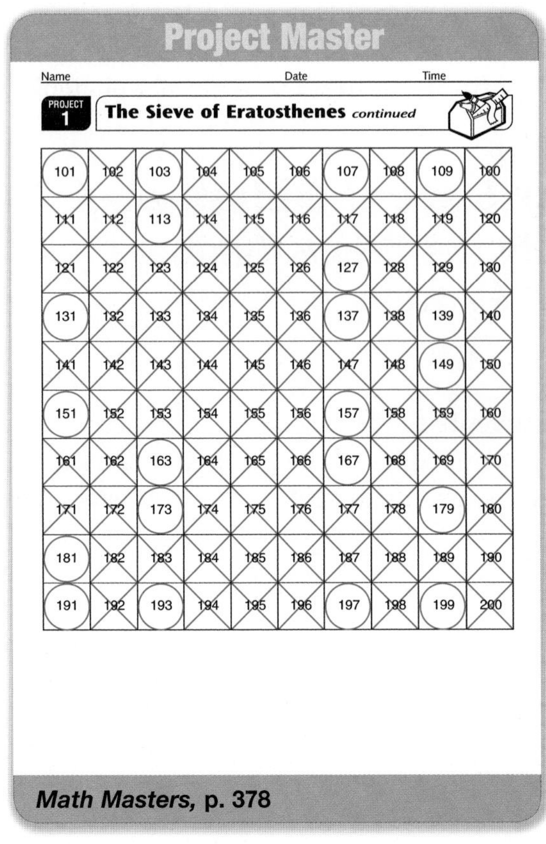
Project Master

Name Date Time

PROJECT 1 **The Sieve of Eratosthenes** *continued*

101	102	103	104	105	106	107	108	109	110
111	112	113	114	115	116	117	118	119	120
121	122	123	124	125	126	127	128	129	130
131	132	133	134	135	136	137	138	139	140
141	142	143	144	145	146	147	148	149	150
151	152	153	154	155	156	157	158	159	160
161	162	163	164	165	166	167	168	169	170
171	172	173	174	175	176	177	178	179	180
181	182	183	184	185	186	187	188	189	190
191	192	193	194	195	196	197	198	199	200

Math Masters, p. 378

Project 2

Deficient, Abundant, and Perfect Numbers

Objective To explore number properties.

Technology Resources www.everydaymathonline.com

eToolkit

Algorithms Practice

EM Facts Workshop Game™

Family Letters

Assessment Management

Common Core State Standards

Curriculum Focal Points

Interactive Teacher's Lesson Guide

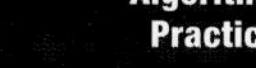

1 Doing the Project

Recommended Use After Unit 1

Key Concepts and Skills

- Factor numbers.
  [Number and Numeration Goal 3]
- Use parentheses to evaluate expressions.
  [Patterns, Functions, and Algebra Goal 3]

Key Activities

Students classify the whole numbers through 50 according to the sums of their proper factors.

Key Vocabulary

factor ◆ proper factor ◆ deficient number ◆ abundant number ◆ perfect number

Materials

- ◆ *Student Reference Book,* p. 306 (optional)
- ◆ *Math Masters,* pp. 379–382
- ◆ calculator

2 Extending the Project

Students find more information on perfect numbers and Mersenne numbers.

Materials

- ◆ encyclopedia
- ◆ computer with Internet access

1 Doing the Project

▶ Introducing Deficient, Abundant, and Perfect Numbers

WHOLE-CLASS DISCUSSION

(*Math Masters,* p. 379)

Ask students to read the definitions on *Math Masters,* page 379. Then go over the definitions of **factor**, **proper factor**, **deficient number**, **abundant number**, and **perfect number**.

Ask questions such as the following:

- What are the factors of 15? 1, 3, 5, 15
- What are the proper factors of 15? 1, 3, 5
- What is the sum of the proper factors of 15? $1 + 3 + 5 = 9$
- Is 15 a deficient, abundant, or perfect number? deficient

If students have no trouble answering these questions, repeat the sequence with a more challenging number, such as 60. Point out that the terms *deficient, abundant,* and *perfect* have historical origins but do not define a number's importance. They are merely labels.

▶ Classifying Whole Numbers by the Sums of Their Proper Factors

SMALL-GROUP ACTIVITY

(*Math Masters,* pp. 379–381)

Have students read the instructions at the bottom of *Math Masters,* page 379. Suggest that each group divide the work among partnerships. Partners should check each other's work. When members of each group have reached agreement on the answers for each number, they record the results in the tables on *Math Masters,* pages 380 and 381. Then they answer the questions at the bottom of *Math Masters,* page 381.

Bring the groups together to report their findings. Problems 5 and 6 reveal an interesting pattern:

- The sum of the proper factors of a power of 2 (2^1, 2^2, 2^3, and so on) is 1 less than the power of 2. For example, $2^4 = 16$, and the sum of the proper factors of 2^4 (16), is $16 - 1 = 15$.
- The sum of all the factors of a power of 2 is equal to the sum of the proper factors plus the power itself. This can be found by doubling the number and subtracting 1. For example, the sum of all the factors of 2^4 (16), is $(2 * 16) - 1 = 31$.

Project Master

Name Date Time

PROJECT 2 **Deficient, Abundant, and Perfect Numbers**

A **factor** of a whole number *N* is any whole number that can be multiplied by a whole number to give *N* as the product. For example, 5 is a factor of 30 because $6 * 5 = 30$. Also, 6 is a factor of 30. Every whole number has itself and 1 as factors.

A **proper factor** of a whole number is any factor of that number except the number itself. For example, the *factors* of 10 are 1, 2, 5, and 10. The *proper factors* of 10 are 1, 2, and 5.

A whole number is a **deficient number** if the sum of its proper factors is less than the number. For example, 10 is a deficient number because the sum of its proper factors is $1 + 2 + 5 = 8$, and 8 is less than 10.

A whole number is an **abundant number** if the sum of its proper factors is greater than the number. For example, 12 is an abundant number because the sum of its proper factors is $1 + 2 + 3 + 4 + 6 = 16$, and 16 is greater than 12.

A whole number is a **perfect number** if the sum of its proper factors is equal to the number. For example, 6 is a perfect number because the sum of its proper factors is $1 + 2 + 3 = 6$.

Exploration

List the proper factors of each number from 1 to 50 in the table on *Math Masters,* pages 380 and 381. Then find the sum of the proper factors of each number, and record it in the third column of the table. Finally, make a check mark in the appropriate column to show whether the number is deficient, abundant, or perfect.

Divide the work with the other members of your group. Have partners use factor rainbows to check each other's work. When you are satisfied that all the results are correct, answer the questions on page 381.

***Math Masters,* p. 379**

Project Master

Name Date Time

PROJECT 2 **Deficient, Abundant, and Perfect Numbers** *cont.*

Number	Proper Factors	Sum of Proper Factors	Deficient	Abundant	Perfect
1		0	✓		
2	1	1	✓		
3	1	1	✓		
4	1, 2	3	✓		
5	1	1	✓		
6	1, 2, 3	6			✓
7	1	1	✓		
8	1, 2, 4	7	✓		
9	1, 3	4	✓		
10	1, 2, 5	8	✓		
11	1	1	✓		
12	1, 2, 3, 4, 6	16		✓	
13	1	1	✓		
14	1, 2, 7	10	✓		
15	1, 3, 5	9	✓		
16	1, 2, 4, 8	15	✓		
17	1	1	✓		
18	1, 2, 3, 6, 9	21		✓	
19	1	1	✓		
20	1, 2, 4, 5, 10	22		✓	
21	1, 3, 7	11	✓		
22	1, 2, 11	14	✓		
23	1	1	✓		
24	1, 2, 3, 4, 6, 8, 12	36		✓	
25	1, 5	6	✓		
26	1, 2, 13	16	✓		
27	1, 3, 9	13	✓		
28	1, 2, 4, 7, 14	28			✓
29	1	1	✓		
30	1, 2, 3, 5, 6, 10, 15	42		✓	
31	1	1	✓		
32	1, 2, 4, 8, 16	31	✓		
33	1, 3, 11	15	✓		
34	1, 2, 17	20	✓		

***Math Masters,* p. 380**

The classification of whole numbers according to the sums of their proper factors can help students choose the best possible numbers when playing *Factor Captor.* Encourage students to refer to the tables on *Math Masters,* pages 380 and 381 when they play the game (*Student Reference Book,* page 306).

Looking for Additional Perfect Numbers

INDEPENDENT ACTIVITY

(*Math Masters,* p. 382)

Students work independently or in small groups to find the third and fourth perfect numbers. They use the method described on *Math Masters,* page 382.

Adjusting the Activity

Have students try to find the fifth perfect number. The next starting number whose factors add up to a prime number is 4,096. The sum of its factors is (2 ∗ 4,096) − 1 = 8,191. The product of 4,096 and 8,191 is 33,550,336, which is the fifth perfect number.

AUDITOR ◆ KINESTHETIC ◆ TACTILE ◆ VISUAL

2 Extending the Project

Learning More about Perfect Numbers

INDEPENDENT ACTIVITY

The search for perfect numbers is based on the ideas presented on *Math Masters,* page 382. As noted earlier, the sum of the proper factors of a power of 2 is equal to 1 less than the power of 2, or $2^n - 1$. Numbers of this form are called *Mersenne numbers*. If a Mersenne number is a prime number, it is called a *Mersenne prime*. Mersenne primes are used to generate perfect numbers.

Have students use encyclopedias or other reference books to find more information on perfect numbers and Mersenne numbers. Many Internet sites are devoted to prime numbers, perfect numbers, and Mersenne primes. For example, see http://www.mersenne.org/prime.htm.

Project Master

Name Date Time

PROJECT 2 **Deficient, Abundant, and Perfect Numbers** *cont.*

Number	Proper Factors	Sum of Proper Factors	Deficient	Abundant	Perfect
35	1, 5, 7	13	✓		
36	1, 2, 3, 4, 6, 9, 12, 18	55		✓	
37	1	1	✓		
38	1, 2, 19	22	✓		
39	1, 3, 13	17	✓		
40	1, 2, 4, 5, 8, 10, 20	50		✓	
41	1	1	✓		
42	1, 2, 3, 6, 7, 14, 21	54		✓	
43	1	1	✓		
44	1, 2, 4, 11, 22	40	✓		
45	1, 3, 5, 9, 15	33	✓		
46	1, 2, 23	26	✓		
47	1	1	✓		
48	1, 2, 3, 4, 6, 8, 12, 16, 24	76		✓	
49	1, 7	8	✓		
50	1, 2, 5, 10, 25	43	✓		

Source: *The Math Teacher's Book of Lists.* San Francisco: Jossey-Bass, 2005.

Refer to the results in your table.

1. What are the perfect numbers up to 50? 6 and 28
2. Is there an abundant number that is not an even number? No
3. Are all deficient numbers odd numbers? No
4. What is the next number greater than 50 for which the sum of its proper factors is 1? 53
5. The sum of the proper factors of 4 is 1 less than 4. List all the numbers through 50 for which the sum of the proper factors is 1 less than the number itself. 2, 4, 8, 16, 32
6. What do you think is the next number greater than 50 for which the sum of its proper factors is 1 less than the number itself? 64

Math Masters, p. 381

Project Master

Name Date Time

PROJECT 2 **A Perfect-Number Challenge**

Perfect numbers become big very quickly. The third perfect number has 3 digits, the fourth has 4 digits, the fifth has 8 digits, the sixth has 10 digits, and the thirty-second has 455,663 digits! In other words, perfect numbers are hard to find.

You can find perfect numbers without having to find the sum of the proper factors of every number. Here is what you do:

1. Complete the pattern of starting numbers in the first column of the table.
2. List the factors of each starting number in the second column.
3. Write the sum of the factors of each starting number in the third column.
4. If the sum of the factors of the starting number is prime, multiply this sum by the starting number itself. The product is a perfect number. Record it in the last column.

The first perfect number is 6. Try to find the next three perfect numbers.

Starting Number	Factors	Sum of Factors	Perfect Number
2	*1, 2*	*3*	*6*
4	1, 2, 4	7	28
8	1, 2, 4, 8	15	
16	1, 2, 4, 8, 16	31	496
32	1, 2, 4, 8, 16, 32	63	
64	1, 2, 4, 8, 16, 32, 64	127	8,128
128	1, 2, 4, 8, 16, 32, 64, 128	255	

People have been fascinated by perfect numbers for centuries. The ancient Greeks knew the first four. No one found the fifth perfect number until the year 1456. Computers now carry on the search for perfect numbers. When this book went to press, 42 perfect numbers had been identified. All the perfect numbers found so far are even numbers.

Math Masters, p. 382

Project 3

An Ancient Multiplication Algorithm

Objective To explore number theory concepts and multiplication algorithms.

Technology Resources www.everydaymathonline.com

eToolkit

Algorithms Practice

EM Facts Workshop Game™

Family Letters

Assessment Management

Common Core State Standards

Curriculum Focal Points

Interactive Teacher's Lesson Guide

1 Doing the Project

Recommended Use During or after Unit 2

Key Concepts and Skills

- Use exponential notation to represent whole numbers. [Number and Numeration Goal 4]
- Use paper-and-pencil algorithms to multiply whole numbers. [Operations and Computation Goal 3]
- Explain how multiplication strategies work. [Operations and Computation Goal 3]

Key Activities

Students examine a multiplication algorithm that was invented in Egypt more than 4,000 years ago. They compare multiplication algorithms and list their advantages and their disadvantages.

Key Vocabulary

powers of 2 ◆ partial products

Materials

- ◆ *Math Masters,* pp. 383–385
- ◆ Class Data Pad
- ◆ transparency (optional)

2 Extending the Project

Students use the Egyptian algorithm with hieroglyphs and Roman numerals.

Students use the Internet to learn more about different numeral systems.

Materials

- ◆ *Math Masters,* p. 386
- ◆ computer with Internet access

1 Doing the Project

▶ Exploring an Ancient Method of Multiplication

(*Math Masters,* pp. 383 and 384)

Read and discuss the introduction and Problems 1 and 2 on *Math Masters,* page 383 as a class. On the Class Data Pad, list the **powers of 2** from the table on the *Math Masters* page. Model the steps for the Egyptian method of multiplication on the board or a transparency. Allow partners time to discuss Problem 3. Then ask volunteers to share their responses. Some students may have analyzed the Egyptian algorithm in Part 3 of Lesson 2-9; consider having these students lead the discussion.

Have students solve the three multiplication problems at the top of *Math Masters,* page 384 using the Egyptian algorithm.

Finally, have students look at the first two problems at the bottom of *Math Masters,* page 384, which have been solved using a variation of the Egyptian algorithm. Ask students to solve the third problem by the same method. Recreational mathematics books call this method the Russian Peasant Algorithm. It is performed by repeatedly halving the number in the left column, ignoring any nonzero remainders, and doubling the number in the right column. All rows that have an even number in the left column are crossed out, and the remaining numbers in the right column are added. The sum of these **partial products** is the answer to the multiplication problem.

▶ Comparing Multiplication Algorithms

(*Math Masters,* p. 385)

Have students consider the multiplication algorithms they know and record the advantages and the disadvantages of each on *Math Masters,* page 385. This should help students decide which algorithm works best for them. However, this need not be the only algorithm they use. It is also important to emphasize that a paper-and-pencil algorithm might not be the most efficient way to solve a problem. Mental computation, a calculator, or an estimate might be a better choice.

When students have completed their comparison charts, bring them together to share preferences. Have students support their choices with examples.

Project Master

Name Date Time

PROJECT 3 An Ancient Multiplication Method

Thousands of years ago, the Egyptians developed one of the earliest multiplication methods. Their method uses an idea from number theory.

Every positive whole number can be expressed as a sum of powers of 2.

2^0	2^1	2^2	2^3	2^4	2^5	2^6
1	2	4	8	16	32	64

Write a number sentence to show each of the numbers below as the sum of powers of 2. For example, 13 = 1 + 4 + 8.

1. 19 = 1 + 2 + 16 **2.** 67 = 1 + 2 + 64

Follow the steps below to use the Egyptian method to multiply 19 * 62.

Step 1 List the powers of 2 that are less than the first factor, 19.

Step 2 List the products of the powers of 2 and the second factor, 62. Notice that each product is double the product before it.

Step 3 Put a check mark next to the powers of 2 whose sum is the first factor, 19.

Step 4 Cross out the remaining rows.

Step 5 Add the partial products that are not crossed out.
62 + 124 + 992 = 1,178
So 19 * 62 = 1,178

19 * 62 =	
1	62
2	124
4	248
8	496
16	992

19 * 62 = 1,178	
✓ 1	62
✓ 2	124
~~4~~	~~248~~
~~8~~	~~496~~
✓ 16	992

3. Explain why you don't have to multiply by any number other than 2 to write the list of partial products when you use the Egyptian method.
Once you begin the list, think of the powers of 2 as repeated-factor expressions. So each time you multiply, it's the previous product multiplied by 2. This is because each time you are multiplying by one more factor of 2. For example, $2^3 * 62 = 2 * 2 * 2 * 62$, or 8 * 62, and $2^4 * 62$ can be thought of as 8 * 62 * 2. So if you know that $2^3 * 62 = 496$, then $2^4 * 62 = 496 * 2$.

Math Masters, p. 383

Project Master

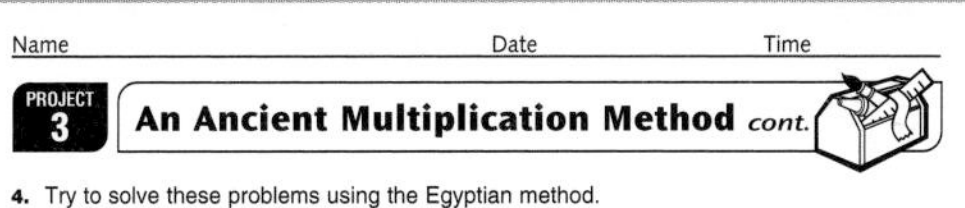
Name Date Time

PROJECT 3 An Ancient Multiplication Method *cont.*

4. Try to solve these problems using the Egyptian method.

85 * 14 = 1,190		38 * 43 = 1,634		45 * 29 = 1,305	
✓ 1	14	~~1~~	~~43~~	✓ 1	29
~~2~~	~~28~~	✓ 2	86	~~2~~	~~58~~
✓ 4	56	✓ 4	172	✓ 4	116
~~8~~	~~112~~	~~8~~	~~344~~	✓ 8	232
✓ 16	224	~~16~~	~~688~~	~~16~~	~~464~~
~~32~~	~~448~~	✓ 32	1,376	✓ 32	928
✓ 64	896		1,634		1,305
	1,190				

Try This

5. Here is another ancient multiplication method, based on the Egyptian method. People living in rural areas of Russia, Ethiopia, and the Near East still use this method. See whether you can figure out how it works. Then try to complete the problem in the third box, using this method.

13 * 25 = 325		38 * 43 = 1,634		45 * 29 = 1,305	
13	25	~~38~~	~~43~~	45	29
~~6~~	~~50~~	19	86	~~22~~	~~58~~
3	100	9	172	11	116
1	200	~~4~~	~~344~~	5	232
	325	~~2~~	~~688~~	~~2~~	~~464~~
		1	1,376	1	928
			1,634		1,305

Math Masters, p. 384

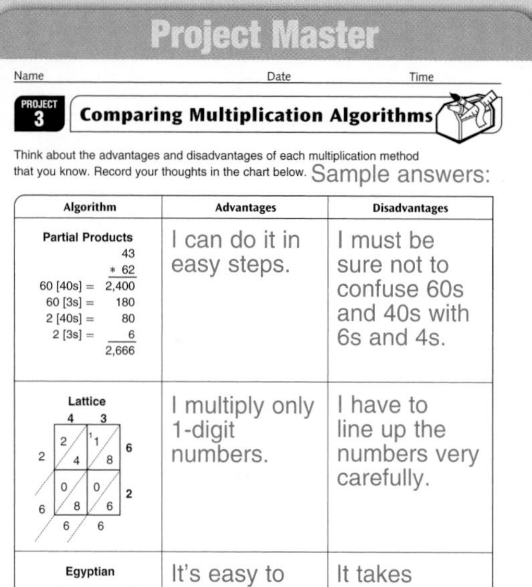
Project Master

Name ______ Date ______ Time ______

PROJECT 3 **Comparing Multiplication Algorithms**

Think about the advantages and disadvantages of each multiplication method that you know. Record your thoughts in the chart below. Sample answers:

Algorithm	Advantages	Disadvantages
Partial Products 43 * 62 60 [40s] = 2,400 60 [3s] = 180 2 [40s] = 80 2 [3s] = 6 2,666	I can do it in easy steps.	I must be sure not to confuse 60s and 40s with 6s and 4s.
Lattice (4 3 / 6 2 lattice; 2,666)	I multiply only 1-digit numbers.	I have to line up the numbers very carefully.
Egyptian 43 * 62 ✓ 1 62 ✓ 2 124 ~~4 248~~ ✓ 8 496 ~~16 992~~ ✓ 32 1,984 2,666	It's easy to work with doubles of numbers.	It takes too long to double numbers.

Math Masters, p. 385

Hindu-Arabic	0	1	2	3	4	5	6	7	8	9	10
Babylonian		▼	▼▼	▼▼▼	▼▼▼▼	▼▼▼▼▼	▼▼▼▼▼▼	▼▼▼▼▼▼▼	▼▼▼▼▼▼▼▼	▼▼▼▼▼▼▼▼▼	<
Egyptian		|	||	|||	||||	|||||	||||||	|||||||	||||||||	|||||||||	∩
Mayan	(shell)	•	••	•••	••••	—	•—	••—	•••—	••••—	=
Greek		α	β	γ	δ	ε	ϛ	ζ	η	θ	ι
Roman		I	II	III	IV	V	VI	VII	VIII	IX	X

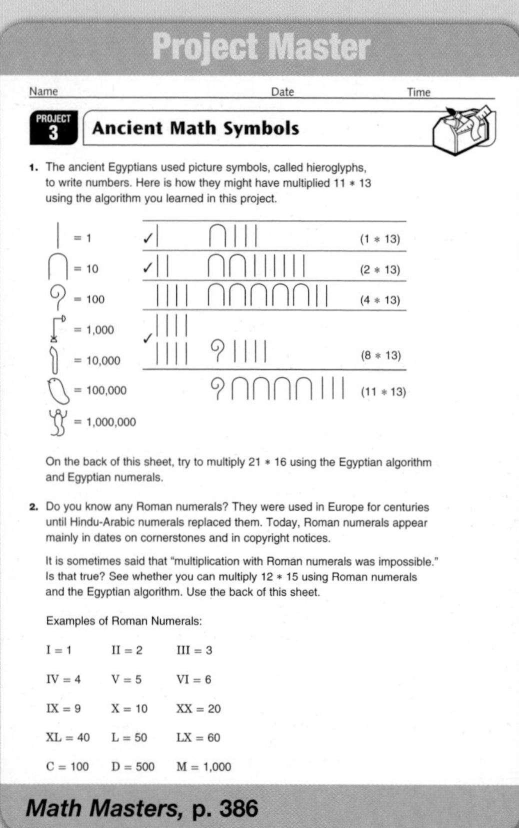
Project Master

Name ______ Date ______ Time ______

PROJECT 3 **Ancient Math Symbols**

1. The ancient Egyptians used picture symbols, called hieroglyphs, to write numbers. Here is how they might have multiplied 11 * 13 using the algorithm you learned in this project.

= 1; = 10; = 100; = 1,000; = 10,000; = 100,000; = 1,000,000

(1 * 13) (2 * 13) (4 * 13) (8 * 13) (11 * 13)

On the back of this sheet, try to multiply 21 * 16 using the Egyptian algorithm and Egyptian numerals.

2. Do you know any Roman numerals? They were used in Europe for centuries until Hindu-Arabic numerals replaced them. Today, Roman numerals appear mainly in dates on cornerstones and in copyright notices.

It is sometimes said that "multiplication with Roman numerals was impossible." Is that true? See whether you can multiply 12 * 15 using Roman numerals and the Egyptian algorithm. Use the back of this sheet.

Examples of Roman Numerals:

I = 1	II = 2	III = 3
IV = 4	V = 5	VI = 6
IX = 9	X = 10	XX = 20
XL = 40	L = 50	LX = 60
C = 100	D = 500	M = 1,000

Math Masters, p. 386

2 Extending the Project

▶ Using Ancient Numerals in Multiplication Algorithms

PARTNER ACTIVITY

(*Math Masters,* p. 386)

Problem 1 on *Math Masters,* page 386 shows how the ancient Egyptians might have used their hieroglyph numerals and algorithm to multiply two numbers. Ask students to solve Problem 1 using hieroglyph numerals. When most students have finished, have volunteers share their solutions on the board.

Problem 2 asks students to use the Egyptian algorithm to multiply with Roman numerals. Ask students to solve Problem 2 using Roman numerals. It is sometimes said that "multiplication with Roman numerals was impossible," but, at least for smaller numbers, it seems possible with this algorithm. Have volunteers share their solutions on the board.

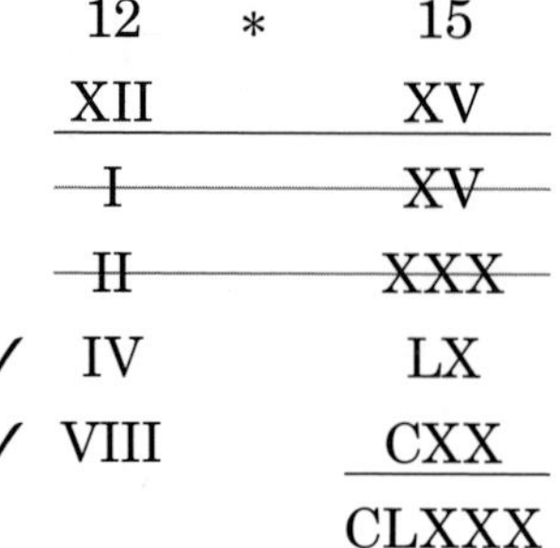

Ask the class if they feel it would be possible to multiply Roman numerals for larger numbers using the Egyptian algorithm. Allow partners time to explore multiplying Roman numerals for larger numbers.

▶ Learning More about Number Systems

Much information about Egyptian mathematics is found on a scroll called the Rhind papyrus. This scroll, copied about 1650 B.C., is named after the man who purchased it in Egypt in A.D. 1858. It is now in the British Museum in London.

Invite students to use the Internet to learn more about different numeral systems, such as the Egyptian, Roman, and Babylonian numeral systems. (The Babylonian numeral system uses a base of 60.) Consider having students make Venn diagrams to compare the similarities and differences between the base-10 number system and a different numeral system of their choice.

The Web site below offers links to a variety of Internet sites on number systems: http://mathforum.org/alejandre/numerals.html

Project 4

"Magic" Computation Tricks

Objective To explore properties of arithmetic.

Technology Resources www.everydaymathonline.com

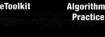

eToolkit | Algorithms Practice | EM Facts Workshop Game™ | Family Letters | Assessment Management | Common Core State Standards | Curriculum Focal Points | Interactive Teacher's Lesson Guide

1 Doing the Project

Recommended Use During or after Unit 2

Key Concepts and Skills

- Identify places in whole numbers and the values of the digits in those places. [Number and Numeration Goal 1]
- Use algorithms to add and subtract whole numbers. [Operations and Computation Goal 1]
- Apply properties of arithmetic. [Patterns, Functions, and Algebra Goal 4]

Key Activities

Students read a description of a "magic" computation trick and try to figure out how it is done. They learn how to perform the trick and then teach it to other students. After completing this project, students should be able to perform and explain three computation tricks.

Materials

- *Math Masters,* pp. 387–393
- calculator
- 6 six-sided dice

2 Extending the Project

Students explore variations of their computation tricks.

Materials

- *Math Masters,* pp. 391–393
- computer with Internet access (optional)

Project Master

Name Date Time

PROJECT 4 **Computation Trick #1—Super Speedy Addition**

Set the Stage: Tell a friend that you have become a whiz at addition. To prove it, you are going to add five 3-digit numbers in your head within seconds.

Props Needed: calculator

Performing the Trick:	**Examples:** Trial 1	Trial 2	Trial 3
1. Ask your friend to jot down a 3-digit number on a piece of paper. Each digit must be different.	493	261	682
2. Ask your friend to write another 3-digit number below the first number. Each digit must be different.	764	503	149
3. One more time. (This is the "notice-me number.")	175	935	306
4. Now it is your turn. Write a number so that the sum of your number and the first number is 999. (For example, in Trial 1, 493 + 506 = 999.)	506	738	317
5. Write another number so that the sum of this number and the second number is 999. (For example, in Trial 1, 764 + 235 = 999.)	+ 235	+ 496	+ 850
6. Pause a few seconds, and then give the sum of the five numbers. Have your friend check your super speedy addition on a calculator.	2,173	2,933	2,304

Figure out how to do this trick. How does it work?

You know that your partner's first 2 numbers and your last 2 numbers total 2 less than 2,000. Subtract 2 from the third number. Add the result to 2,000.

Math Masters, p. 387

Project Master

Name Date Time

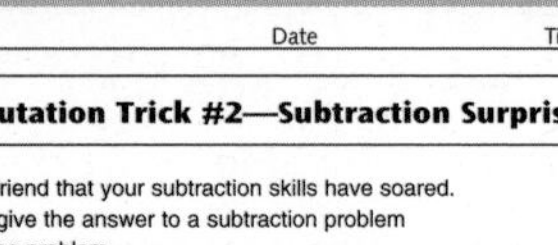

PROJECT 4 **Computation Trick #2—Subtraction Surprise**

Set the Stage: Tell a friend that your subtraction skills have soared. You are now able to give the answer to a subtraction problem without ever seeing the problem.

Props Needed: calculator

Performing the Trick:	**Examples:** Trial 1	Trial 2
1. Ask your friend to secretly write a 3-digit number on a piece of paper. Each digit must be different.	135	562
2. Tell your friend to reverse the digits and write the new number below the first number.	531	265
3. Now have your friend use a calculator to subtract the smaller number from the larger number.	531 − 135 = 396	562 − 265 = 297
4. Say: *Tell me either the digit in the hundreds place or the digit in the ones place.*	3 in the hundreds place	7 in the ones place
5. Pause a few seconds, and then give the answer.	396	297

Figure out how to do this trick. How does it work?

The sum of the digits in the ones place and the hundreds place is always 9. The tens place is always 9.

Math Masters, p. 388

1 Doing the Project

Demonstrating a Magic Number Trick with Dice

WHOLE-CLASS DISCUSSION

Play "magician" and announce that you are going to perform a magic number trick. Tell students to watch you carefully and to try to figure out how you did it.

Ask a student to roll 5 dice and find the sum of all the numbers on the top and bottom of the dice. Before the student has had much time to think, announce that the sum of all the numbers on the top and bottom of the dice is 35.

Perform the trick again, this time with 6 dice. Again, give the answer quickly, 42. Repeat with other numbers of dice. Ask each time whether anyone has figured out how to do the trick. The sum is equal to 7 times the number of dice rolled. For example, the sum is 28 with 4 dice; the sum is 56 with 8 dice; and so on.

At some point, someone is likely to notice the pattern. If no one figures it out, share it with the class:

▷ On a six-sided die, the sum of the numbers on each pair of opposite faces is 7. Therefore, with 5 dice, the sum of the numbers on the top and bottom is $7 * 5 = 35$, no matter which numbers come up on top when the dice are rolled. With 6 dice, the sum is $7 * 6 = 42$, and so on.

Learning a Magic Computation Trick

SMALL-GROUP ACTIVITY

(*Math Masters,* pp. 387–393)

Divide the class into three equal groups. Tell students that each group will figure out how to do a magic computation trick. When they have figured it out, each student in the group will teach it to one member in each of the other two groups.

Give each student in one group a copy of *Math Masters,* page 387. Give each student in a second group one copy of *Math Masters,* page 388 and each student in the third group a copy of *Math Masters,* pages 389 and 390. Give the groups 10–15 minutes to figure out how the tricks work and to write a brief explanation.

Then give one or more copies of *Math Masters,* page 391 to the first group; *Math Masters,* page 392 to the second group; and *Math Masters,* page 393 to the third group. The top section of each page explains the group's original trick. Ask students to compare their explanations with the *Math Masters* page. Then have each group work together until all members are certain they can perform and explain the trick.

▶ Teaching Computation Tricks to Other Students

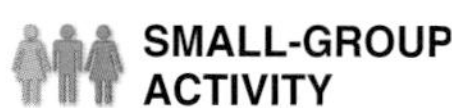
SMALL-GROUP ACTIVITY

Mix up the groups and form groups of three students, consisting of one student from each of the original three groups. Each student in a group performs a trick and teaches it to the other two students in the group.

You can form groups of three by having students in each of the original groups count off "1, 2, 3, ..." Then all the 1s form a group, all the 2s form another group, and so on. If the original groups do not have the same number of members, you can team up a pair of students to present the same trick in one of the other groups.

▶ Discussing the Computation Tricks

WHOLE-CLASS DISCUSSION

Bring students together to discuss the computation tricks. Possible questions:

- Which trick did you find easiest to learn? The hardest to learn?
- Was it easy or hard to teach your trick to others? Why?
- Which trick would you most like to share with someone at home? Why?

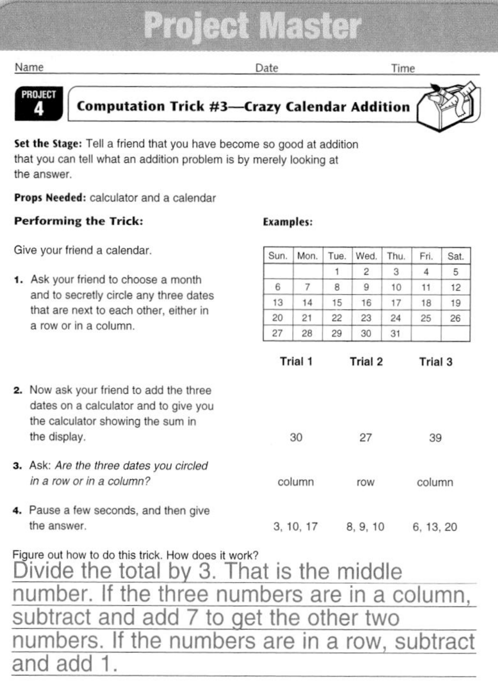

Project Master

Name Date Time

PROJECT 4 **Computation Trick #3—Crazy Calendar Addition**

Set the Stage: Tell a friend that you have become so good at addition that you can tell what an addition problem is by merely looking at the answer.

Props Needed: calculator and a calendar

Performing the Trick:

Give your friend a calendar.

1. Ask your friend to choose a month and to secretly circle any three dates that are next to each other, either in a row or in a column.

Examples:

Sun.	Mon.	Tue.	Wed.	Thu.	Fri.	Sat.
		1	2	3	4	5
6	7	8	9	10	11	12
13	14	15	16	17	18	19
20	21	22	23	24	25	26
27	28	29	30	31		

	Trial 1	Trial 2	Trial 3
2. Now ask your friend to add the three dates on a calculator and to give you the calculator showing the sum in the display.	30	27	39
3. Ask: *Are the three dates you circled in a row or in a column?*	column	row	column
4. Pause a few seconds, and then give the answer.	3, 10, 17	8, 9, 10	6, 13, 20

Figure out how to do this trick. How does it work?

Divide the total by 3. That is the middle number. If the three numbers are in a column, subtract and add 7 to get the other two numbers. If the numbers are in a row, subtract and add 1.

Math Masters, p. 389

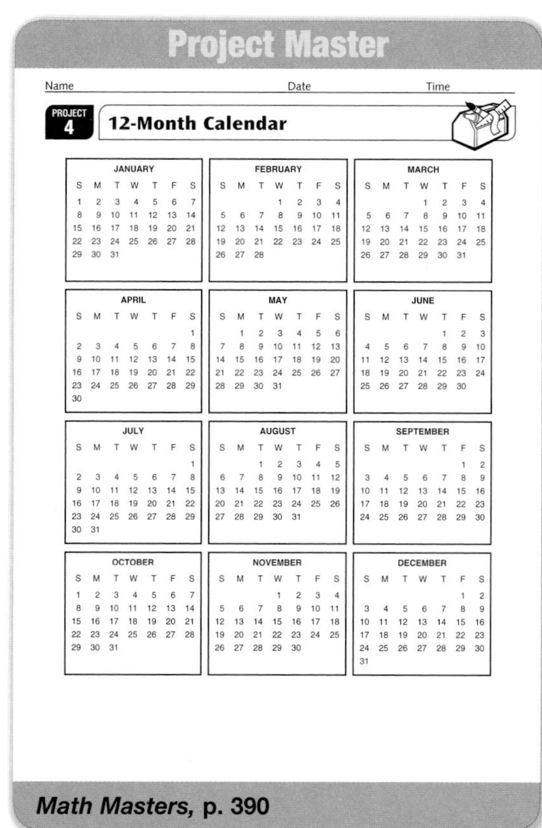

Project Master

Name Date Time

PROJECT 4 **12-Month Calendar**

JANUARY

S	M	T	W	T	F	S
1	2	3	4	5	6	7
8	9	10	11	12	13	14
15	16	17	18	19	20	21
22	23	24	25	26	27	28
29	30	31				

FEBRUARY

S	M	T	W	T	F	S
			1	2	3	4
5	6	7	8	9	10	11
12	13	14	15	16	17	18
19	20	21	22	23	24	25
26	27	28				

MARCH

S	M	T	W	T	F	S
			1	2	3	4
5	6	7	8	9	10	11
12	13	14	15	16	17	18
19	20	21	22	23	24	25
26	27	28	29	30	31	

APRIL

S	M	T	W	T	F	S
						1
2	3	4	5	6	7	8
9	10	11	12	13	14	15
16	17	18	19	20	21	22
23	24	25	26	27	28	29
30						

MAY

S	M	T	W	T	F	S
	1	2	3	4	5	6
7	8	9	10	11	12	13
14	15	16	17	18	19	20
21	22	23	24	25	26	27
28	29	30	31			

JUNE

S	M	T	W	T	F	S
				1	2	3
4	5	6	7	8	9	10
11	12	13	14	15	16	17
18	19	20	21	22	23	24
25	26	27	28	29	30	

JULY

S	M	T	W	T	F	S
						1
2	3	4	5	6	7	8
9	10	11	12	13	14	15
16	17	18	19	20	21	22
23	24	25	26	27	28	29
30	31					

AUGUST

S	M	T	W	T	F	S
		1	2	3	4	5
6	7	8	9	10	11	12
13	14	15	16	17	18	19
20	21	22	23	24	25	26
27	28	29	30	31		

SEPTEMBER

S	M	T	W	T	F	S
					1	2
3	4	5	6	7	8	9
10	11	12	13	14	15	16
17	18	19	20	21	22	23
24	25	26	27	28	29	30

OCTOBER

S	M	T	W	T	F	S
1	2	3	4	5	6	7
8	9	10	11	12	13	14
15	16	17	18	19	20	21
22	23	24	25	26	27	28
29	30	31				

NOVEMBER

S	M	T	W	T	F	S
			1	2	3	4
5	6	7	8	9	10	11
12	13	14	15	16	17	18
19	20	21	22	23	24	25
26	27	28	29	30		

DECEMBER

S	M	T	W	T	F	S
					1	2
3	4	5	6	7	8	9
10	11	12	13	14	15	16
17	18	19	20	21	22	23
24	25	26	27	28	29	30
31						

Math Masters, p. 390

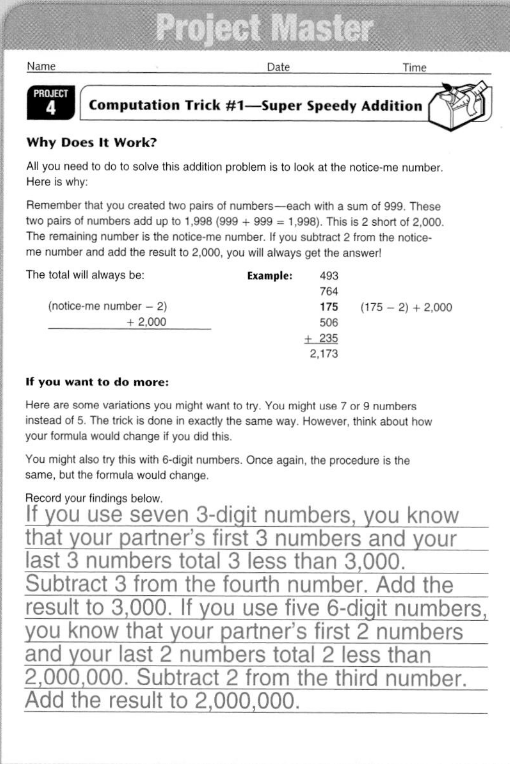

Project Master

Name Date Time

PROJECT 4 **Computation Trick #1—Super Speedy Addition**

Why Does It Work?

All you need to do to solve this addition problem is to look at the notice-me number. Here is why:

Remember that you created two pairs of numbers—each with a sum of 999. These two pairs of numbers add up to 1,998 (999 + 999 = 1,998). This is 2 short of 2,000. The remaining number is the notice-me number. If you subtract 2 from the notice-me number and add the result to 2,000, you will always get the answer!

The total will always be:

(notice-me number – 2)
+ 2,000

Example:

493
764
175 (175 – 2) + 2,000
506
+ 235
2,173

If you want to do more:

Here are some variations you might want to try. You might use 7 or 9 numbers instead of 5. The trick is done in exactly the same way. However, think about how your formula would change if you did this.

You might also try this with 6-digit numbers. Once again, the procedure is the same, but the formula would change.

Record your findings below.

If you use seven 3-digit numbers, you know that your partner's first 3 numbers and your last 3 numbers total 3 less than 3,000. Subtract 3 from the fourth number. Add the result to 3,000. If you use five 6-digit numbers, you know that your partner's first 2 numbers and your last 2 numbers total 2 less than 2,000,000. Subtract 2 from the third number. Add the result to 2,000,000.

Math Masters, p. 391

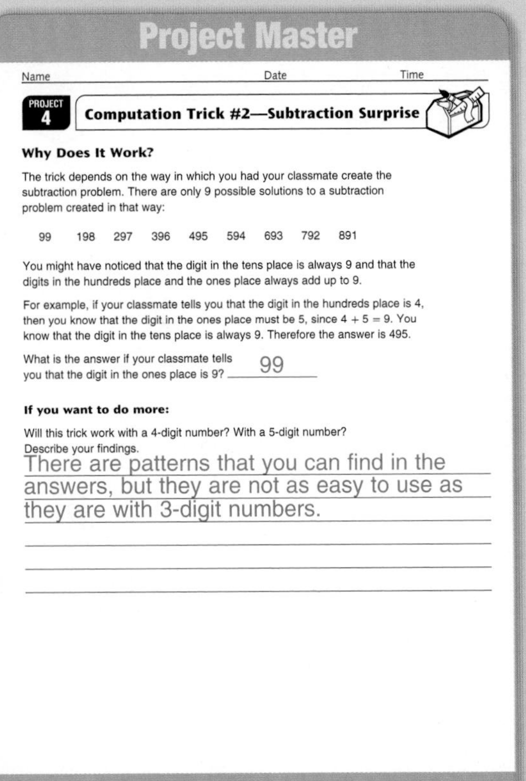

Project Master

Name Date Time

PROJECT 4 **Computation Trick #2—Subtraction Surprise**

Why Does It Work?

The trick depends on the way in which you had your classmate create the subtraction problem. There are only 9 possible solutions to a subtraction problem created in that way:

99 198 297 396 495 594 693 792 891

You might have noticed that the digit in the tens place is always 9 and that the digits in the hundreds place and the ones place always add up to 9.

For example, if your classmate tells you that the digit in the hundreds place is 4, then you know that the digit in the ones place must be 5, since 4 + 5 = 9. You know that the digit in the tens place is always 9. Therefore the answer is 495.

What is the answer if your classmate tells you that the digit in the ones place is 9? 99

If you want to do more:

Will this trick work with a 4-digit number? With a 5-digit number? Describe your findings.

There are patterns that you can find in the answers, but they are not as easy to use as they are with 3-digit numbers.

Math Masters, **p. 392**

Project Master

Name Date Time

PROJECT 4 **Computation Trick #3—Crazy Calendar Addition**

Why Does It Work?

If three numbers are evenly spaced, you can find the middle number by dividing the sum of the numbers by 3.

Example:

Sun.	Mon.	Tue.	Wed.	Thu.	Fri.	Sat.
		1	2	3	4	5
6	7	8	9	10	11	12
13	14	15	16	17	18	19
20	21	22	23	24	25	26
27	28	29	30	31		

The numbers in a row and the numbers in a column of a calendar are evenly spaced.

- The numbers in a row are consecutive whole numbers. They are 1 apart.
- The numbers in a column are 7 apart. This is because there are 7 days in a week.

After you find the middle number by dividing the sum of the numbers by 3, it is easy to find the other two numbers.

- If the three numbers are in a row, subtract 1 from the middle number to get the first number. Add 1 to the middle number to get the third number.
- If the three numbers are in a column, subtract 7 from the middle number to get the first number. Add 7 to the middle number to get the third number.

If you want to do more:

What would happen if the three dates chosen were on a diagonal? Would the trick still work? Why or why not?

You could still find the number in the middle, but you would have to know which way the diagonal points. If the diagonal points down to the right, add and subtract 8. If it points up to the right, add and subtract 6.

Math Masters, **p. 393**

2 Extending the Project

▶ Exploring More Tricks

INDEPENDENT ACTIVITY

(*Math Masters,* pp. 391–393)

Math Masters, pages 391–393 contain variations of the computation tricks at the bottom of each page under the heading If You Want to Do More. Invite students to try these.

There are many books and Internet sites on recreational mathematics. The sites listed below provide a variety of links and approaches:

http://archives.math.utk.edu/popmath.html

www-history.mcs.st-andrews.ac.uk/HistTopics/Mathematical_games.html

Encourage students to find more computation tricks to share with the class.

Project

5

How Would You Spend $1,000,000?

Objectives To provide experiences with large number computation; fraction, decimal, and percent conversions; and data display.

Technology Resources www.everydaymathonline.com

eToolkit

Algorithms Practice

EM Facts Workshop Game™

Family Letters

Assessment Management

Common Core State Standards

Curriculum Focal Points

Interactive Teacher's Lesson Guide

1 Doing the Project

Recommended Use During or after Unit 5

Key Concepts and Skills

- Solve problems involving percents. [Number and Numeration Goal 2]
- Convert between fractions, decimals, and percents. [Number and Numeration Goal 5]
- Collect and organize data to create a circle graph. [Data and Chance Goal 1]

Key Activities

In this long-term project, students work independently to research and plan how they would spend $1,000,000 while guided by a consistent, original theme. Students group their purchases into categories and record the items purchased in each category. They present their results to the class, using any appropriate format, such as a written report or a display board.

Key Vocabulary

major category ◆ unit price

Materials

- ◆ *Math Masters,* pp. 394–398
- ◆ calculator

2 Extending the Project

Students apply percent skills to analyze their project data and make circle graphs.

Materials

- ◆ *Math Masters,* pp. 399 and 400
- ◆ Geometry Template
- ◆ calculator

Additional Information

Allow about two weeks, outside of class time, for the project.

The project used as a model was done by Emily Maneck, a student in Glenview, Illinois. The project design was created by Catherine Tucci and Gayle Zis, teachers in Glenview, Illinois.

Advance Preparation

Each student will need several copies of *Math Masters,* page 398, one for each of their determined major categories.

Project Master

Name Date Time

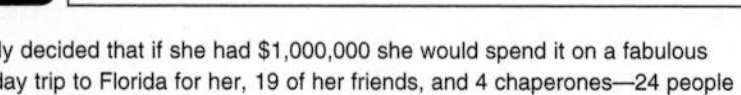

PROJECT 5 **How Would You Spend $1,000,000?—Emily's Idea**

Emily decided that if she had $1,000,000 she would spend it on a fabulous 10-day trip to Florida for her, 19 of her friends, and 4 chaperones—24 people altogether. With $1,000,000, she knew that she could make this a trip no one would ever forget.

Emily began by thinking about everything she and her friends might need for their trip. She visited a local department store to find out how much different items cost. She decided to purchase a **vacation wardrobe** for everyone, including the chaperones, at a cost of $50,750. Her next stop was a **sporting goods** store for items such as snorkel gear, swimsuits, and sunglasses. The store clerk calculated that all of her purchases there would cost $24,100.

Emily knew that she would need **transportation** to Florida and for traveling around while there. She made a few telephone calls to find out the prices for transportation. Emily found that when she politely explained her project to people, most of them were willing to help her. After doing some research, she chartered an airplane for a flight from Chicago to Orlando and back ($54,780). She purchased two stretch limos to use in Florida ($165,160 + $10,000 for gas and two around-the-clock chauffeurs). She also purchased a minivan to carry the chaperones and the luggage ($20,700) while in Florida.

Lodging was another consideration. Emily decided that her group would stay at one of the resorts inside a theme park ($33,550). She went to a travel agency to get some information about the **activities** that she and her friends might try while they were there. For $177,200, Emily made reservations for several special breakfasts as well as dinner shows, rented a water park for 12 hours, and purchased 10-day passes to the theme park where she and her group were staying.

Math Masters, p. 394

Project Master

Name Date Time

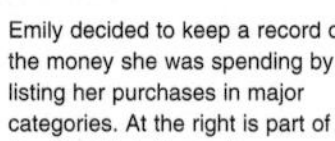

PROJECT 5 **How Would You Spend $1,000,000?** *cont.*

Emily decided to keep a record of the money she was spending by listing her purchases in major categories. At the right is part of the chart that she made.

Emily also decided that for each category she would keep a detailed record so that she would know exactly how she was spending the $1,000,000.

Major Category	Cost
Vacation Wardrobe	$ 50,750
Sports Equipment	$ 24,100
Transportation	$ 250,640
Lodging	$ 33,550
Activities	$ 177,200

Below is an example of her record for one category.

Major Category—Vacation Wardrobe			
Item	Quantity	Unit Price	Total Price
Boxer shorts	100	$ 12.50	$ 1,250.00
Socks	200	$ 5.50	$ 1,100.00
Shorts	240	$ 38.00	$ 9,120.00
T-shirts	200	$ 32.00	$ 6,400.00
Swimsuits	100	$ 36.00	$ 3,600.00
Jeans	100	$ 34.00	$ 3,400.00
Shoes	60	$ 50.00	$ 3,000.00
Flip-flops	60	$ 24.00	$ 1,440.00
Sunglasses	20	$ 29.50	$ 590.00
Long-sleeve shirts	40	$ 57.00	$ 2,280.00
Tax			$ 2,570.00
Chaperones → Wardrobe Allotment		$4,000.00 per person	$ 16,000.00
		Total	$50,750.00

These are examples of just a few of the expenses for Emily's amazing trip.

About how much money has Emily spent so far? $536,240

About how much money does Emily have left to spend? $463,760

Math Masters, p. 395

1 Doing the Project

Introducing the Project

WHOLE-CLASS DISCUSSION

(*Math Masters,* pp. 394 and 395)

Ask students to imagine that they have $1,000,000 and to think about ways they would spend it. Then have them share a few of their ideas.

Ask students to read *Math Masters,* pages 394 and 395. The essay describes how Emily decided on a theme and began her investigation of how she would spend $1,000,000. Discuss the essay to model an approach to the project. Include the following points:

▷ Emily's theme for spending her $1,000,000 was a Florida vacation.

Emily researched her project by going to stores and making phone calls. She found that when she politely explained her project to people, they were happy to help her. (Explain that not everyone students speak to will be enthusiastic about answering hypothetical purchasing questions. Realistically, many people do not have the time. Encourage students to politely thank those who are too busy to help and to try again somewhere else.)

▷ Emily organized her purchases into **major categories** and listed the items that made up each category.

Point out that the term ***unit price*** refers to the cost for one item. Unit costs should be rounded to the nearest dollar or half-dollar. Encourage students to round larger prices to larger values, for example, to the nearest $10 or nearest $100 for major category costs.

▷ Emily has spent about $536,240 for the items listed. She has about $463,760 left over for more purchases.

Assigning the Project

WHOLE-CLASS DISCUSSION

(*Math Masters,* pp. 396–398)

The guidelines for completing the project are given on *Math Masters,* page 396. Review them with the class. The guidelines provide students with a common framework to begin. However, try to keep the spirit of the project as open-ended as possible.

Encourage students to pursue their own creative ideas, to imagine projects that entertain or make a profit, and to explore projects that benefit society. Projects have included starting a sports grill and ice-cream shop, modernizing a food depository, opening an animal shelter, investing in the stock market, and renovating the children's wing of a hospital.

One benefit of this project is that it provides students with the opportunity to investigate subjects of their own choosing. In gathering information, students will need to use a variety of resources and possibly speak with many different people. Because some students will have greater access to resources than others will, expect some projects to be more detailed than others.

Have students use *Math Masters,* pages 397 and 398 to organize and to record their purchases.

The goal of the project is to spend as close to $1,000,000 as possible, without going over. As this might be difficult to do, allow students to contribute a specified amount (for example, not less than $10,000 and not more than $50,000) to a charity to bring the total to $1,000,000. This contribution could be used to account for small, unspent amounts of money.

▶ Presenting the Project

Schedule time for students to present their completed projects to the class. Students will enjoy sharing their plans for spending $1,000,000, as well as hearing how other students choose to spend it. The presentations can be brief—students can give quick summaries of their themes and highlight any special parts of their projects.

Collect the accounting sheets (*Math Masters,* pages 397 and 398) from students after their presentations. Verify that the totals in all the categories do indeed total $1,000,000. If not, return the sheets to the students for correction before proceeding to the next activity.

2 Extending the Project

▶ Displaying Project Data

(*Math Masters,* pp. 399 and 400)

Distribute the accounting sheets that you collected after the students' presentations. Students use their data to complete *Math Masters,* pages 399 and 400.

You might need to clarify the directions on *Math Masters,* page 400. Because each percent has been rounded to the nearest whole percent, the percents might not total 100%. To compensate for this, the smaller categories should be graphed first and the largest one graphed last. If a category is only 2% of the total, and it is off by 1%, that is a relatively large error. However, if a category is 34% of the total, and it is off by 1%, the error is much less significant. By starting with the smallest category, the relative errors can be minimized.

Consider making a display of students' graphs.

Project Master

Name Date Time

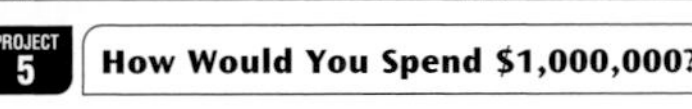

Project Guidelines

Imagine that you have just inherited $1,000,000. One of the conditions for receiving the money is that you must investigate, research, and present exactly how you will spend it. You must follow the guidelines below.

Theme The $1,000,000 must be spent carrying out one particular plan.

For example: A plan that would help save the rain forest; a plan to build new parks and playgrounds in your city; a plan for a trip around the world; or a plan to open a ballet studio.

Goal Spend as close to $1,000,000 as possible, but not more than $1,000,000.

Research Include all of the expenses involved in carrying out the details of your plan.

For example: If you are opening a ballet studio, you must consider how many teachers you will need and how much you will pay them. If you are buying a car, you will need to consider the cost of gas, maintenance, and insurance for the length of time you will own the car.

Accounting In an organized way, record exactly how you will spend the $1,000,000. The purchases needed to carry out your plan should be organized in several major categories. Each major category must total at least $10,000.

For example: Think about how Emily organized the purchases for her Florida vacation, as described on *Math Masters,* pages 394 and 395.

Display Present the research and accounting for your plan in a report, on a display board, on a poster, or in a portfolio. You might even make a video production.

For example: Emily presented her project as a report. In addition to her calculations, she included pictures and sample receipts whenever possible.

***Math Masters,* p. 396**

Project Master

Name Date Time

PROJECT 5 **How Would You Spend $1,000,000?—Graph**

Make a circle graph of your categories for spending $1,000,000. Use your Percent Circle and the information on *Math Masters,* page 399.

Begin by drawing the section for the smallest part of the $1,000,000. Continue with the larger parts. Mark the largest part last. Because of rounding, the percents may not add up to exactly 100%.

Give the graph a title and label each section.

Sample answer:

Vacation with My Friends

Sports equipment

Lodging

Vacation wardrobe

Activities

Other

Transportation

***Math Masters,* p. 400**

Project 6

Sports Areas

Objectives To provide experiences with calculating the areas of rectangles, converting between units, and converting mixed units to decimals.

Technology Resources www.everydaymathonline.com

eToolkit

Algorithms Practice

EM Facts Workshop Game™

Family Letters

Assessment Management

Common Core State Standards

Curriculum Focal Points

Interactive Teacher's Lesson Guide

1 Doing the Project

Recommended Use During or after Unit 9

Key Concepts and Skills

- Use appropriate formulas to calculate the areas of rectangles.
  [Measurement and Reference Frames Goal 2]
- Describe relationships among U.S. customary units for area, and convert units.
  [Measurement and Reference Frames Goal 3]

Key Activities

Students are given the dimensions of the playing field or surface for a variety of sports. They calculate the area of each and identify areas greater than 1 acre.

Key Vocabulary

scale drawing ◆ perspective drawing

Materials

◆ *Math Masters,* pp. 401 and 402
◆ calculator
◆ ruler

2 Extending the Project

Students convert the ground area of several large buildings to estimated area in acres.

Materials

◆ *Math Masters,* p. 403
◆ calculator

1 Doing the Project

▶ Discussing Scale Drawings and Dimensions of Sports Surfaces

WHOLE-CLASS DISCUSSION

(*Math Masters,* pp. 401 and 402)

The dimensions of the playing surface for each sport are given in the rules for that sport. Playing areas vary greatly from sport to sport.

Discuss the two scale drawings on *Math Masters,* pages 401 and 402. Include the following points:

▷ The drawings are **scale drawings**. The relationships between lengths in a scale drawing are the same as the relationships between lengths in the actual object. For example, the playing surface for field hockey is 300 feet by 180 feet, or 100 yards by 60 yards. Its scale drawing on *Math Masters,* page 402 is 100 millimeters by 60 millimeters.

▷ The drawings are not **perspective drawings**. In perspective drawings, parallel lines that move away from the viewer are drawn so they come together at a vanishing point. The proportions in a perspective drawing are not the same as the proportions of the actual object.

The surfaces for contact sports shown on *Math Masters,* page 401 are drawn to a scale of 1 millimeter to 1 foot. Have students measure the boxing ring or one of the other surfaces with a ruler and use the scale to convert their measurements to feet. They can check their measurements against the dimensions listed below the drawing.

The surfaces for other popular sports shown on *Math Masters,* page 402 were too large to draw with the same scale used on *Math Masters,* page 401. The scale is 1 millimeter to 1 yard (3 feet). If each length and width of the scale drawing on page 402 were enlarged to three times the current size, then the playing surfaces shown on both pages would be drawn to the same scale.

Remind students of the work they did in Lesson 4-3, when they learned how to use a map scale to measure distances on a map. For example, 1 inch on a map might represent 10 miles. On another map, 1 inch might represent 100 miles.

Work through at least one problem from each page with the class. Have students write the formula for area at the bottom of page 401. $A = b * h$, or $A = l * w$ Point out that some dimensions are given in feet and inches. Such measures must be converted to decimals to enter them into a calculator.

Project Master

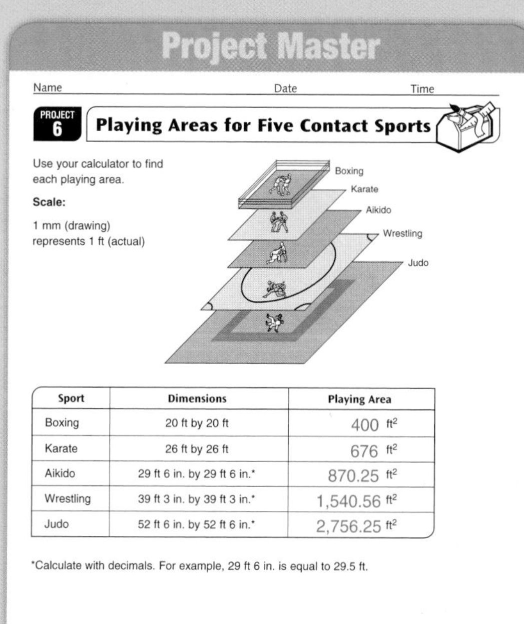

Name Date Time

PROJECT 6 **Playing Areas for Five Contact Sports**

Use your calculator to find each playing area.

Scale:

1 mm (drawing) represents 1 ft (actual)

Sport	Dimensions	Playing Area
Boxing	20 ft by 20 ft	400 ft²
Karate	26 ft by 26 ft	676 ft²
Aikido	29 ft 6 in. by 29 ft 6 in.*	870.25 ft²
Wrestling	39 ft 3 in. by 39 ft 3 in.*	1,540.56 ft²
Judo	52 ft 6 in. by 52 ft 6 in.*	2,756.25 ft²

*Calculate with decimals. For example, 29 ft 6 in. is equal to 29.5 ft.

Source: *COMPARISONS* by the Diagram Group. Reprinted by permission of St. Martin's Press.

***Math Masters,* p. 401**

Project Master

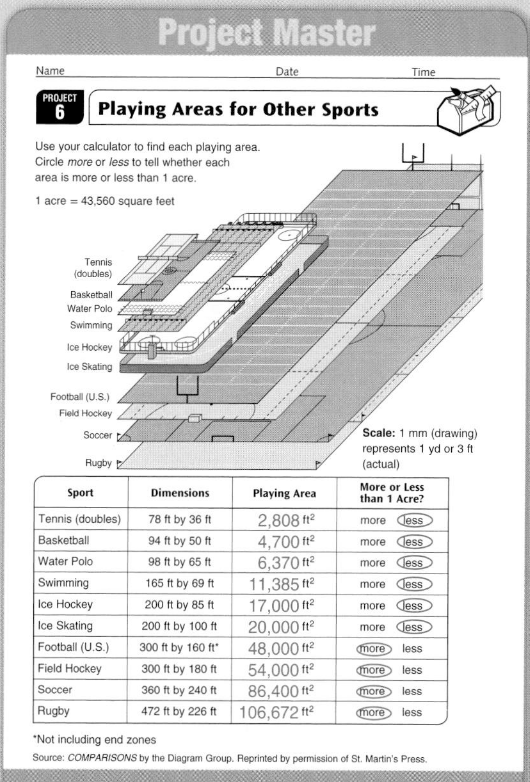

Name Date Time

PROJECT 6 **Playing Areas for Other Sports**

Use your calculator to find each playing area. Circle *more* or *less* to tell whether each area is more or less than 1 acre.

1 acre = 43,560 square feet

Sport	Dimensions	Playing Area	More or Less than 1 Acre?
Tennis (doubles)	78 ft by 36 ft	2,808 ft²	more (less)
Basketball	94 ft by 50 ft	4,700 ft²	more (less)
Water Polo	98 ft by 65 ft	6,370 ft²	more (less)
Swimming	165 ft by 69 ft	11,385 ft²	more (less)
Ice Hockey	200 ft by 85 ft	17,000 ft²	more (less)
Ice Skating	200 ft by 100 ft	20,000 ft²	more (less)
Football (U.S.)	300 ft by 160 ft*	48,000 ft²	(more) less
Field Hockey	300 ft by 180 ft	54,000 ft²	(more) less
Soccer	360 ft by 240 ft	86,400 ft²	(more) less
Rugby	472 ft by 226 ft	106,672 ft²	(more) less

*Not including end zones

Source: *COMPARISONS* by the Diagram Group. Reprinted by permission of St. Martin's Press.

***Math Masters,* p. 402**

▶ Calculating Sports Areas

PARTNER ACTIVITY

(*Math Masters,* pp. 401 and 402)

Have students complete *Math Masters,* pages 401 and 402. Remind them that they can compare an area to an acre if they know the area in square feet. A sports area of more than 43,560 square feet will be more than 1 acre.

Students might note that a football field (minus the end zones) is about 1 acre. They will have little difficulty identifying football, field hockey, soccer, and rugby as sports whose playing areas exceed 1 acre.

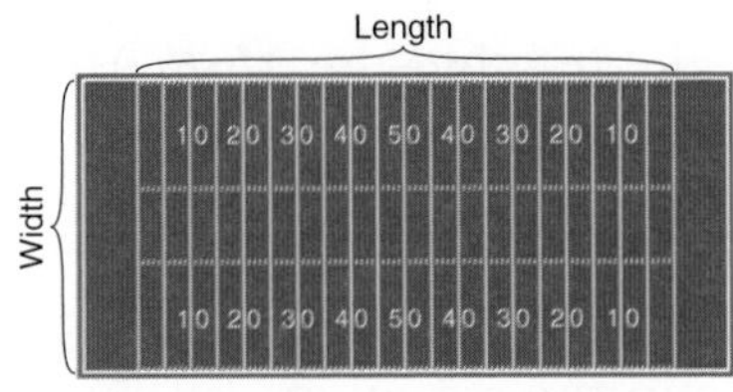

The area of a football field without the end zones is approximately 1 acre.

2 Extending the Project

▶ Finding the Footprints of Famous Buildings

PARTNER ACTIVITY

(*Math Masters,* p. 403)

Students are given the ground areas in square feet, or footprints, of seven famous, large buildings. Using an equivalence of 1 acre to about 50,000 ft^2, they convert these areas to acres.

Project Master

Name Date Time

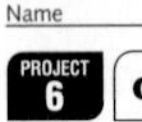

PROJECT 6

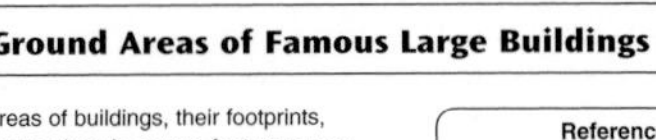

Ground Areas of Famous Large Buildings

The ground areas of buildings, their footprints, are almost always given in square feet or square meters. Some buildings have very large ground areas. When their areas are given in square feet, the numbers are so large that it is hard to imagine how big the buildings really are.

For large buildings, if you convert the area in square feet to an estimate in acres, you can get a better idea of the size of the building.

Reference

1 acre = 43,560 square feet

For estimating, think of 1 acre as about 50,000 square feet.

A football field (excluding the end zones) is approximately 1 acre.

Estimate the ground area, in acres, of each building in the table below:

Example: The Colosseum, in Italy, covers an area of about 250,000 ft^2.

One acre is about 50,000 ft^2.

So 5 acres is about 250,000 ft^2.

The Colosseum covers an area of about 5 acres (5 football fields).

Building	Country	Date Built	Ground Area (ft^2)	Estimated Area (in acres)
Colosseum	Italy	70–224	250,000 ft^2	5 acres
Pyramid of Cheops	Egypt	c. 2600 B.C.	571,500 ft^2	11 acres
Chartres Cathedral	France	1194–1514	60,000 ft^2	1 acres
St. Peter's Basilica	Vatican City	1506–1626	392,300 ft^2	8 acres
Taj Mahal	India	1636–1653	78,000 ft^2	1.5 acres
Pentagon	U.S. (Virginia)	1941–1943	1,263,000 ft^2	25 acres
Ford Parts Center	U.S. (Michigan)	1936	2,800,000 ft^2	56 acres

Math Masters, p. 403

Project 7

Polygon Areas and Pick's Formula

Objective To explore Pick's Formula for finding the area of a polygon.

Technology Resources www.everydaymathonline.com

eToolkit · Algorithms Practice · EM Facts Workshop Game™ · Family Letters · Assessment Management · Common Core State Standards · Curriculum Focal Points · Interactive Teacher's Lesson Guide

1 Doing the Project

Recommended Use During or after Unit 9

Key Concepts and Skills

- Measure length with tools to the nearest millimeter. [Measurement and Reference Frames Goal 1]
- Use appropriate formulas to calculate the areas of polygons. [Measurement and Reference Frames Goal 2]

Key Activities

Students extend the rectangle method or choose other methods to find areas of polygons. They are introduced to Pick's Formula as an alternative way to find the area of a figure drawn on a square grid or formed on a geoboard.

Key Vocabulary

grid points ◆ vertices ◆ interior

Materials

- *Math Masters,* pp. 404 and 405
- Geometry Template or ruler
- Class Data Pad
- calculator
- for demonstration: overhead geoboard and elastic bands or transparency of geoboard dot paper
- per partnership: geoboard and rubber bands or geoboard dot paper

2 Extending the Project

Students use Pick's Formula to find the area of an irregular path.

Materials

- *Math Masters,* p. 406

Advance Preparation

As an alternative to an overhead geoboard and elastic bands, make a transparency of geoboard dot paper.

Project Master

Name ________ Date ________ Time ________

PROJECT 7 **Finding Areas with Standard Methods** 

Use any method you want to find the area of each polygon below. Record the area in the table to the right. You can use different methods with different figures. If you use any area formulas, remember that height is always measured perpendicular to the base you choose. Measure base and height very carefully.

Figure	Area
A	about 4.5 cm^2
B	about 13 cm^2
C	about 7 cm^2
D	about 12 cm^2
E	about 7.5 cm^2
F	about 7.5 cm^2

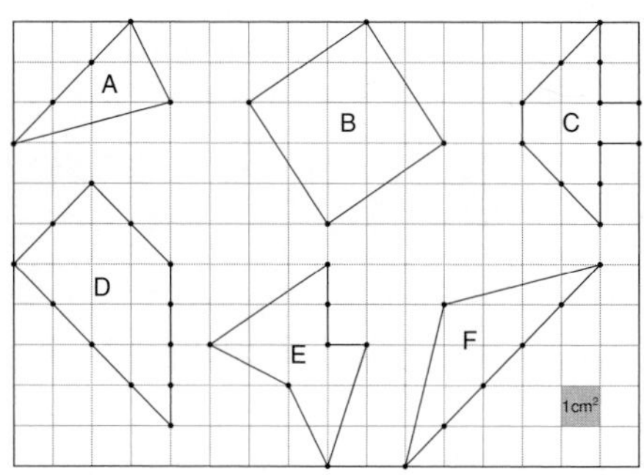

***Math Masters,* p. 404**

Project Master

Name ________ Date ________ Time ________

PROJECT 7 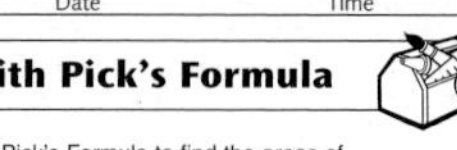 **Finding Areas with Pick's Formula**

Read the paragraphs below, and then use Pick's Formula to find the areas of the polygons on the previous page. Record your results in the table below. Compare them to the results you recorded in the table on the previous page. You should expect some differences—measures are always estimates.

Pick's Formula for Finding Polygon Areas by Counting

In 1899, Georg Pick, an Austrian mathematician, discovered a formula for finding the area of a polygon on a square grid (such as graph paper). If a polygon has its vertices at grid points, its area can be found by counting the number of grid points on the polygon (P) and the number of grid points in the interior of the polygon (I) and then by using the formula $A = (\frac{1}{2} * P) + I - 1$. The unit of area is one square on the grid.

For figure B on the previous page, the unit of area is cm^2.

$P = 4$ (grid points on polygon)

$I = 12$ (grid points in interior)

$A = (\frac{1}{2} * P) + I - 1$

$= (\frac{1}{2} * 4) + 12 - 1$

$= 13 \text{ cm}^2$

Figure	P	I	Area $= (\frac{1}{2} * P) + I + - 1$
A	5	3	4.5 cm^2
B	4	12	13 cm^2
C	12	2	7 cm^2
D	12	7	12 cm^2
E	7	5	7.5 cm^2
F	7	5	7.5 cm^2

Draw two polygons. Be sure that the vertices are at grid points.
Use Pick's Formula to find the areas of the polygons.

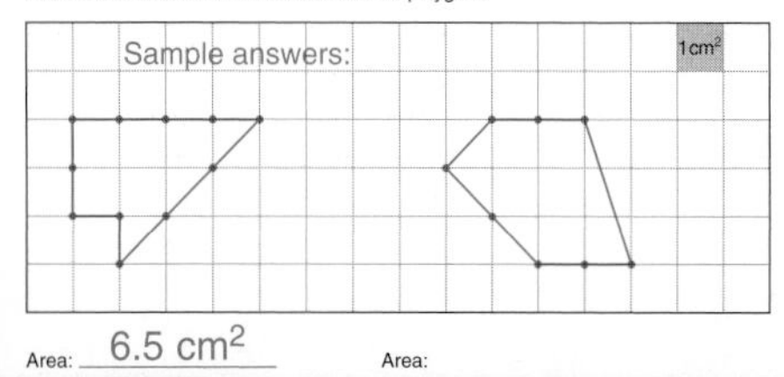

Area: 6.5 cm^2 Area: ________

***Math Masters,* p. 405**

1 Doing the Project

▶ Finding Areas of Polygons

 PARTNER ACTIVITY

(*Math Masters,* p. 404)

Students find the areas of the polygons on *Math Masters,* page 404 and record them in the table. Encourage students to use any of the strategies they know for finding areas.

NOTE For figures that are "tilted" on the grid, it might not be possible to read lengths of bases or heights directly from the grid. Advise students using area formulas to measure slant lengths very carefully (in millimeters) and to use their calculators to multiply the resulting decimals to get close approximations of the areas.

When most students have completed the page, discuss the methods they used to find the areas, and list the strategies on the Class Data Pad. The rectangle method can be used with all the figures. Examples of other strategies:

▷ **Figure A**
Measure a base and height, and use the formula for the area of a triangle. Remind students that the height of the triangle must be measured perpendicular to the base of the triangle.

▷ **Figure B**
Carefully measure the sides (about 3.6 cm each), and use the formula for the area of a rectangle.

▷ **Figure C**
Count squares and half-squares to find the area of the figure.

▷ **Figure D**
Partition the trapezoid into a square and a triangle. Measure bases and heights carefully. Then calculate the areas, and add them together

▷ **Figure E**
This figure is challenging to most students. The rectangle method works very nicely here. Partitioning the polygon into many triangles is possible but tedious.

▷ **Figure F**
Measure carefully, and use the formula for the area of a triangle. Once again, remind students that the height of the triangle is measured perpendicular to the base of the triangle.

▶ Introducing Pick's Formula

 WHOLE-CLASS DISCUSSION

(*Math Masters,* p. 405)

Pick's Formula can be used to find the area of any polygon that has its vertices at grid points on a square grid or geoboard.

Have students read the description of Pick's Formula and the example on *Math Masters,* page 405. Discuss the formula. Be sure students understand how P (the number of **grid points** on the polygon, including **vertices**) and I (the number of grid points in the **interior** of the polygon) are counted and how they are used in the calculation of area.

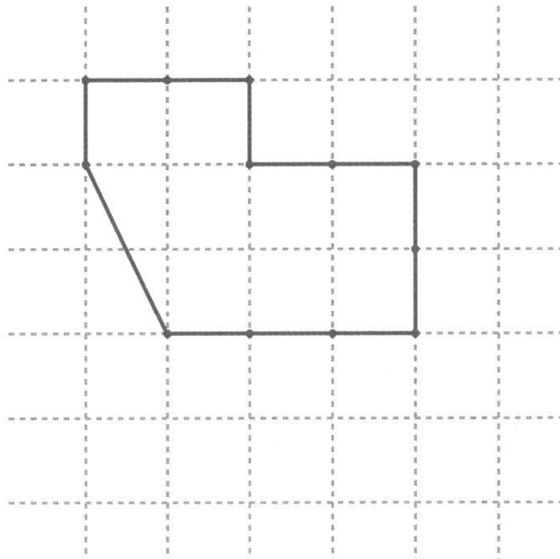

Use an overhead geoboard, or draw several figures on a transparency of geoboard dot paper. Work through Pick's Formula with the class to find the areas of the figures.

NOTE Pick's Formula, also called *Pick's Theorem,* was first published in 1899 by Austrian mathematician Georg Alexander Pick (1859–1942). The proof of this odd, but elegant formula is beyond the scope of this book, as is the proof that it is equivalent to the formula linking the number of edges (e), faces (f), and vertices (v) of any polyhedron: $e = f + v - 2$.

Using Pick's Formula

PARTNER ACTIVITY

(*Math Masters,* pp. 404 and 405)

Have students use Pick's Formula to find the areas of the polygons on *Math Masters,* page 404. They record the areas on *Math Masters,* page 405.

If students have geoboards, have them form the figures before using Pick's Formula. Encourage partners who finish early to create new problems for each other on a geoboard or geoboard dot paper.

2 Extending the Project

Using Pick's Formula to Find the Area of an Irregular Path

INDEPENDENT ACTIVITY

(*Math Masters,* p. 406)

Have students use Pick's Formula to find the area of the path on *Math Masters,* page 406. This path appeared in Lesson 9-6 (*Math Masters,* page 273). When students have completed the page, discuss whether they think Pick's Formula is an efficient method for calculating this area.

Project Master

Name Date Time

PROJECT 7 **Finding Areas with Pick's Formula** *cont.*

You might have found the area of this shaded path in Lesson 9-6.

Now use Pick's Formula to find the area.

1 cm²

1. The area of the path is 33 cm².
2. Do you think Pick's Formula is a good way to find this area? Answers vary.
   Explain. Answers vary.

Math Masters, p. 406

Project

8 Pendulums

Objectives To provide experiences with collecting, displaying, and analyzing data.

Technology Resources www.everydaymathonline.com

eToolkit

Algorithms Practice

EM Facts Workshop Game™

Family Letters

Assessment Management

Common Core State Standards

Curriculum Focal Points

Interactive Teacher's Lesson Guide

1 Doing the Project

Recommended Use During or after Unit 10

Key Concepts and Skills

- Collect and organize data to create a line graph.
  [Data and Chance Goal 1]
- Predict the outcomes of experiments, test the predictions using manipulatives, and summarize the results.
  [Data and Chance Goal 4]

Key Activities

Students record and graph the time and length of pendulum swings. They investigate whether the length of a pendulum affects the duration of one complete swing of the pendulum; whether the length of the arc of a pendulum affects the duration of the swing; and whether the amount of weight at the end of a pendulum affects the duration of the swing.

Key Vocabulary

pendulum ◆ complete swing

Materials

◆ *Math Masters,* pp. 407–409

Per small group:

◆ string pendulum
◆ ruler or meterstick
◆ watch or clock to time seconds (preferable to tenths of a second)
◆ 10 metal washers or similar weights

2 Extending the Project

Students research pendulums.

Materials

◆ encyclopedia
◆ *Longitude*
◆ *Sea Clocks: The Story of Longitude*
◆ computer with Internet access (optional)

Advance Preparation

Prepare one string pendulum for each small group. Cut as many $1\frac{1}{2}$ m strings as there are groups. Tie a paper clip to one end of each string. Use a marker to mark each string 5 cm, 10 cm, 20 cm, 30 cm, 50 cm, 75 cm, and 1 m from the end of the paper clip. Open up the clip so large metal washers or similar weights can be hung on it.

Prepare one additional pendulum with a string at least 2 m long and a paper clip at one end for demonstration purposes. Mark the string 50 cm, 75 cm, and 2 m from the paper clip.

For Part 2, obtain a copy of ***Longitude*** by Dava Sobel (Walker, 2005) and/or ***Sea Clocks: The Story of Longitude*** by Louise Bordon (Margaret K. McElderry, 2004).

1 Doing the Project

▶ Discussing Pendulums

WHOLE-CLASS DISCUSSION

Explain that according to legend, Galileo discovered the principle of the pendulum in 1583 while watching a hanging lamp swing back and forth in a cathedral in Pisa. Galileo and Christiaan Huygens (1656) are each credited with designing a clock controlled by the motion of a pendulum.

A **pendulum** consists of an object, called the bob, suspended from a fixed support in such a way that the object can swing freely back and forth under the influence of gravity.

Ask students to describe the instances of pendulums they have seen. One example would be the pendulum in a clock. Some students might have been to a science museum and seen a very long pendulum (a Foucault pendulum) that demonstrates the rotation of the Earth.

▶ Demonstrating and Timing a Pendulum

WHOLE-CLASS ACTIVITY

(*Math Masters,* p. 407)

Demonstrate how to set up a string pendulum on a desk or table (*see margin*):

▷ Form a pendulum that is 50 cm long.

▷ Hold the pendulum fairly high (approximately parallel to the floor) and release the bob. In a **complete swing,** the pendulum swings forward, stops for an instant, swings back (almost) to its starting position, and stops for an instant. Swinging in just one direction is a half-swing.

Tell students that they will perform experiments to try to answer the question, *Does the time it takes a pendulum to make a complete swing depend on the length of the string?* Ask students to predict what the answer will be.

Now use the pendulum to demonstrate how to time 10 complete swings of the pendulum:

1. Ask a student to keep time with a seconds timer.
2. Pull the pendulum to one side. As you release it, say, *Go.* The student starts timing.
3. With the class, count out 10 complete swings (not half-swings).
4. When the pendulum finishes its tenth complete swing, say, *Stop.* The student stops timing.
5. The student gives the elapsed time (to the nearest tenth of a second, if possible).

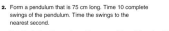

Project Master

Name Date Time

PROJECT 8 **The Swing Time of Pendulums**

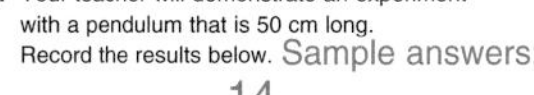

1. Your teacher will demonstrate an experiment with a pendulum that is 50 cm long. Record the results below. Sample answers:
   a. It took about 14 seconds for 10 complete swings of the pendulum.
   b. About how much time did it take for one swing? Round your answer to the nearest 0.1 second. 1.4 second(s)

heavy object

2. Form a pendulum that is 75 cm long. Time 10 complete swings of the pendulum. Time the swings to the nearest second.

   Practice timing 10 complete swings several times. Then time 10 swings and record the results below. Sample answers:
   a. It took about 17 seconds for 10 complete swings of the pendulum.
   b. About how much time did it take for one swing? Round your answer to the nearest 0.1 second. 1.7 second(s)

3. Record the results for a 50-cm and a 75-cm pendulum in the table at the right. Sample answers:
4. Experiment with different lengths of pendulum string.

   Find the time for 10 complete swings for each of the other pendulum lengths. Time the 10 swings to the nearest 0.1 second. Record your results in the table.

   After collecting your data, divide each of the times by 10 to estimate the time for one complete swing. Record your answers in the table, rounded to the nearest 0.1 second.

Length of Pendulum	Time for: Ten Complete Swings (to nearest 0.1 sec)	One Complete Swing (to nearest 0.1 sec)
5 cm	4.5 sec	0.5 sec
10 cm	6.3 sec	0.6 sec
20 cm	9.0 sec	0.9 sec
30 cm	11.0 sec	1.1 sec
50 cm	14.0 sec	1.4 sec
75 cm	17.4 sec	1.7 sec
100 cm	20.0 sec	2.0 sec
200 cm	28.4 sec	2.8 sec

Math Masters, p. 407

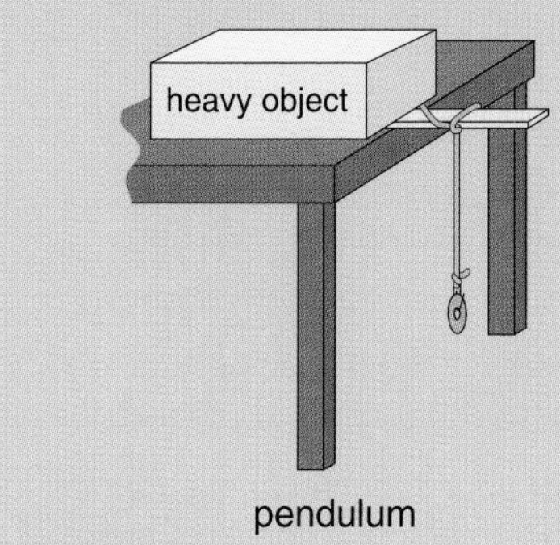

pendulum

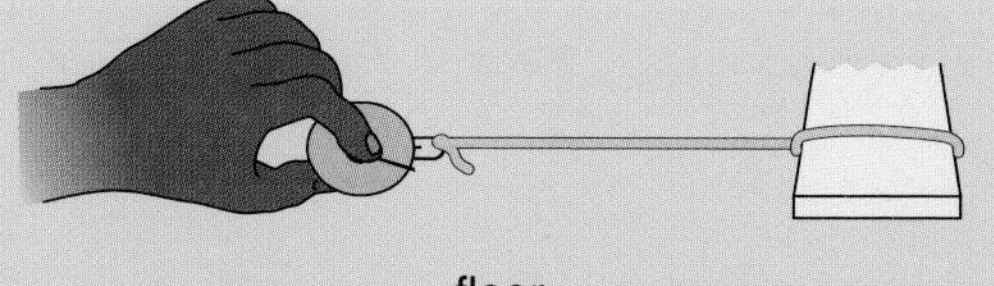

Hold pendulum parallel to floor.

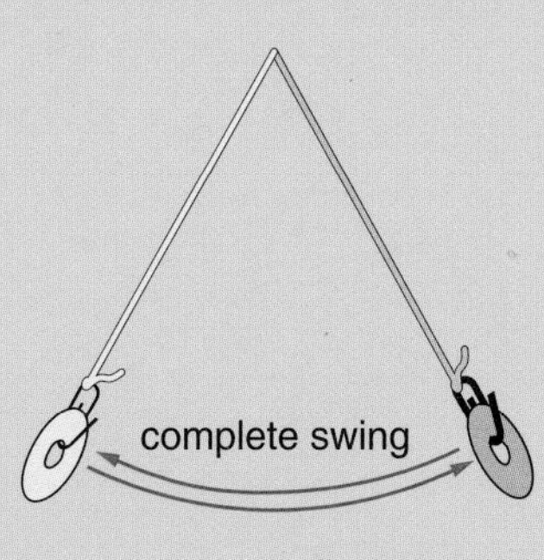

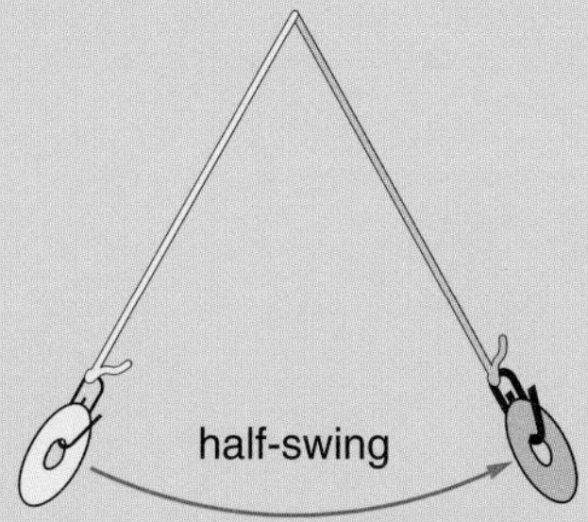

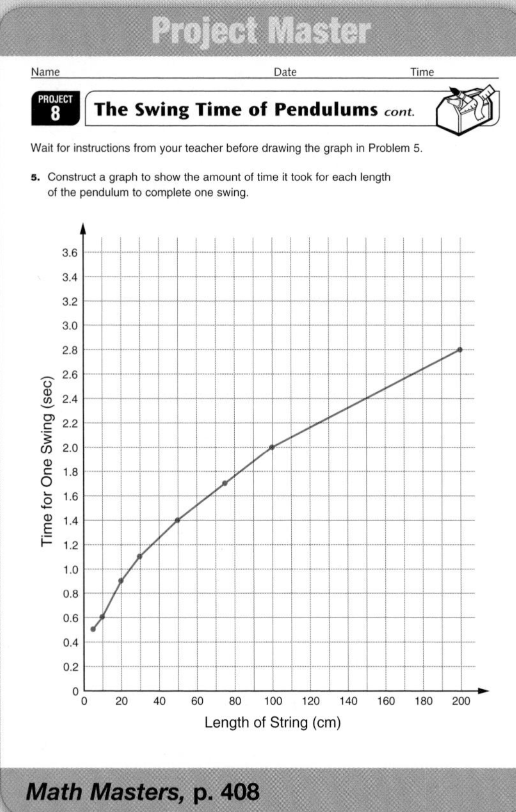
Project Master

Name Date Time

PROJECT 8 **The Swing Time of Pendulums** *cont.*

Wait for instructions from your teacher before drawing the graph in Problem 5.

5. Construct a graph to show the amount of time it took for each length of the pendulum to complete one swing.

Math Masters, p. 408

NOTE For your information, the formula for calculating the time of a complete swing of a pendulum is based on its length.

Time in seconds $= 2 * \pi * \sqrt{\frac{\text{length in meters}}{9.8}}$

Ask students to use the time for 10 swings to calculate the approximate time for one complete swing, to the nearest tenth or hundredth of a second. Divide by 10. Have students record the times for 10 swings and for 1 swing in Problem 1 on *Math Masters,* page 407, and in the table at the bottom of the page.

Some students might wonder why it is necessary to time 10 complete swings to obtain an accurate time measurement for a single swing. Why not simply time a single swing? Point out that timing a single, complete swing can be tricky, and the chance of error is great. But timing 10 swings is easy—even the shortest pendulum will take about 5 seconds for 10 swings.

Investigating the Swing Times for Pendulums of Various Lengths

SMALL-GROUP ACTIVITY

(*Math Masters,* pp. 407 and 408)

1. **Practicing Timing Swings of a 75-centimeter Pendulum** Have each group form a 75-centimeter pendulum and time 10 swings. Ask groups to do several additional practice trials. Circulate and assist.

   When students have demonstrated that they have acquired the knack for timing the pendulum, have them do a final trial that they will record. They should then record the time for 10 complete swings and 1 complete swing in Problem 2 and in the table at the bottom of *Math Masters,* page 407.

2. **Collecting Data for Pendulums of Various Lengths** Ask for three volunteers. Two students stand on chairs about 2 meters apart. One of them holds the demonstration pendulum by the weighted end. The other holds the string at the 2-meter mark. The third student prepares to keep time. The volunteers then time 10 complete swings of this pendulum. Students calculate the duration of one swing and record the results in the table.

NOTE If a group's results are markedly different from the others, discuss how this might have happened (for example, counting half-swings instead of complete swings; timing is started or stopped too early or too late; making the pendulum the wrong length). In such cases, suggest that the group use data from another group for the graphing exercise.

Adjusting the Activity

Suggest students make long pendulums that they can safely swing from high places, time the swings, and report the results to the class. Have students prepare a larger graph incorporating the results.

AUDITORY ◆ KINESTHETIC ◆ TACTILE ◆ VISUAL

Have students work in groups to continue the investigation by timing 10 swings for pendulums with 5 cm, 10 cm, 20 cm, 30 cm, and 1 m string lengths. Circulate and assist. Each student records the time for 10 swings and then divides by 10 to find the average time for a single swing, to the nearest tenth of a second.

Check the reasonableness of data entries of groups that finish early. They may go on to Problem 6 on *Math Masters,* page 409 while waiting for the others to catch up. They should not begin the graphing exercise in Problem 5 on *Math Masters,* page 408 until their data entries have been checked.

3. **Graphing the Results**
After all groups have completed their trials and found the average time for 10 swings to the nearest tenth of a second, help students plot one or two data points on the grid in Problem 5 on *Math Masters,* page 408. Students then plot the rest of the results recorded in the table on *Math Masters,* page 407.

Ask students to connect the dots to form a broken-line graph. In discussing the graph, ask questions such as the following:

- Does the length of the string affect the duration of the swing? The time for one complete swing increases as the length of the pendulum string increases. Some students might notice that quadrupling the length of the pendulum string doubles the swing time.
- About how many seconds, to the nearest tenth of a second, would it take for a complete swing of a 150-centimeter pendulum? About 2.4 sec
- About how long is a pendulum that takes 2 seconds to complete a swing? 100 cm
- Based on the results, what might be the swing time for a much longer pendulum—say 10 m, 20 m, or even 30 m long? Possible responses: 10 m: about 6 sec; 20 m: about 9 sec; 30 m: about 11 sec

Investigating the Effect of the Arc on Swing Time

SMALL-GROUP ACTIVITY

(*Math Masters,* p. 409)

Have students start the swing of a pendulum at various positions. They try to answer the question, *Does the size of the arc make much difference in the amount of time it takes for 10 complete swings?* They record their answer in Problem 6 on *Math Masters,* page 409. For a given pendulum length, the position of the starting point should not significantly affect the time for a complete swing.

Project Master

Name Date Time

PROJECT 8 **The Swing Time of Pendulums** *cont.*

6. Experiment with different arc sizes. The largest arc is formed when the string of the pendulum is in a horizontal position. Does the size of the arc make much difference in the amount of time it takes for 10 complete swings?

No

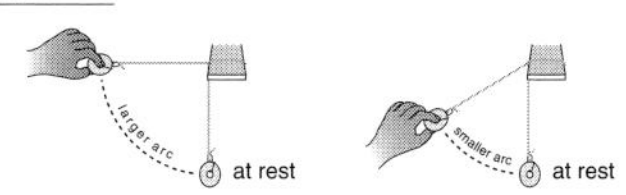

7. Does the weight of the object at the end of a pendulum affect the time for a complete swing? Using a pendulum with a string 50 cm long, try different numbers of objects to find out if weight makes a difference in the time of the swing.

Length of Pendulum	Number of Weights (washers or other objects)	Time for 10 Swings (to nearest 0.1 sec)	Time for One Swing (to nearest 0.1 or 0.01 sec)
50 cm	1	14 sec	1.4 sec
50 cm	3	14 sec	1.4 sec
50 cm	5	14 sec	1.4 sec
50 cm	10	14 sec	1.4 sec

My conclusion: It seems that the weight of the attached object does not affect the duration of a complete swing.

Math Masters, p. 409

Investigating the Effect of Weight on Swing Time

(*Math Masters,* p. 409)

Have students explore whether the amount of weight at the end of a pendulum affects the time for 10 complete swings. Using the 50-centimeter pendulum, students vary the weight by adding or removing washers. For a given pendulum length, different weights should make little difference in the time for a complete swing. However, the heavier the weight is, the longer the pendulum is likely to keep swinging. They record their conclusions in Problem 7 on *Math Masters,* page 409.

2 Extending the Project

Learning More about Pendulums

Invite students to find out more about the history, types, and uses of pendulums by looking in encyclopedias or searching the Internet.

Pendulums were integral to the development of clocks. Clocks, in turn, made possible the long-sought solution to measuring longitude. Two books that discuss this solution are *Longitude* and *Sea Clocks: The Story of Longitude.*

Longitude
Summary: This is the story of the search for a way to determine longitude aboard ships at sea. The solution came in the 18th century in the form of precise clocks designed so a ship's motion and variations in temperature and humidity did not affect the clocks' pendulums.

Sea Clocks: The Story of Longitude
Summary: This juvenile literature biography is the dramatic story of John Harrison. Harrison dedicated more than 40 years of his life to the design of the perfect sea clock.

Project 9

Adding Volumes of Solid Figures

Objectives To find the volumes of solid figures composed of two non-overlapping rectangular prisms.

Technology Resources www.everydaymathonline.com

eToolkit

Algorithms Practice

EM Facts Workshop Game™

Family Letters

Assessment Management

Common Core State Standards

Curriculum Focal Points

Interactive Teacher's Lesson Guide

1 Doing the Project

Recommended Use During or after Unit 9

Key Concepts and Skills

- Use unit cubes to calculate volume.
  [Measurement and Reference Frames Goal 2]
- Use a formula to calculate the volumes of rectangular prisms.
  [Measurement and Reference Frames Goal 2]
- Explore properties of solid figures.
  [Geometry Goal 2]
- Write number sentences with variables to model volume problems.
  [Patterns, Functions, and Algebra Goal 2]

Key Activities

Students use centimeter cubes and formulas to explore the volumes of solid figures composed of two rectangular prisms.

Key Vocabulary

unit cube

Materials

- *Math Journal 2,* Activity Sheet 8
- *Math Masters,* p. 410
- transparent tape
- per group of students: about 100 centimeter cubes

2 Extending the Project

Students find the volumes of rectangular prisms to find the total approximate volume of Willis Tower.

Materials

- *Math Masters,* p. 410A

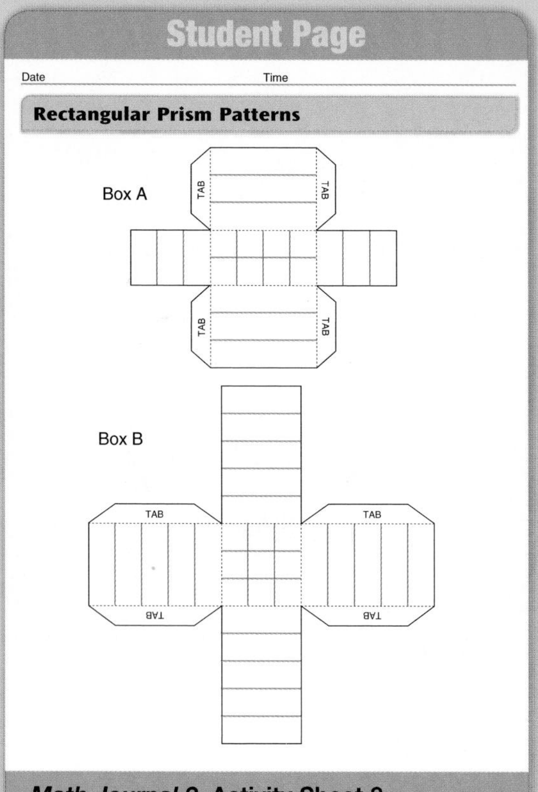

Math Journal 2, Activity Sheet 8

1 Doing the Project

▶ Exploring the Volumes of Solid Figures

(*Math Journal 2,* Activity Sheet 8)

Provide each group of students with about 100 centimeter cubes. In each group, students should display the two open boxes that they constructed in Lesson 9-8 from Activity Sheet 8. If the constructed boxes are no longer available, distribute copies of Activity Sheet 8 as needed.

Have students tape together Boxes A and B to form one solid figure. Specify that they should put the prisms together so that two faces are together and edges line up where possible. Note that students may tape the prisms together in different ways. The figure below is one example.

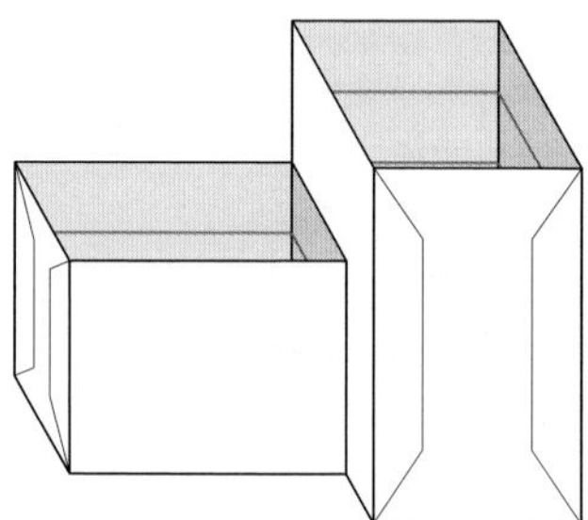

Ask: *Suppose each box has a lid so that each is a rectangular prism. Is the figure formed by the two rectangular prisms also a rectangular prism? Explain.* Sample answer: No. A rectangular prism is formed by six faces that are rectangles. The new figure that is formed has more than six rectangular faces. Mention that a three-dimensional shape that is not of a specific type is simply called a *solid figure.*

Ask: *How could you use the centimeter cubes to find the volume of the solid figure you formed?* Sample answer: Fill each box with centimeter cubes. Add or count the cubes used in all. *What is the volume of the solid figure?* 69 cubic centimeters

Ask students to attach the two prisms in different ways (such as one above the other or one next to the other) and compare the volume of each new solid that has been formed. Students should recognize that the volume is the same no matter how the prisms are attached. Ask a volunteer to explain why this is so. Sample answer: The two prisms have the same volumes no matter how they are put together, so the sum of the two volumes is the same.

Explain that in this case we can consider each dimension of a centimeter cube as being 1 unit long. Mention that a cube with side lengths of 1 unit is called a **unit cube.** Explain that in general, when a solid figure can be packed without gaps and overlaps using n unit cubes, the volume of the solid figure is n cubic units.

Building a Solid Figure to Find Volume

SMALL-GROUP ACTIVITY

(*Math Masters,* p. 410)

Have students use the centimeter cubes to build the two rectangular prisms in each of Problems 1–3 on *Math Masters,* page 410. Students find the volume of each prism and then find the volume of the solid figure formed by the two prisms. Encourage students to use a formula (either $V = B * h$ or $V = l * w * h$) to find the volumes of the rectangular prisms. Students should use the cubes to check their results.

When students complete Problem 4, they should conclude that you can find the volume of a solid figure formed by two rectangular prisms by adding the two volumes. So, finding the volume of a solid figure that includes more than one rectangular prism is an additive process. You may want to explain that if a solid figure has overlapping parts, as in the solid figure below, you add the volumes of the *non-overlapping* parts to the volumes of the parts that overlap.

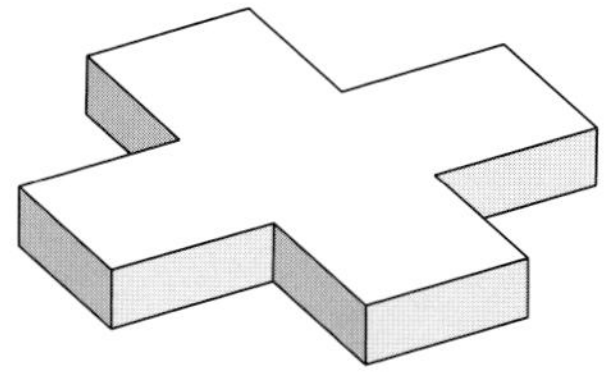

2 Extending the Project

Finding the Volume of Willis Tower in Chicago

INDEPENDENT ACTIVITY

(*Math Masters,* p. 410A)

Mention that at 1,450 feet tall (excluding antennas), Willis Tower in Chicago (formerly named Sears Tower) is the tallest building in the United States. When it was built in 1974, it was the tallest building in the world.

Project Master

Name Date Time

PROJECT 9 **Building a Solid Figure to Find Volume**

For Problems 1–3, do the following:

a. Use centimeter cubes to build each rectangular prism.
b. Find the volume of each rectangular prism.
c. Find the volume of the solid figure formed by the two rectangular prisms.

1.

	Length l	Width w	Height h	Volume V (cubic units)
Rectangular Prism A	1	2	3	6
Rectangular Prism B	2	3	4	24
Solid Figure Formed by Prisms A and B				30

2.

	Length l	Width w	Height h	Volume V (cubic units)
Rectangular Prism C	5	3	2	30
Rectangular Prism D	2	3	5	30
Solid Figure Formed by Prisms C and D				60

3.

	Length l	Width w	Height h	Volume V (cubic units)
Rectangular Prism E	12	3	1	36
Rectangular Prism F	3	3	3	27
Solid Figure Formed by Prisms E and F				63

4. Explain how to find the volume of a solid figure made from two rectangular prisms, one with dimensions 3 cm by 4 cm by 5 cm and one with dimensions 2 cm by 5 cm by 4 cm.
Sample answer: I would use the formula $V = l * w * h$ to find the volume of each rectangular prism and then add the volumes. So, the total volume is $3 * 4 * 5 + 2 * 5 * 4 = 60 + 40$, or 100 cm^3.

Math Masters, p. 410

Project Master

Name ______ Date ______ Time ______

Finding the Volume of Willis Tower

Willis Tower

At 1,450 feet tall, Willis Tower in Chicago is the tallest building in the United States. It is composed of nine rectangular prisms known as "tubes." The tubes are built in a 3-by-3 arrangement. Although the tubes are of various heights, each one has a square base that measures 75 feet on a side.

1. What is the area of the base of each tube?
   5,625 ft²

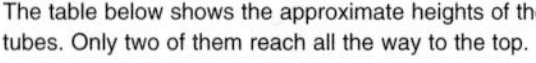

The table below shows the approximate heights of the tubes. Only two of them reach all the way to the top.

2. What formula could you use to find the volume of one tube? Sample answer: $V = B * h$

3. Complete the table to find the volume of one tube at each given height. Then find the total volume of the tubes for each height.

Approximate Height of Tube	Number of Tubes at this Height	Volume of One Tube at this Height (ft^3)	Total Volume of Tubes at this Height (ft^3)
646 ft	3	3,633,750	10,901,250
672 ft	2	3,780,000	7,560,000
1,200 ft	2	6,750,000	13,500,000
1,450 ft	2	8,156,250	16,312,500

4. Describe what you will do to find the total approximate volume of Willis Tower.
   Sample answer: I will find the sum of the total volumes of the tubes for each height.

5. The total volume of Willis Tower is about 48,273,750 ft³.

Math Masters, p. 410A

The building consists of nine square "tubes" constructed in a 3-by-3 arrangement. Each tube measures 75 feet on a side. Ask students to explain how to find the dimensions of the entire base of Willis Tower. Sample answer: There are three tubes on a side, and each is 75 feet long. So each side is 225 feet long, making the dimensions of the base 225 ft by 225 ft. Ask: *What is the area of the base?* $225 * 225$, or 50,625 ft^2

Explain that the nine tubes are of various heights, with some being the same height. For example, although all nine tubes extend up through the 49th story, only two tubes extend to the full height of 110 stories. So to find the volume of Willis Tower, you need to find the volumes of the different tubes and then add. Of course, multiplication could be used to find the total volume of tubes with the same dimensions.

Math Masters, page 410A guides students in finding the approximate volume of Willis Tower.

Algorithm 1 Project

U.S. Traditional Addition

Objective To introduce U.S. traditional addition.

Technology Resources www.everydaymathonline.com

eToolkit | Algorithms Practice | EM Facts Workshop Game™ | Family Letters | Assessment Management | Common Core State Standards | Curriculum Focal Points | Interactive Teacher's Lesson Guide

1 Doing the Project

Recommended Use After Lesson 2•2

Key Concepts and Skills

- Identify places in whole numbers and the values of the digits in those places. [Number and Numeration Goal 1]
- Add multidigit whole numbers. [Operations and Computation Goal 1]
- Solve addition number stories. [Operations and Computation Goal 1]
- Make reasonable estimates for addition problems. [Operations and Computation Goal 6]

Key Activities

Students explore and practice U.S. traditional addition with multidigit whole numbers.

Key Vocabulary

U.S. traditional addition

Materials

- ◆ *Math Journal 1* or *2,* pp. 1P and 2P
- ◆ *Student Reference Book,* p. 24A

2 Extending the Project

Students solve multidigit addition problems, first using the focus algorithm (partial-sums addition) and then using any algorithm they choose.

Materials

- ◆ *Math Journal 1* or *2,* pp. 3P and 4P
- ◆ Online Additional Practice, pp. 4A–4D
- ◆ *Student Reference Book,* pp. 13, 14, and 24A

Student Page

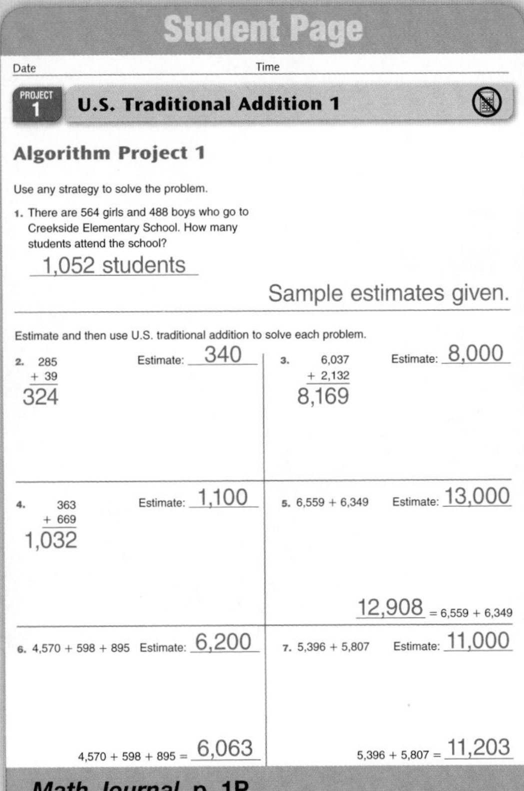

Date Time

PROJECT 1 **U.S. Traditional Addition 1**

Algorithm Project 1

Use any strategy to solve the problem.

1. There are 564 girls and 488 boys who go to Creekside Elementary School. How many students attend the school?
   1,052 students

Sample estimates given.

Estimate and then use U.S. traditional addition to solve each problem.

2. 285 + 39 = 324 Estimate: 340	3. 6,037 + 2,132 = 8,169 Estimate: 8,000
4. 363 + 669 = 1,032 Estimate: 1,100	5. 6,559 + 6,349 Estimate: 13,000 12,908 = 6,559 + 6,349
6. 4,570 + 598 + 895 Estimate: 6,200 4,570 + 598 + 895 = 6,063	7. 5,396 + 5,807 Estimate: 11,000 5,396 + 5,807 = 11,203

Math Journal, p. 1P

NOTE Reinforce the use of estimation by asking students to make an estimate prior to solving each problem. The estimate is then used to check the reasonableness of the solution to the problem.

1 Doing the Project

▶ Solving an Addition Problem

INDEPENDENT ACTIVITY

(*Math Journal 1* or *2*, p. 1P)

Ask students to solve Problem 1 on journal page 1P. Tell them they may use any methods they wish, but they may not use calculators.

▶ Discussing Solutions

WHOLE-CLASS ACTIVITY

(*Math Journal 1* or *2*, p. 1P)

Discuss students' solutions to Problem 1 on journal page 1P. 564 + 488 = 1,052 students Expect that students will use several different methods, including partial-sums addition, column addition, and the opposite-change rule for addition. Some students may also use U.S. traditional addition. *Possible strategies:*

▷ Using partial-sums addition

		564
		+ 488
Add the 100s.	500 + 400 →	900
Add the 10s.	60 + 80 →	140
Add the 1s.	4 + 8 →	12
Add the partial sums.	900 + 140 + 12 →	**1052**

▷ Using column addition

	100s	10s	1s
	5	**6**	**4**
	+ 4	**8**	**8**
Add the numbers in each column.	9	14	12
Trade 10 ones for 1 ten.	9	15	2
Trade 10 tens for 1 hundred.	**10**	**5**	**2**

▷ Using the opposite-change rule for addition

Adjust 564 down (by 2) to 562 and adjust 488 up (by 2) to 490.
Adjust 562 down (by 10) to 552 and adjust 490 up (by 10) to 500.

564 + 488
562 + 490
552 + 500
1052

▷ Using U.S. traditional addition

```
  1 1
  5 6 4
+ 4 8 8
-------
1 0 5 2
```

▶ Introducing U.S. Traditional Addition

WHOLE-CLASS ACTIVITY

After you have discussed students' solutions, and even if one or more students used **U.S. traditional addition,** demonstrate it as described below.

Example 1: 564 + 488

Step 1:

Add the 1s: 4 + 8 = 12.
12 = 1 ten + 2 ones
Write 2 in the 1s place below the line.
Write 1 above the numbers in the 10s place.

```
     1
  5 6 4
+ 4 8 8
-------
      2
```

Step 2:

Add the 10s: 1 + 6 + 8 = 15.
15 tens = 1 hundred + 5 tens
Write 5 in the 10s place below the line.
Write 1 above the numbers in the 100s place.

```
   1 1
  5 6 4
+ 4 8 8
-------
    5 2
```

Step 3:

Add the 100s: 1 + 5 + 4 = 10.
10 hundreds = 1 one thousand + 0 hundreds
Write 0 in the 100s place below the line.
Write 1 in the 1,000s place below the line.

```
   1 1
  5 6 4
+ 4 8 8
-------
1 0 5 2
```

564 + 488 = 1,052
There are 1,052 students at Creekside Elementary School.

NOTE Throughout the discussion of U.S. traditional addition, be sure that students understand the values of the digits. For instance, in Step 2 of Example 1, 1 + 6 + 8 = 15 means 1 ten + 6 tens + 8 tens = 15 tens (1 hundred + 5 tens) or 10 + 60 + 80 = 150.

Example 2: 7,446 + 3,579

Step 1:

Add the 1s: 6 + 9 = 15.
15 = 1 ten + 5 ones
Write 5 in the 1s place below the line.
Write 1 above the numbers in the 10s place.

```
       1
  7 4 4 6
+ 3 5 7 9
---------
        5
```

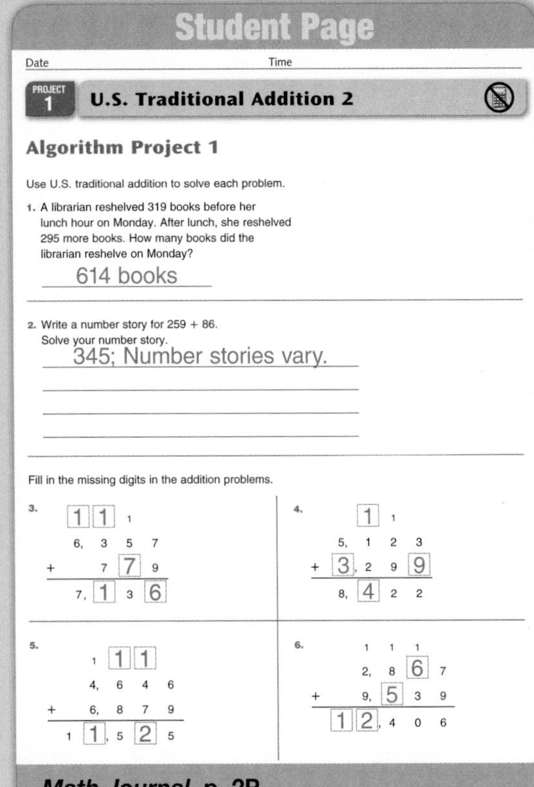

Student Page

Date Time

PROJECT 1 **U.S. Traditional Addition 2**

Algorithm Project 1

Use U.S. traditional addition to solve each problem.

1. A librarian reshelved 319 books before her lunch hour on Monday. After lunch, she reshelved 295 more books. How many books did the librarian reshelve on Monday?
614 books

2. Write a number story for 259 + 86. Solve your number story.
345; Number stories vary.

Fill in the missing digits in the addition problems.

3.
```
 1 1 1
 6, 3 5 7
+   7 7 9
 7, 1 3 6
```

4.
```
 1   1
 5, 1 2 3
+3, 2 9 9
 8, 4 2 2
```

5.
```
 1 1 1
 4, 6 4 6
+6, 8 7 9
1 1, 5 2 5
```

6.
```
 1 1 1
 2, 8 6 7
+9, 5 3 9
1 2, 4 0 6
```

Math Journal, p. 2P

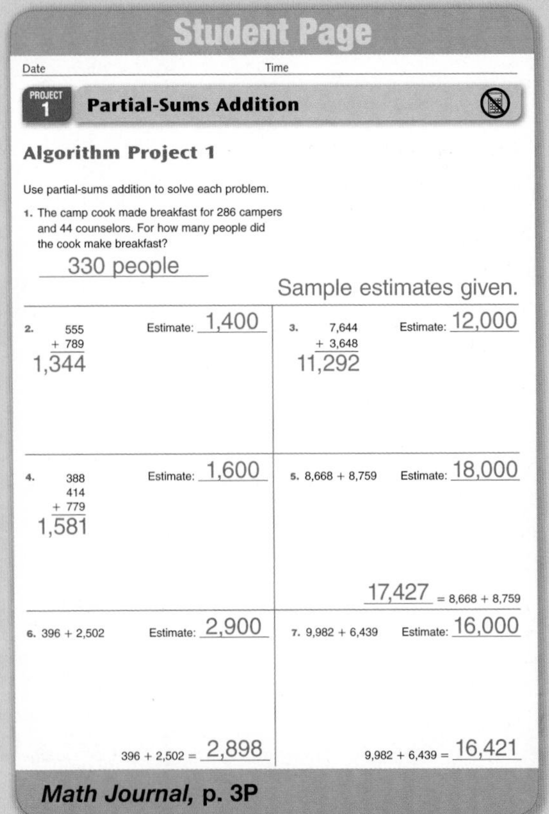

Student Page

Date Time

PROJECT 1 **Partial-Sums Addition**

Algorithm Project 1

Use partial-sums addition to solve each problem.

1. The camp cook made breakfast for 286 campers and 44 counselors. For how many people did the cook make breakfast?
330 people

Sample estimates given.

2. 555 + 789 = 1,344 Estimate: 1,400

3. 7,644 + 3,648 = 11,292 Estimate: 12,000

4. 388 + 414 + 779 = 1,581 Estimate: 1,600

5. 8,668 + 8,759 Estimate: 18,000
17,427 = 8,668 + 8,759

6. 396 + 2,502 Estimate: 2,900
396 + 2,502 = 2,898

7. 9,982 + 6,439 Estimate: 16,000
9,982 + 6,439 = 16,421

Math Journal, p. 3P

Step 2:

Add the 10s: 1 + 4 + 7 = 12.
12 tens = 1 hundred + 2 tens
Write 2 in the 10s place below the line.
Write 1 above the numbers in the 100s place.

```
   1 1
 7 4 4 6
+3 5 7 9
     2 5
```

Step 3:

Add the 100s: 1 + 4 + 5 = 10.
10 hundreds = 1 thousand + 0 hundreds
Write 0 in the 100s place below the line.
Write 1 above the numbers in the 1,000s place.

```
 1 1 1
 7 4 4 6
+3 5 7 9
   0 2 5
```

Step 4:

Add the 1,000s: 1 + 7 + 3 = 11.
11 thousands = 1 ten thousand + 1 thousand
Write 1 in the 1,000s place below the line.
Write 1 in the 10,000s place below the line.

```
  1 1 1
  7 4 4 6
+ 3 5 7 9
1 1 0 2 5
```

7,446 + 3,579 = 11,052

You may want to work several more examples with the whole class.

Suggestions:

▷ 77 + 58 = ? 135

▷ 581 + 69 = ? 650

▷ 517 + 362 = ? 879

▷ 763 + 245 + 528 = ? 1,536

▷ 8,075 + 6,997 = ? 15,072

▷ 6,488 + 7,556 = ? 14,044

▶ Practicing U.S. Traditional Addition

(*Math Journal 1* or *2,* pp. 1P and 2P; *Student Reference Book,* p. 24A)

When students are ready, have them estimate and then solve Problems 2–7 on journal page 1P. They may find the example on *Student Reference Book,* page 24A helpful.

Journal page 2P provides students with additional practice using U.S. traditional addition. Use this journal page as necessary.

2 Extending the Project

▶ Solving Multidigit Addition Problems

INDEPENDENT ACTIVITY

(*Math Journal 1* or *2,* pp. 3P and 4P; Online Additional Practice, pp. 4A–4D; *Student Reference Book,* pp. 13, 14, and 24A)

Journal pages 3P and 4P provide students with additional practice solving multidigit addition problems. Use these journal pages as necessary.

Encourage students to estimate and then use the focus algorithm (partial-sums addition) to solve the problems on journal page 3P. Invite them to use any algorithm they wish to solve the problems on journal page 4P. Online practice pages 4A–4D provide students with additional practice with multidigit addition problems.

Students may find the examples on *Student Reference Book,* pages 13, 14, and 24A helpful.

Student Page

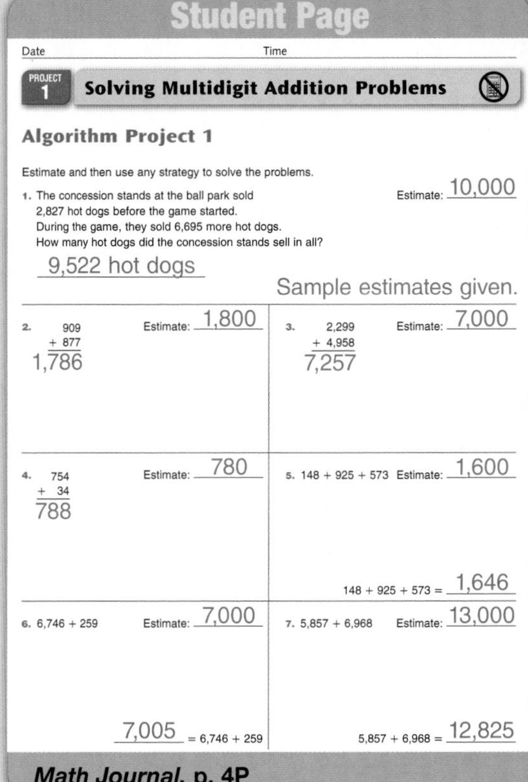
Date Time

PROJECT 1 **Solving Multidigit Addition Problems**

Algorithm Project 1

Estimate and then use any strategy to solve the problems.

1. The concession stands at the ball park sold 2,827 hot dogs before the game started. During the game, they sold 6,695 more hot dogs. How many hot dogs did the concession stands sell in all? Estimate: 10,000
   9,522 hot dogs

Sample estimates given.

2. 909 + 877 = 1,786 Estimate: 1,800
3. 2,299 + 4,958 = 7,257 Estimate: 7,000
4. 754 + 34 = 788 Estimate: 780
5. 148 + 925 + 573 Estimate: 1,600
   148 + 925 + 573 = 1,646
6. 6,746 + 259 Estimate: 7,000
   7,005 = 6,746 + 259
7. 5,857 + 6,968 Estimate: 13,000
   5,857 + 6,968 = 12,825

Math Journal, p. 4P

Go to www.everydaymathonline.com to access the additional practice pages.

Online Master

Name Date Time

PROJECT 1 **Solving Multidigit Addition Problems 1**

Online Additional Practice

Algorithm Project 1

Estimate and then use any strategy to solve the problems.

1. Lamar and his classmates held a food drive. They collected 1,973 cans of food and 2,634 boxes of food. How many food items did they collect in all? Estimate: 5,000
   4,607 food items

Sample estimates given.

2. 492 + 627 = 1,119 Estimate: 1,100
3. 8,230 + 3,576 = 11,806 Estimate: 12,000
4. 133 + 209 + 75 = 417 Estimate: 400
5. 7,138 + 4,593 Estimate: 12,000
   11,731 = 7,138 + 4,593
6. 2,945 + 382 + 68 = 3,395 Estimate: 3,400
7. 5,792 + 8,821 Estimate: 15,000
   5,792 + 8,821 = 14,613

Online Additional Practice, p. 4A

Algorithm

2

Project

U.S. Traditional Addition: Decimals

Objective To introduce U.S. traditional addition for decimals.

Technology Resources www.everydaymathonline.com

eToolkit

Algorithms Practice

EM Facts Workshop Game™

Family Letters

Assessment Management

Common Core State Standards

Curriculum Focal Points

Interactive Teacher's Lesson Guide

1 Doing the Project

Recommended Use After Lesson 2•2

Key Concepts and Skills

- Identify places in whole numbers and decimals and the values of the digits in those places.
  [Number and Numeration Goal 1]
- Add decimals.
  [Operations and Computation Goal 1]
- Solve addition number stories with decimals.
  [Operations and Computation Goal 1]
- Make reasonable estimates for addition with decimals.
  [Operations and Computation Goal 6]

Key Activities

Students explore and practice U.S. traditional addition with decimals.

Materials

- *Math Journal 1* or *2,* pp. 5P–8P
- *Student Reference Book,* p. 54A
- base-10 blocks (optional)

2 Extending the Project

Students solve decimal addition problems, first using the focus algorithm (partial-sums addition) and then using any algorithm they choose.

Materials

- Online Additional Practice, pp. 8A–8D
- *Student Reference Book,* pp. 34, 35, and 54A

1 Doing the Project

▶ Solving a Decimal Addition Problem

INDEPENDENT ACTIVITY

(*Math Journal 1* or *2,* p. 5P)

Ask students to solve Problem 1 on journal page 5P. Tell them they may use base-10 blocks, paper and pencil, or any other tools they wish, except calculators.

▶ Discussing Solutions

WHOLE-CLASS ACTIVITY

(*Math Journal 1* or *2,* p. 5P)

Discuss students' solutions to Problem 1 on journal page 5P. \$4.85 + \$2.69 = \$7.54 Expect that students will use several different methods, including base-10 blocks, partial-sums addition, and column addition. Some students may also use U.S. traditional addition. *Possible strategies:*

▷ Modeling with base-10 blocks

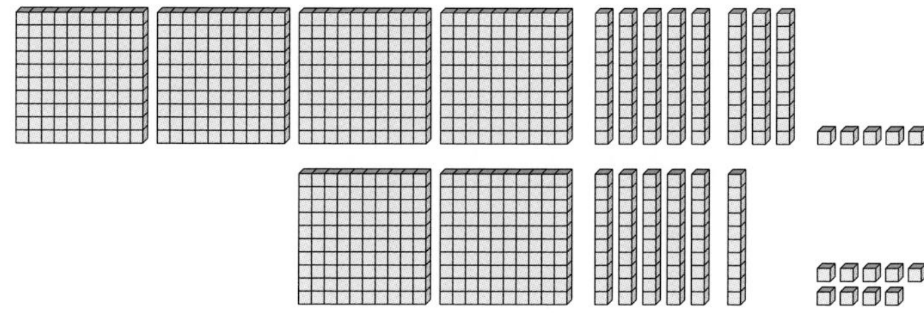

Show 4.85 and 2.69 with blocks.

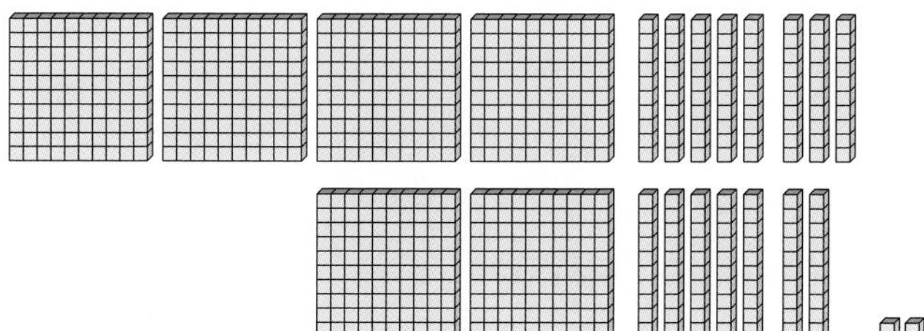

Trade 10 cubes for 1 long.

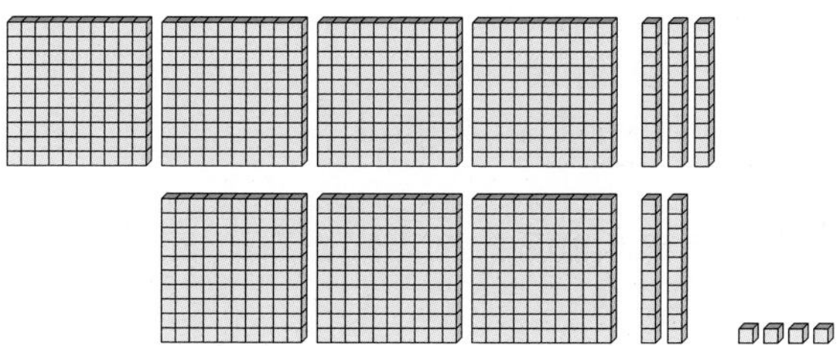

Trade 10 longs for 1 flat.

\$4.85 + \$2.69 = \$7.54

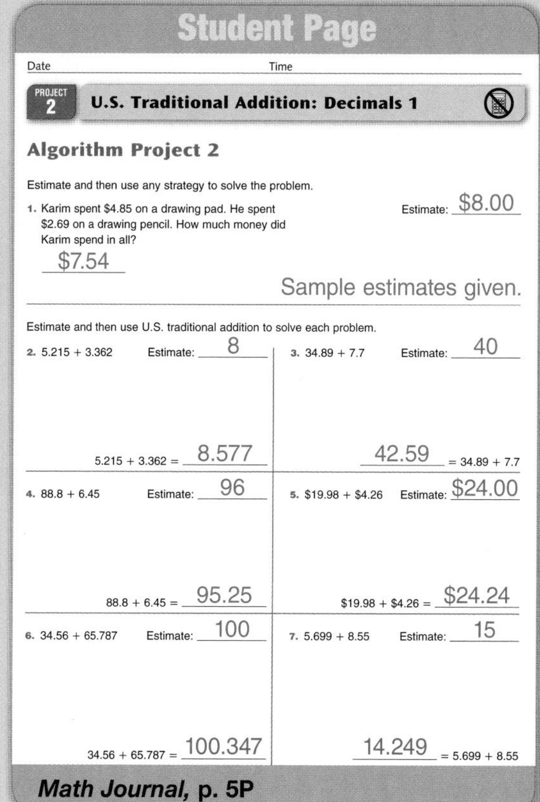

Student Page

Date Time

PROJECT 2 **U.S. Traditional Addition: Decimals 1**

Algorithm Project 2

Estimate and then use any strategy to solve the problem.

1. Karim spent \$4.85 on a drawing pad. He spent \$2.69 on a drawing pencil. How much money did Karim spend in all? Estimate: \$8.00

\$7.54

Sample estimates given.

Estimate and then use U.S. traditional addition to solve each problem.

2. 5.215 + 3.362 Estimate: 8 — 5.215 + 3.362 = 8.577
3. 34.89 + 7.7 Estimate: 40 — 42.59 = 34.89 + 7.7
4. 88.8 + 6.45 Estimate: 96 — 88.8 + 6.45 = 95.25
5. \$19.98 + \$4.26 Estimate: \$24.00 — \$19.98 + \$4.26 = \$24.24
6. 34.56 + 65.787 Estimate: 100 — 34.56 + 65.787 = 100.347
7. 5.699 + 8.55 Estimate: 15 — 14.249 = 5.699 + 8.55

***Math Journal,* p. 5P**

NOTE Reinforce the use of estimation by asking students to make an estimate prior to solving each problem. The estimate is then used to check the reasonableness of the solution to the problem.

▷ Using shorthand pictures of base-10 blocks

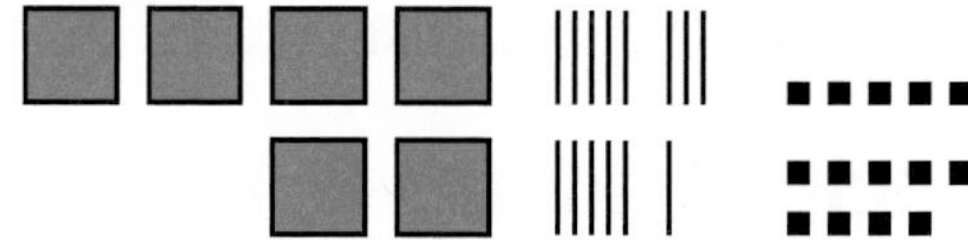

Draw a picture for each number.

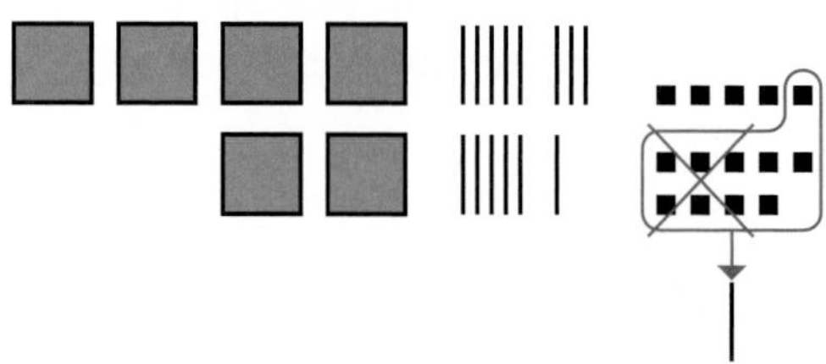

Draw a ring around 10 cubes and trade them for 1 long.

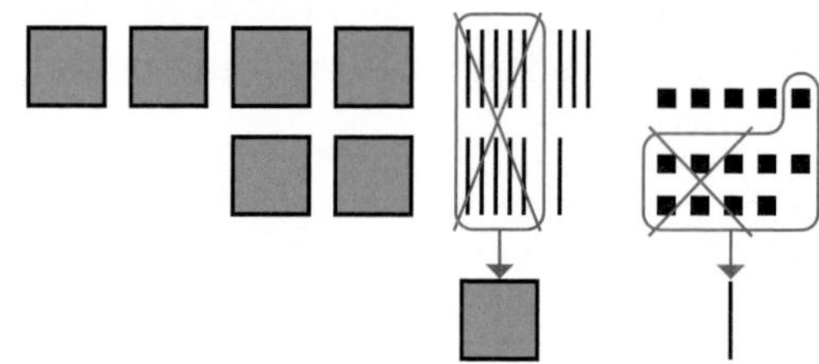

Draw a ring around 10 longs and trade them for 1 flat.

This drawing shows 7.54.

$4.85 + $2.69 = $7.54

▷ Using partial-sums addition

		4.85
		+ 2.69
Add the 1s.	4 + 2 →	6.00
Add the 0.1s.	0.8 + 0.6 →	1.40
Add the 0.01s.	0.05 + 0.09 →	0.14
Add the partial sums.	6.00 + 1.40 + 0.14 →	**7.54**

$6.00 + $1.40 + $0.14 = $7.54

▷ Using column addition

1s	0.1s	0.01s
4 .	**8**	**5**
+ 2 .	**6**	**9**
6 .	14	14
6 .	15	4
7 .	**5**	**4**

Add the numbers in each column.
Trade 14 hundredths for 1 tenth and 4 hundredths.
Trade 15 tenths for one and 5 tenths.

$4.85 + $2.69 = $7.54

▷ Using U.S. traditional addition

```
  1 1
  4.85
+ 2.69
  7.54
```

$4.85 + $2.69 = $7.54

▶ Introducing U.S. Traditional Addition for Decimals

WHOLE-CLASS ACTIVITY

After you have discussed students' solutions, and even if one or more students used U.S. traditional addition, demonstrate it again as described below.

Example 1: \$4.85 + \$2.69

Step 1:

Start with the 0.01s: 5 + 9 = 14.
14 hundredths = 1 tenth + 4 hundredths

$$\begin{array}{r} {\scriptstyle 1} \\ 4.8\mathbf{5} \\ +\,2.6\mathbf{9} \\ \hline \mathbf{4} \end{array}$$

Step 2:

Add the 0.1s: 1 + 8 + 6 = 15.
15 tenths = 1 whole + 5 tenths

$$\begin{array}{r} {\scriptstyle 1\;1\;\;} \\ 4.\mathbf{8}5 \\ +\,2.\mathbf{6}9 \\ \hline \mathbf{5}\,4 \end{array}$$

Step 3:

Add the 1s: 1 + 4 + 2 = 7.
Remember to include the decimal point in the answer.

$$\begin{array}{r} {\scriptstyle 1\;1\;\;} \\ \mathbf{4}.85 \\ +\,\mathbf{2}.69 \\ \hline \mathbf{7}.54 \end{array}$$

\$4.85 + \$2.69 = \$7.54

Karim spent \$7.54.

Be sure that students understand how to properly line up the places when adding decimals so that hundredths are added to hundredths, tenths to tenths, and so on. In the example below, write 28.38 as 28.380 so that both numbers have the same number of digits after the decimal point.

Example 2: 37.966 + 28.38

Step 1:

Start with the 0.001s: 6 + 0 = 6.

$$\begin{array}{r} 37.96\mathbf{6} \\ +\,28.38\mathbf{0} \\ \hline \mathbf{6} \end{array}$$

Step 2:

Add the 0.01s: 6 + 8 = 14.
14 hundredths = 1 tenth + 4 hundredths

$$\begin{array}{r} {\scriptstyle 1\;\;} \\ 37.9\mathbf{6}6 \\ +\,28.3\mathbf{8}0 \\ \hline \mathbf{4}\,6 \end{array}$$

Step 3:

Add the 0.1s: 1 + 9 + 3 = 13.
13 tenths = 1 whole + 3 tenths

$$\begin{array}{r} {\scriptstyle 1\;1\;\;\;} \\ 37.\mathbf{9}66 \\ +\,28.\mathbf{3}80 \\ \hline \mathbf{3}\,46 \end{array}$$

Step 4:

Add the 1s: 1 + 7 + 8 = 16.
16 = 1 ten + 6 ones

$$\begin{array}{r} {\scriptstyle 1\,1\;\;1\;\;\;} \\ 3\mathbf{7}.966 \\ +\,2\mathbf{8}.380 \\ \hline \mathbf{6}\;\;346 \end{array}$$

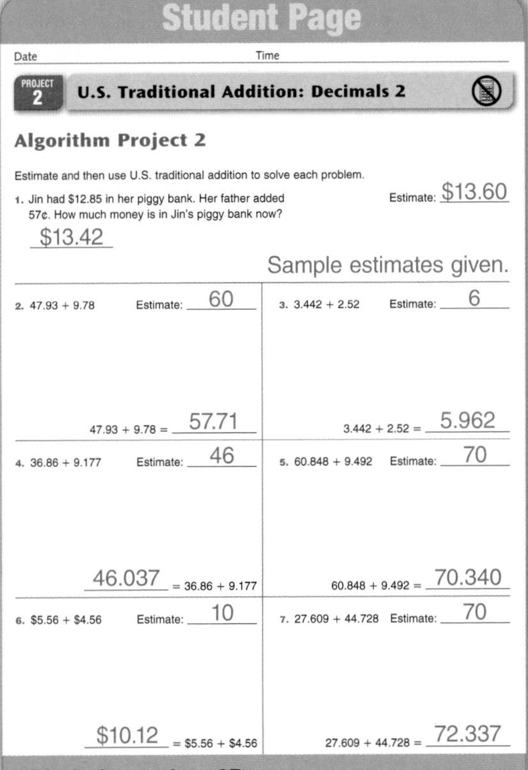
Student Page

Date Time

PROJECT 2 **U.S. Traditional Addition: Decimals 2**

Algorithm Project 2

Estimate and then use U.S. traditional addition to solve each problem.

1. Jin had \$12.85 in her piggy bank. Her father added 57¢. How much money is in Jin's piggy bank now? Estimate: \$13.60
\$13.42

Sample estimates given.

2. 47.93 + 9.78 Estimate: 60
47.93 + 9.78 = 57.71

3. 3.442 + 2.52 Estimate: 6
3.442 + 2.52 = 5.962

4. 36.86 + 9.177 Estimate: 46
46.037 = 36.86 + 9.177

5. 60.848 + 9.492 Estimate: 70
60.848 + 9.492 = 70.340

6. \$5.56 + \$4.56 Estimate: 10
\$10.12 = \$5.56 + \$4.56

7. 27.609 + 44.728 Estimate: 70
27.609 + 44.728 = 72.337

Math Journal, p. 6P

NOTE Throughout the discussion of U.S. traditional addition, be sure that students understand the values of the digits. For example, in Step 1 of Example 1, 5 + 9 = 14 means 5 hundredths + 9 hundredths = 14 hundredths (1 tenth + 4 hundredths), or 0.05 + 0.09 = 0.14. The same structure applies to the carry digits.

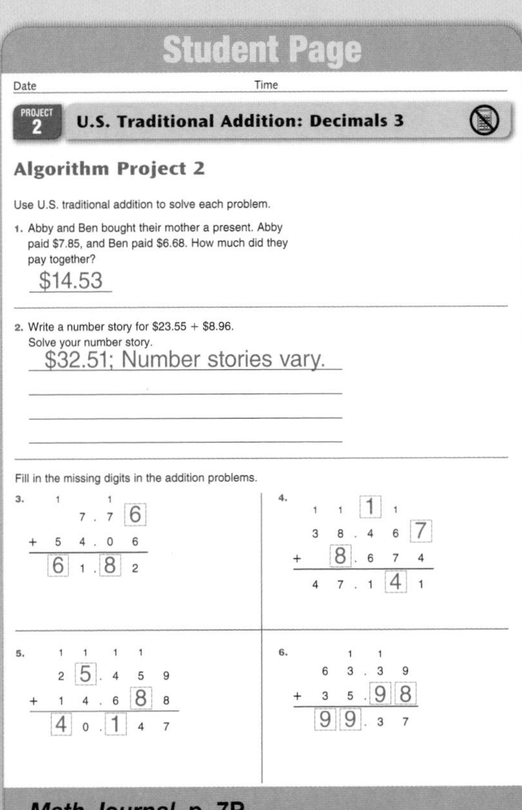
Student Page

Date Time

PROJECT 2 **U.S. Traditional Addition: Decimals 3**

Algorithm Project 2

Use U.S. traditional addition to solve each problem.

1. Abby and Ben bought their mother a present. Abby paid \$7.85, and Ben paid \$6.68. How much did they pay together?
\$14.53

2. Write a number story for \$23.55 + \$8.96. Solve your number story.
\$32.51; Number stories vary.

Fill in the missing digits in the addition problems.

3. 7.7[6] + 54.06 = [6]1.[8]2 (carries: 1, 1)

4. 38.46[7] + [8].674 = 47.1[4]1 (carries: 1, 1, [1], 1)

5. 2[5].459 + 14.6[8]8 = [4]0.[1]47 (carries: 1, 1, 1, 1)

6. 63.39 + 35.[9][8] = [9][9].37 (carries: 1, 1)

Math Journal, p. 7P

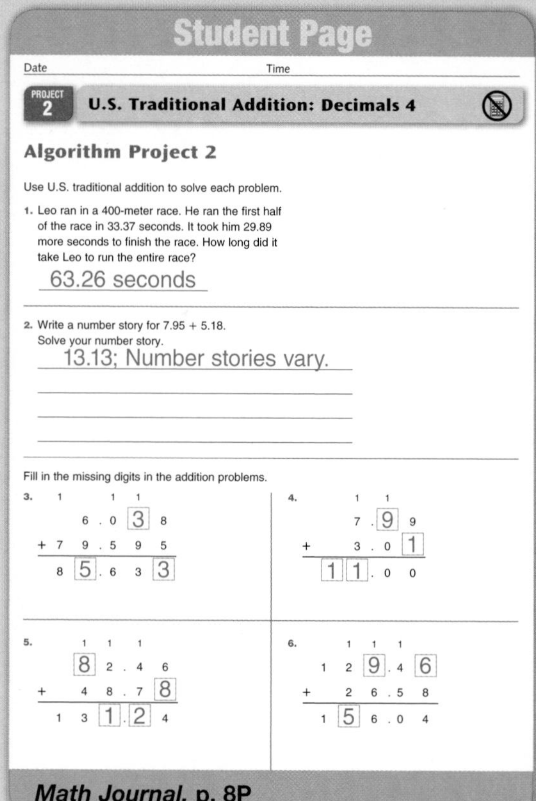
Student Page

Date Time

PROJECT 2 **U.S. Traditional Addition: Decimals 4**

Algorithm Project 2

Use U.S. traditional addition to solve each problem.

1. Leo ran in a 400-meter race. He ran the first half of the race in 33.37 seconds. It took him 29.89 more seconds to finish the race. How long did it take Leo to run the entire race?
63.26 seconds

2. Write a number story for 7.95 + 5.18. Solve your number story.
13.13; Number stories vary.

Fill in the missing digits in the addition problems.

3.
```
  1     1  1
    6 . 0 [3] 8
+ 7  9 . 5  9  5
  8 [5]. 6  3 [3]
```

4.
```
      1   1
      7 .[9] 9
+     3 . 0 [1]
  [1][1]. 0  0
```

5.
```
      1  1  1
    [8] 2 . 4  6
+    4  8 . 7 [8]
  1  3 [1].[2] 4
```

6.
```
    1  1  1
  1  2 [9]. 4 [6]
+    2  6 . 5  8
  1 [5] 6 . 0  4
```

Math Journal, p. 8P

Go to www.everydaymathonline.com to access the additional practice pages.

Online Master

Name Date Time

PROJECT 2 **Partial-Sums Addition: Decimals** Online Additional Practice

Algorithm Project 2

Estimate and then use any strategy to solve the problems.

1. Denzel bought 12.8 pounds of peaches. He also bought 4.5 pounds of berries. How many pounds of fruit did Denzel buy altogether? Estimate: 15
17.3 pounds

Sample estimates given.

2. 4.733 + 5.1 Estimate: 10 9.833 = 4.733 + 5.1	3. \$7.55 + \$5.77 Estimate: \$14.00 \$7.55 + \$5.77 = \$13.32
4. 95.4 + 4.95 Estimate: 100 95.4 + 4.95 = 100.35	5. 70.86 + 45.694 Estimate: 120 70.86 + 45.694 = 116.554
6. 18.922 + 55.49 Estimate: 80 74.412 = 18.922 + 55.49	7. 39.53 + 1.862 Estimate: 42 41.392 = 39.53 + 1.862

Online Additional Practice, p. 8A

Step 5:

Add the 10s: 1 + 3 + 2 = 6.
Remember to include the decimal point in the answer.

```
   1 1   1
   3 7 . 9 6 6
 + 2 8 . 3 8 0
   6 6 . 3 4 6
```

37.966 + 28.38 = 66.346

You may want to work several more examples with the whole class.

Suggestions:

▷ \$2.32 + \$6.55 = ? \$8.87

▷ 7.809 + 1.395 = ? 9.204

▷ 4.77 + 8.259 = ? 13.029

▷ 63.9 + 8.72 = ? 72.62

▷ \$38.83 + \$94.07 = ? \$132.90

▷ 60.498 + 45.664 = ? 106.162

▶ Practicing U.S. Traditional Addition for Decimals

(*Math Journal 1* or *2,* pp. 5P–8P; *Student Reference Book,* p. 54A)

When students are ready, have them estimate and then solve Problems 2–7 on journal page 5P. They may find the example on *Student Reference Book,* page 54A helpful.

Journal pages 6P–8P provide students with additional practice using U.S. traditional addition. Use these journal pages as necessary.

2 Extending the Project

▶ Solving Decimal Addition Problems

(Online Additional Practice, pp. 8A–8D; *Student Reference Book,* pp. 34, 35, and 54A)

Online practice pages 8A–8D provide students with additional practice solving decimal addition problems. Use these pages as necessary.

Encourage students to use the focus algorithm (partial-sums addition) to solve the problems on practice page 8A. Invite them to use any algorithm they wish to solve the problems on the remaining pages.

Students may find the examples on *Student Reference Book,* pages 34, 35, and 54A helpful.

Algorithm **3** Project

U.S. Traditional Subtraction

Objective To introduce U.S. traditional subtraction.

Technology Resources www.everydaymathonline.com

eToolkit

Algorithms Practice

EM Facts Workshop Game™

Family Letters

Assessment Management

Common Core State Standards

Curriculum Focal Points

Interactive Teacher's Lesson Guide

1 Doing the Project

Recommended Use After Lesson 2•3

Key Concepts and Skills

- Identify places in whole numbers and the values of the digits in those places.
  [Number and Numeration Goal 1]
- Subtract multidigit numbers.
  [Operations and Computation Goal 1]
- Solve subtraction number stories.
  [Operations and Computation Goal 1]
- Make reasonable estimates for subtraction problems.
  [Operations and Computation Goal 6]

Key Activities

Students explore and practice U.S. traditional subtraction with multidigit whole numbers.

Key Vocabulary

U.S. traditional subtraction

Materials

- *Math Journal 1* or *2,* pp. 9P and 10P
- *Student Reference Book,* p. 24B
- play money (optional)
- base-10 blocks (optional)

2 Extending the Project

Students solve multidigit subtraction problems, first using the focus algorithm (trade-first subtraction) and then using any algorithm they choose.

Materials

- *Math Journal 1* or *2,* pp. 11P and 12P
- Online Additional Practice, pp. 12A–12D
- *Student Reference Book,* pp. 15–17 and 24B

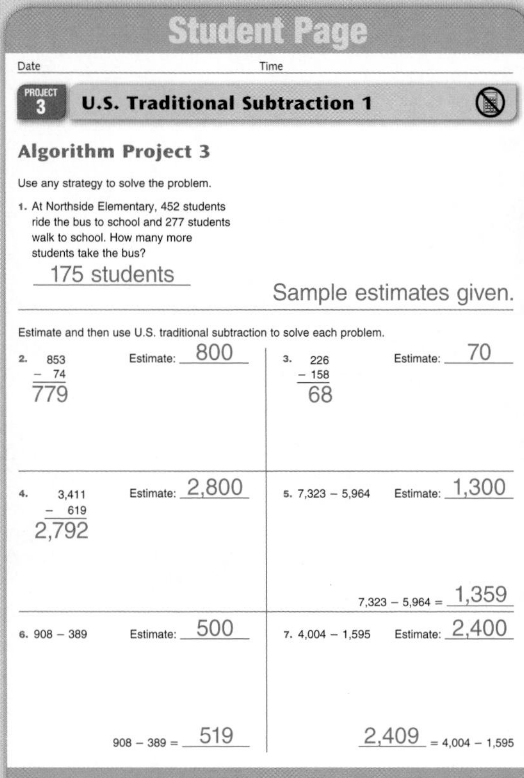

Student Page

Date Time

PROJECT 3 **U.S. Traditional Subtraction 1**

Algorithm Project 3

Use any strategy to solve the problem.

1. At Northside Elementary, 452 students ride the bus to school and 277 students walk to school. How many more students take the bus?

175 students

Sample estimates given.

Estimate and then use U.S. traditional subtraction to solve each problem.

2. 853 − 74 = 779 Estimate: 800
3. 226 − 158 = 68 Estimate: 70
4. 3,411 − 619 = 2,792 Estimate: 2,800
5. 7,323 − 5,964 Estimate: 1,300

   7,323 − 5,964 = 1,359
6. 908 − 389 Estimate: 500

   908 − 389 = 519
7. 4,004 − 1,595 Estimate: 2,400

   2,409 = 4,004 − 1,595

Math Journal, p. 9P

NOTE Reinforce the use of estimation by asking students to make an estimate prior to solving each problem. The estimate is then used to check the reasonableness of the solution to the problem.

1 Doing the Project

Solving a Subtraction Problem

INDEPENDENT ACTIVITY

(*Math Journal 1* or *2,* 9P)

Ask students to solve Problem 1 on journal page 9P. Tell them they may use base-10 blocks, play money, paper and pencil, or any other tools they wish, except calculators.

Discussing Solutions

WHOLE-CLASS ACTIVITY

(*Math Journal 1* or *2,* p. 9P)

Discuss students' solutions to Problem 1 on journal page 9P. 452 – 277 = 175 students Expect that students will use several different methods. Some may use base-10 blocks, play money, or other manipulatives. Others may use paper-and-pencil methods, including the same-change rule, counting up, partial-differences subtraction, and trade-first subtraction. Some students may also use U.S. traditional subtraction. *Possible strategies:*

▷ Using the same-change rule

$$\begin{array}{rcr} \mathbf{452} & \text{(add 23)} & 475 \\ \mathbf{-\ 277} & \text{(add 23)} & -\ 300 \\ \hline & & \mathbf{175} \end{array}$$

▷ Counting up

$$277 \xrightarrow{+3} 280 \xrightarrow{+20} 300 \xrightarrow{+100} 400 \xrightarrow{+52} 452$$

$$\begin{aligned} 277 + 3 &= 280 \\ 280 + 20 &= 300 \\ 300 + 100 &= 400 \\ 400 + 52 &= 452 \end{aligned}$$

$3 + 20 + 100 + 52 = 175$
$452 - 277 = 175$

▷ Using partial-differences subtraction

		452 − 277
Subtract the 100s.	400 – 200 →	+ 200
Subtract the 10s.	50 – 70 →	− 20
Subract the 1s.	2 – 7 →	− 5
Find the total.	200 – 20 – 5 →	**175**

▷ Using trade-first subtraction

	14	
3	~~4~~	12
~~4~~	~~5~~	~~2~~
− 2	7	7
1	7	5

▷ Using U.S. traditional subtraction

	14	
3	~~4~~	12
~~4~~	~~5~~	~~2~~
− 2	7	7
1	7	5

NOTE Trade-first subtraction resembles U.S. traditional subtraction, except that in trade-first subtraction, as the name implies, all the trading is done before any subtractions are carried out, allowing the person to concentrate on one task at a time.

▶ Introducing U.S. Traditional Subtraction

After you have discussed students' solutions, and even if one or more students used **U.S. traditional subtraction,** demonstrate it again as described below.

Example 1: 452 – 277

Step 1:

Start with the 1s.

Since 7 > 2, you need to regroup.

Trade 1 ten for 10 ones:
452 = 4 hundreds + 4 tens + 12 ones.

Subtract the 1s: 12 – 7 = 5.

	4	**12**
4	~~**5**~~	~~**2**~~
− 2	7	**7**
		5

Step 2:

Go to the 10s.

Since 7 > 4, you need to regroup.

Trade 1 hundred for 10 tens:
452 = 3 hundreds + 14 tens + 12 ones.

Subtract the 10s: 14 – 7 = 7.

	14	
3	~~**4**~~	12
~~**4**~~	~~5~~	~~2~~
− 2	**7**	7
	7	5

Step 3:

Go to the 100s. You don't need to regroup.
Subtract the 100s: 3 – 2 = 1.

452 – 277 = 175

There are 175 more students who take the bus.

	14	
3	~~4~~	12
~~4~~	~~5~~	~~2~~
− **2**	7	7
1	7	5

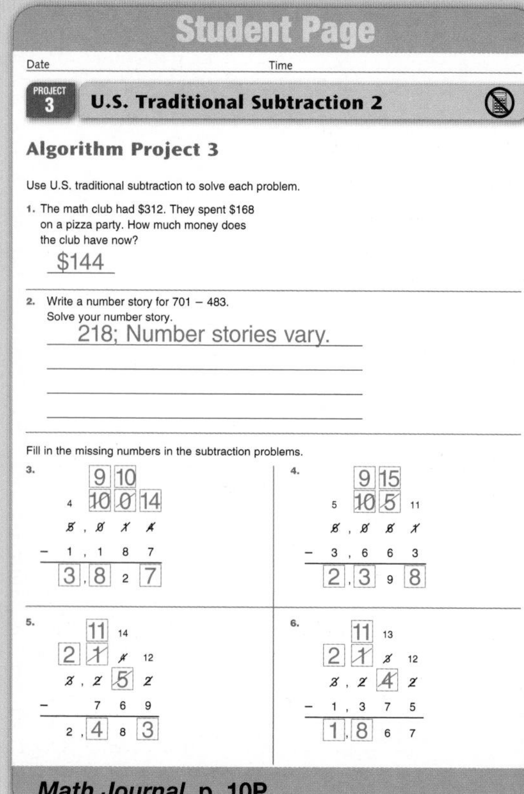
Student Page

Date　　　　Time

PROJECT 3 **U.S. Traditional Subtraction 2**

Algorithm Project 3

Use U.S. traditional subtraction to solve each problem.

1. The math club had $312. They spent $168 on a pizza party. How much money does the club have now?
$144

2. Write a number story for 701 – 483. Solve your number story.
218; Number stories vary.

Fill in the missing numbers in the subtraction problems.

3.
	9	10	
4	10	0	14
5,	0	1	4
– 1,	1	8	7
3,	8	2	7

4.
	9	15	
5	10	5	11
6,	0	6	1
– 3,	6	6	3
2,	3	9	8

5.
	11	14	
2	1	4	12
3,	2	5	2
–	7	6	9
2,	4	8	3

6.
	11	13	
2	1	3	12
3,	2	4	2
– 1,	3	7	5
1,	8	6	7

Math Journal, p. 10P

Example 2: 503 – 386

Step 1:

Start with the 1s.

Since 6 > 3, you need to regroup.

There are no tens in 503, so trade 1 hundred for 10 tens and then trade 1 ten for 10 ones: 503 = 4 hundreds + 9 tens + 13 ones.

Subtract the 1s: 13 – 6 = 7.

	9	
4	10	13
5	0	3
– 3	8	6
		7

Step 2:

Go to the 10s. You don't need to regroup.

Subtract the 10s: 9 – 8 = 1.

	9	
4	10	13
5	0	3
– 3	8	6
	1	7

Step 3:

Go to the 100s. You don't need to regroup.

Subtract the 100s: 4 – 3 = 1.

503 – 386 = 117

	9	
4	10	13
5	0	3
– 3	8	6
1	1	7

You may want to work several more examples with the whole class.

Suggestions:

▷ 231 – 69 = ? 162

▷ 643 – 447 = ? 196

▷ 5,318 – 349 = ? 4,969

▷ 707 – 488 = ? 219

▷ 4,610 – 1,773 = ? 2,837

▷ 8,002 – 3,626 = ? 4,376

Student Page

Date　　　　Time

PROJECT 3 **Trade First Subtraction**

Algorithm Project 3

Estimate and then use trade-first subtraction to solve each problem.

1. Ms. Gibbons owns 527 books. If she has 78 books that are biographies, how many of her books are not biographies? Estimate: 400
449 books

Sample estimates given.

2. 444 – 288 = 156　Estimate: 150

3. 8,135 – 3,577 = 4,558　Estimate: 4,500

4. 506 – 159 = 347　Estimate: 350

5. 6,004 – 4,885　Estimate: 1,000
1,119 = 6,004 – 4,885

6. 2,252 – 687　Estimate: 1,600
2,252 – 687 = 1,565

7. 763 – 266　Estimate: 500
763 – 266 = 497

Math Journal, p. 11P

▶ Practicing U.S. Traditional Subtraction

PARTNER ACTIVITY

(*Math Journal 1* or *2,* pp. 9P and 10P; *Student Reference Book,* p. 24B)

When students are ready, have them estimate and then solve Problems 2–7 on journal page 9P. They may find the example on *Student Reference Book,* page 24B helpful.

Journal page 10P provides students with additional practice using U.S. traditional subtraction. Use this journal page as necessary.

2 Extending the Project

▶ Solving Multidigit Subtraction Problems

INDEPENDENT ACTIVITY

(*Math Journal 1* or *2,* pp. 11P and 12P; Online Additional Practice, pp. 12A–12D; *Student Reference Book,* pp. 15–17 and 24B)

Journal pages 11P and 12P provide students with additional practice solving multidigit subtraction problems. Use these journal pages as necessary. Encourage students to use the focus algorithm (trade-first subtraction) to solve the problems on journal page 11P. Invite them to use any algorithm they wish to solve the problems on journal page 12P.

Online practice pages 12A–12D provide students with additional practice with multidigit subtraction problems.

Students may find the examples on *Student Reference Book,* pages 15–17 and 24B helpful.

Student Page

Date Time

PROJECT 3 **Solving Multidigit Subtraction Problems**

Algorithm Project 3

Estimate and then use any strategy to solve the problems.

1. On Saturday, 5,007 people went to the county fair. On Sunday, 3,889 people went to the county fair. How many more people went to the fair on Saturday? Estimate: 1,000

1,118 people

Sample estimates given.

2. 402 − 234 = 168 Estimate: 200

3. 7,430 − 3,583 = 3,847 Estimate: 4,000

4. 624 − 86 = 538 Estimate: 500

5. 945 − 277 Estimate: 700

945 − 277 = 668

6. 3,613 − 859 Estimate: 2,600

2,754 = 3,613 − 859

7. 521 − 333 Estimate: 200

521 − 333 = 188

Math Journal, p. 12P

Go to www.everydaymathonline.com to access the additional practice pages.

Online Master

Name Date Time

PROJECT 3 **Solving Multidigit Subtraction Problems 1**

Algorithm Project 3

Estimate and then use any strategy to solve the problems.

1. The winner of the student-council election received 368 votes. The runner-up received 179 votes. How many more votes did the winner receive? Estimate: 200

189 votes

Sample estimates given.

2. 761 − 83 = 678 Estimate: 700

3. 314 − 235 = 79 Estimate: 100

4. 7,020 − 514 = 6,506 Estimate: 6,500

5. 4,189 − 2,999 Estimate: 1,000

4,189 − 2,999 = 1,190

6. 756 − 177 Estimate: 600

579 = 756 − 177

7. 6,150 − 2,459 Estimate: 4,000

3,691 = 6,150 − 2,459

Online Additional Practice, p. 12A

Algorithm

Project

U.S. Traditional Subtraction: Decimals

Objective To introduce U.S. traditional subtraction with decimals.

Technology Resources www.everydaymathonline.com

eToolkit

Algorithms Practice

EM Facts Workshop Game™

Family Letters

Assessment Management

Common Core State Standards

Curriculum Focal Points

Interactive Teacher's Lesson Guide

1 Doing the Project

Recommended Use After Lesson 2•3

Key Concepts and Skills

- Identify places in whole numbers and decimals and the values of the digits in those places.
  [Number and Numeration Goal 1]
- Subtract decimals.
  [Operations and Computation Goal 1]
- Solve subtraction number stories with decimals.
  [Operations and Computation Goal 1]
- Make reasonable estimates for subtraction with decimals.
  [Operations and Computation Goal 6]

Key Activities

Students explore and practice U.S. traditional subtraction for decimals.

Materials

- *Math Journal 1* or *2,* pp. 13P–16P
- *Student Reference Book,* p. 54B
- play $10 and $1 bills (optional)
- dimes, pennies (optional)
- base-10 blocks (optional)

2 Extending the Project

Students solve decimal subtraction problems, first using the focus algorithm (trade-first subtraction) and then using any algorithm they choose.

Materials

- Online Additional Practice, pp. 16A–16D
- *Student Reference Book,* pp. 34–37 and 54B

1 Doing the Project

▶ Solving a Decimal Subtraction Problem

INDEPENDENT ACTIVITY

(*Math Journal 1* or *2,* p. 13P)

Ask students to solve Problem 1 on journal page 13P. Tell them they may use base-10 blocks, play money, paper and pencil, or any other tools they wish, except calculators.

▶ Discussing Solutions

WHOLE-CLASS ACTIVITY

(*Math Journal 1* or *2,* p. 13P)

Discuss students' solutions to Problem 1 on journal page 13P. $7.24 – $5.86 = $1.38 Expect that students will use several different methods, including modeling with base-10 blocks, counting up, using partial-differences subtraction, and using trade-first subtraction. Some students may also use U.S. traditional subtraction. *Possible strategies:*

▷ Modeling with base-10 blocks

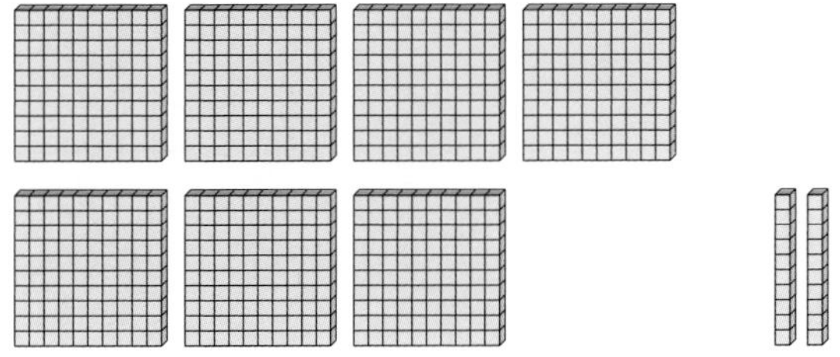

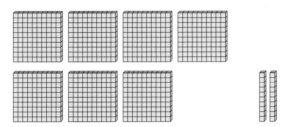

Show 7.24 with blocks.

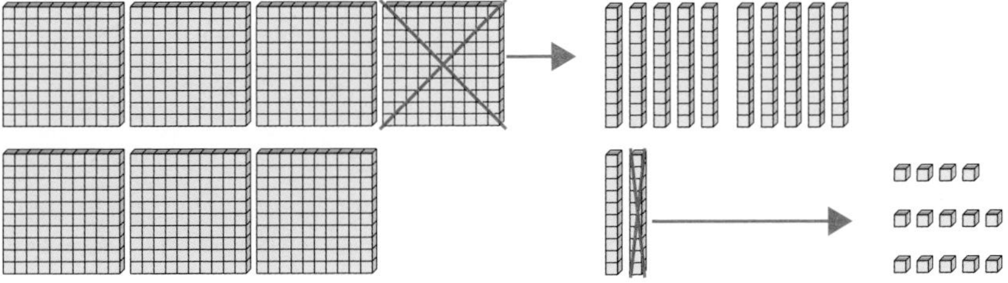

You want to take away 5.86. To do this, you need to first trade 1 flat for 10 longs and 1 long for 10 cubes.

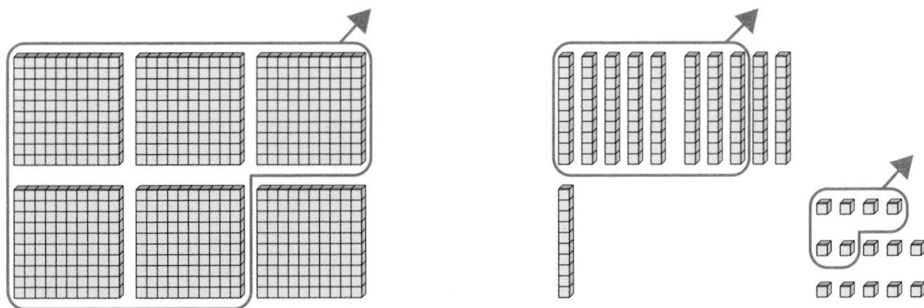

Now remove 5 flats, 8 longs, and 6 cubes (5.86). One flat, 3 longs, and 8 cubes are left. These blocks show 1.38.

Student Page

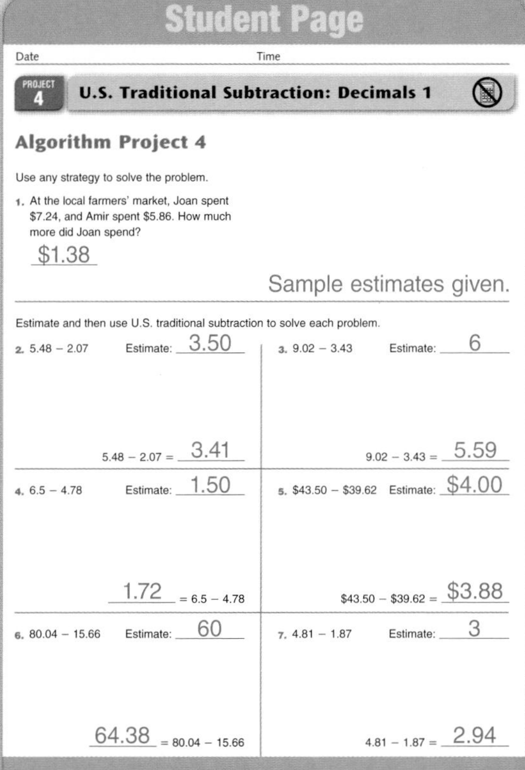

Date Time

PROJECT 4 **U.S. Traditional Subtraction: Decimals 1**

Algorithm Project 4

Use any strategy to solve the problem.

1. At the local farmers' market, Joan spent $7.24, and Amir spent $5.86. How much more did Joan spend?
$1.38

Sample estimates given.

Estimate and then use U.S. traditional subtraction to solve each problem.

2. 5.48 – 2.07 Estimate: 3.50
5.48 – 2.07 = 3.41

3. 9.02 – 3.43 Estimate: 6
9.02 – 3.43 = 5.59

4. 6.5 – 4.78 Estimate: 1.50
1.72 = 6.5 – 4.78

5. $43.50 – $39.62 Estimate: $4.00
$43.50 – $39.62 = $3.88

6. 80.04 – 15.66 Estimate: 60
64.38 = 80.04 – 15.66

7. 4.81 – 1.87 Estimate: 3
4.81 – 1.87 = 2.94

***Math Journal,* p. 13P**

NOTE Reinforce the use of estimation by asking students to make an estimate prior to solving each problem. The estimate is then used to check the reasonableness of the solution to the problem.

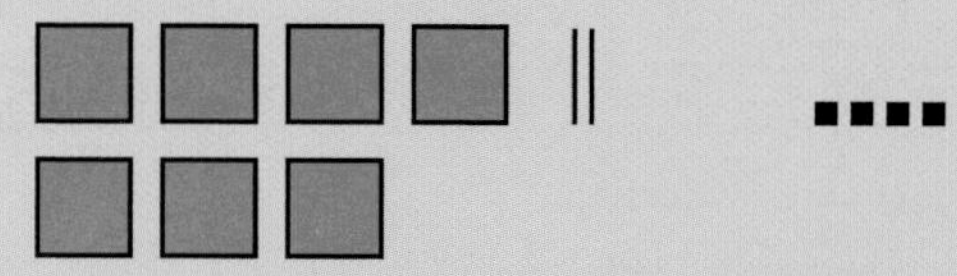

Draw a picture for 7.24.

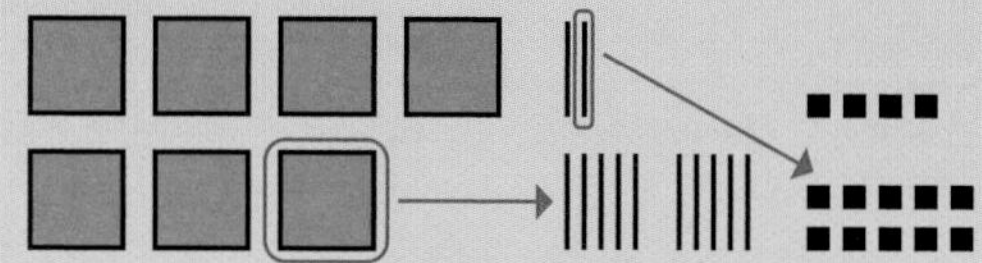

Trade 1 flat for 10 longs and 1 long for 10 cubes.

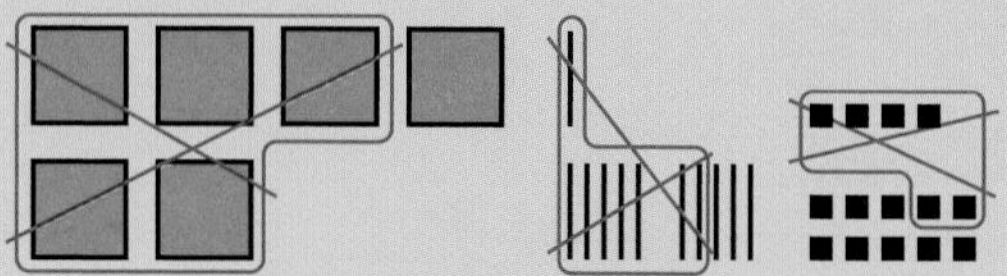

Remove 5 flats, 8 longs, and 6 cubes. The drawing shows 1.38.

$7.24 – $5.86 = $1.38

▷ Using shorthand pictures of base-10 blocks (*See margin.*)

▷ Counting up

5.86	
+(0.04)	
5.90	
+(0.10)	0.04
6.00	0.10
+(1.24)	+ 1.24
7.24	1.38

$7.24 – $5.86 = $1.38

▷ Using partial-differences subtraction

		7. 2 4
		– 5. 8 6
Subtract the 1s.	7 – 5 →	2. 0 0
Subtract the 0.1s.	0.2 – 0.8 →	– 0. 6 0
Subtract the 0.01s.	0.04 – 0.06 →	– 0. 0 2
Find the total.	2 – 0.60 – 0.02 →	**1. 3 8**

$7.24 – $5.86 = $1.38

▷ Using trade-first subtraction

1s	0.1s	0.01s
	11	
6	~~1~~	14
~~7~~.	~~2~~	~~4~~
– 5.	8	6
1.	3	8

$7.24 – $5.86 = $1.38

▷ Using U.S. traditional subtraction

1s	0.1s	0.01s
	11	
6	~~1~~	14
~~7~~.	~~2~~	~~4~~
– 5.	8	6
1.	3	8

$7.24 – $5.86 = $1.38

NOTE Trade-first subtraction resembles U.S. traditional subtraction, except that in trade-first subtraction, as the name implies, all the trading is done before any subtractions are carried out, allowing the person to concentrate on one task at a time.

▶ Introducing U.S. Traditional Subtraction for Decimals

WHOLE-CLASS ACTIVITY

After you have discussed students' solutions, and even if one or more students used U.S. traditional subtraction, demonstrate it again as described on the next page.

Example 1: 7.24 – 5.86

Step 1:

Start with the 0.01s.

Since 6 > 4, you need to regroup.

Trade 1 tenth for 10 hundredths:
7.24 = 7 ones + 1 tenth + 14 hundredths.

Subtract the 0.01s: 14 – 6 = 8.

$$\begin{array}{rcccc} & & & 1 & 14 \\ & 7 & . & \cancel{2} & \cancel{4} \\ - & 5 & . & 8 & 6 \\ \hline & & & & 8 \end{array}$$

Step 2:

Go to the 0.1s.

Since 8 > 1, you need to regroup.

Trade 1 one for 10 tenths:
7.24 = 6 ones + 11 tenths + 14 hundredths.

Subtract the 0.1s: 11 – 8 = 3.

$$\begin{array}{rcccc} & & & 11 & \\ & 6 & & \cancel{1} & 14 \\ & \cancel{7} & . & \cancel{2} & \cancel{4} \\ - & 5 & . & 8 & 6 \\ \hline & & & 3 & 8 \end{array}$$

Step 3:

Go to the 1s. You don't need to regroup.

Subtract the 1s: 6 – 5 = 1.

Remember to include the decimal point in the answer.

$$\begin{array}{rcccc} & & & 11 & \\ & 6 & & \cancel{1} & 14 \\ & \cancel{7} & . & \cancel{2} & \cancel{4} \\ - & 5 & . & 8 & 6 \\ \hline & 1 & . & 3 & 8 \end{array}$$

\$7.24 – \$5.86 = \$1.38

Joan spent \$1.38 more than Amir.

Example 2: 62.05 – 34.29

Step 1:

Start with the 0.01s.

Since 9 > 5, you need to regroup.

There are no tenths in 62.05, so trade 1 one for 10 tenths and then trade 1 tenth for 10 hundredths: 62.05 = 6 tens + 1 one + 9 tenths + 15 hundredths.

Subtract the 0.01s: 15 – 9 = 6.

$$\begin{array}{rccccc} & & & & 9 & \\ & & 1 & & \cancel{10} & 15 \\ & 6 & \cancel{2} & . & \cancel{0} & \cancel{5} \\ - & 3 & 4 & . & 2 & 9 \\ \hline & & & & & 6 \end{array}$$

Step 2:

Go to the 0.1s.

You don't need to regroup.

Subtract the 0.1s: 9 – 2 = 7.

$$\begin{array}{rccccc} & & & & 9 & \\ & & 1 & & \cancel{10} & 15 \\ & 6 & \cancel{2} & . & \cancel{0} & \cancel{5} \\ - & 3 & 4 & . & 2 & 9 \\ \hline & & & & 7 & 6 \end{array}$$

Step 3:

Go to the 1s.

Since 4 > 1, you need to regroup.

Trade 1 ten for 10 ones:

62.05 = 5 tens + 11 ones + 9 tenths + 15 hundredths.

Subtract the ones: 11 – 4 = 7.

$$\begin{array}{rccccc} & & 11 & & 9 & \\ & 5 & \cancel{1} & & \cancel{10} & 15 \\ & \cancel{6} & \cancel{2} & . & \cancel{0} & \cancel{5} \\ - & 3 & 4 & . & 2 & 9 \\ \hline & & 7 & & 7 & 6 \end{array}$$

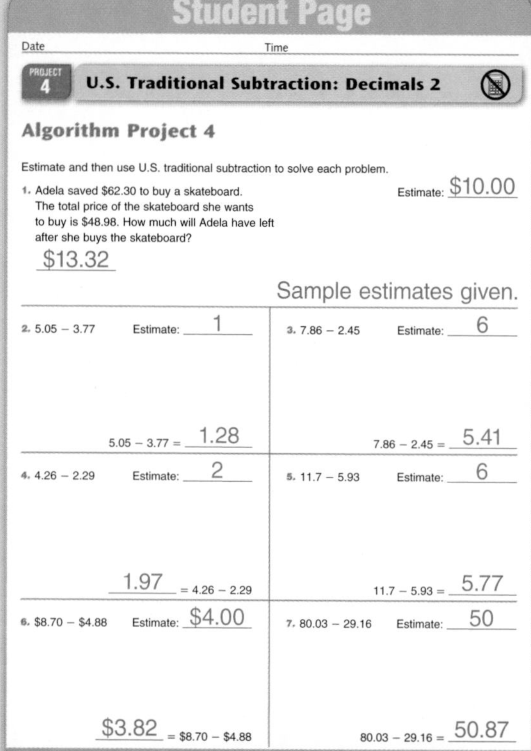

Student Page

Date Time

PROJECT 4 **U.S. Traditional Subtraction: Decimals 2**

Algorithm Project 4

Estimate and then use U.S. traditional subtraction to solve each problem.

1. Adela saved $62.30 to buy a skateboard. The total price of the skateboard she wants to buy is $48.98. How much will Adela have left after she buys the skateboard? Estimate: $10.00
   $13.32

Sample estimates given.

2. 5.05 – 3.77 Estimate: 1 5.05 – 3.77 = 1.28	3. 7.86 – 2.45 Estimate: 6 7.86 – 2.45 = 5.41
4. 4.26 – 2.29 Estimate: 2 1.97 = 4.26 – 2.29	5. 11.7 – 5.93 Estimate: 6 11.7 – 5.93 = 5.77
6. $8.70 – $4.88 Estimate: $4.00 $3.82 = $8.70 – $4.88	7. 80.03 – 29.16 Estimate: 50 80.03 – 29.16 = 50.87

Math Journal, p. 14P

Student Page

Date Time

PROJECT 4 **U.S. Traditional Subtraction: Decimals 3**

Algorithm Project 4

Use U.S. traditional subtraction to solve each problem.

1. Wenona bought a sandwich and a bowl of soup. The total cost (before tax) was $6.35. The sandwich cost $3.79. How much did the soup cost?
   $2.56

2. Write a number story for $47.25 – $25.89. Solve your number story.
   $21.36; Number stories vary.

Fill in the missing numbers in the subtraction problems.

3.
```
     9
  3 10 12
  4 . 0  2
– 1 . 5  7
  2 . 4  5
```

4.
```
    18
  7  8 15
  8 . 9  5
– 1 . 9  6
  6 . 9  9
```

5.
```
      9  9
  7 10 10 14
  8  0 . 0  4
– 3  5 . 3  8
  4  4 . 6  6
```

6.
```
     11 14
  5  1  4 10
  6  2 . 5  0
– 2  8 . 6  4
  3  3 . 8  6
```

Math Journal, p. 15P

Step 4:

Go to the 10s.
You don't need to regroup.
Subtract the 10s: 5 – 3 = 2.
Remember to include the decimal point in the answer.

```
      11  9
   5   1 10 15
   6   2 . 0  5
 – 3   4 . 2  9
   2   7 . 7  6
```

62.05 – 34.29 = 27.76

Example 3: 8.3 – 2.74

Step 1:

Write the problem in columns.
Be sure to line up the places correctly.
Since 2.74 has two decimal places, write 8.3 as 8.30.

```
   8 . 3  0
 – 2 . 7  4
```

Step 2:

Start with the 0.01s.
Since 4 > 0, you need to regroup.
Trade 1 tenth for 10 hundredths:
8.30 = 8 ones + 2 tenths + 10 hundredths.
Subtract the 0.01s: 10 – 4 = 6.

```
       2 10
   8 . 3  0
 – 2 . 7  4
          6
```

Step 3:

Go to the 0.1s.
Since 7 > 2, you need to regroup.
Trade 1 one for 10 tenths:
8.30 = 7 ones + 12 tenths + 10 hundredths.
Subtract the 0.1s: 12 – 7 = 5.

```
      12
   7   2 10
   8 . 3  0
 – 2 . 7  4
       5  6
```

Step 4:

Go to the 1s. You don't need to regroup.
Subtract the 1s: 7 – 2 = 5.
Remember to include the decimal point in the answer.

```
      12
   7   2 10
   8 . 3  0
 – 2 . 7  4
   5 . 5  6
```

8.3 – 2.74 = 5.56

You may want to work several more examples with the whole class.

Suggestions:

▷ $5.65 – $3.22 = ? $2.43

▷ 7.32 – 1.47 = ? 5.85

▷ 3.03 – 2.36 = ? 0.67

▷ 8.4 – 5.69 = ? 2.71

▷ $62.25 – $49.89 = ? $12.36

▷ 70.06 – 38.88 = ? 31.18

Practicing U.S. Traditional Subtraction for Decimals

(*Math Journal 1* or *2,* pp. 13P–16P; *Student Reference Book*, p. 54B)

When students are ready, have them estimate and then solve Problems 2–7 on journal page 13P. They may find the example on *Student Reference Book,* page 54B helpful.

Journal pages 14P–16P provide students with additional practice using U.S. traditional subtraction. Use these journal pages as necessary.

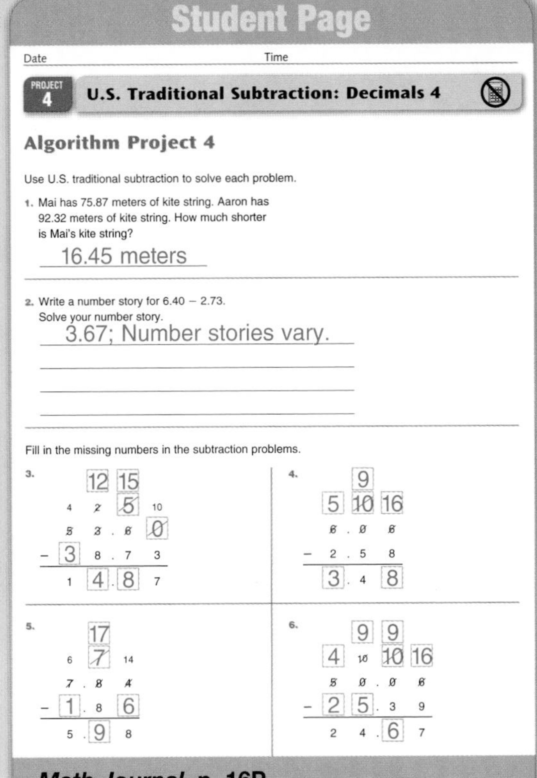

Student Page

Date Time

PROJECT 4 **U.S. Traditional Subtraction: Decimals 4**

Algorithm Project 4

Use U.S. traditional subtraction to solve each problem.

1. Mai has 75.87 meters of kite string. Aaron has 92.32 meters of kite string. How much shorter is Mai's kite string?
   16.45 meters

2. Write a number story for 6.40 − 2.73. Solve your number story.
   3.67; Number stories vary.

Fill in the missing numbers in the subtraction problems.

3.
12 15
4 2 5 10
5 3 . 6 0
− 3 8 . 7 3
1 4 . 8 7

4.
9
5 10 16
6 . 0 6
− 2 . 5 8
3 . 4 8

5.
17
6 7 14
7 . 8 4
− 1 . 8 6
5 . 9 8

6.
9 9
4 10 10 16
5 0 . 0 6
− 2 5 . 3 9
2 4 . 6 7

Math Journal, p. 16P

2 Extending the Project

Solving Decimal Subtraction Problems

(Online Additional Practice, pp. 16A–16D; *Student Reference Book,* pp. 34–37 and 54B)

Online practice pages 16A–16D provide students with additional practice solving decimal subtraction problems. Use these pages as necessary.

Encourage students to use the focus algorithm (trade-first subtraction) to solve the problems on practice page 16A. Invite them to use any algorithm they wish to solve the problems on the remaining pages.

Students may find the examples on *Student Reference Book,* pages 34–37 and 54B helpful.

Go to www.everydaymathonline.com to access the additional practice pages.

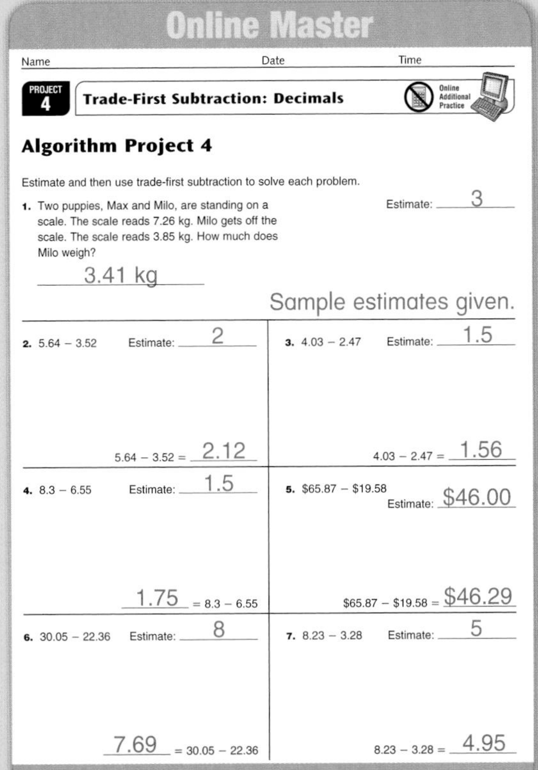

Online Master

Name Date Time

PROJECT 4 **Trade-First Subtraction: Decimals**

Algorithm Project 4

Estimate and then use trade-first subtraction to solve each problem.

1. Two puppies, Max and Milo, are standing on a scale. The scale reads 7.26 kg. Milo gets off the scale. The scale reads 3.85 kg. How much does Milo weigh? Estimate: 3
   3.41 kg

Sample estimates given.

2. 5.64 − 3.52 Estimate: 2
   5.64 − 3.52 = 2.12

3. 4.03 − 2.47 Estimate: 1.5
   4.03 − 2.47 = 1.56

4. 8.3 − 6.55 Estimate: 1.5
   1.75 = 8.3 − 6.55

5. $65.87 − $19.58 Estimate: $46.00
   $65.87 − $19.58 = $46.29

6. 30.05 − 22.36 Estimate: 8
   7.69 = 30.05 − 22.36

7. 8.23 − 3.28 Estimate: 5
   8.23 − 3.28 = 4.95

Online Additional Practice, p. 16A

Algorithm **5** Project

U.S. Traditional Multiplication

 **Objective** To introduce U.S. traditional multiplication.

Technology Resources www.everydaymathonline.com

eToolkit

Algorithms Practice

EM Facts Workshop Game™

Family Letters

Assessment Management

Common Core State Standards

Curriculum Focal Points

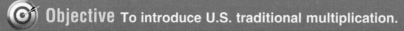

Interactive Teacher's Lesson Guide

1 Doing the Project

Recommended Use After Lesson 2•9

Key Concepts and Skills

- Identify places in whole numbers and the values of the digits in those places. [Number and Numeration Goal 1]
- Use multiplication facts to find products of multidigit whole numbers. [Operations and Computation Goal 3]
- Multiply multidigit whole numbers. [Operations and Computation Goal 4]
- Solve multiplication number stories. [Operations and Computation Goal 4]
- Make reasonable estimates for multiplication problems. [Operations and Computation Goal 6]

Key Activities

Students explore and practice U.S. traditional multiplication with multidigit whole numbers.

Key Vocabulary

U.S. traditional multiplication

Materials

- *Math Journal 1* or *2,* pp. 17P–20P
- *Student Reference Book,* pp. 24C and 24D

2 Extending the Project

Students solve multidigit multiplication problems, first using the focus algorithm (partial-products multiplication) and then using any algorithm they choose.

Materials

- Online Additional Practice, pp. 20A–20D
- *Student Reference Book,* pp. 19, 20, 24C, and 24D

1 Doing the Project

▶ Solving a Multiplication Problem

INDEPENDENT ACTIVITY

(*Math Journal 1* or *2,* p. 17P)

Ask students to solve Problem 1 on journal page 17P. Tell them they may use any methods they wish, except calculators.

▶ Discussing Solutions

WHOLE-CLASS ACTIVITY

(*Math Journal 1* or *2,* p. 17P)

Discuss students' solutions to Problem 1 on journal page 17P. 86 * 24 = 2,064 bottles Expect that students will use several different methods, including partial-products multiplication and lattice multiplication. Some students may also use U.S. traditional multiplication. *Possible strategies:*

▷ Using partial-products multiplication

$$\begin{array}{rr} & 86 \\ * & 24 \\ \hline 20 * 80 \rightarrow & 1600 \\ 20 * 6 \rightarrow & 120 \\ 4 * 80 \rightarrow & 320 \\ 4 * 6 \rightarrow & 24 \\ \hline & 2064 \end{array}$$

▷ Using lattice multiplication

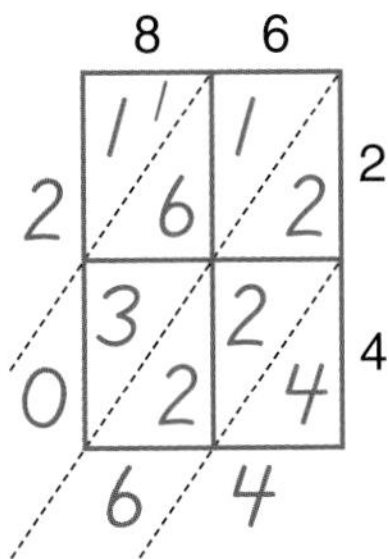

▷ Using U.S. traditional multiplication

$$\begin{array}{rr} & 1 \\ & 2 \\ & 86 \\ * & 24 \\ \hline & 344 \\ + & 1720 \\ \hline & 2064 \end{array}$$

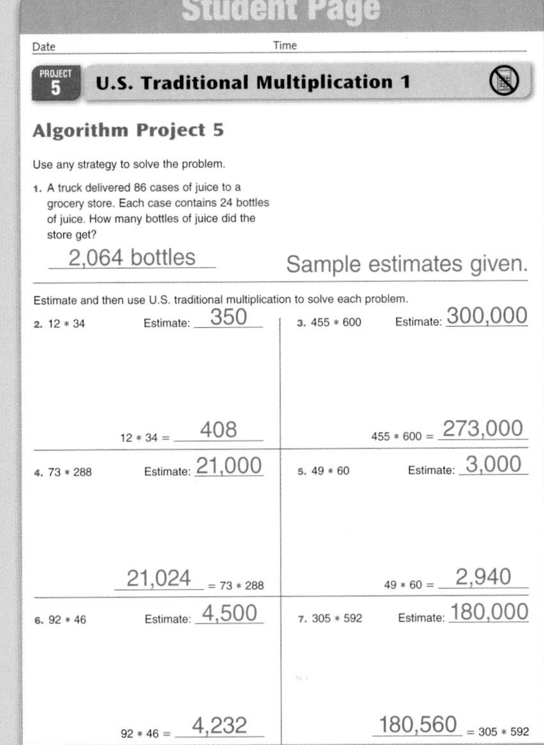

Student Page

Date Time

PROJECT 5 **U.S. Traditional Multiplication 1**

Algorithm Project 5

Use any strategy to solve the problem.

1. A truck delivered 86 cases of juice to a grocery store. Each case contains 24 bottles of juice. How many bottles of juice did the store get?

2,064 bottles Sample estimates given.

Estimate and then use U.S. traditional multiplication to solve each problem.

2. 12 * 34 Estimate: 350 — 12 * 34 = 408
3. 455 * 600 Estimate: 300,000 — 455 * 600 = 273,000
4. 73 * 288 Estimate: 21,000 — 21,024 = 73 * 288
5. 49 * 60 Estimate: 3,000 — 49 * 60 = 2,940
6. 92 * 46 Estimate: 4,500 — 92 * 46 = 4,232
7. 305 * 592 Estimate: 180,000 — 180,560 = 305 * 592

Math Journal, p. 17P

NOTE Reinforce the use of estimation by asking students to make an estimate prior to solving each problem. The estimate is then used to check the reasonableness of the solution to the problem.

▶ Introducing U.S. Traditional Multiplication

After you have discussed students' solutions, and even if one or more students used **U.S. traditional multiplication,** demonstrate it again as described below.

Example 1: 24 ∗ 86

Step 1:

Multiply 86 by the 4 in 24, as if the problem were 4 ∗ 86.

```
     2
    86
 *  24
 -----
   344  ← The partial product
          4 * 86 = 344
```

Step 2:

Multiply 86 by the 2 in 24, as if the problem were 2 ∗ 86.

The 2 in 24 stands for 2 tens, so write the partial product one place to the left.

Write a 0 in the 1s place to show you are multiplying by tens.

Write the new carry above the old carry.

```
     1
     2
    86
 *  24
 -----
   344
  1720  ← 20 * 86 = 1,720
```

Step 3:

Add the two partial products to get the final answer.

```
     1
     2
    86
 *  24
 ------
   344
 + 1720
 ------
  2064  ← 24 * 86 = 2,064
```

24 ∗ 86 = 2,064

The store purchased 2,064 bottles of juice.

NOTE U.S. traditional multiplication is so familiar that the details of its working may appear more meaningful than they are. Consider the following example:

```
    1 2
    3 5
   147
 *  38
 ------
   1176
 + 4410
 ------
   5586
```

Many people, when asked why the "2" carried from "3 ∗ 7" is written in the 10s place, will explain that it stands for "2 tens." But this "2" really means "2 hundreds" because the "3" is really "3 tens." U.S. traditional multiplication is efficient—though not as efficient as a calculator—but it is not, despite its familiarity, conceptually transparent.

Example 2: 237 * 456

Step 1:

Multiply 456 by the 7 in 237, as if the problem were 7 * 456.

$$\begin{array}{r} 3\,4 \\ \mathbf{4\,5\,6} \\ * \;\; 2\,3\,\mathbf{7} \\ \hline \mathbf{3\,1\,9\,2} \end{array} \leftarrow \text{The partial product } 7 * 456 = 3{,}192$$

Step 2:

Multiply 456 by the 3 in 237, as if the problem were 3 * 456.

The 3 in 237 stands for 3 tens, so write the partial product one place to the left.

Write a 0 in the 1s place to show you are multiplying by tens.

Write the new carries above the old carries.

$$\begin{array}{r} \mathbf{1\,1} \\ 3\,4 \\ \mathbf{4\,5\,6} \\ * \;\; 2\,\mathbf{3}\,7 \\ \hline 3\,1\,9\,2 \\ \mathbf{1\,3\,6\,8\,0} \end{array} \leftarrow 30 * 456 = 13{,}680$$

Step 3:

Multiply 456 by the 2 in 237, as if the problem were 2 * 456.

The 2 in 237 stands for 2 hundreds, so write the partial product two places to the left.

Write 0s in the 10s and 1s places to show you are multiplying by hundreds.

Write the new carries above the old carries.

$$\begin{array}{r} \mathbf{1\,1} \\ 1\,1 \\ 3\,4 \\ \mathbf{4\,5\,6} \\ * \;\; \mathbf{2}\,3\,7 \\ \hline 3\,1\,9\,2 \\ 1\,3\,6\,8\,0 \\ \mathbf{9\,1\,2\,0\,0} \end{array} \leftarrow 200 * 456 = 91{,}200$$

Step 4:

Add the three partial products to get the final answer.

$$\begin{array}{r} 1\,1 \\ 1\,1 \\ 3\,4 \\ 4\,5\,6 \\ * \;\; 2\,3\,7 \\ \hline \mathbf{3\,1\,9\,2} \\ \mathbf{1\,3\,6\,8\,0} \\ + \;\mathbf{9\,1\,2\,0\,0} \\ \hline \mathbf{1\,0\,8\,0\,7\,2} \end{array} \leftarrow 237 * 456 = 108{,}072$$

237 * 456 = 108,072

You may want to work several more examples with the whole class.

Suggestions:

- ▷ 320 * 21 = ? 6,720
- ▷ 48 * 73 = ? 3,504
- ▷ 675 * 50 = ? 33,750
- ▷ 59 * 302 = ? 17,818
- ▷ 700 * 36 = ? 25,200
- ▷ 284 * 77 = ? 21,868

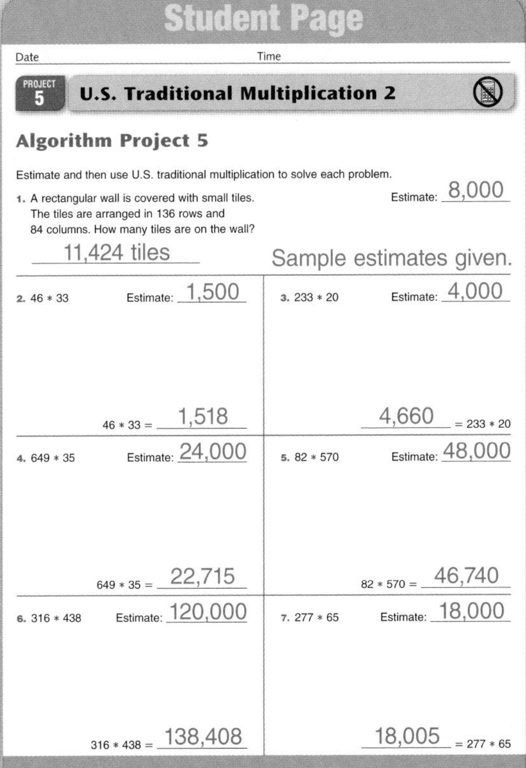

Student Page

Date Time

PROJECT 5 **U.S. Traditional Multiplication 2**

Algorithm Project 5

Estimate and then use U.S. traditional multiplication to solve each problem.

1. A rectangular wall is covered with small tiles. The tiles are arranged in 136 rows and 84 columns. How many tiles are on the wall? Estimate: 8,000

11,424 tiles

Sample estimates given.

2. 46 * 33 Estimate: 1,500 — 46 * 33 = 1,518
3. 233 * 20 Estimate: 4,000 — 4,660 = 233 * 20
4. 649 * 35 Estimate: 24,000 — 649 * 35 = 22,715
5. 82 * 570 Estimate: 48,000 — 82 * 570 = 46,740
6. 316 * 438 Estimate: 120,000 — 316 * 438 = 138,408
7. 277 * 65 Estimate: 18,000 — 18,005 = 277 * 65

Math Journal, p. 18P

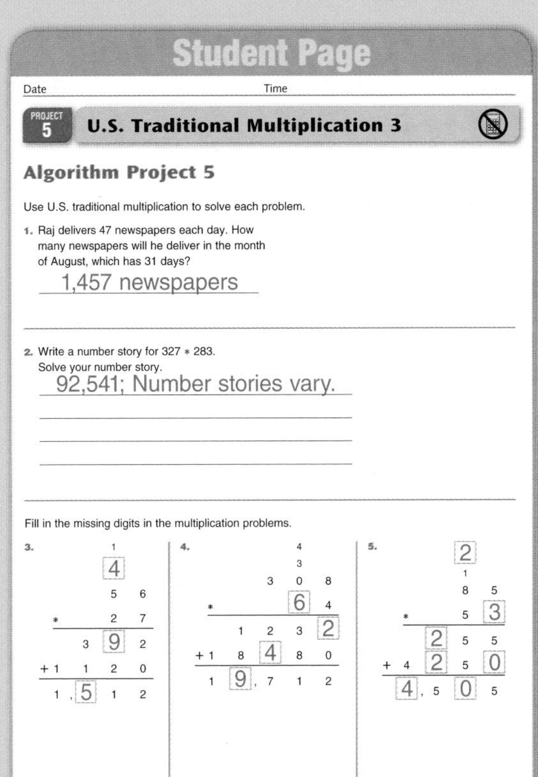

Student Page

Date Time

PROJECT 5 **U.S. Traditional Multiplication 3**

Algorithm Project 5

Use U.S. traditional multiplication to solve each problem.

1. Raj delivers 47 newspapers each day. How many newspapers will he deliver in the month of August, which has 31 days?

1,457 newspapers

2. Write a number story for 327 * 283. Solve your number story.

92,541; Number stories vary.

Fill in the missing digits in the multiplication problems.

3.
$$\begin{array}{r} 1 \\ \boxed{4} \\ 5\;6 \\ * \;\; 2\;7 \\ \hline 3\;\boxed{9}\;2 \\ +1\;\;1\;2\;0 \\ \hline 1,\boxed{5}\;1\;2 \end{array}$$

4.
$$\begin{array}{r} 4 \\ 3 \\ 3\;0\;8 \\ * \;\; \boxed{6}\;4 \\ \hline 1\;2\;3\;\boxed{2} \\ +1\;\;8\;\boxed{4}\;8\;0 \\ \hline 1\;\boxed{9},7\;1\;2 \end{array}$$

5.
$$\begin{array}{r} \boxed{2} \\ 1 \\ 8\;5 \\ * \;\; 5\;\boxed{3} \\ \hline \boxed{2}\;5\;5 \\ +\;4\;\;\boxed{2}\;5\;\boxed{0} \\ \hline \boxed{4},5\;\boxed{0}\;5 \end{array}$$

Math Journal, p. 19P

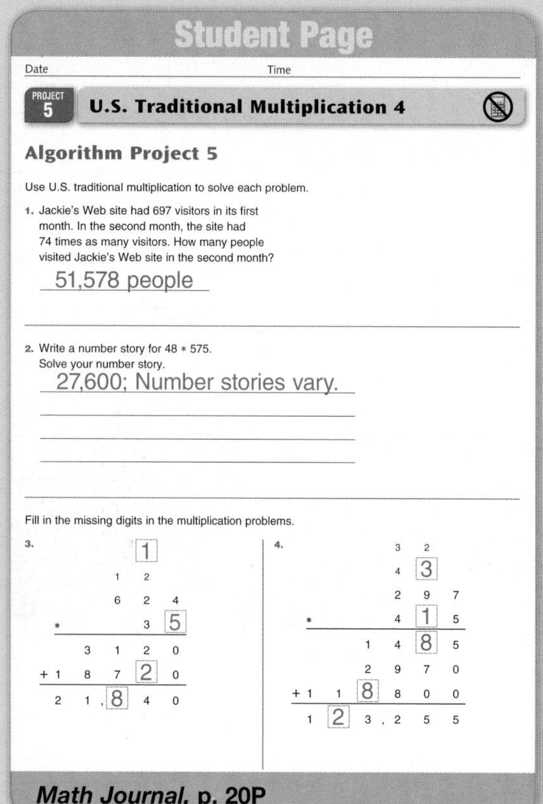

Student Page

Date Time

PROJECT 5 **U.S. Traditional Multiplication 4**

Algorithm Project 5

Use U.S. traditional multiplication to solve each problem.

1. Jackie's Web site had 697 visitors in its first month. In the second month, the site had 74 times as many visitors. How many people visited Jackie's Web site in the second month?

   51,578 people

2. Write a number story for 48 * 575. Solve your number story.

   27,600; Number stories vary.

Fill in the missing digits in the multiplication problems.

3.
```
        [1]
      1  2
      6  2  4
*        3 [5]
   3  1  2  0
+1 8  7 [2] 0
 2 1 ,[8] 4  0
```

4.
```
            3  2
            4 [3]
            2  9  7
*           4 [1] 5
      1  4 [8] 5
      2  9  7  0
+1 1 [8] 8  0  0
 1 [2] 3 , 2  5  5
```

Math Journal, p. 20P

▶ Practicing U.S. Traditional Multiplication

PARTNER ACTIVITY

(*Math Journal 1* or *2,* pp. 17P–20P; *Student Reference Book,* pp. 24C and 24D)

When students are ready, have them estimate and then solve Problems 2–7 on journal page 17P. They may find the examples on *Student Reference Book,* pages 24C and 24D helpful.

Journal pages 18P–20P provide students with additional practice using U.S. traditional multiplication. Use these journal pages as necessary.

Go to www.everydaymathonline.com to access the additional practice pages.

Online Master

Name Date Time

PROJECT 5 **Partial-Products Multiplication** Online Additional Practice

Algorithm Project 5

Estimate and then use partial-products multiplication to solve each problem.

1. Last week, a theater showed a popular movie 35 times. Each time, all 218 seats in the theater were full. How many people saw the movie at that theater last week? Estimate: 8,000

   7,630 people

Sample estimates given.

2. 300 * 21 Estimate: 6,000 300 * 21 = 6,300	3. 75 * 363 Estimate: 28,000 27,225 = 75 * 363
4. 23 * 84 Estimate: 1,600 23 * 84 = 1,932	5. 38 * 59 Estimate: 2,400 38 * 59 = 2,242
6. 60 * 504 Estimate: 30,000 60 * 504 = 30,240	7. 182 * 797 Estimate: 160,000 145,054 = 182 * 797

Online Additional Practice, p. 20A

2 Extending the Project

▶ Solving Multidigit Multiplication Problems

INDEPENDENT ACTIVITY

(Online Additional Practice, pp. 20A–20D; *Student Reference Book,* pp. 19, 20, 24C, and 24D)

Online practice pages 20A–20D provide students with additional practice solving multidigit multiplication problems. Use these pages as necessary.

Encourage students to use the focus algorithm (partial-products multiplication) to solve the problems on practice page 20A. Invite them to use any algorithm they wish to solve the problems on the remaining pages.

Students may find the examples on *Student Reference Book,* pages 19, 20, 24C, and 24D helpful.

Algorithm 6 Project

U.S. Traditional Multiplication: Decimals

Objective To introduce U.S. traditional multiplication for decimals.

Technology Resources www.everydaymathonline.com

eToolkit

Algorithms Practice

EM Facts Workshop Game™

Family Letters

Assessment Management

Common Core State Standards

Curriculum Focal Points

Interactive Teacher's Lesson Guide

1 Doing the Project

Recommended Use After Lesson 2•9

Key Concepts and Skills

- Identify places in whole numbers and decimals and the values of the digits in those places.
  [Number and Numeration Goal 1]
- Calculate products of decimals and whole numbers and of decimals and decimals.
  [Operations and Computation Goal 3]
- Solve multiplication number stories with decimals.
  [Operations and Computation Goal 3]
- Make reasonable estimates for multiplication with decimals.
  [Operations and Computation Goal 6]

Key Activities

Students explore and practice U.S. traditional multiplication with decimals.

Materials

- *Math Journal 1* or *2,* pp. 21P–24P
- *Student Reference Book,* pp. 54C and 54D
- play money (optional)

2 Extending the Project

Students solve decimal multiplication problems, first using the focus algorithm (partial-products multiplication) and then using any algorithm they choose.

Materials

- Online Additional Practice, pp. 24A–24D
- *Student Reference Book,* pp. 37–40, 54C, and 54D

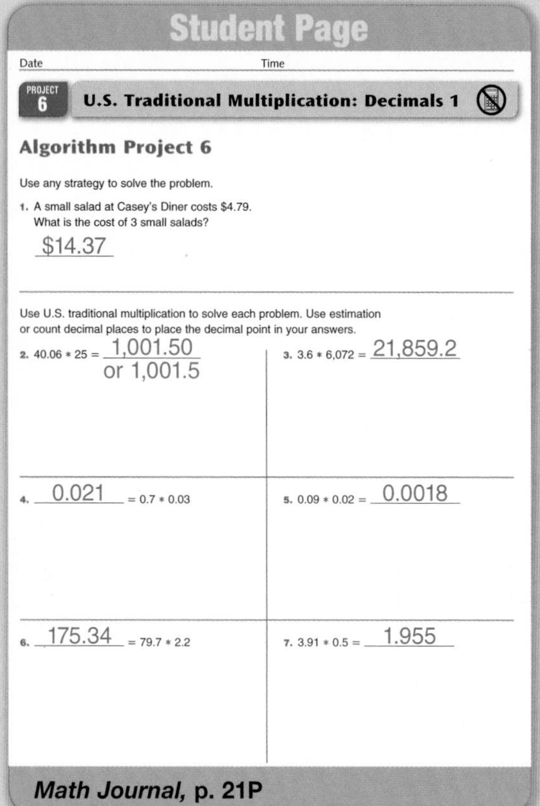
Student Page

Date Time

PROJECT 6 **U.S. Traditional Multiplication: Decimals 1**

Algorithm Project 6

Use any strategy to solve the problem.

1. A small salad at Casey's Diner costs $4.79. What is the cost of 3 small salads? $14.37

Use U.S. traditional multiplication to solve each problem. Use estimation or count decimal places to place the decimal point in your answers.

2. 40.06 * 25 = 1,001.50 or 1,001.5
3. 3.6 * 6,072 = 21,859.2
4. 0.021 = 0.7 * 0.03
5. 0.09 * 0.02 = 0.0018
6. 175.34 = 79.7 * 2.2
7. 3.91 * 0.5 = 1.955

Math Journal, p. 21P

1 Doing the Project

▶ Solving a Decimal Multiplication Problem

INDEPENDENT ACTIVITY

(*Math Journal 1* or *2,* p. 21P)

Ask students to solve Problem 1 on journal page 21P. Tell them they may use play money, paper and pencil, or any other tools they wish, except calculators.

▶ Discussing Solutions

WHOLE-CLASS ACTIVITY

(*Math Journal 1* or *2,* p. 21P)

Discuss students' solutions to Problem 1 on journal page 21P. $4.79 ∗ 3 = $14.37 Expect that students will use several different methods, which may include modeling with play money, using repeated addition, using lattice multiplication, and using partial-products multiplication. Some students may also use U.S. traditional multiplication. *Possible strategies:*

▷ Modeling with play money

$1	$1	$1
$1	$1	$1
$1	$1	$1
$1	$1	$1
Ⓓ Ⓓ Ⓓ	Ⓓ Ⓓ Ⓓ	Ⓓ Ⓓ Ⓓ
Ⓓ Ⓓ Ⓓ	Ⓓ Ⓓ Ⓓ	Ⓓ Ⓓ Ⓓ
Ⓓ	Ⓓ	Ⓓ
Ⓟ Ⓟ Ⓟ	Ⓟ Ⓟ Ⓟ	Ⓟ Ⓟ Ⓟ
Ⓟ Ⓟ Ⓟ	Ⓟ Ⓟ Ⓟ	Ⓟ Ⓟ Ⓟ
Ⓟ Ⓟ Ⓟ	Ⓟ Ⓟ Ⓟ	Ⓟ Ⓟ Ⓟ

Use play money to show the cost of 3 salads.

4 [$1] + 4 [$1] + 4 [$1] = 12 [$1] or 1 [$10] and 2 [$1]

Combine the bills.

7 Ⓓ + 7 Ⓓ + 7 Ⓓ = 21 Ⓓ or 2 [$1] and 1 Ⓓ

Combine the dimes.

9 Ⓟ + 9 Ⓟ + 9 Ⓟ = 27 Ⓟ or 2 Ⓓ and 7 Ⓟ

Combine the pennies.

1 [$10] + 2 [$1] + 2 [$1] + 1 Ⓓ + 2 Ⓓ + 7 Ⓟ = $14.37

Combine the bills and coins.

▷ Using repeated addition

$4.79	$9.58
+ $4.79	+ $4.79
$8.00	$13.00
$1.40	$1.20
+ $0.18	+ $0.17
$9.58	$14.37

$4.79 * 3 = $14.37

▷ Using lattice multiplication

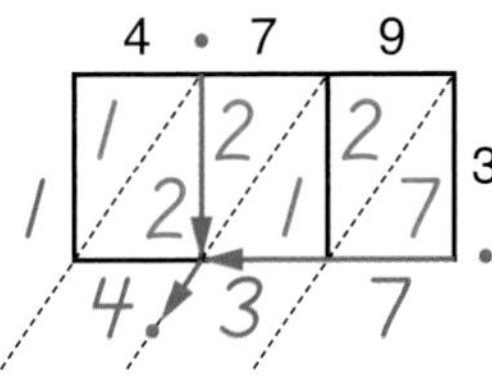

$4.79 * 3 = $14.37

▷ Using partial-products multiplication

```
                  $4 . 7 9
                *        3
3 [$4.00s] →     1 2 . 0 0
3 [$0.70s] →       2 . 1 0
3 [$0.09s] →   +   0 . 2 7
                 $1 4 . 3 7
```

$4.79 * 3 = $14.37

▷ Using U.S. traditional multiplication

```
       2   2
    $4 . 7 9
  *        3
   $1 4 . 3 7
```

$4.79 * 3 = $14.37

Introducing U.S. Traditional Multiplication for Decimals

WHOLE-CLASS ACTIVITY

After you have discussed students' solutions, and even if one or more students used U.S. traditional multiplication, demonstrate it again as described below.

Example 1: $4.79 * 3

Step 1:

Start with the pennies.
3 * 9 pennies = 27 pennies
27 pennies = 2 dimes + 7 pennies

```
        2
  4 . 7 9
*       3
        7
```

Step 2:

Multiply the dimes.
3 * 7 dimes = 21 dimes
Remember the 2 dimes from Step 1.
21 dimes + 2 dimes = 23 dimes in all
23 dimes = $2 + 3 dimes

```
    2   2
  4 . 7 9
*       3
      3 7
```

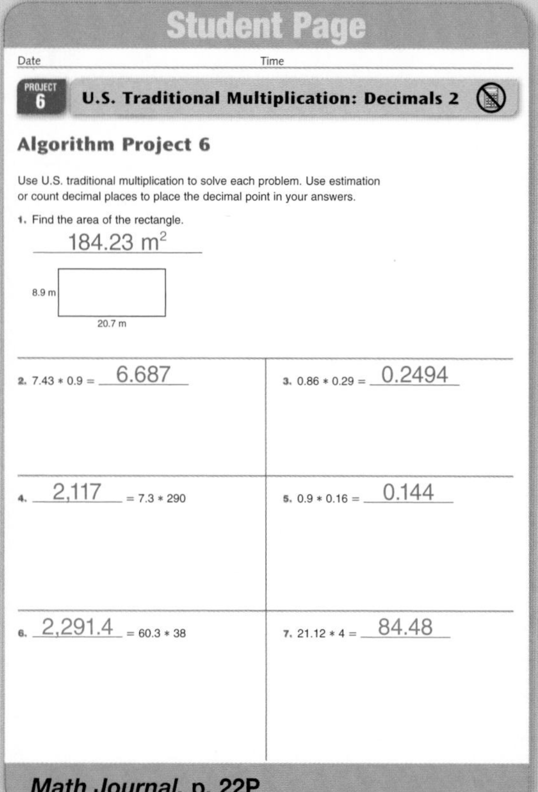

Student Page

Date ____ Time ____

PROJECT 6 **U.S. Traditional Multiplication: Decimals 2**

Algorithm Project 6

Use U.S. traditional multiplication to solve each problem. Use estimation or count decimal places to place the decimal point in your answers.

1. Find the area of the rectangle. 184.23 m^2

8.9 m, 20.7 m

2. 7.43 ∗ 0.9 = 6.687
3. 0.86 ∗ 0.29 = 0.2494
4. 2,117 = 7.3 ∗ 290
5. 0.9 ∗ 0.16 = 0.144
6. 2,291.4 = 60.3 ∗ 38
7. 21.12 ∗ 4 = 84.48

Math Journal, p. 22P

NOTE This second method for multiplying decimals (used in Example 3) is useful when there are many decimal places in the factors, making it difficult to estimate the answer. For example, 0.078 ∗ 0.029 = 0.002262.

Student Page

Date ____ Time ____

PROJECT 6 **U.S. Traditional Multiplication: Decimals 3**

Algorithm Project 6

Use U.S. traditional multiplication to solve each problem. Use estimation or count decimal places to place the decimal point in your answers.

1. A model train caboose is 7.75 inches long. The actual caboose is 48 times as long as this. How long is the actual caboose? 372.00 or 372 in.
2. Write a number story for 40.06 ∗ 67. Solve your number story. 2,684.02; Number stories vary.

Fill in the missing digits in the multiplication problems.

3.
```
      1 3
      1 4
      3 2 . 7
  *     5 . 6
    1 9 6 2
+ 1 6 3 5 0
  1 8 3 . 1 2
```

4.
```
      3
    8 . 0 5
  *   0 . 6
  4 . 8 3 0
```

5.
```
       4
    0 . 1 9
  *   0 . 5
  0 . 0 9 5
```

Math Journal, p. 23P

Step 3:

Multiply the dollars.

3 ∗ $4 = $12

Remember the $2 from Step 2.

$12 + $2 = $14 in all

$14 = 1 [$10] + 4 [$1]s

Remember to include the decimal point.

```
     2 2
    4 . 7 9
  *       3
  1 4 . 3 7
```

$4.79 ∗ 3 = $14.37

Three small salads cost $14.37.

One way to use U.S. traditional multiplication with decimals is to multiply the factors as though they were whole numbers and then use estimation to place the decimal point.

Example 2: 6.07 ∗ 0.5

Step 1:

Multiply as though both factors were whole numbers.

```
     3
   6 0 7
 *     5
 3 0 3 5
```

Step 2:

Estimate the product: 6.07 ∗ 0.5 ≈ 6 ∗ 0.5 = 3.

Step 3:

Use the estimate to place the decimal point in the answer. The estimate is 3, so place the decimal point to make the answer close to 3: 3.035 is close to 3.

6.07 ∗ 0.5 = 3.035

Another way to use U.S. traditional multiplication with decimals is to multiply as though both factors were whole numbers and then find the total number of places to the right of the decimal points of both factors to decide where to place the decimal point.

Example 3: 0.47 ∗ 0.82

Step 1:

Multiply as though both factors were whole numbers.

```
       5
       1
     4 7
 *   8 2
     9 4
 + 3 7 6 0
   3 8 5 4
```

Step 2:

Count the total number of places to the right of the decimal points of both factors. There are 2 places to the right of the decimal point in 0.47. There are 2 places to the right of the decimal point in 0.82. There are 4 decimal places in all.

Step 3:

Place the decimal point 4 places from the right.

0.47 ∗ 0.82 = 0.3854

You may want to work several more examples with the whole class.

Suggestions:

▷ 4.64 ∗ 24 = ? 111.36

▷ 30.8 ∗ 52 = ? 1,601.6

▷ 5.3 ∗ 953 = ? 5,050.9

▷ 0.8 ∗ 0.38 = ? 0.304

▷ 0.71 ∗ 0.04 = ? 0.0284

▷ 82.9 ∗ 8.1 = ? 671.49

Practicing U.S. Traditional Multiplication for Decimals

PARTNER ACTIVITY

(*Math Journal 1* or *2,* pp. 21P–24P; *Student Reference Book,* pp. 54C and 54D)

When students are ready, have them solve Problems 2–7 on journal page 21P. They may find the examples on *Student Reference Book,* pages 54C and 54D helpful.

Journal pages 22P–24P provide students with additional practice using U.S. traditional multiplication. Use these journal pages as necessary.

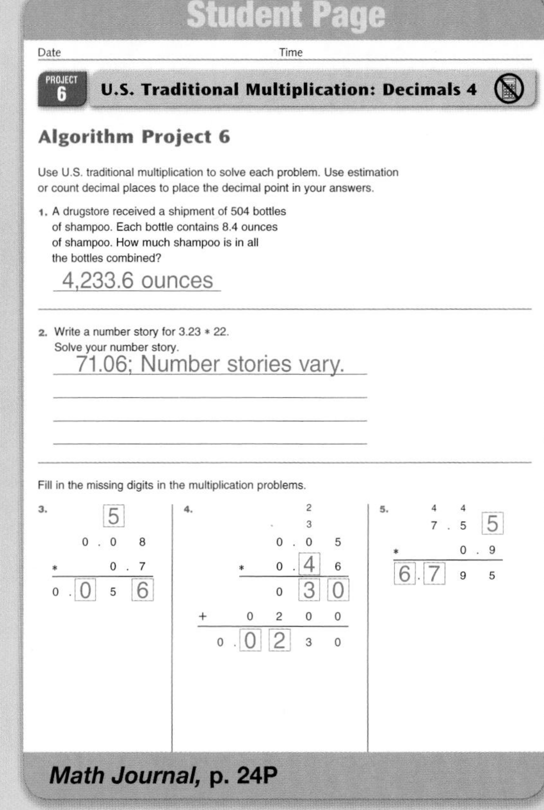

Student Page

Date Time

PROJECT 6 **U.S. Traditional Multiplication: Decimals 4**

Algorithm Project 6

Use U.S. traditional multiplication to solve each problem. Use estimation or count decimal places to place the decimal point in your answers.

1. A drugstore received a shipment of 504 bottles of shampoo. Each bottle contains 8.4 ounces of shampoo. How much shampoo is in all the bottles combined?
4,233.6 ounces

2. Write a number story for 3.23 ∗ 22. Solve your number story.
71.06; Number stories vary.

Fill in the missing digits in the multiplication problems.

3.
```
      [5]
   0 . 0 8
 *     0 . 7
 0 .[0] 5 [6]
```

4.
```
          2
          3
    0 . 0 5
 *  0 .[4] 6
      0 [3][0]
 +  0 2 0 0
  0 .[0][2] 3 0
```

5.
```
      4 4
    7 . 5 [5]
 *      0 . 9
 [6].[7] 9 5
```

Math Journal, p. 24P

2 Extending the Project

Solving Decimal Multiplication Problems

INDEPENDENT ACTIVITY

(Online Additional Practice, pp. 24A–24D; *Student Reference Book,* pp. 37–40, 54C, and 54D)

Online practice pages 24A–24D provide students with additional practice solving decimal multiplication problems. Use these pages as necessary.

Encourage students to use the focus algorithm (partial-products multiplication) to solve the problems on practice page 24A. Invite them to use any algorithm they wish to solve the problems on the remaining pages.

Students may find the examples on *Student Reference Book,* pages 37–40, 54C, and 54D helpful.

Go to www.everydaymathonline.com to access the additional practice pages.

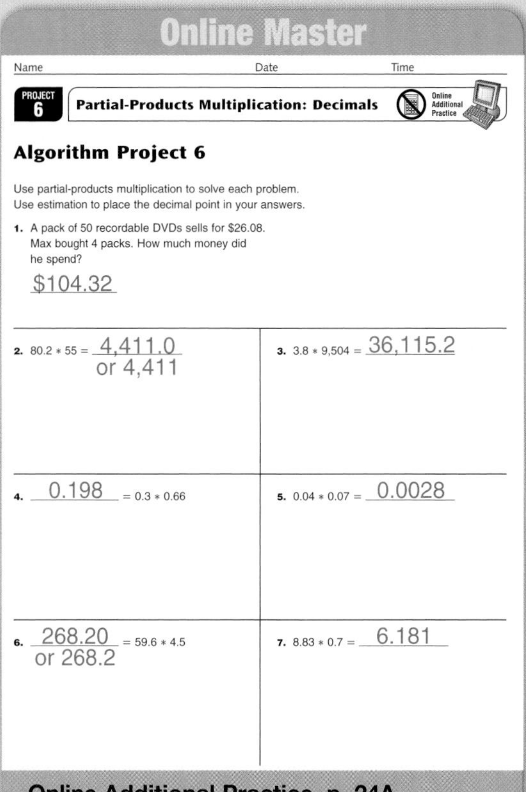

Online Master

Name Date Time

PROJECT 6 **Partial-Products Multiplication: Decimals** Online Additional Practice

Algorithm Project 6

Use partial-products multiplication to solve each problem. Use estimation to place the decimal point in your answers.

1. A pack of 50 recordable DVDs sells for $26.08. Max bought 4 packs. How much money did he spend?
$104.32

2. 80.2 ∗ 55 = 4,411.0 or 4,411

3. 3.8 ∗ 9,504 = 36,115.2

4. 0.198 = 0.3 ∗ 0.66

5. 0.04 ∗ 0.07 = 0.0028

6. 268.20 or 268.2 = 59.6 ∗ 4.5

7. 8.83 ∗ 0.7 = 6.181

Online Additional Practice, p. 24A

Algorithm 7 Project

U.S. Traditional Long Division

Objective To review and practice U.S. traditional long division with whole numbers.

Technology Resources www.everydaymathonline.com

eToolkit

Algorithms Practice

EM Facts Workshop Game™

Family Letters

Assessment Management

Common Core State Standards

Curriculum Focal Points

Interactive Teacher's Lesson Guide

1 Doing the Project

Recommended Use After Lesson 4•2

Key Concepts and Skills

- Apply multiplication and division facts with long division.
  [Operations and Computation Goal 2]
- Use long division to divide whole numbers by single-digit and multidigit whole numbers.
  [Operations and Computation Goal 3]
- Use estimation to carry out long division efficiently.
  [Operations and Computation Goal 6]

Key Activities

Students review, practice, and extend U.S. traditional long division with whole numbers.

Key Vocabulary

U.S. traditional long division ◆ dividend ◆ divisor ◆ quotient ◆ remainder

Materials

- *Math Journal 1* or *2,* pp. 25P–28P
- *Student Reference Book,* pp. 24E–24H
- play money (optional)

2 Extending the Project

Students create and solve long division puzzles.

For additional practice, students solve division problems, first using the focus algorithm (partial-quotients division) and then using any algorithm they choose.

Materials

- *Math Journal 1* or *2,* p. 28P
- *Math Masters,* p. 415
- Online Additional Practice, pp. 28A–28D
- *Student Reference Book,* pp. 22, 23, and 24E–24H

1 Doing the Project

Reviewing Long Division with Single-Digit Divisors

WHOLE-CLASS DISCUSSION

(*Math Journal 1* or *2*, p. 25P)

Have students solve Problem 1 on journal page 25P. Tell them they may use paper and pencil, or any manipulatives or tools that they wish, except calculators.

Have volunteers explain their solutions. \$2,365 / 6 = \$394 R\$1 Expect that students will use several different methods, including partial-quotients division, various informal paper-and-pencil approaches, dealing with manipulatives, and drawing pictures. Some students may also use U.S. traditional long division, which was introduced and practiced in fourth-grade algorithm projects. *For example:*

▷ Using partial-quotients division

6) 2365	
− 1200	200
1165	
− 600	100
565	
− 300	50
265	
− 240	40
25	
− 24	4
1	394

\$2365 ÷ 6 = \$394 R\$1

▷ Using an informal paper-and-pencil method

\$2365	
− 600	← \$100 for each worker
1765	
− 600	← \$100 for each worker
1165	
− 600	← \$100 for each worker
565	
− 300	← \$50 for each worker
265	
− 240	← \$40 for each worker
25	
− 24	← \$4 for each worker

▷ Using U.S. traditional long division (*See margin.*)

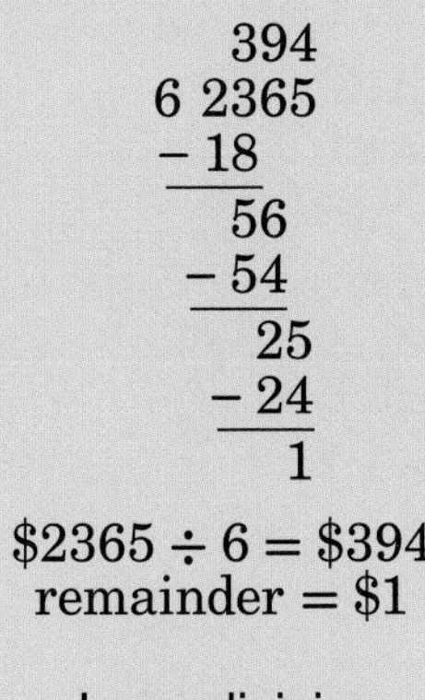

Long division

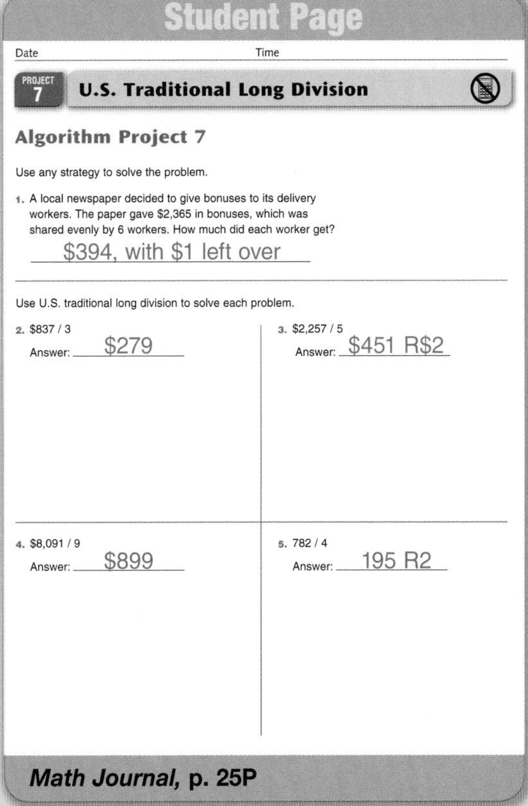

Student Page

Date Time

PROJECT 7 **U.S. Traditional Long Division**

Algorithm Project 7

Use any strategy to solve the problem.

1. A local newspaper decided to give bonuses to its delivery workers. The paper gave \$2,365 in bonuses, which was shared evenly by 6 workers. How much did each worker get?
\$394, with \$1 left over

Use U.S. traditional long division to solve each problem.

2. \$837 / 3 Answer: \$279
3. \$2,257 / 5 Answer: \$451 R\$2
4. \$8,091 / 9 Answer: \$899
5. 782 / 4 Answer: 195 R2

Math Journal, p. 25P

NOTE Although the largest note in circulation today is the $100 bill, in the past, limited numbers of much larger bills have been issued, including $1,000, $10,000, and $100,000 bills. These notes were withdrawn from circulation by President Nixon because they were rarely used and were attractive to counterfeiters.

NOTE Sharing money is a useful context for teaching and learning long division. The process of sharing bills of various denominations ($100 bills, $10 bills, and $1 bills) and coins (dimes and pennies), starting with the largest denomination and trading for smaller denominations as necessary, is broadly parallel to the steps in long division.

Review how to solve the problem using **U.S. traditional long division.** Illustrate each step with pictures and, if possible, model the steps using play money. Emphasize the connections between the steps in long division and the process of sharing money.

Step 1

Bonus to be Shared

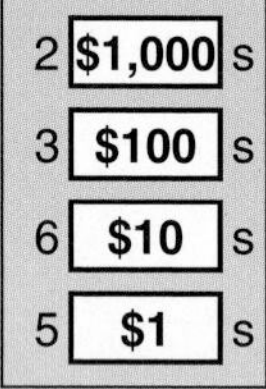

Step 1:

Write the problem $2,365 / 6 in the long division format on the board or a transparency.

6)2 3 6 5 ← $2,365 is to be shared: $2,365 is the **dividend.**
↑
The money is to be
shared by 6 workers:
6 is the **divisor.**

Step 2

Bonus to be Shared

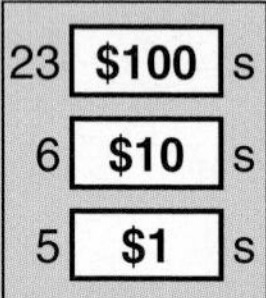

Step 2:

Encourage students to think about sharing actual bills: 2 [$1,000]s, 3 [$100]s, 6 [$10]s, and 5 [$1]s. There are not enough [$1,000]s for 6 equal shares, so trade the 2 [$1,000]s for 20 [$100]s. There were 3 [$100]s already, so there are 20 + 3 = 23 [$100]s after the trade.

6)2 3 6 5 ← 20 [$100]s from the 2 [$1,000]s +
3 [$100]s = 23 [$100]s

Step 3

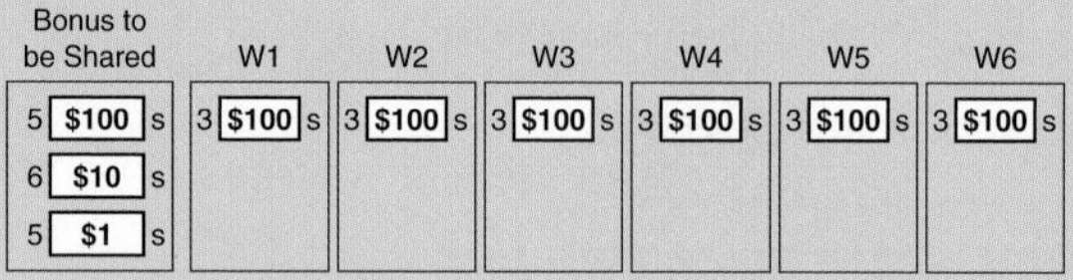

Step 3:

Share the 23 [$100]s. Each worker gets 3 [$100]s; 5 [$100]s are left over.

3 ← Each worker gets 3 [$100]s.
6)2 3 6 5
− 1 8 ← 3 [$100]s each for 6 workers = 18 [$100]s
5 ← 5 [$100]s are left.

Step 4

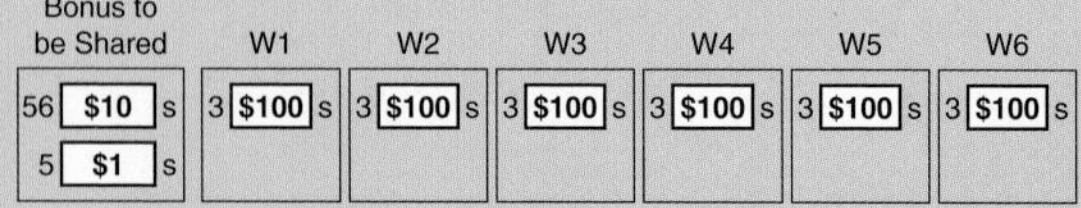

Step 4:

Trade the 5 [$100]s for 50 [$10]s. There were 6 [$10]s already, so there are 50 + 6 = 56 [$10]s.

3
6)2 3 **6** 5
− 1 8 ↓
5 6 ← 50 [$10]s from the 5 [$100]s + 6 [$10]s = 56 [$10]s

Step 5:

Share the 56 [$10]s. Each worker gets 9 [$10]s; there are 2 [$10]s left over.

```
   3 9   ← Each worker gets 9 [$10]s.
6)2 3 6 5
 -1 8
   5 6
  -5 4   ← 9 [$10]s each for 6 workers = 54 [$10]s
     2   ← 2 [$10]s are left.
```

Step 6:

Trade the 2 [$10]s for 20 [$1]s. There were 5 [$1]s already, so there are 20 + 5 = 25 [$1]s.

```
   3 9
6)2 3 6 5
 -1 8   ↓
   5 6  ↓
  -5 4  ↓
     2 5 ← 20 [$1]s from the 2 [$10]s + 5 [$1]s = 25 [$1]s
```

Step 7:

Share the 25 [$1]s. Each worker gets 4 [$1]s; 1 [$1] is left over.

```
   3 9 4 ← Each worker gets 4 [$1]s.
6)2 3 6 5
 -1 8
   5 6
  -5 4
     2 5
    -2 4 ← 4 [$1]s each for 6 workers = 24 [$1]s
       1 ← 1 [$1] is left.
```

Step 8:

Each worker gets $394: $394 is the **quotient.** The $1 that is left over is the **remainder.** A number model is a good way to show the answer:

$2,365 / 6 → $394 R$1

U.S. traditional long division is complicated, so consider working one or two more examples with the whole class. Continue to use sharing money as a context and drawing pictures to show actions with money, as needed.

Suggestions:

- ▷ $4,967 / 6 $827 R$5
- ▷ $2,850 / 8 $356 R$2
- ▷ $705 / 5 $141
- ▷ $1,008 / 9 $112
- ▷ $2,048 / 4 $512
- ▷ $402 / 4 $100 R$2
- ▷ $4,290 / 7 $612 R$6
- ▷ $2,040 / 8 $255

Step 5

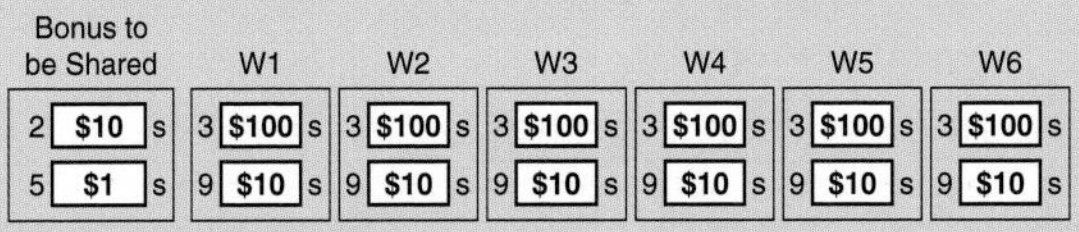

Bonus to be Shared	W1	W2	W3	W4	W5	W6
2 [$10]s	3 [$100]s	3 [$100]s	3 [$100]s	3 [$100]s	3 [$100]s	3 [$100]s
5 [$1]s	9 [$10]s	9 [$10]s	9 [$10]s	9 [$10]s	9 [$10]s	9 [$10]s

Step 6

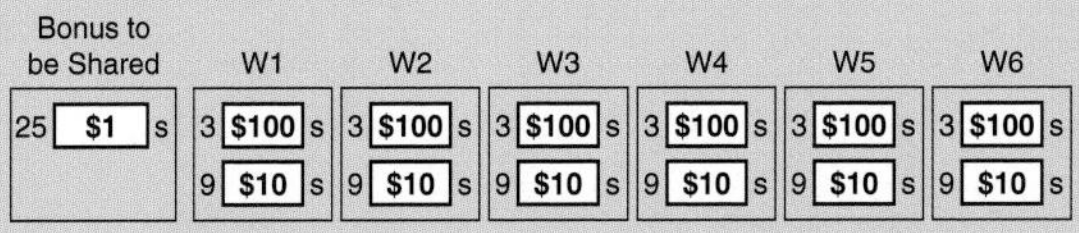

Bonus to be Shared	W1	W2	W3	W4	W5	W6
25 [$1]s	3 [$100]s	3 [$100]s	3 [$100]s	3 [$100]s	3 [$100]s	3 [$100]s
	9 [$10]s	9 [$10]s	9 [$10]s	9 [$10]s	9 [$10]s	9 [$10]s

Step 7

Bonus to be Shared	W1	W2	W3	W4	W5	W6
1 [$1]s	3 [$100]s	3 [$100]s	3 [$100]s	3 [$100]s	3 [$100]s	3 [$100]s
	9 [$10]s	9 [$10]s	9 [$10]s	9 [$10]s	9 [$10]s	9 [$10]s
	4 [$1]s	4 [$1]s	4 [$1]s	4 [$1]s	4 [$1]s	4 [$1]s

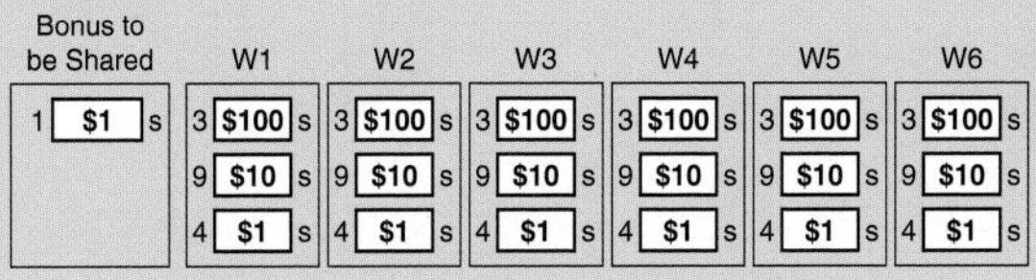

$2,365 shared by 6 workers

NOTE Some students may benefit from seeing long division on a computation grid that shows place-value column names.

	Thousands	Hundreds	Tens	Ones
		3	9	4
6	2	3	6	5
–	1	8		
		5	6	
	–	5	4	
			2	5
		–	2	4
				1

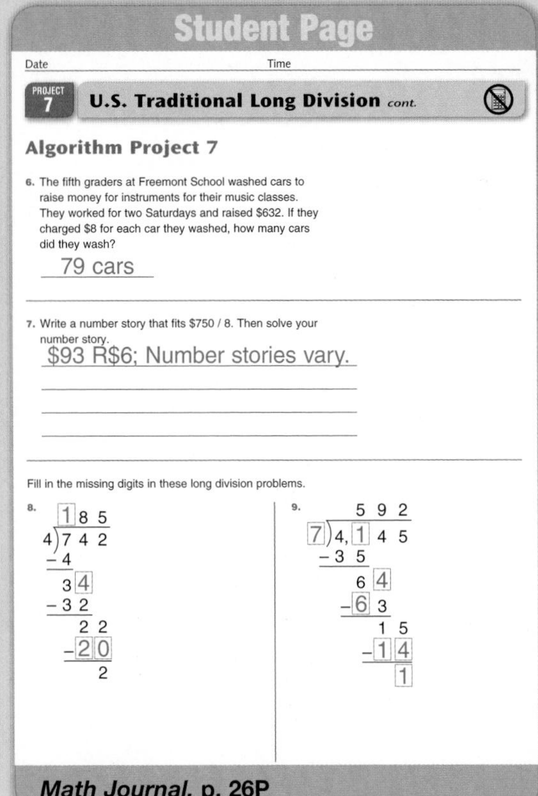

Student Page

Date ______ Time ______

PROJECT 7 **U.S. Traditional Long Division** *cont.*

Algorithm Project 7

6. The fifth graders at Freemont School washed cars to raise money for instruments for their music classes. They worked for two Saturdays and raised $632. If they charged $8 for each car they washed, how many cars did they wash?
   79 cars

7. Write a number story that fits $750 / 8. Then solve your number story.
   $93 R$6; Number stories vary.

Fill in the missing digits in these long division problems.

8.
```
    [1]8 5
 4)7 4 2
  -4
   3[4]
  -3 2
     2 2
    -[2][0]
       2
```

9.
```
       5 9 2
 [7])4,[1] 4 5
    -3 5
       6[4]
      -[6]3
         1 5
        -[1][4]
           [1]
```

Math Journal, p. 26P

▶ Solving Long Division Problems with One-Digit Divisors

(*Math Journal 1* or *2,* pp. 25P and 26P; *Student Reference Book,* pp. 24E and 24F)

Have students use U.S. traditional long division to solve Problems 2–9 on journal pages 25P and 26P. They might find the examples on *Student Reference Book,* pages 24E and 24F helpful.

▶ Introducing Long Division with Multidigit Divisors

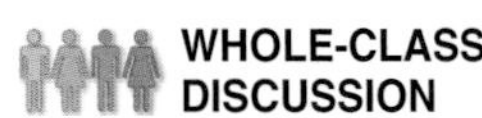

(*Math Journal 1* or *2,* p. 27P)

Have students solve Problem 1 on journal page 27P. Circulate and assist.

When most students have finished, discuss students' solutions. $6,714 / 27 → $248 R$18 Expect that students will use various methods.

```
27)6714 |
 - 2700 | 100
   4014 |
 - 2700 | 100
   1314 |
  - 540 |  20
    774 |
  - 540 |  20
    234 |
  - 135 |   5
     99 |
   - 54 |   2
     45 |
   - 27 |   1
     18 | 248
```

$6714 \div 27 \rightarrow 248\text{ R}18$

Partial quotients

```
     248
27)6714
  - 54
    131
  - 108
     234
   - 216
      18
```

$27 * 1 = 27$
$27 * 2 = 54$
$27 * 3 = 81$
$27 * 4 = 108$
$27 * 5 = 135$
$27 * 6 = 162$
$27 * 8 = 216$
$27 * 10 = 270$

$6714 \div 27 \rightarrow 248\text{ R}18$

Long division

Demonstrate how to solve the problem using long division. Illustrate each step on the board or a transparency.

Carrying out long division with multidigit divisors can be challenging, particularly for students whose estimation skills are not well developed. Have students make a table of simple multiples of the divisor to use in deciding how many to share at each step.

Student Page

Date ______ Time ______

PROJECT 7 **Long Division with Multidigit Divisors**

Algorithm Project 7

Use any strategy to solve the problem.

1. Holmes School had a carnival to raise money for classroom supplies. The carnival raised $6,714, which was to be shared equally by all 27 teachers at Holmes. How much should each teacher have received?
   $248, with $18 left over

Use U.S. traditional long division to solve each problem.

2. $4,864 / 32
   Answer: $152

3. $17,187 / 43
   Answer: $399 R$30

4. 5,238 / 27
   Answer: 194

5. 4,785 / 87
   Answer: 55

Math Journal, p. 27P

Example: Solve: $6,714 / 27

$6,714 has only 6 [$1,000]s, which are not enough to share among 27 teachers. Trade the 6 [$1,000]s for 60 [$100]s, which makes 67 [$100]s in all. Share the 67 [$100]s among the 27 teachers. Use the table of multiples to help decide how many each teacher should get.

```
      2        ← Each teacher gets 2 [$100]s.
27)6 7 1 4     ← Trade 6 [$1,000]s for 60 [$100]s.
  -5 4           There are 67 [$100]s to share
   1 3           2 [$100]s * 27 teachers
                 13 [$100]s are left.
```

Trade the 13 [$100]s for 130 [$10]s. There was 1 [$10] already, so there are 131 [$10]s after the trade. Share the 131 [$10]s among the 27 teachers.

```
      2 4      ← Each teacher gets 4 [$10]s.
27)6 7 1 4
  -5 4
   1 3 1       ← 13 [$100]s + 1 [$10] = 131 [$10]s
  -1 0 8       ← 4 [$10]s * 27 teachers
     2 3       ← 23 [$10]s are left.
```

Trade the 23 [$10]s for 230 [$1]s. There were 4 [$1]s already, so there are 234 [$1]s altogether. Share the 234 [$1]s among the 27 teachers.

```
      2 4 8    ← Each teacher gets 8 [$1]s.
27)6 7 1 4
  -5 4
   1 3 1
  -1 0 8
     2 3 4     ← 23 [$10]s + 4 [$1] = 234 [$1]s
    -2 1 6     ← 8 [$1] * 27 teachers
       1 8     ← 18 [$1]s are left.
```

$6,714 / 27 → $248 R$18

Each teacher gets $248. $18 are left over.

Discuss what the remainder means in this problem. It's the part of the original $6,714 raised by the carnival that is left over after each of the 27 teachers receives $248. Ask students what they think should be done with the leftover money. Some students may want to continue dividing. The $18 left over could be traded for 180 dimes, shared 27 ways, and so on. The quotient, even carried to pennies, won't come out evenly. There will be 18 pennies left over. However, by continuing the division, a bit more of the carnival proceeds could be distributed. Project 8 will extend long division to decimal dividends. Some students might want to attempt to extend the method on their own.

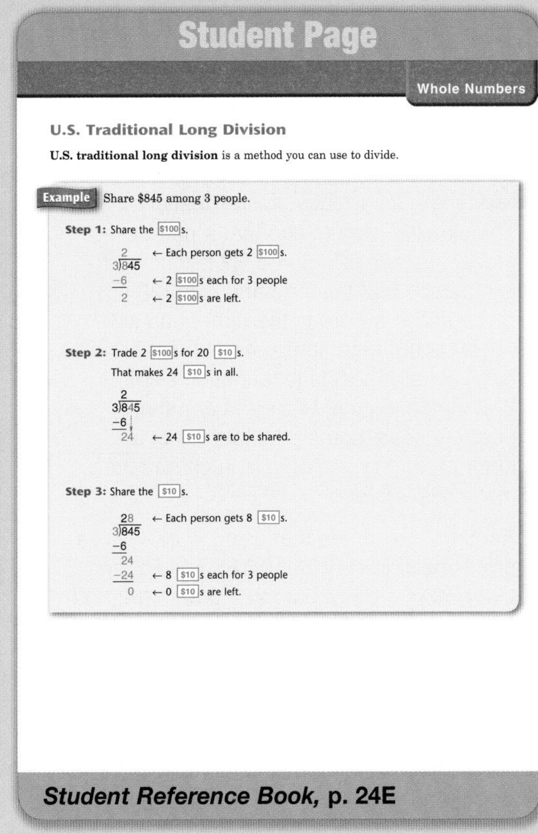

Student Page

Whole Numbers

U.S. Traditional Long Division

U.S. traditional long division is a method you can use to divide.

Example Share $845 among 3 people.

Step 1: Share the [$100]s.

```
  2     ← Each person gets 2 [$100]s.
3)845
 -6     ← 2 [$100]s each for 3 people
  2     ← 2 [$100]s are left.
```

Step 2: Trade 2 [$100]s for 20 [$10]s. That makes 24 [$10]s in all.

```
  2
3)845
 -6
  24    ← 24 [$10]s are to be shared.
```

Step 3: Share the [$10]s.

```
  28    ← Each person gets 8 [$10]s.
3)845
 -6
  24
 -24    ← 8 [$10]s each for 3 people
   0    ← 0 [$10]s are left.
```

Student Reference Book, p. 24E

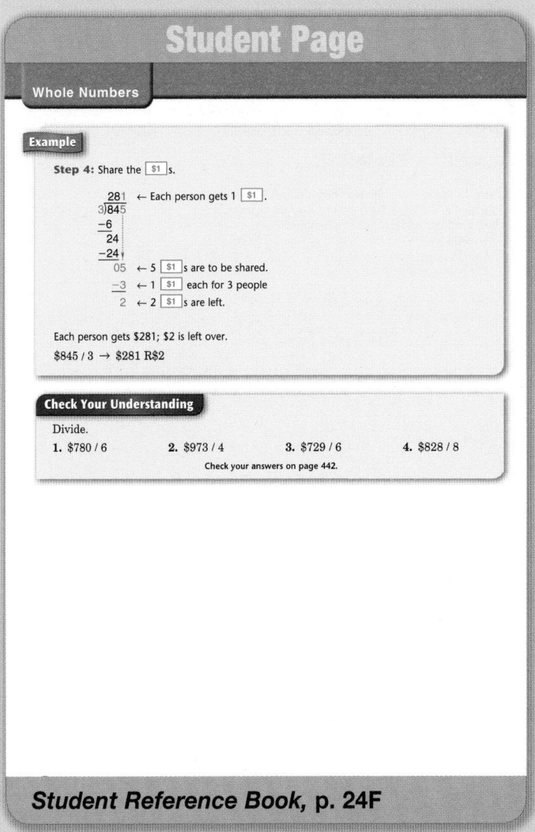

Student Page

Whole Numbers

Example

Step 4: Share the [$1]s.

```
  281   ← Each person gets 1 [$1].
3)845
 -6
  24
 -24
   05   ← 5 [$1]s are to be shared.
   -3   ← 1 [$1] each for 3 people
    2   ← 2 [$1]s are left.
```

Each person gets $281; $2 is left over.

$845 / 3 → $281 R$2

Check Your Understanding

Divide.

1. $780 / 6 2. $973 / 4 3. $729 / 6 4. $828 / 8

Check your answers on page 442.

Student Reference Book, p. 24F

NOTE *Everyday Mathematics* uses → rather than = in number models showing division with remainders because = is technically incorrect in such situations. The simplest way to see that a number model such as 22 / 5 = 4 R2 is incorrect is to notice that the left-hand side (22 / 5) is a number, whereas the right-hand side (4 R2) is not a number—numbers, after all, don't usually include letters such as *R*. But something that is a number cannot possibly equal something that is not a number, so the use of = in such number models is improper.

Another way to see that using = can cause problems is to consider 22 / 5 = 4 R2 and 202 / 50 = 4 R2. If both 22 / 5 and 202 / 50 were equal to 4 R2, one would have to conclude that 22 / 5 and 202 / 50 are equal to each other (since equality is a transitive relation). But 22 / 5 and 202 / 50 are not equal to each other: 22 / 5 > 202 / 50. This shows that using = in such number models can cause problems. Accordingly, in *Everyday Mathematics,* we use the → notation when there are remainders.

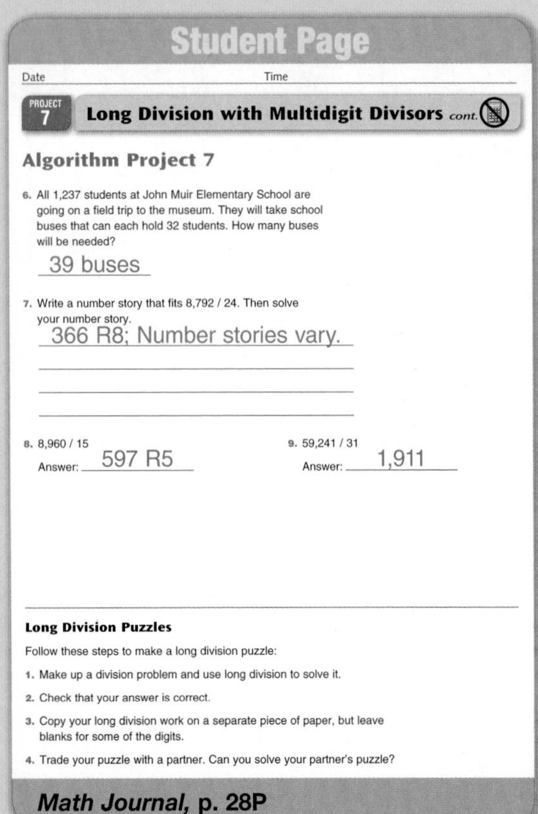

Student Page

Date Time

PROJECT 7 **Long Division with Multidigit Divisors** *cont.*

Algorithm Project 7

6. All 1,237 students at John Muir Elementary School are going on a field trip to the museum. They will take school buses that can each hold 32 students. How many buses will be needed?

39 buses

7. Write a number story that fits 8,792 / 24. Then solve your number story.

366 R8; Number stories vary.

8. 8,960 / 15

Answer: 597 R5

9. 59,241 / 31

Answer: 1,911

Long Division Puzzles

Follow these steps to make a long division puzzle:

1. Make up a division problem and use long division to solve it.
2. Check that your answer is correct.
3. Copy your long division work on a separate piece of paper, but leave blanks for some of the digits.
4. Trade your puzzle with a partner. Can you solve your partner's puzzle?

Math Journal, p. 28P

Work more examples as necessary until students understand the procedure.

Suggestions:

- ▷ $9,475 / 26 $364 R$11
- ▷ $19,240 / 33 $583 R$1
- ▷ $16,248 / 13 $1,249 R$11
- ▷ $5,535 / 12 $461 R$3
- ▷ $7,089 / 47 $150 R$39
- ▷ $3,749 / 25 $149 R$24

▶ Solving Long Division Problems with Multidigit Divisors

(*Math Journal 1* or *2,* pp. 27P and 28P; *Student Reference Book,* pp. 24G and 24H)

Have students use U.S. traditional long division to solve Problems 2–9 on journal pages 27P and 28P. They may find the examples on *Student Reference Book,* pages 24G and 24H helpful.

One of the hardest steps in carrying out U.S. traditional long division is accurately estimating the quotient at each step. As traditionally performed, any wrong estimate, either too high or too low, will cause the algorithm to fail—the incorrect estimate must be erased and replaced. Using a table of easy multiples is one way to address this problem.

Another approach, which combines features of Partial Quotients Division with U.S. Traditional Long Division, is illustrated below. The stacked digits in the place-value positions of the quotient represent partial quotients that must be added to yield the final quotient. For example, the 6 in the hundreds place is from 6 ∗ 7 = 42 (actually 600 ∗ 7 = 4,200). The 2 above the 6 is from 2 ∗ 7 = 14 (actually 200 ∗ 7 = 1,400). The 6 and 2 must be added to determine the hundreds digit in the final quotient. Similarly, the 8 and the 1 must be added to determine the ones digit in the final quotient. So, the final quotient for 6,225 / 7 is 889 R2.

```
   2   1
   6 8 8   → 889 R2
7)6 2 2 5
 -4 2
   2 0
 -1 4
     6 2
   - 5 6
       6 5
     - 5 6
           9
         - 7
           2
```

2 Extending the Project

▶ Long Division Puzzles

PARTNER ACTIVITY

(*Math Journal 1* or *2,* p. 28P; *Math Masters,* p. 415)

Have partners follow the directions at the bottom of journal page 28P. Provide copies of the computation grid (*Math Masters,* page 415). Ask volunteers to explain how they checked their answers in Step 2. Consider having students make long division puzzles for classroom display.

▶ Solving Division Problems

(Online Additional Practice, pp. 28A–28D; *Student Reference Book,* pp. 22, 23, and 24E–24H)

Online practice pages 28A–28D provide students with additional practice solving division problems. Use these pages as necessary.

Encourage students to use the focus algorithm (partial-quotients division) to solve the problems on practice page 28A. Invite them to use any algorithm they wish to solve the problems on the remaining pages. Students may find the examples on *Student Reference Book,* pages 22, 23, and 24E–24H helpful.

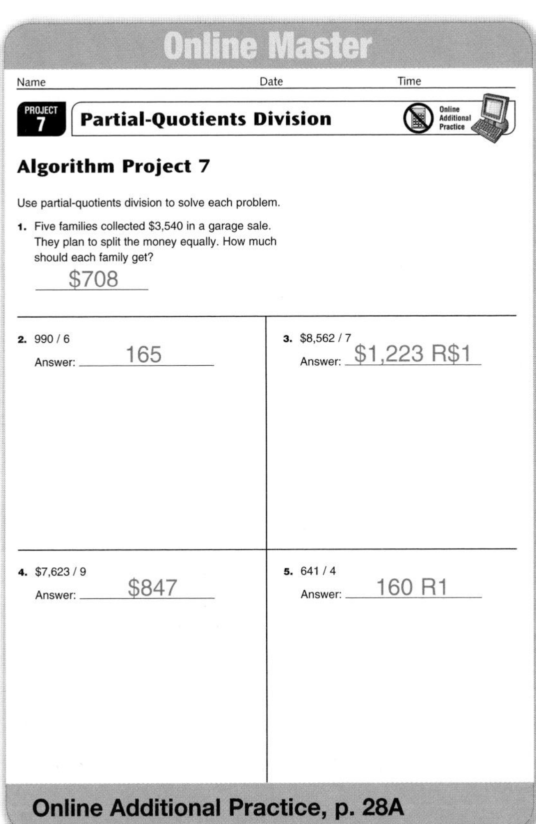

Online Master

Name Date Time

PROJECT 7 **Partial-Quotients Division**

Algorithm Project 7

Use partial-quotients division to solve each problem.

1. Five families collected $3,540 in a garage sale. They plan to split the money equally. How much should each family get?
   $708

2. 990 / 6
   Answer: 165

3. $8,562 / 7
   Answer: $1,223 R$1

4. $7,623 / 9
   Answer: $847

5. 641 / 4
   Answer: 160 R1

Online Additional Practice, p. 28A

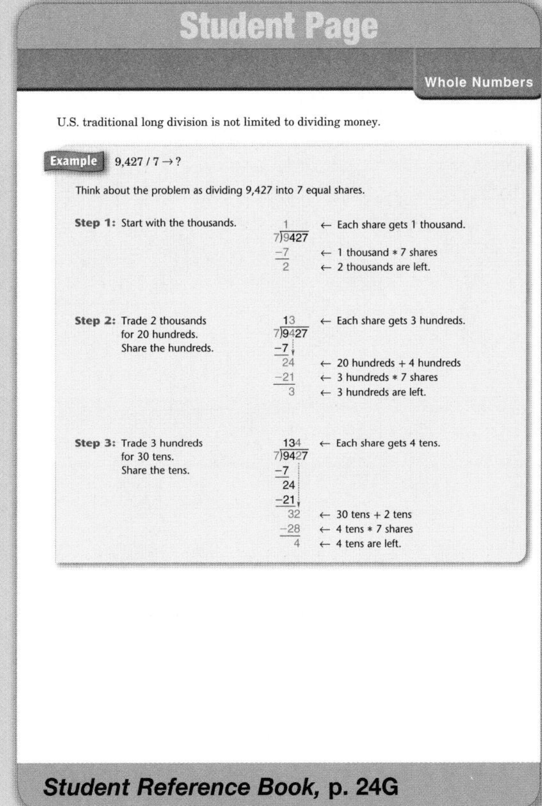

Student Page

Whole Numbers

U.S. traditional long division is not limited to dividing money.

Example 9,427 / 7 → ?

Think about the problem as dividing 9,427 into 7 equal shares.

Step 1: Start with the thousands.

```
   1        ← Each share gets 1 thousand.
7)9427
 -7         ← 1 thousand * 7 shares
  2         ← 2 thousands are left.
```

Step 2: Trade 2 thousands for 20 hundreds. Share the hundreds.

```
   13       ← Each share gets 3 hundreds.
7)9427
 -7
  24        ← 20 hundreds + 4 hundreds
 -21        ← 3 hundreds * 7 shares
   3        ← 3 hundreds are left.
```

Step 3: Trade 3 hundreds for 30 tens. Share the tens.

```
   134      ← Each share gets 4 tens.
7)9427
 -7
  24
 -21
   32       ← 30 tens + 2 tens
  -28       ← 4 tens * 7 shares
    4       ← 4 tens are left.
```

***Student Reference Book*, p. 24G**

Go to www.everydaymathonline.com to access the additional practice pages.

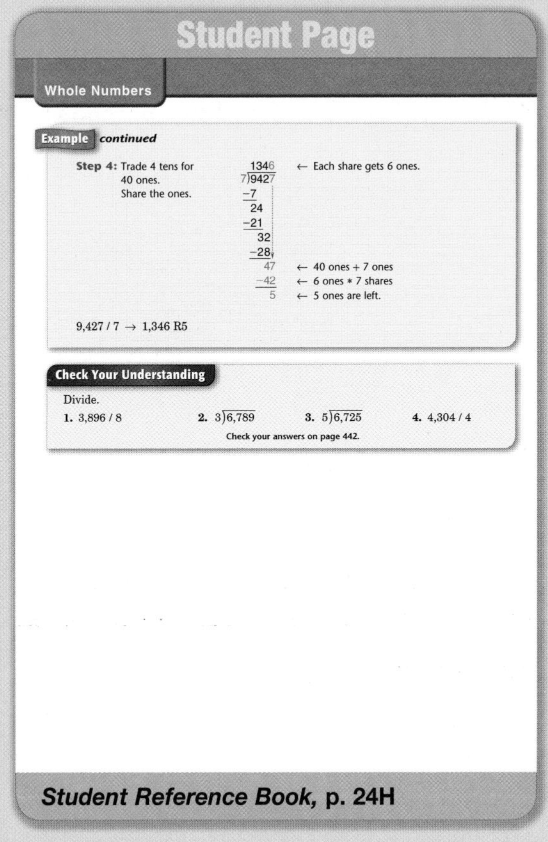

Student Page

Whole Numbers

Example *continued*

Step 4: Trade 4 tens for 40 ones. Share the ones.

```
   1346     ← Each share gets 6 ones.
7)9427
 -7
  24
 -21
   32
  -28
    47      ← 40 ones + 7 ones
   -42      ← 6 ones * 7 shares
     5      ← 5 ones are left.
```

9,427 / 7 → 1,346 R5

Check Your Understanding

Divide.

1. 3,896 / 8 2. 3)6,789 3. 5)6,725 4. 4,304 / 4

Check your answers on page 442.

***Student Reference Book*, p. 24H**

Algorithm

Project

U.S. Traditional Long Division with Decimal Dividends

Objective To extend long division to problems in which a decimal is divided by a whole number.

Technology Resources www.everydaymathonline.com

eToolkit

Algorithms Practice

EM Facts Workshop Game™

Family Letters

Assessment Management

Common Core State Standards

Curriculum Focal Points

Interactive Teacher's Lesson Guide

1 Doing the Project

Recommended Use After Lesson 4•5 and Algorithm Project 7

Key Concepts and Skills

- Apply multiplication facts in carrying out long division.
  [Operations and Computation Goal 2]
- Use long division to solve division problems with decimal dividends.
  [Operations and Computation Goal 3]
- Estimate products and quotients.
  [Operations and Computation Goal 6]
- Find average speeds, given times and distances.
  [Operations and Computation Goal 7]

Key Activities

Students extend the whole-number long division algorithm to decimal dividends.

Materials

- *Math Journal 1* or *2,* pp. 29P and 30P
- *Student Reference Book,* pp. 54E and 54F

2 Extending the Project

Students use long division to rename fractions as decimals.

For additional practice, students solve division problems, first using the focus algorithm (partial-quotients division) and then using any algorithm they choose.

Materials

- *Math Journal 1* or *2,* p. 31P
- *Student Reference Book,* pp. 42, 43, 54E, 54F, 54I, and 54J
- Online Additional Practice, pp. 31A–31C

1 Doing the Project

▶ Long Division with Dollars and Cents

WHOLE-CLASS DISCUSSION

(*Math Journal 1* or *2,* p. 29P; *Student Reference Book,* pp 54E and 54F)

Have students solve Problems 1–3 on journal page 29P. When most students have finished, write Emma's long division work from the journal page introduction on the board or a transparency. Ask questions such as the following:

- Where does the 53 in the fourth line of Emma's method come from? The 53 refers to 53 dimes, 50 dimes from the $5 left over after the whole dollars were shared and 3 dimes in the original dividend: 50 dimes + 3 dimes = 53 dimes.
- Where does the 48 in the fifth line of Emma's method come from? The 48 is the number of dimes shared when each of 6 shares gets 8 dimes: 6 ∗ 8 dimes = 48 dimes.
- What is the 1 at the very bottom? It is the remainder; it represents $0.01 that is left over after $17.35 is divided by 6.

Have students make up a number story that fits 17.35 / 6. Ask volunteers to share their number stories and explain what should be done with the remainder in each case. Emphasize that what to do with the remainder depends on the problem situation.

Have partners complete journal page 29P. Students may find the examples on *Student Reference Book,* pages 54E and 54F helpful.

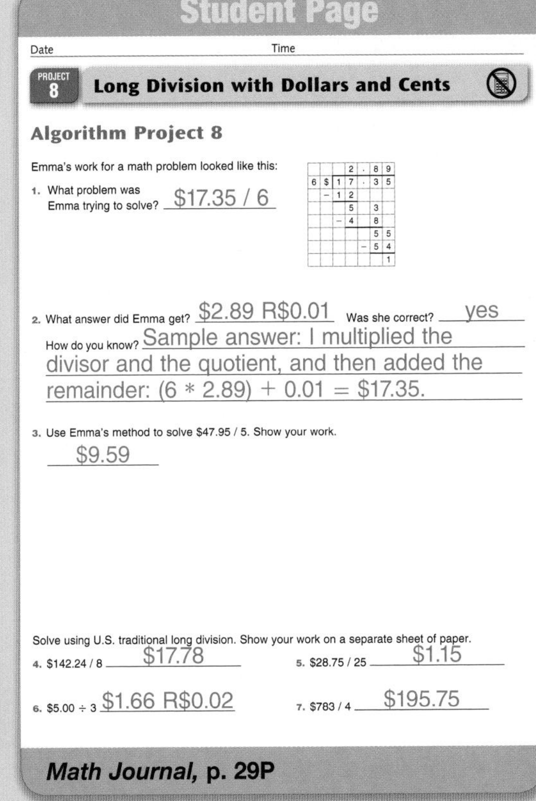
Student Page

Date Time

PROJECT 8 **Long Division with Dollars and Cents**

Algorithm Project 8

Emma's work for a math problem looked like this:

			2	.	8	9
6	$	1	7	.	3	5
	−	1	2			
			5		3	
		−	4		8	
					5	5
				−	5	4
						1

1. What problem was Emma trying to solve? $17.35 / 6

2. What answer did Emma get? $2.89 R$0.01 Was she correct? yes
How do you know? Sample answer: I multiplied the divisor and the quotient, and then added the remainder: (6 ∗ 2.89) + 0.01 = $17.35.

3. Use Emma's method to solve $47.95 / 5. Show your work.
$9.59

Solve using U.S. traditional long division. Show your work on a separate sheet of paper.

4. $142.24 / 8 $17.78
5. $28.75 / 25 $1.15
6. $5.00 ÷ 3 $1.66 R$0.02
7. $783 / 4 $195.75

Math Journal, p. 29P

NOTE Extending whole-number long division to money in dollars-and-cents notation is relatively straightforward. One of the most useful characteristics of our base-10 place-value number system is that many whole-number algorithms can be easily adapted to work with decimals.

▶ Long Division with Decimal Dividends

WHOLE-CLASS DISCUSSION

(*Math Journal 1* or *2,* p. 30P)

Have students solve Problems 1 and 2 on journal page 30P. For Problem 2, remind students that a decimal point and trailing 0s can be attached to the dividend: 224 = 224.000 . . . and that a table of easy multiples of 12 might be helpful. Problem 2 involves a division that will never come out evenly and introduces students to a process that repeats forever. This idea is explored further in Part 2 of this project.

Student Page

Date Time

PROJECT 8 **Long Division with Decimal Dividends**

Algorithm Project 8

Use long division to solve these problems. Give your answers to the nearest hundredth.

1. A garden snail travels 7.95 feet in 3 minutes. What is the snail's average speed in feet per minute?
2.65 feet/minute (unit)

2. In 2004, Andrew Otto set a record for the men's course of the Davis 12-hour Challenge bicycle race in Winters, California. He rode 224 miles in 12 hours. What was Otto's average speed in miles per hour?
18.67 miles/hour (unit)

3. In 2000, Sandy Earl set a record for the women's course of the Davis 12-hour Challenge. She rode 214 miles in 12 hours. What was Earl's average speed in miles per hour?
17.83 miles/hour (unit)

Sources: *Encyclopaedia Britannica,* www.britannica.com
Davis Bike Club, www.davisbikeclub.org

Math Journal, p. 30P

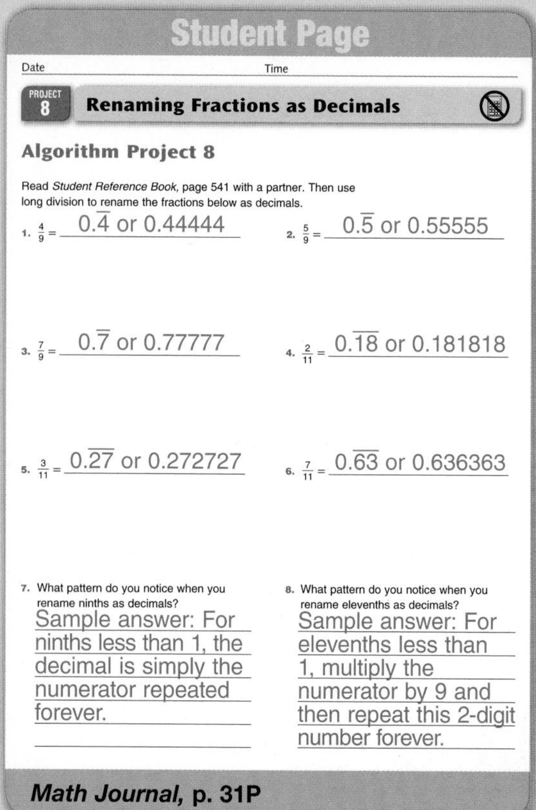
Student Page

Date Time

PROJECT 8 **Renaming Fractions as Decimals**

Algorithm Project 8

Read *Student Reference Book,* page 541 with a partner. Then use long division to rename the fractions below as decimals.

1. $\frac{4}{9}$ = $0.\overline{4}$ or 0.44444
2. $\frac{5}{9}$ = $0.\overline{5}$ or 0.55555
3. $\frac{7}{9}$ = $0.\overline{7}$ or 0.77777
4. $\frac{2}{11}$ = $0.\overline{18}$ or 0.181818
5. $\frac{3}{11}$ = $0.\overline{27}$ or 0.272727
6. $\frac{7}{11}$ = $0.\overline{63}$ or 0.636363
7. What pattern do you notice when you rename ninths as decimals? Sample answer: For ninths less than 1, the decimal is simply the numerator repeated forever.
8. What pattern do you notice when you rename elevenths as decimals? Sample answer: For elevenths less than 1, multiply the numerator by 9 and then repeat this 2-digit number forever.

Math Journal, p. 31P

Go to www.everydaymathonline.com to access the additional practice pages.

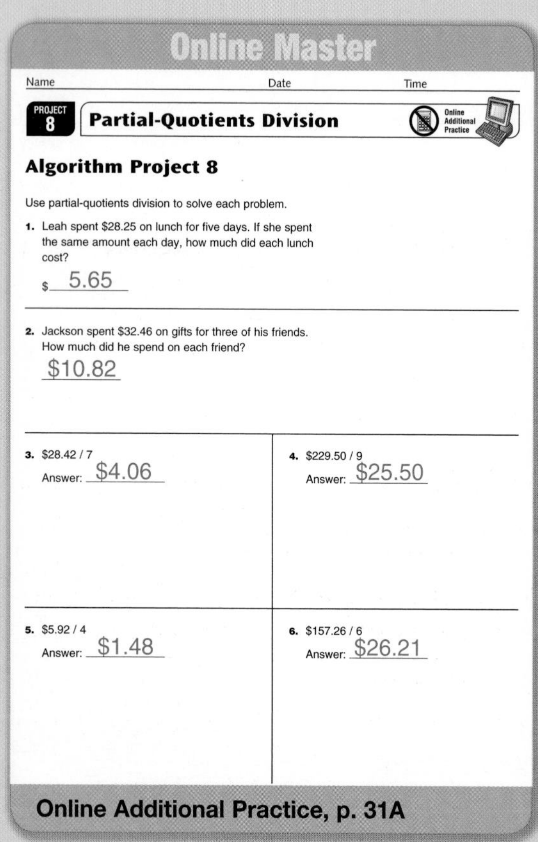
Online Master

Name Date Time

PROJECT 8 **Partial-Quotients Division**

Algorithm Project 8

Use partial-quotients division to solve each problem.

1. Leah spent $28.25 on lunch for five days. If she spent the same amount each day, how much did each lunch cost? $ 5.65
2. Jackson spent $32.46 on gifts for three of his friends. How much did he spend on each friend? $10.82
3. $28.42 / 7 Answer: $4.06
4. $229.50 / 9 Answer: $25.50
5. $5.92 / 4 Answer: $1.48
6. $157.26 / 6 Answer: $26.21

Online Additional Practice, p. 31A

When most students have finished, have volunteers copy their work on the board or a transparency and explain their solutions. Ask questions such as the following:

Problem 1

- Why does dividing 7.95 by 3 give the average speed in feet per minute? Feet per minute means feet in 1 minute. At the average speed, the snail would go 7.95 feet in 3 minutes; 7.95 / 3 gives the distance traveled in 1 minute.

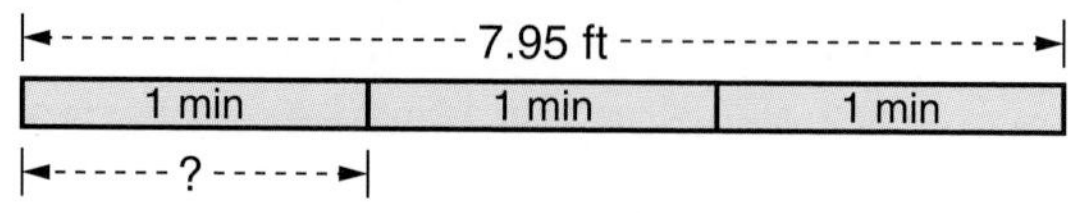

- What does the digit 2 in the quotient mean? If 7 feet are shared into 3 equal parts, then each part would get 2 feet with 1 foot left over.

Problem 2

- Why does dividing 224 by 12 give the average speed in miles per hour? Miles per hour means miles in 1 hour. At the average speed, Otto would go 224 miles in 12 hours. 224 / 12 gives the distance traveled in 1 hour.

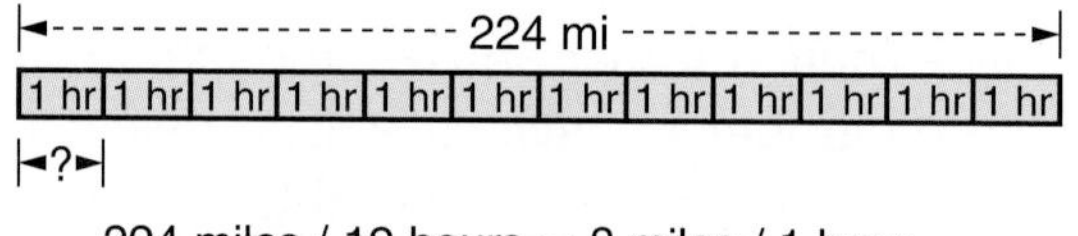

Have partners complete journal page 30P.

2 Extending the Project

Using Long Division to Rename Fractions as Decimals

(*Student Reference Book,* pp. 54I and 54J; *Math Journal 1* or *2,* p. 31P)

Have students solve Problems 1–8 on journal page 31P.

Solving Division Problems

INDEPENDENT ACTIVITY

(Online Additional Practice, pp. 31A–31C; *Student Reference Book,* pp. 42, 43, 54E, 54F, 54I, and 54J)

Online practice pages 31A–31C provide students with additional practice solving division problems. Use these pages as necessary.

Encourage students to use the focus algorithm (partial-quotients division) to solve the problems on practice page 31A. Invite them to use any algorithm they wish to solve the problems on the remaining pages. Students may find the examples on *Student Reference Book,* pages 42, 43, 54E, 54F, 54I, and 54J helpful.

Algorithm 9 Project

U.S. Traditional Long Division: Decimals

Objective To extend long division to problems in which both the divisor and the dividend are decimals.

Technology Resources www.everydaymathonline.com

eToolkit

Algorithms Practice

EM Facts Workshop Game™

Family Letters

Assessment Management

Common Core State Standards

Curriculum Focal Points

Interactive Teacher's Lesson Guide

1 Doing the Project

Recommended Use After Lesson 4•5 and Algorithm Project 8

Key Concepts and Skills

- Use the Multiplication Rule to find equivalent fractions. [Number and Numeration Goal 5]
- Use long division to solve division problems with decimal divisors. [Operations and Computation Goal 3]
- Multiply numbers by powers of 10. [Operations and Computation Goal 3]
- Explore the meaning of division by a decimal. [Operations and Computation Goal 7]

Key Activities

Students explore the meaning of division by a decimal and extend long division to decimal divisors.

Key Vocabulary

decimal divisors

Materials

- *Math Journal 1* or *2,* p. 32P
- *Student Reference Book,* pp. 37, 54G, 54H, and 60

2 Extending the Project

Students express the remainder in a division problem as a whole number, a fraction, an exact decimal, and a decimal rounded to the nearest hundredth.

For additional practice, students solve division problems, first using the focus algorithm (partial-quotients division) and then using any algorithm they choose.

Materials

- *Math Journal 1* or *2,* p. 33P
- *Student Reference Book,* pp. 54E–54J
- Online Additional Practice, pp. 33A–33B

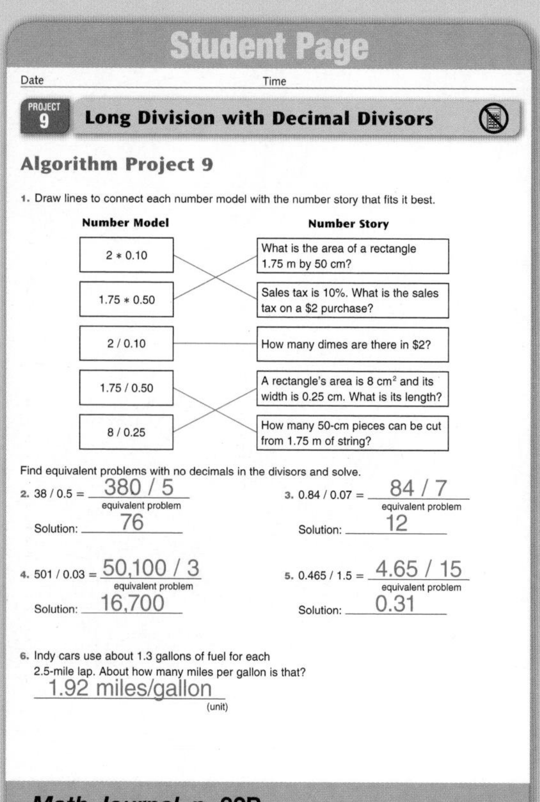

Student Page

Date Time

PROJECT 9 **Long Division with Decimal Divisors**

Algorithm Project 9

1. Draw lines to connect each number model with the number story that fits it best.

Number Model	Number Story
2 * 0.10	What is the area of a rectangle 1.75 m by 50 cm?
1.75 * 0.50	Sales tax is 10%. What is the sales tax on a $2 purchase?
2 / 0.10	How many dimes are there in $2?
1.75 / 0.50	A rectangle's area is 8 cm² and its width is 0.25 cm. What is its length?
8 / 0.25	How many 50-cm pieces can be cut from 1.75 m of string?

Find equivalent problems with no decimals in the divisors and solve.

2. 38 / 0.5 = 380 / 5 (equivalent problem) Solution: 76

3. 0.84 / 0.07 = 84 / 7 (equivalent problem) Solution: 12

4. 501 / 0.03 = 50,100 / 3 (equivalent problem) Solution: 16,700

5. 0.465 / 1.5 = 4.65 / 15 (equivalent problem) Solution: 0.31

6. Indy cars use about 1.3 gallons of fuel for each 2.5-mile lap. About how many miles per gallon is that?
1.92 miles/gallon (unit)

Math Journal, p. 32P

Student Page

Date Time

PROJECT 9 **Representing Remainders as Decimals**

Algorithm Project 9

You might write the answer to a problem such as 17 / 6 in two ways: 17 / 6 → 2 R5, or by rewriting the remainder as a fraction: 17 / 6 = $2\frac{5}{6}$.

With decimal long division, you can show the quotient as a decimal: 17 / 6 = $2.8\overline{3}$. The repeat bar means that the 3s repeat forever. But, in most situations, having infinitely many 3s is not practical, so answers are often rounded to some reasonable number of decimal places, usually two or three: 17 / 6 = 2.83, or 17 / 6 = 2.833.

Notice that 17 / 6 = 2.83 is not actually true. You can check this by multiplying 2.83 by 6. You won't get 17. But, for most practical purposes, 2.83 or 2.833 is close enough to 17 / 6 that most people aren't bothered by a rounded number model.

Complete the table.

Problem	Answer as: Quotient and Remainder	Mixed Number	Exact Decimal	Decimal Rounded to Hundredths
1. 17 / 6	2 R5	$2\frac{5}{6}$	$2.8\overline{3}$	2.83
2. 15 / 4	3 R3	$3\frac{3}{4}$	3.75	3.75
3. 5 / 8	0 R5	$\frac{5}{8}$	0.625	0.63
4. 17 / 3	5 R2	$5\frac{2}{3}$	$5.\overline{6}$	5.67
5. 56 / 9	6 R2	$6\frac{2}{9}$	$6.\overline{2}$	6.22

Math Journal, p. 33P

1 Doing the Project

Exploring Meanings for Decimal Division

(*Math Journal 1* or *2*, p. 32P)

Have partners solve Problem 1 on journal page 32P. When most students have finished, have volunteers explain their solutions. Use student responses to emphasize the following ideas:

▷ One way to think about division is as "How many ___ are in ___?"

▷ Think of missing factors. Given the area and one dimension of a rectangle, for example, we can use division to find the other dimension.

▷ Numbers in problems can be represented one way in the problem's number story and another way in the matching number model. For example, 10% in one of the number stories corresponds to 0.10 in the matching number model.

▷ The idea that multiplication makes bigger and division makes smaller, which many students have formed from their work with whole numbers, does not apply to multiplication and division by numbers less than 1.

Dividing with Decimal Divisors

(*Math Journal 1* or *2*, p. 32P)

Remind students of two key facts that may be used to solve division problems with **decimal divisors:**

- A fraction can be interpreted as a division problem, and vice versa.
- Multiplying the numerator and denominator of a fraction by the same nonzero number results in an equivalent fraction.

Write 27 / 0.3 = ? on the board or a transparency. Using division methods such as partial quotients and long division is cumbersome with decimal divisors. Ask students how they might use multiplication to rename the problem to an equivalent problem that is easier to solve.

27 / 0.3 can be thought of as $\frac{27}{0.3}$.

$\frac{27}{0.3} = \frac{27}{0.3} * \frac{10}{10} = \frac{270}{3}$

But $\frac{270}{3}$ can be thought of as 270 / 3.

So, 27 / 0.3 = 270 / 3.

The resulting problem, 270 / 3, is easier to solve than the original problem, 27 / 0.3, but has the same answer.

Work through similar problems until students understand the principle:

Multiplying the dividend and the divisor in a division problem by the same nonzero number does not change the quotient.

Suggestions:

▷ 45 / 0.9 $45 / 0.9 = \frac{45}{0.9} * \frac{10}{10} = \frac{450}{9} = 450 / 9 = 50$

▷ 12 / 0.03 $12 / 0.03 = \frac{12}{0.03} * \frac{100}{100} = \frac{1,200}{3} = 1,200 / 3 = 400$

▷ 105 / 0.015 $105 / 0.015 = \frac{105}{0.015} * \frac{1,000}{1,000} = \frac{105,000}{15} = 105,000 / 15 = 7,000$

Have students complete journal page 32P. Circulate and assist.

2 Extending the Project

▶ Using Long Division to Rename Fractions as Decimals

PARTNER ACTIVITY

(*Student Reference Book,* pp. 54I and 54J; *Math Journal,* p. 33P)

Have partners read *Student Reference Book,* pages 54I and 54J and then complete journal page 33P. When students have finished, discuss any difficulties or curiosities they encountered.

NOTE *Student Reference Book,* pages 54G and 54H provide a detailed step-by-step explanation of how to "clear decimals" in the divisor so that the long division algorithm can be applied. Other relevant *Student Reference Book* pages include page 37 (multiplication by powers of 10) and 60 (using multiplication to find equivalent fractions).

▶ Solving Division Problems

INDEPENDENT ACTIVITY

(Online Additional Practice, pp. 33A and 33B; *Student Reference Book,* pp. 42, 43, and 54E–54J)

Online practice pages 33A and 33B provide students with additional practice solving division problems. Use these pages as necessary.

Encourage students to use the focus algorithm (partial-quotients division) to solve the problems on practice page 33A. Invite them to use any algorithm they wish to solve the problems on the remaining page. Students may find the examples on *Student Reference Book,* pages 42, 43, and 54E–54J helpful.

Student Page

Decimals and Percents

U.S. Traditional Long Division: Renaming Fractions as Decimals

U.S. traditional long division can be used to rename fractions as decimals.

Did You Know?
Any whole number can be written as a decimal by attaching a decimal point and one or more 0s; the value of the number remains the same: 5 = 5.0.
With all decimal numbers, attaching one or more zeros to the right of the digit that is furthest to the right will not change the value of the number: 8.3 = 8.3000.

Example Use U.S. traditional long division to rename $\frac{5}{8}$ as a decimal.

Step 1: Write $\frac{5}{8}$ as a division problem. Write 5 with several 0s after the decimal point: 5.000. (You can always add more 0s if you need them.)
8)5.000

Step 2: Solve the division problem. Stop when the remainder is 0, or when you have enough precision for your purposes, or when you notice a repeating pattern.

```
   .625
8)5.000
 -4 8
    20
   -16
     40
    -40
      0
```

This division problem divided evenly in three decimal places.

$\frac{5}{8} = 0.625$

Student Reference Book, **p. 54I**

Go to www.everydaymathonline.com to access the additional practice pages.

Online Master

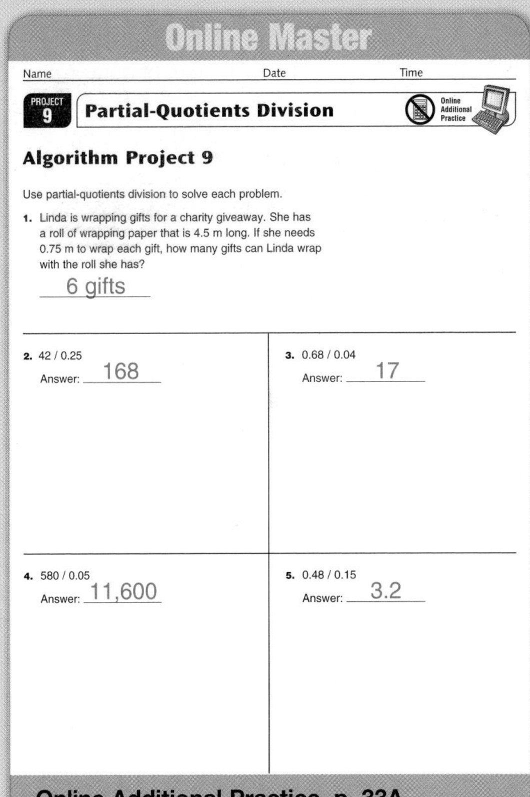
Name Date Time

PROJECT 9 **Partial-Quotients Division**

Online Additional Practice

Algorithm Project 9

Use partial-quotients division to solve each problem.

1. Linda is wrapping gifts for a charity giveaway. She has a roll of wrapping paper that is 4.5 m long. If she needs 0.75 m to wrap each gift, how many gifts can Linda wrap with the roll she has?
6 gifts

2. 42 / 0.25
Answer: 168

3. 0.68 / 0.04
Answer: 17

4. 580 / 0.05
Answer: 11,600

5. 0.48 / 0.15
Answer: 3.2

Online Additional Practice, p. 33A

Fifth Grade Key Vocabulary

For a more comprehensive glossary that includes additional entries and illustrations, please refer to the *Teacher's Reference Manual.*

NOTE: Within a definition, terms in italics are defined elsewhere in the glossary.

account balance An amount of money that you have or that you owe. See *"in the black"* and *"in the red."*

acute angle An angle with a measure less than 90°.

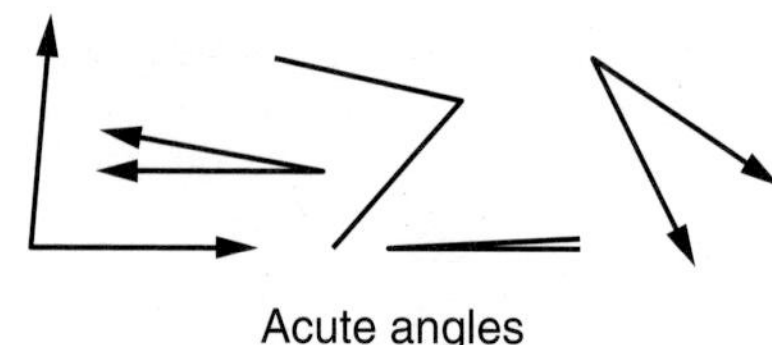

Acute angles

adjacent angles Two angles with a common side and *vertex* that do not otherwise overlap.

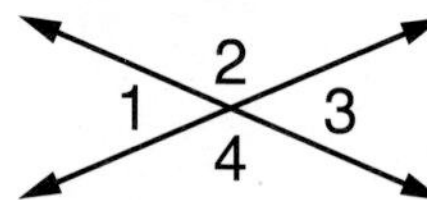

Angles 1 and 2, 2 and 3, 3 and 4, and 4 and 1 are pairs of adjacent angles.

adjacent sides (1) Two sides in a *polygon* that share a common *vertex.* (2) Two sides of a *polyhedron* with a common *edge.*

algebraic expression An *expression* that contains a *variable.* For example, if Maria is 2 inches taller than Joe and if the variable M represents Maria's height, then the algebraic expression $M - 2$ represents Joe's height.

algorithm A set of step-by-step instructions for doing something, such as carrying out a computation or solving a problem. The most common algorithms are those for basic arithmetic computation, but there are many others. Some mathematicians and many computer scientists spend a great deal of time trying to find more efficient algorithms for solving problems.

apex In a *pyramid* or *cone,* the *vertex* opposite the *base.* In a pyramid, all the nonbase faces meet at the apex.

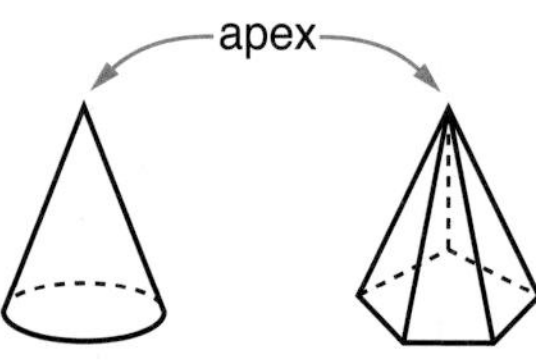

arc of a circle A part of a circle between and including two endpoints on the circle. For example, the endpoints of the *diameter* of a circle define an arc called a semicircle. An arc is named by its endpoints.

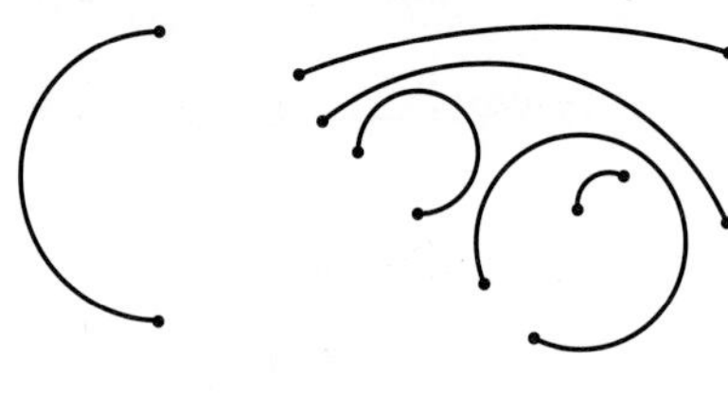

Arcs

area The amount of *surface* inside a 2-dimensional figure. The figure might be a triangle or rectangle in a plane, the curved surface of a *cylinder,* or a state or country on Earth's surface. Commonly, area is measured in *square units* such as square miles, square inches, or square centimeters.

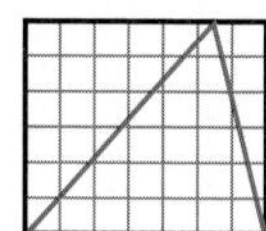

A triangle with area 21 square units

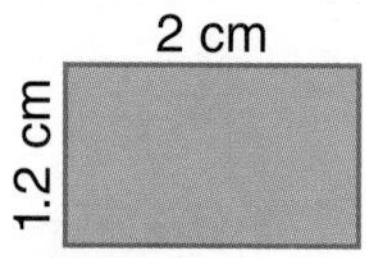

A rectangle with area 1.2 cm * 2 cm = 2.4 square centimeters

The area of the United States is about 3,800,000 square miles.

area model (1) A model for multiplication in which the length and width of a rectangle represent the *factors,* and the *area* of the rectangle represents the *product.*

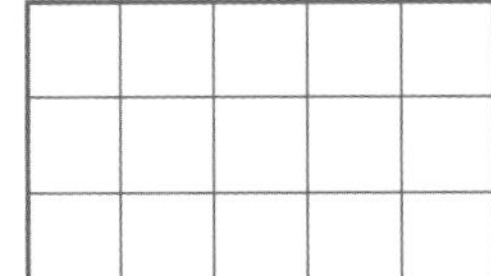

Area model for $3 * 5 = 15$

(2) A model showing fractions as parts of a whole. The *whole* is a region, such as a circle or a rectangle, representing the number *ONE.*

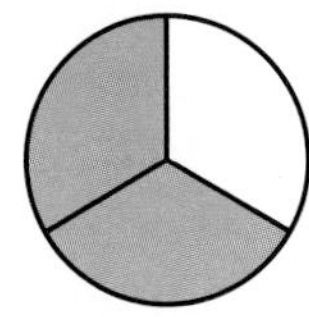

Area model for $\frac{2}{3}$

Associative Property A property of addition and multiplication (but not of subtraction or division) that says that when you add or multiply three numbers, it does not matter which two you add or multiply first. For example:

$$(4 + 3) + 7 = 4 + (3 + 7)$$

and

$$(5 * 8) * 9 = 5 * (8 * 9)$$

attribute blocks A set of blocks in which each block has one each of four attributes including color, size, thickness, and shape. The blocks are used for attribute identification and sorting activities. Compare to *pattern blocks.*

axis of a coordinate grid Either of the two number lines used to form a *coordinate grid.* Plural is axes.

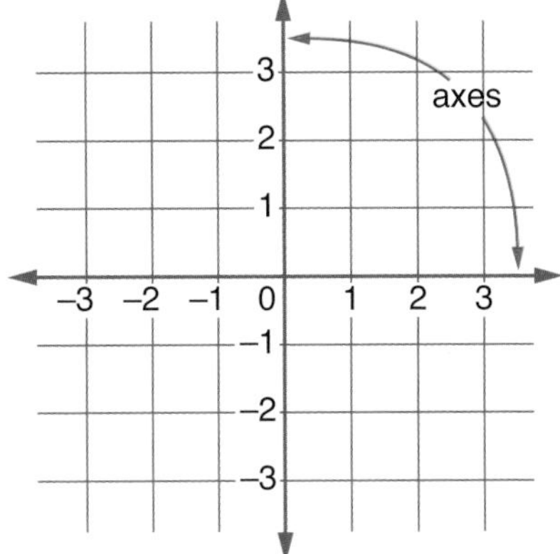

axis of rotation A line about which a solid figure rotates.

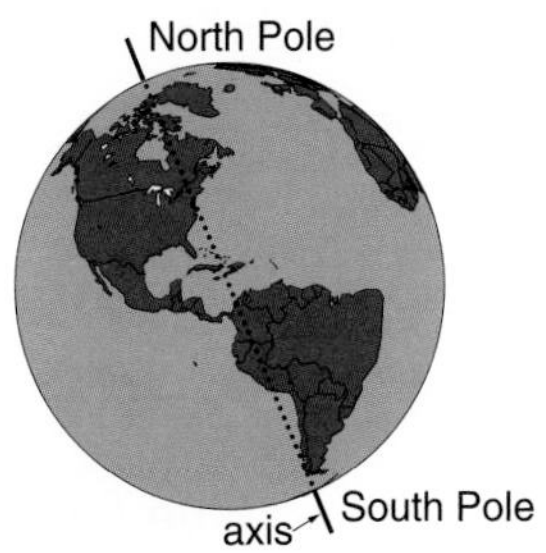

B

ballpark estimate A rough *estimate;* "in the ballpark." A ballpark estimate can serve as a check of the reasonableness of an answer obtained through some other procedure, or it can be made when an exact value is unnecessary or is impossible to obtain.

bar graph A graph with *horizontal* or *vertical* bars that represent data.

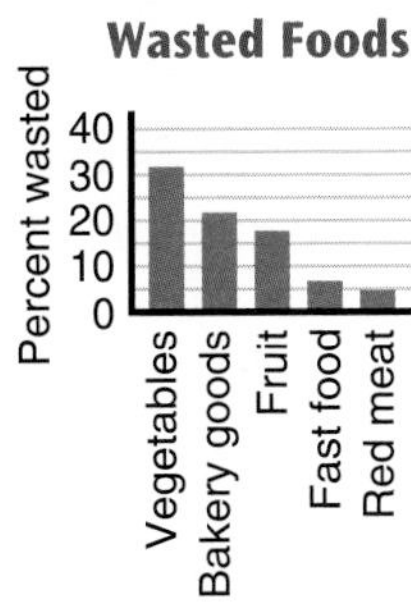

Source: *The Garbage Product*

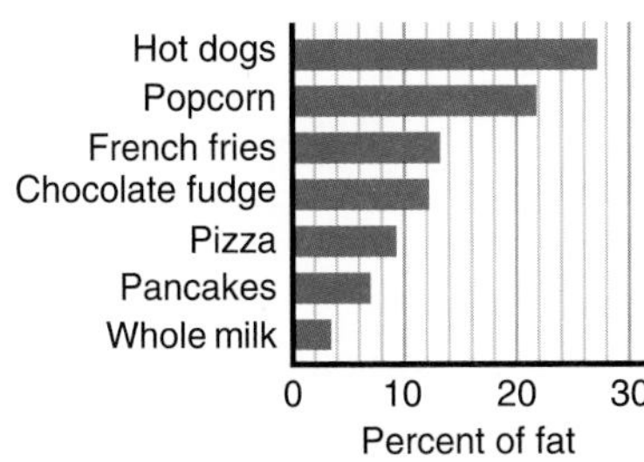

Source: *The New York Public Library Desk Reference*

base (in exponential notation) A number that is raised to a *power.* For example, the base in 5^3 is 5.

base of a parallelogram (1) The side of a *parallelogram* to which an altitude is drawn. (2) The *length* of this side. The *area* of a parallelogram is the length of the base times the altitude or *height perpendicular* to it.

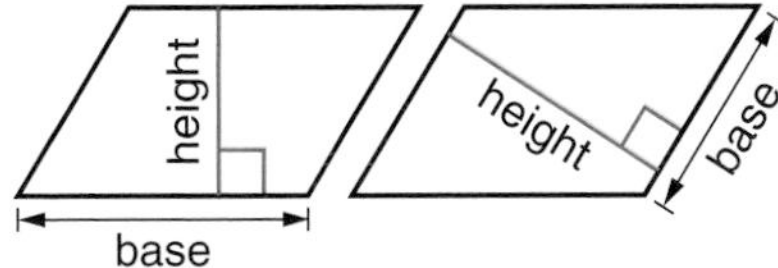

base of a prism or cylinder Either of the two parallel and congruent *faces* that define the shape of a *prism* or *cylinder.* In a cylinder, the base is a circle.

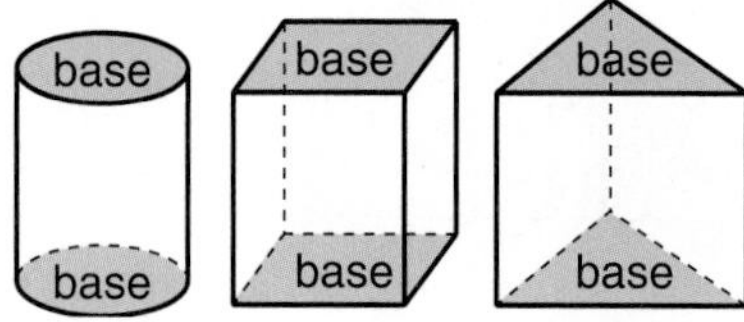

base of a pyramid or cone The *face* of a *pyramid* or *cone* that is opposite its *apex.* The base of a cone is a circle.

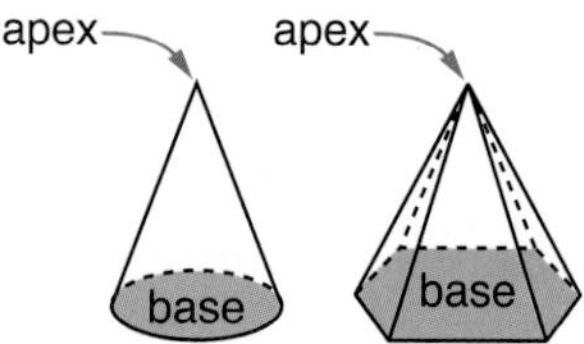

base of a rectangle (1) One of the sides of a rectangle. (2) The *length* of this side. The *area* of a rectangle is the length of the base times the altitude, or *height.*

base of a triangle (1) Any side of a triangle to which an *altitude* is drawn. (2) The *length* of this side. The *area* of a triangle is half the length of the base times the altitude, or *height.*

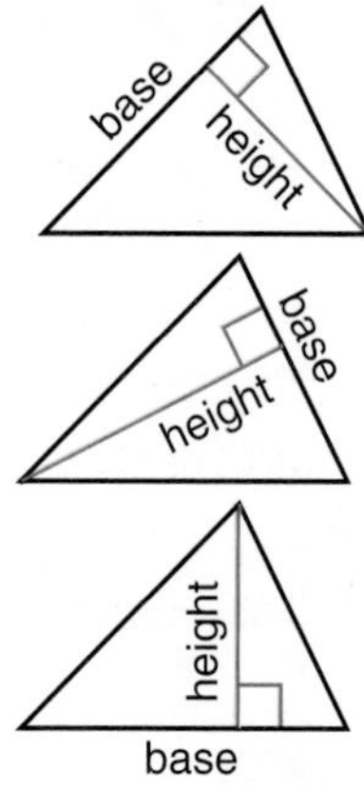

base-10 blocks A set of blocks to represent ones, tens, hundreds, and thousands in the base-10 *place-value* system. In *Everyday Mathematics,* the unit block, or *cube,* has 1-cm edges; the ten block, or long, is 10 unit blocks in *length;* the hundred block, or flat, is 10 longs in width; and the thousand block, or big cube, is 10 flats high.

benchmark A well-known count or measure that can be used to evaluate the reasonableness of other counts, measures, or estimates. The benchmarks often used when estimating with fractions are 0, $\frac{1}{2}$, and 1.

biased sample A *sample* that does not fairly represent the total *population* from which it was selected. A sample is biased if every member of the population does not have the same chance of being selected for the sample.

calibrate (1) To divide or mark a measuring tool with gradations, such as the degree marks on a *thermometer.* (2) To test and adjust the accuracy of a measuring tool.

capacity (1) The amount of space occupied by a 3-dimensional figure. Same as *volume.* The amount a container can hold. Capacity is often measured in *units* such as *quarts,* gallons, *cups,* or *liters.* (2) The maximum weight a scale can measure.

census An official count of population and the recording of other demographic data such as age, gender, income, and education.

center of a circle The point in the plane of a circle equally distant from all points on the circle.

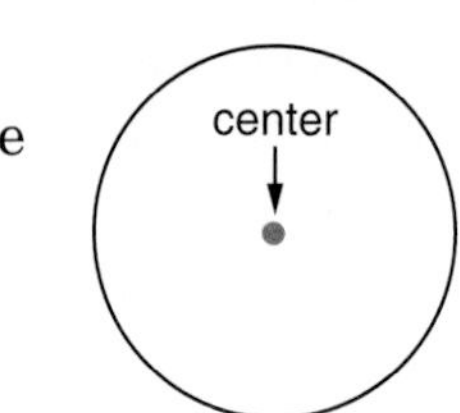

century One hundred years.

change diagram A diagram used in *Everyday Mathematics* to model situations in which quantities are either increased or decreased by addition or subtraction. The diagram includes a starting quantity, an ending quantity, and an amount of change.

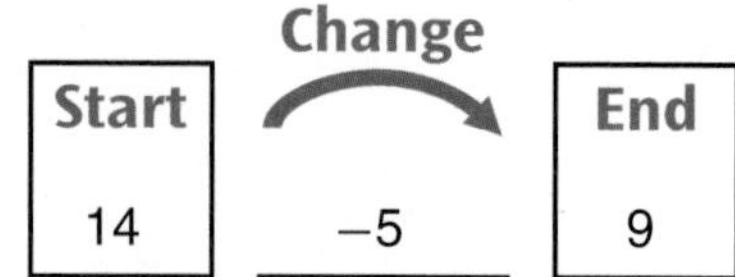

A change diagram for 14 − 5 = 9

change-to-less story A number story about a change situation in which the ending quantity is less than the starting quantity. For example, a story about spending money is a change-to-less story. Compare to *change-to-more story.*

change-to-more story A number story about a change situation in which the ending quantity is more than the starting quantity. For example, a story about earning money is a change-to-more story. Compare to *change-to-less story.*

circle graph A graph in which a circle and its interior are divided into *sectors* corresponding to parts of a set of data. The whole circle represents the whole set of data. Same as *pie graph* and sometimes called a pie chart.

circumference The distance around a circle; its *perimeter.* The circumference of a *sphere* is the circumference of a circle on the sphere with the same center as the sphere.

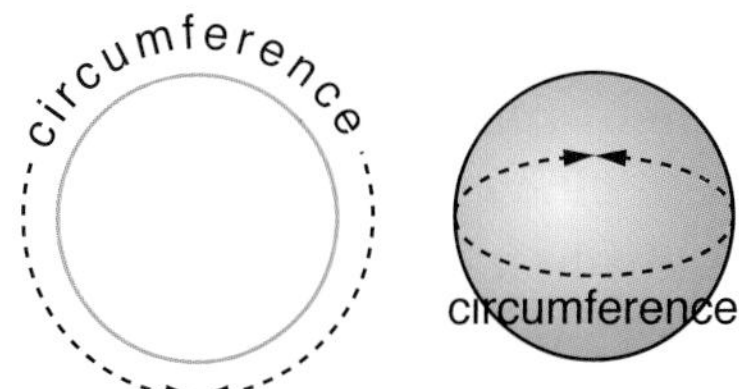

coefficient The number, or constant, *factor* in a *variable* term in an *expression.* For example, in $3c + 8d$, 3 and 8 are coefficients.

column addition An addition *algorithm* in which the addends' *digits* are first added in each *place-value* column separately, and then 10-for-1 trades are made until each column has only one digit. Lines may be drawn to separate the place-value columns.

combine like terms To rewrite the sum or difference of like terms as a single term. For example, $5a + 6a$ can be rewritten as $11a$, because $5a + 6a = (5 + 6)a = 11a$. Similarly, $16t - 3t = 13t$.

common denominator A nonzero number that is a multiple of the *denominators* of two or more fractions. For example, the fractions $\frac{1}{2}$ and $\frac{2}{3}$ have common denominators 6, 12, 18, and other multiples of 6. Fractions with the same denominator already have a common denominator.

common factor A *factor* of each of two or more counting numbers. For example, 4 is a common factor of 8 and 12.

Commutative Property of Multiplication A property of multiplication that two numbers can be multiplied in either order without changing the *product.* For example, $5 * 10 = 10 * 5$. In *Everyday Mathematics,* this is called a turn-around fact, and the two Commutative Properties are called *turn-around rules.* In symbols:

For any numbers a and b, $a * b = b * a$.

Division is not commutative. For example, $10 / 5 \neq 5 / 10$ because $2 \neq \frac{1}{2}$.

complement of a number *n* (1) In *Everyday Mathematics,* the *difference* between n and the next multiple of 10. For example, the complement of 4 is $10 - 4 = 6$ and the complement of 73 is $80 - 73 = 7$. (2) The difference between n and the next higher *power of 10.* In this definition, the complement of 73 is $100 - 73 = 27$.

composite number A counting number greater than 1 that has more than two *factors.* For example, 10 is a composite number because it has four factors: 1, 2, 5, and 10. A composite number is divisible by at least three whole numbers. Compare to *prime number.*

cone A *geometric solid* with a circular *base,* a *vertex* called an *apex* not in the plane of the base, and all of the line segments with one endpoint at the apex and the other endpoint on the *circumference* of the base.

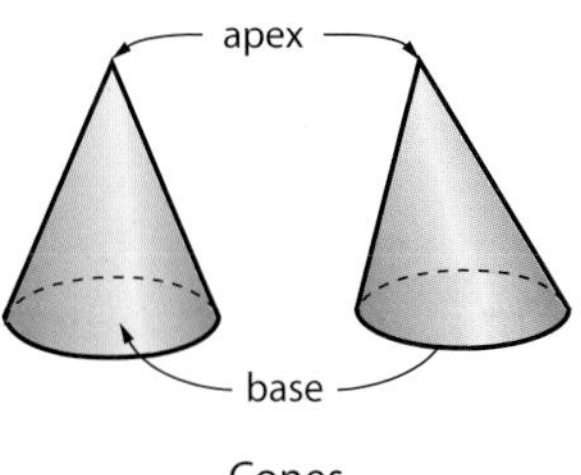

Cones

congruent figures (≅) Figures having the same size and shape. Two figures are congruent if they match exactly when one is placed on top of the other after a combination of *slides,* flips, and/or turns. In diagrams of congruent figures, the corresponding congruent sides may be marked with the same number of hash marks. The symbol ≅ means "is congruent to."

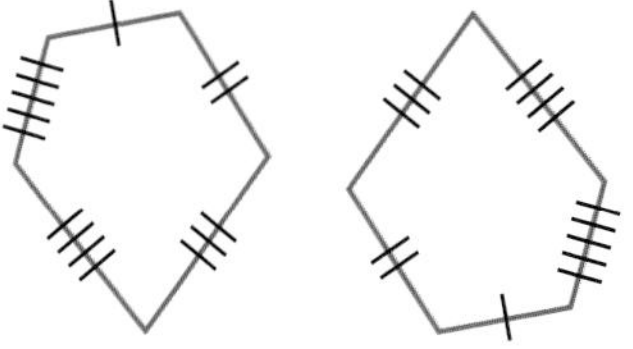
Congruent pentagons

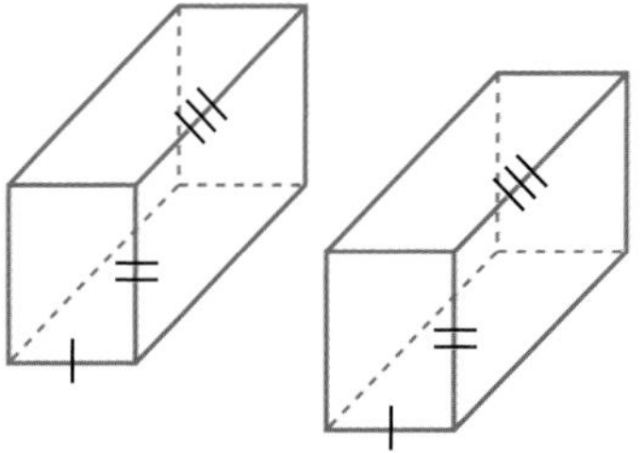
Congruent prisms

contour line A curve on a map through places where a measurement such as temperature, elevation, air pressure, or growing season is the same. Contour lines often separate regions that have been differently colored to show a range of conditions. See *contour map.*

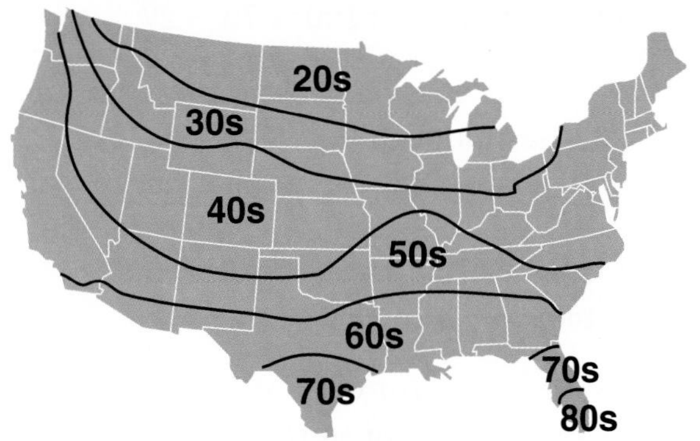

A contour map

contour map A map that uses *contour lines* to indicate areas having a particular feature, such as elevation or climate.

coordinate (1) A number used to locate a point on a number line; a point's distance from an *origin.* (2) One of the numbers in an *ordered pair* or triple that locates a point on a *coordinate grid* or in coordinate space, respectively.

coordinate grid (rectangular coordinate grid) A reference frame for locating points in a plane by means of *ordered pairs* of numbers. A rectangular coordinate grid is formed by two number lines that intersect at *right angles* at their zero points.

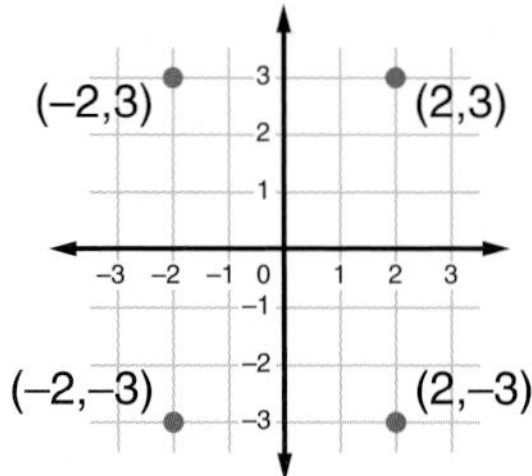

A coordinate grid

cube (1) A regular *polyhedron* with 6 square *faces.* A cube has 8 *vertices* and 12 *edges.*

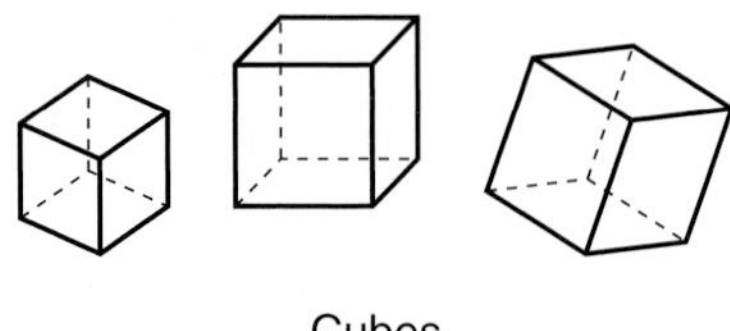

Cubes

(2) In *Everyday Mathematics,* the smaller cube of the *base-10 blocks,* measuring 1 cm on each edge.

cube of a number The *product* of a number used as a *factor* three times. For example, the cube of 5 is $5 * 5 * 5 = 5^3 = 125$.

cubic centimeter (cc or cm^3) A metric *unit* of *volume* or *capacity* equal to the volume of a *cube* with 1-cm edges. 1 cm^3 = 1 milliliter (mL).

cubic unit A *unit* such as *cubic centimeters,* cubic inches, cubic feet, and cubic meters used to measure *volume* or *capacity.*

cubit An ancient *unit* of *length,* measured from the point of the elbow to the end of the middle finger. The cubit has been standardized at various times between 18 and 22 inches. The Latin word "cubitum" means elbow.

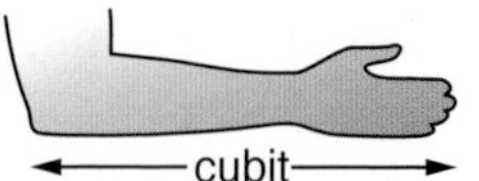

cup (c) A U.S. customary *unit* of *volume* or *capacity* equal to 8 fluid ounces or $\frac{1}{2}$ pint.

curved surface A 2-dimensional surface that does not lie in a plane. *Spheres, cylinders,* and *cones* each have one curved surface.

cylinder A *geometric solid* with two congruent, parallel circular regions for *bases* and a curved *face* formed by all the segments with an endpoint on each circle that are parallel to a segment with endpoints at the centers of the circles. Also called a circular cylinder.

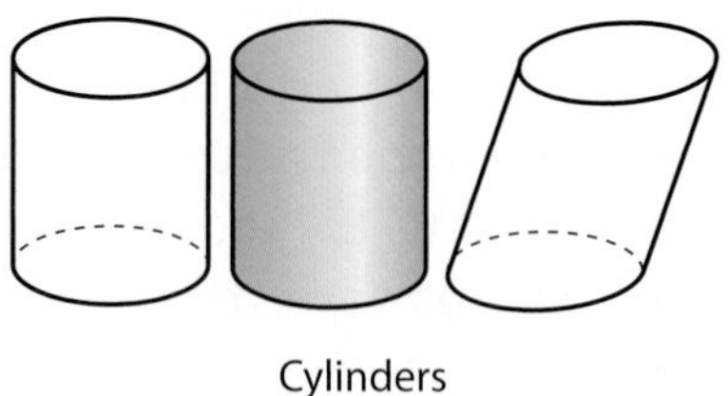

Cylinders

D

data bank (1) In *Third Grade Everyday Mathematics,* a collection of data sets presented in posters, tables, graphs, and maps. (2) In general, any established data set or database.

debit An amount subtracted from a bank balance; a withdrawal.

decade Ten years.

decimal point A mark used to separate the ones and tenths places in decimals. A decimal point separates dollars from cents in *dollars-and-cents notation.* The mark is a dot in the U.S. customary system and a comma in Europe and some other countries.

denominator The nonzero divisor b in a fraction $\frac{a}{b}$ and a/b. In a part-whole fraction, the denominator is the number of equal parts into which the *whole,* or ONE, has been divided. Compare to *numerator.*

diameter (1) A line segment that passes through the *center of a circle* or *sphere* and has endpoints on the circle or *sphere.* (2) The *length* of such a segment. The *diameter* of a circle or sphere is twice the length of the *radius.*

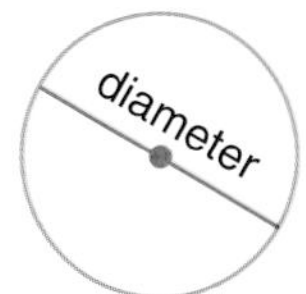

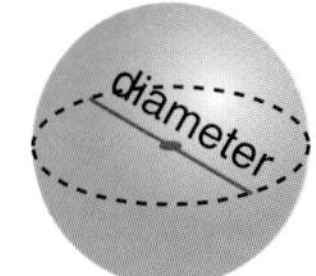

difference The result of subtracting one number from another. For example, the difference of 12 and 5 is $12 - 5 = 7$.

digit (1) Any one of the symbols 0, 1, 2, 3, 4, 5, 6, 7, 8, and 9 in the base-10 numeration system. For example, the numeral 145 is made up of the digits 1, 4, and 5. (2) Any one of the symbols in any number system. For example, A, B, C, D, E, and F are digits along with 0–9 in the base-16 notation used in some computer programming.

discount The amount by which a price of an item is reduced in a sale, usually given as a fraction or *percent* of the original price or as a percent off. For example, a \$4 item on sale for \$3 is discounted to 75% or $\frac{3}{4}$ of its original price. A \$10.00 item at 10% off costs \$9.00, or $\frac{1}{10}$ less than the usual price.

displacement method A method for estimating the *volume* of an object by submerging it in water and then measuring the volume of water it displaces. The method is especially useful for finding the volume of an irregularly shaped object. Archimedes of Syracuse (circa 287–212 B.C.) is famous for having solved a problem of finding the volume and density of a king's crown by noticing how his body displaced water in a bathtub and applying the method to the crown. He reportedly shouted "Eureka!" at the discovery, so similar insights are today sometimes called "Eureka moments."

Distributive Property A property that relates multiplication and addition or subtraction. This property gets its name because it "distributes" a factor over terms inside parentheses.

Distributive Property of Multiplication over Addition:

$$a * (b + c) = (a * b) + (b * c),$$
$$\text{so } 2 * (5 + 3) = (2 * 5) + (2 * 3) = 10 + 6 = 16.$$

Distributive Property of Multiplication over Subtraction:

$$a * (b - c) = (a * b) - (b * c),$$
$$\text{so } 2 * (5 - 3) = (2 * 5) - (2 * 3) = 10 - 6 = 4.$$

dividend The number in division that is being divided. For example, in 35 / 5 = 7, the dividend is 35.

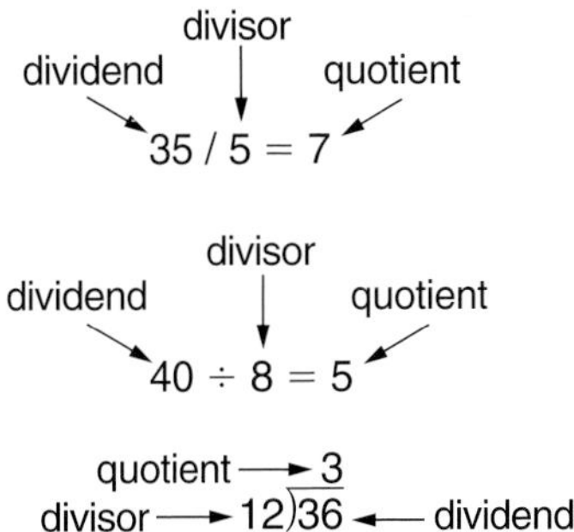

divisibility rule A shortcut for determining whether a counting number is *divisible by* another counting number without actually doing the division. For example, a number is divisible by 5 if the *digit* in the ones place is 0 or 5. A number is divisible by 3 if the sum of its digits is divisible by 3.

divisibility test A test to see if a *divisibility rule* applies to a particular number.

divisible by If the larger of two counting numbers can be divided by the smaller with no *remainder,* then the larger is divisible by the smaller. For example, 28 is divisible by 7, because 28 / 7 = 4 with no remainder. If a number n is divisible by a number d, then d is a *factor* of n. Every whole number except 0 is divisible by itself.

divisor In division, the number that divides another number, the *dividend.* For example, in 35 / 7 = 5, the divisor is 7.

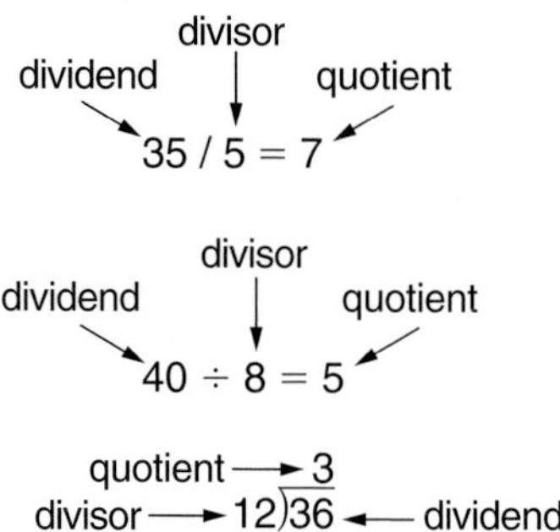

dollars-and-cents notation The U.S. customary notation for writing amounts of money as a number of dollars and hundredths of dollars (cents). The decimal is preceded by the $ symbol, as in $8.98, meaning "eight dollars and 98 cents."

double-stem plot A *stem-and-leaf plot* in which each stem is split into two parts. Numbers on the original stem ending in 0–4 are plotted on one half of the split, and numbers ending in 5–9 are plotted on the other half. Double-stem plots are useful if the original stem-and-leaf plot has many leaves falling on few stems. The following plot shows eruption duration in minutes of the Old Faithful Geyser. For example, the first two stems show one observation each of durations lasting 42, 44, 45, 48, and 49 minutes.

Eruption Duration of Old Faithful (minutes)

Stems (tens)	Leaves (ones)
4	2 4
4	5 8 9
5	0 1 1 1 3 3 3 4
5	5 5 6 6 7 7 8
6	0 1 1
6	6 7 7 8 8 9
7	0 0 1 1 2 2 3 3 4 4
7	5 5 6 6 6 7 7 8 8 9 9 9
8	0 0 1 1 1 2 2 3 3 4 4 4
8	5 6 6 6 6 8 8 9
9	
9	

A double-stem plot

edge (1) Any side of a *polyhedron's faces.* (2) A line segment or curve where two *surfaces* of a *geometric solid* meet.

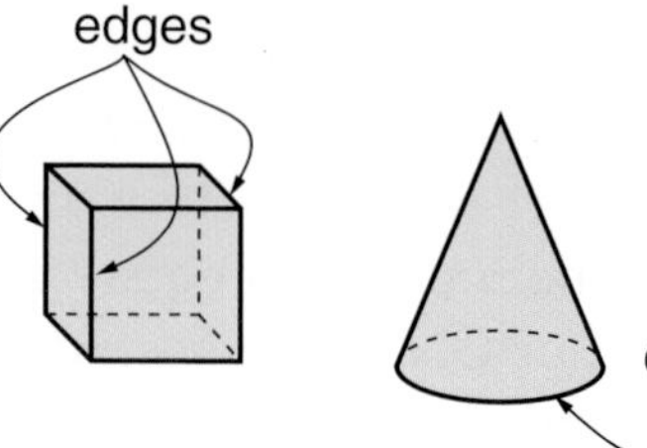

elapsed time The *difference* in two times. For example, between 12:45 P.M. and 1:30 P.M., 45 minutes have elapsed.

equal The same in value but possibly in a different form. For example, $\frac{1}{2}$, 0.5, and 50% are all equivalent.

equal parts Equivalent parts of a *whole.* For example, dividing a pizza into 4 equal parts means each part is $\frac{1}{4}$ of the pizza and is equal in size to the other 3 parts.

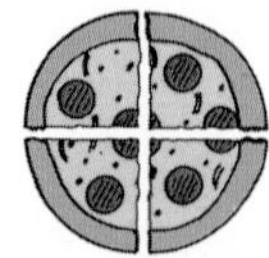

4 equal parts, each $\frac{1}{4}$ of a pizza

equally likely outcomes Outcomes of a chance experiment or situation that have the same *probability* of happening. If all the possible outcomes are equally likely, then the probability of an event is equal to:

$$\frac{\text{number of favorable outcomes}}{\text{number of possible outcomes}}$$

equation A *number sentence* that contains an equal sign. For example, $5 + 10 = 15$ and $P = 2l + 2w$ are equations.

equilateral polygon A *polygon* in which all sides are the same *length.*

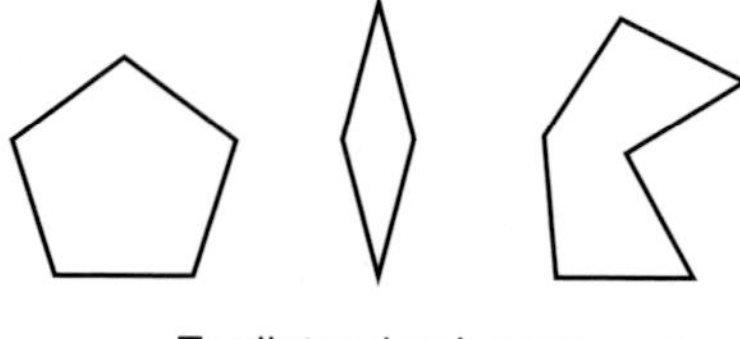

Equilateral polygons

equilateral triangle A triangle with all three sides equal in *length*. Each angle of an equilateral triangle measures 60°, so it is also called an equiangular triangle.

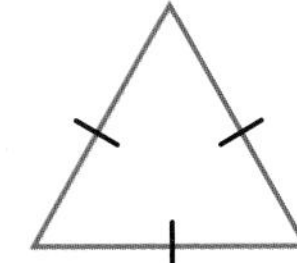

An equilateral triangle

equivalent fractions Fractions with different *denominators* that name the same number.

estimate (1) An answer close to, or approximating, an exact answer. (2) To make an estimate.

even number (1) A counting number that is *divisible by* 2. (2) An integer that is divisible by 2. Compare to *odd number*.

expanded notation A way of writing a number as the sum of the values of each *digit*. For example, 356 is 300 + 50 + 6 in expanded notation. Compare to *number-and-word notation, scientific notation,* and *standard notation*.

exponent A small raised number used in *exponential notation* to tell how many times the *base* is used as a *factor*. For example, in 5^3, the base is 5, the exponent is 3, and $5^3 = 5 * 5 * 5 = 125$. Same as *power*.

exponential notation A way of representing repeated multiplication by the same *factor*. For example, 2^3 is exponential notation for $2 * 2 * 2$. The *exponent* 3 tells how many times the *base* 2 is used as a factor.

2^3 ← exponent

↑ base

expression (1) A mathematical phrase made up of numbers, *variables, operation symbols,* and/or grouping symbols. An expression does not contain *relation symbols* such as =, >, and ≤. (2) Either side of an *equation* or inequality.

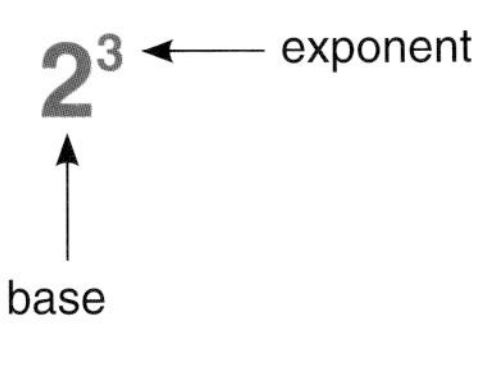

Expressions

F

face (1) In *Everyday Mathematics,* a flat *surface* on a 3-dimensional shape. Some special faces are called *bases*. (2) More generally, any 2-dimensional surface on a 3-dimensional shape.

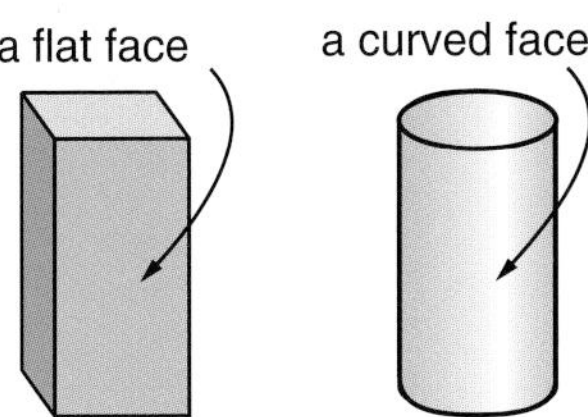

fact power In *Everyday Mathematics,* the ability to automatically recall basic arithmetic facts. Knowing the facts automatically is as important to arithmetic as knowing words by sight is to reading.

factor (1) Each of the two or more numbers in a *product*. For example, in $6 * 0.5$, 6 and 0.5 are factors. (2) To represent a number as a product of factors. For example, factor 21 by rewriting as $7 * 3$.

factor pair Two *factors* of a counting number *n* whose product is *n*. A number may have more than one factor pair. For example, the factor pairs for 18 are 1 and 18, 2 and 9, and 3 and 6.

factor rainbow A way to show *factor pairs* in a list of all the *factors* of a number. A factor rainbow can be used to check whether a list of factors is correct.

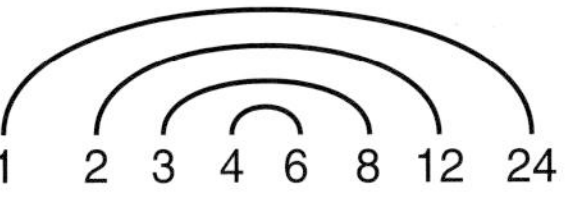

A factor rainbow for 24

factor string A counting number written as a *product* of two or more of its counting-number *factors* other than 1. The *length of a factor string* is the number of factors in the string. For example, $2 * 3 * 4$ is a factor string for 24 with length 3. By convention, $1 * 2 * 3 * 4$ is not a factor string for 24 because it contains the number 1.

factor tree A way to get the *prime factorization* of a counting number. Write the original number as a *product* of *factors.* Then write each of these factors as a product of factors, and continue until the factors are all *prime numbers.* A factor tree looks like an upside-down tree, with the root (the original number) at the top and the leaves (the factors) beneath it. See *tree diagram.*

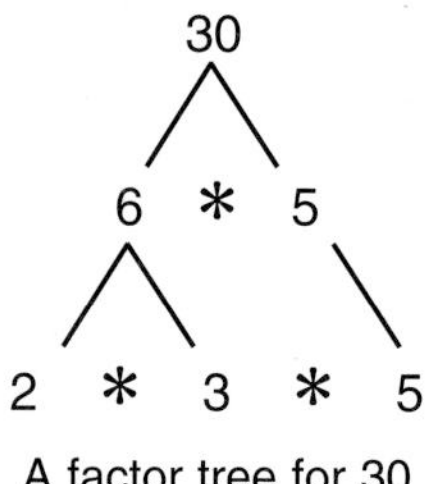

A factor tree for 30

fair game A game in which every player has the same chance of winning.

false number sentence A *number sentence* that is not true. For example, $8 = 5 + 5$ is a false number sentence. Compare to *true number sentence.*

fathom A *unit* of *length* equal to 6 feet, or 2 yards. It is used mainly by people who work with boats and ships to measure depths underwater and lengths of cables.

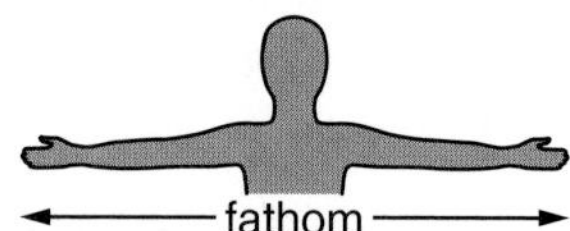

flat surface A *surface* contained entirely in one plane.

formula A general rule for finding the value of something. A formula is usually an *equation* with quantities represented by letter *variables.* For example, a formula for distance traveled d at a rate r over a time t is $d = r * t$. The *area* of a triangle A with base length b and height h is given below.

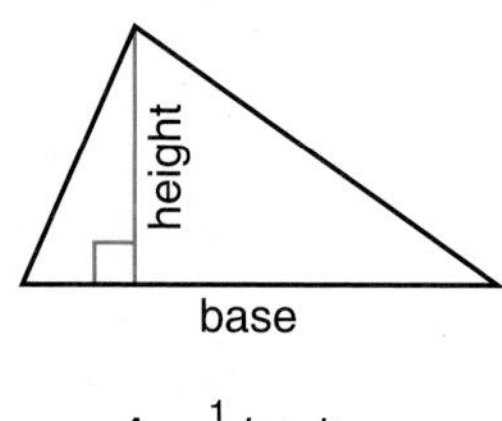

$$A = \frac{1}{2}b * h$$

fraction stick In *Fifth* and *Sixth Grade Everyday Mathematics,* a diagram used to represent simple fractions.

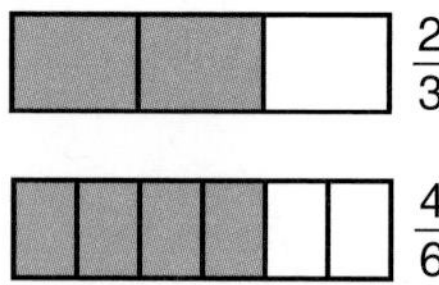

fractional part Part of a *whole.* Fractions represent fractional parts of numbers, sets, or objects.

frequency (1) The number of times a value occurs in a set of data. (2) A number of repetitions per *unit* of time. For example, the vibrations per second in a sound wave.

frequency graph A graph showing how often each value occurs in a data set.

Colors in a Bag of Gumdrops

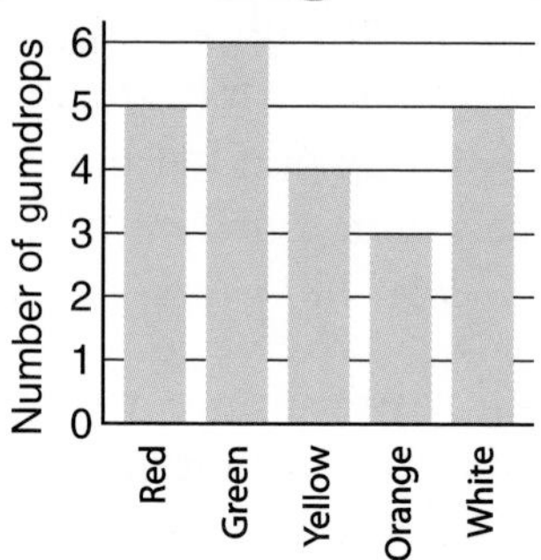

frequency table A table in which data are tallied and organized, often as a first step toward making a *frequency graph.*

Color	Number of Gumdrops
Red	~~////~~
Green	~~////~~ /
Yellow	////
Orange	///
White	~~////~~

generate a random number To produce a random number by such methods as drawing a card without looking from a shuffled deck, rolling a fair die, and flicking a fair spinner. In *Everyday Mathematics,* random numbers are commonly generated in games.

geoboard A manipulative 2-dimensional *coordinate* system made with nails or other posts at equally-spaced intervals relative to both axes. Students loop rubber bands around the posts to make *polygons* and other shapes.

geometric solid The *surface* or surfaces that make up a 3-dimensional figure such as a *prism, pyramid, cylinder, cone,* or *sphere.* Despite its name, a geometric solid is hollow, that is, it does not include the points in its interior. Informally, and in some dictionaries, a solid is defined as both the surface and its interior.

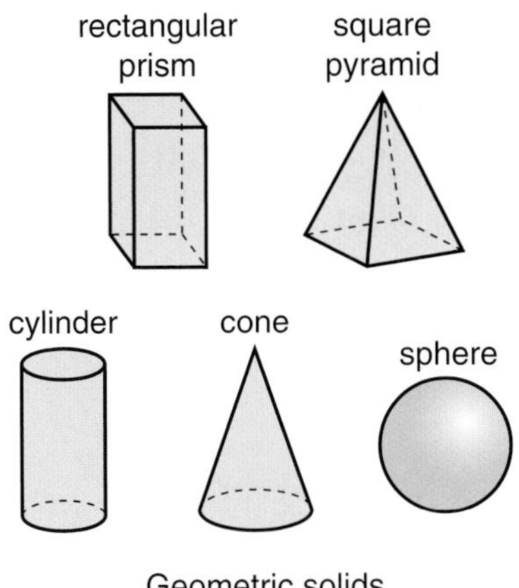

Geometric solids

Geometry Template A *Fourth* through *Sixth Grade Everyday Mathematics* tool that includes a millimeter ruler, a ruler with $\frac{1}{16}$-inch intervals, half-circle and full-circle protractors, a *Percent Circle, pattern-block* shapes, and other geometric figures. The template can also be used as a compass.

greatest common factor (GCF) The largest *factor* that two or more counting numbers have in common. For example, the common factors of 24 and 36 are 1, 2, 3, 4, 6, and 12, and their greatest common factor is 12.

great span The distance from the tip of the thumb to the tip of the little finger (pinkie), when the hand is stretched as far as possible. The great span averages about 9 inches for adults. Compare to *normal span.*

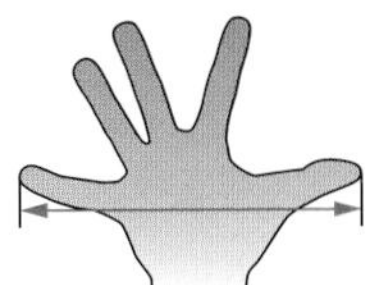

Great span

height (altitude) (1) In *Everyday Mathematics,* same as height of a figure. See *height of a parallelogram, height of a rectangle, height of a prism or cylinder, height of a pyramid or cone,* and *height of a triangle.*

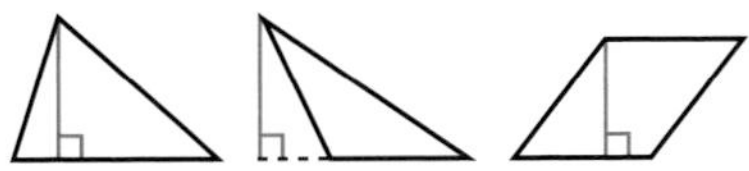

Altitudes of 2-D figures are shown in red.

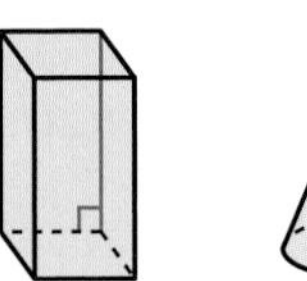
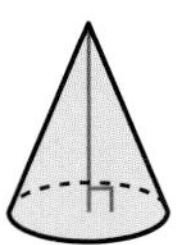

Altitudes of 3-D figures are shown in red.

(2) Distance above sea level.

height of a parallelogram (1) The *length* of the shortest line segment between a *base of a parallelogram* and the line containing the opposite side. The height is *perpendicular* to the base. (2) The line segment itself. See *base of a parallelogram.*

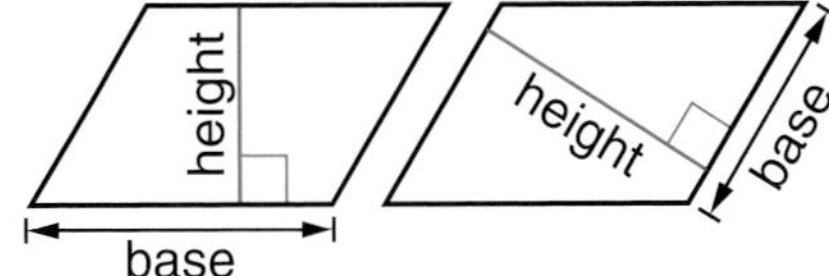

height of a prism or cylinder (1) The *length* of the shortest line segment from a *base of a prism or cylinder* to the plane containing the opposite base. The height is *perpendicular* to the bases. (2) The line segment itself.

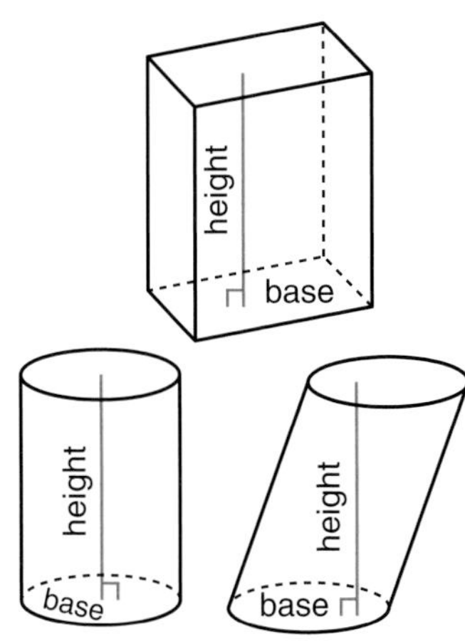

height of a pyramid or cone (1) The *length* of the shortest line segment from the *apex* of a *pyramid* or *cone* to the plane containing the *base.* The height is *perpendicular* to the *base.* (2) The line segment itself.

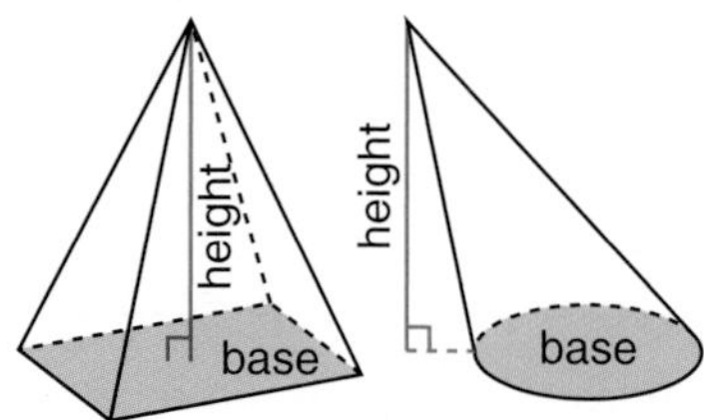

height of a rectangle The *length* of a side *perpendicular* to a *base of a rectangle.*

height of a triangle (1) The *length* of the shortest segment from a *vertex* of a triangle to the line containing the opposite side. The height is *perpendicular to the base.* (2) The line segment itself. *See base of a triangle.*

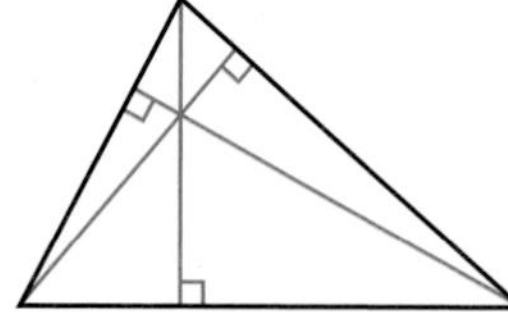

The heights of the triangle are indicated in red.

horizontal In a left-to-right orientation. Parallel to the horizon. Compare to *vertical.*

improper fraction A fraction with a *numerator* that is greater than or equal to its *denominator.* For example, $\frac{4}{3}$, $\frac{5}{2}$, $\frac{4}{4}$, and $\frac{24}{12}$ are improper fractions. In *Everyday Mathematics,* improper fractions are sometimes called "top-heavy" fractions.

instance of a pattern In *Everyday Mathematics,* a specific example of a general pattern. For example, $6 + 6 = 12$ is a special case of $y + y = 2y$ and $9 = 4.5 * 2$ is a special case of $A = l * w$.

interest A charge for using someone else's money. Interest is usually a *percent* of the amount borrowed.

interpolate To *estimate* an unknown value of a function between known values. Graphs are useful tools for interpolation.

"in the black" Having a positive *account balance;* having more money than is owed.

"in the red" Having a negative *account balance;* owing more money than is available.

irrational numbers Numbers that cannot be written as fractions where both the *numerator* and *denominator* are integers and the denominator is not zero. For example, $\sqrt{2}$ and π are irrational numbers. An irrational number can be written as a nonterminating, nonrepeating decimal. For example, $\pi = 3.141592653\ldots$ continues forever without any known pattern. The number 1.10100100010000 . . . is irrational because its pattern does not repeat.

irregular polygon A *polygon* with sides of different *lengths* or angles of different measures.

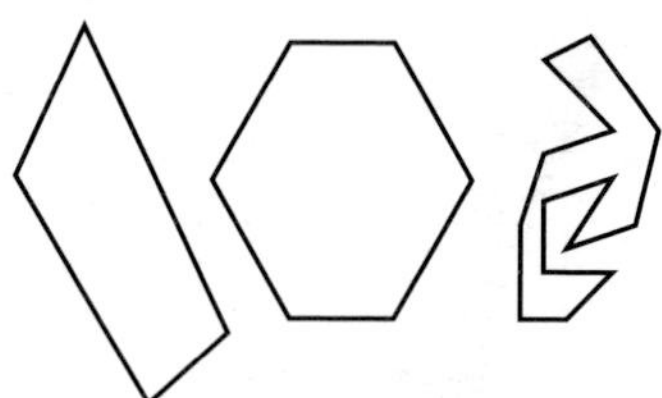

Irregular polygons

isosceles triangle A triangle with at least two sides equal in *length.* Angles opposite the congruent sides are congruent to each other.

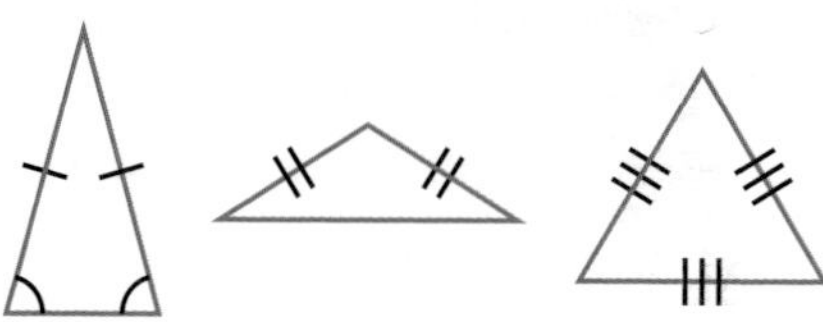

Isosceles triangles

kite A quadrilateral with two distinct pairs of adjacent sides of equal *length.* In *Everyday Mathematics,* the four sides cannot all have equal length; that is, a rhombus is not a kite. The diagonals of a kite are *perpendicular.*

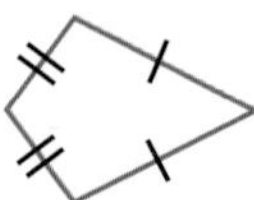

A kite

landmark In *Everyday Mathematics,* a notable feature of a data set. Landmarks include the *median, mode, mean, maximum, minimum,* and *range.*

latitude A degree measure locating a place on Earth north or south of the equator. A location at 0° latitude is on the equator. The North Pole is at 90° north latitude, and the South Pole is at 90° south latitude. Compare to *longitude.* See *lines of latitude.*

lattice multiplication A very old *algorithm* for multiplying multidigit numbers that requires only basic multiplication facts and addition of 1-digit numbers in a lattice diagram.

least common multiple (LCM) The smallest number that is a multiple of two or more given numbers. For example, common multiples of 6 and 8 include 24, 48, and 72. The least common multiple of 6 and 8 is 24.

length The distance between two points on a 1-dimensional figure. For example, the figure might be a line segment, *arc,* or a hiking path. Length is measured in *units* such as inches, kilometers, and miles.

length of a factor string The number of factors in a *factor string.*

line graph A graph in which data points are connected by line segments.

line plot A sketch of data in which check marks, Xs, or other symbols above a labeled line show the *frequency* of each value.

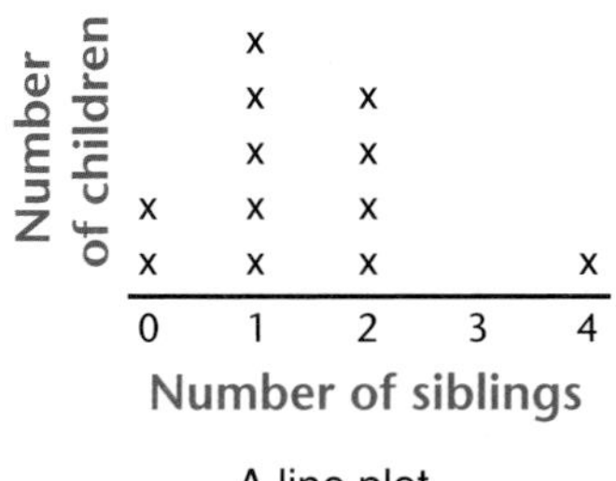

A line plot

lines of latitude Lines of constant *latitude* drawn on a 2-dimensional map or circles of constant latitude drawn on a globe. Lines of latitude are also called "parallels" because they are parallel to the equator and to each other. On a globe, latitude lines (circles) are intersections of planes parallel to the plane through the equator. Compare to *lines of longitude.*

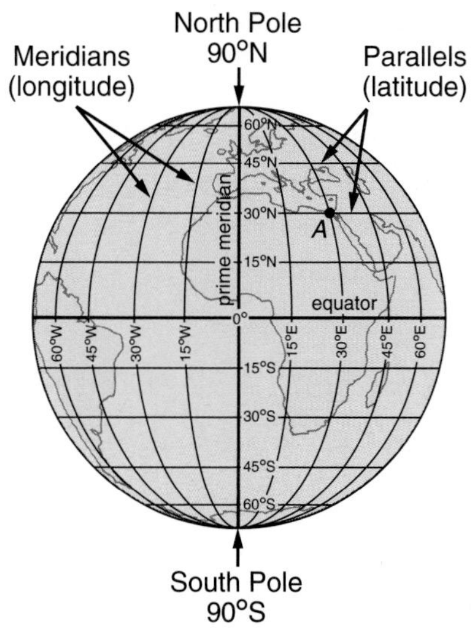

Point *A* is located at 30°N, 30°E.

lines of longitude Lines of constant *longitude* drawn on a 2-dimensional map or semicircles of constant longitude drawn on a globe connecting the North and South Poles. Lines of longitude are also called "meridians." Compare to *lines of latitude.*

liter (L) A metric *unit* of *volume* or *capacity* equal to the volume of a *cube* with 10-cm-long *edges.* 1 L = 1,000 mL = 1,000 cm^3. A liter is a little larger than a *quart.*

longitude A degree measure locating a place on Earth east or west of the prime meridian. A place at 0° longitude is on the prime meridian. A place at 180° east or west longitude is on or near the international date line, which is based on the imaginary semicircle opposite the prime meridian. Compare to *latitude.* See *lines of longitude.*

M

magnitude estimate A rough *estimate* of whether a number is in the tens, hundreds, thousands, or other *powers of 10.* For example, the U.S. national debt per person is in the tens of thousands of dollars. In *Everyday Mathematics*, children give magnitude estimates for problems such as *How many dimes are in $200?* or *How many halves are in 30?*

map direction symbol A symbol on a map that identifies north, south, east, and west. Sometimes only north is indicated.

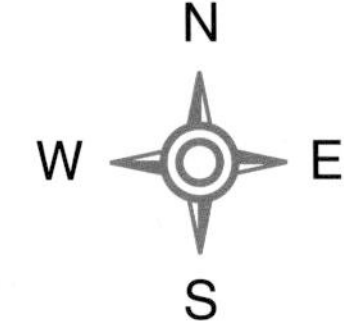

map legend (map key) A diagram that explains the symbols, markings, and colors on a map.

map scale The *ratio* of a distance on a map, globe, or drawing to an actual distance. For example, 1 inch on a map might correspond to 1 real-world mile. A map scale may be shown on a segment of a number line, given as a ratio of distances such as $\frac{1}{63,360}$ or 1:63,360 when an inch represents a mile, or by an informal use of the = symbol such as "1 inch = 1 mile."

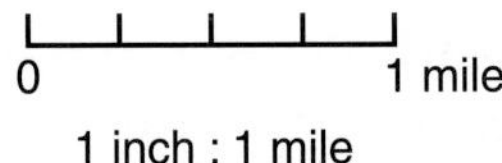

maximum The largest amount; the greatest number in a set of data. Compare to *minimum.*

mean (average) For a set of numbers, their sum divided by the number of numbers. Compare to the other data *landmarks, median* and *mode.*

median The middle value in a set of data when the data are listed in order from smallest to largest or vice versa. If there is an *even number* of data points, the median is the *mean* of the two middle values. Compare to other data *landmarks, mean* and *mode.*

memory in a calculator Where numbers are stored in a calculator for use in later calculations. Most calculators have both a short-term memory and a long-term memory.

milliliter (mL) A metric *unit* of *volume* or *capacity* equal to $\frac{1}{1,000}$ of a *liter,* or 1 *cubic centimeter.*

minimum The smallest amount; the smallest number in a set of data. Compare to *maximum.*

minuend In subtraction, the number from which another number is subtracted. For example, in $19 - 5 = 14$, the minuend is 19. Compare to *subtrahend.*

mirror image Same as a *reflection* image.

mixed number A number that is written using both a whole number and a fraction. For example, $2\frac{1}{4}$ is a mixed number equal to $2 + \frac{1}{4}$.

mode The value or values that occur most often in a set of data. Compare to other *landmarks, mean* and *median.*

multiple of a number *n* (1) A *product* of *n* and a counting number. For example, the multiples of 7 are 7, 14, 21, 28, ... (2) A product of *n* and an integer. For example, the multiples of 7 are . . . , −21, −14, −7, 0, 7, 14, 21, ...

multiples of equal groups A *multiple* of a *rate* in an equal-grouping situation. For example, *How many balloons are there altogether in 6 packages with 20 balloons per package?* is a multiple of an equal-group problem.

multiplication counting principle A way of determining the total number of possible outcomes for two or more separate choices. For example, suppose you roll a typical die and then flip a coin. There are 6 choices for which a number on the die lands up (1, 2, 3, 4, 5, or 6) and 2 choices for which side of the coin lands up (HEADS *H* or TAILS *T*). So there are $6 * 2 = 12$ possible outcomes altogether: (1, *H*), (1, *T*), (2, *H*), (2, *T*), (3, *H*), (3, *T*), (4, *H*), (4, *T*), (5, *H*) (5, *T*), (6, *H*), (6, *T*).

N

name-collection box In *Everyday Mathematics,* a diagram that is used for collecting equivalent names for a number.

25
37 − 12
20 + 5

twenty-five
veinticinco

negative numbers Numbers less than 0; the opposites of the positive numbers, commonly written as a positive number preceded by a – or OPP. Negative numbers are plotted left of 0 on a *horizontal* number line or below 0 on a *vertical* number line.

nested parentheses Parentheses within parentheses in an *expression.* Expressions are evaluated from within the innermost parentheses outward.

normal span The distance from the end of the thumb to the end of the index (first) finger of an outstretched hand. For estimating *lengths,* many people can adjust this distance to approximately 6 inches or 15 centimeters. Same as *span.* Compare to *great span.*

number-and-word notation A notation consisting of the significant *digits* of a number and words for the *place value.* For example, 27 billion is number-and-word notation for 27,000,000,000. Compare to *expanded notation, scientific notation,* and *standard notation.*

number model A *number sentence, expression,* or other representation that models a number story or situation. For example, the story *Sally had $5, and then she earned $8* can be modeled as the number sentence 5 + 8 = 13, or as the expression 5 + 8, or by

$$\begin{array}{r} 5 \\ +\ 8 \\ \hline 13 \end{array}$$

number sentence Two *expressions* with a *relation symbol.* For example,

$$5 + 5 = 10$$
$$2 - ? = 8$$
$$16 \leq a * b$$
$$a^2 + b^2 = c^2$$

Number sentences

numerator The dividend a in a fraction $\frac{a}{b}$ or a/b. In a part-whole fraction, in which the *whole* (the ONE or unit whole) is *divided* into a number of equal parts, the numerator is the number of equal parts being considered. Compare to *denominator.*

O

obtuse angle An angle with measure between 90° and 180°.

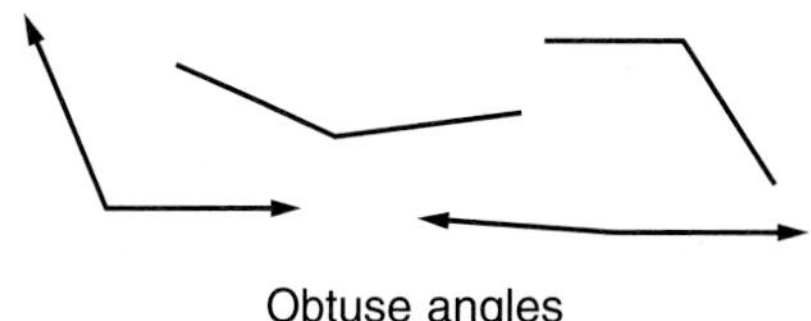

Obtuse angles

odd number A counting number that is not *divisible by* 2. Compare to *even number.*

open proportion A proportion with one or more *variables.* An open proportion is an *open sentence* and is neither true nor false. For example, $\frac{2}{3} = \frac{a}{5}$ and $\frac{z}{15} = \frac{y}{3}$ are open proportions.

open sentence A *number sentence* with one or more *variables.* An open sentence is neither true nor false. For example, 9 + ___ = 15, ? – 24 < 10, and $7 = x + y$ are open sentences.

operation symbol A symbol used in *expressions* and *number sentences* to stand for a particular mathematical operation. Symbols for common arithmetic operations are listed below:

addition	+
subtraction	–
multiplication	×, *, •
division	÷, /
powering	^

opposite angles Same as *vertical angles.*

opposite of a number *n* A number that is the same distance from 0 on a number line as *n,* but on the opposite side of 0. In symbols, the opposite of a number n is $-n$ and, in *Everyday Mathematics,* OPP(n). If n is a *negative number,* $-n$ is a positive number. For example, the opposite of –5 is 5. The sum of a number n and its opposite is zero; $n + -n = 0$.

order of operations Rules that tell the order in which operations in an *expression* should be carried out. The conventional order of operations is as follows:

1. Do operations inside grouping symbols. Work from the innermost set of grouping symbols outward. Inside grouping symbols, follow Rules 2–4.
2. Calculate all expressions with *exponents.*
3. Multiply and divide in order from left to right.
4. Add and subtract in order from left to right.

For example:

$$\begin{aligned} 5^2 + (3 * 4 - 2) / 5 &= 5^2 + (12 - 2) / 5 \\ &= 5^2 + 10 / 5 \\ &= 25 + 10 / 5 \\ &= 25 + 2 \\ &= 27 \end{aligned}$$

order of rotation symmetry The number of times a rotation image of a figure coincides with the figure before completing a 360° rotation.

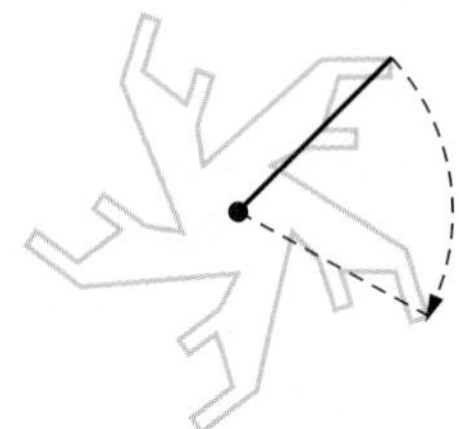

A figure with order 5 rotation symmetry

ordered pair (1) Two numbers, or *coordinates,* used to locate a point on a rectangular *coordinate grid.* The first coordinate *x* gives the position along the *horizontal* axis of the grid, and the second coordinate *y* gives the position along the *vertical* axis. The pair is written (*x*,*y*). (2) Any pair of objects or numbers in a particular order, as in letter-number spreadsheet-cell names or map coordinates.

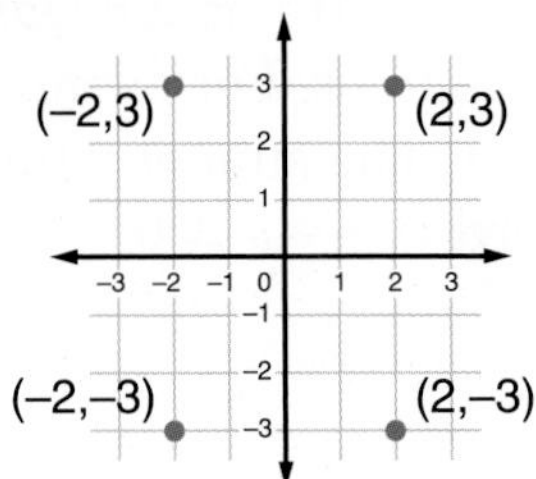

Ordered pairs

origin The zero point in a *coordinate* system. On a number line, the origin is the point at 0. On a *coordinate grid,* the origin is the point (0,0) where the two axes intersect.

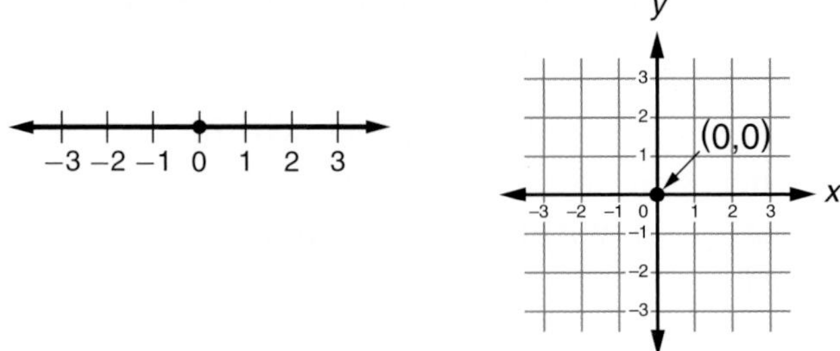

The points at 0 and (0,0) are origins.

outlier A value far from most of the others in a data set. Commonly, outliers are much larger or smaller than other values.

pan balance A device used to weigh objects or compare their weights.

parallel lines Lines in a plane that never meet. Two parallel lines are always the same distance apart. Line segments or rays on parallel lines are parallel to each other.

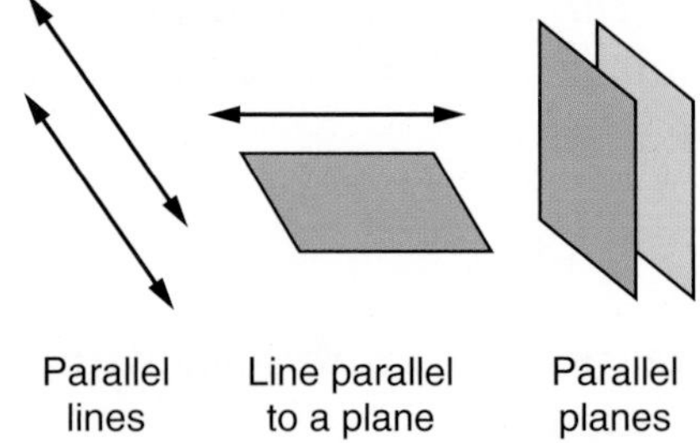

Parallel lines | Line parallel to a plane | Parallel planes

parallel planes Planes in space that never meet. Two parallel planes are always the same distance apart. A figure in one plane is parallel to the other plane. *Polygons* in one plane are said to be parallel to polygons in the other plane. However, 1-dimensional shapes such as lines, segments, and rays in one plane are not necessarily parallel to 1-dimensional shapes in a parallel plane.

parallelogram A quadrilateral with two pairs of parallel sides. Opposite sides of a parallelogram have the same *length,* and *opposite angles* have the same measure. All rectangles are parallelograms, but not all parallelograms are rectangles because parallelograms do not necessarily have *right angles.*

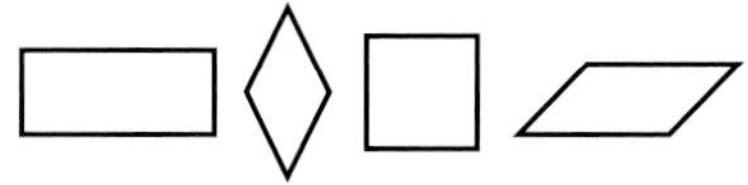

Parallelograms

partial-differences subtraction A subtraction *algorithm* in which separate differences are computed for each *place value* of the numbers and then added to get a final difference.

partial-products multiplication A multiplication *algorithm* in which partial products are computed by multiplying the value of each *digit* in one *factor* by the value of each digit in the other factor. The final *product* is the sum of the partial products.

partial-quotients division A division *algorithm* in which a partial quotient is computed in each of several steps. The final *quotient* is the sum of the partial quotients.

partial-sums addition An addition *algorithm* in which separate sums are computed for each *place value* of the numbers and then added to get a final sum.

parts-and-total diagram In *Everyday Mathematics,* a diagram used to model problems in which two or more quantities (parts) are combined to get a total quantity.

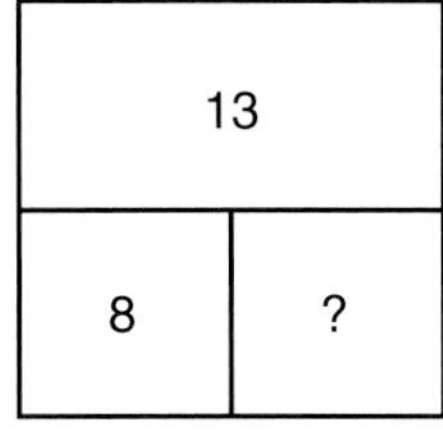

Total
13
Part 8
Part ?

Parts-and-total diagrams for 13 = 8 + ?

parts-and-total story A number story in which a *whole* is made up of distinct parts. For example, *There are 15 girls and 12 boys in Mrs. Dorn's class. How many students are there in all?* is a parts-and-total story. In other stories, the total and one or more parts may be known and the last part unknown.

pattern blocks A set of *polygon*-shaped blocks of varying sizes in which smaller blocks can be placed on larger blocks to show fractional parts. The blocks are used for geometric-shape identification and fraction activities. Compare to *attribute blocks.*

pentagon A 5-sided *polygon.*

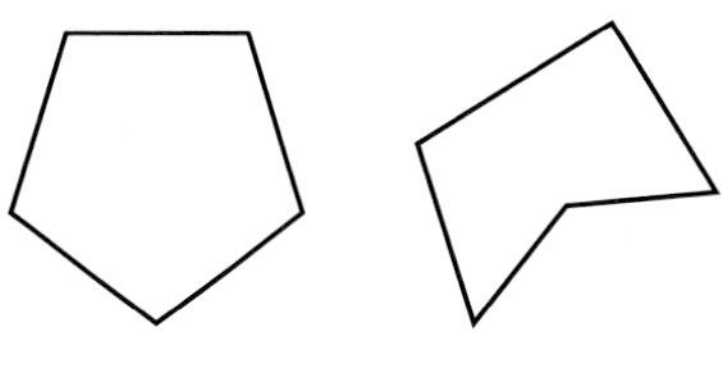

Pentagons

per For each, as in "ten chairs per row" or "six tickets per family."

percent (%) Per hundred, for each hundred, or out of a hundred. $1\% = \frac{1}{100} = 0.01$. For example, *48% of the students in the school are boys* means that, on average, 48 of every 100 children in the school are boys.

Percent Circle A tool on the *Geometry Template* that is used to measure and draw figures that involve *percents,* such as *circle graphs.*

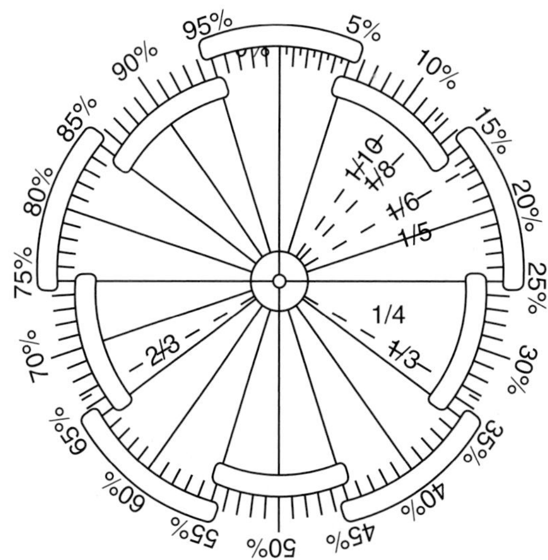

perimeter The distance around the boundary of a 2-dimensional figure. The perimeter of a circle is called its *circumference.* A formula for the perimeter P of a rectangle with *length* l and width w is $P = 2 * (l + w)$. Perimeter comes from the Greek words for "around measure."

perpendicular (⊥) Two lines or two planes that intersect at *right angles.* Line segments or rays that lie on perpendicular lines are perpendicular to each other. The symbol ⊥ means "is perpendicular to."

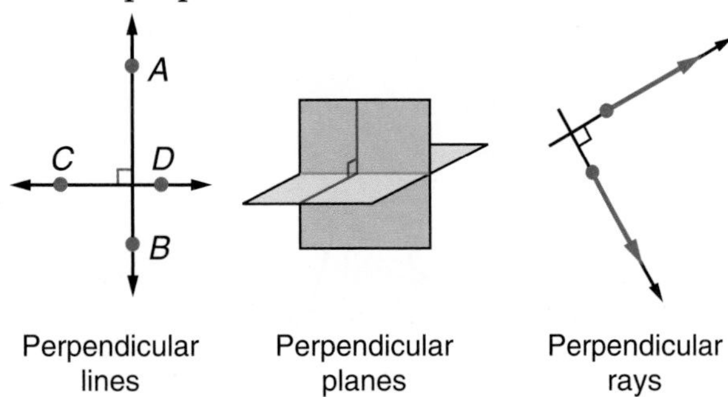

Perpendicular lines Perpendicular planes Perpendicular rays

perpendicular bisector A line, ray, or segment that bisects a line segment at a *right angle.*

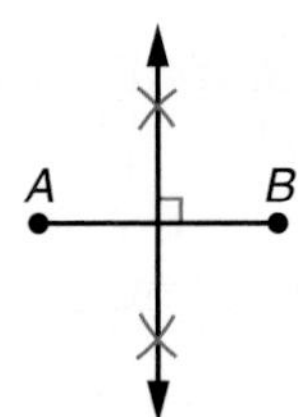

Construction of a perpendicular bisector of $\overline{AB}$

perpetual calendar A table that can be used to determine the correct day of the week for any date in a wide *range* of years.

personal-measurement reference A convenient approximation for a standard *unit* of measurement. For example, many people have thumbs that are approximately one inch wide.

pi (π) The *ratio* of the *circumference* of a circle to its *diameter.* Pi is also the ratio of the *area* of a circle to the square of its *radius.* Pi is the same for every circle and is an *irrational number* that is approximately equal to 3.14. The symbol π is the sixteenth letter of the Greek alphabet.

pie graph Same as *circle graph.*

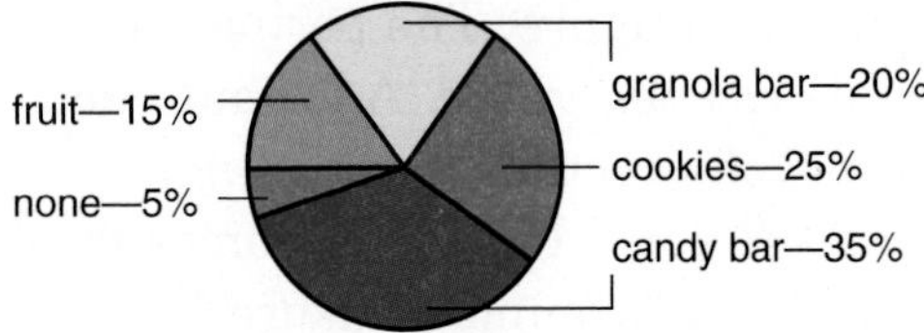

place value A system that gives a *digit* a value according to its position, or place, in a number. In our standard, base-10 (decimal) system for writing numbers, each place has a value 10 times that of the place to its right and 1 tenth the value of the place to its left.

thousands	hundreds	tens	ones	.	tenths	hundredths

A place-value chart

polygon A 2-dimensional figure formed by three or more line segments (sides) that meet only at their endpoints (*vertices*) to make a closed path. The sides may not cross one another.

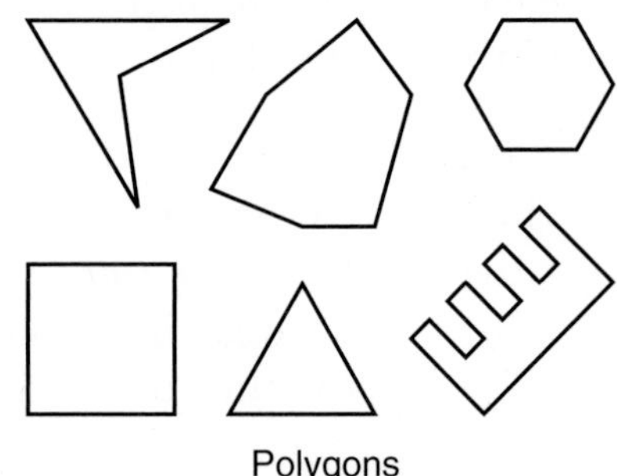

Polygons

polyhedron A 3-dimensional figure formed by *polygons* with their interiors (*faces*) and having no holes. Plural is polyhedrons or polyhedra.

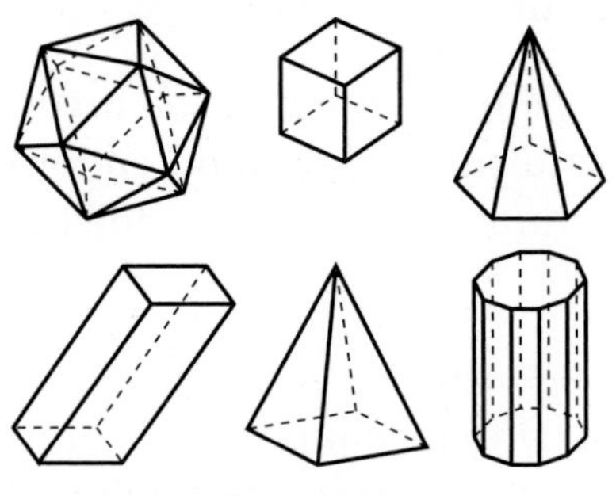

Polyhedrons

population (1) The total number of people living within a defined geographic region. (2) In data collection, the group of people or objects that is the focus of study. Large populations are often studied by picking a representative random *sample* from the population.

power Same as *exponent.*

power of a number A *product* of *factors* that are all the same; the result of a^b for any numbers a and b. For example, $5^3 = 5 * 5 * 5 = 125$ is read "5 to the third *power*" or "the third power of 5" because 5 is a factor 3 times.

power of 10 (1) In *Everyday Mathematics,* a number that can be written in the form 10^a, where a is a counting number; that is, the numbers $10 = 10^1$, $100 = 10^2$, $1{,}000 = 10^3$, and so on, that can be written using only 10s as *factors.* Same as positive power of 10. (2) More generally, a number that can be written in the form 10^a, where a is an integer, that is, all the positive and negative powers of 10 together, along with $10^0 = 1$.

precipitation Condensed atmospheric moisture that falls to the ground, including rain, snow, and hail. In the United States, rainfall is typically measured in inches. Snow and hail are first melted and then measured like rain.

predict In mathematics, to say what will happen in the future based on experimental data or theoretical calculation.

prime factorization A counting number written as a *product* of *prime-number factors.* Every counting number greater than 1 has a unique prime factorization. For example, the prime factorization of 24 is $2 * 2 * 2 * 3$.

prime number A counting number greater than 1 that has exactly two whole-number *factors,* 1 and itself. For example, 7 is a prime number because its only factors are 1 and 7. The first five prime numbers are 2, 3, 5, 7, and 11. Also simply called "primes." Compare to *composite number.*

prism A *polyhedron* with two parallel and congruent polygonal regions for *bases* and lateral *faces* formed by all the line segments with endpoints on corresponding edges of the bases. The lateral faces are all *parallelograms.* Lateral faces intersect at lateral *edges.* In a *right prism,* the lateral faces are rectangular. Prisms get their names from the shape of their bases.

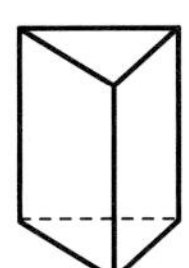

A triangular prism

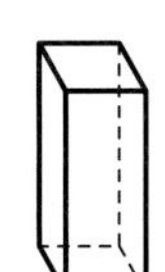

A rectangular prism

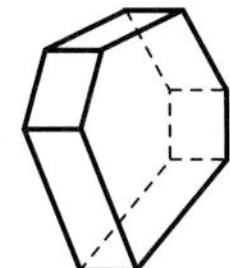

A hexagonal prism

probability A number from 0 through 1 giving the likelihood of an event happening. The closer a probability is to 1, the more likely the event is to happen. The closer a probability is to 0, the less likely the event is to happen. For example, the probability that a fair coin will show HEADS is $\frac{1}{2}$.

Probability Meter In *Fifth* and *Sixth Grade Everyday Mathematics,* a tool used to show *probabilities* as fractions, decimals, and *percents.*

product The result of multiplying two numbers, called *factors.* For example, in $4 * 3 = 12$, the product is 12.

program a calculator To instruct a calculator to repeat a calculation using its *memory* instead of having the user enter a key sequence over and over. In *Everyday Mathematics,* students program their calculators to skip count using the machines' built-in constant operation feature.

pyramid A *polyhedron* made up of any polygonal region for a *base,* a point (*apex*) not in the plane of the base, and all of the line segments with one endpoint at the apex and the other on an *edge* of the base. All *faces* except the base are triangular. Pyramids get their names from the shape of their bases.

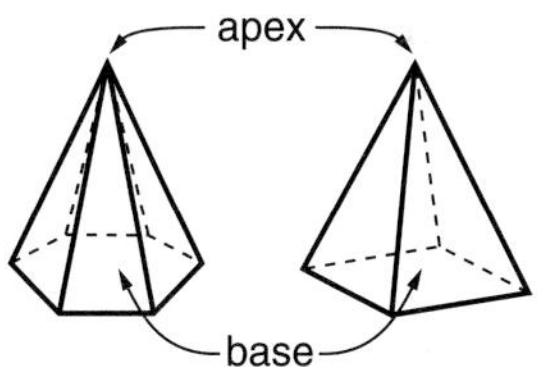

A hexagonal pyramid   A square pyramid

Q

quadrangle A polygon that has four angles.

quart (qt) A U.S. customary *unit* of *volume* or *capacity* equal to 32 fluid ounces, 2 pints, or 4 *cups.*

quick common denominator (QCD) The *product* of the *denominators* of two or more fractions. For example, the quick common denominator of $\frac{3}{4}$ and $\frac{5}{6}$ is $4 * 6 = 24$. In general, the quick common denominator of $\frac{a}{b}$ and $\frac{c}{d}$ *is* $b * d$. As the name suggests, this is a quick way to get a *common denominator* for a collection of fractions, but it does not necessarily give the least common denominator.

quotient The result of dividing one number by another number. For example, in 10 / 5 = 2, the quotient is 2.

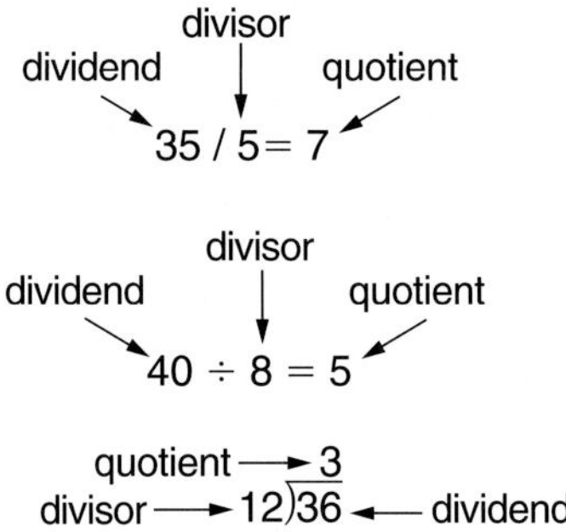

radius (1) A line segment from the *center of a circle* (or sphere) to any point on the circle (or *sphere*). (2) The *length* of this line segment. The length of a radius is half the length of a *diameter.* Plural is radiuses or radii.

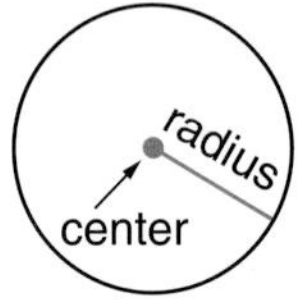

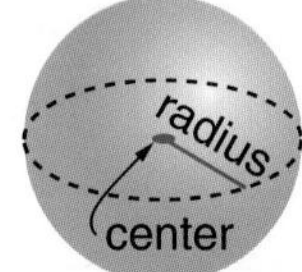

random draw Taking an object from a set of objects in which each object has an *equally likely* chance of being chosen. For example, drawing a card from a deck or drawing a domino from a bag of dominos are random draws.

range The *difference* between the *maximum* and the *minimum* in a set of data. Used as a measure of the spread of the data.

rate A comparison by division of two quantities with different *units.* For example, traveling 100 miles in 2 hours is an average rate of $\frac{100 \text{ mi}}{2 \text{ hr}}$, or 50 miles *per* hour. Compare to *ratio.*

rate-multiplication story A number story in which one quantity is a *rate* times another quantity. A typical rate is speed, which multiplied by a time traveled gives distance traveled. There are many other rates such as price *per* pound or hours per person. For example, *8 people work a total of 20 hours. What is the average number of work hours per person?* is a rate-multiplication story.

ratio A comparison by division of two quantities with the same *units.* Ratios can be fractions, decimals, *percents,* or stated in words. Ratios can also be written with a colon between the two numbers being compared. For example, if a team wins 3 games out of 5 games played, the ratio of wins to total games is $\frac{3}{5}$, 3 / 5, 0.6, 60%, 3 to 5, or 3:5 (read "three to five"). Compare to *rate.*

rectangle method A strategy for finding the *area* of a *polygon* in which one or more rectangles are drawn around all or parts of the polygon through its *vertices.* The sides of the drawn rectangle(s), together with the sides of the original figure, define regions that are either rectangles or triangular halves of rectangles. Add and/or subtract the areas of these rectangular and triangular regions to get the *area* of the original polygon. For example, rectangle *RYSX* was drawn around the original triangle *XYZ.*

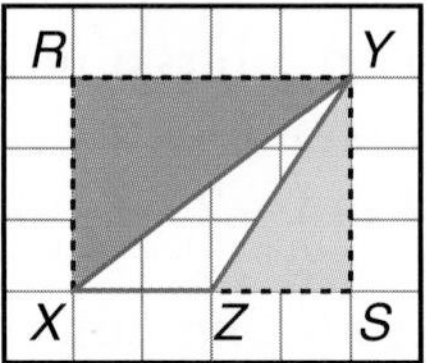

Area of $\triangle XYZ$ = area of rectangle *RYSX* − area of $\triangle XRY$ − area of $\triangle YSZ$

rectangular array An arrangement of objects in rows and columns that form a rectangle. All rows have the same number of objects, and all columns have the same number of objects.

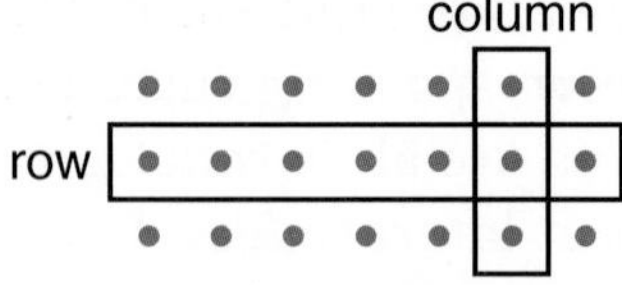

A rectangular array

rectanglar prism A *prism* with rectangular *bases.* The four *faces* that are not bases are either rectangles or *parallelograms.* For example, a shoe box models a rectangular prism in which all sides are rectangles.

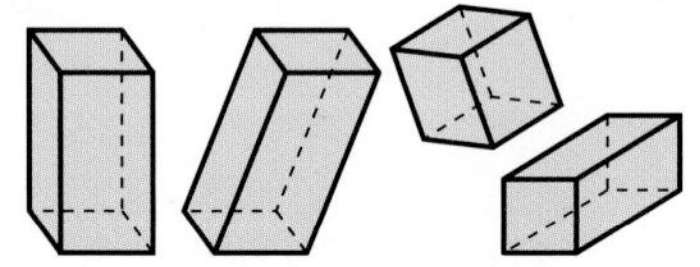

Rectangular prisms

reflection A *transformation* in which the image of a figure is a *mirror image* of the figure over a line of reflection. Each point A on the figure and its corresponding point A' on the image are the same distance from the line of reflection on a line *perpendicular* to it. Informally called a flip.

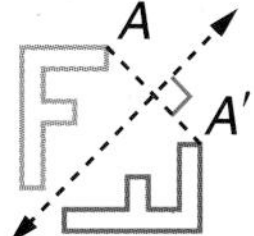

A reflection

reflex angle An angle with a measure between 180° and 360°.

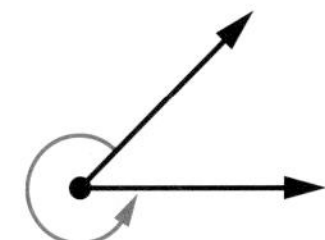
A reflex angle

regular polygon A *polygon* in which all sides are the same *length* and all angles have the same measure.

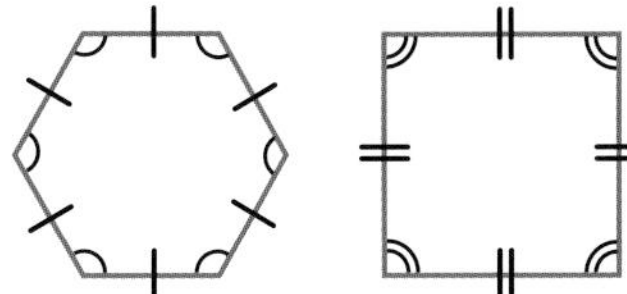
Regular polygons

regular tessellation A *tessellation* of one *regular polygon.* The only three regular tessellations are shown below.

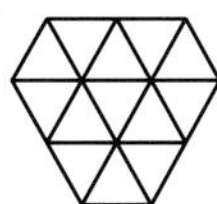 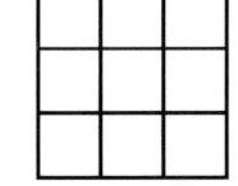 
The three regular tessellations

relation symbol A symbol used to express a relationship between two quantities.

Relation Symbol	Meaning
$=$	is equal to
$\neq$	is not equal to
$<$	is less than
$>$	is greater than
$\leq$	is less than or equal to
$\geq$	is greater than or equal to
$\approx$	is approximately equal to
$\cong$	is congruent to

remainder An amount left over when one number is divided by another number. For example, in 16 / 3 → 5 R1, the *quotient* is 5 and the remainder (R) is 1.

repeating decimal A decimal in which one *digit* or a group of digits is repeated without end. For example, 0.3333. . . and $0.\overline{147}$ are repeating decimals.

right angle A 90° angle.

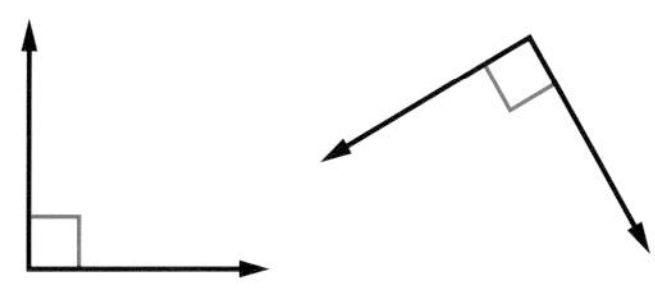
Right angles

right cone A *cone* whose *base* is *perpendicular* to the line segment joining the *apex* and the center of the base.

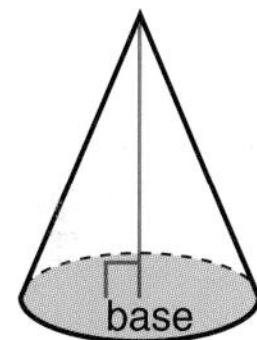

A right circular cone

right cylinder A *cylinder* whose *bases* are *perpendicular* to the line segment joining the centers of the bases.

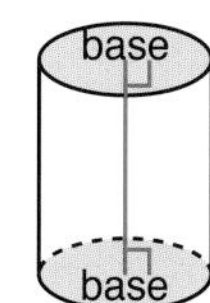

A right circular cylinder

right prism A *prism* whose *bases* are *perpendicular* to all of the *edges* that connect the two bases.

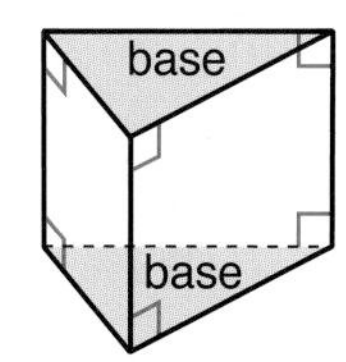

A right triangular prism

right triangle A triangle with a *right angle.*

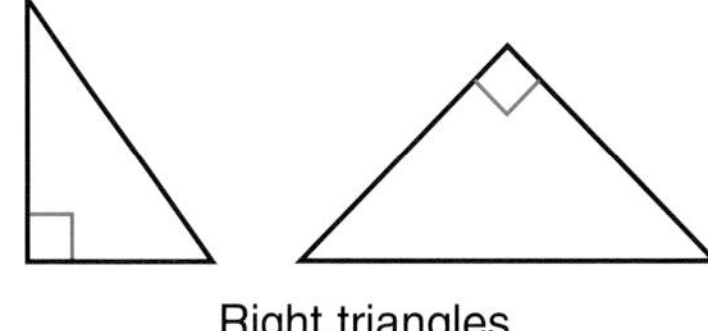
Right triangles

round To approximate a number to make it easier to work with, or to make it better reflect the precision of the data. "Rounding up" means to approximate larger than the actual value. "Rounding down" means to approximate smaller than the actual value.

round to the nearest To *round* a number up or down in a particular decimal place, depending on which approximation is closer to the actual value.

S

sample A part of a *population* intended to represent the whole population.

scalene triangle A triangle with sides of three different *lengths.* The three angles of a scalene triangle have different measures.

scientific notation A system for representing numbers in which a number is written as the product of a *power of 10* and a number that is at least 1 and less than 10. Scientific notation allows you to write large and small numbers with only a few symbols. For example, in scientific notation, 4,300,000 is $4.3 * 10^6$, and 0.00001 is $1 * 10^{-5}$. Scientific calculators display numbers in scientific notation. Compare to *expanded notation* and *standard notation.*

sector A region bounded by, and including, an *arc* and two *radii* of a circle. A sector resembles a slice of pizza. *Circle graphs* are made with sectors corresponding to parts of a data set. Also called a wedge.

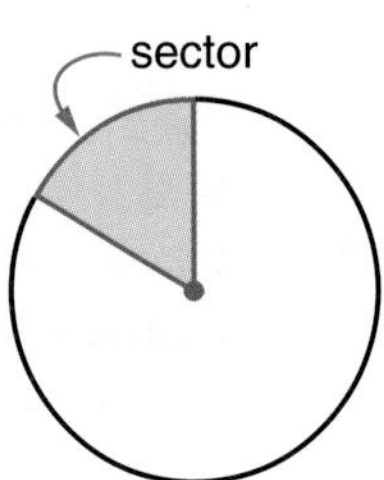

simplest form of a fraction A fraction that cannot be renamed in simpler form. A *mixed number* is in simplest form if its fractional part is in simplest form. Simplest form is not emphasized in *Everyday Mathematics* because other equivalent forms are often equally or more useful. For example, fractions with *common denominators* are easier to compare or add than fractions in simplest form but with different denominators.

situation diagram A diagram used to organize information in a problem situation in one of the addition/subtraction or multiplication/division use classes.

slide An informal name for a *translation.*

solution of an open sentence A value or values for the *variable(s)* in an *open sentence* that make the sentence true. For example, 7 is the solution of $5 + n = 12$. Although *equations* are not necessarily *open sentences,* the solution of an open sentence is commonly referred to as a "solution of an equation."

span Same as *normal span.*

sphere The set of all points in space that are an equal distance from a fixed point called the center of the sphere. The distance from the center to the sphere is the *radius* of the sphere. The *diameter* of a sphere is twice its radius. Points inside a sphere are not part of the sphere.

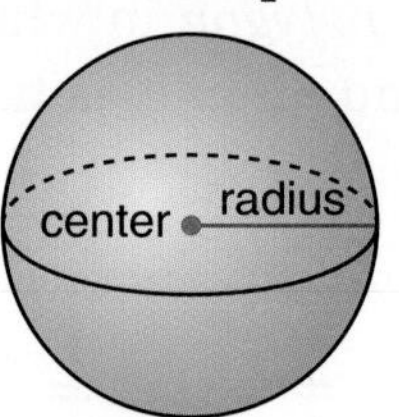

A sphere

square array A *rectangular array* with the same number of rows as columns. For example, 16 objects will form a square array with 4 objects in each row and 4 objects in each column.

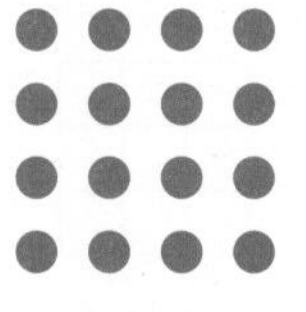

A square array

square corner Same as a *right angle.*

square numbers Figurate numbers that are the *product* of a counting number and itself. For example, 25 is a square number because $25 = 5 * 5$. A square number can be represented by a *square array* and as a number squared, such as $25 = 5^2$.

square root of a number *n* A number that multiplied by itself is *n*, commonly written as $\sqrt{n}$. For example, 4 is a square root of 16, because $4 * 4 = 16$. Normally, square root refers to the positive square root, but the *opposite* of a positive square root is also a square root. For example, -4 is also a square root of 16 because $-4 * -4 = 16$.

square unit A *unit* to measure *area*. A model of a square unit is a square with each side a related unit of *length*. For example, a square inch is the area of a square with 1-inch sides. Square units are often labeled as the length unit squared. For example, 1 cm^2 is read "1 square centimeter" or "1 centimeter squared."

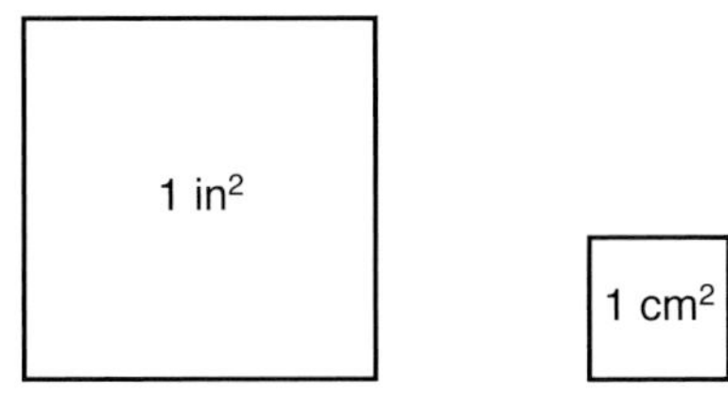

Square units

standard notation Our most common way of representing whole numbers, integers, and decimals. Standard notation is base-10 *place-value* numeration. For example, standard notation for three hundred fifty-six is 356.

stem-and-leaf plot A display of data values in which *digits* with larger *place values* are "stems" and digits with smaller place values are "leaves."

Data List: 24, 24, 25, 26, 27, 27, 31, 31, 32, 32, 36, 36, 41, 41, 43, 45, 48, 50, 52

Stems (tens)	Leaves (ones)
2	4 4 5 6 7 7
3	1 1 2 2 6 6
4	1 1 3 5 8
5	0 2

A stem-and-leaf plot

step graph A 2-dimensional coordinate graph that looks like steps because the *vertical* values of points are the same over an interval of *horizontal* values and then change, or "step," for another interval. Horizontal values in a step graph often represent time.

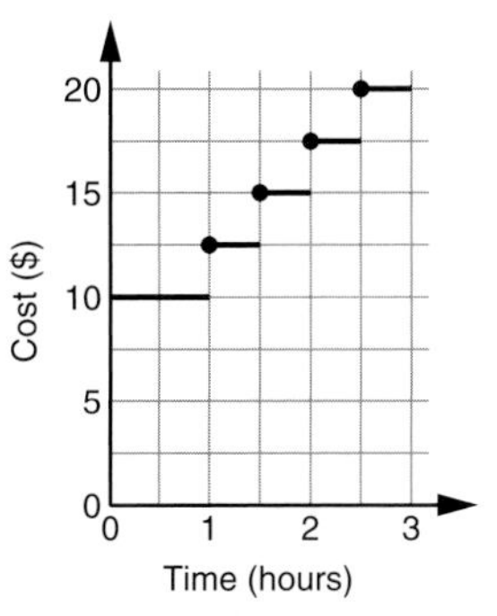

A step graph

straight angle A 180° angle.

A straight angle

subtrahend The number being taken away in a subtraction problem. For example, in $15 - 5 = 10$, the subtrahend is 5. Compare to *minuend*.

summer solstice The longest day of the year, when the sun is farthest north of Earth's equator. The number of hours of daylight depends on the *latitude* of a location. In Colorado, the summer solstice averages a little less than 16 hours of daylight.

surface (1) The boundary of a 3-dimensional object. The part of an object that is next to the air. Common surfaces include the top of a body of water, the outermost part of a ball, and the topmost layer of ground that covers Earth. (2) Any 2-dimensional layer, such as a plane or a *face* of a *polyhedron*.

surface area The *area* of the *surface* of a 3-dimensional figure. The surface area of a *polyhedron* is the sum of the areas of its *faces*.

survey A study that collects data. Surveys are commonly used to study "demographics" such as people's characteristics, behaviors, interests, and opinions.

tessellate To make a *tessellation;* to tile a *surface.*

tessellation A pattern of shapes that covers a *surface* completely without overlaps or gaps.

A tessellation

thermometer A tool to measure temperature in degrees according to a fixed scale. The most common scales are Celsius and Fahrenheit.

trade-first subtraction A subtraction *algorithm* in which all necessary trades between places in the numbers are done before any subtractions are carried out. Some people favor this algorithm because they can concentrate on one thing at a time.

transformation An operation on a geometric figure (the preimage) that produces a new figure (the image). The study of transformations is called transformation geometry. Transformations are often based on rules for how points behave, as in the translation below. Although the preimage does not actually move under a transformation, it is convenient to think and talk about transformations as moving a figure from one place to another and sometimes changing its size or shape. So *Everyday Mathematics* encourages using informal terms such as flip, turn, and *slide.* See *reflection* and *translation.*

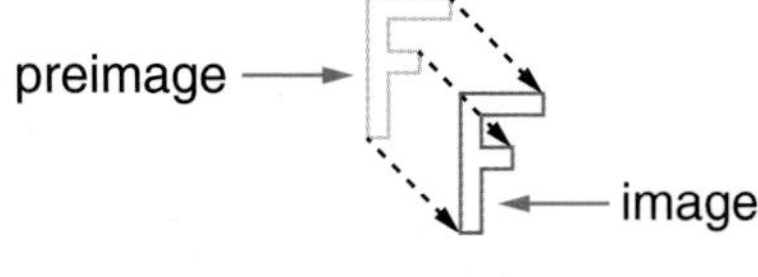

A translation

translation A *transformation* in which every point in the image of a figure is at the same distance in the same direction from its corresponding point in the figure. Informally called a *slide.*

tree diagram A network of points connected by line segments and containing no closed loops. *Factor trees* and *probability* trees are diagrams used, respectively, to *factor* numbers and to represent probability situations in which there is a series of events. The first tree diagram below shows the *prime factorization* of 30. The second tree diagram models flipping one coin two times.

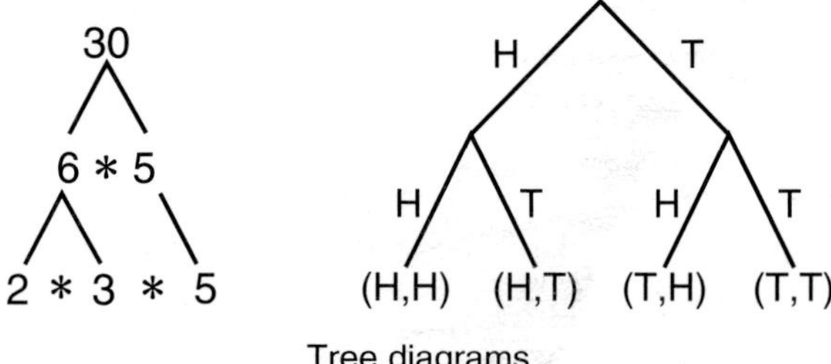

Tree diagrams

true number sentence A *number sentence* stating a correct fact. For example, $75 = 25 + 50$ is a true number sentence. Compare to *false number sentence.*

turn-around rule A rule for solving addition and multiplication problems based on the *Commutative Properties of Multiplication* and Addition. For example, if you know that $6 * 8 = 48$, then, by the turn-around rule, you also know that $8 * 6 = 48$.

unit A label used to put a number in context. In measuring *length,* for example, inches and centimeters are units. In a problem about 5 apples, apple is the unit. In *Everyday Mathematics,* students keep track of units in unit boxes.

unit fraction A fraction whose *numerator* is 1. For example, $\frac{1}{2}$, $\frac{1}{3}$, $\frac{1}{12}$, $\frac{1}{8}$, and $\frac{1}{20}$ are unit fractions. Unit fractions are especially useful in converting among *units* within measurement systems. For example, because 1 foot = 12 inches you can multiply a number of inches by $\frac{1}{12}$ to convert to feet.

unit percent One *percent* (1%).

unlike denominators *Denominators* that are different, as in $\frac{1}{2}$ and $\frac{1}{3}$.

unlike fractions Fractions with *unlike denominators.*

V

value of a variable A specific number or quantity represented by a *variable.* For example, in $y = 4x + 3$, if the value of x is 7, then the value of y that makes the *equation* true is 31.

variable A letter or other symbol that represents a number. A variable can represent a single number, as in $5 + n = 9$, because only $n = 4$ makes the sentence true. A variable may also stand for many different numbers, as in $x + 2 < 10$, because any number x less than 8 makes the sentence true. In *formulas* and properties, variables stand for all numbers. For example, $a + 3 = 3 + a$ for all numbers a.

Venn diagram A picture that uses circles or rings to show relationships between sets. In this diagram, $22 + 8 = 30$ girls are on the track team, and 8 are on both the track and the basketball teams.

Numbers of Girls on Sports Teams

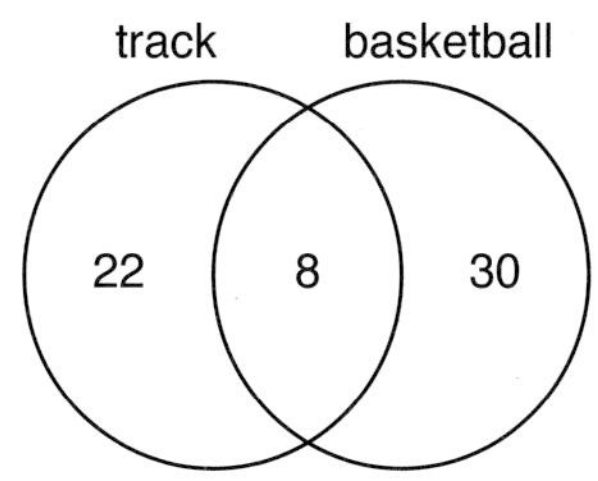

A Venn diagram

vertex The point at which the rays of an angle, the sides of a *polygon,* or the *edges* of a *polyhedron* meet. Plural is vertexes or vertices.

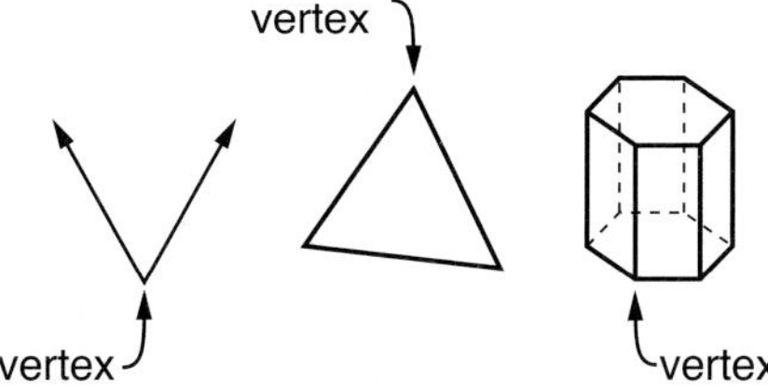

vertical Upright; *perpendicular* to the horizon. Compare to *horizontal.*

vertical angles The angles made by intersecting lines that do not share a common side. Same as *opposite angles.* Vertical angles have equal measures.

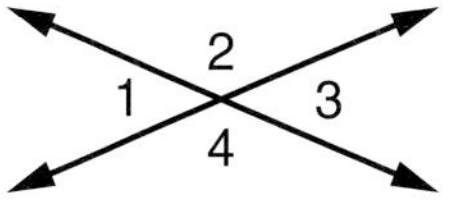

Angles 1 and 3 and angles 2 and 4 are pairs of vertical angles.

volume (1) The amount of space occupied by a 3-dimensional figure. Same as *capacity.* (2) The amount a container can hold. Volume is often measured in *cubic units,* such as cm^3, cubic inches, or cubic feet.

W

whole (ONE, unit whole) An entire object, collection of objects, or quantity being considered in a problem situation; 100%.

Grade-Level Goals

Everyday Mathematics organizes content through Program Goals and Grade-Level Goals. The Grade-Level Goals Chart shows the units in which goal content is taught and then practiced and applied. For more information, see the *Assessment Handbook*.

The Grade-Level Goals are divided according to the content strands below.

Content Strands — Pages

How to Read the Grade-Level Goals Chart

Each section of the chart includes Grade-Level Goals organized by content strand. The three grade-level columns divided into units indicate in which units the goals are addressed.

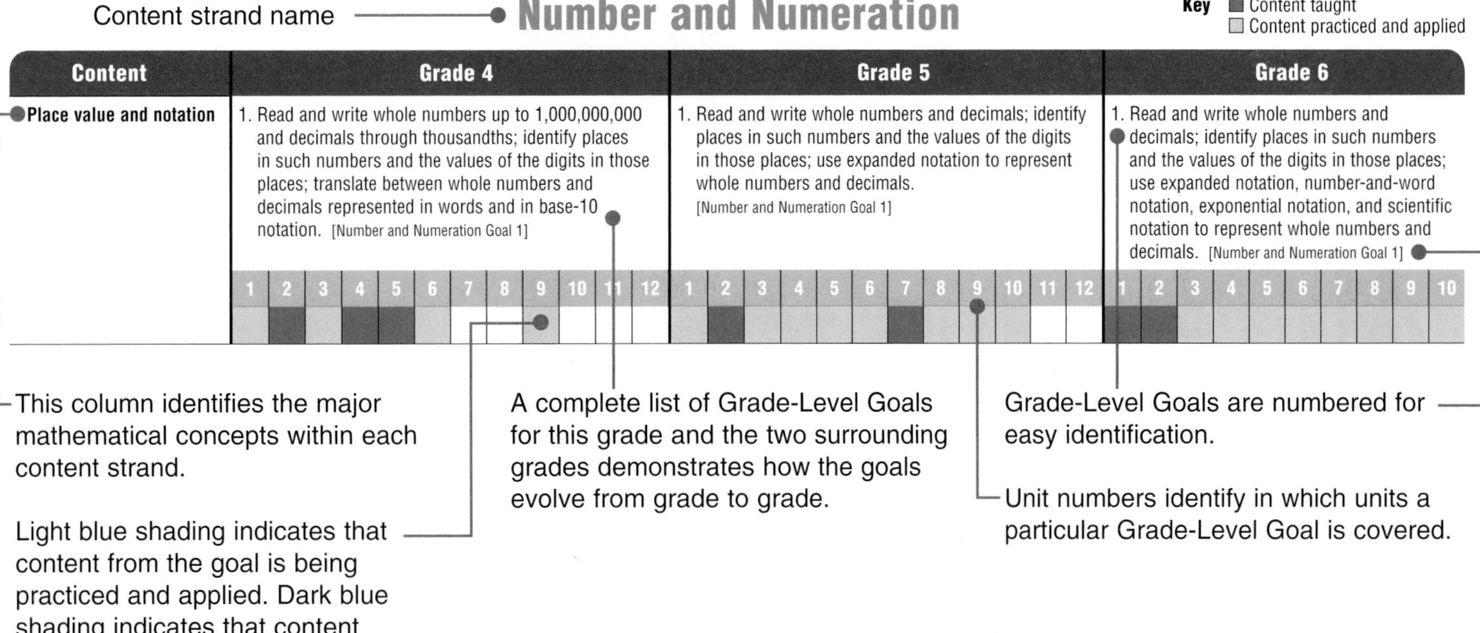
Content strand name
Number and Numeration
Key
Content taught
Content practiced and applied
Content
Grade 4
Grade 5
Grade 6
Place value and notation
1. Read and write whole numbers up to 1,000,000,000 and decimals through thousandths; identify places in such numbers and the values of the digits in those places; translate between whole numbers and decimals represented in words and in base-10 notation. [Number and Numeration Goal 1]
1. Read and write whole numbers and decimals; identify places in such numbers and the values of the digits in those places; use expanded notation to represent whole numbers and decimals. [Number and Numeration Goal 1]
1. Read and write whole numbers and decimals; identify places in such numbers and the values of the digits in those places; use expanded notation, number-and-word notation, exponential notation, and scientific notation to represent whole numbers and decimals. [Number and Numeration Goal 1]
1 2 3 4 5 6 7 8 9 10 11 12
1 2 3 4 5 6 7 8 9 10 11 12
1 2 3 4 5 6 7 8 9 10
This column identifies the major mathematical concepts within each content strand.
Light blue shading indicates that content from the goal is being practiced and applied. Dark blue shading indicates that content from the goal is being taught.
A complete list of Grade-Level Goals for this grade and the two surrounding grades demonstrates how the goals evolve from grade to grade.
Grade-Level Goals are numbered for easy identification.
Unit numbers identify in which units a particular Grade-Level Goal is covered.

Number and Numeration

Key
- Content taught
- Content practiced and applied

Content	Grade 4	Grade 5	Grade 6
Place value and notation	1. Read and write whole numbers up to 1,000,000,000 and decimals through thousandths; identify places in such numbers and the values of the digits in those places; translate between whole numbers and decimals represented in words and in base-10 notation. [Number and Numeration Goal 1]	1. Read and write whole numbers and decimals; identify places in such numbers and the values of the digits in those places; use expanded notation to represent whole numbers and decimals. [Number and Numeration Goal 1]	1. Read and write whole numbers and decimals; identify places in such numbers and the values of the digits in those places; use expanded notation, number-and-word notation, exponential notation, and scientific notation to represent whole numbers and decimals. [Number and Numeration Goal 1]
	1 2 3 4 5 6 7 8 9 10 11 12	1 2 3 4 5 6 7 8 9 10 11 12	1 2 3 4 5 6 7 8 9 10
Meanings and uses of fractions	2. Read, write, and model fractions; solve problems involving fractional parts of a region or a collection; describe and explain strategies used; given a fractional part of a region or a collection, identify the unit whole. [Number and Numeration Goal 2]	2. Solve problems involving percents and discounts; describe and explain strategies used; identify the unit whole in situations involving fractions. [Number and Numeration Goal 2]	2. Solve problems involving percents and discounts; explain strategies used; identify the unit whole in situations involving fractions, decimals, and percents. [Number and Numeration Goal 2]
	1 2 3 4 5 6 7 8 9 10 11 12	1 2 3 4 5 6 7 8 9 10 11 12	1 2 3 4 5 6 7 8 9 10
Number theory	3. Find multiples of whole numbers less than 10; identify prime and composite numbers; find whole-number factors of numbers. [Number and Numeration Goal 3]	3. Identify prime and composite numbers; factor numbers; find prime factorizations. [Number and Numeration Goal 3]	3. Use GCFs, LCMs, and divisibility rules to manipulate fractions. [Number and Numeration Goal 3]
	1 2 3 4 5 6 7 8 9 10 11 12	1 2 3 4 5 6 7 8 9 10 11 12	1 2 3 4 5 6 7 8 9 10

Content	Grade 4	Grade 5	Grade 6
Equivalent names for whole numbers	4. Use numerical expressions involving one or more of the basic four arithmetic operations and grouping symbols to give equivalent names for whole numbers. [Number and Numeration Goal 4] 1 2 3 4 5 6 7 8 9 10 11 12	4. Use numerical expressions involving one or more of the basic four arithmetic operations, grouping symbols, and exponents to give equivalent names for whole numbers; convert between base-10, exponential, and repeated-factor notations. [Number and Numeration Goal 4] 1 2 3 4 5 6 7 8 9 10 11 12	4. Apply the order of operations to numerical expressions to give equivalent names for rational numbers. [Number and Numeration Goal 4] 1 2 3 4 5 6 7 8 9 10
Equivalent names for fractions, decimals, and percents	5. Use numerical expressions to find and represent equivalent names for fractions and decimals; use and explain a multiplication rule to find equivalent fractions; rename fourths, fifths, tenths, and hundredths as decimals and percents. [Number and Numeration Goal 5] 1 2 3 4 5 6 7 8 9 10 11 12	5. Use numerical expressions to find and represent equivalent names for fractions, decimals, and percents; use and explain multiplication and division rules to find equivalent fractions and fractions in simplest form; convert between fractions and mixed numbers; convert between fractions, decimals, and percents. [Number and Numeration Goal 5] 1 2 3 4 5 6 7 8 9 10 11 12	5. Find equivalent fractions and fractions in simplest form by applying multiplication and division rules and concepts from number theory; convert between fractions, mixed numbers, decimals, and percents. [Number and Numeration Goal 5] 1 2 3 4 5 6 7 8 9 10
Comparing and ordering numbers	6. Compare and order whole numbers up to 1,000,000,000 and decimals through thousandths; compare and order integers between –100 and 0; use area models, benchmark fractions, and analyses of numerators and denominators to compare and order fractions. [Number and Numeration Goal 6] 1 2 3 4 5 6 7 8 9 10 11 12	6. Compare and order rational numbers; use area models, benchmark fractions, and analyses of numerators and denominators to compare and order fractions and mixed numbers; describe strategies used to compare fractions and mixed numbers. [Number and Numeration Goal 6] 1 2 3 4 5 6 7 8 9 10 11 12	6. Choose and apply strategies for comparing and ordering rational numbers; explain those choices and strategies. [Number and Numeration Goal 6] 1 2 3 4 5 6 7 8 9 10

Operations and Computation

Key ■ Content taught □ Content practiced and applied

Content	Grade 4	Grade 5	Grade 6
Addition and subtraction facts	1. Demonstrate automaticity with addition and subtraction fact extensions. [Operations and Computation Goal 1] 1 2 3 4 5 6 7 8 9 10 11 12	1 2 3 4 5 6 7 8 9 10 11 12	1 2 3 4 5 6 7 8 9 10

Operations and Computation (cont.)

Key ■ Content taught □ Content practiced and applied

Content	Grade 4	Grade 5	Grade 6
Addition and subtraction procedures	2. Use manipulatives, mental arithmetic, paper-and-pencil algorithms and models, and calculators to solve problems involving the addition and subtraction of whole numbers and decimals through hundredths; describe the strategies used and explain how they work. [Operations and Computation Goal 2] 1 2 3 4 5 6 7 8 9 10 11 12	1. Use manipulatives, mental arithmetic, paper-and-pencil algorithms and models, and calculators to solve problems involving the addition and subtraction of whole numbers, decimals, and signed numbers; describe the strategies used and explain how they work. [Operations and Computation Goal 1] 1 2 3 4 5 6 7 8 9 10 11 12	1. Use mental arithmetic, paper-and-pencil algorithms and models, and calculators to solve problems involving the addition and subtraction of whole numbers, decimals, and signed numbers; describe the strategies used and explain how they work. [Operations and Computation Goal 1] 1 2 3 4 5 6 7 8 9 10
Multiplication and division facts	3. Demonstrate automaticity with multiplication facts through 10 ∗ 10 and proficiency with related division facts; use basic facts to compute fact extensions such as 30 ∗ 60. [Operations and Computation Goal 3] 1 2 3 4 5 6 7 8 9 10 11 12	2. Demonstrate automaticity with multiplication and division fact extensions. [Operations and Computation Goal 2] 1 2 3 4 5 6 7 8 9 10 11 12	1 2 3 4 5 6 7 8 9 10
Multiplication and division procedures	4. Use manipulatives, mental arithmetic, paper-and-pencil algorithms and models, and calculators to solve problems involving the multiplication of multidigit whole numbers by 2-digit whole numbers and the division of multidigit whole numbers by 1-digit whole numbers; describe the strategies used and explain how they work. [Operations and Computation Goal 4] 1 2 3 4 5 6 7 8 9 10 11 12	3. Use manipulatives, mental arithmetic, paper-and-pencil algorithms and models, and calculators to solve problems involving the multiplication of whole numbers and decimals and the division of multidigit whole numbers and decimals by whole numbers; express remainders as whole numbers or fractions as appropriate; describe the strategies used and explain how they work. [Operations and Computation Goal 3] 1 2 3 4 5 6 7 8 9 10 11 12	2. Use mental arithmetic, paper-and-pencil algorithms and models, and calculators to solve problems involving the multiplication and division of whole numbers, decimals, and signed numbers; describe the strategies used and explain how they work. [Operations and Computation Goal 2] 1 2 3 4 5 6 7 8 9 10
Procedures for addition and subtraction of fractions	5. Use manipulatives, mental arithmetic, and calculators to solve problems involving the addition and subtraction of fractions and mixed numbers; describe the strategies used. [Operations and Computation Goal 5] 1 2 3 4 5 6 7 8 9 10 11 12	4. Use mental arithmetic, paper-and-pencil algorithms and models, and calculators to solve problems involving the addition and subtraction of fractions and mixed numbers; describe the strategies used and explain how they work. [Operations and Computation Goal 4] 1 2 3 4 5 6 7 8 9 10 11 12	3. Use mental arithmetic, paper-and-pencil algorithms and models, and calculators to solve problems involving the addition and subtraction of fractions and mixed numbers; describe the strategies used and explain how they work. [Operations and Computation Goal 3] 1 2 3 4 5 6 7 8 9 10

Key Content taught / Content practiced and applied

Content	Grade 4	Grade 5	Grade 6
Procedures for multiplication and division of fractions		5. Use area models, mental arithmetic, paper-and-pencil algorithms and models, and calculators to solve problems involving the multiplication of fractions and mixed numbers; use visual models, paper-and-pencil methods, and calculators to solve problems involving the division of fractions; describe the strategies used. [Operations and Computation Goal 5]	4. Use mental arithmetic, paper-and-pencil algorithms and models, and calculators to solve problems involving the multiplication and division of fractions and mixed numbers; describe the strategies used and explain how they work. [Operations and Computation Goal 4]
Computational estimation	6. Make reasonable estimates for whole number and decimal addition and subtraction problems, and whole number multiplication and division problems; explain how the estimates were obtained. [Operations and Computation Goal 6]	6. Make reasonable estimates for whole number and decimal addition, subtraction, multiplication, and division problems and fraction and mixed number addition and subtraction problems; explain how the estimates were obtained. [Operations and Computation Goal 6]	5. Make reasonable estimates for whole number, decimal, fraction, and mixed number addition, subtraction, multiplication, and division problems; explain how the estimates were obtained. [Operations and Computation Goal 5]
Models for the operations	7. Use repeated addition, skip counting, arrays, area, and scaling to model multiplication and division. [Operations and Computation Goal 7]	7. Use repeated addition, arrays, area, and scaling to model multiplication and division; use ratios expressed as words, fractions, percents, and with colons; solve problems involving ratios of parts of a set to the whole set. [Operations and Computation Goal 7]	6. Use ratios and scaling to model size changes and to solve size-change problems; represent ratios as fractions, percents, and decimals, and using a colon; model and solve problems involving part-to-whole and part-to-part ratios; model rate and ratio number stories with proportions; use and explain cross multiplication and other strategies to solve proportions. [Operations and Computation Goal 6]

Data and Chance

Key
- Content taught
- Content practiced and applied

Content	Grade 4	Grade 5	Grade 6
Data collection and representation	1. Collect and organize data or use given data to create charts, tables, graphs, and line plots. [Data and Chance Goal 1]	1. Collect and organize data or use given data to create graphic displays with reasonable titles, labels, keys, and intervals. [Data and Chance Goal 1]	1. Collect and organize data or use given data to create graphic displays with reasonable titles, labels, keys, and intervals. [Data and Chance Goal 1]
Data analysis	2. Use the maximum, minimum, range, median, mode, and graphs to ask and answer questions, draw conclusions, and make predictions. [Data and Chance Goal 2]	2. Use the maximum, minimum, range, median, mode, and mean and graphs to ask and answer questions, draw conclusions, and make predictions. [Data and Chance Goal 2]	2. Use data landmarks, measures of spread, and graphs to ask and answer questions, draw conclusions, and make predictions; compare and contrast the median and mean of a data set. [Data and Chance Goal 2]
Qualitative probability	3. Describe events using *certain, very likely, likely, unlikely, very unlikely, impossible,* and other basic probability terms; use *more likely, equally likely, same chance, 50-50, less likely,* and other basic probability terms to compare events; explain the choice of language. [Data and Chance Goal 3]	3. Describe events using *certain, very likely, likely, unlikely, very unlikely, impossible,* and other basic probability terms; use *more likely, equally likely, same chance, 50-50, less likely,* and other basic probability terms to compare events; explain the choice of language. [Data and Chance Goal 3]	
Quantitative probability	4. Predict the outcomes of experiments and test the predictions using manipulatives; summarize the results and use them to predict future events; express the probability of an event as a fraction. [Data and Chance Goal 4]	4. Predict the outcomes of experiments, test the predictions using manipulatives, and summarize the results; compare predictions based on theoretical probability with experimental results; use summaries and comparisons to predict future events; express the probability of an event as a fraction, decimal, or percent. [Data and Chance Goal 4]	3. Use the Multiplication Counting Principle, tree diagrams, and other counting strategies to identify all possible outcomes for a situation; predict results of experiments, test the predictions using manipulatives, and summarize the findings; compare predictions based on theoretical probability with experimental results; calculate probabilities and express them as fractions, decimals, and percents; explain how sample size affects results; use the results to predict future events. [Data and Chance Goal 3]

Measurement and Reference Frames

Key ■ Content taught □ Content practiced and applied

Content	Grade 4	Grade 5	Grade 6
Length, weight, and angles	1. Estimate length with and without tools; measure length to the nearest $\frac{1}{4}$ inch and $\frac{1}{2}$ centimeter; use tools to measure and draw angles; estimate the size of angles without tools. [Measurement and Reference Frames Goal 1]	1. Estimate length with and without tools; measure length with tools to the nearest $\frac{1}{8}$ inch and millimeter; estimate the measure of angles with and without tools; use tools to draw angles with given measures. [Measurement and Reference Frames Goal 1]	1. Estimate length with and without tools; measure length with tools to the nearest $\frac{1}{16}$ inch and millimeter; estimate the measure of angles with and without tools; use tools to draw angles with given measures. [Measurement and Reference Frames Goal 1]
Area, perimeter, volume, and capacity	2. Describe and use strategies to measure the perimeter and area of polygons, to estimate the area of irregular shapes, and to find the volume of rectangular prisms. [Measurement and Reference Frames Goal 2]	2. Describe and use strategies to find the perimeter of polygons and the area of circles; choose and use appropriate methods, including formulas, to find the areas of rectangles, parallelograms, and triangles, and the volume of a prism; define *pi* as the ratio of a circle's circumference to its diameter. [Measurement and Reference Frames Goal 2]	2. Choose and use appropriate formulas to calculate the circumference of circles and to solve area, perimeter, and volume problems. [Measurement and Reference Frames Goal 2]
Units and systems of measurement	3. Describe relationships among U.S. customary units of measure and among metric units of measure. [Measurement and Reference Frames Goal 3]	3. Describe relationships among U.S. customary units of measure and among metric units of measure. [Measurement and Reference Frames Goal 3]	
Coordinate systems	4. Use ordered pairs of numbers to name, locate, and plot points in the first quadrant of a coordinate grid. [Measurement and Reference Frames Goal 4]	4. Use ordered pairs of numbers to name, locate, and plot points in all four quadrants of a coordinate grid. [Measurement and Reference Frames Goal 4]	3. Use ordered pairs of numbers to name, locate, and plot points in all four quadrants of a coordinate grid. [Measurement and Reference Frames Goal 3]

Geometry

Key
- Content taught
- Content practiced and applied

Content	Grade 4	Grade 5	Grade 6
Lines and angles	1. Identify, draw, and describe points, intersecting and parallel line segments and lines, rays, and right, acute, and obtuse angles. [Geometry Goal 1] 1 2 3 4 5 6 7 8 9 10 11 12	1. Identify, describe, compare, name, and draw right, acute, obtuse, straight, and reflex angles; determine angle measures in vertical and supplementary angles and by applying properties of sums of angle measures in triangles and quadrangles. [Geometry Goal 1] 1 2 3 4 5 6 7 8 9 10 11 12	1. Identify, describe, classify, name, and draw angles; determine angle measures by applying properties of orientations of angles and of sums of angle measures in triangles and quadrangles. [Geometry Goal 1] 1 2 3 4 5 6 7 8 9 10
Plane and solid figures	2. Describe, compare, and classify plane and solid figures, including polygons, circles, spheres, cylinders, rectangular prisms, cones, cubes, and pyramids, using appropriate geometric terms including *vertex, base, face, edge,* and *congruent.* [Geometry Goal 2] 1 2 3 4 5 6 7 8 9 10 11 12	2. Describe, compare, and classify plane and solid figures using appropriate geometric terms; identify congruent figures and describe their properties. [Geometry Goal 2] 1 2 3 4 5 6 7 8 9 10 11 12	2. Identify and describe similar and congruent figures and describe their properties; construct a figure that is congruent to another figure using a compass and straightedge. [Geometry Goal 2] 1 2 3 4 5 6 7 8 9 10
Transformations and symmetry	3. Identify, describe, and sketch examples of reflections; identify and describe examples of translations and rotations. [Geometry Goal 3] 1 2 3 4 5 6 7 8 9 10 11 12	3. Identify, describe, and sketch examples of reflections, translations, and rotations. [Geometry Goal 3] 1 2 3 4 5 6 7 8 9 10 11 12	3. Identify, describe, and sketch (including plotting on the coordinate plane) instances of reflections, translations, and rotations. [Geometry Goal 3] 1 2 3 4 5 6 7 8 9 10

Patterns, Functions, and Algebra

Key Content taught / Content practiced and applied

Content	Grade 4	Grade 5	Grade 6
Patterns and functions	1. Extend, describe, and create numeric patterns; describe rules for patterns and use them to solve problems; use words and symbols to describe and write rules for functions that involve the four basic arithmetic operations and use those rules to solve problems. [Patterns, Functions, and Algebra Goal 1]	1. Extend, describe, and create numeric patterns; describe rules for patterns and use them to solve problems; write rules for functions involving the four basic arithmetic operations; represent functions using words, symbols, tables, and graphs and use those representations to solve problems. [Patterns, Functions, and Algebra Goal 1]	1. Extend, describe, and create numeric patterns; describe rules for patterns and use them to solve problems; represent patterns and rules using algebraic notation; represent functions using words, algebraic notation, tables, and graphs; translate from one representation to another and use representations to solve problems involving functions. [Patterns, Functions, and Algebra Goal 1]
Algebraic notation and solving number sentences	2. Use conventional notation to write expressions and number sentences using the four basic arithmetic operations; determine whether number sentences are true or false; solve open sentences and explain the solutions; write expressions and number sentences to model number stories. [Patterns, Functions, and Algebra Goal 2]	2. Determine whether number sentences are true or false; solve open number sentences and explain the solutions; use a letter variable to write an open sentence to model a number story; use a pan-balance model to solve linear equations in one unknown. [Patterns, Functions, and Algebra Goal 2]	2. Determine whether equalities and inequalities are true or false; solve open number sentences and explain the solutions; use a pan-balance model to solve linear equations in one or two unknowns; use trial-and-error and equivalent equations strategies to solve linear equations in one unknown. [Patterns, Functions, and Algebra Goal 2]
Order of operations	3. Evaluate numeric expressions containing grouping symbols; insert grouping symbols to make number sentences true. [Patterns, Functions, and Algebra Goal 3]	3. Evaluate numeric expressions containing grouping symbols and nested grouping symbols; insert grouping symbols and nested grouping symbols to make number sentences true; describe and use the precedence of multiplication and division over addition and subtraction. [Patterns, Functions, and Algebra Goal 3]	3. Describe and apply the conventional order of operations. [Patterns, Functions, and Algebra Goal 3]
Properties of the arithmetic operations	4. Describe and apply the Distributive Property of Multiplication over Addition. [Patterns, Functions, and Algebra Goal 4]	4. Describe and apply properties of arithmetic. [Patterns, Functions, and Algebra Goal 4]	4. Describe and apply properties of arithmetic and multiplicative and additive inverses. [Patterns, Functions, and Algebra Goal 4]

Scope and Sequence Chart

Throughout *Everyday Mathematics*, students repeatedly encounter skills in each of the content strands. Each exposure builds on and extends students' understanding. They study important concepts over consecutive years through a variety of formats. The Scope and Sequence Chart shows the units in which these exposures occur. The symbol ● indicates that the skill is introduced or taught. The symbol ■ indicates that the skill is revisited, practiced, or extended. These levels refer to unit content within the *K–6 Everyday Mathematics* curriculum.

The skills are divided according to the content strands below.

Content Strands Pages

How to Read the Scope and Sequence Chart

Each section of the chart includes a content strand title, three grade-level columns divided by units or sections, and a list of specific skills grouped by major concepts.

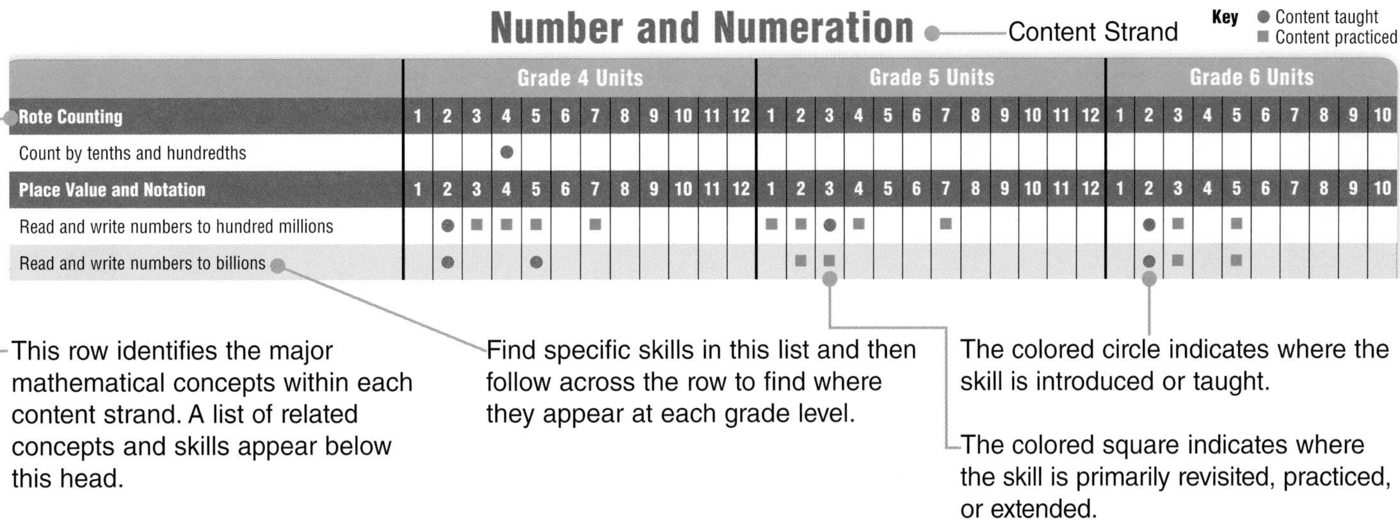

Number and Numeration
Content Strand
Key ● Content taught ■ Content practiced
Grade 4 Units
Grade 5 Units
Grade 6 Units
Rote Counting
Count by tenths and hundredths
Place Value and Notation
Read and write numbers to hundred millions
Read and write numbers to billions
This row identifies the major mathematical concepts within each content strand. A list of related concepts and skills appear below this head.
Find specific skills in this list and then follow across the row to find where they appear at each grade level.
The colored circle indicates where the skill is introduced or taught.
The colored square indicates where the skill is primarily revisited, practiced, or extended.

Number and Numeration

Key ● Content taught ■ Content practiced

	Grade 4 Units												Grade 5 Units												Grade 6 Units									
Rote Counting	1	2	3	4	5	6	7	8	9	10	11	12	1	2	3	4	5	6	7	8	9	10	11	12	1	2	3	4	5	6	7	8	9	10
Count by tenths and hundredths				●																														
Place Value and Notation	1	2	3	4	5	6	7	8	9	10	11	12	1	2	3	4	5	6	7	8	9	10	11	12	1	2	3	4	5	6	7	8	9	10
Read and write numbers to hundred millions		●	■	■	■		■						■	■	●	■			■							●	■		■					
Read and write numbers to billions		●			●									■	■											●	■		■					
Explore numbers to trillions					●									●					●						■	●	■				■			
Investigate or identify place value in numbers to hundred millions		●	■	■			■						■	■	■	■			■						■	●	■						■	
Identify place value in numbers to billions		●			●									■	■								■		■	●	■						■	
Name the values of digits in numbers to billions		●			●										■										■	●	■						■	
Make exchanges among place values		●		■										■			■	■	■							■					■			
Investigate and apply powers of 10					■								■	■	■				●							●	■	■						■
Investigate and apply expanded notation		■			■									●		■		■	●							■			■	■				
Read and write numbers to trillions in standard and expanded notation		●	■		●																				●	●	■				■			■
Investigate, use, or apply exponential notation					●	■		■					●	■			■	■	●							●	■	■	■	■		■		■
Investigate and apply scientific notation																			●							●	■	■		■				■
Use dollar-and-cents notation			■	●		■	●	■	●		■	●																						
Explore uses of decimals				■																														
Model decimals with base-10 materials				●																														
Read and write decimals to ten-thousandths in standard and expanded notation				●	■				●					●	■				■						■	●			■					
Identify place value in decimals through ten-thousandths; compare decimals				●	■	■							■	●	■	■			■		■	■			●	●	■	●				●	●	
Investigate and apply expanded notation of decimals				■											■					■						●								
Translate words into numerical expressions													■		■															●				
Meanings and Uses of Fractions	1	2	3	4	5	6	7	8	9	10	11	12	1	2	3	4	5	6	7	8	9	10	11	12	1	2	3	4	5	6	7	8	9	10
Explore uses of fractions			■				●										●					■		■										

Key ● Content taught ■ Content practiced

Meanings and Uses of Fractions (cont.)	1	2	3	4	5	6	7	8	9	10	11	12	1	2	3	4	5	6	7	8	9	10	11	12	1	2	3	4	5	6	7	8	9	10
Identity fractional parts of regions					■	■	●	■	●	■							●	■		●					■			●						
Identify fractional parts of a set				●		■	●	■									●			■									■	■	■			
Decompose a fraction							●																											
Identify the whole for fractions							●		●						■		●	■	■	●								■				●		
Identify fractions on a number line						■	●	■				■					●	●									■							
Identify/find fractional parts of units of money							■													●												●		
Find a fraction of a number				●		■	●		●								●	■	■	●			■	●				●	■	■	■		■	
Use percents to describe real-life situations								■	●																							■		
Find a percent of a number								■	●			■					■	■	■	●			■	■			●	●	■	■	●	●	●	
Find the whole, given a percent of the whole									●											●				■								●	■	
Solve percent problems								■	■	■							●			●						■	●	●	■	■	●	●	●	
Estimate and calculate percent								■	●								●			●						■	●	●	■	■	●	●	●	
Find the unit fraction or unit percent to calculate unit prices												●								●		●									■	●		
Determine the better buy												●								■			●				●					●	■	
Number Theory	**1**	**2**	**3**	**4**	**5**	**6**	**7**	**8**	**9**	**10**	**11**	**12**	**1**	**2**	**3**	**4**	**5**	**6**	**7**	**8**	**9**	**10**	**11**	**12**	**1**	**2**	**3**	**4**	**5**	**6**	**7**	**8**	**9**	**10**
Identify even and odd numbers													●																	■				
Find the factors of numbers			●		■		■					■	●	■	■	■	■			■			■	●			■	■					●	
Investigate, identify, or apply the concepts of prime and composite numbers			●										●											●				●		■				
Find the prime factorization of numbers													●	■	■	■	■				■		■	●				■						
Find multiples of a number or the least common multiple of two numbers			●	■							■		●					■		■	■			●			■	●		●		■		
Find the greatest common factor of two numbers													●							■				●			■	●			●		●	
Investigate or identify square numbers, square roots, and absolute value			●										●										■				■			●			●	
Understand properties of rational numbers																					■		■			■				●	■			

Number and Numeration (cont.)

Key ● Content taught ■ Content practiced

	Grade 4 Units												Grade 5 Units												Grade 6 Units									
Equivalent Names for Whole Numbers	**1**	**2**	**3**	**4**	**5**	**6**	**7**	**8**	**9**	**10**	**11**	**12**	**1**	**2**	**3**	**4**	**5**	**6**	**7**	**8**	**9**	**10**	**11**	**12**	**1**	**2**	**3**	**4**	**5**	**6**	**7**	**8**	**9**	**10**
Find equivalent names for numbers	■	●	■	■	■	■				■		■	●	■	■	●	■	■	●		■	■			●	●		■				■	●	■
Rename numbers written in exponential notation					●	■							●						●							●	■	■	■	■		■		■
Equivalent Names for Fractions, Decimals, and Percents	**1**	**2**	**3**	**4**	**5**	**6**	**7**	**8**	**9**	**10**	**11**	**12**	**1**	**2**	**3**	**4**	**5**	**6**	**7**	**8**	**9**	**10**	**11**	**12**	**1**	**2**	**3**	**4**	**5**	**6**	**7**	**8**	**9**	**10**
Find equivalent fractions						■	●	■	■							■	●	●	■	●			■	●				●			■	●		
Rename fractions as decimals				●			●		●	■				■			●	■									■	●	●	■	■	■		
Relate fractions and decimals				●			●	■	●	■		■					●								●	●		●	■	■	■	■	■	
Convert between fractions and decimals							●	■	●	■							●			■							■	●	■	■	■	■		
Estimate equivalent percents for fractions																	●											●	●	■	■	●	■	
Rename fractions and mixed numbers in simplest forms																	■	●	■	●			■	■			■	●		■	■	■	■	
Convert between fractions, mixed numbers, decimals, and/or percents			●	●			■		●	■			■	■	■		●	●		●	■			■	●	■	■	●	■	●	●	●	■	
Use a calculator to rename any fraction as a decimal or percent									●								●	●									■	●	●		●	●		
Comparing and Ordering Numbers	**1**	**2**	**3**	**4**	**5**	**6**	**7**	**8**	**9**	**10**	**11**	**12**	**1**	**2**	**3**	**4**	**5**	**6**	**7**	**8**	**9**	**10**	**11**	**12**	**1**	**2**	**3**	**4**	**5**	**6**	**7**	**8**	**9**	**10**
Compare numbers using <, >, and = symbols	■	■	■	■	■	■	●	■			■	■	■					●	●	●	■		■	■	●	■		●		●			■	
Compare larger numbers					●	■								■					●						■	■								
Compare and order decimals			■	●	■	■			■			■	■		■	■	■		■		■			■		●	■			■		■		
Compare and order integers										●	■	■							●						●	■			■	●	■	■		
Compare and order fractions with or without benchmarks							●		■	■		■		■		■	●	●	■	●	■			■			■	●		■		■		
Plot and compare decimals on a number line																									●	■				■				
Explore uses for positive and negative numbers										●	●								●		●								■	●	■			
Use properties of positive and negative numbers										●	■	■							●							■	●		■	●	■			
Explore reference points for zero										●	■												●	●			■			■				

Operations and Computation

Key ● Content taught ■ Content practiced

	Grade 4 Units												Grade 5 Units												Grade 6 Units									
Addition and Subtraction Facts	1	2	3	4	5	6	7	8	9	10	11	12	1	2	3	4	5	6	7	8	9	10	11	12	1	2	3	4	5	6	7	8	9	10
Practice basic facts and extended facts	■	■											■	■		■			■			■	■			■			●		■	■		
Practice extensions of basic facts		■													■											■				■				
Add/subtract multiples of 10 or 100		●																																
Addition and Subtraction Procedures	1	2	3	4	5	6	7	8	9	10	11	12	1	2	3	4	5	6	7	8	9	10	11	12	1	2	3	4	5	6	7	8	9	10
Use addition/subtraction algorithms		●		●	■								■	●	■										■	●	■			■		■		
Add/subtract using a calculator		●		●																						■					■	■		
Add/subtract multidigit numbers	■	●	●		●								■	●	■										■	●		■	■		■			
Solve addition/subtraction number stories		■	●	■	●									●	■										■							■		
Add/subtract multidigit whole numbers and decimals		●	■	●	■		■							●	■	■					■	■			■	●	■			■		■		
Use estimation or algorithms to add/subtract money amounts/decimals; make change			■	●		■				●	●	●		●	■	■	■	■	■	■					■	●	■	■					■	
Solve decimal addition/subtraction number stories				●															■							●								
Add/subtract positive and negative numbers; model addition and subtraction on a number line										●	●	■							●			■	■				●	■	●	●		■		
Compute with positive and negative integers											■	■							●								■			●	■	■		
Multiplication and Division Facts	1	2	3	4	5	6	7	8	9	10	11	12	1	2	3	4	5	6	7	8	9	10	11	12	1	2	3	4	5	6	7	8	9	10
Use a Multiplication/Division Facts Table			●										■																					
Practice multiplication/division facts			●	■	■	■	■						●	■	■	●			■	■		■	■			●	●	●	■	●		●		
Practice extended multiplication/division facts			●		●	■							■	■	■	●						■				●	■					■		
Solve multiplication/division problems involving multiples of 10, 100, and 1,000					●	■							■	●	■	●									■	●	■	●	■		■	■		
Understand the relationship between multiplication and division			●			●							■			●				■			■	■						●				
Multiplication and Division Procedures	1	2	3	4	5	6	7	8	9	10	11	12	1	2	3	4	5	6	7	8	9	10	11	12	1	2	3	4	5	6	7	8	9	10
Model multiplication with arrays			■		■								●																					
Use mental arithmetic to multiply/divide		■		■	●									■	■	●		■					■	■	●	●				■		■		
Use multiplication/division algorithms					●	●	■	■	●					●	■	●					■	■		■	●	●	■	■	■		■	●		

Operations and Computation (cont.)

Key ● Content taught ■ Content practiced

	Grade 4 Units												Grade 5 Units												Grade 6 Units									
Multiplication and Division Procedures (cont.)	1	2	3	4	5	6	7	8	9	10	11	12	1	2	3	4	5	6	7	8	9	10	11	12	1	2	3	4	5	6	7	8	9	10
Relate fractions and division			■						●								■	■	●								■	●	■	■		■		
Divide by 1-digit numbers						●			■				●			●		■						■	■	●				■		■		
Divide by 2-digit numbers						●			■							●	■									●				■		■		
Use a calculator to multiply/divide					■							●	●			●		■	■			■			●	●		●	■			■	■	
Identify or investigate square numbers			●										●														■						●	
Solve multiplication/division number stories		■	■		■	●			■		■	●				●	■	■								●		■	■			■	■	
Solve multidigit multiplication/division problems					●	■								●	■	●					■	■		■	●	●	■				■			
Multiply/divide decimals by powers of 10														■	■				■			■				●	■	●		■		■		
Multiply decimals by whole numbers									●	■	■			●	■			■	■						●	●		●	■			●		
Divide decimals by whole numbers									●	■	■					●		■								●	■					■		
Multiply/divide money amounts						■			●	●		●		●		●				●	■	●				●	■					●	●	
Solve multiplication/division decimal number stories									●														■					●				■	●	
Interpret a remainder in division problems					■	●			■			●				●	■									■		●				■		
Express remainders as fractions or decimals						●						■				●										●	■	●		■		■	■	
Express quotients as mixed numbers or decimals						●											■	■								●	■	●		■		■		
Locate the decimal point in a product or quotient									●	■	■			●												●		●	■					
Round a decimal quotient to a specified place																		■			■					●		●				●		
Multiply decimals by decimals														●											■	●						●		
Multiply by positive and negative powers of 10																			●		■					●	■							
Multiply/divide positive and negative numbers																											■			●	■	■		
Use divisibility tests to determine if a number is divisible by another number													●		■	■	■	■			■	■				■	■	●						
Procedures for Addition and Subtraction of Fractions	1	2	3	4	5	6	7	8	9	10	11	12	1	2	3	4	5	6	7	8	9	10	11	12	1	2	3	4	5	6	7	8	9	10
Use benchmarks to add and subtract fractions																		●		■	■													
Use models to add/subtract fractions and mixed numbers							●		■	■	■						●	●	■	●								■						

Key ● Content taught ■ Content practiced

Procedures for Addition and Subtraction of Fractions (cont.)	1	2	3	4	5	6	7	8	9	10	11	12	1	2	3	4	5	6	7	8	9	10	11	12	1	2	3	4	5	6	7	8	9	10
Add/subtract fractions with like denominators							●	■	■	■								●		●							■	●			●	■	●	
Add/subtract fractions with unlike denominators							●	■	■	■								●		●	■			■				●	■	■	●	■	●	
Solve fraction addition/subtraction number stories; model addition and subtraction with pictures or words							●				■						●	■	■	■	■			■				●	■			■		
Use an algorithm to add/subtract mixed numbers with like denominators							●													●				■			■	●						
Use an algorithm to add/subtract mixed numbers with unlike denominators							●										■	■	■	●				■				●	■			■		
Procedures for Multiplication and Division of Fractions	**1**	**2**	**3**	**4**	**5**	**6**	**7**	**8**	**9**	**10**	**11**	**12**	**1**	**2**	**3**	**4**	**5**	**6**	**7**	**8**	**9**	**10**	**11**	**12**	**1**	**2**	**3**	**4**	**5**	**6**	**7**	**8**	**9**	**10**
Find common denominators																		●		●				■				●	■	●	●	■		
Use an algorithm to multiply fractions by whole numbers							●	■		■										●								■		■				
Use an algorithm to multiply fractions																				●	■			■				●	■	●	●	●	■	■
Use an algorithm to multiply mixed numbers																				●	■			■				●	■	●		●		■
Solve multiplication/division fraction number stories							●			■										●	■							■	■			●		
Solve "fraction-of-a-fraction" problems																				●										■	●	■	■	
Use a common denominator to divide fractions																			■	●														
Use an algorithm to multiply/divide fractions and mixed numbers; use area models to demonstrate							●													●	■							●	■	●		●	■	■
Understand the effect of multiplying fractions by a number less than 1, equal to 1, or greater than 1																				●														
Computational Estimation	**1**	**2**	**3**	**4**	**5**	**6**	**7**	**8**	**9**	**10**	**11**	**12**	**1**	**2**	**3**	**4**	**5**	**6**	**7**	**8**	**9**	**10**	**11**	**12**	**1**	**2**	**3**	**4**	**5**	**6**	**7**	**8**	**9**	**10**
Round whole numbers to a given place				■	●	■							■	■		●		■							■	●	■						●	
Use estimation to add/subtract		●	■	●	●			■						●						●	■							■		●		●		
Use estimation to multiply/divide					●			■						●	●	●								■	■		■	■						■
Make magnitude estimates to solve *, ÷ problems					●									●		●		●				■			■	■		■						■
Estimate sums/differences of fractions																				■	■	■						■						
Round decimals to a given place									■		■	■		●	■	●										●	■	●	■			●	■	

Operations and Computation (cont.)

Key ● Content taught ■ Content practiced

	Grade 4 Units												Grade 5 Units												Grade 6 Units									
Computational Estimation (cont.)	1	2	3	4	5	6	7	8	9	10	11	12	1	2	3	4	5	6	7	8	9	10	11	12	1	2	3	4	5	6	7	8	9	10
Estimate costs				■		■			■								■								■									
Estimate products and multiply decimals									●	■	■			●										■	■	●								■
Estimate the quotient and divide a decimal by a whole number									●	■	■					●	■									●	■	●		■				
Models for the Operations	1	2	3	4	5	6	7	8	9	10	11	12	1	2	3	4	5	6	7	8	9	10	11	12	1	2	3	4	5	6	7	8	9	10
Understand multiplicative comparisons		■	●	●	●	■		●					■		■	■				■														
Understand additive comparisons				●	●																													
Find unit rates												●										●					■				■	●	■	
Collect and compare rate data; evaluate reasonableness of rate data												●										●		●			●					●		
Use rate tables to solve problems												●										●		●			●					●		
Represent rates with formulas, tables, and graphs												●										●		●			●			■	■	●	■	
Solve rate and ratio number stories; find equivalent ratios												●								■		●		●			●				■	●	●	
Explore uses of ratios and ways of expressing ratios; differentiate between rate and ratio												●										●		●							■	●	●	
Find opposites and reciprocals of numbers																				■							●			●		■		
Solve problems involving a size-change factor																																●	●	
Write open proportions to solve model problems																								●							■	●	●	
Use cross-multiplication to solve open proportions																															■	●	■	

Data and Chance

	Grade 4 Units												Grade 5 Units												Grade 6 Units									
Data Collection and Representation	1	2	3	4	5	6	7	8	9	10	11	12	1	2	3	4	5	6	7	8	9	10	11	12	1	2	3	4	5	6	7	8	9	10
Collect data by counting/interviewing		●							●			●					●	●							●		■	■						
Collect data from print sources		●	●	■	■	■	■	■	■	■	■	■						■	■						●	■								
Collect data from a map			●	■	●	●						■			■			●					■									●		

Key ● Content taught ■ Content practiced

Data Collection and Representation (cont.)	1	2	3	4	5	6	7	8	9	10	11	12	1	2	3	4	5	6	7	8	9	10	11	12	1	2	3	4	5	6	7	8	9	10
Find locations on a map or globe		●	●		●	●	■		■		■										●													
Collect and compare rate data												●										●		●			●					●		
Conduct a survey									●									●		●					●	■								
Organize and tabulate survey data									●									●							●									
Make a tally chart		●																●													■			
Record data in a table/chart		●	●						●	■		●						●		■		●	●	●	●		●			■	■	■	●	
Record data on a map									●																									
Record/compare numerical data		●					●	■	●			●		●				●						●	●		●	●				■		
Create/interpret bar graphs		●		■	■	■			■	■	■	■		■			●	●							●	■		■			■			
Create/interpret box plots																									●	■	■							
Create/interpret broken-line graphs and line plots		■	●				■				■	■		●				●	●	■	■	●	■	●	●	■	●			■	■			
Create/interpret circle graphs with or without a Percent Circle			■	■	■	■										■	●	●		■		■	■		●	■		●	●	■		■		
Create/interpret step graphs																									●									
Create/interpret Venn diagrams	■		■		■						■						■		●				●	■					■		●	■		
Create/interpret number-line plots		●					●				●			●				●							●	■								
Create/interpret stem-and-leaf plots		■																●	■			●			●	■		■					■	
Interpret mystery graphs																						●				■	■			■			■	
Use technology to create graphs																									■									
Use a spreadsheet																											●	■				■	●	
Explore misleading ways of presenting data																									●	■								
Data Analysis	**1**	**2**	**3**	**4**	**5**	**6**	**7**	**8**	**9**	**10**	**11**	**12**	**1**	**2**	**3**	**4**	**5**	**6**	**7**	**8**	**9**	**10**	**11**	**12**	**1**	**2**	**3**	**4**	**5**	**6**	**7**	**8**	**9**	**10**
Interpret tables, graphs, and maps	■		●	■	■	■			●					●	■	■	●	●	●	●	■	●	■	●	●	■	●	■				●	■	
Use a map scale			●	■	■	●	■	●	■					●		●																●	●	
Use a mileage map					●									●		●																●		
Make and interpret scale drawings								●													■											●	●	
Identify locations for given latitudes and longitudes						●															●													

Data and Chance (cont.)

Key ● Content taught ■ Content practiced

	Grade 4 Units												Grade 5 Units												Grade 6 Units									
Data Analysis (cont.)	1	2	3	4	5	6	7	8	9	10	11	12	1	2	3	4	5	6	7	8	9	10	11	12	1	2	3	4	5	6	7	8	9	10
Find latitude and longitude for given locations						●			■												●													
Summarize and interpret data		■		■				■				●		●				●	●	●		●		●	●	■	●	■				■	■	
Compare two sets of data; compare graphical representations of the same data		■						■	■			■		●	●		●	●	●	●		●		●	●	■	■							
Make predictions about data		■					●		●			■						●				●		●	●		●	●			●			
Find/use the minimum/maximum		●		■				●		■			■	●	●	■	■	●	■		■	■	■	●	●	■	■						■	
Find/use the range		●	■	■	■		■			■			■	●	■		■	●	■		■		■	●	●	■	■						■	
Find/use the median		●	●		■		■	●		■		●	■	●	●	■	■	●	■			●	■	●	●	■	■	■					■	
Find/use the mode		●		■			■	●		■				●	■	■	■	●			■		■		●	■	■						■	
Find/use the mean		■	●	■			■					■		●	■	■	■	●			■		■		●	■	●	■	●				■	
FInd/use the lower quartile, upper quartile, and the interquartile range																									●	■	■							
Understand how sample size or outliers affect results		■					■											●							●	■		■						
Determine whether the mean, median, or mode provides the most useful information in a given situation		■	■									■						●							●	■	■	■						
Use data in problem solving		■	●					■				●						●				●			●	■	●				■	■		
Qualitative Probability	1	2	3	4	5	6	7	8	9	10	11	12	1	2	3	4	5	6	7	8	9	10	11	12	1	2	3	4	5	6	7	8	9	10
Explore likelihood of events						■	●		■		■	■		●										●						■	●			
Explore fair and unfair games							●										■	●													●			
Quantitative Probability	1	2	3	4	5	6	7	8	9	10	11	12	1	2	3	4	5	6	7	8	9	10	11	12	1	2	3	4	5	6	7	8	9	10
Predict outcomes; solve problems involving chance outcomes							●	■	■					●				■						●						■	●	■		
Conduct experiments							●							●				■						●							●			
Record outcomes							●							●				■						●							●	■		
Use fractions to record probabilities of events							●		■															●						■	■	■		
Compute the probability of equally-likely outcomes							●	■	■		■			■										●						■	●	■		
Calculate and express the probability of simple events						■	●	■	■	■	■	■					■		■		■			●						■	●			

Key ● Content taught ■ Content practiced

Quantitative Probability (cont.)	1	2	3	4	5	6	7	8	9	10	11	12	1	2	3	4	5	6	7	8	9	10	11	12	1	2	3	4	5	6	7	8	9	10
Understand and apply the concept of random numbers to probability situations																															●			
Understand how increasing the number of trials affects experimental results																		●						■	●						●	■		
Investigate/apply the Multiplication Counting Principle, tree diagrams, lists, and other counting strategies to identify all possible outcomes for a situation			■																					●						■	●	■		
Explore random sampling									●									●							●						●			

Measurement and Reference Frames

	Grade 4 Units												Grade 5 Units												Grade 6 Units									
Length, Weight, and Angles	1	2	3	4	5	6	7	8	9	10	11	12	1	2	3	4	5	6	7	8	9	10	11	12	1	2	3	4	5	6	7	8	9	10
Add and subtract units of length, weight, and capacity			●		■		■		■		■												■											
Estimate and compare lengths/heights of objects			■	●	■		■																●										●	●
Measure to the nearest foot								●																										
Measure to the nearest inch			■				■									●								●										
Measure to the nearest $\frac{1}{2}$ inch			●																■						■							●	●	●
Measure to the nearest $\frac{1}{4}$ inch					■	■		●						■		■	●			■					■				■			●	●	
Measure to the nearest $\frac{1}{8}$ inch														■				■							■			●	■	●		●	●	
Draw or measure line segments to the nearest centimeter		●	■	●				●								■		●							■				■				■	
Measure to the nearest $\frac{1}{2}$ centimeter		●		■																														
Draw or measure line segments to the nearest millimeter				●	■	■												●		■					■				■			●	●	
Investigate the meter				●																														
Express metric measures with decimals				●																						■								
Estimate and compare distances			●	●	●	●		●						●		●					■													●
Solve length/height/distance number stories			●		■		■		■		■										■					■						●	■	
Estimate and compare weights										■	●																					■		
Estimate/weigh objects in ounces or grams											●																			■				

Measurement and Reference Frames (cont.)

Key ● Content taught ■ Content practiced

	Grade 4 Units												Grade 5 Units												Grade 6 Units									
Length, Weight, and Angles (cont.)	1	2	3	4	5	6	7	8	9	10	11	12	1	2	3	4	5	6	7	8	9	10	11	12	1	2	3	4	5	6	7	8	9	10
Use a pan balance/spring scale											●											●												
Solve weight number stories											●											●	●											
Estimate the measure of an angle			■			■	■			■					●	■												■	■					■
Use full-circle and half-circle protractors to measure and draw angles						●	■	■	■	■					●		■	●										■	●			■		
Measure angles with degree units to within 2°						●	■							■	●	■	■	●	■									■	●				■	■
Area, Perimeter, Volume, and Capacity	1	2	3	4	5	6	7	8	9	10	11	12	1	2	3	4	5	6	7	8	9	10	11	12	1	2	3	4	5	6	7	8	9	10
Investigate area and perimeter			■				■	●	■												●			■	●	■	●					■	●	
Find the areas of regular shapes								●	■	■							■			■	●	■	●		●	■	●	●		●		■	●	
Find the perimeters of regular shapes			■					●	■	■					■		■				■		■		■	■	●					■	●	
Find the areas of irregular shapes								●													●		■					■					■	
Find the perimeters of irregular shapes								■	■												■		■										■	■
Estimate area								●													●							■					●	
Compare perimeter and area								■	■			■									■		■	■	■								●	
Find the area of a figure by counting unit squares and fractions of unit squares inside the figure							■	●													●					■							■	
Use formulas to find areas of rectangles, parallelograms, and triangles; understand the relationship between these formulas								●	■												●		●		■	■	●			●		■	●	■
Find the surface areas of prisms, cylinders, and pyramids																					■		●					●					■	
Investigate/understand the concept of volume of a figure											●										●	■	■										●	■
Understand the relationships between the volumes of pyramids and prisms, and the volumes of cones and cylinders																							●										●	
Estimate volume or surface area								●			●										●												●	
Find and use an approximate value for π (pi)																						●											●	
Use a formula to find the circumference of a circle																						■	■	■									●	■
Use a formula to find the area of a circle																						●	●	■			●					■	●	■
Distinguish between circumference and area of a circle																						●	■	■									●	

Key ● Content taught ■ Content practiced

Area, Perimeter, Volume, and Capacity (cont.)	1	2	3	4	5	6	7	8	9	10	11	12	1	2	3	4	5	6	7	8	9	10	11	12	1	2	3	4	5	6	7	8	9	10
Solve cube-stacking volume problems with unit cubes and fractions of unit cubes											■										●	■	■										■	
Use formulas to calculate volumes of 3-dimensional shapes											●	■									●	■	●			■				■			●	■
Investigate/understand the concept of capacity											●	■									●		●							■			●	
Estimate and calculate capacity											●	■									●		●							■			●	■
Solve capacity number stories											●	■											●							■			●	■
Units and Systems of Measurement	**1**	**2**	**3**	**4**	**5**	**6**	**7**	**8**	**9**	**10**	**11**	**12**	**1**	**2**	**3**	**4**	**5**	**6**	**7**	**8**	**9**	**10**	**11**	**12**	**1**	**2**	**3**	**4**	**5**	**6**	**7**	**8**	**9**	**10**
Identify equivalent customary units of length	■	■	■					●	■		■			●							■	■										●	●	■
Identify equivalent metric units of length				●		■												■			■	■			■						■	■	●	
Convert between metric/customary measures			■	●				■		■	●	■						■							●	●				■		■	●	■
Use personal references for metric/customary units of length				●	■										■			●			●													
Identify equivalent customary units of weight										■	●											■	■									■		
Identify equivalent metric units of weight				■							●											■	●									■		
Identify metric units of capacity											●	■									●	■	●										●	
Identify equivalent metric units of capacity											●	■									●	■	●									■	●	
Examine the relationships among the liter, milliliter, and cubic centimeter																					●		●										●	
Use personal references for common units of area																					●				■			■					■	
Money	**1**	**2**	**3**	**4**	**5**	**6**	**7**	**8**	**9**	**10**	**11**	**12**	**1**	**2**	**3**	**4**	**5**	**6**	**7**	**8**	**9**	**10**	**11**	**12**	**1**	**2**	**3**	**4**	**5**	**6**	**7**	**8**	**9**	**10**
Compare money amounts	■		■	■					■			●																						
Temperature	**1**	**2**	**3**	**4**	**5**	**6**	**7**	**8**	**9**	**10**	**11**	**12**	**1**	**2**	**3**	**4**	**5**	**6**	**7**	**8**	**9**	**10**	**11**	**12**	**1**	**2**	**3**	**4**	**5**	**6**	**7**	**8**	**9**	**10**
Read, record, and convert units of temperature									■													■					●					■	●	
Time	**1**	**2**	**3**	**4**	**5**	**6**	**7**	**8**	**9**	**10**	**11**	**12**	**1**	**2**	**3**	**4**	**5**	**6**	**7**	**8**	**9**	**10**	**11**	**12**	**1**	**2**	**3**	**4**	**5**	**6**	**7**	**8**	**9**	**10**
Investigate 1-minute intervals						●						●																						
Calculate elapsed time		■	●		■	●																●												
Convert units of time		■			●													●		■				■								■		

Measurement and Reference Frames (cont.)

Key ● Content taught ■ Content practiced

	Grade 4 Units												Grade 5 Units												Grade 6 Units									
Time (cont.)	1	2	3	4	5	6	7	8	9	10	11	12	1	2	3	4	5	6	7	8	9	10	11	12	1	2	3	4	5	6	7	8	9	10
Solve time number stories			●		●								■																					
Coordinate Systems	1	2	3	4	5	6	7	8	9	10	11	12	1	2	3	4	5	6	7	8	9	10	11	12	1	2	3	4	5	6	7	8	9	10
Plot ordered number pairs on a one or four-quadrant coordinate grid						●	■	■	■	■		■								■	●	■		●	■	■	■		●		■		■	
Use ordered number pairs to name points in four quadrants																				■	●	■			■	■	■		■			■		■
Find distances between ordered number pairs along lines																													●	●				■

Geometry

	Grade 4 Units												Grade 5 Units												Grade 6 Units									
Lines and Angles	1	2	3	4	5	6	7	8	9	10	11	12	1	2	3	4	5	6	7	8	9	10	11	12	1	2	3	4	5	6	7	8	9	10
Identify and name points	●														■										■			■	●					■
Identify and name line segments	●		■												■					■								■	●				■	
Draw line segments to a specified length	●	●													●						■				■				●					
Identify parallel and nonparallel line segments	●				■										■														●	■		■	■	
Identify and name lines	●														■														●	■		■	■	
Identify and name intersecting lines					■										■														●	■		■	■	
Identify and name rays	●			■																														
Name, draw, and label line segments, lines, and rays	●														■										■			■	●					■
Identify and name acute, obtuse, right, straight, and reflex angles	●					●			■					■	●	■				■				■				■	●				●	
Identify and describe right angles, parallel lines, skew lines, and line segments	●													■	■													■	●			■	■	
Use full-circle and half-circle protractors to measure and draw angles						●	■	■	■	■					●		■	●										■	●			■		■
Use a compass and a protractor to draw and measure angles formed by intersecting lines															●														●					■
Solve degree problems						●	■	■	■						■														●				■	

Key ● Content taught ■ Content practiced

Lines and Angles (cont.)	1	2	3	4	5	6	7	8	9	10	11	12	1	2	3	4	5	6	7	8	9	10	11	12	1	2	3	4	5	6	7	8	9	10
Determine angle measures based on relationships among common angles					■	●	■	■	■						●													■	●					■
Find angle sums for geometric shapes						■									●														●				■	■
Apply properties of adjacent, supplementary, complementary, and vertical angles; recognize properties in real-world settings						●	■		■						●														●	■		■	●	■
Apply properties of sums of angle measures of triangles and quadrilaterals															●	■								■				■	●			■	■	■
Apply properties of angles of parallelograms															●														●				■	●
Apply properties of angles formed by two parallel lines and a transversal																													●	■		■	■	■
Explore the relationship between endpoints and midpoints																													●					
Make turns and fractions of turns; relate turns to angles						●				■					●									■					●				■	●
Solve construction problems															●														●			■		
Plane and Solid Figures	**1**	**2**	**3**	**4**	**5**	**6**	**7**	**8**	**9**	**10**	**11**	**12**	**1**	**2**	**3**	**4**	**5**	**6**	**7**	**8**	**9**	**10**	**11**	**12**	**1**	**2**	**3**	**4**	**5**	**6**	**7**	**8**	**9**	**10**
Explore shape relationships	●						●	●		●					●						■								■			●	●	■
Identify characteristics of 2-dimensional shapes; use symbolic notation to denote these characteristics	●						●	●	■	●				■	●						●					■			●			●	●	
Identify 2-dimensional shapes	●	■	■				●	●							●					■	■					■			●			■	●	■
Construct/draw 2-dimensional shapes; create designs with 2-dimensional shapes	●	■					■	●		●					●										■				●			●	●	
Use a compass and a straightedge to construct geometric figures	●	■					■	■							●														●			■		
Identify the bases and heights of triangles and parallelograms								●													●											■	●	■
Use a compass to draw a circle with a given radius or diameter, and angles formed by intersecting lines															●														●				■	
Investigate the relationship between circumference and diameter																						●					■						■	
Form shapes by combining polygons							●	■																										
Identify properties and characteristics of polygons	●	■	■	■	■			●	■	●				■	●	●					■				■	■			●			●	●	●
Classify and name polygons	●						●	●	■						●					■	■				■				●				■	■
Classify triangles and quadrilaterals according to side and angle properties	●							●							●					■					■				●				●	●

Geometry (cont.)

Key ● Content taught ■ Content practiced

	Grade 4 Units												Grade 5 Units												Grade 6 Units									
Plane and Solid Figures (cont.)	1	2	3	4	5	6	7	8	9	10	11	12	1	2	3	4	5	6	7	8	9	10	11	12	1	2	3	4	5	6	7	8	9	10
Name, draw, and label angles, triangles, and quadrilaterals	●							●							●					■					●			■	●					■
Identify types of triangles								●							●	■				■					■									
Verify and apply the Pythagorean Theorem																																	●	
Solve problems involving 2-dimensional shapes	■	■					●	●							●						●				■				●			●	●	
Identify and classify 3-dimensional shapes											●									■	●		●						■				●	
Identify characteristics of 3-dimensional shapes; compare them with their 2-D faces											●										●	■	●						■				●	
Construct 3-dimensional shapes											●										●		●										●	
Describe properties of geometric solids											●										●		●						■				●	■
Identify faces, edges, vertices, and bases of prisms and pyramids											●	■											●						■				●	
Perform and identify topological transformations																													■					●
Identify congruent figures															●					■			■					●	●	■		●		●
Draw or form a figure congruent to a given figure										●					●						■								●					■
Identify and draw similar figures								■							●														■			●	●	
Describe relationships among angles, side lengths, perimeter, and area of similar polygons								■																						■	■	●	●	
Transformations and Symmetry	1	2	3	4	5	6	7	8	9	10	11	12	1	2	3	4	5	6	7	8	9	10	11	12	1	2	3	4	5	6	7	8	9	10
Identify lines of reflection, reflected figures, and figures with line symmetry										●											●								●					■
Use a transparent mirror to draw the reflection of a figure										●																								■
Identify symmetrical figures										●											■													■
Identify lines of symmetry									■	●											■												■	■
Translate figures on a coordinate grid																					●								●					●
Rotate figures										■	■										●								●					●
Model clockwise/counterclockwise turns/rotations						●				■														■					●					
Explore transformations of geometric figures in a plane; identify preimage and image											■										●								●				■	●
Explore rotation and point symmetry										■					●																			●

Patterns, Functions, and Algebra

Key ● Content taught ■ Content practiced

Patterns and Functions	Grade 4 Units												Grade 5 Units												Grade 6 Units									
	1	2	3	4	5	6	7	8	9	10	11	12	1	2	3	4	5	6	7	8	9	10	11	12	1	2	3	4	5	6	7	8	9	10
Explore and extend visual patterns	■						●			●			●							●	●	■							●					●
Create patterns with 2-dimensional shapes	■						●			●																								■
Define and create tessellations/frieze patterns										●					●																		■	●
Identify and use notation for semiregular tessellations																																	■	●
Identify regular tessellations															●																		■	●
Find and extend numerical patterns		■	■		■						●				■			■	■	■		●				●	●	■	●			●	●	
Make/complete a sequence with a number line		●		●	■		●	■				■	●			■		■				■												
Solve "What's My Rule?" (function machine) problems; find a rule for a set of problems		■	●	■	■	■	■		■	■							●	■	●	●	■					●	■			■			■	■
Solve pan-balance problems		■																				●	■	■						●	■		●	
Describe a pattern with a number sentence that has one to three variables																											●			●		■	●	■
Find patterns in addition, subtraction, multiplication, and division facts		■	■		■								●								■					●	■	●		●	■	●	●	
Find number patterns in data; complete a table of values								●				●										●		●		●	●	●				●	●	
Solve and graph solutions for inequalities																														●	■		■	
Combine like terms to simplify expressions and equations																																	●	■
Write and identify equivalent expressions and equivalent equations													●				■	■			●								●	●			●	
Write and solve equations that represent problem situations			●		■	●	●	■	■	■						●											■			●		■	●	■
Algebraic Notation and Solving Number Sentences	1	2	3	4	5	6	7	8	9	10	11	12	1	2	3	4	5	6	7	8	9	10	11	12	1	2	3	4	5	6	7	8	9	10
Compare numbers using <, >, and = symbols	■	■	■	■	■	■	●	■			■	■						●	●	●			■	■	●			●	■	●			■	
Evaluate expressions using <, >, =, and ≈ symbols																■						■			●		●	●	■	●	■	●	●	
Translate number stories into expressions			●		■	●	●	■	■	■				●		●			●			●		●			●	■	■	●			●	
Write/solve addition and subtraction number sentences	■	●			■		■						■	●	■						■				■	■	●	■	■	●			●	
Write/solve multiplication/division number sentences			●		■	■			■				■	●		●					■				■	■	●		■	●		●	●	■
Use variables to describe general patterns																											●	■		●		●	●	

Patterns, Functions, and Algebra (cont.)

Key ● Content taught ■ Content practiced

	Grade 4 Units												Grade 5 Units												Grade 6 Units									
Algebraic Notation and Solving Number Sentences (cont.)	1	2	3	4	5	6	7	8	9	10	11	12	1	2	3	4	5	6	7	8	9	10	11	12	1	2	3	4	5	6	7	8	9	10
Determine the value of a variable		■		■		■		■		■	■	■		●	■	●		■	■	■	■	●	■	●			●	●	●	●	■	●	●	
Write and solve open sentences or number sentences with variables			●		■	●		■	■		■	■		●	■	●	■		●	●	■	●	■	●			●	●	●	●	■	●	●	
Determine if number sentences are true or false		■	●	■	■												■		●	■									■	●	■	■		
Write or evaluate algebraic expressions and formulas to describe situations			●		■	●			■													●		■			●	■		●		■	●	■
Use variables and formulas in spreadsheets																											●	■				■	●	
Evaluate formulas																					●		●			■	●	■		●		■	●	■
Use formulas to solve problems																					●		●			■	●	●		●		■	●	■
Identify dependent and independent variables																											●							
Order of Operations	1	2	3	4	5	6	7	8	9	10	11	12	1	2	3	4	5	6	7	8	9	10	11	12	1	2	3	4	5	6	7	8	9	10
Apply the use of parentheses in number sentences			●	■	■	■	■		■		■							■	●	■	■			■	■		●		■	●		■	●	■
Understand and apply the order of operations to evaluate expressions and solve number sentences																			●	■	■	●	■		■	●		■	■	●	■	■	●	■
Simplify expressions and equations that have parentheses																			●										■	●		■	●	■
Properties of Arithmetic Operations	1	2	3	4	5	6	7	8	9	10	11	12	1	2	3	4	5	6	7	8	9	10	11	12	1	2	3	4	5	6	7	8	9	10
Investigate properties of multiplication/division			●			■							●	■		●										■				●	■	■	■	
Understand and apply the Commutative Property for addition and multiplication																				■										●	■		●	
Apply the Distributive Property					●	■	■	■	■																			●		●		■	●	■
Understand and apply the Identity Property for multiplication																												●		●		●		
Understand and apply the Associative Property for addition and multiplication																	●		●		■		●					●		●			●	

Index

A

B

L

Z

Notes

Notes

Notes

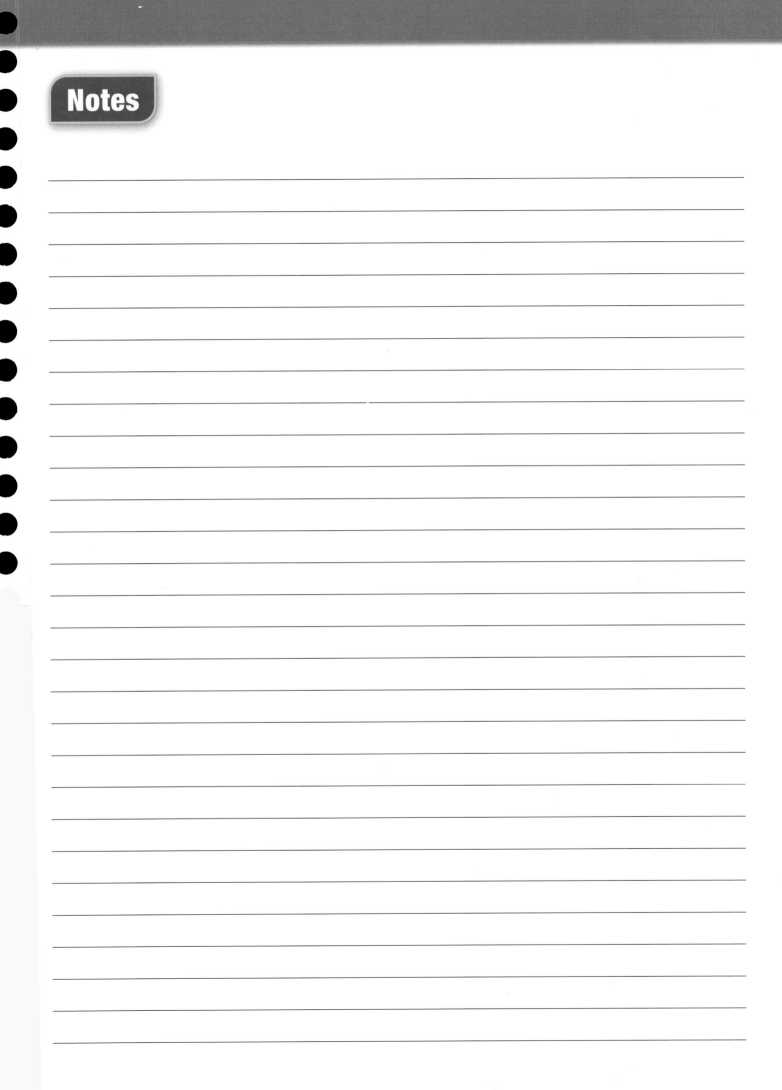

Notes

Notes

Notes